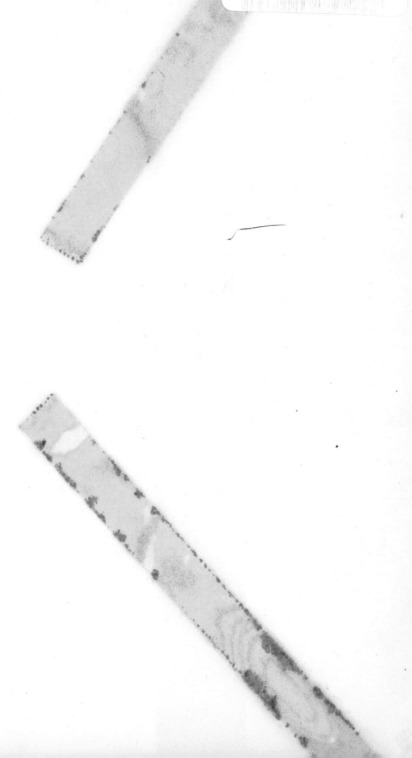

HANDBOOK OF MENTAL DEFICIENCY

Psychological Theory and Research

McGRAW-HILL SERIES IN PSYCHOLOGY
HARRY F. HARLOW, *Consulting Editor*

John F. Dashiell was Consulting Editor of this series from its inception in 1931 until January 1, 1950. Clifford T. Morgan was Consulting Editor of this series from January 1, 1950 until January 1, 1959.

HANDBOOK OF MENTAL DEFICIENCY

Psychological Theory and Research

NORMAN R. ELLIS, Editor
George Peabody College for Teachers

McGRAW-HILL BOOK COMPANY
New York   San Francisco   Toronto   London

Handbook of Mental Deficiency

CONTRIBUTORS

Alfred Baumeister
Gershon Berkson
Gordon N. Cantor
Rue L. Cromwell
Norman R. Ellis
Sol L. Garfield
Irving I. Gottesman
Samuel Guskin
William Hawkins
Betty House
Frank Kodman, Jr.
Ronald Lipman
A. R. Luria
Brendan Maher
Leslie F. Malpass
Lorene Childs Quay
Sheldon Rosenberg
Herman H. Spitz
George Spivack
Joseph Spradlin
Harold W. Stevenson
Mary Woodward
David Zeaman

FOREWORD

When Itard undertook to teach the wild boy of Aveyron, with sympathy, patience, and an optimism about the plasticity of the human mind that was characteristic of his time, he engaged the interest of educated men everywhere. He used the most enlightened instructional methods of his time. When he was unable to lead the boy to complete normalcy, he felt himself a failure, and apparently the world agreed with him. An air of hopelessness settled over the retarded and has scarcely been lifted since.

Now, some 165 years later, a new measure is being taken of the problem of mental retardation. There is emerging a reasoned optimism, justified by modest advances in basic knowledge and encouraged by a quickened public conscience. There is also emerging a new strategy that eschews the quick cure but insists that we begin to use the knowledge we already have while intensifying our search for new and basic understandings.

This book is an expression of this last important commitment, a search for new and basic understandings. Though formidable in size, its scope is wisely limited to one domain, to that of behavior; and it seeks to assess where we are and how we may most profitably proceed to build a behavior science for the mentally retarded.

The editor and his colleagues share two important ideas: that mental retardation should not be an isolated study; that, on the contrary, its special problems can best be cast in general behavior theory terms. As a corollary to this, they hold and have here demonstrated that the field of mental retardation offers many opportunities and challenges to the behavioral scientist who has reached a point of no return with his subjects who cannot use language, that most human of human functions. This book is as important for psychology in general as it is for the field of mental retardation.

All that is here is new, especially written for this book. Excepting one chapter written by an eminent Russian scholar, there are no great names after chapter titles, or, more accurately, the names are not great yet, though some will surely be. These are people who have cut a new way and whom others will follow.

Nicholas Hobbs

The purpose of this book is to assess the status of behavioral research and theory in mental deficiency. Part I is devoted mainly to theory, and Part II includes empirical findings categorized according to conventional areas of investigation. Some repetition of materials is intentional since the theoretical treatment must rely upon experimental results and, therefore, should be cited at that point. The summaries of empirical findings include much of the same material, which appears in the interest of the reader since this provides a complete review of research fairly divorced from theory. In the main, the theoretical treatments are extensions of those developed to explain the behavior of the normal organism. In some instances, however, modification of the existing theory is far-reaching. Most of the research upon which this book is based has been conducted within the past decade or so. The theories, as applied to mental deficiency, are of recent origin. The reader will find little formal attention to the history of mental deficiency, parent adjustment problems, administrative matters, social welfare issues, and other materials which are usually included in a book on mental deficiency. Rather we have attempted to come to grips with the basic problem, the *behavior* of the inadequate organism.

The problem of nomenclature is largely ignored. The reader will find the population referred to as mental defectives, mental retardates, mentally deficients, etc. How a "thing" is called is of little consequence. The defining operations are of central importance and the scientist is well aware of this. A term may have undesirable emotional connotations, but changing the term is only a temporary remedial measure. Some terms used to establish categories within the group are unfortunate from a rational standpoint. The terms educable, trainable, and untrainable, for example, tend to be used in an absolute rather than a relative sense, and, perhaps, preclude serious effort in remediation.

Much ambiguity and contradiction will be found in the results of research reported here. This should not prove discouraging, for the systematic study of mental deficiency by the behavioral sciences is still in an embryonic state. However, there is clear evidence of rapid, healthy growth.

This book is the result of a cooperative enterprise. Not only have the authors made formal contributions, but they have also provided counsel throughout the project. I am especially grateful to my colleague Rue Cromwell who has provided a constant source of encouragement and guidance. Paul S. Siegel of the University of Alabama was instrumental in this publication also. His critical evaluation of the manuscript was of invaluable assistance. William Sloan is due a note of appreciation for his technical advice as well as his personal encouragement. Lloyd Dunn provided assistance at critical times. Raymond C. Norris also served as critical reader. Many others made contributions in varying amounts. A number of graduate students offered pertinent criticism on different chapters.

My wife, Kay, worked diligently at editorial duties as well as "running interference" while I worked on the book.

Acknowledgment of permission to quote and reproduce materials from other sources is made to the following: American Psychological Association Journals; *American Journal of Mental Deficiency*; *Journal of Mental Deficiency*; *Psychological Reports*; *Perceptual and Motor Skills*; The Journal Press; *Journal of Clinical Psychology*; *The Lancet*; *American Journal of Orthopsychiatry*; *Exceptional Children*; John Wiley & Sons, Inc., Prentice-Hall, Inc.; The Macmillan Company; Baillière, Tindall & Cox Ltd.; Oxford University Press; Pergamon Press; Grune & Stratton, Inc.; Sidgwick & Jackson Ltd.; Annual Reviews, Inc.; Doubleday & Company, Inc.; Basic Books, Inc.; The Williams & Wilkins Company; Harper & Row, Publishers, Incorporated; The University of Wisconsin Press. We are also grateful to the many authors who permitted their work to be reproduced here.

Norman R. Ellis

CONTENTS

Part I

Part II

INTRODUCTION

Man, unlike animals lower in the phyletic scale, protects the maimed and crippled organism. In this age of humanitarian reform, the conscience of society demands humane care as well as a sharper focus of scientific technology on the inadequate member and the problem of adaptation. The scientific study of the inadequate human is a recent innovation in history. Genetics has given insight into seemingly complex phenomena. Medical science has made remarkable progress in freeing mankind from many afflictions. However, some conditions have been resistant to scientific advance. Cerebral palsy, epilepsy, the choreas, psychosis, alcoholism, and mental deficiency are examples which have behavioral involvement. Preventive measures have reduced the incidence of some. In the main, attempts at remediation have met with little success.

For the conditions in which man's commerce with his environment is inadequate, the onus for care and remediation falls, in large part, on the behavioral sciences. This is particularly true for the *mental* afflictions. Of these, mental deficiency, perhaps, has received less attention. From a humane standpoint, care and treatment of the defective have improved. Social agencies are more sensitive to the needs of the defective living in the community. Institutional care has become better, although it still falls far below society's aspirations. Both innovations have made serious demands upon the economy as well as upon professional and scientific talent. The methods and techniques of care and training have changed little since the turn of the century. Pedagogical procedures, vocational training regimens, psychological treatments, and social and self-help training are largely those employed with the normal individual or with some other clinical population.

1

Thus, those directly concerned with the defective use techniques appropriate for another occasion or else "common sense." No doubt the latter is more germane in most instances.

Behavioral science assumes two roles in mental deficiency, service and research. The service function has consisted largely in evaluation and diagnosis, guidance, and some small, unsuccessful commitment to psychotherapeutic procedures. To date, the clinical psychology of mental deficiency has consisted of little more than psychometric procedures, quite often applied indiscriminately and without clear purpose. Conventionally, parents, teachers, administrators, and others concerned with the defective expect the psychologist to "test" the children. In some instances the mental tester plays an important role in the placement and care of children, but quite often the service could be rendered without a mental test and by someone with much less formal training. The writer estimates that the typical psychologist working in the field spends, at a minimum, 50 per cent of his time directly or indirectly occupied with mental tests. It is indeed unfortunate that a greater part of his time is not devoted to procedures designed to bring about more nearly adequate behavior in the subject. Recently some discontent with mental testing has been in evidence, as reflected by comments which range from "Discard the IQ" to "Our tests are inadequate: develop better tests." Many of the most popular intelligence tests are highly reliable instruments which predict some aspects of adaptive behavior fairly well. Used with discretion they provide a valuable datum; current indiscriminate usage represents the behavior of psychologist in a cul-de-sac.

Research in mental deficiency has provided little supporting information for the clinician. Much of the past research has been conducted by the individual trained for a service role and is quite often performed in his "spare time." It has consisted mainly in analyses of data collected for clinical purposes. Only in the last decade or so has the trained experimentalist turned to the scientific analysis of defective behavior. Probably, several factors account for this trend including a general increase in the number of available experimentalists, exemplary medical and genetic research in the field, changing social attitudes, and increased support for research by governmental and private agencies.

Behavioral research in mental deficiency may attempt to solve an immediate practical problem, or its objective may be that of establishing general laws of behavior. For those with vision, frequently, the well-conceived experiment sheds light on both. Too often the results of laboratory research are applied prematurely and unsuccessfully to practical situations. Several reasons may account for this occurrence, including failure to consider important variables operating in either or both situations, the unreliability of the laboratory findings, and the lack of astuteness on the part of the one making the application. Applying laboratory findings to a real life situation usually requires intermediary research in which successive approximations to the practical setting are examined. The orientation of many researchers in the field is toward application which leads occasionally to over-generalized statements based on narrow research findings. The critics of pure research in mental deficiency have been in the majority, but their number is diminishing. The solution to a practical problem frequently comes about through pure rather than applied research.

Many issues face the researcher in the field; some are quixotic, others genuine. The problem of nomenclature has occupied much of the researcher's time. For the scientist the matter is resolved by subscription to the principles of operationism. For the educator, administrator, social worker, or the physician, differing definitions may be desirable. Perhaps there is some advantage in a common nomenclature for all disciplines, but this issue is not resolved easily. The clear specification of operations is important.

The question of which discipline should do a certain type of research has been of concern. Should the experimental analysis of special educational techniques be left to the special educator? Should drug studies be the exclusive domain of the physician or pharmacologist? Or, is the psychologist to be trusted with electroencephalography? Perhaps there are not adequate answers to such questions. In some instances, for legal as well as other reasons, the research has to be a collaborative effort, but not necessarily a team approach. All too often team research, particularly that conducted on a grand scale, yields little. Science, as has been said before, seems to be an individual enterprise. More mundane problems also beset the researcher. Obtaining permission for children to participate in research can tax the prowess of the most ingenious investigator. Educators are reluctant to have their classes disrupted, and administrators of institutions must defend research to parents and, unfortunately, at times to legislators. Research projects in institutions designed for service functions frequently meet with seemingly insurmountable hurdles in terms of regulations, legal and whimsical. Above all, the well-being of the child as a subject must be ensured, which precludes many research procedures. The investigator who must do research in his spare time finds himself in an awkward position, particularly if he takes service functions seriously. The availability of personnel to run subjects can present a formidable problem.

The issues which bear directly on scientific aspects of the experimenter's work are tactical and may involve his ultimate objectives. Should he adopt a theoretical or an atheoretical approach? Are single organism or group data more appropriate for the population studied? Is reductionism ultimately necessary to explain mental deficiency? What type of subjects should be included in control groups? What constitutes explanation of inadequate behavior? Should the analysis of inadequate behavior be attempted within the models or theories based upon the normal organism, or are special models to be constructed? What is the value of comparative research in which interspecies or intraspecies comparisons of organisms are made? Most of these issues are debatable. In the writer's view the most significant variable determining the contributions of an investigator is not based upon issues such as the preceding, but rather the perspicacity of the investigator himself. Did he have a clear objective for his research; i.e., did he ask a question pertaining to a significant source of behavioral variability? Was his methodology such that his results can be viewed with confidence? Other issues such as the type of control to be used are no longer germane.

As an example of a widely debated issue, consider further the question of control groups. If the investigator wants to know how a normal 7-year-old child differs on some dimension from a defective whose performance on an IQ test is equivalent to that of the normal child, then he should match for MA. However, if the intelligence test includes a broad sampling of fundamental behaviors, then the investigator is likely to have equalized his subjects on the independent variable with the matching device. He can expect differences between groups in the dependent measure only to the extent that the variance is not accounted for by the matching variable, assuming, of course, that there is a between-groups difference in the dependent variable. To elaborate on this issue, assume that behavior B is determined by five variables, A, C, D, E, G; that is, $B = (f)$ A, C, D, E, G. If a group of defectives and a group of normals are equated on MA, the differences between the groups on B will reflect only the variance in A, C, D, E, and G, which is independent of MA. If the IQ test *measures* behaviors found in A, C, D, E, and G, then we could expect no between-group differences in B. However, IQ tests do not measure all adaptive behaviors, and therefore, quite often differences are found in B. In the instance where A, C, D, E, and G are of approximately equal value in the normal, but quite unevenly distributed in the defective, the prediction of a difference on the dependent variable is complex. Graphically, such a distribution of determinants is presented in Figure I-1.

In this example we assume that the two Ss are equated on MA. The *average* of the determinants is of equal value. Whether or not differences in B occur is dependent upon the relative contribution of A, C, D, E, and G to B. If the main determinants of B are A and F, then the defective will be found superior. On the other hand, if C and E are more heavily weighted, then the defective will be found inferior. Of course MA may be unrelated to these particular determinants of B and, in such a case, differences in B may or may not obtain between MA matched groups. In brief, when subjects are matched on MA, differences in a dependent variable reflect variance not accounted for by the IQ test. This may result from matching the subjects on a single-score MA, which derives from uneven values of the components making up the score, with B in turn depending differentially upon the components. Or, B may reflect determinants not measured by the IQ test.

Figure I-1. Values of behavioral determinants.

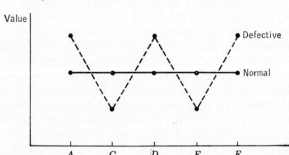

Behavioral comparison of subjects with equal CAs poses another some-what different methodological dilemma. Here we wish to determine why two subjects of, say, 16 years of age manifest different behavior. In the writer's view the equal-CA comparison appears more fruitful since the former methodology may have resulted in equalizing the differences in which the investigator is interested. It would appear that the central concern is why children of the same CA differ rather than why two children who are similar on one measuring instrument differ on another. The CA match-ing approach outlines a broader problem, bringing into play all variables for which the experimenter must account.

The use of "intelligence," as measured by a test, as an explanatory variable is questionable. If the tests were ideal and actually measured man's adaptive behavior, then to explain a given behavior (or a difference in behavior) by referring to "intelligence" would be somewhat analogous to explaining Babe Ruth's batting record by saying that he possessed high athletic ability. IQ is usually a low-order explanatory variable. A child sent to a clinic with a school learning problem may be found to have an IQ of 50 with an absence of other conditions (e.g., personality disorder or defective eyesight) which result in poor academic performance. This finding is explanatory in the sense that the likelihood is high that the child's in-adequate behavior is due to some CNS state (disease, trauma, genetic endowment, or cultural impoverishment) of long standing, which is likely to continue. The IQ score as an "explanation" leads to prognostic state-ments made with some confidence. The scientific study of behavior requires a more nearly elemental analysis than that provided by constructs such as IQ or MA.

Although the purpose here is not to attempt a treatise on methodology, some further comments on "explanation" seem invited. Frequently, subjects are selected who possess certain characteristics, low IQ, for example, and are compared with subjects of normal intelligence. Assume that a prediction is made that differences will obtain. Suppose, further, that the results support the hypothesis. Does such an outcome constitute "explanation"? We do know that the dependent variable is related to certain characteristics of organisms, although the independent variable, organismic characteristic, cannot be manipulated. Subjects can be *selected* who possess the character-istic. Such findings commonly are described as correlative. Many research efforts are of this type. CA, clinical-type, anxiety scale score, or other "stable" personality variables are often used as selection criteria in such studies, instead of IQ. Although many studies of this type provide extremely valu-able data, they do not constitute high-order explanation. In the writer's view, the explanation of differences in a dependent variable must neces-sarily involve the *manipulation* of a variable. As an illustration, suppose it is expected that normals and defectives will learn at different rates because defectives attend to irrelevant cues more than do normals. The experimenter proceeds to compare the learning rate of the two groups in a situation that contains irrelevant cues and finds the predicted difference. His hypothesis should not be offered as an explanation of the difference. To test the hypothesis, the number of or some aspect of the irrelevant cue dimension must be varied and the magnitude of the behavioral difference related to this variation.

Mental deficiency is said to be a collection of many different conditions, not a unitary state. From an etiological standpoint, mental deficiency is not a unitary condition, rather there are many causes. To assume that they are a heterogeneous group behaviorally is quite another matter, but it is a step commonly taken. Empirical evidence for etiological factors producing distinctive behavioral syndromes is indeed rare. For example, much of the research purporting to show that brain injury leads to a particular pattern of behavior is difficult to interpret in view of poorly formulated hypotheses, inadequate experimental design, and evangelical experimentation. Perhaps the strongest supportive evidence for viewing defectives as a behaviorally heterogeneous group (not qualitatively heterogeneous) is that showing that variability in performance on a task is usually much greater among defectives than among normals. This is particularly true for learning and related tasks. Obviously, such a finding is expected since the behavioral capacity of the defective ranges from near zero to normal. Adaptive behavior within the normal range and above is much more homogeneous, at least on commonly used laboratory measuring devices.

The preceding discussion raises the issue of what level of retardation to use in research. If the purpose of the research is to provide normative data or to provide data for inter- or intraspecies comparison, then the issue vanishes. For research which is more directly theory-oriented, the question is a tactical one. Much depends upon the nature of the specific problem that is posed. The researcher studying classical conditioning does not employ a tone as a CS with a deaf patient, nor does he use those with IQ of 20 or less when their performance depends upon complex verbal instructions. The behavior of a severely retarded nonverbal child is as lawful as that of a mildly retarded child or of a normal child. Moreover, orderliness may be more apparent in the child functioning at a lower level. On the other hand, orderliness may be more obscure in these subjects. Of course, some behaviors are not found in the repertoire of the severely retarded, and the experimenter must select a higher level.

There are many other tactical issues confronting the behavioral researcher in mental deficiency. A few have been cited. Some are knotty problems; others can be resolved. There are a number of problem areas that need attention. They present difficult methodological issues. Cultural retardation is an enigma. Does it exist, or is it a measurement artifact? Are the fundamental properties of behavior, such as learning, stimulus generalization, memory, etc., affected by an impoverished environment? If so, is the condition irreversible? The age at which CNS damage occurs is probably of central importance. Even though etiological factors have not been related clearly to distinctive behaviors, this does not mean that the relationship does not obtain. The typical experiment using a sample of brain-injured and familials, for example, may find equal average performance in these groups on certain measures. A more careful individual analysis may turn up widely varying performances in the brain-injured group, as a result of differing amounts and locations of injury as well as age of injury. The *single organism* approach has much merit in such instances. On the surface, it would appear that a child with a genetically inferior CNS or an endocrine disorder which has resulted in CNS impairment would show behavioral differences in memory, for example, when compared with a child suffering localized brain injury.

Another research area of central concern is that of behavioral shaping, developed with lower organisms, mainly the rat and the pigeon. It seems likely that the behavioral repertoire of the defective can be increased notably by shaping techniques, especially the severely retarded patient. Such procedures applied in the development of self-help habits possess the potential for rendering the patient more nearly independent, which would have important economic implications. It seems likely that the *majority* of "untrainable" children can be trained to maintain a dormitory and themselves with a minimum of supervision. Probably, such skills as toilet habits, dressing, making beds, cleaning floors, and serving food can be introduced in many seemingly vegetating ambulatory patients. Quite often the high-level child is viewed as the one with the greatest potential for improvement. Such a view has little support, rational or empirical. Indeed, the more severely retarded child may have the greater relative potential. The establishment of behaviors in a severely defective, such as dressing, bathing, and toilet habits, may represent a much greater (relative) gain in terms of adaptation than would the acquisition of simple arithmetic skills in a mildly defective patient. As a child's behavior capacity deviates from normal, the methods used with normal children become increasingly less appropriate. Consequently, the treatment of the severely defective child is more inadequate than that employed with the mildly defective child.

Society cannot continue its program of employing increasing numbers of attendants to care for increasing numbers of severely retarded patients. Training techniques must be developed. The academic training of the retarded bears careful scrutiny by the researcher. Normative data on achievement rates in patients are needed so that the teacher's time can be most profitably scheduled. Helping the child "realize his full potential" may not mean that he should acquire all the academic skills of which he is capable irrespective of other factors.

The status of research in mental deficiency has improved notably within the past decade or so. New knowledge is available regarding the behavior of defectives, yet there are many gaps. Currently, research is becoming more systematic, which is a healthy sign. There is much unrest and controversy among research workers regarding tactical as well as other fundamental issues. This, too, is symptomatic of healthy growth.

1

FIELD THEORY IN
MENTAL DEFICIENCY

Herman H. Spitz

INTRODUCTION

In this chapter an attempt will be made to apply some aspects of certain
field theoretical (gestalt) concepts to the understanding of mental deficiency.
In order to do this, an operational definition of mental deficiency (or
mental retardation, terms which will be used interchangeably) will be given,
followed by a short summary of the general frame of reference of field
theory. Then, after a limited review of this theory as previously applied
to mental retardation, a series of recent, physiologically oriented gestalt
studies will be discussed in detail. The implications of these more recent
studies will be presented in the form of testable postulates. Finally, some
limitations and advantages of this approach will be suggested.

OPERATIONAL DEFINITION OF MENTAL RETARDATION

Without getting too involved in the controversy over what mental deficiency
really is, some definition must be given which can be of use in our investigations. If an experiment is to be reproducible, not only the parameters of
the experimental situation must be specified but also the universe from
which our subjects (Ss) are drawn.

There is nothing sacred about the standardized intelligence tests, although
they have been shown to correlate with school achievement. There are probably better ways of measuring the capacity for intelligent behavior. Perhaps
problem-solving ability and speed of learning new material will be weighted
more heavily on future tests. But despite its limitations, the IQ measurement has proved invaluable in research. The IQ has sufficient validity, and
it is the most objective and readily communicated measure of intelligent

behavior on hand. It had best not be discarded until it is replaced by a better instrument.

The IQ and its concomitant concept MA will be utilized, therefore, in our operational definition of mental retardation: a condition of retarded mental development as determined by an IQ below 70 on a standardized individual intelligence test—a condition which, to the best of our knowledge, has existed from before the age of 3 years. This frequently used definition obviously utilizes only one of many factors which make up a fuller definition of retardation (Heber, 1959), but it must be emphasized that for certain research purposes there is no need to get involved in the niceties and subtleties of definitions and their implications. We are for the most part dealing with groups of Ss. Whether they are institutionalized or not, and any other such relevant data, should of course always be included in the description of the sample.

Another problem is the differentiation of brain-damaged (exogenous) and familial (endogenous) retardates. One often feels when entering into this problem as if he were entering a morass from which he will never be able to extricate himself. The problems are interminable. The view to be taken here is that all mental retardates are brain-damaged in one way or another. This is not a new approach, but it seems to be the most logical one and is certainly defensible. By brain damage we mean a deficit or defect in the structure and/or functioning of the organism's brain mechanisms which has resulted in a lowered IQ. If an infant is born with a genetically transmitted deficit or defect in either the structure or functioning of his central nervous system (e.g., an endogenous, familial child), he should be no less readily classifiable as brain-damaged than an infant who becomes retarded when his neural mechanisms are injured by disease or trauma. That he is differently damaged is unquestionable. By the same reasoning, however, a birth-injured infant displaying subsequent retardation cannot be lumped in the same (exogenous) category as a child who is retarded owing to a disease contracted in infancy. The disease-injured child is surely as different from the birth-injured as either is from the familial. The subtypes of brain injury are almost infinite. Furthermore, it is a good guess that increasing numbers of retardates who are now classified as endogenous will with improved diagnostic techniques be diagnosed as exogenous.

There have been many experimental demonstrations of exogenous retardates performing in a reliably different manner from endogenous retardates. But there have been just as many instances where this has not been the case. When diagnostic techniques become fine enough, and when and if Ss with different types of damage perform in a consistently reliable and different manner, some such differentiation will be welcomed. In the meantime, if one seeks to differentiate types of retardates, it would seem that the most promising approach would be to search for consistent differences on behavioral tests no matter what the underlying pathology.

Finally, the question of *pseudoretardation* should be mentioned. It is obvious that a percentage of retardates are potentially capable of normal performance and are retarded because of purely functional reasons, but this is certainly a very small percentage of the total retarded population. There is no doubt about the relevance of studying these environmentally induced functional retardates, but the importance of this source should not be magnified and generalized out of all proportion.

One often hears it stated that retardates perform as they do because they are treated differently. Within limits this may be true, but the logical next step is rarely taken; that is, to question why they are treated differently in the first place. Quite obviously it is because, in most cases, they *are* different. They are less capable of displaying intelligent behavior than are normals.

GESTALT PSYCHOLOGY

No attempt at wide coverage will be made in this section. Rather, the clarifying of some frequent misconceptions and the highlighting of some basic areas of disagreement with other schools of psychology may give to the reader some notion of the framework within which field theory operates.

Köhler (1934) states that, "Whenever a process becomes dynamically distributed and arranges itself in accordance with the constellation of determining circumstances in its entire field, that process belongs in the realm of Gestalt psychology" (as quoted by Katz, 1950, p. 91).[1] This approach, stressing as it does the interdependence of parts, which in turn determines the nature of the whole process or the whole structure, found wide application, particularly in the area of perception. A number of laws or principles were derived (Wertheimer, 1923; Katz, 1950), and it became a major purpose of gestalt psychologists to discover under what conditions these part-whole relations apply (Koffka, 1935, p. 22).

Gestaltists recognize, of course, the existence of purely summative distributions where adding, subtracting, or changing one part in no way changes the property of other parts; but Köhler (1920) clearly distinguishes these from the nonadditive processes, which he refers to as *physical systems*. It is in these segregated physical systems that the interdependence and interrelationship of parts become of vital importance, always constrained, to a greater or lesser extent, by the topography of the elements within which they obtain. The central nervous system is an example of one such physical system, one which shall be of large concern within the present paper.

Although the gestalt laws have been demonstrated most often in visual perception, they are applicable also to the other sense modalities. In kinesthetic perception temporal organization appears to play a primary role, perhaps because the figure to be perceived is so often larger than the span of touch. For example, if the raised contour of a 1-inch-diameter circle is placed on the forearm, the discrimination is more difficult than if one is allowed to trace around the contour with his fingers. Since in the kinesthetic modality one must often resort to temporal tracing, blind *S*s who gain their sight may inefficiently transfer this approach to the visual modality and attend particularly to angles while they "trace" around figures with

[1] Originally from von W. Köhler, *Psychologische probleme.* Berlin: Springer, 1934.

eye movements. For this reason it would seem hazardous indeed to generalize about visual processes from blind patients who suddenly gain sight (Hebb, 1949). A recent study with normal *S*s gives no support to the position that the angle or corner of a figure is a separate perceptual element (Pritchard, Heron, & Hebb, 1960), as Hebb had originally suggested.

A frequent misconception is that gestaltists are interested only in the whole to the neglect of the analysis of parts. This is not the case. The interplay of the parts of figures is repeatedly brought under scrutiny. Köhler states, "The very principles of organization refer to the segregation of such parts as much as their unitary character. Analysis in terms of genuine parts is a perfectly legitimate and necessary procedure in Gestalt Psychology" (1947, pp. 168–169).[2] Saying that the whole is more than the sum of its parts is not at all to deny the importance of the parts, but of course the reference here is to *genuine* parts which, in visually perceived segregated objects, for example, would consist of subunits rather than minute local sensations. Sensory stimuli impinge on the retina as a mosaic, and it is only within the nervous system that the sensory units making up this mosaic interact. This process takes time to occur, an incredibly short time, it is true; but nevertheless the final percept is not immediately given. The brain is not a repository of an unchanged mosaic of sensory stimuli.

Gestaltists in general take the position that physical processes inherent in the organism, rather than associations formed in past experience, are the source of the perception of objects as segregated visual entities, of depth perception, and of grouping by similarity and proximity. However, very early in the history of the gestalt approach the influence of set, attitude, and experience on the basic sensory processes had been pointed out. Among his first experiments with apparent movement, Wertheimer (as quoted by Koffka, 1935, pp. 511–512) demonstrated the effect of past experience. The notion of a *trace* and its influence on present processes has been repeatedly invoked. Koffka states, "It is . . . my personal opinion that experience may influence the figure-ground articulation in the sense that one such actualized articulation may facilitate similar ones" (1935, p. 210), a statement empirically supported by Leeper (1935) with ambiguous figures.

Experience, then, may influence perception under certain conditions. Some psychologists, on the other hand, insist that basic perceptual phenomena are originally *formed* only with repeated experience, that things take shape only by means of learning; and they cite as proof experiments in which perceptions are altered by experience, attitude, set, or reduced cues. The reader may be aware of the ingeniously designed experiments which purport to show that perception is a personal prediction, a best guess based on a weighted average of past experience (Ittelson & Kilpatrick, 1951). In these experiments cards are cut up, all but a single cue are eliminated, or *S* must observe with one eye only or from a certain distance, or walls of rooms are built in odd juxtaposition, and so forth. The results of these machinations lead to at least three clear conclusions: (1) humans show

[2] From *Gestalt Psychology*, by Wolfgang Köhler. By permission of Liveright, Publishers, New York. Copyright © 1947, by Liveright Publishing Corporation.

remarkable ingenuity in designing experiments; (2) certain projective techniques are indeed valid, for under conditions of reduced, distorted, or conflicting cues *S* must turn to his inner resources and past experiences; and (3) normal perception is, on the whole, incredibly veridical and highly resistant to all but the most cleverly designed deceptive devices.

The evidence is not conclusive, certainly; but many studies with young organisms from chicks to humans suggest that such things as pattern and depth perception are present at very early ages or when there has been little or no opportunity for learning (Gibson & Walk, 1960; Hess, 1956; Lashley & Russell, 1934).

Another area of disagreement concerns the optimal conditions under which learning takes place. To the gestaltists learning is enhanced by the same processes which facilitate certain perceptions. For this reason the degree of organization and isolation is said to have a more marked effect on learning than does repetitive association. For example, learning will be relatively easy when, in a large number of items, the few items to be learned form, for whatever reason, a separate subgroup. However, the more similar the items of this subgroup become to those of the larger group, the more difficult the learning and the more must *S*'s intent be brought into play (Köhler, 1958a). In association learning, likewise, associations occur spontaneously when organization is spontaneous; and strong intentional organization must be introduced when this is not the case.

Previous application of gestalt theory to problems of mental deficiency

Aside from some isolated studies, as for example those of Aldrich and Doll (1931a, 1931b), two lines of investigation have branched from the main stream of gestalt psychology into the area of mental deficiency, one propagated by Heinz Werner, the other by Kurt Lewin.

The Werner-Strauss approach. The notion of figure-ground differentiation as a fundamental process inherent in the organism is basic to gestalt theory. Starting in the late 1930s, Werner and his coworkers, particularly Strauss, carried on a series of investigations concerned with the performance of high-grade exogenous and endogenous retarded children and, frequently, matched-MA normals. Tests were designed to reveal how a disturbance which results in an impairment or a leveling of figure-ground contrast may affect the organism's functioning. Many excellent reviews of this work may be found elsewhere (Gallagher, 1957; Strauss & Lehtinen, 1947; Werner & Weir, 1956) so that only a cursory review will be given here.

The task of separating the exogenous and endogenous cases was undertaken by Strauss (1939), whose background included experience in training brain-damaged children. The framework of the experiments, on the other hand, with their strong gestalt flavor was obviously Werner's and paralleled in some ways the approach which Goldstein (1939) had used in his investigations of brain-injured adults. Techniques were specifically designed to measure the effect of an interfering background on the ability to perceive and reproduce the figure; experiments were carried out in the visual, tactual, and auditory modalities and included studies of memory and conceptual thinking. In most cases it was found that the exogenous retardates were, under conditions of the experiment, reliably more susceptible to background interference than matched endogenous children, who in turn performed essentially the same as did the equal-MA normals. It should be noted, incidentally, that differences were frequently eliminated when the special experimental conditions were not employed so that, for example, the exogenous group performed as well as the other two groups when given a chance to observe a picture for a few seconds rather than under short tachistoscopic exposure (Werner & Strauss, 1941). In summing up, Werner agrees with Goldstein that the figure-background organization is a fundamental one and concludes that it can be impaired by any number of disturbing factors (Werner & Weir, 1956).

Supported by the results of these investigations, Strauss pursued his original goal and applied the findings to the training of exogenous retardates, describing this extension in books coauthored with Lehtinen (1947) and with Kephart (1955).

This series of studies has come under attack for a number of reasons, and attempts to replicate the results have not been conspicuously successful (Gallagher, 1957). But if the basic experimental findings have stood on uncertain ground, then their hasty application by Strauss and probably by many others is doubly suspect, particularly when compared with more carefully controlled attempts in this direction (Gallagher, 1960). The old problem of selecting exogenous and endogenous retardates crops up again, inevitably. Furthermore, we have not yet reached a point where a brain-damaged child can automatically be categorized without first knowing how he performs on certain tests, especially when the overlap of scores with endogenous *S*s is considered.

Although the application of the results was hasty in the extreme, this series of studies must stand as a landmark in the field of mental deficiency. They were experiments derived from a particular theoretical point of view; they were repeated in different modalities; and they represented a concerted attack on a single problem, often by ingenious means. At a time when anecdote often substituted for procedure, and authority for results, these accomplishments should not be underestimated.

The Lewin-Kounin approach. The attack on the problem by these investigators took quite a different form. Whereas Werner's empirical studies were oriented toward the specific problem of the brain-injured retardate, Lewin (1935) presented a rather elaborate theory to account for the behavior of familial retardates; he derived this theory as much from his more inclusive topological field theory as from the findings of experimental studies. But his was at least a specific, stated theory; and the continuing studies, criticisms, and counterarguments around its structure indicate that it filled, to some extent, the vacuum in the theoretical field. Again the reader is referred to other sources for a more complete review of the theory's history (Zigler, 1962; Luchins and Luchins, 1959), but some elements of the problems will be discussed.

Lewin's constructs form an autonomous system, and his terminology cannot be fully understood without a rather thorough acquaintance with the entire theoretical structure. The extension of the system into the area of retardation rested largely, aside from some anecdotal evidence, on the results of three experiments. The first of these was an experiment in behavioral (as distinguished from cortical) satiation, the results of which may with charity be called inconclusive. It was found that 10- to 11-year-old retardates drew "moon faces" for longer periods of time than did equal-CA normals, but there were no such differences in the 9- to 10- year-old groups, and in the 8- to 9-year-old groups the *normals* drew for longer periods of time. Lewin claims, however, that the course of satiation was different, that the retardate was either definitely immersed in the task or interrupted it completely, while the normals were much more flexible, much less "either-or." In the second and third experiments Köpke found that 8- to 9-year-old retardates returned more often to an incompleted task than did 7- to 8-year-old normals, even when a substitute activity of high or low similarity was added.

The theory into which Lewin fits these results states in part that differentiation of the organism's *psychical regions* increases with age. Retardates are said to be less differentiated than equal-CA normals and in this respect are more like younger normals; but even when the degree of differentiation is the same, the boundaries between the regions are more rigid in the retardates. This rigidity of the boundaries results in a decreased mobility of the psychical systems, which accounts for the either-or effect. Lewin enlarges on these and other points and explains certain peculiarities of the retardates' behavior in terms of the theory.

Kounin (1941a), working within the Lewinian framework, postulated that the rigidity of region boundaries is a positive monotonous function of CA as well as of degree of retardation. On the basis of this postulate, he made five specific derivations and tested each in separate experiments. His three experimental groups consisted of older retardates, younger retardates, and normals, all matched on MA, with the same Ss used for each experiment. All predictions were supported by the results. In a follow-up paper (1941b), Kounin commends Lewin's theory as an example of a high-level hypothetico-deductive one which leads to testable derivations, explains a wide range of behavior, and subsumes many other concepts and theories. He makes special note of the fact that theory-based predictions, which were just the opposite of what one might expect, were made and verified and that certain apparently paradoxical findings can be clearly understood on the basis of the theory.

Since the publication of these experiments (which, incidentally, comprised his doctoral dissertation), Kounin performed no further studies in the area and neither, as far as I could find, did Lewin. Up to the Zigler and Stevenson studies (to be discussed shortly), there were some isolated experiments derived from the theory (cf., for example, Shaw & Bensberg, 1955; Plenderleith, 1956), with subsidiary efforts put into theoretical criticisms and replies.

The first of these criticisms came from Goldstein (1943), who agreed that rigidity is an important symptom of retardation and that it is a positive monotonous function of CA; but he argued that its role is not the most important one. He postulated two types of rigidity: primary, most frequently resulting from lesions in the subcortical ganglia; and secondary, resulting from cortical damage or malformation.

Primary rigidity is said to manifest itself in rigidity of set or, as Goldstein terms it, *einstellung*. He cited some observational evidence from a single case and went on to claim that for Kounin's *S*s drawing new figures did not represent a new task. Rather, drawing in general represented an *einstellung*. Secondary rigidity is defined as an impairment of the "abstract attitude" frequently leading to a catastrophic reaction. It is this catastrophic reaction, or fear of it, which results in very rigid, perseverative, or distractible types of behavior.

Thus Goldstein explains the behavior of retardates in terms of the general scheme he uses in analyzing the behavior of brain-damaged patients and even normals (Goldstein, 1939, 1940). Basically, any task which is beyond a person's capacity and which results in failure will lead to very rigid or very distractible behavior; and retardates, because of their limited capacities, more often meet catastrophic situations. However, no experimental evidence is presented to support these speculations about the behavior of retardates or the statement that retardates with subcortical damage behave in a predictably different manner from retardates with cortical damage.

The second major critical paper came from Werner (1946a) and provoked a reply from Kounin (1948). The disagreement centers primarily around the term "rigidity," a term which lends itself so readily to varying definitions. Much of Werner's criticism was based on his own findings with the brain-damaged (1946b), and in the process he also raised some questions about Goldstein's primary-secondary distinction. Kounin replied, in part, that Werner's was a phenotypical concept of rigidity, while his own definition placed it in the realm of a genotypic construct.

But the most extensive attack on the Lewin-Kounin position has come from Zigler, whose series of studies, initiated with Stevenson, have recently been fully summarized (Zigler, 1962). At first they took the position, backed by empirical evidence, that Kounin's results were due to a motivational factor: the desire by institutionalized retardates, who generally have preinstitutional histories with unusual amounts of social deprivation and negative experience, to seek the adult contact and approval which has been denied them. Two additional factors were later added on the basis of further results. The first of these posits that institutionalized retardates also have a "higher negative reaction tendency" toward adults, a result of their frequent negative experiences with adults. The final factor states that, "The positions of various reinforcers in a reinforcer hierarchy differ as a function of environmental events," and institutionalization will act as one variable influencing the position of a reinforcer (see also Brand, Benoit, & Ornstein, 1953).

Although both negative and positive reaction tendencies are higher in retarded than in normal children, the negative reaction tendency is much more susceptible to change than is the positive tendency. For this reason, if *E* is very supportive on an initial or pre-experimental task, a reduction of the negative tendency becomes strengthened (Shallenberger & Zigler,

1961). The opposite effect could be achieved, nevertheless, by failure-punishment conditions. If this is true, as the evidence presented suggests, then the reaction tendencies must be highly susceptible to change.

Zigler sums up his position as follows: "The author and his colleagues have opposed emphasizing the inherent differences between feebleminded and normals. Their position has been that all that is required to understand the performance of the familial feebleminded is his MA and the particular environmental conditions which underlie his motivation" (1962, p. 160). This last task, incidentally, is a rather formidable one.

This position implies that differences between equal-MA *S*s, where there is no brain damage involved, must be due only to motivational factors. If this generalization is intended to be applied to a wide variety of learning, perceptual and cognitive tasks, it is a very sweeping suggestion, and if confirmed, it must have wide impact.

The task of determining what events when experienced lead to the kinds of behavior manifested by retarded children is a difficult one, however; and for the theory to be consistent we must also know the forces operating on the normal control. It must be clearly shown, in any case, that institutionalized retardates have had, and still have, more frequent negative encounters at the hands of adults than noninstitutionalized retardates, or than noninstitutionalized normals for that matter. Zigler has buttressed this contention by the findings of his recently developed social deprivation rating scale.

One final point, which is more of a logical one, must be made. The MA is obtained from scores on an intelligence test. Since the total score is made up of a number of subtests and since many equal-MA *S*s could not possibly have produced the same pattern of scores, it follows that the resultant MA itself is derived from performance differences which could not be attributed to motivation.

The position to be taken in the present paper is that, in fact, the emphasis should be placed precisely on inherent differences and that where differences in the performances of equal-MA *S*s are found, they cannot always, or even usually, be ascribed to motivation. The lines of the two theoretical approaches are clearly drawn.

CORTICAL SATIATION

The theory of cortical satiation introduced most fully in the monograph by Köhler and Wallach (1944) was the natural culmination of a long line of thinking which identified physical, inorganic, self-distributing processes—as demonstrated particularly by electrical phenomena—with the self-distribution of psychological, and particularly perceptual, processes. A cornerstone of this approach is the conception of a structural and functional identity between the organism's experiences and the physiological process underlying these experiences. As Köhler (1947) states it: "when the visual field exhibits a thing as a detached entity, the corresponding process in the brain is relatively segregated from surrounding processes" (p. 344).[3] This

[3] *Ibid.*

principle of psychophysical isomorphism further holds that the distribution and structure of the stimulus, and the functional interrelationship between parts and wholes, correspond to the distribution, structure, and functional interrelationship of its representation in the brain. Furthermore, brain processes are held to be essentially the same as certain physical forms and processes of inorganic nature, such as electrical charges and currents, which distribute themselves in such a way that, functionally, every part of the system depends on all other parts. In fact, cortical currents which accompany the perceiving of visual objects and the hearing of sounds have actually been registered (Köhler, 1958b).

Such perceptual processes as reversible figures and figural aftereffects lend themselves to an interpretation in these terms and were used to demonstrate satiation theory. Although reversible figures are well known, figural aftereffects are not quite so familiar; they can, however, be readily demonstrated. On the left side of Figure 1-1, with your eyes fixated on the small *x*, you will note that the two squares look equal. Now cover the squares and fixate the small *x* between the two circles for about 45 seconds (you may blink, of course). At the end of 45 seconds, cover the circles and switch your fixation back again to the small *x* between the two squares. Most people will now see the lower square as smaller than the upper one.

Figure 1-1. An example of figures used to obtain a visual figural aftereffect.

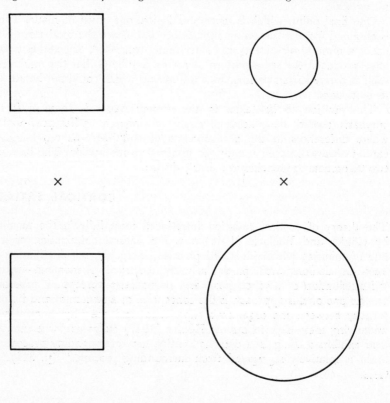

This is an example of a visual figural aftereffect in which a change in size is obtained. Simple displacements and distortions can also be demonstrated, as well as changes in luminosity and in depth, effects which appear to be independent of each other. Aftereffects have been demonstrated with switching monocular viewing, presumably indicating that they occur centrally. They have also been shown to exist in the kinesthetic and auditory modalities.

For one explanation of figural aftereffects, we turn now to the Köhler-Wallach theory of satiation. Only a cursory explanation of the theory can be given here, but the interested reader is referred to the original monograph (1944) as well as to some recent reviews of work in the area (McEwen, 1958; Sagara & Oyama, 1957; Spitz, 1958).

According to the theory, the cortex of the brain acts as a continuous volume conductor. When a figure, for example a single black line on a white ground, is projected onto the brain, the frequency of the impulses of the cortical cells representing the figure is at a different level from those representing the ground. As a consequence the chemical output of the cells is also different, such that the fluid surrounding the more active fibers will be pervaded by a higher concentration of the particular chemical released by the active cells. Since the chemicals in the fluid are dissociated into ions, the differential concentration of participating ions creates an electromotive force, an electric current, from the level of greater activity and greater concentration of ions to the level of lesser activity and lesser ionic concentration, with the cell surfaces constituting the third medium. In other words the two chemically different regions of the tissue fluid plus the adjacent cells set up a current system.[4] This current is greatest at the boundary line of figure and ground. It circles everywhere into the field surrounding the contour of the figure, and the shape of the figure will help to determine the distribution of the current. At some distance from the line, where the current can spread freely, it will be much less dense than within the enclosed area of the line, which is pervaded by current from all directions.

The continued presence of this direct current acts just as do other electric currents. That is, it polarizes all cell surfaces and establishes the condition of electrotonus or—as Köhler and Wallach call it—satiation. In essence, the continued presence of the electric current acts to block its own recurrence; the electric current is progressively self-limiting. The cell surfaces become less and less permeable. Current activity is gradually turned away from this area of increasing impermeability or impedance and into areas of relatively greater permeability.

Now then, let us return to the demonstration in Figure 1-1. Fixating on the *x* between the two circles sets up an area of satiation or impedance in those parts of the cortex representing the contours of the two circles. Upon subsequent fixation of the two squares, the contours of the lower square will fall *within,* while the upper square will *surround,* the area of satiation set up by the contours of the previously inspected circles.

[4] Köhler (personal communication) now feels that this cannot be the *main* cause of such strong currents.

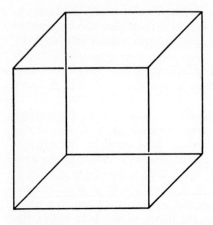

Figure 1-2. The Necker cube.

Consequently, since the lower square falls within the satiated area, its contours will be deflected inwardly away from the area of impedance; and the square will appear to have shrunk. The current representing the contours of the upper square, on the other hand, since they surround the satiated area, will be deflected in an outward direction away from the area of impedance; and that square will appear to have grown.

Satiation theory has also been applied to the understanding of reversible figures, such as the Necker cube shown in Figure 1-2. According to the theory, when one aspect of the cube is forward, the isomorphic cortical representation of that aspect is electrically active and sets up by its continuing activity an area of satiation or impedance. At some critical point the current activity is sufficiently blocked and deflected into the surrounding area so that, phenomenally, the second aspect of the cube stands out, and a reversal has occurred. Naturally, the longer the period of observation, the greater the number of reversals, up to a point.

The value of satiation theory is not primarily in its capacity for explaining figural aftereffects and reversible figures. The real value lies in the fact, if we assume the above explanations to be correct, that aftereffects demonstrate processes upon which gestaltists, and Köhler in particular, have always placed much stress. For example, they have insisted on the primary importance of relational processes in psychological experience, and satiation is said to be produced by the relational effect of the ionic distribution in figure and ground. They have insisted that a percept field spreads in and around a figure and that changes in any part of a field will affect all parts of that field. Within certain time limits the satiation process can be demonstrated to spread in decreasing strength—with the exception of the *distance paradox*—from the contours of the figure into the surrounding field, and reversible figures demonstrate that the current distribution in any portion of the field is dependent upon the current flow in all parts of the field. Finally, the exact same stimulus is phenomenally perceived in different ways depending on the state of processes occurring within the organism.

Many writers have made extensions from Köhler and Wallach's basic investigations and have suggested that individual differences in figural aftereffects reflect underlying physiological differences (Wertheimer & Wertheimer, 1954), although it is now apparent that these differences, perhaps because of permanent effects or input variability, must be confined to particular modalities (Spitz & Lipman, 1960a).

Before demonstrating an application of cortical satiation to the study of mental retardation, certain confusions about the theory should be clarified. One of these is that satiation is a synonym for all kinds of inhibition processes. Actually, satiation may be characterized as a type of autoinhibition created by repeated stimulation in a particular area; it is closest in definition to Hull's concept of reactive inhibition (Duncan, 1956). It is quite different from reciprocal inhibition, for example, or retroactive inhibition, or inhibition of a different response. It will be suggested that a nervous system which exhibits a limitation in autoinhibition is also likely to be limited in displaying other types of inhibition, but this is clearly an inference which does not at all stem directly from tests of cortical satiation.

It should also be pointed out that cortical satiation is not adaptation, nor is it due to the nerve's refractory period. An unresponding adapted nerve will react if the strength of the stimulus is increased (Brazier, 1958, p. 116), but such an increase would not restore to normal cortically satiated tissue; and recovery from both adaptation and the refractory period is almost instantaneous, whereas satiation lasts at least for many minutes. In this respect satiation is more like a fatigue process than anything else.

One final point should be made. Cross-modal aftereffects, although smaller and less stable, have been demonstrated (Jaffe, 1956). It is possible that information concerning local cortical changes is sent by means of some central processing unit to other modalities, which then react in a parallel manner. But in any case, this would have nothing to do with the causes of the initial local change, which is the major concern of satiation theory.

Cortical satiation in retardates

At the Johnstone laboratories a series of studies have been completed in which institutionalized retardates have been compared with equal-CA normals on tests of aftereffects, reversible figures, and certain illusions. I should like now to review briefly only the experiments which stem directly from the theory. Results on experiments using the Müller-Lyer illusion (Spitz & Blackman, 1958) and the spiral aftereffect (Spitz & Lipman, 1959) were not as clear-cut as those obtained when utilizing tasks by which Köhler (1940) had originally demonstrated satiation. It seems that the further we moved from the original tests, the less the differences between retardates and normals.

Visual figural aftereffect experiment.   In the first experiment (Spitz & Blackman, 1959), employing the figures illustrated in Figure 1-1, it was found that retarded boys did not report perceiving the aftereffect as readily or as often as did normal adolescent boys of equal CA. Furthermore, once the aftereffect was perceived, it persisted for a relatively longer period of time than it did with normals. Very tentatively, then, it was suggested that mentally retarded *S*s show a limited capacity to satiate and take longer periods of fixation before they do satiate, and that satiation effects tend to persist longer relative to original satiation levels.

However, it is obvious that the experiment had a number of flaws. It is not easy to maintain fixation although there was always a second *E* observing *S* in order to remind him, when necessary, to fixate. If *S* was unable to do so, he was dropped from the study. Also, the results of the experiment were dependent upon the validity of *S*'s verbal response, a procedure which with retardates is not always defensible.

Kinesthetic aftereffect experiment. A second experiment, using kinesthetic aftereffects (Spitz & Lipman, 1961b), eliminated these flaws. Even though individual differences on visual and kinesthetic aftereffects are not correlated (Spitz & Lipman, 1960a), there is no reason why retardates as a group should not show a limited capacity for satiation in another modality, if indeed this is a true description of retardate functioning.

For the kinesthetic aftereffect test, *S* was blindfolded and asked to judge the width of a straight wooden standard block presented to his left hand by finding the point of subjective equality on a tapered block presented to his right hand. After making four such judgments, he relaxed his right hand and with his left rubbed a larger block of wood for a prescribed period of time—a process which is, incidentally, analogous to fixating circles in the visual test. Immediately after rubbing the larger block, *S* once again had to find the point of subjective equality of the original standard block. If the area cortically representing the contours of the larger inspection block becomes satiated by the rubbing, the standard block will now feel narrower than it did originally, exactly the way the bottom square in Figure 1-1 seemed to have shrunk; and *S*'s point of subjective equality will change accordingly.

The advantages of this test are obvious. "Fixation" by rubbing is not a difficult task. Furthermore, *S*'s responses are now actual judgments, no verbal report being required. High-grade male and female retardates were used, and their preinspection judgments were as accurate as those of their equal-CA controls. But once again the effect of the satiating process, in this case rubbing the wood, was not as great in retardates as it was in normals. After having rubbed the larger block, the standard block shrank to a lesser extent with retardates than it did with normals. This appeared to constitute further evidence that retardates satiate less than do equal-CA normals.

There is some evidence that normal children of 10- to 12-years CA demonstrate kinesthetic aftereffects which are as large as, or even slightly larger than, those of adults (Barthol, 1959). This suggests that retardates may also be characterized as displaying a lowered capacity for cortical satiation than equal-MA normals; but this, of course, requires much more confirmation.

Necker cube experiment. There is one other experiment, carried out in collaboration with R. S. Lipman and published here for the first time, which completes this small series. In this experiment a Necker cube, similar to the one shown in Figure 1-2, was used. The *S*s were asked to say "now" every time the cube reversed. Each S observed the cube steadily for 2 minutes, then had a 2-minute rest, and then observed the cube again for four 30-second periods interspersed with 30-second intertrial rests. The characteristics of the experimental and control groups are given in Table 1-1.

In an attempt to ensure reliable reports from the retardates, prior to the experiment they were shown a wire three-dimensional copy of the cube and told to report "now" each time the cube changed the direction it faced. E then manually shifted the wire cube just as the two-dimensional drawn cube would appear to shift once the experiment began. Only Ss who could perform this introductory task were included in the experiment. Of course, no such preliminary was necessary for the control group. Again, although no fixation point was used, another E always sat to the side to make certain that S continually observed the cube.

Once the experiment began, the behavior of the retarded Ss was convincing. In general, they seemed genuinely startled when reversals occurred, and their behavior at each reversal provided some corroboration for their verbal reports. Most of them were convinced that E was causing the reversals, and their task became one of catching E every time he made the box change—though in reality, of course, the reversals were occurring only within S.

The results, scored as number of reversals reported over 30-second time periods, are shown in Figure 1-3.

Before analyzing these results, a word should be said about some studies which contribute to our knowledge of the relative influence of retinal factors, central factors, and familiarity on reversal rate. Notice that over the first 2 minutes of steady observation, the curves in Figure 1-3 may be characterized as negatively accelerated, a function which can be produced under both fixated and nonfixated conditions (Spitz & Lipman, 1960b). The existence of this type of curve allows for some crucial tests. If, for example, the increase in reversal rate is due to a retinal process, then a switch from one eye to the other after 1 minute—but with the cube still projected onto the same cortical area—will cause a sudden drop in number of reversals. In an experimental test of this possibility, no such drop was found (Spitz & Lipman, 1961a). If, on the other hand, the increasing rate of reversal stems from a central, cortical process, then switching the cube by means of suitably placed fixation points from one brain hemisphere to the other should cause a drop in number of reversals. From results in the same experiment it was found that under these conditions a significant

TABLE 1-1

Composition of retarded and normal groups in Necker cube experiment

	N	Mean age	σ	Mean IQ	σ
Retardates	44	18–4	1.87	58.00	11.46
Normals	46	18–8	0.98		

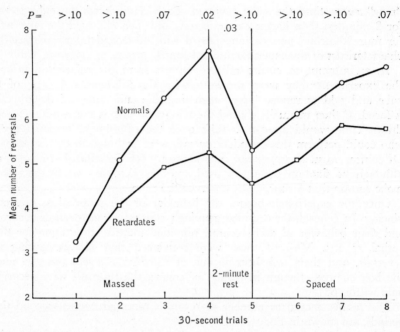

Figure 1-3. A comparison of retardates and equal-CA normals on the Necker cube test. Odd-even reliability for retardates is .94, for normals .93. For the significance of the drop after a 2-minute rest, $P < .10$ for retardates, $< .001$ for normals. P values for the differences between the groups at each point, and for the differences in the size of the drop after a 2-minute rest, are given at the top of the figure.

drop does, in fact, occur; and although familiarity did play a role, it was a relatively minor one. In other words, switching to a fresh retina but maintaining the same cortical area causes no drop in number of reversals, while switching to a fresh retina plus a fresh cortical area does. It would seem reasonable to assume, then, that any differences in reversal rate are due primarily to a central physiological process (see also Cohen, 1959a).

The performance of the retardates on the Necker cube experiment lends further confirmation to the results of the initial visual figural aftereffect experiment. On the average their reversals increase at a slower rate, never reach the same level, and, with rest, decrease at a slower rate than do those of normals. If the buildup in reversal rate is caused by the buildup of cortical satiation, while the drop in number of reversals with a 2-minute rest is caused by recovery of the brain medium from the effects of the satiation process, then it may be inferred that retardates as a group build up and dissipate cortical satiation at slower rates than do equal-CA normals.

Implications. Of the structures presumed to be involved in the satiation process, cortical cells play a major role. It will be recalled that brightness differences between figure and ground set up differential firing of stimulated cells, which in turn produce different concentrations of the emitted chemicals. When, over time, impedance occurs, it is said to occur at the cell membranes. With rest the cell surfaces presumably recover their permeability. It would not be illogical, then, to reason that a reduced capacity to satiate might be caused by reduced cellular functioning. The same impaired functioning would also be responsible for the cells' slowness in regaining their former permeability. The conclusion drawn is that retardates as a group are characterized by a lowered capacity for cellular modifiability or, to use a term introduced by Wertheimer and Wertheimer (1954), by reduced cortical modifiability. On the basis of this conclusion, a group of postulates will be offered. First, however, two alternative hypotheses will be discussed.

Alternative hypotheses. There has been one major attempt to give an alternative physiological explanation for visual figural aftereffects (Osgood & Heyer, 1952). Against this alternative hypothesis a number of objections have already been raised, objections far more serious than those raised against the Köhler-Wallach theory (McEwen, 1958). For example, the Osgood-Heyer theory rests on the notion that small, natural saccadic movements of the eyes are instrumental in setting up the central conditions creating aftereffects; and yet experiments have demonstrated that both visual aftereffects and reversible figures are still obtained when the figures are stabilized on the retina (Krauskopf, 1960; Pritchard, 1958).

However, there is a more serious alternative, not to the explanation of figural aftereffects, but to our explanation of why retardates perform differently from normals on these tasks. Köhler and Adams (1958) have demonstrated a significant positive relationship between attention and the size of visual and kinesthetic figural aftereffects. Furthermore, in the study with stabilized retinal images mentioned above, Pritchard demonstrated that under certain conditions attention may play a role in increasing the reversal rate of a reversible figure. In still another study using stabilized retinal images (Pritchard, Heron, & Hebb, 1960), attention influenced the length of time a figure remained in view before it faded out of sight.

There would seem to be some way in which, as Köhler and Adams put it, attending increases the energy input to a particular part of the field. In an attempt to explain their findings, the principles of natural science are again invoked. Köhler (1955) considers the organism an open system in which energy absorbed from the outside intensifies the processes in the interior. As a consequence, existing differences will be enhanced, resulting in sharpened articulation and greater differentiation. Greater energy input, for example, will intensify the current process between figure and ground, thereby also accelerating the subsequent satiation process. This is said to explain the larger figural aftereffects under conditions of increased attention.

Zeaman (1959) has argued cogently that an attentional deficit plays a major role in certain differences between retardates and normals. We have considered that perhaps something like an attentional deficit may also explain the differences in aftereffects and in reversible figures. However, there are some problems in applying this attractive and parsimonious explanation to our data. For example, attention—or motivation or learning —cannot be successfully invoked to explain differences in number of reversals under massed and spaced conditions (Spitz & Lipman, 1960b) nor can it explain the drop in number of reversals after a 2-minute rest or when the cube is projected to a fresh cortical area. Since the increase in reversal rate cannot be due primarily to an attention factor, it is therefore doubtful that the retardates' lower rate of reversal is due to an attentional deficit.

Furthermore, we have recently found that very high satiaters on the kinesthetic aftereffect test also evidence reliably smaller reminiscence gains and lower postmassing spaced performance on the pursuit rotor task than do low satiaters (Lipman & Spitz, 1961). Greater attention on the part of the high satiaters could hardly cause them to perform more poorly on the pursuit rotor task unless one posits that greater attention during the massing condition caused greater amounts of inhibition to build up. But then, no differences were found between high and low satiaters on a pure spaced condition in which one might expect greater attention to result in a higher score.

The problem, obviously, is not easily resolved. The two processes, cellular torpidity and attentional deficit, may be intimately interwoven, one operating at the cortical level and the other at the level of the reticular activating system. However, until further evidence is forthcoming, our thinking and theorizing will continue to be based on the postulated deficit in cortical modifiability.

FOUR POSTULATES

The inferences up to this point have not strayed too far from the data. All those which follow, however, may be considered second-, third-, and fourth-level inferences (depending upon your outlook) and should be judged accordingly. Nevertheless, it is felt that such theoretical abstractions rooted in varying degrees to experimental findings have their place in a growing science.

Lewin's notions of rigidity summarized previously will not be dragged kicking into these postulates. There are a number of crucial differences. For one thing, the present postulates will be said to hold primarily for mental retardates when they are compared with equal-CA normals. It is hoped that the postulates can be utilized for other comparisons in which case they might be classified, in terms of the probability of successful application, in the manner indicated below. The first-named group would be expected to perform—relative to their comparison group—as the retardates would perform relative to their equal-CA group.

Good degree of probability:

Low-grade retardates versus high-grade retardates of equal CA

Fair degree of probability:

1. Retardates versus equal-MA normals
2. Brain-damaged nonretardates versus normals of equal IQ

This may be an overly cautious approach, but it is felt that at this stage of our knowledge it is best to get a clear idea of where the substantial differences lie before we close in on the finer, more subtle distinctions. Of course, unless the postulates can in fact be extended, their usefulness will be quite limited.

Another major difference is that the present postulates have been molded within a physiological framework, although always with an attempt at constant interplay between physiological mechanisms and behavioral data. Such terms as "differential systems" and "rigid boundaries" may be useful abstractions, but it is the present writer's prejudice to question *what* systems are differentiated and *what* boundaries are rigid. Having no particular affinity for these terms, there will be no attempt to answer such questions. Also, it should be stated that although the present hypothetical constructs are obviously derived from a particular mode of thinking, they cannot be considered a product of any single "school" of psychology.

No theory, or set of postulates, can ever hope to be completely correct. The most that can be hoped is that it becomes a link in that particular chain of theories which is approaching nearer to some more enlightening and more unifying concept. With this thought in mind and with a frightening realization of the pitfalls, the following postulates are offered.

Let us assume from the satiation studies as previously described that—when compared with equal-CA normals—retardates as a group can be physiologically characterized by the following four postulates:

Postulate I. In retardates, it takes longer to induce temporary, as well as permanent, electrical, chemical, and physical changes in stimulated cortical cells.

This postulate does not refer only to the excitation of cells, for it must be remembered that cell excitation does not occur in a vacuum but is accompanied by other changes throughout the brain field. Among these is the reciprocal inhibition which accompanies excitation. Consequently, both excitation and inhibition of cell activity are covered in Postulate I. Also, the delay in inducing change may be somewhat compensated for by an increase in energy input.

Postulate II. Once stimuli induce temporary chemical and electrical modification of cortical cells, it takes longer for these cells to return to their previous state.

Postulate III. In retardates, once stimuli induce permanent chemical, electrical and/or physical changes in cortical cells, it will be more difficult and take a longer period of time to switch consequent like—or relatively similar—stimuli away from these particular cell traces or current patterns so as to form new, or different, traces or patterns.

The terms *temporary* and *permanent* will be further discussed in a later section; but, briefly, by temporary cellular change is meant the electrochemical change that is relatively short-lived and leaves no lasting imprint or physical trace, as opposed to the imprinting of some permanent physical change in the affected cells. (The reader will note that Postulate III is a pure extrapolation since aftereffect studies give no information on permanent effects.) It is assumed that a permanent change made by a particular type of stimulus, or complex of stimuli, is more likely to be the path taken, the pattern reproduced, or the activity elicited by the subsequent reintroduction of that stimulus or like stimuli. It is further assumed, however, that the human organism is an open system in which new trace patterns can be produced not only by the more "passive" natural redistribution of the electrochemical cellular activity but also by the active, forced redistribution of this activity by the input of new elements.

Postulate IV. In retardates, there is less spread of electrochemical activity from stimulated cells into the surrounding cortical field.

Since all four postulates bank on the notion of a torpidity or sluggishness in the cortical cells of retardates, a word should be said, before discussing the applicability of the postulates, about the possible causes of such torpidity. Wertheimer (1955) has suggested lowered metabolic efficiency as a possible source of lowered capacity to satiate. Indeed, when one has a glimpse of the incredibly delicate balance in cellular activity as well as in the metabolic interplay of sugar and oxygen supply, in the sensitive ionic interchange across the membrane of the nerve fiber, and in the chemical and electrical activity of the brain field in general, it is not too difficult to reason that any powerful assault on these physiological mechanisms, whether by the genetic transmission of inadequate mechanisms or by traumatic insult (particularly at an early stage of development), would be enough to upset the balance and timing of these operations. For example, although cells fire on an all-or-none principle, the state of the cells determines the threshold at which they are triggered.

Another point should be made here. Sluggish cellular activity does not necessarily mean sluggish behavior, only less modifiable behavior. That is, a very distractible, overactive organism would find it difficult to slow down and concentrate, just as an overly ponderous organism would find it difficult to accelerate his behavior.

Application of the postulates
Since the postulates are presented in physiological terminology, their usefulness will be limited unless they can be translated into behavioral terms. An attempt to do this will be made by using the postulates to explain some empirical findings and to generate measurable predictions. Necessarily, only a few areas of psychological study will be touched upon, some of these only because they lend themselves to the postulates. The writer is fully cognizant of the fact that each area and each subarea is tremendously complex, and this is in no sense an attempt to be comprehensive.

Visual perception. It has frequently been reported that nonretarded brain-damaged Ss perform more poorly on embedded figure and reversible figure tests than do normals, even when matched for intelligence (Battersby, Krieger, Pollack, & Bender, 1953; Cobrinik, 1959; Dolphin & Cruickshank, 1951; Spivack & Levine, 1957; Spivack & Levine, 1959; Teuber, Battersby, & Bender, 1951; Teuber & Weinstein, 1956; Yacorzynski & Davis, 1945). One surprising exception is the greater number of Necker cube fluctuations reported by *S*s with bilateral frontal lesions (Cohen, 1959b). McMurray (1954) found a lower reversal rate on a moving reversible figure for exogenous as compared with endogenous retardates, but he used no normal control. For some reason the embedded figure test has rarely been used with retardates. Werner and Strauss (1939) reported no differences on this test between exogenous and endogenous retardates, one of their rare failures in this regard.

One problem with the embedded figure test is the lack of standard procedure. The same figures are not always employed. In some experiments the simple figure is withdrawn before presentation of the complex figure (Newbigging, 1954; Witkin, 1950), making memory a contaminating factor. In other experiments the simple figure remains in view but with different multiple-choice procedures (Cobrinik, 1959; Thurstone, 1944). No time limit may be imposed, or there may be time limits of varying amounts.

There is almost always a good reason for these differences in procedure, but it is obviously hazardous to make comparisons and generalizations from embedded figure tests, as well as from other tests, when there are differences in procedure and instructions (Miller & Spitz, 1960). But the prediction from Postulate I is obvious: that retardates will take longer and perform more poorly than normals on embedded figure tests, probably even when matched for MA. The following posited explanation of the processes involved will make this prediction quite clear and is the type of reasoning which may be employed in other areas as well.

There is no reason to change our approach in order to describe what happens when *S* seeks out the embedded figure. We still posit a current distribution set up by the interaction of the currents propagated by the figure contours. Since there are fewer contours in the simpler figure—which is to be sought out in the larger, more complex embedding figure—its contours are relatively isolated with a current distribution quite different from that of the complex figure. When *S* is asked to find in the complex figure the contours of the simple figure, he must break into the existing current distribution of the larger figure. This is quite different from the ordinary matching of like figures in which the shape, and consequently the current distribution, of the two figures is the same even if their size is not. Only by actively breaking into the organization of the more complex figure, only by the active redistribution of the current pattern by the input of new energy or new elements (Köhler & Adams, 1958), can the like pattern be discovered or the like contour matched.

The current pattern established by a contour serving one figure has to be redistributed when the contour now serves another figure. What is being suggested here is that in some organisms this current redistribution is more difficult to induce. The more a contour serves the larger figure, and consequently the greater the investment of its current process in that figure, the greater the force and the longer the time required for a redistribution; and in many cases it may never be accomplished. It is for this reason that figures hidden with shared contours are so much more difficult to perceive than those covered by intersecting contours (Ghent, 1956; Cobrinik, 1959) and that a Necker cube embedded in a larger figure will not cause the same reaction as an isolated Necker cube (Cohen, 1959a).

This same process, a single contour serving two different figures, also occurs in reversible figures; but because of the structure of the reversible figure a more "passive" process, such as satiation, results in a more rapid current redistribution. In order to find a hidden figure, on the other hand, an active part must be played by the perceiving organism. Perhaps this accounts for the fact that individual scores on these two tests do not correlate (Cattell & Tiner, 1949; Thurstone, 1944) or correlate at only a low level (Newbigging, 1954). Nevertheless, because of the postulated crucial involvement of cortical cells in both active and passive redistribution, large groups of disparate Ss may be expected to perform at different levels. It is of incidental interest in this regard that females as a group report significantly fewer reversals (Newbigging, 1954), do significantly poorer on embedded figures tests (Witkin, 1950), and have significantly smaller figural aftereffects (Rechtschaffen & Bookbinder, 1960) than do males.

For the same reason that increasing the contrast between figure and ground will cause an increase in number of reversals (Cipywnyk, 1959; Lynn, 1961), poorer discrimination capacity would be predicted for retardates. That is, anything, be it an interior (Postulate I) or an exterior factor, which retards the intensity of the initial current flow will reduce the discriminability of objects. By the same token two point discriminations should also be poor, especially since spreading inhibition appears to play a role.

From Postulate IV the immediately obvious prediction for retardates is a higher threshold of apparent movement (Werner & Thuma, 1942). It would follow also that retardates should display less capacity for grouping perceptual stimuli, but this would apply only when figures have no strong inherent organization. In such cases, since the "good" figure requires the minimal amount of current process, it must be predicted that retardates would have difficulty in breaking into, or in breaking up, the strongly organized unit. Furthermore, under conditions in which a figure approaches completion into a "strong" or "good" figure, the retardates should have more difficulty than normals in resisting the tendency for closure. In other words, under these circumstances the inability to resist or change the course of an established current flow (Postulate II) or a distribution which requires minimal energy should overcome the weakened spread of activity (Postulate IV), and this will become especially evident with increasing time from the presentation of the original stimulus.

Learning.   Since Postulates II and III differentiate temporary and permanent learning in physiological terms, they should now be interpreted in behavioral terms. This is not a simple task. It has been claimed with some justification that nothing learned is ever forgotten and that all stimuli which impinge upon the sense organs and are relayed to the brain leave *some* trace, perhaps revealed only under certain circumstances, such as hypnosis.

Operationally, however—and circularly, it might be added—in temporary learning, material is forgotten within a very short time, say an hour or so after it is first learned. An example might be a series of seven meaningless numbers which *S* can immediately reproduce but soon forgets. In "permanent" learning, material is retained for years or longer. There might be many reasons for this longer retention; e.g., the material was very thoroughly learned by repetition, its initial introduction to *S* was very startling or had strong personal meaning, it was not soon interfered with, or it was easily incorporated into an already well-organized memory.

With number of trials equated, the retardates will learn more slowly than normals (Postulate I) but forget relatively less, that is, relative to the amount originally learned (Postulate II). They will still, of course, end up retaining less absolute amount of material. We refer here to verbal learning type of tasks, not psychomotor tasks that introduce the contaminating factor of muscular coordination. Since it takes longer to induce change in retardates (Postulate I), they should display less retroactive inhibition when the original task is well learned and the interfering task is introduced for a very short period of time. When one is comparing groups on memory and interference effects, some statistical technique which takes into account differences at different stages of learning, such as an analysis of covariance, might profitably be employed (Pryer, 1960).

But the problem of temporal and spatial grouping and organization is also intimately related to the problem of learning. In a great many instances the retardates' slower learning ability will be hampered still further by a deficit in the organization or grouping of the material to be learned. When, for example, the task is to reproduce six digits, if during the initial presentation normals tend to group the digits into two groups of three digits each, and retardates do not, then in essence the retardates are attempting to learn more bits of information than are the normals. Under such circumstances incoming material must often be overwhelming. The retardates' impoverished capacity to isolate a relevant abstraction is an example of this problem (Griffith, Spitz, & Lipman, 1959; Spitz, 1959; but see also Osborn, 1960). Again, the ability to organize and isolate material which is not naturally organized and articulated presumably requires—just as it does in an embedded figure test—a level of neural flexibility (and energy input) which is generally beyond their threshold.

It would follow, then, that for retardates to learn best, the material must be presented, as far as possible, in a highly organized and articulated state. This brings up the further question of whether training in organizing material would prove valuable, and beyond that whether or not it would generalize to other tasks. In this regard Postulate III generates the deduction that once material is learned well by retardates, it is unlikely to be serviceable in instances which are not directly related to the original learning experience.

Conditioning should take longer to achieve in retardates as should the inhibition of an established conditioned response. A learning set should be reached more slowly, but it should take longer to induce a reversal in the learning set. In both these areas the findings thus far have been contradictory.

Transposition. Where the size differences between them are not too great, two figures, such as a small and large square, placed close together form an organized group which may be labeled a *small-large* unit (Köhler, 1947, pp. 199–202). The ability to learn the absolute size of either figure is tantamount to breaking into the organized group or unit. Once again we have a situation analogous to the embedded figure test, and the same explanation would be applied to the greater difficulty retardates have in making absolute responses under conditions of transposition (Rudel, 1959, 1960). However, the greater the differences between the small and large subunits, so that each becomes more naturally isolated, the less must intent come into play and the more likely are retardates to respond absolutely. Of course, the trace of the total unit would be stronger than the trace of either subunit, so that relational responses are much more likely to occur when there is a period of delay between original learning and the transposition test (Stevenson & Langford, 1957).

Generalization. In hue, pitch, or intensity generalization, it would follow that retardates, as poor discriminators (Postulate I), would produce a flatter generalization curve than normals (Smith, 1961). In spatial generalization, however, where discrimination is usually less of a problem, the prediction is more difficult. On the one hand, a deficit in the ability to inhibit a response suggests greater generalization. On the other hand, from Postulates III and IV we should expect less responsiveness to another stimulus and less spread of the response to the neighboring area. The amount of original learning of the training stimulus would be a crucial factor (Postulate III)—the greater the original learning, the less the relative amount of stimulus generalization in retardates (not supported by Barnett, 1958). Latency of response is another crucial variable. If S is forced to respond within a short period of time, we should expect the inhibition deficit to become dominant and generalization to be greater.

Incidentally, when rewards or verbal reinforcement is given for the correct stimulus (Mednick & Wild, 1958), it might prove useful also to take away rewards or verbally castigate when a response is incorrect, so that S has something to lose by responding to other stimuli. It is worth inquiring, too, whether the ability to inhibit a response is more difficult when S is required to press down on a key, as compared with conditions under which he is required to release a key.

Problem solving. Thinking is conceived of by many gestaltists (Koffka, 1935) as a form process governed by the same laws that apply to perception (Fox, 1959). In order to solve a problem, one must bring out certain aspects and inhibit others. Since there must be a reorganization of the field, the prediction for retardates is obvious. But of particular importance is the application of Postulate III to this area. Retardates would have special difficulty in the adapting of objects or ideas which have been used repeatedly in one type of situation for novel use in the same or in a different context, as, for example, using bricks for book ends or the heel of a shoe one is wearing to hammer a tack, and so forth. For some reason the study of the mental retardates' cognitive processes has been almost totally neglected, though one would think that in studying the parameters of retarded intellectual behavior it would be of principal importance.

LIMITATIONS

It should be quite obvious to the reader by now that the primary interest is in finding some general principles and that individual differences have been disregarded in the process. At the present time, there can be no valid way of applying our findings to the training of retardates. The very presence of large individual differences in all our tasks raises some further serious questions. The extensive overlap between normals and retardates on tests of satiation indicates that the satiation variable must be only a very small one in the total complex of intelligent behavior. It does not, in general, correlate with IQ; it merely differentiates the average performance of two distinct groups.

Furthermore, the test-retest reliability of the scores of retardates is not impressive (Spitz & Lipman, 1961b). There is no intercorrelation of individual scores across certain of the satiation tasks given in different modalities (Spitz & Lipman, 1960a), and even in the same modality correlations have been moderate (Spitz & Blackman, 1958) or nonexistent (Spivack & Levine, 1959).

Finally, there are other theories which would explain the behavior of retardates quite as adequately as ours. In defense, however, it should be noted that the present approach is a deductive attempt to find some element which threads its way across many aspects of intellectually deficient behavior. It is a very broad approach, vulnerable because it is spread so wide. But it has many advantages which, it is felt, outweigh its disadvantages, particularly at the present stage of development in this area. By itself it could not stand, but as a counterpoint to careful empirical studies it makes its contribution.

A POINT OF VIEW

Although physiological psychology is a respected, often required subject for advanced degrees in psychology, for some reason it often becomes—once the student has graduated—an area to be looked at askance. Attempts to include other areas, such as biology and physics, as substantial parts of the study of human behavior are censored outright as being outside the bounds of psychology. Granting even that this may be the case, and aside from the question of who is to delineate these boundaries, can any discipline be confined within a circumscribed area and still survive? More importantly, can scientific curiosity be so restricted? What kind of investigator, pursuing an interesting lead which takes him into another area, would restrain himself because it is purportedly outside his field? His restraint may stamp him as a faithful psychologist, but he will surely be labeled an incomplete scientist (Köhler, 1940).

A view reiterated with parrot-like insistence is the idea that we know too little about brain processes to apply such knowledge to psychological problems. This viewpoint continues despite the increasing fund of information building up with geometric rapidity, and one sometimes suspects that those who defend it most insistently have expended the least effort in discovering the state of knowledge in this area. Allied with this view is the comment that we cannot speculate about things we cannot see, although this is a common procedure in science, as for example when astronomers accurately plot from the course and speed of known planets the presence and course of unseen planets. There are many other examples.

Support of one manner of approaching a problem does not mean a depreciation of the importance of other approaches. If *reductionism* means that there is only one way to study human behavior, there must be very few, if any, reductionists (Cantor & Cromwell, 1957). One approach may be preferred as being more productive in the long run, but this is a wholly different matter. Knowledge of brain processes by itself would probably alter very little the educational and environmental problems of dealing with mental retardates and would be of very little help in understanding group processes, although even in these instances it cannot be ignored. But the more we know about the way in which the brain operates, the more we will know about the sources of the mental retardates' limited intellectual behavior. In any case, if the primary driving force and purpose of the basic researcher is the desire to know and understand what is not yet known and understood, any attempt to defend such research on practical or applied grounds is superfluous.

In a world where the natural sciences have been advancing at a rapid pace, some of the most exciting research is being carried out in attempts to understand the neurophysiological processes which underlie behavior. There have been some dramatic descriptions of the manner in which these incredibly complex processes are thought to occur, such as Sherrington's famous and beautifully literate analysis of brain processes as "an enchanted loom where millions of flashing shuttles weave a dissolving pattern, always a meaningful pattern though never an abiding one; a shifting harmony of subpatterns" (1951, p. 178); and Lashley's "network of cells, organized in various structures and systems, subject to constant excitation from the sense organs, and capable of developing and maintaining a great variety of patterns of activity" (1958, p. 17). Both authors, widely distant from each other in basic viewpoint, nevertheless see a constantly active brain with ever-changing patterns.

If the present standpoint is nothing more than an antidote to the often stodgy, arbitrary, rigid approaches on the one hand, as well as to the unscientific, subjectively based approaches on the other, it will have achieved some purpose. If it arouses eagerness and curiosity in the minds of some students who will one day contribute to our knowledge of the way the brain functions, it will be a great success; and the mentally deficient among others will be the beneficiaries.

REFERENCES

ALDRICH, C. G., & DOLL, E. A. Problem solving among idiots. *J. comp. Psychol.*, 1931, 12, 137–169. (a)

ALDRICH, C. G., & DOLL, E. A. Problem solving among idiots: The use of implements. *J. soc. Psychol.*, 1931, 2, 306–336. (b)

BARNETT, C. D. Stimulus generalization in normals and retardates on a visual-spatial task requiring a voluntary response. Unpublished masters dissertation, George Peabody Coll. for Teachers, 1958.

BARTHOL, R. P. Cortical conductivity: Age differences and other findings. *Psychol. Rec.*, 1959, 9, 153–158.

BATTERSBY, W. S., KRIEGER, H. P., POLLACK, M., & BENDER, M. B. Figure-ground discrimination and the "abstract attitude" in patients with cerebral neoplasms. *A.M.A. Arch. Neurol. Psychiat.*, 1953, 70, 703–712.

BRAND, H., BENOIT, E. P., & ORNSTEIN, G. N. Rigidity and feeblemindedness: An examination of the Kounin-Lewin theory. *J. clin. Psychol.*, 1953, 9, 375–378.

BRAZIER, M. A. B. *The electrical activity of the nervous system.* New York: Macmillan, 1958.

CANTOR, G. N., & CROMWELL, R. L. The principle of reductionism and mental deficiency. *Amer. J. ment. Defic.*, 1957, 61, 461–466.

CATTELL, R. B., & TINER, E. G. The varieties of structural rigidity. *J. Pers.*, 1949, 17, 321–341.

CIPYWNYK, D. Effect of degree of illumination on rate of ambiguous figure reversal. *Canad. J. Psychol.*, 1959, 13, 169–174.

COBRINIK, L. The performance of brain-injured children on hidden figure tasks. *Amer. J. Psychol.*, 1959, 72, 566–571.

COHEN, L. Rate of apparent change of a Necker cube as a function of prior stimulation. *Amer. J. Psychol.*, 1959, 72, 327–344. (a)

COHEN, L. Perception of reversible figures after brain injury. *A.M.A. Arch. Neurol. Psychiat.*, 1959, 81, 765–775. (b)

DOLPHIN, J. E., & CRUICKSHANK, W. M. The figure-background relationship in children with cerebral palsy. *J. clin. Psychol.*, 1951, 7, 228–231.

DUNCAN, C. P. On the similarity between reactive inhibition and neural satiation. *Amer. J. Psychol.*, 1956, 69, 227–235.

ELLIS, W. D. *A source book of gestalt psychology.* London: Routledge, 1938.

FOX, J. Köhler's satiation theory and individual differences in problem solving. *Psychol. Newsltr*, 1959, 10, 119–122.

GALLAGHER, J. J. A comparison of brain-injured and non-brain-injured mentally retarded children on several psychological variables. *Monogr. Soc. Res. Child Develpm.*, 1957, 22, No. 2 (Whole No. 65).

GALLAGHER, J. J. *The tutoring of brain-injured mentally retarded children.* Springfield, Ill.: Charles C Thomas, 1960.

GHENT, L. B. Perception of overlapping and embedded figures by children of different ages. *Amer. J. Psychol.*, 1956, 69, 575–587.

GIBSON, E. J., & WALK, R. D. The "visual cliff." *Sci. Amer.*, 1960, 202, 64–71.

GOLDSTEIN, K. *The organism.* New York: American Book, 1939.

GOLDSTEIN, K. *Human nature in the light of psychopathology.* Cambridge, Mass.: Harvard, 1940.

GOLDSTEIN, K. Concerning rigidity. *Charact. & Pers.*, 1943, 11, 209–226.

GRIFFITH, B. C., SPITZ, H. H., & LIPMAN, R. S. Verbal mediation and concept formation in retarded and normal subjects. *J. exp. Psychol.*, 1959, 58, 247–251.

HEBB, D. O. *The organization of behavior.* New York: Wiley, 1949.

HEBER, R. A manual on terminology and classification in mental retardation. *Amer. J. ment. Defic., Monogr. Suppl.*, 1959, 64, No. 2.

HESS, E. H. Space perception in the chick. *Sci. Amer.*, 1956, 195, 71–80.

ITTELSON, W. H., & KILPATRICK, F. P. Experiments in perception. *Sci. Amer.*, 1951, 185, 50–55.

JAFFE, R. The influence of visual stimulation on kinesthetic figural after-effects. *Amer. J. Psychol.,* 1956, 69, 70–75.

KATZ, D. *Gestalt psychology.* New York: Ronald, 1950.

KOFFKA, K. *Principles of gestalt psychology.* New York: Harcourt, Brace, 1935.

KÖHLER, W. Die physischen Gestalten in Ruhe und im stationären Zustand, Eine naturphilosophische Untersuchung, Erlangen, 1920. As cited by W. D. Ellis, *A source book of gestalt psychology.* London: Routledge, 1938, pp. 17–54.

KÖHLER, W. *Dynamics in psychology.* New York: Liveright, 1940.

KÖHLER, W. *Gestalt psychology.* New York: Liveright, 1947.

KÖHLER, W. Direction of processes in living systems. *Sci. Month.,* 1955, 80, 29–32.

KÖHLER, W. Perceptual organization and learning. *Amer. J. Psychol.,* 1958, 71, 311–315. (a)

KÖHLER, W. The present situation in brain physiology. *Amer. Psychol.,* 1958, 13, 150–154. (b)

KÖHLER, W., & ADAMS, P. A. Perception and attention. *Amer. J. Psychol.,* 1958, 71, 489–503.

KÖHLER, W., & WALLACH, H. Figural after-effects: An investigation of visual processes. *Proc. Amer. phil. Soc.,* 1944, 88, 269–357.

KOUNIN, J. S. Experimental studies of rigidity. I. The measurement of rigidity in normal and feeble-minded persons. *Charact. & Pers.,* 1941, 9, 251–272. (a)

KOUNIN, J. S. Experimental studies of rigidity. II. The explanatory power of the concept of rigidity as applied to feeble-mindedness. *Charact. & Pers.,* 1941, 9, 273–282. (b)

KOUNIN, J. S. The meaning of rigidity: A reply of Heinz Werner. *Psychol. Rev.,* 1948, 55, 157–166.

KRAUSKOPF, J. Figural after-effects with a stabilized retinal image. *Amer. J. Psychol.,* 1960, 73, 294–297.

LASHLEY, K. S. Cerebral organization and behavior. *Proc. Ass. Res. nerv. ment. Dis.,* 1958, 36, 1–18.

LASHLEY, K. S., & RUSSELL, J. T. The mechanism of vision. XI. A preliminary test of innate organization. *J. genet. Psychol.,* 1934, 45, 136–144.

LEEPER, R. A. A study of a neglected portion of the field of learning—the development of sensory organization. *J. genet. Psychol.,* 1935, 46, 41–75.

LEWIN, K. A. *A dynamic theory of personality.* New York: McGraw-Hill, 1935.

LIPMAN, R. S., & SPITZ, H. H. The relationship between kinesthetic satiation and inhibition in rotary pursuit performance. *J. exp. Psychol.,* 1961, 62, 468–475.

LUCHINS, A. S., & LUCHINS, E. H. *Rigidity of behavior: A variational approach to the effect of Einstellung.* Eugene: Univer. Ore. Books, 1959.

LYNN, R. Reversible perspective as a function of stimulus-intensity. *Amer. J. Psychol.,* 1961, 74, 131–133.

MCEWEN, P. Figural after-effects. *Brit. J. Psychol., Monogr. Suppl.,* 1958, Whole No. 31.

MCMURRAY, J. G. Visual perception in exogenous and endogenous mentally retarded children. *Amer. J. ment. Def.,* 1954, 58, 659–663.

MEDNICK, S. A., & WILD, C. Stimulus generalization in brain-damaged children. Final Rep., USPHS grant M-1519, 1958.

MILLER, M. B., & SPITZ, H. H. Differences in reversal rate of ambiguous figures as a function of stimulus "meaningfulness" in a retarded group: An exploratory study. In R. L. Cromwell (Ed.), *Abstracts of Peabody studies in mental retardation.* Nashville: George Peabody Coll. for Teachers, 1960, Vol. 1, Abstr. No. 63.

NEWBIGGING, P. L. The relation between reversible perspective and embedded figures. *Canad. J. Psychol.,* 1954, 8, 204–208.

OSBORN, W. J. Associative clustering in organic and familial retardates. *Amer. J. ment. Defic.,* 1960, 65, 351–357.

OSGOOD, C. E., & HEYER, A. W., JR. A new interpretation of figural after-effects. *Psychol. Rev.,* 1952, 59, 98–118.

PLENDERLEITH, M. Discrimination and discrimination reversal learning in normal and feebleminded children. *J. genet. Psychol.,* 1956, 88, 107–112.

PRITCHARD, R. M. Visual illusions as stabilized retinal images. *Quart. J. exp. Psychol.,* 1958, 10, 77–81.

PRITCHARD, R. M., HERON, W., & HEBB, D. O. Visual perception approached by the method of stabilized images. *Canad. J. Psychol.,* 1960, 14, 67–77.

PRYER, R. S. Retroactive inhibition in normals and defectives as a function of temporal position of the interpolated task. *Amer. J. ment. Defic.,* 1960, 64, 1004–1015.

RECHTSCHAFFEN, A., & BOOKBINDER, L. J. Introversion-extraversion and kinesthetic aftereffects. *J. abnorm. soc. Psychol.,* 1960, 61, 495–496.

RUDEL, R. G. The absolute response in tests of generalization in normal and retarded children. *Amer. J. Psychol.,* 1959, 72, 401–408.

RUDEL, R. G. The transposition of intermediate size by brain-damaged and mongoloid children. *J. comp. physiol. Psychol.,* 1960, 53, 89–94.

SAGARA, M., & OYAMA, T. Experimental studies on figural aftereffects in Japan. *Psychol. Bull.,* 1957, 54, 327–338.

SHALLENBERGER, P., & ZIGLER, E. Rigidity, negative reaction tendencies, and cosatiation effects in normal and feebleminded children. *J. abnorm. soc. Psychol.,* 1961, 63, 20–26.

SHAW, M. E., & BENSBERG, G. J. Level of aspiration phenomena in mentally deficient persons. *J. Pers.,* 1955, 24, 134–144.

SHERRINGTON, C. *Man on his nature.* (2nd ed.) New York: Cambridge Univ. Press, 1951.

SMITH, J. Stimulus generalization in mental defectives. Paper read at East. Psychol. Ass., Philadelphia, April, 1961.

SPITZ, H. H. The present status of the Köhler-Wallach theory of satiation. *Psychol. Bull.,* 1958, 55, 1–28.

SPITZ, H. H. Cortical satiation as a common factor in perception and abstraction: Some postulated relationships based on the performances of atypical groups. *Amer. J. ment. Defic.,* 1959, 63, 633–638.

SPITZ, H. H., & BLACKMAN, L. S. The Müller-Lyer illusion in retardates and normals. *Percept. mot. Skills,* 1958, 8, 219–225.

SPITZ, H. H., & BLACKMAN, L. S. A comparison of mental retardates and normals on visual figural aftereffects and reversible figures. *J. abnorm. soc. Psychol.,* 1959, 58, 105–110.

SPITZ, H. H., & LIPMAN, R. S. Some parameters in the perception of the spiral aftereffect. *Percept. mot. Skills,* 1959, 9, 81.

SPITZ, H. H., & LIPMAN, R. S. Reliability and intercorrelation of individual differences on visual and kinesthetic figural aftereffects. *Percept. mot. Skills,* 1960, 10, 159–166. (a)

SPITZ, H. H., & LIPMAN, R. S. Some effects of spacing, massing and rest on the rate of Necker cube reversals. Paper read at East. Psychol. Ass., New York, April, 1960. (b)

SPITZ, H. H., & LIPMAN, R. S. Retinal and central factors in Necker cube reversals. Paper read at Amer. Psychol. Ass., New York, Sept., 1961. (a)

SPITZ, H. H., & LIPMAN, R. S. A comparison of mental retardates and normals on kinesthetic figural aftereffects. *J. abnorm. soc. Psychol.,* 1961, 62, 686–687. (b)

SPIVACK, G., & LEVINE, M. The spiral aftereffect and reversible figures as measures of brain damage and memory. *J. Pers.,* 1957, 25, 767–778.

SPIVACK, G., & LEVINE, M. Spiral aftereffect and measures of satiation in brain-injured and normal subjects. *J. Pers.,* 1959, 27, 211–227.

STEVENSON, H. W., & LANGFORD, T. Time as a variable in transposition by children. *Child Develpm.,* 1957, 28, 365–370.

STRAUSS, A. A. Typology in mental deficiency. *Proc. Amer. Ass. ment. Def.,* 1939, 44, 85–90.

STRAUSS, A. A., & KEPHART, N. C. *Psychopathology and education of the brain-injured child.* New York: Grune & Stratton, 1955.

STRAUSS, A. A., & LEHTINEN, L. E. *Psychopathology and education of the brain-injured child.* New York: Grune & Stratton, 1947.

TEUBER, H.-L., BATTERSBY, W. S., & BENDER, M. B. Performance of complex visual tasks after cerebral lesions. *J. nerv. ment. Dis.,* 1951, 114, 413–429.

TEUBER, H.-L., & WEINSTEIN, S. Ability to discover hidden figures after cerebral lesions. *A.M.A. Arch. Neurol. Psychiat.,* 1956, 76, 369–379.

THURSTONE, L. L. *A factorial study of perception.* Chicago: Univer. Chicago, 1944.

WERNER, H. The concept of rigidity: A critical review. *Psychol. Rev.,* 1946, 53, 43–52. (a)

WERNER, H. Abnormal and subnormal rigidity. *J. abnorm. soc. Psychol.,* 1946, 41, 15–24. (b)

WERNER, H., & STRAUSS, A. A. Types of visuo-motor activity in their relation to low and high performance ages. *Proc. Amer. Ass. ment. Def.,* 1939, 44, 163–168.

WERNER, H., & STRAUSS, A. A. Pathology of figure-background relation in the child. *J. abnorm. soc. Psychol.,* 1941, 36, 236–248.

WERNER, H., & THUMA, B. D. A deficiency in the perception of apparent motion in children with brain injury. *Amer. J. Psychol.,* 1942, 55, 58–67.

WERNER, H., & WEIR, A. The figure-ground syndrome in the brain-injured child. *Int. Rec. Med. G.P. Clin.,* 1956, 169, 362–367.

WERTHEIMER, M. Untersuchungen zur Lehre von der Gestalt. II. *Psychol. Forsch.,* 1923, 4, 301–350. As cited by W. D. Ellis, *A source book of gestalt psychology.* London: Routledge, 1938, pp. 71–88.

WERTHEIMER, M. Figural aftereffects as a measure of metabolic efficiency. *J. Pers.,* 1955, 24, 56–73.

WERTHEIMER, M., & WERTHEIMER, N. A metabolic interpretation of individual differences in figural aftereffects. *Psychol. Rev.,* 1954, 61, 279–280.

WITKIN, H. A. Individual differences in ease of perception of embedded figures. *J. Pers.,* 1950, 19, 1–15.

YACORZYNSKI, G. K., & DAVIS, L. An experimental study of the functions of the frontal lobes in man. *Psychosom. Med.,* 1945, 7, 97–107.

ZEAMAN, D. Discrimination learning in retardates. *Trng. Sch. Bull.,* 1959, 56, 62–67.

ZIGLER, E. Rigidity in the feebleminded. In E. P. Trapp and P. Himelstein (Eds.), *Readings on the exceptional child.* New York: Appleton-Century-Crofts, 1962.

2

A SOCIAL LEARNING APPROACH
TO MENTAL RETARDATION[1]

Rue L. Cromwell

The clinical psychologist, as he performs his professional chores, cannot say he has a thorough identification and understanding of all the important factors involved in his activities. Psychodiagnostic, psychotherapeutic, and consultative work, when it is successful and when it is not, is yet greatly a product of the artistic and wise use of common sense rather than of scientific understandings. This truth calls for no apology. The history and present status of other scientifically based service disciplines are reassuring enough. The concern of the clinician about this matter need only be for ways to advance and refine his skills in service to individuals.

That basic research is effective for making these changes is a premise of this chapter and of this book. To have better psychodiagnostic constructs and methods, better therapeutic approaches, or better consultative work on the environmental and organismic conditions necessary for behavior to become what we now call "adjusted" and "habilitated," more advanced understandings are needed of the underlying phenomena. That these advanced understandings will lead to improved clinical practices is the premise of the basic research clinician. This does not imply that research should not be done concurrently on the applied level or that service work should not advance and thereby provide a wake of ideas for the basic researcher. Let each person follow his own interests and skills. An implication is indeed

[1] Acknowledgment is given to Maurine Behrens, Irv Bialer, Earl Butterfield, William I. Gardner, Samuel Guskin, Rick F. Heber, Thomas R. McConnell, Jr., Robert B. McIntyre, Martin B. Miller, James W. Moss, Daniel Ringelheim, Dorothy Shipe, Joseph E. Spradlin, Donald Stedman, and Wolf Wolfensberger, who have argued, developed, and researched the ideas presented here. Acknowledgment is also given to Bob King, manager of the Hiway Pup.

tenable, however, that the sound advancement of applied clinical techniques depends on systematic investigation of the basic variables involved.

The clinical problem of mental retardation, as it exists today, is largely a paradox. The conventional continuity from diagnosed syndrome or etiology to treatment and prognosis is rarely present. The etiologies and syndromes of retarded conditions, described in neurophysiological or biochemical constructs, suggest curative and remedial approaches most infrequently. Those rare instances which do have distinctive, medically treatable syndromes are overpopularized, as if to keep alive the traditional physical etiology → treatment concept. Meanwhile, the major and formidable clinical problem with retarded individuals is to educate and habilitate them toward the greatest degree of behavior efficiency and happiness possible. If true to the paradox, this problem will continue to demand a sophisticated analysis of the individual which is in great part independent of what etiological factor caused the retarded condition. This paradox is still not fully realized, especially by the educator and the psychologist in whose areas the problem greatly resides.

Constructs such as intelligence, differential ability, social competency, perceptual-motor linkages, and personality factors must continue to evolve and be refined in order to give better indications about how and where the clinician, teacher, and other workers should be spending their time. As crude as they may be at present, these and the other psychoeducational constructs are in the vast majority of cases more important than primary etiology constructs when it comes to restoring the typical retarded child to maximal functioning.

One segment of this basic research, the personality factors, is approached in this chapter through social learning theory (SLT) (Rotter, 1954). The following questions have been considered important. What personality effects accrue as a result of limited behavioral efficiency? How do these factors affect the long-term functioning of the retarded individual? To what extent do *psychogenic* or *sociogenic* factors depress functioning? Whether the research attempted here provides basic knowledge which will be ultimately useful awaits judgment at a later time.

A LITTLE PHILOSOPHY OF SCIENCE

The research described here deals with such constructs as expectancy, generalized expectancy, locus of control, higher-level skills for increased effort, approach and avoidance tendencies, and so on. The notion is rejected that these are entities or even "correct" or irrevocable constructs. They merely seem to be the best constructs to use, although the best constructs today are none too good. The point of view here is that no constructs, even those with established levels of utility, merit a continued existence if others are developed which do a still better job of predicting the same phenomena. For example, one would not have to assume that organisms learn, acquire habit, etc., if constructs were available which predicted behavior acquisition phenomena in a way better than present-day learning constructs. A good theory will characteristically promote enough research to evolve its own constructs out of current usage. A poor theory, well popularized but with untestable hypotheses, may survive longer.

The nature of the subject matter is viewed here within the framework of Kantor (1958). The subject matter of all sciences consists of events occurring within a framework of time and space. Scientific disciplines are partitioned from each other as a function of the arbitrary divisions of labor among the various disciplines. Psychology has as its subject matter those events which concern the interaction of the individual with stimulus objects in his environment. The interest of the personality psychologist is limited still further to those events which allow predictions about the long-term, recurring behavior patterns characteristic of a single individual. The scientific method, involving (1) sharable observations of these events, (2) recording of them into protocol, (3) analysis of the protocol with mathematics and logic, and (4) the scientific construction of these findings, is a process which is common to all sciences. Psychology has no special sanctions in method and no unique universe of subject matter.

The present research should perhaps be discussed in terms of its philosophy of hypothesis development. Researchers vary greatly on this score. Some prefer to take as little as possible for granted, to work out as clearly as possible the functions of each variable before proceeding on to hypotheses which involve new variables. Others choose to make larger "leaps" in their investigations by introducing a greater number of assumptions and using assumptions which are often based on conjectures about reality rather than on firm data about reality. It is the latter philosophy which is more often implicit here. For example, a number of studies discussed later proceed from the assumption that a typical retarded child has more failure experience than a typical normal child. This is a broader conjecture about reality than some theorists would wish. No one has observed the life situations of retarded and normal children and counted the number of unsuccessful goal-directed behavior attempts. However, the assumption that this conjecture may be true has led to a number of different testable hypotheses.

Although one strategy is chosen primarily, the point of view here is that each strategy of hypothesis development is admirable if it is carried out conscientiously and well. Each has its merits and its disadvantages. The former strategy is obviously a more meticulous and cautious approach to research. By chipping off each unknown a piece at a time one is in a much better position at any one time to say what is known for sure and what is not known for sure. The major disadvantage is that this strategy promotes slow theory development.

The other strategy allows one to wade further and faster into new ideas. One says, "*If* A is true, and *if* B is true, and *if* C is true—we do not know for sure, of course, but if they *are* true—then we should predict that X has an effect on Y." So, one has the opportunity to move ahead to X and Y without ever having verified the verifiable aspects of A, B, and C. In other words, "Why worry about the number of assumptions if the hypotheses continue to be confirmed?" The progress can be exciting, but the pitfalls are many. If one gets positive results in the research on X and Y, one assumes he is on the right track and that A, B, and C are useful assumptions. One can then skip ahead to another study. However, positive results are possible because unidentified factors, other than A, B, and C, bear upon X and Y. If this possibility obtains, one may perhaps propagate an inadequate theoretical explanation in the literature which may take years to invalidate and decades for people to unlearn. Furthermore, if one gets negative results, one has a long way to back up. Figuratively, one has fallen flat on his assumptions. All the assumptions may be adequate but one; they may all be inadequate; or, as usual, there is the possibility that all were adequate but the methodology to test X and Y was poor. In the "step-by-step" strategy, although assumptions are still involved, one does not have so far to back up when negative results are incurred. The factors to which negative results may be attributed are fewer. Nonetheless, the myth is rejected here that negative results are ever interpretable, i.e., attributable to a true independence of the relationship between X and Y. No matter how tight the assumptions, there are always the possibilities that the theory or assumption(s) was inadequate, that the hypothesis was deduced and translated incorrectly into operational terms, that the methodology was sloppy with error variance and did not measure what was proposed for measurement, that an extraneous variable not considered in either the theory or methodology was operating, and finally that the theoretical hypothesis as such was incorrect. Perhaps the greatest—and most often overlooked—value of negative results is that they can stimulate enlightened research based on new assumptions about why they were negative.

These strategies of hypothesis development are only relatively different, and the advantages and pitfalls are likewise only relatively different. Let each researcher choose the strategy which is comfortable to his personality. Why not?

A BIT OF ORTHODOX SLT

The social learning theory of Rotter (1954) provides the basis of departure for the research and theoretical formulations to be described in this chapter. The antecedents of this theory reflect themselves in various ways. For example, his scientific philosophy and basic postulates often have the orientation of Kantor. The working constructs, such as expectancy and reinforcement value, are reminiscent of Lewin, Hull, and Tolman. The application within a social context shows the influence of Adler.

In line with Kantor, Rotter postulates that "the unit of investigation for the study of personality is the interaction of the individual and his meaningful environment" (1954, p. 85). An additional assumption is made, however, when Rotter postulates that this interaction, "as described by personality constructs, has a directional aspect" (1954, p. 97). This assumption sets a tone for much that follows in the use of the theory. It assumes that a referent point in the *meaningful environment* may be identified toward which or away from which the individual is moving, hence the notions of approach and avoidance behavior. The assumption breaks through an earlier behavioristic tradition that the laws in psychology must relate immediate stimulus conditions to behavior (S-R laws). Here, although any lawful relationship among factors in the event is properly allowable, attention is placed on goal objects or threat objects (whether physically present or not) toward which the individual's behavior is predictable.

Since all constructs are defined in terms of the interaction of the individual with his meaningful environment, all internally couched or dualistic concepts are rejected. Fascinatingly enough, in contrast to other theories, the term *need,* therefore, becomes equivalent to *goal.* Each is inferred from the same directional behavior of the individual. When it is desirable that the language emphasize aspects of the environment, the term goal is used. When aspects of the individual are to be emphasized, the term need is used. In each case, however, the same concept and referent are employed.

Finally, Rotter postulates that "the occurrence of a behavior of a person is determined not only by the nature or importance of goals or reinforcements but also by the person's anticipation or expectancy that these goals will occur" (1954, p. 102). This postulate gives a basis for the working concepts of the theory. Of these, there are four: expectancy, situation, reinforcement value, and behavior potential. The major working formula for molecularly described situations interrelates these concepts as follows:

$$BP_{x,s_1,r_a} = f(E_{x,R_a,s_1}, \ \& \ RV_a)$$

The formula may be read as follows: The potential for behavior x to occur in situation 1 in relation to reinforcement a is a function of the expectancy of the occurrence of reinforcement a following behavior x in situation 1 and the value of reinforcement a in situation 1 (Rotter, 1954, p. 108).

This formula illustrates how the theory cuts across the conventional distinctions between S-R and R-R laws (Spence, 1944). *RV* is typically measured through the response of the individual (thus yielding an R-R prediction), but it may on occasion be inferred culturally. The use of E to predict *BP* is typically an R-R prediction since E is measured from some verbal or behavioral response of the individual. On occasion, however, it is roughly inferred from the objective schedule of reinforcements given the individual, thus, in these cases, an S-R prediction. The $s,$ the situation variable, which serves to limit the generalizability of the formula, is likewise independent of the usual distinction. Although the use of objective situational stimuli as a measurement provides an S-R prediction, it is sometimes used in an R-R fashion when measured as a verbally mediated response of the subject, i.e., the situation as reported by the subject.

Both *RV* and E break down into components. *RV* is a function of the expectancy that the present reinforcement will lead to other reinforcements, together with the values of these subsequent reinforcements (Rotter, 1954, p. 152). E is a function of E' (the situational expectancy developed as a function of the schedule of reinforcements in the situation in question) and GE (the generalized expectancy developed from reinforcements in other situations and generalized to the present situation) (Rotter, 1954, pp. 165–168). The formula is thus $E = f(E' \ \& \ GE)$. The latter component,

GE, is one of those regarded as having special relevance to mental retardation.

Going beyond this basic formula, an additional assumption is made which opens the way to a more general formula: "a person's behaviors and goals are not independent but belong in functionally related systems." More specifically, a person's behaviors are interrelated, and on occasion intersubstitutable, as a function of leading to the same or similar types of reinforcements (Rotter, 1954, p. 101). These interrelated sets of behaviors are referred to as need categories (goal categories, need clusters, goal clusters). For example, one behavior may be viewed as related to or intersubstitutable for another, if each leads to the same love and affection goal, dependency goal, or achievement goal, etc.

This gives rise to the formula:

$$NP = f(FM \ \& \ NV)$$

This is the molar version of the basic formula. It is independent of specific situations but assumes some broad category of situations. It predicts the occurrence of classes of behaviors rather than individual behaviors. It may be read as follows: Need potential (the probability of behaviors occurring within a given need category) is a function of the freedom of movement (the mean expectancy that behaviors within this category will lead to reinforcement) and the need value (the mean RVs of the various kinds of reinforcements within this category) (Rotter, 1954, p. 110). No inclusive set of need categories has been established. Their development depends on the prior experiences of the individual. Love and affection, dependency, independence, dominance, and recognition status are specific categories whose generality has been established (Rockwell, 1950).

The system of constructs in social learning theory was formulated for the purpose of making predictions of behavior in complex social situations, in clinical diagnosis, and in psychotherapy. It is also felt that extrapolations from the theory would be useful in making predictions of group behavior within a social science framework.

AN EXPLORATION OF MENTAL RETARDATION

The research presented here represents deductions and departures from social learning theory in the area of mental retardation. The theory has been a tool in producing hypotheses and organizing facts.

Two preliminary studies. Among the many questions which could represent a starting point for a series of research projects, the following general question was focused on: How does the retarded individual modify his behavior as a function of success or failure in prior experience? From the theory one would make the simple prediction that the expectancy increment or decrement resulting from a particular experience would affect the immediately subsequent behavior. This preliminary notion was examined in two different ways, once by Starkman and Cromwell (1958), once by Ringelheim (1960). In each case the results were what has modestly been called "significant at the point-oh-shucks level."

Starkman and Cromwell (1958) predicted that subjects who had a positive evaluation of their accomplishments on an initial performance would have a greater increment (practice effect) during a second performance. Forty-two institutionalized mentally defective subjects were given a digit-symbol task which offered no objective basis by which to evaluate performance. They were then asked how well they did. The answers, forced into a four-point good-bad dimension, were mostly positive. The subjects then repeated the task. The verbal evaluation was used to predict the practice effect from the first to second performance, with initial performance level being controlled through analysis of covariance. The results showed no relationship between stated evaluation of performance and subsequent practice effects.

Ringelheim (1960) gave 20 retarded subjects a digit-symbol task after asking each how he thought he would do. Answers were again arranged on a good-bad dimension. Half of the subjects were given a fixed goal point of 50 substitutions and were stopped 10 cells short of the goal. The other half performed the same amount with no specified goal or indication of failure. The major finding was that *all* subjects gave a verbal expectancy of good performance, and *no* significant shifts occurred in these statements as a function of the objective failure.

Four subsequent notions. These two preliminary studies led to the following notions about research with the mentally retarded: (1) Failure, after all, is a socially learned phenomenon. The retardate is impaired in ability to conceptualize himself as having failed or not failed. (2) The *verbal* reaction to perceived failure is a complex thing which demands a more refined investigation. (2) Studies of verbal behavior should be avoided in favor of studies with motor-behavior criteria in order to get reliable results. The retardate's verbal behavior is unreliable. (4) The retardate tends to use his language to please or as wish fulfillment rather than to describe what reality is.

Actually, all four of these notions were pursued. Regarding the first notion, Bialer (1957) obtained inconclusive results in a study which attempted to show that retardates with inconsistent self-labeling were oblivious of failure. Later, his study of the development of success and failure conceptualization (Bialer, 1960) amply supported the notion that retardates were impaired in this area. This study will be discussed later in the chapter. The second notion, regarding the need for a more refined investigation of verbal reactions to success and failure, was followed up at a later time by Ringelheim (1958). This is also discussed later in the chapter. The third notion, involving the use of motor behavior in assessing the reactions to success and failure, was followed up by Gardner (1957) and Heber (1959). The fourth notion was pursued shortly thereafter by Cromwell and Moss (1959). Research based on the latter two notions will be discussed briefly.

In pursuing the fourth notion, Cromwell and Moss (1959) studied the effects of reward value on stated expectancies in mentally retarded subjects. If retardates use their language extensively in the direction of wish fulfillment, then it would be predicted that the value of a particular event would greatly influence the stated expectancy. To examine this, 80 retardates were each presented a card-guessing task under three different conditions. In each condition the subject was to guess what color card would come up in a series of 80 cards, 40 black and 40 yellow. The cards were always randomized by shuffling and were out of sight until the subject made each guess. In the first condition the subjects guessed the series without reward. In the next two conditions the appearance of a card of one particular color always brought a reward regardless of the subject's response. Another reward was given if the subject guessed any card correctly. These two conditions differed only in amount of reward. Theoretically, a stated expectancy is a verbal behavior, the potential of which is a function of E and RV. Thus, the reward conditions would be predicted to yield an increased stated expectancy for the valued card according to the magnitude of each reward condition. As predicted, the reward conditions brought significantly more guessing of the valued card than would be expected by chance. Contrary to prediction, the high- and low-reward conditions did not differ significantly from each other. A further pilot study indicated that the amount of influence of reward value upon stated expectancies was comparable to that found in normal individuals. Thus, within the limits of this investigation, no support was found for the notion that retardates are more prone than normals to use language for wish fulfillment.

The third notion, focusing on the use of motor-behavior criteria, was, in part, introduced by Heber (1959). Thirty-six retardates were matched into two groups on the basis of performance on a motor task similar to the experimental task. All subjects were asked to rank a set of prizes in a manner typically used to measure RV, so that a high- and low-incentive object was identified for each subject. The two groups were then given trials on a form-board task under high- and low-incentive conditions, respectively. After 12 trials the incentive conditions were reversed. As predicted (from Hullian theory), the high-incentive group attained a higher speed of performance than the low-incentive group. Then, when the incentives were reversed, the original low- and high-incentive groups made rapid shifts upward and downward, respectively, in performance. If viewed in SLT terms, the RV was independently varied while E was controlled and the expected shifts were observed in BP. Thus, in the study Heber demonstrated that educable retardates were sensitive to changes in reward value.

Gardner (1957) investigated the effects of interpolated success and failure experience on motor task performance in mental defectives. Forty-five subjects, divided into three groups and matched on the basis of performance on a task similar to that being used for the experiment, performed for 2 minutes on a simple card-sorting task. Then, one group was given success experience on a different motor task. A second group was given failure experience, and the third group performed the same task without knowledge of success or failure. After this all groups were tested on the original experimental task. In terms of gain scores, the success group exceeded the failure and control groups. The failure and control groups did not differ from each other.

Gardner then examined a fourth group which was given an interpolated experience called *partial failure*. This involved working for an interim prize and receiving three successful trials toward achieving the prize. Then, on the fourth and final trial, the subject was failed and did not receive the prize. Gardner found that this type of interpolated failure experience brought a deficit in performance so that the gain scores were significantly less than those of the control and total-failure groups.

The studies just described showed fairly clearly that reactions to the relative shift in reward value and to interpolated success and partial-failure experiences were sensitively reflected in motor speed measures. Also of value for future research was the finding that total failure had an effect no different from the control condition, while partial failure did have a debilitating effect.

The third phase: generalized expectancy and avoidance behavior. The next series of investigations was based on theoretical assumptions that the average retardate has a lower *GE* for success (see Figure 2-1) and a higher tendency toward avoidant behavior than the average normal subject. If constitutional limitations of the average retardate cause him to have more failure experiences than the average normal child, then we should expect from the theory that this experience would lead to a low *GE* for success. Since *GE* is a component of *E* which in turn is a predictor of *BP*, we should assume lowered *BP*s for the kinds of behaviors and goals associated with the failure. Along with the decreased *BP*s for these goal-directed behaviors, the *BP*s for avoidant behavior could become relatively higher in the heirarchy. Thus, the likelihood of further failure is increased; not only the constitutional impairment but also the depressed *BP*s would lower the behavior efficiency. Since the depressed *BP*s are likely to increase the probability of failure, the *GE* would be lowered still further, and so on, in a cyclic effect.

Heber (1957) advanced this line of thinking by investigating expectancy

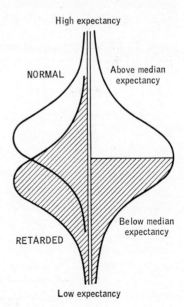

Figure 2-1. Illustration of expectancy levels in retarded and normal groups.

changes in retardates and normals. In a novel task situation one assumes that only *GE* is operating. In the formula $E = f(E' \& GE)$, no E' has developed because the subject has not yet had experience in the situation. Thus, $E = f(GE)$ for the novel situation. Then, as experience is obtained in the situation the predictive weight (not necessarily the value) of E' becomes greater while the predictive weight (not the value) of *GE* becomes less and less. This is expressed in the formula, $E = f[GE/(N+1) \& E']$, where *N* is the number of trials or amount of experience in the situation.

From these theoretical positions Heber assumed that when retarded and normal children were matched on initial performance on a task, the retarded children were potentially better in terms of constitutional ability because their initial matching performance was somewhat depressed owing to low *GE*. If true, a series of predominantly success trials would build a high E' for success, and the predictive importance of *GE* would become less. In this way, the retardate should soon excel the normal in performance. On the other hand, if the matched retarded and normal subjects were given a series of predominantly failure experiences, the constructs would lead one to predict a decrement in *BP*s and, therefore, in performance. This decrement would be expected in both groups. The normal group, initially higher in *GE*, would show the greater decrement.

To test these predictions, Heber gave mentally retarded and normal boys a series of 24 trials on a simple reaction-time task. The normal children were younger (aged 7 to 9½) than the retarded children (aged 9½ to 15) so that comparable performance could be attained. A reaction-time task was chosen because no learning curve or sequence effects are demonstrable in normals and retardates. Initial trials for matching purposes were given with no knowledge of results. Then, half of each group was given predominantly success experience. The other half was given predominantly failure experience. After the subjects were run, the present author matched

Figure 2-2. Mean (reciprocal) reaction-time performance under a series of predominantly success trials. *Note:* Speed of response measure is based on the reciprocal of the latency score.

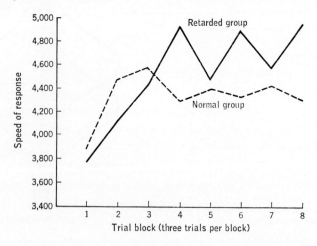

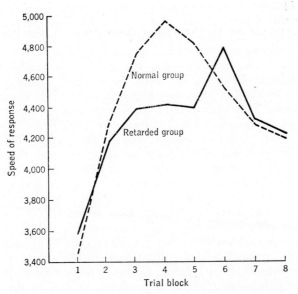

Figure 2-3. Mean (reciprocal) reaction-time performance under a series of predominantly failure trials.

retardates and normals by initial performance without having knowledge of their subsequent performance. This yielded 30 matched pairs of subjects for the success condition and 30 matched pairs of subjects for the failure condition.

The results are presented in Figure 2-2 for the success condition and in Figure 2-3 for the failure condition. As predicted, the increment from initial to final performance for the retarded group, under the success condition, is greater than the increment for the normal group. The utility of the *GE* construct was demonstrated in the correct prediction of these results. Contrary to prediction, however, the failure condition produced an increment and then a subsequent decrement in each group. These data could not be handled by the constructs heretofore employed.[2]

The distinctively contrary findings in the failure condition indicated that further constructs should be invoked to describe reactions to failure. Specifically, a failure experience seemed to have situational cue properties as well as reinforcing properties. The Heber prediction about failure had been made on the assumption that only reinforcing properties, which would effect *E'*, were operating. Of greater importance, perhaps, was the *s* variable. His subjects categorized the situation as one where particular behaviors, such as increased effort or withdrawal from threat, were appropriate. Here, in a mild failure situation, the subjects seemed to be using the failure as a cue calling for increased effort responses. Then, continued failure cues brought a subsequent recategorization that the situation was hopeless.

[2] A third phase of Heber's study, concerned with testing the independence of *E* and *RV* in normals, is not reported here.

Gardner (1958), in examining these reformulations, built his assumptive structure in the following way: First, he incorporated the previously held assumptions about the roles of *GE* and *E'* with normals and retardates. Second, he incorporated the revised notion that failure has situational cue properties for recategorizing the situation and has the reinforcement properties of negative *RV* as well. Third, he assumed the magnitude of a failure was a function of the discrepancy between the *E* level and the actual failure outcome. This means that if one's expectancy for success is low, the magnitude of the failure is low. On the other hand, if the *E* level is high, the failure is of greater magnitude. Fourth, he assumed that situational cue properties of failure bring forth previously learned *BPs* and *Es* for behaviors which avoid or cope with failure. Fifth, he thought that these failure-reactive behaviors may be described usefully in terms of increased effort and psychological withdrawal or decreased effort. Sixth, he felt that normals have had more opportunity than retardates to learn that increased effort after failure may lead to success. The retardate, because of limited ability, would less often have acquired success by "trying harder next time." Seventh, regardless of the direction of the failure-reactive behavior, the absolute magnitude of behavior change was assumed to be a function of the magnitude of the failure, as previously defined by the expectancy-outcome discrepancy (Gardner, 1958, pp. 28–38).

On the basis of these assumptions, Gardner examined the reactions of retarded boys after experimentally induced failure. Sixty retarded and sixty normal subjects attending regular classes were matched on a simple card-sorting task closely similar to the one used in the experimental study. Then, in the experiment proper, as shown in Table 2-1, the subjects were given a pretest on a card-sorting task, as neutral in reinforcement effects as possible with no knowledge of results. After this, the 40 normals and 40 retardates of group I received failure in an interpolated pencil-marking task while working for a highly valued prize. The groups were subdivided according to the type of failure. One group received total failure, or lack of success, on every interpolated trial; and the other group, with partial failure, was allowed success on all but the final trial. The 20 normal and 20

TABLE 2-1

The effects of interpolated failure on card-sorting speed

	Initial phase	Middle phase	Final phase
Normal group I	Card sorting	Failure $\begin{cases} \text{total} \\ \text{partial} \end{cases}$	Card sorting
Retarded group I	Card sorting	Failure $\begin{cases} \text{total} \\ \text{partial} \end{cases}$	Card sorting
Normal group II	Card sorting	No failure	Card sorting
Retarded group II	Card sorting	No failure	Card sorting

Gardner

Reactions to interpolated failure experience

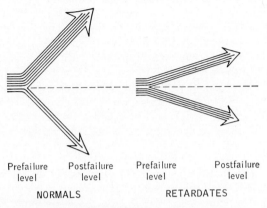

Prefailure level	Postfailure level	Prefailure level	Postfailure level
NORMALS		RETARDATES	

Figure 2-4. Illustration of Gardner's hypotheses.

retarded children in group II performed on the same interpolated task without any prize or experimentally defined failure.

From the assumptions it was predicted that the absolute magnitude of change would be greater for the normals than for the retardates, that the normals would more often increase in performance after the failure, and that the partial-failure subgroups would have a greater magnitude of change than the total-failure subgroups. These hypotheses are partially illustrated in Figure 2-4 with the directions and angles of the arrows indicating the direction and magnitudes of change after failure, respectively. The thickness of the arrows illustrates the relative frequency of subjects choosing a particular direction.

As predicted, the normal group showed a greater absolute magnitude of change than did the retarded group after failure. Also, as predicted, the number of retardates to increase their performance following failure was considerably less than the number of normals to do so (see Table 2-2). This retarded-normal difference is significant in spite of the tendencies of both groups to increase their performance. Also, as predicted, the control group comparisons of retardates and normals revealed no differences. When subjects received no experimentally induced failure, there were no differences in absolute change scores or tendencies to show increased effort. Con-

TABLE 2-2

	Persons increasing after failure	Persons decreasing after failure	Direction of change in performance following failure
Normal *S*s	37	3	
Retarded *S*s	25	15	

Gardner

trary to expectations, no differences were found between the total- and partial-failure subgroups.

These findings lent general support to the notions that a greater magnitude of failure is experienced by normals as a function of not expecting it and that normals more often than retardates learn to increase effort in the face of failure. On the other hand, the results did not substantiate the notion that a partial failure (or, $+ + + -$) sequence could experimentally produce a temporarily increased expectancy which would give rise to a greater magnitude of reaction to failure. It will be recalled that Gardner's earlier study (1957) did yield the expected differences between partial- and total-failure conditions.

It will be noted that Heber and Gardner, while examining hypotheses based on advanced theoretical assumptions, were using criteria involving motor performance. Ringelheim (1958), on the other hand, persisted in his inquiry of how success and failure are mediated through verbal reactions in the retardate. In order to do this, he used the vertical lift apparatus, as adapted by the present author (Cromwell, 1959; Rotter, 1961; Sky, 1950), to allow complete control of the subject's success or failure without the necessity of verbal feedback from the experimenter (see Figure 2-5). The subject's task is to pull a cord which lifts a carriage by pulley to the top of a vertical shaft. On the carriage is a steel ball. The object of the task is to lift the carriage to the top without letting the ball fall off. The shaft has graduated markings so that if the ball is carried beyond the designated point, a prize can be awarded. Unknown to the subject, the carriage has concealed within it an electromagnet. Since the top surface of the carriage is slightly sloped, the ball will fall off whenever the experimenter presses a hidden switch cutting the current to the electromagnet. Invariably, the subject perceives the ball's falling off to be a result of his own inability to guide the carriage smoothly to the top of the shaft. (In Figure 2-5, the experimenter holds the switch in view, the ball is falling, and the subject is closer to the apparatus than usual.)

Ringelheim placed a goal marker midway on the shaft of the vertical lift. This allowed subjects to "win" or "lose" by varying degrees depending on how close the ball was to the goal marker when it fell off. Each subject was given eight chips preceding each trial and was required to bet a self-chosen number on his ability to raise the ball at least as far as the goal marker. He tested 48 retarded and 48 normal boys in four groups, each group having a predetermined schedule of success and failure. Group I began with excessively poor performance and improved continuously throughout the 24 trials. After the twelfth trial, the ball surpassed the goal marker each time, allowing for success in increasing degrees. Group II started with perfect and successful performance on the first trial and had decreasing performance from there on. After the twelfth trial the ball fell off below the goal marker allowing failure of greater and greater magnitude. Group III began with minimal winning performance (barely above the goal marker) and increased for 12 trials. Then, minimal failing performance (barely below the marker) began, with decreasing performance occurring

Figure 2-5. The vertical lift apparatus.

in the final 12 trials. Group **IV** began with this same minimal failure performance and continued to decrease for 12 trials. Then, they were given minimal success followed by increasing (successful) performance on the final 12 trials.

This design allowed Ringelheim to examine the verbal (betting) reactions to the failure and success conditions. Would the retardates make lower bets in the beginning because of lower *GE*s? Would they have greater variability in betting, thus attesting to the "unreliability" of retardate language as suggested in earlier studies? What would happen in critical situations where internal and external reinforcement were opposed, i.e., where the subject's performance was continually improving but was still failing (losing chips), or where the subject was successful (winning chips) but decreasing trial by trial in performance? Would the subject's betting be determined by the direction of change in his own performance or by the fact that he was winning or losing chips with respect to the goal-marker position? Would normals and retardates differ in this respect?

The results were straightforward. The retardates did not differ from normals in initial betting level. They were not more variable than normals in betting. Nowhere- was there evidence that the increase or decrease in performance (or, closeness of performance with respect to the goal marker) had an effect on betting. Instead, the *external reinforcement* (reaching marker and winning chips) produced an increasing gradient of betting amounts. This was true whether the winning performance had a trial-by-trial increase or decrease. No such declining gradient occurred with continual failure (losing chips) due to substandard performance; however, the general level of betting was lower in the failure than in the success conditions.

An unexpected finding was that the betting performance of retardates became significantly lower than in the case of normals during a failure sequence which followed a success sequence. This finding was reminiscent of the finding by Gardner (1957) that partial failure (failure following initial success) is more debilitating than complete failure. Thus, the expectancy-outcome discrepancy, as defined by Gardner (1958), may still have possible utility in predicting a detrimental behavior effect.

Except for this one unexpected finding, the betting patterns of retardates were very much like normals. The different external failure and success conditions produced highly similar betting behavior. Figure 2-6 shows the betting behavior of subjects in groups I and IV, where external failure was followed by external success. It also shows the betting behavior of subjects in groups II and III, where external success was followed by external failure.

These findings by Ringelheim support the possibility that somehow or other the verbal or stated expectancy measures of retardates do not differ greatly from those of normals. However, motor-behavior measures do reflect differences which can be theoretically predicted by differences in expectancy.

At about this time more attention began to be focused on avoidant behavior in retardates (Moss, 1958). This was done through extending some of the theoretical assumptions. The basic assumption was Rotter's directionality postulate, which

> . . . led to the consideration that the description of behavior in approach and avoidance terms would have some utility. Behavior could be described as "approach" if the individual were observed to respond primarily to goal-related cues in his environment. It could be described as "avoidant" if the individual responded primarily to cues associated with potential threat. Thus, two behaviors which may appear identical could differ dynamically in that one could be in response to threat elements of the field while the other could be in response to positive goal elements [Moss, 1958, p. 2 (abstract)].

From this directionality notion and the concept of *GE*, which had already been employed, a new construct was introduced:

(The) inference was drawn that an individual with a low generalized

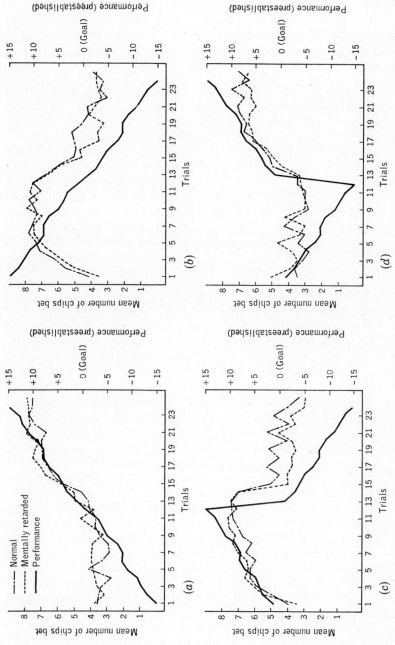

Figure 2-6. Betting of normal and mentally retarded subjects as a function of ascending and descending vertical lift performance: (a) ascending performance (group I); (b) descending performance (group II); (c) ascending descending (group III); (d) descending ascending (group IV).

expectancy for success would, in fact, give up trying to be successful as a general rule. Rather, he would be primarily concerned with the prevention of additional failure.

These concepts of directionality led to the formulation of the "success-striving vs. failure-avoiding" construct. At one pole of the continuum, the *success-striving* individual was described as one with a high generalized expectancy for success who responded primarily to cues which would point the way to continued success. The *failure-avoiding* person, at the opposite end of the continuum, was described as one with a very low generalized expectancy for success who responded primarily to cues in the environment (negative cues) which would lead to the prevention of additional failure [Moss, 1958, p. 3 (abstract)].

Differences in learning approach were formulated as follows:

It would seem apparent that the failure-avoider would function under a handicap in an open-system learning situation; i.e., one where the subject would not be led to the "correct" response through the identification of the "incorrect" response. Being threatened by possible failure, he would not attend to cues leading to success until he had identified and learned the cues associated with possible failure in the situation. Thus, he would have two sets of cues to learn (positive and negative) as compared with the success-striver who would concern himself with the positive cues only. The failure-avoider would not find himself under such a handicap in a closed system task where the avoidance of the "incorrect" response would lead (simultaneously) to a "correct" response [Moss, 1958, p. 4 (abstract)].

On the basis of the previous research, it seemed plausible to associate the failure-avoiding tendency with the retarded individual. Therefore, to examine the formulation, Moss selected 39 mentally retarded children, having low achievement scores but in regular public school classes, as the failure-avoiding group. A group of 38 second-grade children, having achievement scores at or above the median and IQs from 95 to 120, were designated the success-striving group. A multiple alternative discrimination (MAD) box was designed which allowed up to four discrimination stimuli to be presented at the same time. A finger press on one stimulus, regardless of its position, produced a red light (correct) signal, and the same response to another stimulus produced a buzzer (incorrect) signal. Instructions were given to associate the red light and buzzer with success and failure, respectively, and this association was perpetuated throughout the experiment by verbal comments of approval and disapproval.

After becoming familiar with the routine, the subject was given a standard four-stimuli task until he could identify the one correct stimulus to a criterion of six consecutive correct responses. Then the subject was asked which of the other three stimuli was the "incorrect" one. (The other two stimuli gave no signal.) He continued trying until he could identify it. Each subject was then presented with a two-alternative discrimination task with a reinforcement signal only for the correct stimulus.

The following was hypothesized: (1) The failure-avoiding (retarded) group, being more sensitive to the negative stimulus signal, would learn to avoid it and make fewer responses to it during the multiple alternative learning series; (2) the failure-avoiding group, matched on number of trials to the criterion, would be more able to identify the negative stimulus after learning than would the success-striving (normal) group; (3)the failure-avoiding group, having performed both an avoidance and an approach learning activity during the first task, would be able to learn the double-alternative task more quickly than the success-striving group, when matched for trials to criterion on the original task; and (4) subjects, without regard to experimental group, who identified the negative stimulus of the first task on the first try would learn the two-alternative task more quickly than subjects who needed three guesses to identify the negative stimulus. In the latter hypothesis a new success-striving group and failure-avoiding group were essentially being formulated on the basis of awareness of the "incorrect" stimulus in the original task. Thus, the normal-retarded classification was ignored.

When the results were analyzed, none of the hypotheses was confirmed. In fact, none showed a hint of approaching significance. Much speculation has been carried out, especially by Bialer (1960), Butterfield, and Moss himself (1958), regarding the possible reasons for nonsignificance. This speculation, as usual, has led to further studies. Meanwhile, other studies were cropping up which lent results quite compatible with the success-striving versus failure-avoiding (SS-FA) formulation. It would be well to look at these for a moment rather than to let the formulation die immediately.

One of the implications of the success-striving versus failure-avoiding formulations in classical conditioning is that conditionability would depend in part on the individual's reaction to the UCS. The failure avoiders, being more reactive to the negative cues, would be expected to have learning facilitated by a negative UCS. The opposite might be true for the success strivers. And, indeed, as one looks into the literature on conditioning, one finds that Razran (1933) reports a study by Osipova (1926) where subnormal children conditioned faster than normal children in a shock-avoidance situation. Another study is described (Mateer, 1918) where normal children conditioned faster than retardates in a food-approach situation. These studies, if well controlled and reported correctly, are astounding, but they support the formulation studied by Moss. Recent studies (Cromwell, Palk, & Foshee, 1961; Franks & Franks, 1962), suggesting the independence of eyelid conditioning and intelligence, leave some question about how to interpret these results.

In recent years much attention has been placed on the relationship between eyelid conditioning and the Taylor Manifest Anxiety Scale (e.g., Spence & Farber, 1953). This relationship is typically interpreted in terms of the Taylor scale's being a measure of generalized drive. Jessor and Hammond (1957), however, criticized this interpretation because the items of the scale did not follow logically from the Hullian concept of generalized drive. Since predictive validity is nonetheless present, one is led to wonder what the Taylor scale is measuring. Could it be measuring, in part, a learned avoidance drive, as would be suggested by the SS-FA construct? If so, one would expect the Taylor scale to be related to avoidance (such as eyelid) conditioning but not to approach conditioning.

Bindra, Patterson, and Strzelecki (1955) found some indirect evidence for the avoidance interpretation in that the Taylor scale did not predict food-approach salivary conditioning. Hilgard, Jones, and Kaplan (1951) seem to regard anxiety, such as that measured by the Taylor scale, as a specific defensive drive rather than a generalized drive. This seems similar, if not identical, to the present formulation.

In an attempt to find additional evidence of the relationship between the Taylor scale and avoidant behavior, Cromwell, Moss, and Duke (1960) reexamined the eyelid conditioning and Taylor scale data of Caldwell and Cromwell (1959). They correlated each item on the Taylor scale with the rate of eyelid conditioning in 51 college subjects. Judges classified the Taylor scale items into three major categories: (1) physiological, (2) generalized avoidance, and (3) specific avoidance. The latter two were distinguished according to whether some particular object or situation was being avoided or whether there was a general negative feeling state or reactivity to negative cues. The biserial item correlations were then analyzed to see which categories carried the major weight in predicting conditioning. As hypothesized, the item correlations of the generalized avoidance category were significantly positive and those in the physiological category were not. Contrary to prediction, the items in the specific avoidance category fell short of positive significance. Some degree of support is therefore offered for the notion that the Taylor scale is a measure of a learned avoidance tendency. Meanwhile, Miller and Cromwell (1961) have also found results with the Taylor scale supporting an anxiety-as-avoidance rather than anxiety-as-drive concept.

With this degree of support for an approach-avoidance construct, such as SS-FA, let us now turn to the question of the degree to which we can associate the avoidance end of the construct continuum with mentally retarded individuals. Returning to the differential reactions in a learning paradigm, as described by Moss, it will be recalled that the success-striving individual will be oriented toward the cues which represent success, whereas the failure-avoiding individual will be oriented toward cues which allow him to avoid the greatest amount of failure. These reactions seem to be illustrated by the studies of Stevenson and Zigler (1958) and Shipe (1960) in probability learning with retardates and normals.

Stevenson and Zigler (1958) had three groups of children press response keys. Two of the keys were never reinforced. The third key was reinforced 100 per cent of the time in one group, 67 per cent of the time in another, and 33 per cent of the time in the third group. Under 33 and 67 per cent reinforcement, the retardates predominantly chose the reinforced key, therefore reaching a higher asymptote of correct performance than the normals, who varied their choices and responded less frequently to the "correct" key.

Shipe (1960) compared retardates and normals on probability learning where subjects guessed which stimulus would occur as the two stimuli were presented in (1) 60 to 40 per cent ratio and (2) 80 to 20 per cent ratio. The retardates reached a higher asymptote of guessing the 60 per cent stimulus than the normals. The retardates' asymptote exceeded the 60 per cent level in choosing the more frequent stimulus. They did not differ from the normals in choosing the 80 per cent stimulus. The choices of both groups asymptoted at 80 per cent in the second study.

If these two studies were to be viewed within the framework of the present formulations, it would seem reasonable to say that the normals, being success striving toward 100 per cent correct response, varied their behavior in an attempt to find the "perfect" sequence and in so doing lowered their level of success. The retardates, being content only to avoid the failure associated with the choices which were paying off poorly, did not try for the completely successful sequence of choices. They focused predominantly on the high-probability stimulus even though it was not paying off 100 per cent of the time. If such an interpretation is valid, it is in support of the SS-FA formulation.

A more recent study by Butterfield and Zigler (1961) offers partial support for the SS-FA formulation as applied to mental defectives. On the assumption that in a task with a restricted number of alternative responses the FA (retarded) subjects would learn better with negative verbal incentives and SS (average) subjects would learn better with positive verbal incentives, a probability learning task was administered to retardates and normals with preestablished incentive conditions. A significant interaction, as predicted, between incentive condition and intelligence gave partial support to the SS-FA formulation.

The SS-FA distinction has also received support in studies of persistence (Green & Zigler, 1961; Shallenberger & Zigler, 1961; Zigler, Hodgden, & Stevenson, 1958; Butterfield, 1961c).

Why, then, did Moss fail to get results in support of the SS-FA formulation? Although many possibilities have been offered, one will be discussed here since it was valuable in leading into the next major phase of the research.

The fourth phase: locus of control. Moss described his subjects as often seemingly unconcerned about whether the outcome of his discrimination task had anything to do with their own behavioral skill. They often seemed more involved with the activity than the achieving of criterion. The possibility therefore occurred that the subjects he used were too young to conceptualize success and failure. If so, the utility of the SS-FA construct could not actually be validated with them. Whether this is the crucial reason for negative results might be decided at a time when the Moss experiment is applied carefully to older individuals. Meanwhile, however, Bialer and Cromwell (1960), Spradlin (1960), and Miller (1961) obtained firm evidence of developmental changes in the reaction of young children to success and failure. These investigators gave educable retarded children two puzzles to complete. Each child was allowed to complete one and was interrupted on the other. Also, he was informed of his success and failure, respectively, at the end of each task. The subject was then given the choice of returning to the failed or completed task in a nontest situation. This is the repetition-choice procedure introduced by Rosenzwieg (1933). As predicted from the 1933 report, the older retardates tended to return more to the failure (interrupted) task, while the younger children tended to return more to the successful (completed) task. Thus, this one-item test seemed to give firm evidence of differences between younger and older noninstitutionalized retarded children in success-failure conceptualization.[3]

At this point a redefinition was made of success and failure, and a tentative theoretical formulation was built to serve as a basis for the next study. Success and failure up to this point had been thought of operationally in terms of the observed attainment or nonattainment of a goal, respectively. At this point, the following definitions were introduced: Success is the attainment of a goal under conditions where the individual attributes the attainment to his own effectiveness. Failure is the nonattainment of a goal under conditions where the individual attributes the outcome to his own (lack of) effectiveness.

This redefinition of success and failure, although similar to previous ones (e.g., Lewin, 1935, p. 250; Sears, 1940, p. 499; Keister, 1937, p. 31), tends to thicken the plot as far as the present series of research studies is concerned. Some of the previous interpretations must be reconsidered. For example, as was intended, the generality of the SS-FA construct has to be restricted. Not all avoidant behavior would be failure avoidant. Some noxious objects and situations would be avoided even though the individual would perceive no responsibility or would not see his own behavioral effectiveness at stake. Not all goal attainments would be success-striving activities. In some situations the individual may see his goal attainment as owing to chance or as the result of another person's efforts rather than his own. Thus, if this awareness of one's own control in the outcome of events develops with age, we should expect the SS-FA construct to apply more often to older individuals and only to situations where an individual conceptualized himself as being in control. The type of avoidance reflected in eyelid conditioning and the Taylor scale may not be failure avoidance.

Another problem, a semantic one perhaps, concerns the way in which failure and success have been used in the investigations up to this point. What has been called experimentally induced failure (e.g., Heber, 1957; Gardner, 1958; Ringelheim, 1958) may not have been failure. Or, it may not have been failure for all subjects. There seems to be no simple word already in existence to describe nonattainment of a goal without using the term failure inappropriately. A child who has "failed" to fit a puzzle together has not failed unless he maturely conceptualized the activity as a measure of his own effectiveness; he has merely encountered a situation which might in hedonic terms be described as unpleasant or frustrating.

Special attention must also be paid to the systematic distinction between *GE* and the proneness to see oneself in control of the outcome of events. Could the latter construct account for the results previously ascribed to *GE*? These things should be kept in mind as we proceed.

[3] McConnell (1961a) failed to find this developmental trend in institutionalized retardates.

With the new success-failure definition and the developmental assumption about it, the following formulation was then developed:

> In the early stages of development, there is no conception between the outcome of events and one's own behavior. Consequently, young children, as a group, tend to view their experiences as being externally controlled. If the child's goal-directed behavior is blocked or frustrated, he categorizes it as an unpleasant (or noxious) experience—probably imposed upon him by some outside agency. If an undertaking is pursued to a satisfactory conclusion, or gratification is achieved, it is categorized as pleasant experience.

> As development proceeds, the child begins to note that he is often able to influence the outcome of events by his own actions. Therefore, as the child grows older, he is more likely to view many of his goal-directed experiences as being internally controlled. With the shift in the conceptualization of locus of control from external to internal there evolves, by definition, the ability of the child to categorize the outcomes of certain goal-directed behaviors in terms of success and failure. If an activity is gratifyingly fulfilled, and its outcome is recognized by the child as being due to his own ability, it is now not only categorized as a pleasant experience; it is also construed as a successful one. By the same token, when the child can conceive of an unfavorable outcome as being due to his own shortcomings, this outcome is not only unpleasant, it is also construed as failure [Bialer, 1960, pp. 3–4 (abstract)].

At this point, Bialer incorporates the concepts of ego-involvement and tension-maintenance into the formulation:

> However, while internal locus of control is a necessary condition for the awareness of success and failure, it is not a sufficient one (in order to be motivated with respect to success and failure). Although the child may be able, developmentally, to conceptualize these phenomena, he will probably become aware of and respond to them only in situations which contain elements of competition or ego-involvement. Since ego-involving situations are actually contingent upon the ability to see oneself as an instrument in the outcome of events, it is apparent that the conceptualized internal locus of control (as a personality variable) and competition or ego-arousing cues (as situational variables) interact to bring about the awareness of success and failure in such situations. Moreover, since the above personality and situational variables are dependent on the appropriate prerequisite learning, only the older child is capable of this kind of awareness.

> Along with the ability to perceive internal locus of control and to respond to certain situations as ego-involving (and, therefore, to conceptualize success and failure), there evolves the ability to delay gratification. This latter ability implies the growth in the capacity to sustain biological and/or psychological tension. Given a situation in which the child is

called upon to forego an immediate reward for the sake of a greater reward in the future, the younger child would not be able to tolerate the tension associated with delay. He would respond to cues denoting immediate pleasure and would choose the lesser valued reward—without seeing himself as having failed to get the greater prize. The more mature child, having the ability to maintain the tension generated by the postponement of immediate need-satisfaction, and being able to construe the choice of the lesser reward as failure on his part, would choose to defer his gratification [Bialer, 1960, pp. 4–5 (abstract)].

To summarize the formulation briefly, we posit that the child is born with a simple hedonistic pleasure-pain awareness, that he learns to associate the outcome of events with his own behavior, and that he consequently develops a success-failure awareness. Along with this comes the reactivity to ego-involving or competitive cues in the environment and an ability to be able to maintain a tension (approach or avoidance tendency) over a period of time with respect to these cues and to the success-failure awareness.

At this point an additional assumption is made explicit about the nature of motivational systems. It is perhaps already apparent that a distinction is made here between approach and avoidance motivational systems. This distinction is considered more useful in the behavior predictions attempted here than the assumption of a single generalized drive. The additional assumption now presented is as follows: It is useful to distinguish two levels of motivational systems, one based on the biological drive structure of the organism and the other based on a later developed system (or systems) involving the conceptualized goals of success striving and failure avoiding. In other words, in addition to becoming aware of the *relation* between event outcomes and one's own effectiveness (i.e., aware of success and failure), one becomes motivated toward the express goal of *demonstrating* one's own behavioral effectiveness—and is motivated to avoid situations as threatening where behavioral ineffectiveness might obtain. One becomes motivated expressly to approach success and to avoid failure, independent of the other goals involved in the situation with which the behavior effectiveness is demonstrated.

The distinction between the two systems might be elaborated on as follows. The earlier, biologically based motivational system is described and studied in research on learning founded on primary and secondary rewards. It is viewed as common to both the human and lower animal forms. Within the present framework of description, it would be identified and described in terms of behavior sequences which approach objects and events which are either (1) biologically drive satisfying themselves or (2) originally neutral but have acquired approach value through association with the biologically satisfying events. Likewise included would be those behavior sequences which avoid events and objects which are noxious in a biological context as well as those neutral stimuli which have gained avoidance value through their association with noxious objects and events. For this reason, this system might be simply labeled in hedonistic language, the *pleasure-approach and pain-avoidance* system.

By contrast, the later motivational system is viewed as follows. Rather than approaching objects and events because of their inherent or acquired properties for satisfaction, approach behavior is carried out for the express goal of demonstrating behavioral effectiveness. Avoidant behavior is carried out to avoid situations where personal behavioral effectiveness is threatened. So delineated, it might be called the *success-approach and failure-avoidance* (SA-FA) system. Exactly what is approached in the way of biological and learned goals may vary from food on the one hand to complex social goals of recognition, love and affection, achievement, etc., on the other hand. Common to all of these would be the striving of the individual to demonstrate and to conceptualize himself as personally successful in the goal-directed endeavor in which he is involved. The later system does not replace the earlier system but rather is elaborated from it (see Figure 2-7). Because of the involvement of the motivational system in the conceptual behavior of the individual, one would not expect a counterpart of this system in the non-language-bearing organisms.

How do the two systems evolve? The earlier system, as viewed conventionally, involves stimuli from biologically noxious and depriving situations and, secondly, the secondary reinforcing stimuli which were once neutral but have acquired drive properties by association with the biologically noxious or deprived states. In responding to these drives, the organism is learning what responses lead to drive satisfactions (goal attainments) and what stimulus objects and situations are acquiring negative and positive value. At the same time, however, the organism is involved in another associative learning process. The stimulus information about the event outcomes, whether the goal has been attained or not attained, is fed back and associated with such things as the behavior the individual has just carried out, the thinking or the conceptualizing he was doing at the time of the terminal reinforcement, and the labels, concepts, and behaviors of other people around him as the event was taking place.

Figure 2-7. Relative roles of later and earlier motivational systems.

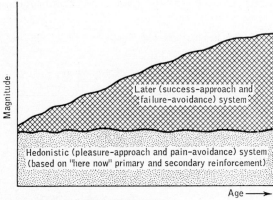

Without attempting to explain *how* the feedback process *initiates* the later system, it is here assumed that the magnitude of the later system develops as a function of the degree to which the child can associate and conceptualize event outcomes with his *own* behavior. In contrast, to the extent that he associates event outcomes with the efforts of people other than himself or to chance, the later system would not be expected to develop with as great a magnitude.

The purpose of Bialer's study (1960) was to test some aspects of this formulation. The first problem was to find different measures from which the magnitude of the later system could be inferred and to see if there was generality or intercorrelation among them. Then, there was the problem of showing that the later system develops together with the conceptual development of the individual.

One of the practical difficulties in getting an operational measure of the magnitude of the later system is that in most life situations it is confounded with the earlier motivational system. That is, what would be pleasant or satisfying (drive reducing, if you wish) in the earlier system would likely be conceptualized as successful in the later system. That described as painful (noxious or depriving) in the earlier system would likely be conceptualized as failure in the later system. These two classes of events would be illustrated by the dotted areas in Figure 2-8. The opportunity to distinguish between the two, therefore, lies in those situations where the confounding does not exist. This would occur in situations where motivation to success or behavioral effectiveness demands the endurance of some deprivation or noxious stimulation in the immediate situation and/or where the acceptance of immediate gratification would be conceptualized as failure. These two classes of events would be illustrated by the check marks in Figure 2-8.

Bialer chose two experimental situations which he assumed discriminated between the two motivational systems. One was the Rosenzweig repetition-choice task which was described earlier. Here it was interpreted that the more mature individual, returning to the failure puzzle, was oriented toward eventual success rather than returning himself to the task with the previously pleasant association. The other task was the classical choice situation involving delayed versus immediate gratification. The more

Figure 2-8. Diagram of congruence and incongruence of the two motivational systems.

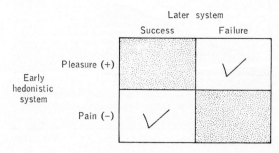

mature individual would be oriented toward the success of getting a larger, although later, reward and would see the choice of the immediate reward as a failure in personal decision making. The less mature individual, not conceptualizing in terms of the later system, would choose the immediate (but lesser) reward since it would represent more "here and now" positive value.

A third avenue with which to assess the later system was a more direct one. Bialer merely asked the child questions. If one assumes that the growing child develops increasing associations of goal outcomes with his own behavior and conceptualizes his own "success" and "failure" capacities as a function of these associations, then he should be able to answer questions about the degree to which he sees himself in control of events around him, as opposed to seeing them as externally controlled. This questionnaire approach to measuring the later system is referred to by Bialer as the *locus of control* measure.

Bialer hypothesized that these three measures, (1) repetition choice (RC), (2) gratification pattern (GP), and (3) locus of control (LC) would change with the increasing mental age (MA) and chronological age (CA) of the subject. The repetition choice would shift from success task repetition to failure task repetition. The gratification pattern would shift from the choice of immediate to delayed gratification. The locus of control questionnaire response would change from external to internal. Thus, with the factor analysis of these three variables and MA and CA, there would appear a general factor with positive loadings from all variables. Since the later motivational system is assumed to be conceptual in nature, it was also predicted that MA would bear a stronger relationship to the three behavioral measures than CA would. This would mean that the shifts would occur at a later period for the retardates. Finally, since the later motivational system is assumed to develop as a function of individual experience, it is predicted that the three behavioral measures would be significantly intercorrelated even when MA and CA were partialled out. This would be reflected in factor analysis by a group factor with no loadings of MA and CA but with positive loadings of repetition choice, gratification pattern, and locus of control.

Eighty-nine children, approximately half retarded and half normal, ranging in CA from 6 to 14 and in MA from 4 to 16, were selected from special and regular classes in the public schools. All subjects individually were given the following treatments: (1) a verbally administered children's locus of control scale, developed by Bialer and the present author, based on the earlier scale by James (1957) and Phares (1955), and measuring the degree to which the subjects perceived the outcome of events as being internally controlled; (2) the Rosenzweig repetition-choice task, measuring the tendency to return to a failed task; and (3) the tendency to delay gratifications in three situations involving pennies now versus more tomorrow, candy now versus more tomorrow, and suppositional car now versus suppositional car and million dollars next year.

As predicted, with increasing age, there was an increasing tendency among all subjects to (1) perceive internal LC, (2) choose the failed rather than succeeded task on RC, and (3) choose to delay gratification to attain a greater reward. This is shown in Table 2-3.

As predicted, MA, rather than CA, was found to be the more relevant variable related to the three measures of development of success-failure conceptualization. In fact, CA was found to carry no predictive weight toward the above tendencies when the effects of MA were partialled out. This is shown in Table 2-4.

As predicted, a factor analysis of the five variables resulted in the derivation of a general factor and one group factor. All variables had positive loadings on the general factor. If one rotates the axes properly, the group factor consists of the behavioral measures (LC, RC, and GP). Contrary to prediction, however, the RC factor was negatively rather than positively loaded. (An alternative rotation solution renders MA, CA, LC, and GP loaded on one factor and MA, CA, and RC loaded on another factor.) The correlational matrix on which the factor analysis was based is presented in Table 2-5. The first rotated factor matrix is presented in Table 2-6.

Essentially, these results are in substantial support of the aspects of the tentative theoretical formulations which were tested, except for the repetition-choice measure. Why this task did not conform to the formulation will be examined later in the chapter.

The implications of Bialer's findings are many. The younger child, responding more to "here and now" gratification of primary and secondary drives, may learn more from experiences involving immediate goal attain-

TABLE 2-3

Multiple correlation coefficients with MA and CA as predictors of the behavior measures

Criterion variable	R	p
LC	.56	$<.01$
RC	.32	$<.05$
GP	.39	$<.01$

TABLE 2-4

Magnitudes, standard errors, and significance levels of the partial beta weights

Criterion variable	Predictor variable					
	MA			CA		
	Magnitude	SE	p	Magnitude	SE	p
LC	.55	.12	$<.005$	.02	.12	NS
RC	.27	.13	$<.025$	.07	.13	NS
GP	.44	.13	$<.005$	$-.08$	.13	NS

ment and noncompetitive activities. Situations of competition, frustration, and deprivation may be viewed as merely painful things to avoid rather than having success-failure meanings. The older child, starting to respond more like an adult, should perhaps receive and be able to profit from failure, competition, and frustration in moderate doses. These experiences could lead to higher-level skills of responding to failure with increased and variable striving. In other words, the emphasis on all success experience possible or, on the other hand, on enforced high standards (leading to increased failure) is a gross oversimplification if it is applied without respect to developmental level.

The retarded would develop these success-failure conceptualization skills at a later time and, therefore, should not be compared with the normal child of the same age any more in personality and conceptual maturity than in intelligence. When the retarded child *can* demonstrate evidence of the later motivational system, however, the need for moderate failure experience may be as important for him as for the normal child in the optimal development of personality functioning.

Regarding psychopathology, suggestions are made that external LC and lack of development of the later system are associated with paranoid syndromes and that extreme internal LC and overdeveloped personal success-failure awareness may be a premorbid condition of depressive syndromes. Also, since feelings of inadequacy or inferiority must inevitably depend on the individual's conceptualization of success and failure as well as behavioral effectiveness, perhaps the important etiology for this type of neurotic condition lies in *later* rather than earlier childhood.

Some social learning theory constructs might also be reconsidered. For example, *RV,* up to now, has been thought of mostly in terms of the bio-

TABLE 2-5

Intercorrelations of developmental and behavior measures ($N = 89$)

Number	Variable	1	2	3	4	5
1	MA	...	.63	.56	.31	.39
2	CA	.63	...	.37	.24	.20
3	LC	.56	.37	...	.06	.47
4	RC	.31	.24	.06	...	.02
5	GP	.39	.20	.47	.02	...

TABLE 2-6

Rotated factor matrix

Number	Variable	I'	II'
1	MA	.84	.10
2	CA	.74	−.10
3	LC	.57	.48
4	RC	.35	−.23
5	GP	.39	.54

logical and psychological value inherent in the goal object. In the case of older individuals, the value of their seeing themselves as successful or influential in determining the event outcome may be as important a component of *RV* as the externally conceived component.

Before the dust settled on Bialer's study of this tentative formulation, Miller (1961) became interested in extending it. He introduced some assumptions with which to predict differences in learning rate directly from responses on the Bialer-Cromwell locus of control scale. These predictions showed shades of the Taylor anxiety scale and eyelid conditioning. They concerned differences in selective perception on the part of internal (ILC) and external locus of control (ELC) subjects. Since there was some support for considering the ILC subject as being more motivated to show his behavior effectiveness (as a function of the development of the success-approach and failure-avoidance system), Miller posited that the ILC individual would be more sensitive to cues which related to this effectiveness. In the typical task where one can get direct knowledge of the results of one's efforts, these would be intratask cues. On the other hand, the ELC individual, being motivated with respect to the hedonistically satisfying or unsatisfying aspects of the situation, was assumed to be more sensitive to the cues which primarily determine the hedonic properties of the situation. These cues are typically extratask cues, consisting of the social responses of others, rewards, punishments, etc., which are present in the situation but not always inherent in the task itself.

Miller then made a further assumption about the reactions of the ELC individual as a function of the kind of hedonic feedback he gets in a situation. He assumed that in a task situation which was hedonistically positive, the ELC individual would develop situational ILC tendencies; that is, he would start paying more attention to cues appropriate to the task and associated with success. This would be described as *task orientation*. In a task situation which was negative or unpleasant, the ELC person would tend to show decreased attention toward the distressing or threatening task. This would be described as *task alienation*.

Another assumption by Miller cuts across some earlier assumptions made in the social learning studies with retardates. Finding in Bialer's data that retardates were significantly more ELC than normals, Miller posits that differential reactions to success and failure in normals and defectives can be explained by differences in locus of control (rather than *GE*). For example, the differences which Heber (1959) and Gardner (1958) explained on the basis of *GE*, Miller was now assuming to be due to locus of control.

Finally, Miller assumed that learning-set formation is influenced by situationally developed ILC tendencies. Within the framework of thinking which he presents, learning set is viewed as a discovery of ways in which one's own behavior is effective on one task; the strategies and techniques connected with this demonstrated effectiveness are then applied to subsequent tasks. If this formulation is correct, learning set could be most effectively demonstrated by a task sequence in ELC subjects where criterion was first achieved (and behavioral effectiveness finally demonstrated) in spite of an unpleasant extratask learning climate of failure. Then, a highly similar task could be presented under a positive learning climate. The latter condition would allow situational ILC tendencies to develop to an optimal degree, and strategies which were learned through having achieved criterion in the first task would be applied. The superior performance expected here would be in contrast to the first task where, in the earlier phase, goals were being lost and attention to behavioral effectiveness was at a low ebb. According to this notion a crucial ingredient of learning set is that the individual must have knowledge of his behavioral effectiveness in the earlier tasks (i.e., knowledge that he has solved them) so that the learning-to-learn phenomenon will manifest itself on later tasks.

In order to test predictions based on these assumptions, Miller chose a serial learning situation with simple pictures. For one reason, this type of task provided a clear distinction between intratask cues (knowledge of results from the memory drum) and extratask cues (giving or taking of chips by the examiner). Second, since the early trials in serial learning involve many errors and the final criterion can be set at two consecutive errorless trials, a number of successes and failures is obtained by each subject. Third, Pryer (1959) has shown that learning set in retardates can be demonstrated with serial learning.

In the first phase of the study, 90 retardates as well as 45 ILC and 45 ELC subjects were subdivided according to their scores on a modified version of the Bialer-Cromwell locus of control scale into three learning climate subgroups. They were given a serial learning task to a criterion of two consecutive errorless trials. The success-climate subgroup (18 ELC and 18 ILC subjects) received prevalued chips for each correct response in the task. Nothing was presented after an incorrect response. The failure-climate subgroup (18 ELC and 18 ILC subjects) received 100 chips, and one chip was removed for each incorrect response. Nothing was presented after a correct response. The neutral climate group (9 ELC and 9 ILC subjects) neither received nor were penalized chips.

The reader must note that in this discription of the study by Miller the terms success and failure do not fit the systematic definitions given earlier on page 62. Since success refers systematically only to goal attainments under ILC orientation, only the ILC subjects (and ELC subjects with situational ILC tendencies) would respond to the positive climate as actually a "success" climate. Only ILC subjects would respond to the negative climate as actually a "failure" climate. Thus, the terms success and failure are used here in the conventionally loose sense rather than in the systematic sense.

In the second phase of the study, 1 day later, the 72 subjects of the success and failure groups were given a second serial learning task. Half of each group repeated the same learning-climate condition. The other half were "shifted" to the opposite learning climate. Thus, in this phase, eight subgroups could be described: success-to-failure shift (SF), failure-to-success shift (FS), failure constant (FF), and success constant (SS), for both ILC and ELC subjects. Nine subjects were in each subgroup. The same performance criterion was used. A ratio of the first over second task scores was computed in order to measure increments and decrements in performance.

The results of the first phase of the study are found in Table 2-7. As may be seen, the performance was uniformly high in the ILC subgroups regardless of learning climate and was also high in the ELC group under the success-emphasis learning-climate condition. However, learning rate was markedly reduced in the ELC groups under failure and neutral emphasis. To examine the hypotheses derived from the assumptions, an analysis of covariance was computed on the criterion scores as a function of success versus failure climate and internal versus external locus of control with intelligence covaried out. As predicted, a significant interaction occurred between locus of control and learning climate. This was in support of the hypothesis that the ELC subjects, being more sensitive to the extratask cues, would show greater differences between the learning climates than the ILC subjects. Although the generality of main effects is limited by this significant interaction, both the main effects were significant: ILCs exceeded ELCs in learning rate; subjects under success climate exceeded subjects under failure climate. The analysis of simple effects yielded the differences and lack of differences already described above from the visual inspection of the data in Table 2-7.

The changes in performance from the first to the second phase of the study, presented in Figure 2-9, were examined by analysis of variance and were broken down into simple effects. Actually, the major attention of the hypotheses is focused on the performance of three of the subgroups, with other subgroups serving as comparison or control conditions. In shifting from success to failure (SF), it was expected that the ILC-SF group would improve and the ELC-SF group would decline in performance. Also, it was predicted that the ELC-FS group would have marked improvement.

The first group, ILC-SF, did as expected: Its increment was (1) significantly greater than zero and (2) significantly greater than those of the control comparison groups—ELC-SF, ILC-FS, ILC-SS, and ILC-FF.

The second group, ELC-FS, showed a decrement, but this decrement was not statistically significant. Thus, the hypothesis was not supported. However, the performance was so low as to be statistically significantly below the comparison groups, ILC-SF, ELC-FF. Thus, some glimmer of credence is given to Miller's notion about ELC subjects having an impeded reaction to a failure (hedonistically unpleasant) climate.

The third group of central concern was the ELC group which went from failure to success. It will be recalled that large learning-set increments were expected in this condition. The hypotheses were confirmed. The ELC-FS

TABLE 2-7

Learning climate	Internal LC	External LC
Success ($N = 18$)	8.94	8.94
Failure ($N = 18$)	8.72	16.78
Neutral ($N = 9$)	9.22	15.89

Serial learning performance (mean trials to criterion) in retardates as a function of locus of control and learning climate

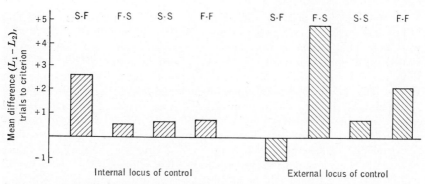

Figure 2-9. Shifts in serial learning performance (list I minus list II) as a function of locus of control and shifts in learning climate.

group had an increment significantly above zero and significantly better than the ILC-FS, ELC-SF, ELC-SS, and ELC-FF comparison groups.

Another general expectation in the second phase of the study was that ELC subjects, being more sensitive to the cues involved in the shifts in climates, would show greater differences in shifts in performance. In examining the interactions (differences between differences), this was not uniformly upheld.

In summary, locus of control does not seem to be a pertinent variable under a condition of success emphasis. Here, presumably, ELC subjects develop situational ILC tendencies, and the measures on the LC personality scale are of no predictive value. Under a condition which emphasizes failure, however, the story is quite different. While ILC subjects, apparently less responsive to the extratask climate cues, perform at about the same level, ELC subjects are markedly impaired under this condition. When no reinforcement schedule is experimentally introduced, the ILC subjects, again as expected, maintain their usual optimal level of performance. The ELC subjects, however, seem to respond to the neutral condition as they do toward a failure emphasis. As viewed in the present theoretical framework, this suggests that the condition of no feedback of information is unpleasant and nonsatisfying. In shifting the learning climates, there was evidence that ILC subjects respond to failure cues, after a period, with increased effort. This was as expected from previous results (Gardner, 1957, 1958; Ringelheim, 1958). The ELC subjects, with a nonsignificant decrement and relatively impaired performance, acted the way retardates in general acted in the Ringelheim and Gardner studies in a success-to-failure shift. The shift upward, expected and found in the ELC subjects shifting from failure to success, dramatically illustrated the responsivity of the ELC subjects to extratask cues when they are shifted from one condition to another. These findings, in general, suggest that the typical nomothetic laws of learning alone are not sufficient in predicting learning and performance. Personality variables and other individual difference constructs must be employed.

While Miller was positing and examining the LC assumptions concerning intra- and extratask cue responsiveness, Butterfield and Butterfield (1961) were examining similar assumptions in a broader learning situation. They assumed ELC individuals would respond more in terms of the values of those around them while ILC individuals would respond more to their own values. To examine this assumption they tested 25 institutionalized, mildly retarded subjects diagnosed as familial (i.e., each had at least one retarded parent and one retarded sibling). The choice of subjects involved the not-too-perilous assumption that they had come from environs with low values for academic achievement. When put into a situation emphasizing values of academic achievement (with a middle-class schoolteacher), one would expect that the ELCs would be more responsive to this foreign set of values than the ILCs. "To the extent that accepting a teacher's values determines what one learns from that teacher, ELC's should learn more than ILC's from teachers whose values differ from theirs" (Butterfield & Butterfield, 1961). When they correlated the subjects' academic achievement levels with the Bialer-Cromwell locus of control scores, with WISC MA partialled out, they managed to get a —.89 correlation to support their hypothesis. In another study, using 40 college students, a significant but lesser partial correlation was similarly found (Butterfield, 1961). It is notable that Stephens[4] reports a positive correlation between LC and grade-point average in a group of high-achieving college students. These hypotheses and findings are notable in that they are opposite the earlier hypotheses by Butterfield (1960) and Behrens[5], who proposed (without successful validation) a positive relationship between LC and achievement. These earlier hypotheses were based on the finding by Liverant[6] that LC had a low but significantly positive correlation with need achievement.

Other locus of control studies. It seems that when a small, easily administered scale is developed, a great amount of research is engendered. Sometimes the research has relevance to the theory out of which the scale was developed; very often, however, the subsequent research is completely without regard to the original theoretical framework. Much recent research on locus of control has been carried out in this way. On a miniature scale, it has been similar to the hubbub of research associated with the Taylor Manifest Anxiety Scale, the California F Scale, and other similar instruments. Such research, although not all of the logically aesthetic hypothetico-deductive variety, seems to find a purpose. No theory is yet broad enough to handle the scope of events which even the researchers, let alone others, are interested in predicting. Therefore, the various positive and negative findings serve to inform about the generality of the construct being measured, the ways in which it is overlapping or identical to constructs in other systematic frameworks, how it has immediate practical value, etc. It seems appropriate that a review of this locus of control research be given here.

The construct, locus of control, originated in social learning theory research as a part of investigations of the skill versus chance situational cate-

---

[4] M. Stephens. Personal communication.
[5] M. Behrens. Unpublished research.
[6] S. Liverant. Personal communication.

gorizations which would affect expectancy learning. It was thought that a questionnaire approach to the construct could measure some personality predisposition to categorize events in one way or another. On this basis, Phares (1955) developed the first scale, a "chance versus self-determinism" scale. Using line- and color-matching tasks where a prearranged series of successes and failures was administered, he found that the ILC subjects had less variability (fewer unusual shifts: up with failure, down with success) and that they made greater increments in expectancy statements with success. James (1957) refined the scale. In his study 160 subjects, divided into two groups according to skill versus chance instructions, were given a line-matching task with a prearranged schedule of success and failure. Then, half of each group did a similar task on angle matching followed by two final trials of line matching. The other half of each group was given extinction. The criterion was the level of expectancy statements. As predicted, subjects with skill instructions had greater, more stable, and more predictable increments in expectancy statements with success instructions than those with chance instructions. Skill-instruction subjects showed more generalization of expectancy statements to a new situation than chance-instruction subjects. Also, as expected, skill-instruction subjects were more resistant to extinction than chance-instruction subjects. The "internal-external" control scale predicted the individual differences among subjects in the same direction as the skill versus chance instructions, respectively.

In a related study James and Rotter (1958) demonstrated differences in extinction in level of expectancy statements as a function of skill versus chance instructions and partial versus total reinforcement. With chance instructions the usual superiority of partial reinforcement over total reinforcement in resistance to extinction prevailed. Under skill instructions, however, the reverse occurred. Total reinforcement led to less rapid extinction than partial reinforcement. These findings have not yet been examined with groups constituted on the basis of locus of control rather than skill-chance instructions.

After this initiation of the locus of control research came a number of studies which were intended primarily for refinement of reliability and validity of scales which measured locus of control. Simmons (1959) related the James-Phares Scale to Rotter ISB, Edwards PPS, Rotter LOA Board, a short personal history questionnaire, and a problem-solving task. ELC males were found to be more defensive in the face of possible failure, had a high need-nurturance measure, and were more maladaptive in response to the Rotter LOA Board. ELC females seemed more disorganized, less planful and goal setting, more fatalistic, and less bright than ILC females.

Liverant[7] developed his forced-choice scale to eliminate some of the response set difficulties of the other scales. It was divided into six categories: academic recognition, social recognition, love and affection, dominance, social-political, and general philosophy. Factor analysis revealed a strong general factor and one group "interpersonal" factor, which included love and affection and dominance. The test-retest (1-week in-

[7] S. Liverant. Personal communication.

terval) reliability of the scale was .93 with 40 male college subjects. A highly significant relationship was found between ELC and dependency, and moderate relationships were found between ILC and the OSPE intelligence measure and the McClelland need achievement measure (Odell, 1959). ELC was related to the California F Scale of authoritarianism. Holden (1958) found the same F scale–ELC relationship with the James-Phares Scale. Barron's Conformity Scale, "a projectivity measure drawn from the MMPI," and a social distrust scale were also related to the Liverant scale. Further research is being carried out to identify *defensive externals,* ILC scorers who behave in an externally controlled manner.

Miller (1960c) tested 100 institutionalized retardates with the Bialer-Cromwell scale and modified it slightly with item analysis. The odd-even reliability (adjusted by the Spearman-Brown formula) was .87. Total test reliability, determined by Rulon's formula, was .94. In another study of 69 retardates Miller (1960a) found ILC higher than ELC subjects on the PPVT intelligence measure, but no relationship existed between LC and children's manifest anxiety scores.

McConnell (1960) developed a locus of control scale in alternate forms for persons with MA over 12 (e.g., ward attendants). (The Bialer scale is better suited to children and the Liverant scale to college students.) Normative data suggested a gradual decline in ILC with later adulthood, similar to the mental age function. Sixty-day test-retest reliability was .90.

Another broad area of locus of control research has been the examination of its relation to life accomplishments. One would expect from the theory that if ILC develops as a function of the success-approach and failure-avoidance motivating system, the ILC person will have been oriented toward attaining more overt accomplishments. Studies of academic achievement have already been mentioned. McConnell (1960) failed to find LC correlated with rank or tenure of institution ward attendants. Brooks (1961) has begun investigation on the relationship of locus of control and anxiety to reading achievements. An interaction between these two variables has been identified.

Regarding achievement aspirations rather than accomplishments, Butterfield (1961a) found that ELC college students had predictions of their own grades which fell into a wider range than ILC college subjects, when WAIS vocabulary scores were held constant. Contrary to prediction, the lowest grade for which ELC subjects reported they were "willing to settle" was higher than that for ILC subjects. This prediction was based on the evidence that ILC subjects have a higher need achievement, whereas the tendency of ELC subjects to respond to values of others in the situation may have been the determiner of this result.

Locus of control has been related to risk taking by Liverant and Scodel (1960). They required subjects to make bets on chance occurrences and found that ILC subjects made more intermediate probability bets then ELC subjects. ILC subjects otherwise tended to be more cautious and less variable in their choice of betting alternatives. These findings about ILC subjects are somewhat similar to those of Atkinson's subjects with high achievement motivation.

From the theoretical formulation presented in this chapter on the development of the later motivational system, one would expect that persistence in the face of physical pain, monotony, or conceptual ambiguity would increase with the development of internal locus of control in children. The only attempt to demonstrate this so far (Shipe, 1960) has been unsuccessful. Tiptoe standing, as a pain persistence measure, seemed to be more related to weight and age of subject than to the experimental variables being studied.

How locus of control develops in children, whether more by direct accrual of associations of event outcomes with behavior or by adopting conceptions and attitudes about the world from parents and other important figures, has been a question raised succinctly by McConnell.[8] No research has yet directly attacked the question. Regarding the Schafer Parent Behavior Inventory measures of subjects' descriptions of parent attitudes (overt control, covert control, protectiveness, and hostility), the following was found by Cromwell, Rosenthal, Shakow, and Zahn (1961). The greater the degree to which normal subjects attributed protective attitudes to their parents, the greater they answered in the direction of external locus of control. This relationship was absent, however, in the ELC-skewed schizophrenic group. Schizophrenics who described parents as exercising greater overt control answered the LC scales in the direction of internal control—the opposite of what might be expected. This relationship was absent in the normal group. Attitudes of covert control did not seem to be greatly related to locus of control response in either group; however, the Liverant scale data indicated that attitudes of hostility were related to external control attitudes in general.

Stedman[9] has presented an unpublished formulation that ELC (perhaps, Catholic) parents would be more accepting of a retarded child in the home than would ILC parents. This formulation has been expanded by him to predict that parents who depend heavily on externally supportive social systems (e.g., religion, welfare agency, lodge, close family ties, etc.) would be more accepting of a retarded child than parents who depend on internal supports when in stress. Although Farber (1959) has studied the acceptance by Catholic parents of retarded children, no research has been done to confirm the locus of control notion.

Attempts have also been made to relate LC to perceptual field dependence-independence. McIntyre (1961), after finding in educable retarded subjects a significant correlation between LC and scores on an embedded figures test, watched this finding dissolve when mental age was partialled out of the correlation. A subsequent attempt to confirm the relationship was also unsuccessful.

McConnell (1961b) has studied the effects of a threatening failure experience on a rigged "masculinity" task on changes in LC scale response. Although behavioral signs of threat were clearly produced, the results indicated that the LC scale was impervious to this kind of recent experience in high school students.

The way of the psychopath and his apparent inability to see behavior consequence and future events in a long-term time perspective have also been

[8] Personal communication.
[9] Personal communication.

viewed as related to locus of control. Heimberg[10] has found the Liverant LC scale to be correlated —.50 with Quay's Psychopathy Scale (ELCs higher on psychopathy score). A scale constructed by Heimberg to measure time perspective correlated .52 with LC. In the same study LC correlated —.41 with Quay's neurotic delinquency measure, —.48 with the anomie (alienation) measure, —.34 with the Taylor manifest anxiety measure, and .30 with intelligence. All correlations, based on a large sample of men in the Armed Forces, were significant. By contrast, Pesetsky (1961), in studying delinquents, reports a significant positive correlation between LC and Quay's psychopathy scale.

Other group comparisons have also been carried out with the LC scale. Cromwell, Rosenthal, Shakow, and Zahn (1961) found schizophrenic patients extremely more oriented to ELC than conscientious objectors. Land (1961) found blind children oriented more to ELC than sighted children, but institutionalized blind were not more oriented to ELC than special-class blind children. McConnell (1961a) has found that the mental age growth function of locus of control, found by Bialer and others, does not occur among children who are growing up in a residential facility for the mentally retarded.

A summary of postulates and possible departure points for future research

The preceding section completes the report of research following the social learning theory line in mental retardation. The present section is an illustration of how the concepts and constructions developed to date could be used to extend this area of research still further. The hypothetico-deductive process involved is enjoyable, and those who take part in it feel creative. For others, of course, it is intolerable to deal in propositions which are based on constructs not yet given the full certitude of empirical validation. From such a point of view, one might at first think that the construction of such linguistic schema is the development of a new art form rather than an attempt to advance science. However, the important distinction comes in how one views the linguistic product. As described previously in the chapter, each instance of hypothesis confirmation and disconfirmation has its particular implication for the theoretical schema. The real danger comes when the theorist or the reader for some reason starts acting as if the theory formulation were true. So long as it is viewed as a useful tool for dreaming up, testing, discarding, revising, and refining probability statements about reality, things are fine.

Postulates from past research.   In order to discuss the departure points, it seems necessary and appropriate to give some of the important assumptions and hypotheses already reached in postulate and theorem form. These propositions may be viewed as continuous with the more basic theoretical propositions of Kantor and Rotter, referred to earlier in the chapter.

Postulate I.   The initial system of motivation of the human organism is to avoid noxious events and to approach satisfying events. This might be

[10] Personal communication.

referred to as the hedonistic pleasure-approach and pain-avoidance, or the earlier, system.

The circularity of hedonistic definition is broken by defining terms within a Kantorian field theory framework. The distinction between reflexive and learned phenomena is not important on this personality level of construction; therefore, the postulate intends to incorporate both the learned and biologically noxious events and the learned and biologically satisfying (drive-reducing, if you will) events as circumscribed by the "here and now" of a given situation. The postulate also intends to convey the assumption that it is useful and meaningful to distinguish between approach and avoidance aspects of motivation rather than to conceptualize in terms of a single summated generalized drive.

Postulate II. The cumulative associations of the outcomes of goal-approach and threat-avoidance events with one's own behavior evolve and become conceptualized over a period of time into a system of motivation to demonstrate one's own behavioral effectiveness. This may be referred to as the success-approach and failure-avoidance, or the later, system.

Typical S-R formulations concentrate on how situational stimuli, organismic variables, and stimuli mediated therefrom predict the subsequent behavior. This postulate, by contrast, concentrates on the feedback information about the event outcome (goal attainment or nonattainment) which may be associated with one's own behavior (as opposed to chance, to the behavior of others, or to other external sources). Without attempting to explain how this feedback process initiates the later motivational system, it is assumed here that the magnitude of the later system develops as a function of the degree to which the individual can associate and conceptualize satisfying and rewarding events with his own behavior (Cromwell, 1961, p. 49).

Corollary II-A. Verbal responses regarding locus of control of events (by self versus not-self) increase with the magnitude of the later motivational system.

Corollary II-B. The tendency to endure a depriving, noxious, or conceptually ambiguous situation in order to achieve success increases with the magnitude of the later motivational system.

The foregoing postulates and corollaries will be recognized as the ones underlying Bialer's research.

Theorem I. Verbal responses expressing an internal locus of control increase as a function of age.

Theorem II. The tendency to choose success (behavioral effectiveness) under hedonistically negative circumstances increases as a function of age.

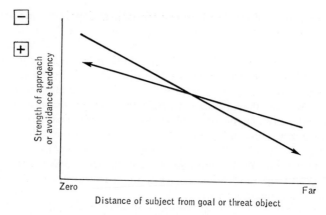

Figure 2-10. Illustration of N. E. Miller's goal-gradient principles.

Theorem III. The tendency to avoid failure under positive hedonistic circumstances will increase as a function of age.

Theorem IV. To the extent that mental age is a measure of the conceptual development of the individual, its magnitude will be more related to the locus of control and other success-approach tendencies than chronological age.

Theorem V. The tendency to choose success under negative hedonistic circumstances, to avoid failure under positive hedonistic circumstances, and to give responses expressing internal locus of control will be intercorrelated independently of developmental level.

It will be recognized that these are the theorems which were tested in Bialer's research.

Postulate III. Independent of developmental level, the magnitude of the earlier system versus the later system determines the relative sensitivity (responsivity) of the individual to cues of hedonistically positive or negative circumstances versus cues relating to success and failure (degree of behavioral effectiveness) in the individual, respectively.

Corollary III-A. Cues relating to the hedonistically positive or negative nature of a situation are determined primarily by the responses of the individual to the external rewards within the situation, whereas cues relating to success and failure (the demonstration of one's behavioral effectiveness) are determined primarily by events within the task involving the goal-directed behavior.

It will be recognized that these assumptions were a part of Miller's research.

A postulate structure for future investigations. The following are postulates and corollaries which project possibilities for future research. They arise mainly from alternative explanations about why the RC task data in Bialer's study did not fit the hypothesis made prior to the study. Notably, it is when hypotheses are not confirmed that theory innovations are produced.

In the first alternative explanation, an attempt is made to integrate N. E. Miller's goal-gradient phenomena (1959), the task recall and task repetition phenomena of Zeigarnik and Rosenzweig, and the formulations presented here. To begin, the propositions of goal-gradient phenomena are incorporated (see Figure 2-10).

Postulate IV. The tendency to approach a goal is stronger the nearer the subject is to it.

Postulate V. The tendency to avoid a threat object is stronger the nearer the subject is to it.

Postulate VI. With a given change in distance the tendency to avoid a threat object changes more rapidly than the tendency to approach a goal object.

Postulate VII. The magnitude of the approach and avoidance motivation affects the elevation (or magnitude) of the approach and avoidance tendencies, respectively, but not the degree of slope (gradient) as a function of distance.

With these assumptions in mind, now let us consider what happens when a particular event has been consummated in which goal-directed behavior has occurred.

Postulate VIII-Y. In older children and in adults, the decay function of approach strength is more rapid when the goal has been attained than when behavior has been blocked prior to goal attainment (see Figure 2-11).

Figure 2-11. Approach strength as a function of attainment versus nonattainment of the goal in older children and adults (Postulate VIII-Y).

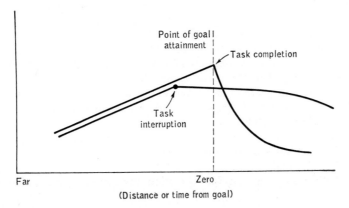

Point of goal attainment

Task completion

Task interruption

Far

Zero

(Distance or time from goal)

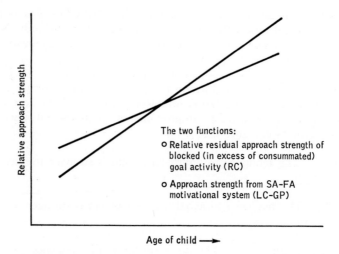

Figure 2-12. Illustration of two hypothetically independent age functions: SA-FA motivational growth and residual approach strength of blocked (in excess of consummated) goal activity.

Here is a relatively simple assumption which shows how approach and avoidance tendencies in states of dissipation can account for the Zeigarnik phenomenon of greater recall for interrupted tasks than completed tasks at a point in time following activity with the tasks. The next step is to qualify this assumption with a further piece of evidence: younger children, not having as much value for completed products as for ongoing activity, will more often retain approach tendencies after a goal (product) is completed. That is, they will "tear it down and build it over again."

Postulate IX-Y. The difference in relative rate of decay between blocked and consummated approach activity becomes greater with the increasing age of the subject.

Now, if we consider the relative difference in decay rate as a function of the age of the child, this difference has an increasing magnitude similar to, but presumably independent of, the increasing magnitude of the SA-FA motivational system (see Figure 2-12). If this is correct, an explanation is offered for the Bialer findings. That is, a developmental function was found through the intercorrelations of CA, MA, and RC (approach decay phenomenon). Another one was found through the intercorrelations of CA, MA, LC, and GP (the SA-FA phenomenon). Then, when the factors are rotated so as to partial out the effects of CA and MA, a small negative loading on RC could occur on the same factors on which LC and GP are positively loaded. This could occur because of relative differences in the slopes of the two developmental phenomena as they were measured in the Bialer study.

One further step in this interpretation renders an explanation about why Rosenzweig (1933) with his ego-involving instructions for the task activities obtained a canceling out (see Bialer, 1957) of the Zeigarnik effect. First of all, he may have used mature subjects, in whom the SA-FA motivational system had developed. Second, he used instructional cues, often called ego-involving, which emphasized to the subject that his personal effectiveness was at stake. Therefore, in applying the assumptions already stated, we should expect that counteracting tendencies would be in play: first, the approach decay function with the tendency being stronger to return to or to recall the blocked rather than consummated activity, and, second, the SA-FA system where the tendency would be stronger to approach (recall, repeat) the events conceptualized as success (completed activities) and to avoid the events conceptualized as failure (interrupted activities) (see Figure 2-13). With relatively equal strength of the two tendencies, no differences in completed versus interrupted activities would be demonstrable. Thus, the explanation would fit Rosenzweig's actual findings.

An alternative postulate structure.   Besides offering constructive changes to the projected postulates just presented, Butterfield (1961b) offers a quite different set of alternative assumptions as another *post hoc* explanation of the RC data in the Bialer study. It is a bit more risky and, therefore, potentially more fruitful. In contrast to the previous assumptions, the formulation by Butterfield assumes that the factor structure of Bialer's data is most meaningful when rotated to the point where GP, LC, and RC are all loaded on one factor, with RC having the negative loading. From this he presumes that the approach-avoidance decay and the SA-FA tendencies are a part of the same developmental system rather than being

Figure 2-13. Illustration of conflicting approach and avoidance tendencies in the Rosenzweig task recall phenomenon: (*A*) approach tendency before goal attainment; (*B*) approach tendency after goal attainment; (*C*) approach tendency before goal blocking; (*D*) approach tendency after goal blocking; (*E*) SA-FA failure-avoidance tendency; (*F*) SA-FA success-approach tendency.

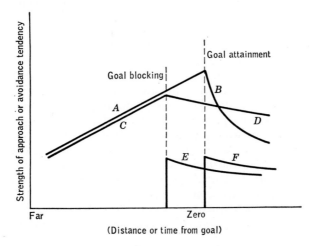

independent developmental phenomena. (It should be clarified that whether they are viewed as the same or separate phenomena in Bialer's data depends on how the factors are rotated.) Finally, he presumes that the negative loading may be an important rather than an insignificant or artifactual phenomenon. (See Table 2-6 for the rotation which is consistent with Butterfield's interpretation.)

Butterfield's first chore, then, is to rationalize this negative RC loading which occurred without prior prediction in the Bialer study. This he does by assuming that locus of control, as a motivational construct, contains two major components: (1) the component variance which is in common with the variance in MA and (2) the component variance which is independent of the variance with MA. Furthermore, it is assumed that these two components represent two different sources of SA-FA motivation. The first component, in common with the variance of MA, would be described as the conceptualized, or anticipatory, motivation, i.e., to approach events for which success is anticipated or conceptualized and to avoid events where failure is anticipated or conceptualized. The second component, independent of the variance of MA, could be described as the *reactive* SA-FA motivation. Following from this motivational component, event classes would be approached which had been experienced as leading to success, while others would be avoided which had been experienced as leading to failure.

Postulate VIII-Z. To the extent locus of control is correlated with mental age, it is a measure of that part of the strength of the later system which is based on (1) approach tendency to objects conceptualized as leading to success and (2) avoidance tendency to objects conceptualized as leading to failure.

Postulate IX-Z. To the extent that locus of control is independent of mental age, it is a measure of that part of the strength of the later system which is based on (1) approach tendency to objects previously associated with success and (2) avoidance tendency to objects previously associated with failure.

At this point one has a basis for predicting differences in behavior among subject groups as a function of the degree to which their differences in LC are in common with differences in MA. If we compare high-MA subjects with low-MA subjects, allowing the LC components independent of MA to vary randomly, the postulates give basis for predicting that high-MA subjects will return to the previously incompleted puzzle and low-MA subjects will return to the previously completed puzzle. Moreover, "the postulates predict that when Ss of different LC and equal MA are presented with the repetition choice task, the high LC subjects will be more likely than the low LC Ss to return to the completed puzzle" (Butterfield, 1961b, p. 13). In the case of Bialer's data, one is dealing with the latter situation in the group factor where MA is partialled out. Thus, the Butterfield formulation suggests that the development of a singular SA-FA motivational system is inferable from an increased tendency to delay gratification, a verbal reaction of increased internal locus of control, and *to the extent that this increased LC is independent of MA development,* a tendency to return to *completed* rather than interrupted activities.

Butterfield proceeds to use this analysis of the components of LC to explain previous results and make further predictions regarding the tendency to delay gratification, the acquisition of serial learning, the response to "ego-involving" cues, the response to failure stress in learning situations, the verbal response to frustration situations, and the tendency to be failure avoiding as opposed to success striving. With these and other research implications, the weight of evidence could decide which alternative formulation is the most useful and the more deserving of being refined and revised.

Need systems research. Aside from the alternative departure points of the more recently developed ideas, research implications are also abundant from the original Rotterian formulations. It will be recalled from the earlier presentation that certain behaviors can be classified together as a function of their leading to the same or similar types of goals. These classes of goal-directed behaviors are referred to as need systems. An investigation of these need systems among institutionalized groups, such as the mentally retarded, would be appropriate. A number of crucial questions regarding need systems remain unanswered. To what extent are need categories developed in institutions and among other culture-restricted groups which are qualitatively different from the need categories which usefully describe the general culture at large? To what extent do these idiosyncratic need categories, if they occur, affect the judgment and rehabilitation of the individual as he moves into the wider society? Once a given need category has developed, so that an intersubstitutability of behaviors and goals is describable, what effect does the attainment (satisfaction) of one particular goal have on the need value for the category in general? When one goal is achieved, is there a lowering of approach tendency for the other related goals (i.e., satiation)? Or, is there an increased approach tendency (i.e., appetite)? Such a question is crucial to the understanding of behavior on the psychological need level of description. The nonmobile setting and restricted range of need development occurring in a residential facility for the mentally retarded make it an ideal place for the advancement of such research.

Social science research. Still another departure point for research would be to apply social learning constructs on a more molar level to social psychology and sociology. SLT constructs are personality constructs; therefore, they are inferred from individual behavior. To apply only these constructs to social psychological and sociological problems would run the risk of being reductionistic in scientific approach. However, to extend these particular constructs to bridge the gap between personality theory and group behavior would seem to be a fruitful undertaking. For example, *group value* (or *ideological need*), as a group-inferred construct, could be defined in terms of the group acceptance versus rejection of a particular issue held in communication by a culture or a group within a culture.

Those particular *BP*s which are relevant to these issues, communicated pro or con in the group or culture, would define the attitude *BP*s. The attitude *BP*s from the appropriate sample of individuals would serve as the operational basis from which group values could be inferred. Thus, the attitude *BP*s and, therefore, the group values could be studied as a function of the degree to which they reflect (1) individual personality characteristics of the individuals concerned and (2) the external group values to which the group members commonly yield. Situations could be identified which are more parsimoniously and economically predicted with group-value constructs. Other situations could be identified where personality constructs would remain the relevant predictive tools. Two constructs may be posited as important in making these distinctions: degree of communication of the group value and individual locus of control tendencies. That is, it seems plausible to hypothesize that (1) the greater the degree to which a group value is discussed, propagandized, or communicated in some other way, (2) the greater the external locus of control for group members, and (3) the greater the identification with (reinforcement source of) the group, the more likely is behavior to be predictable on a mass (group or cultural) basis rather than with individual personality and other psychological constructs.

In considering those events which are most conveniently predicted through group-value constructs, a further question arises: what conditions are necessary for a group value to be formalized into an *institution* (law, social structure)? The construct, institution, could perhaps be defined in terms of conditions where conforming behavior is expected and punishments are given to those whose behavior violates this institutionalized group value.

To illustrate the use of such group-inferred constructs, one might consider such problems as the group values of residential retardates toward sexual activity or learning and rehabilitative skills. Also, the attitudes of educable retardates in special classes and sheltered workshops toward delinquent behavior or toward handling one's savings might be studied. If pertinent variables and laws could be identified here, there is the possibility that sociological and social psychological mass treatment techniques could be used to manage and shape certain behavior more economically and efficiently than individual psychological approaches alone.

SUMMARY

This chapter has introduced social learning theory as a basic and researchable personality theory which is applicable to mental retardation. After discussing critically some of the scientific, methodological, and philosophical habits which characterize the theory, the research, and the researchers, a brief exposition of Rotter's social learning theory was presented. Following this, a chronology of research studies was described in which social learning theory was applied to mental retardation. Early consideration was given to the effect of failure and perceived failure on the retardates' self-evaluation and performance. Gradually, more refined notions were developed about the role of failure and success in human behavior. This led to a major phase of research which proceeded from an assumption that retardates typically experience more failure than average children and therefore have developed greater generalized expectancies for failure. Along with this came the assumption that retardates had stronger tendencies to be failure avoiders than success strivers.

These assumptions led to research which presented evidence that retardates (1) enter a novel situation with a performance level which is depressed below their level of constitutional ability, (2) have fewer tendencies to be "moved" by failure experience than normals, and (3) have fewer tendencies than normals to increase effort following a mild failure experience. Evidence was also obtained which gave partial support to the notion of separate approach and avoidance motivational systems. Stronger avoidance tendency was sometimes but not always shown by retardates. From this research there gradually developed a theoretical formulation which posited a success-approach and failure-avoidance motivational system which was separate from the hedonistic system typically described in terms of primary and secondary drives.

This formulation gave rise to a study which investigated relationships between locus of control, delay of gratification, and tendency to return to interrupted versus completed tasks. The developmental aspects of these variables were demonstrated with mental, rather than chronological, age being the important developmental variable. This research focused attention on the construct locus of control, which has come to be investigated in various ways. Further formulations were then developed which afforded predictions of marked differences in serial learning rates as a function of locus of control in the subject and success versus failure emphasis in the learning situation.

A summary postulate system has been developed which serves to focus on some of the controversial interpretations of evidence in this line of research. Alternative sets of assumptions are presented as a basis for future hypothetico-deductive research. Finally, psychological need systems and social science problems were discussed with the view that social learning theory constructs could produce useful research in these areas.

REFERENCES

BEHRENS, M. Locus of control and academic achievement in institutionalized mental retardates. Unpublished manuscript, 1961.

BIALER, I. Differential task recall in mental defectives as a function of consistency in self labeling. Unpublished master's thesis, George Peabody Coll. for Teachers, 1957.

BIALER, I. *Conceptualization of success and failure in mentally retarded and normal children.* Ann Arbor, Mich.: University Microfilms, 1960. (Also, in brief, *J. Pers.,* 1961, 29, 303–320.)

BIALER, I., & CROMWELL, R. L. Task repetition in mental defectives as a function of chronological and mental age. *Amer. J. ment. Defic.,* 1960, 65, 265–268.

BINDRA, D., PATTERSON, A. L., & STRZELECKI, J. On the relation between anxiety and conditioning. *Canad. J. Psychol.,* 1955, 9, 1–6.

BROOKS, S. Effects of locus of control on the ability of mentally retarded children to use context cues. Unpublished manuscript, 1961.

BUTTERFIELD, E. C. The relationship of locus of control scores to discrepancy between achievement age and mental age in a grade school population. *Abstracts of Peabody studies in mental retardation*, 1960, 1, No. 57.

BUTTERFIELD, E. C. Locus of control, academic aspirations, and achievement. Unpublished manuscript, 1961. (a)

BUTTERFIELD, E. C. Some further applications of the goal gradient hypotheses. Unpublished manuscript, 1961. (b)

BUTTERFIELD, E. C. The interactive effects upon learning of approach strength to an incentive source and the quality of incentive from that source. Unpublished manuscript, 1961. (c)

BUTTERFIELD, E. C., & BUTTERFIELD, G. B. Locus of control and academic achievement in familial retardates. Unpublished manuscript, 1961.

BUTTERFIELD, E. C., & ZIGLER, E. F. The effects of different verbal incentives on learning of mentally retarded and average children. Unpublished manuscript, 1961.

CALDWELL, D. F., & CROMWELL, R. L. Replication report: The relationship of manifest anxiety and electric shock to eyelid conditioning. *J. exp. Psychol.*, 1959, 57, 348–349.

CROMWELL, R. L. A methodological approach to personality research in mental retardation. *Amer. J. ment. Defic.*, 1959, 64, 333–340.

CROMWELL, R. L. Selected aspects of personality development in mentally retarded children. *Exceptional Child.*, 1961, 28, 44–51.

CROMWELL, R. L., & MOSS, J. W. The influence of reward value on stated expectancies of mentally retarded patients. *Amer. J. ment. Defic.*, 1959, 63, 657–661.

CROMWELL, R. L., MOSS, J. W., & DUKE, R. B. The Taylor Scale as a measure of avoidant behavior. *Abstracts of Peabody studies in mental retardation*, 1960, 1, No. 33.

CROMWELL, R. L., PALK, B. E., & FOSHEE, J. G. Studies in activity level. V. The relationships among eyelid conditioning, intelligence, activity level, and age. *Amer. J. ment. Defic.*, 1961, 65, 744–748.

CROMWELL, R. L., ROSENTHAL, D., SHAKOW, D., & ZAHN, T. P. Reaction time, locus of control, choice behavior, and descriptions of parent behavior in schizophrenic and normal subjects. *J. Pers.*, 1961, 29, 363–379.

FARBER, B. Effects of a severely mentally retarded child on family integration. *Monogr. Soc. Res. Child Developm.*, 1959, 24, No. 2.

FRANKS, V., & FRANKS, C. M. Conditioning in defectives and in normals as related to intelligence and organic deficit: The application of a learning theory model to a study of the learning process in the mental defective. *Proc. London Conf. Scientific Stud. ment. Defic.*, 1962.

GARDNER, W. I. Effects of interpolated success and failure on motor task performance in mental defectives. Paper read at Southeast. psychol. Ass., Nashville, 1957.

GARDNER, W. I. *Reactions of intellectually normal and retarded boys after experimentally induced failure—a social learning theory interpretation.* Ann Arbor, Mich.: University Microfilms, 1958.

GREEN, C., & ZIGLER, E. F. Social deprivation and the performance of feeble minded and normal children on a satiation type task. Unpublished manuscript, 1961.

HEBER, R. F. *Expectancy and expectancy changes in normal and mentally retarded boys.* Ann Arbor, Mich.: University Microfilms, 1957.

HEBER, R. F. Motor task performance of high grade mentally retarded males as a function of the magnitude of incentive. *Amer. J. ment. Defic.*, 1959, 63, 667–671.

HEIMBERG, L. Relation of locus of control to other personality variables. Unpublished manuscript, 1961.

HILGRAD, E. R., JONES, L. V., & KAPLAN, S. J. Conditioned discrimination as related to anxiety. *J. exp. Psychol.*, 1951, 42, 94–99.

HOLDEN, K. B. Attitude toward external versus internal control of reinforcement and learning of reinforcement sequences. Unpublished master's thesis, Ohio State Univer., 1958.

JAMES, W. H. *Internal versus external control of reinforcement as a basic variable in learning theory.* Ann Arbor, Mich.: University Microfilms, 1957.

JAMES, W. H., & ROTTER, J. B. Partial and one hundred per cent reinforcement under chance and skill conditions. *J. exp. Psychol.*, 1958, 55, 397–403.

JESSOR, R., & HAMMOND, K. R. Construct validity and the Taylor anxiety scale. *Psychol. Bull.*, 1957, 54, 161–170.

KANTOR, J. R. *Interbehavioral psychology.* Bloomington, Ind.: Principia Press, 1958.

KEISTER, M. E. The behavior of young children in failure: An experimental attempt to discover and to modify undesirable responses of preschool children to failure. *Iowa Univer. Stud. Child Welf.*, 1937, 14, 27–82.

LAND, S. Locus of control: A comparison between blind and sighted children. Unpublished master's thesis, Vanderbilt Univer., 1961.

LEWIN, K. *A dynamic theory of personality.* New York: McGraw-Hill, 1935.

LIVERANT, S., & SCODEL, A. Internal and external control as determinants of decision making under conditions of risk. *Psychol. Rep.*, 1960, 7, 59–67.

MATEER, F. *Child behavior: A critical and experimental study of young children by the method of conditioned reflexes.* Boston: Gorham Press, 1918. Cited by G. H. S. Razran, Conditioned responses in children, *Arch. Psychol., N.Y.*, 1933, No. 148.

MCCONNELL, T. R. Locus of control as a factor in attendant selection. *Abstracts of Peabody studies in mental retardation*, 1960, 1, No. 84.

MCCONNELL, T. R. A comparison of two methods of repetition choice in institutionalized retardates. Unpublished paper, 1961. (a)

MCCONNELL, R. T. Effect of recent threat experience on locus of control. Unpublished manuscript, 1961. (b)

MCINTYRE, R. B. Perceptual field dependency and locus of control. Paper read at Amer. Ass. ment. Defic., Cincinnati, 1961.

MILLER, M. B. Correlational analysis of locus of control, manifest anxiety, and PPVT raw scores (mental age) in an institutionalized mentally retarded sample. *Abstracts of Peabody studies in mental retardation*, 1960, 1, No. 62. (a)

MILLER, M. B. "Rebelliousness" and repetition choice of a puzzle task under relative autonomy or control conditions in adolescent retardates. *Abstracts of Peabody studies in mental retardation*, 1960, 1, No. 74. (b)

MILLER, M. B. Reliability of the Bialer-Cromwell locus of control scale in an institutionalized mentally retarded sample. *Abstracts of Peabody studies in mental retardation*, 1960, 1, No. 73. (c)

MILLER, M. B. *Locus of control, learning climate, and climate shift in serial learning with mental retardates.* Ann Arbor, Mich.: University Microfilms, 1961.

MILLER, M. B., & CROMWELL, R. L. Response competition and the anxiety-as-drive concept: A direct study. Paper read at Southeast. psychol. Ass., Gatlinburg, Tenn., 1961.

MILLER, N. E. Liberalization of basic S-R concepts: Extensions to conflict behavior, motivation, and social learning. In S. Koch (Ed.), *Psychology: A study of a science,* Vol. 2, New York: McGraw-Hill, 1959. Pp. 198–290.

MOSS, J. W. *Failure-avoiding and success-striving behavior in mentally retarded and normal children.* Ann Arbor, Mich.: University Microfilms, 1958.

ODELL, M. Personality correlates of independence and conformity. Unpublished master's thesis. Ohio State Univer., 1959.

OSIPOVA, V. N. Speed of formation of the associated reflex in children. Novoya v reflexologii i fiziologii nervnoy systemy, 1926, 2, 248–255. Cited by G. H. S. Razran, Conditioned responses in children: *Arch. Psych., N.Y.,* 1933, No. 148.

PESETSKY, F. Programmed perception: Variability in the meaning of deviant behavior. Unpublished doctoral dissertation, Vanderbilt Univer., 1961.

PHARES, E. J. *Changes in expectancy in skill and chance situations.* Ann Arbor, Mich.: University Microfilms, 1955.

PRYER, R. S. *Retroactive inhibition in slow and fast learners as a function of temporal position in the interpolated task.* Ann Arbor, Mich.: University Microfilms, 1959.

RAZRAN, G. H. S. Conditioned responses in children. *Arch. Psychol., N.Y.,* 1933, No. 148.

RINGELHEIM, D. *Effects of internal and external reinforcements on expectancies of mentally retarded and normal boys.* Ann Arbor, Mich.: University Microfilms, 1958.

RINGELHEIM, D. The effect of failure on verbal expectancies in male defectives. *Abstracts of Peabody studies in mental retardation,* 1960, 1, No. 14.

ROCKWELL, A. The evaluation of six social learning need constructs. Unpublished doctoral dissertation, Ohio State Univer., 1950.

ROSENZWEIG, S. Preferences in the repetition of successful and unsuccessful activities as a function of age and personality. *J. genet. Psychol.,* 1933, 42, 423–440.

ROSENZWEIG, S. An experimental study of repression with special reference to need persistence and ego-defensive reactions to frustration. *J. exp. Psychol.,* 1943, 32, 64–74.

ROTTER, J. B. *Social learning and clinical psychology.* Englewood Cliffs, N.J.: Prentice-Hall, 1954.

ROTTER, J. B., LIVERANT, S., & CROWNE, D. P. The growth and extinction of expectancies in chance controlled and skilled tasks. *J. Psychol.,* 1961, 52, 161–177.

SEARS, P. S. Levels of aspiration in academically successful and unsuccessful children. *J. abnorm. soc. Psychol.,* 1940, 35, 498–536.

SHALLENBERGER, P., & ZIGLER, E. F. Rigidity, negative reaction tendencies, and cosatiation effects in normal and feeble minded children. Unpublished manuscript, 1961.

SHIPE, D. A comparison of probability learning in mentally retarded and normal children. Unpublished minor research project, George Peabody Coll. for Teachers, 1959.

SHIPE, D. The relationships among locus of control and some measures of persistence in mentally retarded and normal subjects. *Abstracts of Peabody studies in mental retardation,* 1960, 1, No. 58.

SIMMONS, W. L. Personality correlates of the James-Phares scale. Unpublished master's thesis, Ohio State Univer., 1959.

SKY, A. W. An apparatus for a frustration task. *Australian J. Psychol.,* 1950, 2, 116–120.

SPENCE, K. W. The nature of theory construction on contemporary psychology. *Psychol. Rev.,* 1944, 51, 47–68.

SPENCE, K. W., & FARBER, I. E. Conditioning and extinction as a function of anxiety. *J. exp. Psychol.*, 1953, 45, 116–119.

SPRADLIN, J. E. Task resumption phenomena in mentally retarded Negro children. *Abstracts of Peabody studies in mental retardation*, 1960, 1, No. 40.

STARKMAN, S. S., & CROMWELL, R. L. Self-evaluation of performance and subsequent practice effects in mental defectives. *Psychol. Rep.*, 1958, 4, 414.

STEVENSON, H. W., & ZIGLER, E. F. Probability learning in children. *J. exp. Psychol.*, 1958, 56, 185–192.

ZIGLER, E. F., HODGDEN, L., & STEVENSON, H. W. The effect of support on the performance of normal and feebleminded children. *J. Pers.*, 1958, 26, 106–122.

3

HULL - SPENCE BEHAVIOR THEORY AND MENTAL DEFICIENCY

Gordon N. Cantor

INTRODUCTION

Purpose and scope of the chapter

Behavior theory of the Hull-Spence variety is becoming an extensive and highly complex scientific system. Since relevance to the field of mental deficiency is the focus of concern in this volume, an attempt to do full justice to the Hull-Spence approach in the present chapter would, in the writer's opinion, be inappropriate. The ground to be covered would be too extensive. Much of the detail, while highly pertinent to behavior theory per se, would not be of great relevance to mental deficiency.

Accordingly, this chapter will not attempt a thorough survey of Hull-Spence behavior theory. The reader interested in such a presentation is referred to appropriate sections of Hilgard's *Theories of Learning* (1956) and to chapters by Logan (1959) and Koch (1954). The basic writings are of course available in Hull's *Principles of Behavior* (1943), *Essentials of Behavior* (1951), and *A Behavior System* (1952) as well as in Spence's *Behavior Theory and Conditioning* (1956) and *Behavior Theory and Learning* (1960). Theoretical formulations bearing strong family relationships to the Hull-Spence approach are to be found in numerous sources, most notably in the writings of Miller (1959), Mowrer (1960), and Logan (1960).

The strategy to be followed here will be based on the assumption that this book's typical reader is not highly conversant with behavior theory. Selected segments of Hullian theory will be discussed to provide a general familiarity with the system and to lay the groundwork for later consideration of the theory's implications with respect to the area of mental deficiency. In this development, only those concepts which in the writer's opinion are most crucial to the theory or most significant for mental deficiency will be stressed. Some major extensions and modifications of Hullian theory due to Spence and to some of his students will then be reviewed. Finally, specific attention will be focused on the role of individual differences in Hull-Spence theory and the potentially heuristic value of the theory for the field of mental deficiency. Before turning to these topics, however, some general comments regarding behavior theory and mental deficiency would seem to be in order.

Some basic premises about behavior theory and mental deficiency

The major goal of scientists is the discovery of laws about phenomena in the world. In the physical sciences, centuries of effort have resulted in the accumulation of large numbers of laws which workers in these areas have been able to integrate via the construction of theories. The psychologist, as scientist, is concerned with the discovery of laws about behavior. Partly because of the complexity of the phenomena studied and partly owing to the youth of the discipline, relatively few behavioral laws of any high degree of dependability are as yet available. Thus, "theory" construction has a more modest connotation in psychology as contrasted with the physical sciences. In behavioral science, theories are intended to integrate the small number of low-level laws available but serve the more important function of aiding in the discovery of as yet unknown laws.

Occasionally, one hears pleas that "theories of mental deficiency" need to be developed. The nature of such theories is rarely if ever explicated, for understandable reasons. At least in the behavioral area, it is difficult to imagine what such a theory might consist of. Psychology has theories dealing with the concepts of perception, learning, motivation, personality, and intelligence. The notion of a theory of mental deficiency seems to imply that the behavior of the defective individual is to be understood either without reference to the behavioral concepts mentioned above or perhaps by the addition to these of some new, significant concepts which are at present undeveloped.

While it would be absurd to close one's mind to the possibility that such a theory might eventually be constructed, the current state of affairs seems to indicate that the psychologist interested in understanding the behavior of the mental defective will come closest to doing so by working within one of the more promising theoretical frames of reference already in existence. The various chapters in Part I of the present volume are concerned with several such approaches.

Historically, psychologists who *have* been interested in drawing upon available psychological theories in their analyses of the behavior of defectives have tended to stress theoretical developments concerned with the concept of intelligence. The face validity of such an emphasis is apparent—defectives are individuals who are intellectually inadequate, so one is rather inevitably inclined to accept the view that theories of intelligence should help make the behavior of the defective explicable. While this may indeed be the case, a small group of individuals has in the past few years strayed from this beaten path to examine the possibility that one or another of the psychological theories not centrally concerned with the concept of intelligence might provide a fruitful means of studying the defective's behavior processes.[1]

Behavior theory of the type developed by Hull, Spence, and their colleagues constitutes just such an approach. Contrary to some prevalent misconceptions, Hull-Spence theory does provide a definite place in its structure for individual differences, as subsequent sections of this chapter will emphasize; but the primary focus of concern in the theory is on other concepts having to do mainly with learning and motivation. The present writer takes the position that such concepts may prove to be of considerable utility in explaining defective behavior as well as human behavior in general.

The hypothetico-deductive and intervening variable approaches to behavior theory construction

The laws psychologists seek are relationships which allow one to make predictions about behavior (responses) on the basis of knowledge concerning (1) stimulus events (S-R laws); (2) other responses made by the individual (R-R laws); and (3) organic characteristics, properties, or states of the organism (O-R laws). Thus, in any psychological law, the dependent variable, i.e., the phenomenon to be predicted, is a response or set of responses manifested by a behaving organism. The three types of laws indicated above differ in the nature of the independent variables involved, i.e., the variables on the basis of which predictions are made. Thus, a theorist's interest in a particular class of independent variables automatically dictates the kind of lawful relationships with which he is apt to deal.

Theories of intelligence, for example, tend to be concerned with R-R laws, the kinds of relationships revealed in factor analytic studies providing clear prototypes of this variety of relationship. In the area of mental deficiency, an interest in organic characteristics of the subject has resulted in considerable emphasis on O-R laws (e.g., hyperactivity as a function of brain lesions). Because workers in mental deficiency have tended to channel their interests in the direction of concepts relevant to intelligence and organicity, relatively little attention has been paid to S-R laws concerned with the behavior of defectives. Behavior theory of the Hull-Spence type, in contrast, is most concerned with the discovery and integration of S-R laws.[2] This latter emphasis may well be one of the determinants of the fact that workers in mental deficiency have not been inclined over the years to make much use of the Hull-Spence approach.

Psychologists who share the goal of discovering S-R laws do not necessarily endorse the same mode of attack on the problem. Skinner (1950), for example, is committed to the viewpoint that the behavior scientist

---

[1] An early attempt to apply such a theoretical formulation dealt with the Lewinian concept of "rigidity." See Kounin (1943) and Chap. 1 in this volume.
[2] A major exception to this generalization is provided by the work of Spence and his colleagues on the concept of anxiety, a topic to be taken up in a later section of this chapter.

should confine his attention to stimuli and responses, manipulating the former in systematic fashion and studying the behavioral consequences as revealed by variations in the latter. Any reference to concepts, i.e., abstractions introduced to "explain" the S-R relationships, is to be rigorously avoided, as is the testing of principles deductively derived from postulates containing such concepts. It is in this sense that Skinner is considered to be "antitheory." In contrast to this position of radical empiricism, behavior scientists working within the Hull-Spence framework consider the use of abstract concepts highly appropriate. The eminently successful application of such concepts in the physical sciences—particularly physics—is one of the primary justifications for this practice in their thinking. These individuals feel that the proclivity of some to bandy about poorly defined, animistically tinged concepts in the behavioral field (witness the use of "id," "ego," and "superego" in psychoanalytic theory) is no basis for concluding that behavior-oriented concepts of considerable utility cannot be defined in a clear, objective manner. Just as the physicist uses the concepts of mass, force, electron, etc., in his theories, so may the behavior scientist incorporate such concepts as "habit," "drive," and "anxiety" into a theoretical schema which serves to integrate known behavioral laws and to suggest new and testable relationships.

During the earlier years of the development of this system, Hull characteristically devoted sections in both his experimental and theoretical papers to rather extensive statements concerned with the status and role of abstract concepts in behavioral science. His position was perhaps made most explicit in the volume *Principles of Behavior* (1943). Adopting the term "intervening variable" from Tolman's writing (Tolman, 1936), Hull observed that "scientists frequently and usefully employ logical constructs, intervening variables, or symbols to facilitate their thinking" (Hull, 1943, p. 21). Noting that the use of such abstractions is attended by serious hazards, Hull indicated that clarity and objectivity can be attained by the secure anchoring of these concepts to observable antecedent determining conditions (stimuli) and to observable consequent phenomena or events (responses).[3]

Psychologists of Skinnerian persuasion do not share Hull's confidence that behavioral concepts can be objectively defined and utilized. The radical empiricists regard intervening variables as "explanatory fictions" and theoretical postulates containing them as generators of misleading if not downright incorrect preconceptions about reality. But, as Hilgard has pointed out, a position which opposes the setting up of postulates and the testing of relationships deduced from such postulates seems to endorse a return to a Baconian conception of science. "The power achieved by other sciences through theoretical formulation is too convincing for such formulation not to serve at least as a long-range goal for those trying to create a science of behavior" (Hilgard, 1956, pp. 117–118).

[3] For a critical appraisal of the extent to which Hull actually achieved an acceptably secure anchoring of his concepts to antecedent and consequent events, see Koch (1954). An illuminating discussion of the status of abstract concepts in psychology may be found in a paper by Bergmann (1951).

As his contribution to a science of behavior, Clark Hull developed a hypothetico-deductive system containing a hierarchy of intervening variables, most of which are at least programmatically tied down to (i.e., defined in terms of) antecedent, manipulative environmental variables and consequent response events. The theory is hypothetico-deductive in the sense that a series of basic postulates comprise the core of the system. The utility of these postulates is not to be assessed in terms of their "truth," but rather in terms of the truth value of theorems or corollaries deductively derived from them. From the inception of his program of theory construction in 1929 until his death in 1952, Hull was constantly engaged in formulating and reformulating the postulates in his system. The self-correcting nature of the enterprise was a consequence of the testability of the theorems derived from the postulates. Friends and foes of the theory, along with the theorist himself, invested great amounts of energy in the experimental testing of the theorems as well as in the identification of logical inconsistencies within the system. Hull was always ready to revise his postulates in the face of compelling facts or logical arguments signifying the need for such revision. As a consequence, the theory changed appreciably, as one can observe by comparing the first large-scale, formal presentation (*Principles of Behavior,* 1943) with a brief revised version (*Essentials of Behavior,* 1951) and the final, posthumously published statement (*A Behavior System,* 1952).

The work of revising and expanding has continued in such vigorous fashion that Hull has already become something of a historical figure in the field of behavior theory. Kenneth Spence, a student of Hull's, has developed his own position to the extent that he should be labeled "neo-Hullian" rather than "Hullian." But Spence has preserved the emphasis on the intervening variable approach so characteristic of Hull. Several lower-order concepts are introduced in his system, each defined in terms of some manipulable environmental variable. Further, higher-order concepts are then defined in terms of the lower-order constructs, with the eventual generation of a single, highly abstract concept which, finally, is related to observable behavioral consequences. Such is the nature of intervening variable theory.

Mention has already been made of the tendency in Hull-Spence theory to emphasize S-R laws which ignore organic variables and concepts. Before turning to a detailed consideration of this approach and its possible heuristic value for the field of mental deficiency, the nonphysiological nature of the theory calls for further comment, as does still another emphasis in the approach which may make the system seem far removed from the problems of mental deficiency.

Molar analysis of simple learning phenomena

The concepts of "molar" and "molecular" are typically used by psychologists to define two ends of a continuum having to do with the degree of coarseness or fineness of the variables with which one deals. In this sense, sociology is molar relative to psychology, and psychology is molar relative to physiology. Within psychology, the theorist may choose to build his system with or without reference to the functioning of the nervous system. The psychologist who refrains from making use of physiological variables and concepts in his theorizing would thus be engaged in the construction of a molar theory of behavior, whereas the physiologically oriented worker would be regarded as more molecular in his interests.

Hull-Spence theory is explicitly a molar analysis of behavior. While recognizing that every bit of behavior has its physiological correlates, both Hull and Spence have insisted that physiological knowledge is not yet sufficiently advanced to provide much help to present-day psychological theorists. Recognition is clearly given to the likelihood that neurological laws may eventually provide the basic principles for a science of behavior. But in the meantime, stress is placed on the importance of achieving as much as possible at the molar level.[4]

As mentioned previously, the emphasis in Hull-Spence theory on S-R as opposed to O-R laws may account, in part, for the system's lack of appeal to many workers in mental deficiency. One cannot deny that knowledge of the behavioral consequences of organicity is apt to enhance our understanding of the behavior of mental defectives; and, in view of its molar nature, Hull-Spence theory could hardly be considered a framework within which such knowledge would be furthered. But the behavior of the so-called "brain-damaged" individual, while undoubtedly affected by the degree and locus of cerebral insult, is also analyzable at a molar level. Indeed, the limitations of currently available neurophysiological knowledge may justify the argument that the organic's behavior is *more* analyzable at a molar than a molecular level at present. An obvious addendum to this argument concerns that large class of defectives termed *familial*—individuals functioning at a subnormal intellectual level but lacking any positive signs of organic involvement. It may very well turn out to be the case, as many persons have contended, that advancement in neurophysiology will result in the recognition of cortical defects in *all* mental defectives. But this conjecture invites investigative work from the neurophysiologist, not the psychologist; and in the meantime, the latter's choice lies between a molar and a wildly speculative molecular analysis.

One other characteristic of Hull-Spence theory which tends to limit its interest value for workers in mental deficiency relates to the kind of behavioral phenomena with which it is concerned. Leaving aside the fact that much of the theory is based on data obtained from animal research, it must be recognized that the fundamental principles in the system, to the extent that they are relevant to human behavior, are concerned with the simplest kinds of behaviors known—classical and instrumental conditioning. Both Hull and Spence have invested considerable effort in attempting to apply these basic principles to more complex forms of behavior (e.g., discrimination learning, verbal learning, etc.). But even at this level of complexity the tasks involved seem to most practitioners to be far removed from the

[4] Spence (1957) has further clarified his position by quoting with approval the following statement taken from Tolman (1936): "But the psychological facts and laws have also to be gathered in their own right. A psychology cannot be explained by a physiology until one has a psychology to explain." Rather ironically, Tolman apparently abandoned this viewpoint in the latter years of his career.

everyday learning situations faced by the mentally defective child in the classroom. Thus, the specialist with applied interests in mental deficiency is apt to look elsewhere for guiding principles. The position taken by the present writer is that the gulf between the Hull-Spence system and practice is not as wide as it may appear to be. Fundamentally, Hull-Spence theory is concerned with basic laws of learning and behavior, not with practical applications. But the possibility of application definitely exists. The following sections of this chapter will summarize some of the major components of the system. Attention will then be paid to potential significance of the theory for mental deficiency, in both a basic and an applied sense.

SOME MAJOR CONCEPTS IN HULL'S THEORY[5]

Behavior as motivated and adaptive

Hull was greatly impressed with the adaptive nature of mammalian behavior. States of need arise in the organism, and these, together with other forms of internal stimulation plus prevailing external stimulus conditions, determine what responses are made by the individual. To the extent that such responses result in a diminution in need, the behavior in question maximizes the organism's chances of survival, and the probability of recurrence of the behavior under similar conditions increases. This adaptive character of behavior is clearly indicated in Hull's postulate regarding unlearned stimulus-response connections $(_sU_Rs)$. Hull hypothesized that organisms, by virtue of their biological nature, possess certain receptor-effector connections which tend to be manifested in behavior under conditions of need, such behavior being more likely to reduce these needs than are responses drawn at random from the organism's repertoire.

The need conditions referred to above were separated conceptually by Hull into *primary* (basic) and *secondary* (acquired) motivational or drive (D) states. Primary motivation is due to the deprivation of various biologically necessary commodities (e.g., water, food, etc.), to lack of outlet for sexual tensions, and to noxious stimulation. In the presence of such precipitating factors, the organism suffers from drive stimulation (S_D) which is inherently unpleasant. It is in this sense that such motivational states are considered "unlearned." In the case of humans, the reduction of primary needs may be accounted for in only some of the simplest instances by invoking $_sU_Rs$ (e.g., reflex withdrawal of the hand from painful stimulation). For the most part, adaptive responses successful in reducing primary needs in the human must be learned. The concept of secondary or acquired motivation has reference to the fact that initially neutral stimuli may themselves, by virtue of their association with primary need conditions, come to generate states of motivation in the organism. "Learned fear" or anxiety provides the clearest illustration of such a drive state. The young child simultaneously stimulated by

[5] This necessarily cursory summary is based in large part on the 1943 and 1951 versions of the theory (Hull, *Principles of behavior,* 1943; *Essentials of behavior,* 1951). Neither completeness nor fidelity to Hull's latest exposition of his position is intended. The purpose of this section and the ensuing one is merely to acquaint the reader with the *general* nature of Hull-Spence theory.

a burn from a hot stove and the sight of the stove quickly learns to fear the latter, a previously neutral stimulus.

Hull was a leading advocate of what may be termed a *homeostatic* conception of behavior in that he stressed the importance of primary and secondary motive states and the adaptive nature of responses in functioning to reduce the intensity of such states. This conception has been sharply criticized during the past decade as depicting too narrow a view of human motivation.[6] Regardless of the direction taken by future motivational theories, however, it would appear that human behavior will continue to be understood, at least in part, in terms of the existence and reduction of primary and secondary needs, more or less as these were described by Hull. This is particularly apt to be the case with regard to the behavior of lower-grade and young mental defectives.

Habit, drive, and the learning-performance distinction

As already mentioned, innately determined receptor-effector connections ($_sU_Rs$) do not account for much of man's adaptive behavior. The transition from infancy to normal adulthood in the human is overwhelmingly characterized by the acquisition of new responses and the building up of associative connections between stimuli and responses—that is to say, by learning. Hull introduced an intervening variable labeled "habit strength" ($_sH_R$) to refer to such associative, stimulus-response connections. While Hull was convinced that growth of $_sH_R$ reflects some kind of change in the nervous system, he defined the concept at a molar level and emphasized its status as a construct, i.e., as a hypothetical state of the organism. Hull recognized the two basic types of habit formation historically associated, respectively, with the work of E. L. Thorndike and Pavlov—simple associative or elementary trial-and-error learning and conditioned-response learning. While the experimental manipulations involved in these two kinds of learning can be differentiated, Hull contended that both varieties of habit acquisition are based on the same major principle—the *law of reinforcement. All* $_sH_Rs$ are formed or become strengthened as a consequence of the response in question being "reinforced"; and reinforcement, for Hull, is any event that results in primary or secondary drive reduction.

The manner in which habit strength is assumed to grow is indicated in one of the system's major postulates. Hull couched this assumption in the form of a mathematical function, in line with his conviction that intervening variables must be tied down in a precise, quantitative fashion to antecedent and consequent events. His specific assumption regarding the growth of habit is expressed by the function

$$_sH_R = 1 - 10^{-iN} \tag{3-1}$$

[6] See, particularly, Harlow's attacks on the homeostatic model (Harlow, 1953a, 1953b). This critic has emphasized the role played by what he terms *curiosity* and *manipulative* drives, at the same time minimizing the significance for human behavior of homeostatic needs and anxiety states. The most direct answers to Harlow may be found in Brown (1961) and Mowrer (1960). For an attempt to handle the perplexing (for the Hullian) problem of man's tendency to seek increases in stimulation, see Brown (1955).

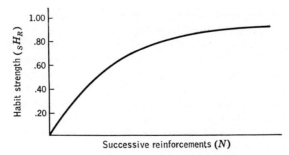

Figure 3-1. The growth of habit strength.

in which N is the number of reinforced response evocations and i is a constant indicating the rate of approach of $_sH_R$ to its limit or asymptote. It would be more accurate to designate i as a *variable constant*, since Hull assumed that individuals differ in regard to the value of this parameter. Equation (3-1) is an example of what is termed a simple positive growth function; it indicates that $_sH_R$ increases in a negatively accelerated fashion with increases in N, the size of the increments in habit being proportional to the amount of possible growth as yet unrealized and thus decreasing in size as training progresses. It should be noted that the number of reinforced responses is the *only* determiner, along with the i parameter, of the magnitude of $_sH_R$, and that habit strength may vary from 0 to 1.00. When $N = 0$, $_sH_R = 0$; when N is very large, $_sH_R$ approaches 1.00 as a limit or asymptotic value.[7] A graphic representation of the growth of the habit factor is presented in Figure 3-1.

Habit strength is *the* associative construct in the theory and refers to a hypothetical (unobservable), relatively permanent state of the organism which increases in a gradual fashion under conditions of reinforcement and, in a rough manner of speaking, constitutes the individual's "know-how." One's appreciation of the generality of the habit concept may be facilitated by noting that the stimuli involved in such stimulus-response associations include a wide array of internal phenomena, e.g., proprioceptive stimulation, motivational or drive stimuli (S_DS), the stimulation involved in covert verbalization, etc., as well as stimulation which excites the exteroceptors (e.g., sights, sounds, smells, etc.).

The reader who is new to the intervening variable approach may well wonder, in view of the unobservable nature of $_sH_R$, how Hull arrived at the positive growth function assumption and how the utility of this assumption is to be assessed. The answers to these questions stem from the premise commonly accepted by modern psychology that the only legitimate data for the behavior scientist consist of stimuli and of observable responses made by the organism under study. On the basis of such responses, one can make *inferences* about hypothetical states such as habit strength. This

[7] In a subsequent section, another form of the simple positive growth function will be discussed which allows for the possibility that the *limit* of $_sH_R$, as well as the rate of approach to the limit, may vary from individual to individual.

is precisely the approach utilized by Hull. The performances of subjects in a variety of learning situations were studied as a function of number of reinforced trials; on the basis of such observations, Hull postulated the simple positive growth function relating $_sH_R$ to N. In part, the utility of this assumption is assessed by examining the extent to which it may be used, in conjunction with other assumptions, to derive the very empirical relationships that generated the postulate in the first place. The patent circularity of this procedure can be circumvented by also using the postulate and additional assumptions to derive predictions about other as yet unobserved behavioral phenomena. The verification of these latter predictions provides the most convincing evidence for the utility of the postulate, as well as of the additional assumptions involved.

Once habit acquisition involving a particular stimulus and a particular response has occurred, the response in question may be evoked with no further training by other stimuli similar in some respect to the training stimulus. Hull used the concept of "stimulus generalization" to refer to this commonly observed phenomenon. Primary stimulus generalization is attributable to the physical similarity among stimuli, "similarity" in this context being conceptualized in either quantitative or qualitative terms. An illustration involving a quantitative dimension may conveniently be utilized here for expository purposes. If an individual has been conditioned to respond to an auditory stimulus of a given intensity (the *training stimulus*), he will also tend to respond to stimuli of other intensities (*test stimuli*), though responses to these latter stimuli have never been reinforced. The more remote the test stimulus is from the training stimulus, the smaller will be the generalized habit tendency involved; this continued diminution in generalized habit strength for stimuli increasingly more distant from the training stimulus is referred to as a generalization "gradient." In similar fashion, such gradients may be obtained involving stimuli ranging along qualitative dimensions (e.g., pitch in the auditory modality, shape in the visual modality, etc.). Generalized habit strength $(_s\bar{H}_R)$ is related to $_sH_R$ in the following fashion:

$$_s\bar{H}_R = {}_sH_R(10^{-jd}) \tag{3-2}$$

In this equation, d represents the magnitude of the difference between the training and test stimuli (in either physical units or *jnd*s, and j is a constant affected by the kind of dimension involved and also, possibly, by individual differences.

Secondary stimulus generalization refers to the same variety of phenomenon, but in situations in which generalization is not due to physical similarity among stimuli. Rather, in this form of generalization, the individual first learns to make the same response to two dissimilar stimuli—say, a verbal response (R_v) to stimuli S_a and S_b. With these habits well formed, the individual may then learn to make a new response, e.g., a motor response (R_m), to S_a. Under ordinary circumstances, and without further training, it will then be observed that S_b also elicits R_m, owing to the stimulus properties of the common mediating response, R_v, already associated with S_a and S_b.

Stimulus generalization is a powerful concept in Hull's system, since the phenomena to which it refers rule out the necessity of requiring that each and every possible stimulus-response association be built up through the reinforcement process. Critics who have attacked the habit strength construct because of its apparent specificity have failed to appreciate the central role given by Hull to the generalization conception.

The existence of a habit tendency in an individual is no guarantee of its manifestation in behavior. Hull conceived of several additional constructs as combining with $_sH_R$ to determine the occurrence of the particular behavior in question. One of the more important of these concepts, already referred to informally in the discussion of motivation presented earlier in this chapter, is drive (D). Hull considered D to be a generalized motivational state contributed to by all need conditions, both primary and secondary, present in the organism at a given time. Thus, D is a nonpermanent, fluctuating condition, the magnitude of which is a function of the individual's prevailing needs. Bypassing other basic concepts in the system for the moment, mention may now be made of a higher-order construct called reaction potential $(_sE_R)$ which provides the basis for anchoring Hull's hierarchy of concepts at the consequent (response) end and which reflects the joint functioning of $_sH_R$ and D (other factors in the system remaining constant). Hull's equation relating $_sE_R$ to $_sH_R$ and D is

$$_sE_R = {_sH_R} \times D \qquad (3\text{-}3)$$

Depending on the nature of the particular response in question, Hull indicated that several different measures are available to which one can relate $_sE_R$ in some sort of monotonic fashion. For example, in a situation which provides the opportunity to measure *amplitude* of response, the greater the amplitude, the greater is the associated $_sE_R$, other things being equal.

The multiplicative assumption indicated in Eq. (3-3) was chosen in preference to another plausible assumption, namely, that $_sH_R$ and D combine in an *additive* fashion, as a result of the examination of performance curves of groups of subjects learning under varying degrees of drive intensity. Plotting performance (e.g., amplitude of response—R_A) as a function of number of reinforced responses (the learning variable—N) for two levels of D, the additive and multiplicative assumptions lead to the contrasting expectations schematized in Figure 3-2. That is, an additive relationship would be reflected in *parallel* curves, whereas a multiplicative assumption would be consistent with a pattern of *diverging* performance curves. Available evidence tends to support the latter conception.

Equation (3-3) indicates clearly the point previously made that sheer possession of a habit tendency does not mean it necessarily will be reflected in behavior, since $_sE_R$ will equal zero when D is zero, irrespective of the magnitude of $_sH_R$. In other words, *learning* $(_sH_R)$ and *performance*

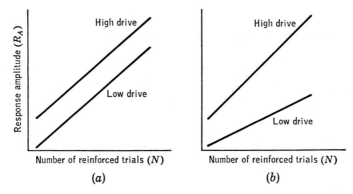

Figure 3-2. The (*a*) additive and (*b*) multiplicative assumptions regarding $_sH_R$ and D.

$(_sE_R)$ must be distinguished; $_sH_R$ is an essential ingredient of and under certain conditions may be inferred from $_sE_R$, but is not the same as $_sE_R$.

Another implication stemming from Eq. (3-3) is that D, irrespective of the particular need states contributing to it, multiplies any and all habit tendencies present in the organism at a given time. As such, D is a generalized energizer of habit tendencies and, in itself, has no directing functions. It is important to recall, however, that associated with drive states are characteristic drive stimuli (S_Ds) and that such stimuli may, via $_sU_Rs$ or $_sH_Rs$, elicit particular responses. Thus, the drive state which results from a condition of hunger indiscriminately energizes *all* habits present in the organism; but the S_Ds characteristic of hunger will tend, either innately or as a result of learning, to elicit responses instrumental in obtaining food. The directing of behavior involved here is a function of the S_Ds and not of D itself.

Incentive motivation and delay of reinforcement

There are, of course, other important contributors to $_sE_R$ in addition to $_sH_R$ and D. One of these—termed incentive motivation (K)—is a hypothetical motivational factor determined, loosely speaking, by the "desirability" of goals or incentives (reinforcers). In the simple case of a hungry laboratory rat, the size and quality (e.g., sweetness) of the food incentive used in a T-maze experiment would be determinants of K. Concern with this construct stems from the common observation that performance in a learning situation tends to improve with increases in the desirability of the incentives involved. In the 1943 version of this theory, Hull considered that such variables as quantity and quality of reward determine the limit to which $_sH_R$ can grow. Subsequently, however, he became convinced that such characteristics of incentives are better conceived as contributors to a *motivational* rather than an associative state. This change was necessitated by experimental evidence (Crespi, 1944; Zeaman, 1949) showing, among other things, that an abrupt shift in magnitude of incentive from a high to a low amount results in a rapid decrease in level of performance in rats. In view of these findings and Hull's conception of $_sH_R$ as a relatively permanent state of the organism, the associative conception of the effects of reward magnitude becomes untenable; a motivational interpretation, in contrast, is consistent with such data.

Hull postulated that the K factor, for situations involving rats as subjects and magnitude of food reward as the independent variable, is a negatively accelerated increasing function of the weight (w) of food given as reinforcement.[8] The specific quantitative function is

$$K = 1 - 10^{-a\sqrt{w}} \tag{3-4}$$

As in the case of D, the K construct combines multiplicatively with $_sH_R$, thus,

$$_sE_R = {_sH_R} \times K \tag{3-5}$$

An additional construct of importance in the theory is delay of reinforcement (J). The manipulable variable in this instance is the time between response evocation and receipt of reward, the empirical finding with respect to this variable being that performance generally is superior when shorter as opposed to longer delays are utilized. Again, the 1943 version of the theory imposed an associative interpretation on the effects of reward delay, but Hull subsequently shifted to a motivational interpretation. The postulate dealing with the J construct indicates that the greater the delay in reinforcement (t), the smaller will be the magnitude of this particular motivational determinant of response strength, the quantitative assumption being

$$J = 10^{-jt} \tag{3-6}$$

Once again, a multiplicative combination with $_sH_R$ is assumed; thus,

$$_sE_R = {_sH_R} \times J \tag{3-7}$$

The considerations which led to the adoption of Eqs. (3-3), (3-5), and (3-7) also served as bases for Hull's decision to postulate the following relationship:

$$_sE_R = {_sH_R} \times D \times K \times J \tag{3-8}$$

Thus, habit strength, drive, incentive motivation, and the delay factor may be thought of as four essential determinants of reaction potential; if any one of the four equals zero, so also does $_sE_R$.

Inhibitory factors

Turning from the major "positive" contributors to $_sE_R$, brief mention may now be made of certain influences conceived of as having inhibitory or negative effects on $_sE_R$. Hull postulated that any response evocation results in an increment in a primary negative drive state called reactive inhibition (I_R)—a condition akin to tissue injury, fatigue, or pain. Following the cessation of responding, I_R is considered to dissipate spontaneously with the

---

[8] Hull has been widely criticized (see Koch, 1954) for generating postulates of supposedly wide generality on the basis of such highly restricted situations. Spence, as will be indicated subsequently, has tended to be considerably more cautious in this respect.

passage of time. Since the cessation of a response is thus inevitably followed by reduction in the strength of a drive, such "nonactivity" becomes conditioned to whatever stimuli are present at the time of response cessation, generating a habit-like state called conditioned inhibition $(_sI_R)$. The determiners of the magnitude of I_R, and thus of $_sI_R$, are the amount of work (W) or energy expenditure involved in the evocation of a particular response and the number of evocations occurring in a given situation. I_R and $_sI_R$ are conceived of as summating in some fashion to constitute an inhibitory aggregate $(\dot{I}_R)$ which, in turn, subtracts from $_sE_R$ to produce effective excitatory potential $(_s\bar{E}_R)$; thus,

$$_s\bar{E}_R = {_sE_R} - \dot{I}_R \tag{3-9}$$

Several behavioral phenomena can be accounted for by principles which make use of Hull's inhibition concepts—most notably, experimental extinction (the decrease in responsivity resulting from nonreinforced trials) and spontaneous recovery (partial recovery of response strength occurring when a period of rest follows extinction). However, the inhibition formulation is beset by numerous difficulties of both a logical and empirical nature; a thorough discussion of these problems is presented by Koch (1954, pp. 37–39, 143–149). As will be indicated later, several investigators have identified some aspect of Hull's inhibition theory as applicable to a differentiation between normals and defectives, so this phase of the system deserves systematic attention in the present chapter, despite Koch's contention that Hull's inhibition assumptions "were among the most inadequate, both in mode of formulation and empirical support, in the entire theory" (Koch, 1954, p. 143).

Threshold, oscillation, and the quantification of reaction potential

In the early stages of development of a habit (i.e., when the value of $_sH_R$ is low), the behavior in question will not be manifest despite the presence of adequate amounts of drive, incentive motivation, and so on. Similarly, with a well-practiced habit (high value of $_sH_R$), reaction potential may be greater than zero but sufficiently low (owing to a low value of drive, for example) that, again, the appropriate behavior will not occur. Hull recognized these possibilities by introducing the concept of reaction threshold $(_sL_R)$, a value of $_s\bar{E}_R$ which exceeds absolute zero of reaction potential and above which a given $_s\bar{E}_R$ must fall in order to be reflected in behavior.

When an organism has practiced on a particular task to a high level of proficiency, and with all (known) relevant variables held constant, variability in performance from moment to moment will still be observed. Under the premise that any and all behavioral phenomena are determined in some lawful fashion, such variability must for the present be treated as "error variance," the assumption being that eventual discovery of as yet unknown relevant variables will eventually lead to an understanding of such fluctuations. The concept used by Hull to refer to this kind of variability in behavior is behavioral oscillation $(_sO_R)$. In his 1943 system, Hull conceived of $_sO_R$ as an additional inhibitory factor subtracting from reaction potential, the resulting quantity being labeled momentary effective reaction potential ($_s\dot{\bar{E}}_R$). Thus,

$$_s\dot{\bar{E}}_R = {_s\bar{E}_R} - {_sO_R} \tag{3-10}$$

Failure of a given habit to be reflected in behavior could thus be attributed to the notion that the associated $_s\bar{E}_R$ value is below threshold, or to the conception of behavioral oscillation carrying a superthreshold value of $_s\bar{E}_R$ to a subthreshold level. In addition, with two competing superthreshold $_s\bar{E}_R$s simultaneously present, Hull postulated that only one of them could be reflected in behavior at any given time. With such $_s\bar{E}_R$s oscillating asynchronously (Hull's assumption), that one with the higher momentary effective reaction potential would predominate by being revealed in behavior.

In the 1943 system, $_s\dot{\bar{E}}_R$ was then related to various response measures in order to anchor the hierarchy of concepts at the consequent, response end. The admittedly programmatic nature of this "anchoring" led Hull and several colleagues (see, e.g., Yamaguchi et al., 1948) to attempt the development of scales by means of which the relationships between reaction potential and various response measures could be objectively stipulated. Briefly, this newer approach (Hull, 1951) makes use of the dispersion (variability) of $_sO_R$ values as a unit of quantification of reaction potential. The extent of such variability is determined by the application of Thurstone's Case III adaptation (Thurstone, 1927a, 1927b, 1932) of the psychophysical method of paired comparison to all possible pairs of responses (i.e., trial 1 versus trial 2, trial 1 versus trial 3, etc.) made by an individual subject in a typical learning situation. By this general method, Hull proposed to relate $_sE_R$ to such response measures as latency (time between stimulus onset and response evocation), response amplitude (vigor of response), and number of trials required to reach complete experimental extinction. Hull postulated that increasing reaction potential is reflected in decreasing latency of response, increasing amplitude of response, and increasing numbers of trials needed to complete the extinction process.

While Hull is reputed to have believed that this quantification procedure represented his most important contribution to behavior theory, critics have taken strong exception to this contention (see, e.g., Koch, 1954, pp. 110ff.). Various criticisms of the assumptions and methodology associated with the quantification procedure led Hilgard (1956, p. 180) to conclude that, "Hull was rightly aware of the task that needed to be done (i.e., quantification of the system's intervening variables), but he failed to accomplish it."

Concluding comments about Hull's theory

This brief overview of Hull's formulation has omitted reference to several important concepts. Examples that should at least be mentioned include the stimulus trace (see Chapter 4); afferent stimulus interaction (a postulated change in an afferent neural impulse due to the simultaneous presence of another such impulse); secondary reinforcement (the acquiring of reinforcing power by a previously neutral stimulus through learning); and stimulus intensity dynamism (V) (a concept related to intensity of stimulation, conceived as combining multiplicatively with $_sH_R$). While all these concepts are of significance to the theory, the writer chose to ignore them in attempting to develop a general account of the nature of Hull's system.

By referring fairly frequently to criticisms of the theory, the writer has tried to avoid any implication that Hull produced a finished product. It is clear that many unsolved problems remain—most notably, the difficult matter of quantification of the various intervening variables. The writer will take the position, to be developed in detail in later sections, however, that despite all its shortcomings the theory has considerable potential for guiding significant psychological research in the field of mental deficiency.

SOME MAJOR MODIFICATIONS AND EXTENSIONS DUE TO SPENCE AND HIS STUDENTS

The nature of Spence's theorizing

First as a student and later as a close associate of Hull's, Kenneth Spence had much to do with the development of Hullian theory. With respect to certain issues, however, Spence and Hull did not agree. Thus, although Spence's own theoretical developments have definitely borne and continue to bear the Hullian stamp, they have also diverged from the parent theory in several significant respects.

In his Silliman lectures, Spence (1956) indicated some of the major ways in which his approach has differed from that of Hull's. For one thing, Spence has avoided the trappings of a hypothetico-deductive system (i.e., the use of postulates and theorems), feeling that psychology's current stage of development does not yet justify this formal mode of presentation. Secondly, Spence has refrained from speculating about the neurophysiological correlates of his behavioral constructs. Hull was prone to conjecture about possible neurophysiological implications with respect to his concepts, despite the essentially molar nature of his theory. Spence, in contrast, has maintained that currently available knowledge at the molecular level allows at best for little more than the addition of physiological labels to one's molar theorizing and, at worst, to speculations which may be misleading in nature. Spence does not *oppose* neurophysiological theory, but insists that molecular concepts must first be significant in their own right (i.e., enter into a network of physiological laws) before they can be helpful to the psychologist. One of the clearest manifestations of this difference in emphasis is found in Spence's symbolism; with regard to his concept of habit strength, for example, Spence avoids any connotation of a receptor-effector connection by omitting the customary subscripts (S and R) and merely referring to habit as H. The mathematical aspects of intervening variable theory construction, Spence insists, can be attacked without reference to such neurophysiological considerations.

A third area of disagreement relates to Hull's reinforcement theory, i.e., the notion that drive reduction is a necessary condition for the occurrence of an increment in habit strength. For many years, Spence held to what he terms a *general* reinforcement position—a viewpoint which recognizes that increments in *excitatory potential* occur when responses are reinforced, but does not attribute *habit* growth to reinforcement. Actually, Spence's most recent (and admittedly tentative) approach involves a two-factor theory suggesting that habit growth in classical conditioning is dependent upon reinforcement, whereas habits mediating instrumental responses do not depend on the occurrence of reinforcements.

Finally, Spence differs from Hull in adopting a much more cautious approach to behavior theory construction. Principles developed to account for data obtained from simple learning situations explain those phenomena only; to go beyond this requires the discovery of additional principles (called composition rules) which make extrapolation to different or more complex phenomena possible and justifiable. In Spence's own words (1956, p. 59),

> What we are trying to accomplish is to provide a theoretical structure that will permit the derivation of the different empirical functions found in the several types of conditioning experiments. That is, the initial objective is to develop a set or system of concepts and postulated inter-relations which, in combination with the different initial and boundary conditions specific to each experimental situation, will provide for the deduction of the many specific empirical relations that have been found in conditioning studies. It is hoped further that this theory, along with the necessary additional composition rules, will permit one to account for more complex learning phenomena.

Spence's initial major venture into independent theory construction (Spence, 1936) was concerned with the behavior of chimpanzees in visual discrimination learning problems. In such situations, the subject is confronted with two discriminable visual stimuli, S^+ and S^-, customarily placed side by side. On half the trials, S^+ is located to the left of S^-, this spatial relationship being reversed on the remaining trials. The subject's problem involves learning to select one stimulus, S^+ (responses to which are always reinforced), and to avoid the second stimulus, S^- (responses to which are never reinforced). Conceiving of leftness (S_L) and rightness (S_R) as additional stimuli, Spence assumed that during the course of learning, two stimulus complexes $(S^+S_L$ and $S^+S_R)$ are reinforced and two $(S^-S_L$ and $S^-S_R)$ are nonreinforced. Further assumptions were made relative to the effects of reinforcement and nonreinforcement on excitatory tendencies to approach the individual components of these four complexes, namely, that reinforcement of a response to a particular component leads to an increment in excitatory tendency to approach that component, whereas nonreinforcement of a response to a particular component weakens the effective tendency to approach that component through the buildup of inhibition. Such effects were conceptualized as being cumulative in nature, with learning occurring when the difference between excitatory tendencies to S^+ and S^- becomes sufficiently great to offset any differential tendency to respond to S_L and S_R.

In a subsequent series of papers (Spence, 1937, 1938, 1940, 1942), this theoretical formulation was applied in critical analyses of various gestalt-oriented interpretations of animal learning phenomena. Emphasis was placed in particular on the essentially continuous or gradual (as opposed to sudden or insightful) nature of such learning and on chimpanzees' responsiveness to individual stimulus components rather than stimulus configurations or wholes. Ingenious use was made of assumptions concerning generalization gradients of both excitation and inhibition, together with specific mathematical assumptions regarding the growth of excitation and the growth of inhibition as functions, respectively, of reinforcement and nonreinforcement.

Since these latter assumptions depended upon information regarding the shapes of learning curves in classical and instrumental conditioning situations, Spence became concerned with the paucity of such data and turned to intensive analyses of these simpler learning phenomena, as indicated by the quotation cited earlier. His work in this respect has ranged over a wide variety of issues, making a succinct summary difficult (see *Behavior Theory and Conditioning*, 1956, and *Behavior Theory and Learning*, 1960, pp. 91–265). This difficulty is compounded by the fact that Spence has always kept his theorizing very close to the available empirical data, with the consequence that the formulation has changed markedly over the years. In the present section of this chapter, several of the more significant contributions will be mentioned briefly; one topic (anxiety as drive) which would appear to have most relevance to the area of mental deficiency will then be dealt with in more detail.

Individual versus group curves. Together with a few other workers in behavior theory, Spence has for some time been sensitive to the fact that group acquisition curves in classical and instrumental conditioning may be quite unrepresentative of the performances of individual learners. Techniques for coping with this problem (e.g., the use of individual curves, Vincentized group curves, etc.) have on occasion been applied in the area of learning. Spence himself has advocated the grouping together of like or homogeneous subjects, the criterion for homogeneity involving either a total score (e.g., the total number of conditioned responses made in a given number of trials) or scores based on performances in the early, middle, and late phases of training. In this fashion, individuals whose scores fall within a relatively narrow range are combined for the purpose of constructing group curves, the end result being group curves which do in fact typify the acquisition patterns of individual subjects. This approach is implicitly, if not explicitly, a comparative one, since different kinds of learners (e.g., slow versus fast) from a given population of subjects are represented in the separate groupings involved. Another variety of comparison, i.e., between groups from different populations (normals and defectives), will be considered in later sections of this chapter.

A reversed two-factor theory. As pointed out previously, Hull developed a "true" reinforcement theory, in the sense that all habit acquisition was considered to be dependent on the occurrence of reinforcement. After taking a general reinforcement position for a number of years (i.e., excitatory potential, but not necessarily habit affected by reward), Spence has recently moved to a two-factor position which considers reinforcement essential for habit acqustion in classical aversive conditioning, but not in instrumental reward learning.[9] This is the reverse of the well-known two-factor theory

[9] In the absence of relevant data from classical reward and instrumental escape learning situations, Spence has refrained from speculating about the role of reinforcement in these types of learning.

endorsed at various times by Schlosberg (1937), Skinner (1938), and Mowrer (1947). The basis for such a stand may be found in a series of studies on classical eyelid conditioning (e.g., Spence, 1953; Spence, Haggard, & Ross, 1958) in which evidence was obtained that habit growth is related to the degree of primary drive reduction occurring in this aversive form of learning. The two-factor stand is a tentative one for Spence. Students of learning are particularly interested in the nonreinforcement or contiguity assumption regarding instrumental learning because of both its theoretical significance and the marked departure from orthodox Hullian theory which it represents.

The fractional anticipatory goal response and incentive motivation. Early in the development of his theory, Hull introduced the concept of the anticipatory goal response (r_g) to account for certain behaviors of rats in maze learning situations. When an animal consumes a food reward in the goal box of a maze, the various cues present (e.g., food cup, goal-box floor, etc.) become conditioned to the eating or goal response (R_G). In the absence of food, and after such conditioning has occurred, these cues are considered to elicit fractional components of the eating response (e.g., chewing, swallowing, etc.), labeled r_gs. Through stimulus generalization and higher-order conditioning, maze cues outside of the goal box also come to elicit r_gs. These implicit responses have stimulus properties (s_gs) which may become conditioned to responses in the same fashion as do any other stimuli. Spence has made frequent use of this r_g-s_g conceptualization, stressing in particular its inherent role in any instrumental reward learning situation. In addition, Spence has indicated how the r_g-s_g notion can provide a relatively objective means of conceiving of animals' expectancies with respect to the magnitude of food reward by relating incentive motivation (K) to the intensity of the r_g. In this context, it should be pointed out that Spence has always held to a motivational interpretation of the effects of reward magnitude. This identification of r_g with K provides a specific account of the mechanism involved. Hull, it will be recalled, first imposed a habit interpretation on the role of magnitude of reward and later shifted to a motivational conception.[10]

The additivity of D and K. In the absence of pertinent information, Hull speculated that drive (D) and incentive motivation (K) (each of which multiplies with habit) combine with one another in a multiplicative fashion [see Eq. (3-8)]. On the basis of small amounts of data, Spence has hazarded the guess that these constructs combine *additively*. Thus, for Spence,

$$E = H(D + K) \qquad (3\text{-}11)$$

The crucial experiment related to this problem would involve the joint manipulation of drive and incentive motivation variables. Support for the additivity assumption would be provided by performance curves which are parallel in form when plotted separately across various drive levels for

---

[10] The r_g-s_g mechanism is representative of a class of phenomena commonly referred to as *mediational*. Several kinds of implicit mediating responses are believed to play important roles in the determination of behavior, the most significant form in human behavior probably involving implicit verbal responses.

different incentive motivation groups. Such a finding has been reported by Ramond (1954).

Delay of reward, inhibition, and extinction. Spence's theorizing with respect to inhibitory factors has always differed considerably from that of Hull. In contrast to the work or fatigue interpretation endorsed by Hull, Spence has maintained that the failure of occurrence of a reinforcer following an instrumental response leads to the development of an inhibitory factor, labeled I_n, which subtracts from excitatory potential and thus leads to the phenomenon of experimental extinction. Another significant deviation from the Hullian formulation involves Spence's notion that the delay of reward variable (i.e., the time between completion of the response and the delivery of reward in instrumental learning situations) also contributes to an inhibitory factor (in this case labeled I_t).[11] A common mechanism accounting for the effects of both I_n and I_t is the acquisition, due to nonreinforcement or delay of reinforcement, of other response tendencies which compete with that of the instrumental response. Spence uses this formulation to interpret the findings of partial reinforcement studies, as well as extinction and delay of reward effects. In his early discrimination learning theorizing, Spence used a "frustration" interpretation to specify the nature of the competing responses which occur as a result of nonreinforcement, indicating that frustration responses are elicited only after the subject has come to expect reward in the situation. This formulation, as will be indicated subsequently, has been elaborately extended by Amsel (1958).

Mathematical developments. Spence's interest in the quantitative aspects of behavior theory has led to a series of highly technical papers dealing with the derivation of relationships between excitatory potential and various response measures. In this context, Spence has shown that certain of Hull's postulates concerned with these relationships are actually superfluous, in the sense that they are derivable from other postulates in the system. Furthermore, one such derivation (Spence, 1954), involving a response latency measure, indicates that Hull's *ad hoc* postulate relating latency to excitatory potential is inconsistent with other postulates in the theory concerning excitatory potential, response threshold, and oscillation.

Anxiety as drive

The phase of Spence's theorizing which has attracted most attention in recent years is that concerned with the variable of anxiety. An analysis of learning in aversive classical conditioning situations provides the primary basis for the theoretical developments in this area.

Starting with Hull's assumption concerning the multiplicative relationship between habit and drive [see Eq. (3-3)], Spence considers the intensity of noxious stimulation (e.g., shock, air puff to the eyelid, etc.) to be the major determinant of drive level in aversive conditioning. Drive, more

[11] Spence has emphasized a differentiation between this form of delay of reward and that involved while a response sequence is being run off ("within-chain" delay), indicating that different principles are probably involved in these two types of delay phenomena. For the case of within-chain delay, Spence stresses the relevance of r_g-s_g and the K construct.

specifically, is assumed to be a function of the magnitude of a hypothetical emotional response, r_e, which in turn is elicited by aversive stimulation. One means of manipulating D would, of course, be through variations in the intensity of the noxious stimulation used in aversive learning situations. But everyday observation, plus various behavioral and physiological data, indicates that different individuals do not respond comparably to the same intensity of noxious stimulation. This hypothesis suggests another way of manipulating D, namely, through the selection of subjects differing in degree of emotional reactivity.

Using this line of reasoning, Janet Taylor, in a doctoral dissertation done under Spence's direction (Taylor, 1951), constructed the Manifest Anxiety Scale (A scale)—a self-inventory instrument designed to assess level of emotional reactivity. Having identified subjects falling at the high and low ends of such a continuum, the research strategy then calls for comparing the performances of the groups in a variety of learning problems. If the task is a very simple one involving only a single or highly dominant response tendency, as in classical conditioning, a high anxiety (and hence high drive) level should result in *superior* performance. If, however, the task is more complex, in the sense that several response tendencies are present which compete with the correct tendency, *impairment* in performance is to be expected, the degree of impairment being directly related to the number and strength of the competing tendencies.

This formulation led to a long series of studies in which high- and low-anxious subjects were compared in a variety of learning situations, including simple classical conditioning, differential conditioning, finger maze learning, and various verbal learning tasks (serial learning, paired-associates learning, etc.). By careful choice of materials, it has been possible to make use of varying levels of complexity within given tasks (e.g., use of high- and low-competition pairs in paired-associates learning) in order to provide explicit tests of the theory. While complete verification has by no means been obtained, the evidence does, in general, point toward the validity of both the A scale and the theoretical position. A summary of relevant studies, as well as of the theoretical formulation, may be found in Spence (1958).

A children's form of the A scale (Castaneda, McCandless, & Palermo, 1956) has been constructed, and it is of considerable interest to note that some of the most convincing evidence for the Spence-Taylor position concerning anxiety as drive has been obtained in studies using children as subjects (e.g., Castaneda, Palermo, & McCandless, 1956; Palermo et al., 1956; Castaneda, 1956). The significance of the anxiety work for the field of mental deficiency, as well as techniques for assessing anxiety level in defectives, will be discussed in a later section of this chapter.

Frustration theory (Amsel) and micromolar theory (Logan)

There is nothing static about behavior theory. Just as Spence has introduced major modifications in orthodox Hullian theory, so have Spence's students, in turn, moved on to new developments of their own. The work of two such theorists will be briefly described here, in order to illustrate the evolving nature of the behavior theory field and because these individuals, in the present writer's opinion, are among the most important of the younger contributors to neo-Hullian theory.

In collaboration with several of his own students, Amsel has developed an elaborate theory concerned with the frustrating effects of nonreinforcement, together with a unique experimental setting designed to provide data relevant to the formulation. Rats are run in a double runway, the sequence of events for a given trial being (1) traversing of runway 1; (2) entry into goal box 1, which may or may not contain a reward; (3) traversing of runway 2; and (4) entry into goal box 2, which always contains a reward. The behavior of primary concern is speed of running in runway 2 as a function of presence or absence of reward in goal box 1. The major empirical finding is that rats tend to run faster in runway 2 after nonreinforcement as compared with reinforcement in goal box 1. This difference is not evident early in training, but becomes so after a certain number of reinforced runs to the first goal box have been experienced.

To account for these findings, Amsel hypothesizes that reinforcement of responses early in training results in the buildup of the fractional anticipatory goal response (r_g). Should nonreinforcement also occur during the early stages of learning (as in partial reinforcement experiments), no substantial effect on the subject's behavior results. When, however, r_g has developed to an appreciable degree (i.e., the subject has come to "expect" reward in the situation), nonreward acquires potent motivational properties as a consequence of its newly acquired *frustrating* nature. The frustration reaction (R_F) that occurs in the empty goal box is, according to the theory, capable of being conditioned in such a fashion that it may occur in anticipatory form prior to the subject's arrival at a goal region, quite as in the case of R_G. This fractional anticipatory frustration response (r_f), together with its characteristic stimulus properties (s_f), is considered to contribute both to a heightened level of drive and to an inhibitory factor involving the elicitation of responses which compete with the running response.

Amsel (1958) makes a convincing case for the utility of this frustration formulation in accounting for the results of several double runway studies conducted in his and other laboratories (e.g., Amsel & Roussel, 1952; Amsel & Hancock, 1957; Wagner, 1957), as well as for the findings of numerous experiments dealing with more traditional learning problems, such as the acquisition of discrimination learning habits, the effects of partial reinforcement on resistance to extinction, etc. Perhaps Amsel's most notable contribution involves the development of a frustration theory based on an experimental setting in which the frustrated response and the criterion response (i.e., the behavior from which the frustration effect is inferred) are clearly separated. The general applicability of the theory has so far only been hinted at; it seems likely, however, that this approach to the concept of frustration will prove to have considerable relevance to a variety of animal and human behaviors.

A more radical revision of traditional Hullian theory is due to Frank Logan, who was closely associated with Hull at Yale after receiving his training under Spence. Logan's micromolar theory emphasizes the assumption that the *intensity* of a response is one of the several things a subject *learns* in the kinds of tasks which behavior theorists study. Thus, the usual assumption that intensity or amplitude of response may serve as an index of excitatory potential, with increasing intensities indicating increasing excitatory potentials, is abandoned in micromolar theory. This formulation presents some discouraging prospects to psychologists, since all response intensities which the subject is capable of differentiating now become *different responses,* as far as the theorist is concerned. Thus, fast and slow runs in a maze alley constitute different responses, just as do, for example, running in a runway and pressing a lever at the end of a runway. But in spite of any complexities which may be added to behavior theory by such an assumption, if the micromolar theory is more effective in accounting for behavioral phenomena, the field will inevitably move toward its adoption.

Logan's recently published book, *Incentive* (Logan, 1960), summarizes the theory and also an extensive research program of relevance to the formulation. The data concern the running speeds of rats in a straight runway, with reinforcement conditions (i.e., magnitude and delay of reward) being manipulated in a systematic and extensive fashion. The subjects are run under *constant* reward treatments (magnitude and delay values remaining the same throughout training) as well as under *varied* conditions involving random shifts between large and small magnitudes and/or between short and long delays. Furthermore, correlated reinforcement schedules are used, with the rats' own speed of response determining the magnitude and/or the delay of reward. One of the more crucial conditions for the theory is a correlated arrangement that is "negative" in nature in the sense that the subject must learn to run *slowly* in order to be rewarded in an optimal fashion (large magnitude and/or short delay). That is, the slower the rat runs, the larger is the magnitude and/or the shorter is the delay of the resulting reward.

In the context of this kind of correlated reinforcement treatment, Logan develops what he terms an *equilibrium model,* which predicts the rats' behavior from the postulates of traditional molar theory. Briefly, the model indicates that the rat will run slowly (and thus experience large magnitudes and/or short delays of reward) in the early stages of training but will gradually increase his speed of response as excitatory potential increases. Faster speeds, however, lead to smaller magnitudes and/or longer delays and thus reduced reaction potential and reduced speeds. In this fashion, excitatory potential and speed of response will shift up and down, with an average speed being predicted which produces the appropriate reward conditions that will balance the reinforcement and extinction effects described above. In general, Logan finds that rats' performances in negatively correlated reinforcement situations deviate from the predictions of the equilibrium model in the direction of producing more optimal conditions than those indicated by the model. Logan concludes that these results provide support for his micromolar assumption.

No matter how Logan's theory fares, it would seem that psychologists must acknowledge his contention that conditions of varied and correlated reinforcement in the laboratory come closer than do constant reward treatments to replicating reinforcement phenomena commonly occurring in everyday life. For this reason, Logan's experimental manipulations and empirical data are undoubtedly of considerable significance for behavior theory.

INDIVIDUAL DIFFERENCES AND HULL-SPENCE THEORY[12]

We are now in a position to consider the role played by individual differences in Hull-Spence theory and, more specifically, the theory's potential for guiding significant research in mental deficiency. Hull proposed that a rather definite place be given to individual differences in his theory, but it is not apparent just what he had in mind when he used the concept. Historically, a variable has been labeled an individual difference variable if it is found that groups of organisms within a species, when categorized on the basis of such a factor, differ reliably on some criterion measure. Thus, one designates *age* as an individual difference variable, since persons of varying ages tend to differ in various important respects, such as speed of learning, etc. The range of variables that traditionally has been included within the rubric individual difference is very wide; this breadth may be given emphasis by noting that at least four categories of such variables may be differentiated, according to one arbitrary classification system.

Physical characteristics. One clear meaning has to do with overt physical characteristics, e.g., height and weight—referents which are not of great relevance here.

Common-sense generic groupings. This category has reference to broad classes of individuals grouped on the basis of such concepts as age, race, sex, socioeconomic level, and ethnic origin. In animals, groupings within a species according to strain, colony, etc., would appear to fall in the present category.

Groupings based on the results of mental tests. Among psychologists, the concept of individual differences is most often encountered in the vocabularies of those interested in the construction and use of mental tests. Differentiation of individuals according to ability level (by means of tests of intelligence, of perceptual-motor skill, and so forth) is one of the most common referents and one of obvious concern to workers in mental deficiency. In the area of personality theory, numerous instruments have been devised to assess individuals with respect to so-called personality differences or *traits*, some well-known examples being the Luchins water jar problem (a test of rigidity), the California F-Scale (designed to measure degree of authoritarianism), the Horowitz Faces Test (prejudice), the Rotter Marble Board (level of aspiration), and so on.

Advocates of these latter kinds of tests often indicate that, in investigating such traits, they are studying individual differences which behavior

[12] Preparation of this section was facilitated by discussions between the writer and Prof. Charles C. Spiker, who also read the entire manuscript and made several helpful suggestions.

theorists ignore. But it would appear perfectly reasonable to contend that traits such as rigidity and authoritarianism may be conceptualized in terms of habits, drives, anticipatory frustration responses, and the like. If one accepts this argument, then it seems clear that the behavior theorists are no less concerned with individual differences in this sense of the term than are the personality theorists.

Biogenic considerations. This final usage carries a meaning apparently having to do with what Hull called "basic physiological determiners" (Hull, 1951, p. 117). In this context, it is assumed that various genetic mechanisms operate to determine (in a *limiting* sense) the quality of one's cortical cells and related neurophysiological characteristics. Such properties are typically thought of as determiners of what have traditionally been called *physiological limits.* In other words, these characteristics set limits on the achievement levels an individual is capable of reaching; how close one comes to approaching such limits depends, of course, on the organism's various life experiences. Furthermore, it is ordinarily assumed that brain damage (from whatever source) can result in physiological limits which are lower than would otherwise have been the case in the absence of such injury. The conceptions represented in this rather vague but undoubtedly important category amount to little more than a recognition of *innate* differences among individuals and of differences more or less immutably imposed on organisms by cortical insult.

As previously indicated, Hull referred to the role of individual differences in his theory in various of his writings (see, e.g., Hull, 1951, pp. 115–117). He intended to publish a book on this topic but unfortunately was not able to complete the work. In the absence of such a volume, it is difficult to be certain what he meant in his use of the concept; it is the present writer's impression, however, that Hull was thinking to some extent in terms of representatives from all four of the categories discussed above. For the purposes of the present chapter, individual differences in intelligence—conceived at a molar level in terms of IQ or MA scores —will be the focus of concern.

The remaining discussion in this section will deal with three topics: (1) mental deficiency in relation to the formal role given by Hull to individual differences in his theory (the *curve-fitting* approach); (2) a more general comparative approach using Hull-Spence theory (called here the *gross comparative* approach); and (3) the *noncomparative* approach to the study of defectives' behavior, pursued within the Hull-Spence framework. The general nature of all three of these methodologies will be discussed, together with studies representative of each of the categories. Reference will also be made to needs for additional research. The final section of the chapter will include some summarizing statements concerning the three approaches to research in mental deficiency about to be discussed in the present section.

Normals versus defectives—the curve-fitting approach

As indicated in earlier sections of this chapter, Hull-Spence behavior theory has been concerned with the discovery of molar behavioral laws or principles, stated in quantitative terms. The equations which state these relationships contain certain values labeled *constants,* and others referred to as *variables.* For example, in the principle concerning the growth of habit strength [see Eq. (3-1)], N (the number of reinforcements) is a variable quantity; i.e., N may take any value from zero to some very large amount, depending on the number of reinforced training trials given the learner. The i value, in contrast, is a parameter or constant for the individual, determining his rate of approach to the limit of habit strength. As noted previously, however, such a parameter may be regarded as a "variable constant"; this is the case because Hull assumed that such *constants* vary from individual to individual within a species. In other words, individual differences are considered by Hull to be reflected in the varying values taken by a given parameter in a given behavioral equation for different individual learners. Another way of stating this principle would be to indicate that the *form* of a given equation (exponential in the case of habit growth) remains invariant for individuals, whereas the value of one or more parameters in the equation (and thus the specific shape of the curve) changes from individual to individual.

In the context of a comparison between the learning of defective and normal subjects, Hull's assumption would call for the obtaining of habit curves for such groups and the subsequent fitting of equations to these curves. Should exponential functions with different i values be found for the two groups, some verifications of the individual difference assumption would be provided.

It would seem reasonable to expect differing *limits* of habit growth, as well as differing rates of approach to the limit, for different individuals. Another form of the exponential habit function may be written as follows:

$$_sH_R = m(1 - 10^{-iN}) \tag{3-12}$$

In this equation, i and N have the same meanings as before, while m designates the asymptotic value of $_sH_R$—a value which may be considered as varying from individual to individual.

Still another possibility concerns the fact that individuals may differ in *initial* level of habit strength when they begin habit acquisition in a particular situation. That is, by virtue of prior experience, individuals may differ in $_sH_R$ before learning in a given situation ever starts. In order to recognize this eventuality, Eq. (3-1) may again be rewritten in the following fashion, using the symbol $_sH_{R_0}$ to refer to initial habit strength:

$$_sH_R = (m - {_sH_{R_0}})(1 - e^{-iN}) + {_sH_{R_0}} \tag{3-13}$$

Inspection of Eq. (3-13) indicates there are now *three* parameters—i, m, and $_sH_{R_0}$—which may be evaluated via a defective-normal comparison in the manner mentioned above.

In similar fashion, this procedure would be appropriate in connection with the parameters included in all other behavioral equations; see, e.g., the j parameter in the function concerning generalized habit strength

[Eq. (3-2)], the *a* parameter in the principle governing the generation of incentive motivation or K [Eq. (3-4)], and the *j* parameter in the function involving the delay of reward factor (*J*) [Eq. (3-6)].

In spite of the fact that Hull's programmatic statements concerning the role of individual differences in his theory have been available for many years, very little has been done with *any* type of subject in the way of actual pursuit of such a research program. This dearth is quite understandable. Two workers who have done some research on individual differences within the Hullian framework had the following to say, in discussing the habit strength function:

> But habit strength is not directly related to behavior, and this fact produces complications which prevent direct empirical check. In theory, habit strengths interact with drives and other factors to produce excitatory potentials, which in turn interact with inhibitory potentials and an oscillatory factor before affecting behavior. Each step in this chain is put into equation form by Hull, and each step involves additional equation constants capable in principle of varying from subject to subject. With individual differences entering at so many possible places in a theoretical superstructure, it becomes a problem to identify a given empirical individual difference with the correct theoretical source . . . (Zeaman & Kaufman, 1955, p. 2).

In other words, extensive difficulties stand in the way of making clear-cut interpretations relating an individual difference variable such as IQ to variations in the value of some one particular parameter.

This interpretative problem is illustrated in the single study with which the writer is familiar that actually utilized a curve-fitting procedure within the context of a defective-normal comparison. Ellis, Pryer, and Barnett (1960a), in a study of habit formation in normal and retarded subjects, reanalyzed some verbal learning data gathered in two earlier studies (Ellis, Pryer, Distefano, & Pryer, 1960; Pryer, 1960), following a type of analysis suggested by Underwood (1954). The latter worker was interested in developing a technique for equating the degree of learning of fast and slow subjects (all normals), so that a more meaningful comparison could be made of retention in such groups. Underwood's approach is termed a *successive probability analysis* and, briefly, involves a determination of the probability that a particular paired-associate verbal learning item will be responded to correctly on a stipulated trial, given the number of correct responses (or what Underwood terms *reinforcements*) which have previously occurred with respect to that item. Using this technique, Underwood plotted curves for fast and slow learners showing the probability of a correct response to a particular item on a given trial as a function of number of previous reinforcements on that item. Ellis et al. applied this type of analysis to serial learning data obtained from the performances of 118 defectives (mean CA = 17.1 years, mean IQ = 64.2) and 75 normals (mean CA = 16.1 years, mean IQ = 102.7). The resulting curves are shown in Figure 3-3. Using the form of the exponential habit function given in Eq. (3-12), Ellis et al. found that equations differing in both the

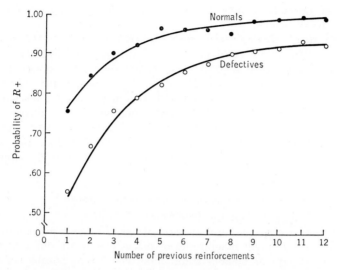

Figure 3-3. Probability of correct response as a function of number of previous reinforcements. (*After Ellis, Pryer, & Barnett, 1960a.*)

m and i parameters fit the two curves nicely. They concluded that these results are favorable to Hull's position that individual differences are reflected as constants in the various behavioral equations.

One interpretive problem with respect to these data stems from the difficulty of stipulating just what constitutes a reinforcement in verbal learning situations. In both paired-associate and serial learning, the subject is ordinarily given feedback regarding the correct response on each trial, irrespective of how he responds. One could thus argue that *every* trial is a reinforced trial in such situations, thus calling into question the appropriateness of the dimension represented in the abscissa in Figure 3-3. A more pertinent difficulty, however, relates to the matter discussed in the quotation from Zeaman and Kaufman, reproduced above. That is, one may raise the question of how certain it is that a habit difference and not some other kind of difference accounts for the curves found in Figure 3-3. In this context, the reader's attention is called to the large initial difference appearing in these curves. The initial decrement for the defectives could be accounted for in terms of lower habit strengths existing prior to any learning in this situation (i.e., lower $_sH_{R_0}$), or perhaps the difference is a result of their learning less in the first few trials. But still another explanation may involve the supposition that the groups were differentially motivated, i.e., that the normals had a higher level of D. If one assumed that the list were a simple one (as indicated by the very high level of performance exhibited by the normals after a relatively small number of trials) and that a fairly high D level thus has facilitating effects in this task, the initial difference could be accounted for on this basis. The fact that the curves do not diverge (as would be expected if there were indeed a difference in D) could be explained by the ceiling effect operating with respect to the normals' performance. Comparable arguments concerning the role of normal-defective differences in still other respects could undoubtedly be developed.

But one study does not serve to confirm or disconfirm the postulates of a theory. The writer considers the analysis presented by Ellis et al. an interesting and valuable one. What is called for, rather obviously, is an extensive program of comparative research in which the curve-fitting technique is utilized in conjunction with systematic manipulations of each of the many variables considered relevant within Hullian theory. In the meantime, one can only conclude that the Ellis-Pryer-Barnett curves are at least consistent with a habit interpretation. Further data and analyses should serve either to bolster their interpretation or to provide support for some alternative interpretation.[13]

Normals versus defectives—the gross comparative approach

Most research done within the framework of Hull-Spence theory involves comparisons of average performances of groups of subjects given differential treatment (e.g., different magnitudes or delays of reward, different degrees of food deprivation or noxious stimulation, etc.). It is possible, of course, to add to such a comparison one involving normal and defective subjects. Thus, one might assign half the subjects in a normal and a defective group to a given treatment (e.g., high drive, via strongly motivating instructions), the remaining subjects in each group being given a second treatment (low drive, via nonmotivating instructions). This sort of comparative research on normals and defectives is termed here the gross comparative approach. Using the illustration just mentioned, a representative design might be one in which the following factors are of interest: (1) a treatment effect involving a variable of relevance to Hull-Spence theory (i.e., high versus low drive); (2) a group effect (normal versus defective); and (3) an interaction effect involving the treatment and group factors.[14] The latter effect would relate to the magnitude of the difference between the performances of high- and low-drive subjects in the normal group, on the one hand, and in the defective group, on the other; a substantial discrepancy between the magnitudes of such differences for the two groups would indicate the presence of a significant interaction between these two factors.

To the extent that IQ is related to performance on the task in question, one would expect the normals, as a group, to exceed the defectives; predictions concerning relative performance of the treatment groups would stem

---

[13] Mention should be made here of the work done by Zeaman and Kaufman (1955). While actual curve-fitting techniques were not used in this study, the authors did make an extensive semi-quantitative analysis of curves in comparing the performances of groups of *normal* adult subjects in a motor task in which the measure was speed of printing letters of the alphabet upside down and backwards. The groups were constituted on the basis of starting score levels. Applying treatments involving spaced and massed practice, and rest periods interpolated during massed practice, plus an elaborate theoretical analysis, these authors concluded that the groups could be differentiated in terms of level of conditioned inhibition ($_sI_R$).

[14] This paradigm conforms to what Lindquist (1953) terms a *factorial* analysis of variance design.

from the theoretical formulation (high-drive superiority if the task is simple, low-drive superiority if the task is complex). Of particular interest would be a significant interaction effect, which would indicate that the law relating the drive variable to performance in normals differs in some fashion from the relationship applicable to the performance of defectives. This gross comparative approach can, of course, be greatly simplified. One might, for instance, merely compare the mean scores of normals and defectives on some criterion measure such as anxiety (e.g., Lipman, 1960). In contrast, it would be feasible to elaborate on the factorial analysis of variance design described above, adding to the treatment and group comparisons one involving, e.g., a trial-block effect. Such a modification would permit assessment of the various subgroups' relative performances in various stages of the training sequence, as well as possible interactions between the treatment and/or group effect, on the one hand, and the trial-block effect, on the other.

Surprisingly few experiments have, in fact, used the gross comparative approach to study variables of central importance in Hullian theory.[15] Brief mention of these, categorized in terms of the concepts being stressed, will serve to indicate the possibilities inherent in this form of experimentation.

Stimulus generalization. It would seem extremely important to know if defectives tend to generalize among stimuli in a manner comparable to that found in normals. Common-sense considerations indicate that defectives should generalize *more* (or, conceived another way, should discriminate less) than do normals. Barnett (1958), using a visual-spatial generalization situation devised by Brown, Bilodeau, and Baron (1951), had 60 normals (mean CA = 17 years, mean IQ = 102) and 60 defectives (mean CA = 18 years, mean IQ = 50) learn to respond to the onset of a light located in the center of a row of 11 lights by lifting a finger from a response button. Half the subjects in each group were given 20 such training trials, the remaining subjects being given only eight trials. The subjects were instructed not to respond if any other light came on. After the training had been completed, all subjects were given test trials involving various of the 10 peripheral lights. The results showed interesting gradient effects indicating that the subjects were more apt to respond to the test lights, the closer these were located to the training light. Significantly flatter gradients occurred for the subjects given 20 as opposed to eight training trials on the center light, as Hullian theory would predict. An unexpected result was the highly comparable generalization gradients obtained for the normal and defective subjects. There was no significant difference between the response patterns of these two groups, nor was there a significant interaction between the amount of training and the intelligence group variables.

It would be of considerable interest to obtain comparable gradients for defectives of lower intellectual level. Since this particular technique, requiring a voluntary response from the individual, would probably not be

---

[15] Numerous studies have used the gross comparative approach in connection with the manipulation of variables not at the present time crucially involved in Hull-Spence theory. See Chaps. 11 and 12 in the present volume.

feasible with low-grade subjects, a comparative study using a classically conditioned, autonomically mediated response (e.g., GSR) would doubtless be more appropriate for such a purpose.

Inhibition. In a rather unusual experiment, Siegel and Foshee (1960) presented 64 defectives (median CA = 28; mean MA = 6 years, 7 months) and 64 normals (median CA = 8 years, 4 months; mean MA = 8 years, 8 months) with a task involving a light signal and four switches. The subjects were told to choose any switch to extinguish the light each time the latter came on. In a series of 33 trials of this sort, the defectives showed significantly less response variability (i.e., more tendency to concentrate choices on particular switches or particular patterns of switches) as compared with the normals. Rejecting a rigidity interpretation, the authors proposed an *ad hoc* explanation which contends that defectives build up less inhibition (I_r) as a function of their peculiar susceptibility to "disinhibition," the latter being attributable to the distracting nature of the environmental surround. While this highly speculative notion may have some merit, it is difficult to reconcile it with Hull's fatigue conception of inhibition. The authors themselves suggest that the inhibition in question may be of a central rather than a peripheral nature. It should also be noted that Hull (1943, pp. 287ff.) discussed the concept of disinhibition (disruption of inhibition by extraneous stimuli) with reference to conditioned inhibition ($_sI_R$) but not reactive inhibition (I_R).

A more conventional treatment of the reactive inhibition concept may be found in a paper by Ellis, Pryer, and Barnett (1960b). These authors ran a group of 80 defectives (mean CA = 18.6 years, mean IQ = 61.2) and a group of 80 normals (mean CA = 16.4 years) on a motor-learning task involving the pursuit rotor. All subjects were given two blocks of twenty 20-second trials (with 20-second rest intervals), the blocks being separated by a 5-minute rest period. Half the subjects in each group were then given 10 additional trials 1 day later, the remaining subjects receiving 10 trials 28 days after original training. The major finding of relatively greater gains made by the normals, as compared with the defectives, following the 5-minute, 1-day, and 28-day rest intervals led Ellis et al. to conclude that greater amounts of I_R were built up in the normals, with greater amounts of dissipation of I_R occurring as a consequence during rest periods.

An implication stemming from these results, namely, that the difference between massed and spaced learning rates should be greater for normals than for defectives, was tested in a subsequent study by Jones and Ellis (1961). Again, a pursuit rotor task was used with 80 defectives (CA range 13–28 years, IQ range 60–75) and 80 normals (CA range 14–16 years). Half the subjects in each group were given *massed* practice (20-second work intervals, 10-second rest intervals) and the remaining subjects received *distributed* practice (20-second work intervals, 30-second rest intervals). All subjects were given 30 trials, a 5-minute rest, and 20 postrest trials. Although the results did not verify the prediction that normals and defectives would be differentially affected by the degree of distribution of practice, a significant difference in amount of "reminiscence" (increment in performance from final prerest trials to initial postrest trials) in favor of the normals did support the notion that greater amounts of inhibition are generated in normals than in defectives.

It is apparent that the normal-defective performance differences found in the studies mentioned above must be accounted for in some fashion. Perhaps an inhibition interpretation fits the data most adequately. But it should be pointed out that Hull's work inhibition theorizing has been far more successful in accounting for motor-learning phenomena, as typified in the pursuit rotor situation, than for other behavioral data which Hull believed should be explainable in inhibition terms. In addition to a lack of congruence between various empirical findings and inhibition theory, the formulation suffers from numerous logical inadequacies. Reference has already been made to Koch's (1954) criticisms in this respect. A recent paper by Jensen (1961) examines Hull's inhibition position, together with several attempts to reformulate the theory, and reaches the conclusion that Spence's approach to inhibition provides the only currently available reformulation showing promise of both logical and empirical adequacy. The present writer tends to agree with this judgment. It consequently seems regrettable that, relatively speaking, so much attention has been paid in normal-defective comparisons to the work inhibition theory, in view of the general paucity of comparative studies dealing with core concepts within Hull-Spence theory. One is led to wonder if comparative studies concerned with Spence's inhibition concepts (I_n as a function of nonreinforcement, I_t as a function of delay in reinforcement) might not constitute a more fruitful investment in time and effort.

Delay of reinforcement. Only one comparative study has dealt with this important variable. Jacobs (1950) ran 40 older institutionalized normals (mean CA = 120.3 months), 40 younger institutionalized normals (mean CA = 77.1 months), and 40 institutionalized defectives (mean IQ = 63; matched for MA level with the younger normals) in a task requiring the learning of associations between three ambiguous visual stimuli and three push buttons. Half the subjects in each group were given pretraining in which they learned verbal labels for the stimuli; the remaining subjects were not given such training. For all subjects, correct responses were signified by the sound of a bell and the delivery of marbles which were later exchangeable for candy; incorrect responses were identified by the onset of a light. For half the subjects, feedback regarding correctness of a response occurred immediately, while for the remaining subjects a delay of 23 seconds intervened between each response and feedback stimulation. The results gave only partial verification of the predictions that the normals would exceed the defectives and that the possession of verbal labels for the stimuli would enhance performance. The treatment involving immediate reinforcement led to clearly superior performance, in comparison with that involving a delay of reward. None of the interactions was significant, indicating, among other things, that the beneficial effects of immediate reinforcement applied comparably to the performances of both normals and defectives.

With the exception of the study just discussed, the variable of delay of reinforcement has remained virtually untouched in comparative and noncomparative research with defective subjects. There is considerable need for studies using a variety of different delay values (including very long delays) and defective subjects representing wider ranges of intellectual ability. The surprising failure to find a significant interaction between intelligence level and the delay variable in the Jacobs study suggests the appropriateness of further investigation into this matter; it is difficult to believe that increasingly long delays of reward do not penalize the defective learner relatively more than the normal learner. Of considerable interest would be experiments making use of varied delay and correlated delay treatments with defectives, much as Logan has applied these techniques with infrahuman subjects.

Discrimination learning and transposition.   In his analyses of discrimination learning, Spence made considerable use of the *transposition* experiment. This term refers to the maintenance of a relational response in a discrimination setting. For example, if a subject learns to choose a small, say, 3 square inches, visual stimulus as opposed to a large one, say, 5 square inches, and is then given the 3-square-inch stimulus paired with a still smaller stimulus (e.g., 1 square inch), transposition is said to have occurred if the subject chooses the 1-square-inch stimulus. One speaks of an "absolute" response if, in contrast, the subject continues to choose the 3-square-inch stimulus. The absolute versus relational controversy with respect to the nature of learning has died down, with Spence (1952) agreeing, at least with respect to certain circumstances (e.g., successive discrimination learning), that relational or "patterned" learning does occur in infrahuman organisms.[16] Irrespective of the status of this controversy, however, psychologists have been interested in determining the conditions which lead to relational or absolute responses in human subjects.

A study by Rudel (1959), using 30 normals (CA 4–5 years) and 20 mongoloid defectives (MA range 2.6–6.4 years), was concerned with this general topic. In view of Rudel's use of an inadequate statistical analysis, a rather unsystematic application of treatments, and a peculiar definition of transposition, it would not appear appropriate to summarize this experiment here. The data do indicate that tendencies to make relational as opposed to absolute responses are affected by both training and testing conditions. Rudel found, for example, that presenting several test stimuli spatially ordered according to size produced results for normal subjects differing from those obtained when the test stimuli were presented in a scrambled spatial order. It is the present writer's impression that studies using Rudel's general approach in a more rigorous fashion could shed considerable light on discrimination behavior in defectives.

Anxiety.   In recent years, workers in mental deficiency have become interested in the possibility that at least some of the defective's inadequacies in learning situations may be attributable to a high anxiety level. Lipman (1960) compared the Children's Manifest Anxiety Scale scores of 217 high-grade defectives with normative scores available in the literature on 367 normals of roughly comparable MA level. Lipman found evidence

[16] It should be noted that Spence's theorizing about discrimination learning has always had reference to infrahuman organisms.

of higher anxiety in female defectives, as compared with certain subgroups of female normals; he concluded that the data provided no basis for believing that anxiety scores can account for performance differences between high-grade defective males and normal males of roughly comparable MAs. The general problem of assessing anxiety level in defectives will be discussed in a subsequent section, as will the application of the "anxiety as drive" formulation to defectives' behavior.

The noncomparative approach to the study of defectives' behavior

It is not unusual to encounter the viewpoint that if behavioral research is to be done on mental defectives at all, it must include control groups consisting of normal subjects. The present writer is not sympathetic with this premise. Granting that comparative work is of great importance, the fact remains that a behavioral law discovered with reference to a group of defectives is useful irrespective of the omission of a normal control group in the research which generates the law. The population to which such a law would be applicable is admittedly restricted, but this is the case with respect to laws obtained from the study of normals' behavior as well. Furthermore, one may point out that the selection of a particular control group of normals is an arbitrary matter; does one match defectives and normals for CA, for MA, or does one not bother to match at all in comparative research? What about such typically confounded variables as socioeconomic level, institutionalization versus noninstitutionalization, etc.?

As is the case with the comparative approach, it is apparent that relatively few studies run with defectives as subjects on a noncomparative basis have been concerned with concepts of crucial importance to Hull-Spence theory. The expository technique of discussing such studies, categorized according to the concept of concern, will again be utilized in this section.

Incentive motivation. This topic is of both theoretical and practical importance, since it concerns a major Hull-Spence construct (K) and also deals with a technique, i.e., manipulation of reward properties, that may provide one of the most effective means of bringing the defective's performance in a learning situation up to the highest level possible.

Cantor and Hottel (1955) were unable to demonstrate with 44 adult male defectives that a high magnitude of food reward (four peanuts per correct response) would result in better performance than would a low magnitude (one peanut per correct response) in a discrimination learning problem. Two obvious ways of accounting for these negative results concern the possibilities that (1) it is impossible to demonstrate a significant magnitude of food reward effect in the absence of a deprivation schedule, and (2) the particular choice of food reward in this instance was inappropriate (evidence from a later study—Heber, [1959]—substantiates this contention).

Heber (1959) used a ranking technique with 36 adult male defectives to manipulate "magnitude" of reward in a different fashion. The subjects were asked individually to indicate the relative desirability of 15 reward objects and were then run on a portion of the Minnesota Spatial Relations Test Board. Half the subjects were started on the task with their most preferred reward object as the incentive; after 12 trials, the subjects were given their rewards and then were asked to work for an additional six trials with their least preferred reward as the incentive in each case. The remaining subjects performed on the first 12 trials for the rewards ranked as least desirable and were then switched to the incentives they ranked highest for an additional six trials of performance. The results showed definite superiority in terms of a response speed measure for the high-magnitude group on the initial 12 trials; an interesting crossover occurred at trial 13, with the high-magnitude (formerly low-magnitude) subjects again being the superior group. This relationship was maintained throughout the six postshift trials. An incidental finding of some interest related to the extensive between-subject variability in the reward preference rankings. This suggests that the individual's idiosyncratic preferences regarding incentives should perhaps be taken into account in both experimental and everyday situations in which incentive motivation is believed to be of importance.

A study by O'Connor and Claridge (1958) provides a replication in defectives of an infrahuman motivational phenomenon which was in part responsible for Hull's change with respect to his interpretation of the effects of reward magnitude. These authors ran four groups of imbecile level, adult defectives on a simple motor task (inserting pins in holes). Four subgroups were constituted: (1) a goal-goal (G-G) group, run throughout the experiment under high-incentive conditions; (2) a goal-control (G-C) group, given ten high-incentive and then eight low-incentive trials; (3) a control-control (C-C) group, run throughout under low-incentive conditions; and (4) a control-goal (C-G) group, given ten low-incentive followed by eight high-incentive trials. "High incentive" in this study referred to the use of verbal encouragement which involved urging of the subject to exceed previous performance levels, praise for success, and sympathy for failure. The "low-incentive" or control treatment consisted of the omission of verbal urging or praise. At the end of the first 10 trials, the two high-incentive groups (G-G and G-C) were performing at a clearly superior level. Following the shift in incentive conditions for the G-C and C-G groups, the data show the C-G group rising quickly to a level superior to that maintained by the G-G group; this is the typical "elation" effect first found in the behavior of rats by Crespi (1942). In contrast to the usual animal findings, however, the G-C group did not drop in performance level when shifted from high to low incentive, although these subjects were inferior to those in the G-G group during the last eight trials (the G-G group continued to improve during these trials, whereas the G-C group's performance tended to stabilize after the incentive shift). In view of the continued superiority of the C-G group and the failure of the G-C group to deteriorate in performance, the authors concluded that incentive conditions have a relatively permanent effect on the performance of imbeciles. This suggests the functioning of some sort of habit or "set" factor, in addition to a motivational phenomenon.

Further evidence for the relevance of incentive magnitude to defectives' performance is found in a study by Blank (1958). A four-choice discrimination task was given to 40 trainable level defectives, with two dominant and two nondominant stimuli involved in the problem. Half the subjects worked for a 25-cent reward, whereas the remaining subjects received 1 cent as a reinforcement. A series of extinction trials followed the acquisition phase of the experiment. The high-incentive group exceeded the low-incentive group in number of correct responses made in acquisition, but this was the case only on those parts of the task in which dominant responses were correct. When nondominant responses were correct, the low-incentive subjects did significantly better. No effect was found when response time was used as a measure of performance in acquisition. In the extinction phase, however, the high-incentive group responded significantly faster in the case of both dominant and nondominant responses.

Anxiety. The assessment of anxiety level in normal adults via the Taylor Manifest Anxiety Scale (MAS) and in normal children via the Children's Manifest Anxiety Scale (CMAS) assumes a certain minimum reading skill (fourth-grade level in the case of the CMAS). This poses a problem with respect to the application of the anxiety concept to defectives' behavior. Rosenblum and Callahan (1958) attacked this difficulty by presenting the CMAS items orally to 30 disturbed school-aged defectives, the responses being marked by the subjects on specially prepared answer sheets. The same subjects were also given the Children's Anxiety Pictures (CAP), a projective test consisting of 40 black and white ambiguous figures (Callahan, 1955). *Anxiety,* as revealed by the CAP, is defined as the subject's tendency to perceive the ambiguous stimuli as *threatening* types of objects. Intercorrelations among the CMAS, the CAP, and the CMAS Lie-Scale (items designed to detect falsification of responses on the CMAS) led these authors to conclude that the administration of the CMAS resulted in the falsifying of responses to an extent which did not characterize the subjects' behavior with reference to the CAP. In addition, clinical evidence was cited indicating that the CAP is less threatening to disturbed defectives than is the CMAS, when the latter is individually administered. Rosenblum and Callahan were led to conclude that the CAP may be a more useful instrument for investigating manifest anxiety in defectives.

Some additional evidence regarding the lack of applicability of the CMAS to defective subjects comes from a study by Keller (1957), which dealt with scores on the WISC digit-span (DS) test and CMAS measures obtained from sixty-three 14-year-old high-grade retardates (mean IQ = 73.3). Twenty-four subjects were selected from this group so as to constitute 12 pairs of individuals, the members within each pair having markedly different DS performances but highly similar Binet IQ scores. Keller found that the high- and low-DS subjects did not differ significantly in anxiety scores (the high-DS subjects tended to be somewhat *less* anxious). Callahan and Keller (1957) retested 21 of these 24 subjects a year later, using the CAP. In this case, the low-DS subjects were found to be significantly more anxious, as Hull-Spence theory would predict.

In an unpublished study, the present writer (Cantor, 1956) attempted to assess anxiety level in adult male defectives by the use of institutional employees' ratings. The raters were asked to study an instruction sheet which defined a concept of anxiety through the listing of a series of characteristics derived from the content of items appearing in both the MAS and the CMAS. The raters were then given 1,485 randomly ordered cards, on each of which appeared a pair of names, assigned at random to a left-right spatial relationship. In toto, the cards contained all possible pairs of the names of 55 residents of the institution.[17] The raters were instructed to check, with respect to each pair, the name of the individual they considered to be "more anxious." They were urged to work together on each decision, but were instructed not to refer back to any card, once it had been marked. An anxiety rank was assigned to each of the 55 subjects, based on the number of times he was rated more anxious. A reliability check was run by examining the data for the 30 subjects falling at the two extreme ends of the anxiety ranking. Within each of these two groups, a random sample of 80 trios of names was obtained. The reliability estimate consisted of a search for *inversions* in the ratings. That is, in a given trio, if subject A was rated more anxious than subject B, and subject B more anxious than subject C, then no inversion would be involved if subject A was rated more anxious than subject C. For the 15 most anxious subjects, 5 inversions out of a possible 80 were found; for the 15 least anxious subjects, only 2 such inversions appeared. The results of this rather crude reliability analysis were considered quite encouraging. Validity of the ratings is another matter. Unfortunately, several of the least anxious subjects were discharged from the institution before an experiment comparing the performances of the most and the least anxious subjects in a learning situation could be run.

To date, attempts to demonstrate interference in defectives' performance as a function of stress conditions have not proved to be successful. For example, Cantor (1960) gave 64 adult male and female defectives the Minnesota Rate of Manipulation Test in a competitive setting involving the pairing of testees. Half the subjects were paired with members of their own sex, the remaining subjects being paired with members of the opposite sex. The prediction that having to compete with members of the opposite sex would engender high anxiety and thus lead to interference in performance was not confirmed by the results. Keller (1957) found that high- and low-stress instructions given to high-grade male retardates had no differential effect on digit-span performance in these subjects.

It seems unlikely that defectives, as a group, are more anxious than normals; but currently available evidence does not indicate that they are any less anxious, at least at the educable level. The formulation regarding the role of anxiety as drive would thus appear to merit serious attention in regard to the learning of defective individuals. The possibility that high anxiety interferes with learning in defectives carries implications of considerable practical significance. The validation of techniques for as-

---

[17] Acknowledgment is due Dr. Willard Segerson, former superintendent of the Tennessee Clover Bottom Home, for his cooperation. The writer is indebted to Mr. Roy McElroy and Mr. Winfred Vance for their excellent work as raters.

sessing anxiety level in defectives would constitute a necessary first step in a research program in this area. One phase of such validation work could very feasibly involve extensive observation of the performances in complex and simple learning situations of defectives identified as low-anxious and high-anxious by the assessment technique in question. In addition, the study of the effects of high and low stress on defectives' performance in such learning situations could shed considerable light on the utility of the Hull-Spence $_sH_R \times D$ formulation for understanding defectives' behavior. This general area has hardly been touched by research workers interested in mental deficiency.

A SUMMING-UP

Theory-oriented behavioral research using defectives as subjects is often criticized on the basis that the experimenters involved are not really interested in mental deficiency. A typical expression of this attitude may be found in a paper by McPherson (1958). After summarizing 14 studies published in the decade prior to 1958 and noting the upsurge in interest in the experimental approach to the study of learning in defectives, McPherson (p. 876) commented as follows: "This impression of increased interest in the experimental approach to learning and mental deficiency is negated somewhat by the realization that four of these papers have utilized mental defectives because of their usefulness for learning data and theory per se, rather than because of an interest in this type of learner."

Persons sharing this attitude rarely, if ever, are explicit about exactly what constitutes a "genuine interest" in the defective learner. The present writer would take the position that the psychologist as scientist is basically concerned with behavioral processes, or, put in other terms, with the discovery of laws that will allow him to predict behavior. Whether the behavior in question happens to be that of the mentally defective, the normal, or some infrahuman species, the scientist's obligation is to make use of the frame of reference which he considers most promising in the way of leading him to such laws. If, in the search for behavioral laws applicable to the behavior of defectives, one is led to abandon more traditional ways of studying defectives' learning processes in favor of a different approach (e.g., the application of Hull-Spence or any other theory), it is difficult to understand why this amounts to a lack of interest in the defective, per se.

In the previous section of this chapter, three approaches within the Hull-Spence framework to the study of defectives' behavior were described and illustrated. All three—the curve-fitting approach, the gross comparative approach, and the noncomparative approach—show considerable promise of being of reciprocal benefit to both the field of behavior theory *and* the field of mental deficiency, in the present writer's opinion. To the extent that such research helps to verify any of the various Hull-Spence postulates, or to show in what fashion they are inadequate, to this extent will behavior theory benefit from the activity. And to whatever extent behavior theory benefits, the understanding of defectives' behavior cannot help but be improved, assuming, of course, some degree of fruitfulness in the Hull-Spence approach. That the theory is a fruitful one is, needless to say, a basic premise of the present chapter; for dissenting opinions expressed by individuals with widely varying orientations, the reader is urged to consult such sources as Skinner (1950), Bruner (1957), and Maslow (1961). The present writer would contend that, whatever the eventual fate of Hull-Spence theory, the utility of some of the formulation's key concepts has already been so well demonstrated that such concepts could scarcely be excluded from behavior theory of the future.

The surface has hardly been scratched in the work of applying the constructs of Hull-Spence theory to analyses of defectives' behavior. From a theoretical standpoint, any meaningful test of a relationship suggested by Hull-Spence theory would appear to constitute a worthwhile endeavor. In terms of practical pay-off, evidence relating the behavior of defectives to the various motivational concepts in the theory would seem to the present writer to be of first importance. Among the most promising possibilities in this context would seem to be those concerned with incentive motivation, the effects of delay of reward and nonreinforcement, and the role of anxiety as an interferer with defectives' performance.

REFERENCES

AMSEL, A.   The role of frustrative nonreward in noncontinuous reward situations. *Psychol. Bull.*, 1958, 55, 102–119.

AMSEL, A., & HANCOCK, W.   Motivational properties of frustration. III. Relation of frustration effect to antedating goal factors. *J. exp. Psychol.*, 1957, 53, 126–131.

AMSEL, A., & ROUSSEL, J.   Motivational properties of frustration. I. Effect on a running response of the addition of frustration to the motivational complex. *J. exp. Psychol.*, 1952, 43, 363–368.

BARNETT, C. D.   Stimulus generalization in normals and retardates on a visual-spatial task requiring a voluntary response. Unpublished Ph.D. dissertation, George Peabody Coll., 1958.

BERGMANN, G.   The logic of psychological concepts. *Phil. Sci.*, 1951, 18, 93–110.

BLANK, J. P.   The effect of magnitude of incentive on acquisition and extinction in mentally retarded children. *Disser. Abstr.*, 1958, 19, 1443.

BROWN, J. S.   Pleasure-seeking behavior and the drive-reduction hypothesis. *Psychol. Rev.*, 1955, 62, 169–179.

BROWN, J. S.   *The motivation of behavior.* New York: McGraw-Hill, 1961.

BROWN, J. S., BILODEAU, E. A., & BARON, M. R.   Bidirectional gradients in the strength of a generalized voluntary response to stimuli on a visual-spatial dimension. *J. exp. Psychol.*, 1951, 41, 52–61.

BRUNER, J. S.   Mechanism riding high. Review of Spence's *Behavior theory and conditioning. Contemp. Psychol.*, 1957, II, 155–157.

CALLAHAN, R. J.   Unrealistic fears as a measure of anxiety in a group of 6th grade children. Unpublished Ph.D. dissertation, Syracuse Univer., 1955.

CALLAHAN, R. J., & KELLER, J. E.   Digit span and anxiety: an experimental group revisited. *Amer. J. ment. Defic.*, 1957, 61, 581–582.

CANTOR, G. N.   Rating of anxiety in defectives by the method of paired-comparisons. Unpublished paper, George Peabody Coll., 1956.

CANTOR, G. N.   Motor performance of defectives as a function of competition with same- and opposite-sex opponents. *Amer. J. ment. Defic.*, 1960, 65, 358–362.

CANTOR, G. N., & HOTTEL, J. V.   Discrimination learning in mental defectives as a function of magnitude of food reward and intelligence level. *Amer. J. ment. Defic.*, 1955, 60, 380–384.

CASTANEDA, A.   Reaction time and response amplitude as a function of anxiety and stimulus intensity. *J. abnorm. soc. Psychol.*, 1956, 53, 225–228.

CASTANEDA, A., MCCANDLESS, B., & PALERMO, D.   The children's form of the Manifest Anxiety Scale. *Child Developm.*, 1956, 27, 317–326.

CASTANEDA, A., PALERMO, D., & MCCANDLESS, B.   Complex learning and performance as a function of anxiety in children and task difficulty. *Child Developm.*, 1956, 27, 327–333.

CRESPI, L. P.   Quantitative variation of incentive and performance in the white rat. *Amer. J. Psychol.*, 1942, 55, 467–517.

CRESPI, L. P.   Amount of reinforcement and level of performance. *Psychol. Rev.*, 1944, 51, 341–357.

ELLIS, N. R., PRYER, M. W., & BARNETT, C. D.   Note on habit formation in normal and retarded subjects. *Psychol. Rep.*, 1960, 6, 385–386. (a)

ELLIS, N. R., PRYER, M. W., & BARNETT, C. D.   Motor learning and retention in normals and defectives. *Percept. mot. Skills*, 1960, 10, 83–91. (b)

ELLIS, N. R., PRYER, M. W., DISTEFANO, M. K., & PRYER, R. S.   Learning in mentally defective, normal, and superior subjects. *Amer. J. ment. Defic.*, 1960, 64, 725–734.

HARLOW, H. F.   Mice, monkeys, men and motives. *Psychol. Rev.*, 1953, 60, 23–32. (a)

HARLOW, H. F.   Motivation as a factor in the acquisition of new responses. In J. S. Brown et al., *Current theory and research in motivation*. Lincoln, Nebr.: Univer. of Nebraska Press, 1953. (b)

HEBER, R. F.   Motor task performance of high grade mentally retarded males as a function of the magnitude of incentive. *Amer. J. ment. Defic.*, 1959, 63, 667–671.

HILGARD, E. R.   *Theories of learning.* (2nd ed.) New York: Appleton-Century-Crofts, 1956.

HULL, C. L.   *Principles of behavior.* New York: Appleton-Century-Crofts, 1943.

HULL, C. L.   *Essentials of behavior.* New Haven: Yale Univer. Press, 1951.

HULL, C. L.   *A behavior system.* New Haven: Yale Univer. Press, 1952.

JACOBS, A.   Performance of children in a discrimination problem as a function of symbolic guidance, delay of reward, and mental ability. Unpublished Ph.D. dissertation, State Univer. of Iowa, 1950.

JENSEN, A. R.   On the reformulation of inhibition in Hull's system. *Psychol. Bull.*, 1961, 58, 274–298.

JONES, R. W., & ELLIS, N. R.   Inhibitory potential in motor skills acquisition by normal and defective subjects. Unpublished paper, George Peabody Coll. for Teachers, 1961.

KELLER, J.   The relationship of auditory memory span to learning ability in high-grade mentally retarded boys. *Amer. J. ment. Defic.*, 1957, 61, 574–580.

KOCH, S.   Clark L. Hull. In W. K. Estes et al., *Modern learning theory*. New York: Appleton-Century-Crofts, 1954.

KOUNIN, J. S.   Intellectual development and rigidity. In R. G. Barker, J. S. Kounin, & H. F. Wright (Eds.), *Child behavior and development*. New York: McGraw-Hill, 1943.

LINDQUIST, E. F.   *Design and analysis of experiments in psychology and education.* Boston: Houghton Mifflin, 1953.

LIPMAN, R. S.   Children's manifest anxiety in retardates and approximately equal M.A. normals. *Amer. J. ment. Defic.*, 1960, 64, 1027–1028.

LOGAN, F. A.   The Hull-Spence approach. In S. Koch (Ed.), *Psychology: a study of a science*, Study I, Vol. 2. New York: McGraw-Hill, 1959.

LOGAN, F. A.   *Incentive*. New Haven: Yale Univer. Press, 1960.

MCPHERSON, M. W.   Learning and mental deficiency. *Amer. J. ment. Defic.*, 1958, 62, 870–877.

MASLOW, A. H.   Are our publications and conventions suitable for the personal sciences? *Amer. Psychol.*, 1961, 16, 318–319.

MILLER, N. E.   Liberalization of basic S-R concepts: extensions to conflict behavior, motivation and social learning. In S. Koch (Ed.), *Psychology: a study of a science*, Study I, Vol. 2. New York: McGraw-Hill, 1959.

MOWRER, O. H.   On the dual nature of learning—a re-interpretation of "conditioning" and "problem-solving." *Harvard educ. Rev.*, 1947, 17, 102–148.

MOWRER, O. H.   *Learning theory and behavior*. New York: Wiley, 1960.

O'CONNOR, N., & CLARIDGE, G. S.   A 'Crespi' effect in male imbeciles. *Brit. J. Psychol.*, 1958, 49, 42–48.

PALERMO, D., CASTANEDA, A., & MCCANDLESS, B.   The relationship of anxiety in children to performance in a complex learning task. *Child Develpm.* 1956, 27, 333–337.

PRYER, R. S.   Retroactive inhibition in normals and defectives as a function of temporal position of the interpolated task. *Amer. J. ment. Defic.*, 1960, 64, 1004–1011.

RAMOND, C. K.   Performance in instrumental learning as a joint function of delay of reinforcement and time of deprivation. *J. exp. Psychol.*, 1954, 47, 248–250.

ROSENBLUM, S., & CALLAHAN, R.   The performance of high-grade retarded, emotionally disturbed children on the Children's Manifest Anxiety Scale and Children's Anxiety Pictures. *J. clin. Psychol.*, 1958, 14, 272–275.

RUDEL, R. G.   The absolute response in tests of generalization in normal and retarded children. *Amer. J. Psychol.*, 1959, 72, 401–408.

SCHLOSBERG, H.   The relationship between success and the laws of conditioning. *Psychol. Rev.*, 1937, 44, 379–399.

SIEGEL, P. S., & FOSHEE, J. G.   Molar variability in the mentally defective. *J. abnorm. soc. Psychol.*, 1960, 61, 141–143.

SKINNER, B. F.   *The behavior of organisms*. New York: Appleton-Century-Crofts, 1938.

SKINNER, B. F.   Are theories of learning necessary? *Psychol. Rev.*, 1950, 57, 193–216.

SPENCE, K. W.   The nature of discrimination learning in animals. *Psychol. Rev.*, 1936, 43, 427–449.

SPENCE, K. W.   The differential response in animals to stimuli varying within a single dimension. *Psychol. Rev.*, 1937, 44, 430–444.

SPENCE, K. W.   Gradual versus sudden solution of discrimination problems by chimpanzees. *J. comp. Psychol.*, 1938, 25, 213–224.

SPENCE, K. W.   Continuous versus non-continuous interpretations of discrimination learning. *Psychol. Rev.*, 1940, 47, 271–288.

SPENCE, K. W.   The basis of solution by chimpanzees of the intermediate size problem. *J. exp. Psychol.*, 1942, 31, 257–271.

SPENCE, K. W.   The nature of the response in discrimination learning. *Psychol. Rev.*, 1952, 59, 89–93.

SPENCE, K. W.   Learning and performance in eyelid conditioning as a function of the intensity of the UCS. *J. exp. Psychol.*, 1953, 45, 57–63.

SPENCE, K. W. The relation of response latency and speed to the intervening variables and N in S-R theory. *Psychol. Rev.*, 1954, 61, 209–216.

SPENCE, K. W. *Behavior theory and conditioning*. New Haven: Yale Univer. Press, 1956.

SPENCE, K. W. The empirical basis and theoretical structure of psychology. *Phil. Sci.*, 1957, 24, 97–108.

SPENCE, K. W. A theory of emotionally based drive (D) and its relation to performance in simple learning situations. *Amer. Psychol.*, 1958, 13, 131–141.

SPENCE, K. W. *Behavior theory and learning*. Englewood Cliffs, N.J.: Prentice-Hall, 1960.

SPENCE, K. W., HAGGARD, D. F., & ROSS, L. E. UCS intensity and the associative (habit) strength of the eyelid CR. *J. exp. Psychol.*, 1958, 55, 404–411.

TAYLOR, J. A. The relationship of anxiety to the conditioned eyelid response. *J. exp. Psychol.*, 1951, 41, 81–92.

THURSTONE, L. L. A law of comparative judgment. *Psychol. Rev.*, 1927, 34, 273–286. (a)

THURSTONE, L. L. Psychophysical analysis. *Amer. J. Psychol.*, 1927, 38, 368–389. (b)

THURSTONE, L. L. Stimulus dispersion in the method of constant stimuli. *J. exp. Psychol.*, 1932, 15, 284–289.

TOLMAN, E. C. Operational behaviorism and current trends in psychology. *Proc. 25th Anniv. Celebration Inaug. Grad. Stud.* Los Angeles: Univer. of Southern California, 1936.

UNDERWOOD, B. J. Speed of learning and amount retained: a consideration of methodology. *Psychol. Bull.*, 1954, 51, 276–282.

WAGNER, A. R. Motivational effects of non-reinforcement as a function of the reinforcement schedule. Unpublished M.A. thesis, State Univer. of Iowa, 1957.

YAMAGUCHI, H. G., HULL, C. L., FELSINGER, J. M., & GLADSTONE, A. I. Characteristics of dispersions based on the pooled momentary reaction potentials $(_s\dot{\bar{E}}_R)$ of a group. *Psychol. Rev.*, 1948, 55, 216–238.

ZEAMAN, D. Response latency as a function of the amount of reinforcement. *J. exp. Psychol.*, 1949, 39, 466–483.

ZEAMAN, D., & KAUFMAN, H. Individual differences and theory in a motor learning task. *Psychol. Monogr.*, 1955, 69, No. 6.

4

THE STIMULUS TRACE
AND BEHAVIORAL INADEQUACY

Norman R. Ellis

This chapter is concerned with behavioral differences between normal and mentally defective humans. Primarily attention is directed to a class of behaviors viewed as dependent upon short-term memory, e.g., digit span or delayed reaction. The stimulus trace is invoked as an "explanatory" mechanism to account for immediate memory, and an individual differences construct is postulated to explain, in part, behavioral inadequacy. Short-term memory would be measured in seconds or minutes as contrasted with long-term memory measured by hours, days, or even years. Many commonly observed behaviors seem to depend upon a short-term storage mechanism; a telephone number is remembered only long enough to dial it, the specific words in a conversation may fade rapidly, or a particular card in a card game may not be remembered shortly after it has been played. Such events are described in the young child as "out of sight, out of mind" phenomena. This paper will develop the thesis that the individual with a *subnormal* central nervous system is characterized by an inadequacy in this function.

An ancillary hypothesis is that the apparent learning deficit in the subnormal organism is due to noncontinuity between events as a result of an impoverished stimulus trace. Even though differences between normal and subnormal organisms are adopted as a basis of speculation, an extension to individual intelligence differences, wherever they may occur, is not precluded.

The plan of the chapter is (1) to provide a brief review of the stimulus trace concept and some of the pertinent research in molar behavior theory, (2) to offer some speculation regarding a possible neurophysiological basis of short-term memory and how it may be affected by CNS pathology, (3) to adduce evidence from previous research in mental deficiency sup-

134

portive of the notion, (4) to establish formal hypotheses to guide further research efforts, and (5) to present experimental results of a priori tests of the theory.

The concept of the stimulus trace is not new. Kohler (1929) invokes a *fading-trace* theory to account for the negative time error in psychophysical judgment. If a stimulus is compared with a standard previously experienced, even though the two stimuli are equal in some dimension (e.g., weight, brightness) the second will be judged greater than the standard. This effect is said to result from a comparison of the second stimulus with a fading trace of the standard, and the longer the interval between the two experiences, the larger the error. With very short intervals, 1.5 seconds or less, the error is usually positive; the second is judged smaller than the first. Some other explanation is needed for the latter effect.

Pavlov (1927) employs the trace notion to explain trace conditioning. Perseverative aftereffects is the central concept in the Muller and Pilzecker (1900) theory of retroactive inhibition. The stimulus trace assumes a central role in Mowrer's theory (1960). Among other things, it is used to explain delay of reinforcement effects. Hull (1952) has used molar stimulus trace as a theoretical construct and has derived a quantitative function for the trace amplitude-time relationship, based on data from eyelid conditioning by Reynolds (1945) and Kimble (1947). According to Hull the trace assumes an important role in an organism's adaptation or survival. Behavioral acts are conditioned to traces of preceding events, and by generalization along the trace, they come to antedate reinforcement. On the basis of this mechanism, behavior sequences are "short-circuited" so that noninstrumental responses are eliminated by the antedating of the critical response. Although Hull states that the physiological basis of the molar trace may reside in the neural response of the stimulated receptor or in a gradual subsiding of muscular contraction, he seems to favor the former. However, the physiological basis of the trace is not central to Hull's formulation since he is concerned with molar properties only, which are anchored to antecedent environmental events and consequently to behavior. The present treatment also adopts the molar model.

Hebb (1949) postulates a dual trace mechanism which resembles the Muller and Pilzecker notion. He suggests that there may be a brief reverberatory trace following a sensory event which could account for immediate memory. Presumably, this trace would serve to produce structural changes in nervous tissue which would constitute the substrate for long-term memory. Hebb hypothesized that the transient trace may carry the memory until structural changes occur.

Although the present formulation is entirely molar, it is of some interest to point out neurophysiological findings which parallel those observed at the behavioral level. As early as 1940, Hilgard and Marquis recognized the reverberatory circuit described by Lorente de No' as a likely basis for short-term memory. More recently, Lorente de No' has observed that a steady state cannot be maintained in a reverberatory circuit and that "either the thing (excitation) begins spreading to involve more and more neurons, or it decrements, after coming to a maximum, and then decays and disappears" (in Jeffress, 1951, p. 62). (It is interesting to note that the latter state of affairs parallels Hull's trace gradient as derived from the eyelid-conditioning studies.)

Gerard observes that reverberatory circuits "free behavior from being time-bound to the stimulus, conduction and synaptic times no longer set the limits between stimulus and response; a neurone chain, once activated by a stimulus might continue to reverberate indefinitely . . ." (1955, p. 229). Some research reported by Gerard, and discussed later in the present paper, indicates that long-term memory may not depend upon indefinite perseveration, however. MuCulloch seems to express the opinion of many neurophysiologists in his eloquent statement:

> It is an eternal idea in a transitory memory wherein the form exists only so long as the reverberation endures. When that ceases, the form is no longer anywhere. Only this kind of memory remains to aged brains in which no new abiding traces can be made and old ones fade. While we are young, use leaves some sort of changes, as freshets cut their channels in the hills, so that aftercoming waters follow and enlarge their beds (in Jeffress, 1951, p. 47).

Several recent investigations have approached the problem of memory from the standpoint of temporal relations in stimulus response paradigms. In those involving the measurement of retention over a long time interval, the assumption that short-term and long-term memory (and by implication learning) are related is necessary, if inferences about the former are to be made from the latter. A similar assumption is required when inferences are drawn from acquisition phenomena in which permanent-type changes occur. In the case of behaviors which depend upon short-term memory no assumptions regarding permanent structural changes are necessary, and measurement is closer to the hypothesized perseverative memory trace.

Evidence for a stimulus trace and a consequent "consolidation" of memory obtains in much clinical literature. Incidents in which memory of a recent event is lost as a result of a blow to the head or some other traumatic insult are fairly common. Numerous experiments utilizing animals have attempted to simulate such an event. Most of these studies adopt the Muller and Pilzecker view as a theoretical point of departure and attempt to show that learning is a matter of consolidating some state of affairs. In the present context, the experiments are important since they tend to demonstrate that there are some perseverative aftereffects of stimulation. It is hypothesized that these effects subserve short-term memory.

Duncan (1949) demonstrated that memory of a discrimination habit in rats is dependent upon the temporal proximity of an electroshock to the end of original learning, with the greatest memory decrement occurring in the animal receiving shock immediately after learning. Gerard (1955) subjected hamsters to deep cold sufficient to stop neural reverberation after learning. A later test showed no memory loss. The deep cold was not introduced shortly after learning, however. Electric shock administered to the hamster soon after learning did have an effect upon long-term memory. If the shock followed learning by as much as 4 hours, no loss occurred.

Memory defects appeared when the interval was reduced to 1 hour; at 15 minutes serious loss resulted, and at 5 minutes, or less, there was complete memory loss.

In a systematic series of experiments, Thompson and his students have obtained results which provide strong evidence for a trace theory. Also, their data bear on the problem of brain injury and its relationship to memory. Their findings seem highly pertinent to the problem of mental subnormality at the human level.

Thompson (1959) trained brain-injured and normal rats in a water T maze to go to alternate arms of the T daily; i.e., right was correct for one day and left for the next. After a criterion of three out of four errorless runs was met, they were given three memory test trials: 1 minute, 1 hour, and 5 hours later. The results showed that animals with a strong position preference performed well on the 1-minute tests on the nonpreferred side but did poorly on the 1- and 5-hour tests, whereas on the preferred side there were negligible differences between performances on the three test trials. This phenomenon seemed to be independent of whether or not the animal was brain-injured. Thompson believed that the temporary reverberatory activity at the 1-minute test was sufficient to overcome the position preference but that after the reverberation subsided, at 1 hour and 5 hours, the position preference was greater than the "structurally" based habit. These findings were interpreted as strongly supporting "the view that the neural memory trace passes through an initial reverberatory state followed by a more permanent structural state" (p. 842).

Pennington (1958) practiced brain-injured rats, defined by anoxic insult, and normal animals on a horizontal-vertical discrimination problem. Immediately after a criterion of learning was reached, ECS was given. A retention test 2 days later revealed that the brain-injured animals suffered the greater memory loss as a result of ECS.

Thompson (1957) has shown that ECS administered soon after learning produces a greater memory loss in the young than in the adult rat. Furthermore the effects of ECS were shown to be related to rate of myelinization in the young animal. This finding was confirmed in a later study (Thompson, Haravey, Pennington, Smith, Gannon & Stockwell, 1958). Thompson and Pryer (1956) demonstrated that anoxia administered within the 2-minute period following learning produces a loss in memory which is inversely related to the temporal interval between the termination of learning and the insult. The anoxia used produces no effects if administered 15 minutes or longer after learning. Visual stimulation interpolated between the learning of a visual problem and a retention test seems to have an effect similar to that of ECS and anoxia (Thompson, 1957).

In summary, the studies by Thompson et al. demonstrate that (1) memory in brain-injured animals is more susceptible to ECS than is memory in normal animals, (2) memory in young animals is more susceptible to ECS than is memory in adult animals, (3) the deleterious effects of ECS on the memory of the young animal seem to be dependent upon stage of myelinization, and (4) ECS-produced memory loss does not seem to depend upon the animals' previous visual experience or cerebral metabolism.

It is apparent that most behavior theorists have recognized the need for a "trace-like" construct. Evidence from neurophysiology supports the notion of a reverberatory circuit and the role of perseverative aftereffects in short-term memory. These considerations along with empirical findings from research with animals lend appeal to the stimulus trace concept and to its promise as an explanatory construct for behavioral differences resulting from CNS insult in the human.

The theory. For heuristic reasons the role of stimulus trace in behavioral inadequacy will be stated more formally. The theoretical structure is designed to serve as a guide for research dealing with subnormal behavior at the human level. It is hypothesized that the mechanism underlying short-term memory varies widely in organisms differing in docility or intelligence. For the present, we are concerned with the behavior of normal and subnormal humans as defined by intelligence tests or other conventional indices of adaptive commerce with the environment.

Two constructs are proposed, stimulus trace (s_t) and central nervous system integrity (n_i). s_t is defined antecedently by an environmental stimulus event (S) and consequently by a behavioral event (B). For the present we shall theorize about unlearned behavior. By *unlearned* is meant behavioral phenomena which seem to depend primarily upon instructions and occur upon initial exposure to the stimulus event. Of course learning is apparently involved in these behaviors: in delayed response, for example. Under some conditions, to be described later, recorded electrical activity from the cerebral cortex EEG may serve as the consequent observable anchor. s_t is viewed as varying in amplitude and duration and, probably, spatially. It is hypothesized that s_t parameters are dependent upon characteristics of S, such as receptor stimulated, intensity, and duration, as well as upon more complex dimensions, such as meaning. n_i, defined by an intelligence test score or other indices of adaptability, serves as a limiting function for s_t. The central hypothesis is that the duration and amplitude of s_t are diminished in the subnormal organism.

The theoretical structure is summarized in symbolic form in Figure 4-1.

It is apparent that the temporal relationship between the stimulus event and the occasion for behavior is of central importance. With *equal* stimulus events for two organisms, one normal and the other subnormal, the duration of stimulus control will be longer for the former. Also the duration of stimulus control in the two organisms may depend differentially upon

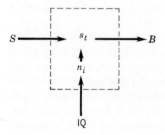

Figure 4-1. The stimulus trace model.

properties of the stimulus, that is to say, there may be an interaction between organism and, for example, intensity of the stimulus as reflected in duration of stimulus control.

The preceding discussion applies to the situation, such as the delayed reaction, in which there is a single stimulus or stimulus complex followed by a temporal interval and then an occasion for a response. There are other models which serve to illustrate the possible role of stimulus trace. In a selective learning or paired-associate learning task in which there are two stimulus events to be associated, the differences between normals and subnormals should, in part, depend upon the temporal separation of the stimuli, with the contiguous situation most favorable for the subnormal and increasing discontiguity retarding their performance relatively more than that of the normal. Still other phenomena may be predicted. The delay of reinforcement gradient should be steeper in the subnormal organism. In a general way the literature supports this prediction. Experimental evidence shows that there is a gradient in the rat and other lower-level organisms, but such a gradient in the human has not been observed. However, in the writer's view, a critical test of the delay effect in humans has not been carried out. It would seem that such a test would minimize the occasion for the organism's learning that reinforcement will follow in, for example, 10 seconds. Since the studies have used uniform delays for a given organism, the stimuli (including the stimulus trace) are constant from trial to trial and therefore maximize the likelihood that mediating responses will be elicited by these cues during the delay interval. Moreover, such studies usually have dealt with the human adult and have used short-delay intervals which had led to gradients in the rat. Few studies have investigated delay gradients in the young child, and apparently none have dealt with the mental defective.

Another example in which trace effects would lead to behavioral differences between normal and subnormal organisms is the partial reinforcement situation. The discrepancy between trials to extinction for subnormals trained under continuous and partial reinforcement schedules should be less than similar differences between normal organisms. If the stimulus trace is more persistent in the normal organism, then the stimulus complex during extinction should be more similar to that during training for the subject undergoing partial reinforcement training. On the other hand, the trace *carryover* for the subnormals should be less, making their performance depend more upon events associated with the contemporary trial and, consequently, upon learned responses to cues other than stimulus traces of preceding trials. The distribution of trials during acquisition could be expected to affect the normal and the subnormal S differently.

These examples will serve to show the likely pervasiveness of the stimulus trace in molar behavior and to point out the nature of predictions based upon the assumption of a trace deficit in the subnormal.

The construct of n_i, perhaps, deserves further elucidation. Even though surplus meanings are likely to be associated with this term, its use does seem appropriate. In view of the large literature, it appears evident that the nervous system is affected in most cases of mental deficiency. Probably in some cases cultural factors have served as causative agents and, no doubt, those agents account for some component of behavioral inadequacy brought about by other conditions. Although n_i has been defined as an intelligence test score, the IQ is nothing more than a sampling device for selecting populations which vary in level of adaptation. Other indices could be used: success in school, institutionalization, and noninstitutionalization, or other criteria which reflect degree of adaptation.

Even though the consequences of neuropathology may result in a common condition described as an impoverished stimulus trace, this may not always be the case. Perhaps each case is unique and an impoverished trace may be a sequela of most but not all cases. Damage may be localized or general, caused by encephalitis, endocrine disorder, physical trauma, or genetic endowment. It may occur before birth or at the age of 5 years. CNS pathology may have a common effect and specific effects, with the latter depending upon etiological factors, or it may have either alone. The damage may be in one system, the visual for example, with all the behavioral deficit stemming from a malfunction in this system alone.

Several lines of evidence favor the notion of common as well as specific effects of CNS pathology. Behavioral research has made a poor case for the dependence of distinctive behavior upon etiological factors; yet there are specific handicaps associated with certain etiological factors, e.g., cerebral palsy. Investigations of the "higher mental process" have failed to link behavior to etiology. Observation of poorly developed sensory and motor functions indicates that they apparently do bear some relationship to certain causative factors. The immature organism, the human infant, possesses behavioral characteristics which are similar to the defective, a fact which has long been noted by the layman, even though the scientist has gone to all lengths to show how their characteristics differ. It would appear that if they differ in some small way, this is grossly more important than finding that a 30-year-old defective possesses mainly the behavioral characteristics of a 2-year-old. From the writer's point of view much would be gained by a study of similarities in addition to the study of differences. With respect to the present theory it is speculated that the young child has a stimulus trace deficit, and the establishment of the adult form of the short-term memory function will show a developmental trend. In view of this, it is not surprising that studies matching immature normal humans and mental defectives rarely fail to find behavioral differences. Thompson's finding that the stability of the memory trace is correlated with the rate of myelinization of nerve fiber in rats seems pertinent here.

In summary, an attempt has been made to account for a significant component of the behavioral differences between normal and subnormal organisms with the notion that the stimulus trace is impoverished as a result of CNS pathology (brain trauma, disease, genetic, etc.). The thesis has been supported indirectly by neurophysiological conceptions and research with CNS-damaged animals. From an overview the behavior of the immature organism resembles that of the defective, and the trace notion has strong appeal because of its explanation of immature behavior.

The nature of the theory favors localizing deficiency in those behaviors dependent directly upon short-term memory and in inadequacies in learning which, in part, indirectly depend upon the immediate memory function. The question may be raised at this point: Is the long-term memory function affected by s_t? Although the theory is not specifically concerned with long-term memory, evidence to be reviewed later suggests that the long-term memory of a mental defective is equal to that of the normal individual. Thus, the focus on the acquisition of behavior seems more appropriate.

Evidence from previous research with mental defectives which bears on the theory will be summarized.

Serial position effects. McCrary and Hunter (1953) have attempted to demonstrate that the percentage distribution of serial position errors in verbal learning is an invariate function for meaningfulness of the items, distribution of practice, and ability level when errors are expressed as a percentage distribution. In the calculations a subject's errors at a serial position are expressed as a per cent of his total errors. From these data curves are plotted depicting group averages. McCrary and Hunter viewed their data as supporting a hypothesis of invariance. However, the interpretation regarding ability level was open to equivocation; and Noble and Fuchs (1959) and Barnett, Ellis, and Pryer (1960b) showed in later studies that the principle of invariance did not obtain in the case of ability level. The former study dealt with normal, slow, and fast learners, the latter with retarded and superior learners. If the serial position curve acquires its characteristic bowed shape from interfering traces of remote forward and backward associations as Lepley (1932) and Hull (1935) hypothesized, then the organism most capable of maintaining a trace would have most difficulty in the middle of the list. Curves for normal, slow, and fast learners as well as for retarded and superior learners indicate that the middle items are relatively more difficult for the fast learners.

More recent data cast some doubt upon the original finding. Girardeau and Ellis (1961) compared normals and defectives on a 10-item serial list with varying interitem intervals, under auditory "distraction" or under a control condition. Analyses of the data supported the invariance hypothesis regarding ability level, interitem interval, and distraction-nondistraction. All serial position curves, expressed as percentage distributions, coincided fairly closely. This study differed from the first one in two ways, which may account for the discrepancy. The IQs of the defectives in the latter study were higher, and the normals' IQs were lower. Secondly, the defectives for the latter study were drawn from public school classes, whereas those for the former came from an institution. Certainly, this issue warrants further study before definitive statements can be made.

Delayed reaction. The study of the delayed reaction (DR) dates back to the early part of this century and classic studies by Walter Hunter (e.g., see Hunter, 1913). In general, the ability to delay has been shown to depend upon phylogenetic level. Damage to the prefrontal cortex in animals results in loss of ability to delay, although Osgood (1953, p. 665) states that loss is not due to the interference of *representative factors* but rather to loss of an inhibitor function which prevents responses to irrelevant stimuli, thus interfering with the appropriate response. The notion that the brain-injured (BI) animal is distractible is not incompatible with the s_t hypothesis. BI would result in an impoverished s_t, thus freeing the organism to respond to external irrelevant stimuli.

Six studies have dealt with DR in mental defectives. Harlow and Israel (1932) tested defectives ranging in MA from 1 to 5 years. They report that half the sample could delay 15 seconds or longer and that no relationship obtained between MA and maximum delay interval. A study by Pascal, Stolurow, Zabarenko, and Chambers (1951) yielded correlations of .61 and .60 between maximum-delay interval and Stanford-Binet MA and IQ, respectively. Pascal and Stolurow (1952) investigated delayed reaction to form and place cues. Scores for form and place were correlated .66 (Rho). Rank-order correlations between maximum place and form delays and MA were .61 and .88, respectively. House and Zeaman (1960) fail to find a relationship between DR performance and MA or IQ in a group of defectives ranging in MA from 2 to 5; also, they find no practice effects over 300 trials. It has been shown (Barnett, Ellis, & Pryer, 1959) that delay performance in defectives can be facilitated by learning names for the cues.

Amos (1959) compared children with and without a history of anoxia at birth on the delayed-reaction test with delay intervals ranging from 1 to 5 minutes. The children with a history of anoxia did worse than the normal children, and the performance loss was relatively greater in the anoxic children for the longer-delay intervals.

The Amos study, along with the studies of Pascal et al., supports the theoretical position presented here. Only the studies by Harlow and Israel (1932) and by House and Zeaman (1961) fail to find a relationship between MA and DR. However, the delay intervals used by Harlow and Israel are much longer than those used in the other studies, and it seems likely that immediate memory effects were qualified by long-term retention effects. The restricted MA range used in the latter study should be noted. A consistent finding of no relationship between some index of adaptive behavior and ability to delay would prove embarrassing. However, present evidence leads to the conclusion that a relationship exists. Probably there are intelligence tests which do not include immediate memory. These tests would seem to be limited measures of man's adaptive capabilities.

EEG. Some recent findings in the field of electroencephalography offer promise of defining s_t by a class of operations other than molar behavior. Berkson (1961), working in Donald B. Lindsley's laboratory, compared various characteristics of alpha block following a visual stimulus in normal and mentally defective subjects. Later, Berkson (1961) repeated the study while working with B. Hermelin and N. O'Connor in England. Of the dimensions investigated, only duration of alpha block significantly differentiated these groups, with the longer duration in the normal subjects. Although there was a clear separation of means, there was considerable overlap in individual scores, and these studies need repeating. It is not suggested that alpha-block duration may compare on an absolute basis with maximal delay time in a typical delayed-reaction situation, for example.

Rather a significant correlation should obtain between alpha-block duration and indices of molar behavior which depend upon short-term memory rather than upon learning. The critical assumption made here is that an alerting stimulus produces changes in the electrical activity in the cortex which persist in time and that the amplitude and duration of the effect is greater in more intelligent organisms. Neurophysiological mechanisms which maintain this activity are presumed to resemble (or be in part identical with) those which serve as a basis for a molar behavioral event following a stimulus remote in time. A deficiency in reverberatory circuits could lead to diminished electrical aftereffects as well as decreased probability of response, depending upon the temporal remoteness of the stimulus.

Factor analysis. A factor analysis by Baumeister and Bartlett (1962) of WISC test profiles produced a factor for defective children which does not appear in an analysis of normal children's records. Loadings for picture arrangement (PA), arithmetic, and coding were found; the highest loading was for coding, with arithmetic next, and PA last. The concept of an s_t factor is an attractive one in this instance. Table 4-1 shows the complete results of the factor analysis.

Fixed-interval operant behavior. A study by Orlando (1961) is especially pertinent to the s_t formulation. Orlando points out that there are two typical FI patterns in retarded children: (1) a low-rate pattern with some scalloping and (2) a stable high-rate pattern. The former indicates that temporal discriminative stimuli S_ds are operative. Orlando postulates that FI performance in these children is dependent upon two behavioral components, the temporal s_d and "withholding from responding in the presence of stimuli associated with nonreinforcement." Thus, FI behavior is attributed mainly to organismic variables rather than to situational or task parameters.

As a test of this notion Orlando devised two tasks other than the FI one.

TABLE 4-1

Factor loadings for the WISC subtests for normals and retardates

Subtest	Normals				Retardates				
	G	V	P	h^2	G	V	P	s_t	h^2
Information	73	47	00	75	57	34	00	00	44
Comprehension	58	44	00	53	38	53	00	00	43
Arithmetic	52	33	00	38	72	10	00	36	66
Similarities	67	39	00	60	67	30	00	00	54
Vocabulary	71	47	00	72	53	74	00	00	83
Picture completion	48	00	40	39	52	00	33	00	38
Picture arrangement	53	00	30	37	71	00	20	20	58
Block design	59	00	51	61	54	00	39	00	44
Object assembly	37	00	80	78	35	00	59	00	47
Coding	52	00	15	29	50	00	10	67	71

One of these tasks was similar to the FI task except that a light or buzzer signaled the end of the fixed interval and remained on until the response was made. The third task used two levers with S_ds (lights) mounted above the levers. Responses made with the lever underneath a light were reinforced. The S_d was switched from one lever to the other on a 30-second variable interval schedule. It was hypothesized that Ss who showed FI performance would also succeed on the "crutch" task and on the two-lever task which required S to withhold responding to a nonreinforced cue. On the other hand it was expected that all Ss solving the last two tasks would not exhibit typical FI behavior since the latter depends upon the "behavioral component" temporal discrimination. The predictions were upheld. Twelve Ss were used: Ten performed efficiently on the two-lever task, eight met a criterion on the crutch task, and four showed FI behavior. Conversely, the four Ss showing FI behavior also withheld from responding on the two-lever task, and all Ss except one who responded appropriately on the two-lever task also met the criterion on the crutch task. From these results it would appear that there are at least two behavioral components which determine performance in these tests, temporal discrimination (which would be attributed to s_t in the present context) and the ability to withhold responding to a nonreinforced cue. It seems likely that the latter also depends upon s_t.

With definite evidence established for s_t differences between normal and subnormal organisms, the theoretical formulation may logically be extended to encompass the relationship between s_t and dimensions of behavior that are described as learned, i.e., behavior which shows systematic improvement over trials and is not ascribable to other conditions. If such an attempt were made, s_t and its relation to B would not be defined by the same operations. The use of serial learning as evidence for s_t and s_t's effect upon serial learning is a case in point, and it was used here for expository rather than explanatory purposes. A logically sound procedure would consist in measuring s_t by such operations as digit span, delayed reaction, or alpha-block duration and with these indices make predictions about learning defined by performance on other tasks such as mazes, rote memorization, and classical conditioning.

Evidence from learning research in mental deficiency seems to support, in a general way, these speculations. Serial learning, shielded finger maze, or verbal memorization clearly differentiates normals and defectives (Ellis, Pryer, Distefano, & Pryer, 1959). On the other hand, there is no evidence that performance on a paired-associate task (with nonverbal highly meaningful materials) will differentiate these groups (Lott, 1958), although there are methodological weaknesses in Lott's study which may account for the results. However, Cantor[1] reports a similar finding from a study which avoids some of the difficulties in the Lott study.

A learning study by Sloan and Berg (1957) using a stylus maze which S could view in its entirety did not differentiate IQ groups within a defective sample. This finding contrasts sharply with those by Ellis et al. using a finger maze shielded from S's view. The latter would appear to depend more

[1] A personal communication.

upon stimulus traces and, for that reason, could be expected to yield a larger correlation.

More generally, the relative difficulty of learning problems for the defective should be predictable on the basis of the S-R (or S-S) time relations, that is, the time elapsing between the materials to be associated. It should be possible to make a rational analysis of various behaviors with respect to their dependence upon immediate memory. The degree of behavioral inadequacy should bear a strong relationship to the rationally derived dimension. Serial anticipation learning should be relatively more difficult for the defective, as compared with the normal, than paired-associate learning of similar materials. The differences between these groups should be greater for double as compared with single alteration. The apparent difficulty the defective experiences with abstract problems may involve the stimulus trace deficit. Certainly, the clinical interpretation of the defective as a *stimulus bound* organism agrees with the s_t deficit concept.

The extension of s_t theorizing to account for differences in learning does not provide for predictions regarding retention. The deficit ascribable to s_t would manifest itself in acquisition as a function of noncontinuity of items to be associated resulting from an impoverished s_t. Any state of affairs (drugs, increase in intensity of stimuli, etc.) which increases the duration of s_t should facilitate learning. For example, an observed deficit in the subnormal organism in trace conditioning may be improved by increasing the intensity of the CS, assuming that stimulus intensity is related to s_t intensity and/or duration. The improvement could exceed that for the normals since their performance is supported by adequate stimulus traces, especially for the shorter CS-UCS interval.

The experimental literature pertaining to learning retention favors a theory which relies upon acquisition inadequacies rather than upon retention weaknesses. Indeed, there is no definitive evidence that a long-term retention deficit obtains in mental defectives (Pryer, 1960; Johnson & Blake, 1960; Ellis, Pryer, & Barnett, 1960; Lott, 1958). This is certainly at variance with popular (and perhaps professional) opinion.

Attempts to replicate the experiments upon which the theoretical formulations for s_t, rest are in order, especially those involving serial learning, DR, EEG, and factor analysis. Other research paradigms may yield data for these speculations. Classical trace conditioning is a case in point. The deleterious effect of increasing CS-UCS interval, that is, beyond the optimal value, should be more pronounced in the mentally defective.

The DR study holds promise. A technique capable of yielding delay functions with high intrasubject reliability would provide a valuable datum by which to judge other parameters. Moreover, this datum could be utilized in investigating the relationship between the duration of s_t and the consolidation of the permanent memory trace. However, the establishment of the temporary trace function should have first priority. A preliminary attempt to derive precise DR data is described later in the chapter.

Attempts should be made to relate alpha-block duration to molar indices of s_t. Also, S characteristics determining alpha blocking should be investigated further in normal and defective humans. Meaning (e.g., as defined by Noble, 1952) seems critical. Jasper has pointed out that "the most obvious and significant changes in the electrical activity of the human cortex occur not necessarily with specific sensory stimuli, but are dependent upon the meaning of these stimuli to the subject" (1958, p. 42).

An observation by Riesen (1958) seems pertinent to the trace notion. He points out that there does not seem to be a relationship between delay of reinforcement and learning in "sophisticated animals and man . . . ," but when "naïve" animals are used, the decay segment of the learning-reinforcement delay function is very similar to that found in classical conditioning. On this basis we might expect the delay function in defectives to resemble that of the naïve organism.

Experimental tests of the s_t hypothesis

Factor analytic. Several studies have been designed with a priori predictions deduced from the s_t hypothesis. The first extension of data bearing on s_t was made in a doctoral dissertation study by Baumeister (1961). He hypothesized that a factor analysis of WISC data including scores from the digit-span subtest would corroborate the earlier findings by Baumeister and Bartlett and in addition find digit span among the higher loadings on the s_t factor. This prediction was made in view of the high face validity of digit span as a test of s_t. Table 4-2 shows the results of the factor analysis of data on 130 "educable" mentally retarded from the Nashville, Tennessee, city schools. The results are clearly in agreement with the prediction.

A second phase of the Baumeister dissertation dealt with validation of s_t. He reasoned that, if the s_t factor measured short-term memory, this factor should predict double-alternation learning in defectives, since this type of learning depends heavily upon immediate memory. On the other hand, a weighting of subtest scores similar to that for arriving at the s_t factor in

TABLE 4-2

Factor matrix of WISC data on retarded Ss enrolled in public schools ($N = 130$)

Subtest	G	V	P	s_t	h^2
Information	.77	.31	.00	.00	.69
Comprehension	.76	.33	.00	.00	.69
Arithmetic	.69	.26	.00	.46	.76
Similarities	.62	.40	.00	.05	.55
Vocabulary	.72	.45	.00	.00	.72
Digit span	.63	.00	.10	.42	.58
Picture completion	.42	.03	.20	.00	.21
Picture arrangement	.68	.00	.33	.18	.60
Block design	.47	.00	.46	.21	.47
Object assembly	.53	.02	.59	.00	.63
Coding	.68	.07	.21	.30	.60
Chronological age	.40	.00	.00	.00	.16

defectives applied to the *trace subtest* of the normal Ss should not predict double-alternation in the latter, since they have traces above some crucial value necessary for performance on these tests. Obviously, this statistical treatment amounts to little more than a test of the validity of the factor analysis and is, in a sense, a logical maneuver. Table 4-3 shows the results. The digit-span data are treated separately since the weighting system was based on that by Baumeister and Bartlett, which did not include digit span. The negative rs indicate a direct relationship between variables.

Again, these results are in line with expectation. The s_t factor does not predict double-alternation performance in normal Ss but predicts quite well for the retardates.

Delayed response. Donald W. Zimmerman and the writer have attempted to develop a new technique for the assessment of DR, since DR, on the face, would appear to be the "purest" measure of s_t. By applying some of the principles of operant conditioning, a device has been constructed which permits automatic programming and control of the events involved in the DR test. Figure 4-2 is a picture of the S panel which is mounted in the wall of a test cubicle. The sample stimulus, which appears in the top window on the panel, may be one of five colors (lights) : red, blue, green, yellow, or white. The duration of this event can be varied by E. We have employed 2.5 seconds. The delay interval follows the offset of the sample. This is variable from trial to trial for a subject. We have used 1, 5, 12, 29, and 68 seconds. At the termination of a delay interval the five colors appear in the five windows in the bottom row. A particular color may appear in any window on a given trial. S is instructed to push the button underneath the one that matches the sample. If the correct button is pressed, a reward (candy, cigarettes, money, etc.) is delivered by a universal feeder into the "cup" shown underneath the panel. Veeder counters summate correct and incorrect responses separately for each delay interval. In our preliminary work Ss were given 100 trials with 20 trials for each of the 5 delay intervals. Serial position of the delay is randomized within each of the 5-trial blocks. The program is such that color of light, delay interval, and position (on panel) of correct response are not related.

The entire test is automatically programmed with all the controlling apparatus located outside the S room. E is required to keep the feeder loaded and to record the data at the end of a session.

Our initial study used six adult female defectives ranging in mental age

TABLE 4-3

Normals			Retardates		
s_t	Digit span	Criterion	s_t	Digit span	Criterion
.41	.41	.03	.57	.57	−.44
.03	−.12	−.12	−.44	−.61	−.61

Intercorrelations of s_t scores, criterion performance, and digit span for normals and retardates

Figure 4-2. Delayed-response apparatus.

from 4 years, 4 months to 8 years, 8 months. These Ss were given 100 trials per day for 10 days. A daily session was approximately 40 to 60 minutes in length. M & M candy was used as the reward. Figure 4-3 shows the results for the first, seventh, and tenth days for the six Ss.

The systematic decay over these fairly short time intervals should be noted.[2] Generally, poorer performance is seen at the 5-second time than at the 1-second time, and still poorer performance at the 12-second time and the longer intervals. There does seem to be some relationship between delay "ability" and MA as measured by the WISC or WAIS although it does not seem particularly high, and we should expect this since MA is a measure of other performances which are independent of s_t. Learning or improvement over days is quite marked in these data, which contrast with the findings by House and Zeaman (1961). Of course our technique differs from theirs. The method holds promise for investigating DR in the young child as well as in the adult. The particular stimuli and delay intervals used in our study seem appropriate for those ranging from approximately an MA of 4 years to 9 years. With the use of miniature stimulus projectors and differing stimuli along with other time intervals, the difficulty of the task could be adapted to S's capabilities.

Reaction time (RT). Terrell (1961) in a master's thesis study has utilized the simple reaction paradigm in a test of the s_t hypothesis. Two groups of Ss, 80 normals and 80 defectives, were each assigned to two subgroups and tested on the RT task. For one subgroup a red warning light came on and remained on (on-on condition) for varying "warning intervals" preceding a buzzer sound to which S was instructed to respond. The warning intervals were 2, 4, 8, and 12 seconds in length. For the other subgroup the warning light came on for 1 second and then went off for the remainder of the warning interval (on-off condition). An interaction between group and con-

[2] After running these Ss we found a small variable error in the timing mechanism which was due to fluctuation in house voltage. Therefore, these data may not be correct on an absolute basis. The general findings are viewed as valid.

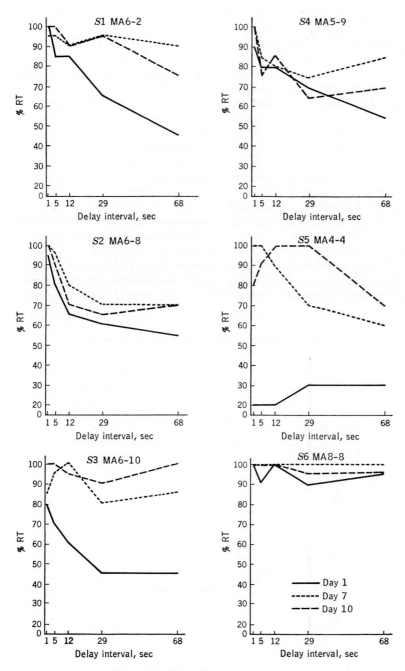

Figure 4-3. Delayed-response functions.

dition was of central concern. Poorer performance was expected in the
on-off condition since *S*'s behavior would be controlled by an *absent*
stimulus; thus the behavior would be dependent upon immediate memory
of the warning signal. However, it was expected that the on-off normals
would be affected relatively little when compared with the on-on normals,
as contrasted with the analogous discrepancy between the defectives tested
under these conditions. It was also expected that the defectives' performance
would deteriorate more, relative to that of the normals, following longer
warning intervals. This would be tested by a group-warning interval interaction. Moreover, an interaction between interval, condition, and group was
predicted since the defectives under the on-off condition were expected to
do worst following the longest warning intervals. Figure 4-4 presents
Terrell's results. The central prediction is clearly confirmed; the performance between the groups under the two conditions is markedly different.
The defectives' performance is far poorer when dependent upon "memory"
of the warning stimulus. There is also an upward inflection of the curve in
the defective on-off group, which suggests that performance in this group
is adversely affected by the longest warning interval. However, there is also
a similar though less pronounced trend in the normal data. The groups by
interval interaction derives mainly from the performance changes *before*

Figure 4-4. RT as a function of warning interval.

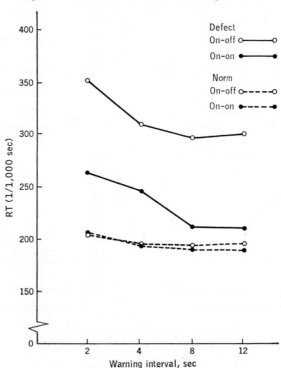

the optimal warning interval is reached and therefore probably involves mechanisms other than s_t. There is a slight trend which suggests that the defective group under the on-off condition may perform more poorly under warning intervals longer than the optimal. However, this trend is slight and not supported by the statistical analysis. Although the s_t construct accounts for the group condition interaction, it is difficult to explain from this position why the differences between the on-on and the on-off condition do not increase with longer warning intervals in the defective groups. It seems likely that behavior following intervals shorter than the optimal must, in part, be accounted for with other constructs. The present experiment was not a fair test of the hypothesis for the interaction effects involving warning intervals since the occasion for the behavior change beyond the optimal interval is scarcely provided. Another explanatory notion suggested by these data is that the defective tends to respond on the basis of some average value of the stimulus population, whereas the normal S responds to the average as well as other characteristics of the stimulus population, the variance, for example. Thus we might expect the normal S to respond approximately in the same fashion to warning intervals throughout the range, whereas the defective would respond on the basis of an average "expectancy." Therefore the defective would do poorly with intervals deviating from the average. The Terrell data may be viewed in this light.

Paired-associate learning

Vergason (1962) investigated paired-associate learning in normals and defectives for the purpose of evaluating acquisition as well as long-term retention. Although his study is not a definitive test of the present formulations, the results are supportive. The task was to associate 13 pairs of familiar items (pictures of objects, such as a horse, tree, and auto) selected from Dunn's Peabody Picture Vocabulary test. The experiment utilized a technique designed to control for differential overlearning, which consisted of dropping items after they had been responded to correctly, rather than retaining them in the task. Sixty-four educable retarded and 64 normal children selected from the same schools were used. The IQs of the retarded ranged from 60 to 75 and the normals, from 90 to 110. The CAs ranged from 12 to about 16.

The two groups were each divided into two subgroups and trained to a criterion of one or five correct trials on an item; i.e., an item was dropped following one correct response, and for subjects in the other groups an item was dropped after five correct responses to it. The four subgroups were each further subdivided into two subgroups each, one of which was tested for retention by the savings method 24 hours later and the other, 30 days later. Figure 4-5 presents the results. The defectives and the normals did not differ on the original learning task. A day later the normals were superior. After 30 days the normals originally trained to the 1 criterion were superior to the defectives, but the defectives trained to a 5 criterion were equal to the normal subjects originally trained to a similar criterion. These data demonstrate that defectives learn at a rate similar to that of normals when the items in the task are familiar. Even though there are no data for com-

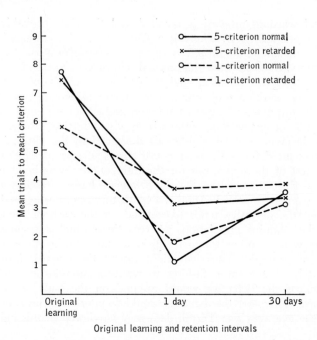

Figure 4-5. Mean trials to 1- and 5-criterion performance on original learning and retention intervals for retarded and normal Ss. (*Vergason study.*)

parison in this particular study, contiguous presentation of the items is viewed as critical. The superiority of the normals after 1 day probably can be ascribed to a reminiscence effect. Some data (Ellis, Pryer, & Barnett, 1960; Jones & Ellis, 1962) are available which suggest that in motor learning normal subjects show more reminiscence than do defectives. The results after 30 days suggest, as predicted, that when original learning is ensured, the defective's retention is equal to that of the normal. This agrees neither with folklore nor with much current professional opinion.

Another study on paired-associate learning supports the conjecture regarding the findings on acquisition in the Vergason study. Blue (1962) trained 48 defective and 48 normal Ss on a task consisting of 10 pairs of items. One member was the name of a color prerecorded and presented with earphones, and the other was a complex geometric design presented with a slide projector. There were two treatments. The auditory stimulus was presented 2 seconds after the onset of the design, which was exposed for 7 seconds, or it occurred 2.75 seconds before the onset of the design. For the other treatment the auditory stimulus was given at an intensity of 40 or 75 decibels. The 48 Ss in each group were assigned to the four treatments deriving from the combinations of these variables. A learning trial was followed by a test trial on which only the design was presented and S was to name the design.

Overall the mean trials to a criterion of one perfect recitation, all 10 items, was 2.98 for the normal Ss and 5.98 for the retarded. This difference

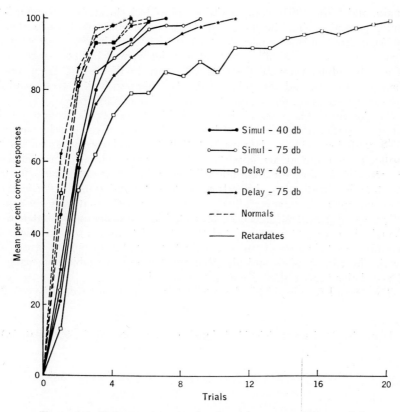

Figure 4-6. Performance curves for the eight groups. (*Blue study.*)

was statistically significant. No other main effects were significant nor were any of the interactions involving intensity of the auditory stimulus. The interaction between group and interstimulus interval was significant, and this is of central interest here. (Since there was marked heterogeneity of variance present, the statistical analysis should be viewed as providing an approximation of probability.) The acquisition of the retarded Ss was seriously affected by the delay condition. The normals learned equally well under all conditions. Figure 4-6 depicts the results. It should be noted that the normal Ss learned more rapidly regardless of the treatment. Possibly these differences could be due to the task involving two sense modalities. This finding, of course, differs from that of the Vergason study. There is a trend in the data suggesting that under the delay condition the defectives do better with the 75-decibel auditory stimulus. If this effect proved reliable, it would be in keeping with the theoretical speculations.

EEG

An attempt to corroborate the earlier finding by Berkson et al. of longer alpha blocking in normal Ss was undertaken in our laboratory. Baumeister,

Spain, and Ellis (1963) compared the alpha-block duration in 10 retardates and 7 normal Ss. The blocking stimulus was a strobiscopic light located 10 inches in front of the S's face. An S received 10 stimulations of 20 ms duration each. The interstimulus interval was determined by the reappearance of a stable alpha wave. The results are shown in Figure 4-7. Even though there was pronounced variability in the data, there is a clear trend, and the group differences are significant at the .05 level of confidence.

Conclusions. The research bearing on the theory holds promise for defining a significant component of behavioral inadequacy in the human with CNS pathology. These data suggest that temporal properties of the retardate's environment are important in the determination of his behavior. It seems likely that the retardate's "slow learning" is not universally true but that his inadequacy depends upon temporal relations in the learning task and upon the *meaningfulness* or *familiarity* of the materials. Of course, only suggestive evidence has been presented here bearing on the latter. Even though these variables are pointed to as two determinants of learning, the possibility that the meaningfulness of the test material is acquired historically by the learning process and also that the temporal variable may have influenced this process should not be overlooked.

The second way in which the retardate's performance would be affected

Figure 4-7. Medians of alpha-block duration. (*Baumeister, Spain, & Ellis study.*)

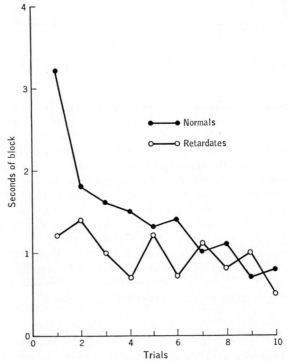

is in behaviors which depend directly upon short-term memory. These may range from phenomena such as the digit span on an intelligence test to the solving of complex problems requiring the individual to keep in mind several aspects of the problem in order to work it out.

Finally, even though the theory does not attempt to describe long-term retention processes, it does tend to ascribe the inadequacy to the process of acquisition and to the immediate stimulus control of behavior. Thus, from the standpoint described here, long-term retention, a process seemingly closely related to the acquisition process, is viewed as "normal" in the retardate, i.e., equivalent to the process in the individual without CNS pathology. This issue, of course, deserves further attention. Perhaps the etiology of the pathology may be of importance. An individual who has had localized brain damage may have difficulty learning; but once the information is stored, presumably in undamaged tissue, we might expect the retention of the information to be adequate. On the other hand the individual with an inadequate CNS owing to genetic factors or endocrine disorder may possess an inadequate storage facility attributable to biochemical or structural characteristics. This amounts to nothing more than speculation. However it does point to meaningful questions for behavioral research involving etiological variables.

Caution should be exercised in attempted application of the findings presented here. Even though they appear germane to such situations as classroom training, the wise practitioner will await further empirical evidence. There is an appreciable gap between theory derived and tested in the laboratory and the application of the finding to the classroom, for example. In the writer's view the gap should be spanned by further research in which the *real life* situation is simulated more closely. Too often in an area in which the problems seem insurmountable, there is premature application of theory which leads to wasted effort and occasionally to disastrous results.

The research vistas suggested here do not require commitments to the use of s_t or n_i, or to the acceptance of the reverberatory circuit concept. Certainly, clear evidence against the last would not damage the position which is essentially molar. As Sidman has aptly put it, "the importance of data is not affected by the sophistication of the hypothesis that may have generated the experiments" (1960, p. 6).

SUMMARY

A theory employing two notions, stimulus trace s_t and integrity of the CNS n_i, has been formalized to account for differences between normal and mentally defective humans in behaviors dependent upon short-term memory. s_t was defined by an environmental stimulus S antecedently, and by a behavioral event B consequently. n_i, defined by IQ or other indices of behavioral inadequacy, was introduced as an individual difference construct. The central problem outlined involved the establishment of the relationship between s_t and n_i.

It was hypothesized that the duration is shortened and the intensity of s_t lessened in the subnormal organism, i.e., the organism with lower n_i. A deficiency of available reverberatory circuits was suggested as a possible neurophysiological substrate underlying individual capacity differences. Consequently, a learning deficit in subnormal organisms could be attributed to noncontinuity between items to be associated.

The role of stimulus trace in molar behavior theory was reviewed, along with opinion regarding a neurological basis for short-term memory. Some recent evidence from animal research was summarized which was pertinent to the general trace concept and to trace as affected by brain subnormality in particular. Evidence from research in mental subnormality in the areas of serial verbal learning, delayed response, EEG, fixed interval operant conditioning, reaction time, and factor analysis was offered in support of the proposed theory. The role of transient neural traces in the consolidation of a permanent trace was described, but limited to the analysis of data from animal research. An extension of this notion appeared to depend upon results of data which bear more directly upon the nature of the trace as defined by molar behavior and electrical activity of the CNS. Evidence for the trace theory deriving from studies designed to test the theory was presented. It was tentatively concluded that a major source of behavioral inadequacy could be attributed to the learning process in the retardate which could in turn be ascribed to a deficit in short-term memory and possibly to the degree of familiarity or meaningfulness of the task materials. A second inadequacy seemed to depend upon behaviors which relied directly upon immediate memory. A third hypothesis was that the long-term retention process in the retardate is equivalent to that in the normal individual. Some cautions against the premature application of the findings were offered.

REFERENCES

AMOS, IRIS E. Delayed response performance at three years of age among children with anoxic and non-anoxic experiences at birth. Unpublished Ph.D. dissertation, Louisiana State Univer., 1959.

BARNETT, C. D., ELLIS, N. R., & PRYER, MARGARET W. Stimulus pretraining and the delayed reaction in defectives. *Amer. J. ment. Defic.*, 1959, 63, 104–111.

BARNETT, C. D., ELLIS, N. R., & PRYER, MARGARET W. Learning in familial and brain-injured defectives. *Amer. J. ment. Defic.*, 1960, 46, 894–901. (a)

BARNETT, C. D., ELLIS, N. R., & PRYER, MARGARET W. Serial position effects in superior and retarded subjects. *Psychol. Rep.*, 1960, 7, 111–113. (b)

BAUMEISTER, A. A. The dimensions of abilities in retardates as measured by the Wechsler intelligence scale for children. A doctoral dissertation, George Peabody Coll. for Teachers, 1961.

BAUMEISTER, A. A., & BARTLETT, C. J. A comparison of the factor structure of normals and retardates. *Amer. J. ment. Defic.*, 1962, 66, 641–646.

BAUMEISTER, A. A., SPAIN, C. J., & ELLIS, N. R. A note on alpha block duration in normals and retardates. *Amer. J. ment. Defic.*, 1963, 67, 723–725.

BERKSON, G. Responsiveness of the mentally deficient. *Amer. J. ment. Defic.*, 1961, 66, 277–286.

BERKSON, G., HERMELIN, B., & O'CONNOR, N. Physiological responses of normals and institutionalized mental defectives to repeated stimuli. *J. ment. Def. Res.*, 1961, 5, 30–39.

BLUE, C. M. The role of short-term memory in the paired-associate learning of normal and retarded subjects. A Ph.D. dissertation, George Peabody Coll. for Teachers, 1962.

DUNCAN, C. P. The retroactive effect of electroshock on learning. *J. comp. physiol. Psychol.,* 1949, 42, 32–44.

ELLIS, N. R., PRYER, MARGARET, W., & BARNETT, C. D. Motor learning and retention in normals and defectives. *Percept. mot. Skills,* 1960, 10, 83–91.

ELLIS, N. R., PRYER, R. S., DISTEFANO, M. K., JR., & PRYER, MARGARET W. Learning in mentally defective, normal and superior subjects. *Amer. J. ment. Defic.,* 1959, 64, 725–734.

GERARD, R. W. Biological roots of psychiatry. *Science,* 1955, 122, 225–230.

GIRARDEAU, F. L., & ELLIS, N. R. Distraction effects in serial and paired-associates learning by normal and mentally defective humans. Unpublished paper, 1961.

HARLOW, H. F., & ISRAEL, R. H. Comparative behavior of primates. IV. Delayed reaction in subnormal humans. *J. comp. Psychol.,* 1932, 14, 253–263.

HEBB, D. O. *The organization of behavior.* New York: Wiley, 1949.

HILGARD, E. R., & MARQUIS, D. G. *Conditioning and learning.* New York: Appleton-Century-Crofts, 1940.

HOUSE, B. J., & ZEAMAN, D. Effects of practice on the delayed response of retardates. *J. comp. physiol. Psychol.,* 1961, 54, 255–260.

HULL, C. L. The conflicting psychologies of learning—a way out. *Psychol. Rev.,* 1935, 42, 491–516.

HULL, C. L. *A behavior system.* New Haven: Yale Univer. Press, 1952.

HUNTER, W. S. The delayed reaction in animals and children. *Animal Behav. Monogr.,* 1913, 2, No. 1.

JASPER, H. Reticular-cortical systems and theories of the integrative action of the brain. In H. F. Harlow & C. N. Woolsey (Eds.), *Biological and biochemical bases of behavior.* Madison: Univer. of Wisconsin Press, 1958.

JEFFRESS, L. A. (ED.) *Cerebral mechanisms in behavior.* New York: Wiley, 1951.

JOHNSON, G. O., & BLAKE, KATHRYN A. *Learning performance of retarded and normal children.* Syracuse: Syracuse Univer. Press, 1960.

JONES, R. W., & ELLIS, N. R. Inhibitory potential in rotary pursuit acquisition by normal and defective subjects. *J. exp. Psychol.,* 1962, 63, 534–537.

KIMBLE, G. A. Conditioning as a function of the time between conditional and unconditional stimuli. *J. exp. Psychol.,* 1947, 37, 1–15.

KOHLER, W. *Gestalt psychology.* New York: Liveright, 1929.

LEPLEY, W. M. A theory of serial learning and forgetting based upon conditioned reflex principles. *Psychol. Rev.,* 1932, 39, 279–288.

LOTT, BERNICE S. E. Paired associate learning, generalization and retention as a function of intelligence. *Amer. J. ment. Defic.,* 1958, 63, 481–489.

MCGRARY, J. W., JR., & HUNTER, W. S. Serial position curves in verbal learning. *Science,* 1953, 117–131.

MCCULLOCH, W. S. Why the mind is in the head. In L. A. Jeffress (Ed.), *Cerebral mechanisms in behavior.* New York: Wiley, 1951.

MOWRER, O. H. *Learning theory and behavior.* New York: Wiley, 1960.

MULLER, G. E., & PILZECKER, A. Experimentelle beitrage zur lehre vom gedachtniss. *Z. Psychol.,* Ergbd., 1900, 1, 1–288.

NOBLE, C. E. An analysis of meaning. *Psychol. Rev.,* 1952, 59, 421–430.

NOBLE, C. E., & FUCHS, J. E. Serial errors in human learning: a test of the McCrary-Hunter hypothesis. *Science,* 1959, 129, 570–571.

ORLANDO, R. Component behaviors in free operant temporal discrimination. *Amer. J. ment. Defic.,* 1961, 65, 615–619.

OSGOOD, C. F. *Method and theory in experimental psychology.* New York: Oxford Univer. Press, 1953.

PASCAL, G. R., & STOLUROW, L. M. Delayed reaction for form and place contrasted. *J. comp. physiol. Psychol.*, 1952, 45, 294–299.

PASCAL, G. R, STOLUROW, L. M., ZABARENKO, R. N., & CHAMBERS, C. S. The delayed reaction in mental defectives. *Amer. J. ment. Defic.*, 1951, 56, 152–160.

PAVLOV, I. P. *Conditional reflexes.* London: Oxford Univer. Press, 1927.

PENNINGTON, D. F. The effect of ECS on retention of a discrimination habit in rats subjected to anoxia. *J. comp. physiol. Psychol.*, 1958, 51, 587–690.

PRYER, R. S. Retroactive inhibition in normals and defectives as a function of temporal position of the interpolated task. *Amer. J. ment. Defic.*, 1960, 64, 1004–1011.

REYNOLDS, B. The acquisition of a trace conditioned response as a function of the magnitude of the stimulus trace. *J. exp. Psychol.*, 1945, 35, 15–30.

RIESEN, A. H. Plasticity of behavior: Psychological series. In H. F. Harlow & C. N. Woolsey (Eds.), *Biological and biochemical bases of behavior.* Madison: Univer. of Wisconsin Press, 1958.

SIDMAN, M. *Tactics of scientific research.* New York: Basic Books, 1960.

SLOAN, W., & BERG, I. A comparison of two types of learning in mental defectives. *Amer. J. ment. Defic.*, 1957, 61, 556–566.

TERRELL, CATHERINE G. Reaction time in normals and defectives following varied warning conditions. A master's thesis, George Peabody Coll. for Teachers, 1961.

THOMPSON, R. The effect of ECS on retention in young and adult rats. *J. comp. physiol. Psychol.*, 1957, 50, 644–646.

THOMPSON, R. Retroactive effect of interpolated visual stimulation. *Psychol. Rep.*, 1957, 3, 183–188.

THOMPSON, R. Transient memory in albino rats. *Science,* 1959, 129, 842–843.

THOMPSON, R., HARAVEY, R., PENNINGTON, D. F., SMITH, J., GANNON, D., & STOCKWELL, F. An analysis of the differential effects of ECS on memory in young and adult rats. *Canad. J. Psychol.*, 1958, 12, 83–96.

THOMPSON, R., & PRYER, R. S. The effect of anoxia on the retention of a discrimination habit. *J. comp. physiol. Psychol.*, 1956, 49, 297–300.

VERGASON, GLENN A. Retention in educable retarded and normal adolescent boys as a function of amount of original training. A Ph.D. dissertation, George Peabody Coll. for Teachers, 1962.

5

THE ROLE OF ATTENTION IN
RETARDATE DISCRIMINATION LEARNING[1]

David Zeaman
Betty J. House

SYNOPSIS

Retardates have been found particularly slow in forming some simple visual habits, even slower than would be expected from their low mental age (Stevenson & Iscoe, 1955; House & Zeaman, 1958a; House & Zeaman, 1960a; Girardeau, 1959). The reasons for the learning deficit do not seem to lie in the area of instrumental learning, but rather in that of *attention*. In support of this notion, data from a series of experiments with moderately retarded, trainable children have been collated here and organized by a theory of attention.

METHOD

Experimental

The experimental techniques we employ are derived from those of Harlow (1959). His Wisconsin General Test apparatus has been adapted for use with retarded children, as it provides a flexible tool for the study of basic discriminative processes. Figure 5-1 depicts the major features of the appa-

[1] The research reported in this paper has been supported by Grant M-1099 of the National Institute of Mental Health of the U.S. Public Health Service.

We gratefully acknowledge the help of several collaborators. Herbert M. Kaufman developed a number of the equations for extensions of the basic model, in particular the $\pi\rho$ submodel. Computer programming was expertly done for us by Lester Hyman. Research contributions were made by USPHS Postdoctoral Fellows, Robert Orlando, Jerome Smith, and Bryan Shepp, as well as a number of others. Without the cooperation of the administration of the Mansfield Training School, Neil Dayton, John Cassell, and Louis Boly, the research reported here would not have been possible.

This work was done in part at the M.I.T. Computation Center, Cambridge, Mass.

159

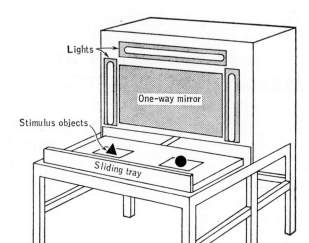

Figure 5-1. Discrimination learning apparatus.

ratus: a tray displaying two stimulus objects (one of which is baited with candy) and a one-way-vision screen separating the subject and experimenter. The experimenter arranges the stimuli on the tray behind the screen, hides a candy under one, and slides the tray out to the subject so a choice can be made. This completes one trial of a two-choice, simultaneous, visual discrimination learning problem. Procedure continues trial by trial for original learning problems, reversals, schedules, changes of incentive, and a variety of transfer operations.

Analysis of discrimination learning curves

Group curves. Analyses of the forms of discrimination learning curves may provide some clues about the nature of underlying processes. Let us begin with a look at some data. For a group of 50 retarded children (MA 2–6) who learned to discriminate between two objects differing in just color and form, Figure 5-2 presents a traditional group learning curve: a plot of trials against percentage correct responses of the group. The curve is gradually rising with overall negative acceleration. From this we might erroneously infer a single gradual underlying process similar to the growth of habit strength in Hull's system.

Homogeneous groups. Such traditional functions, however, are likely to obscure characteristics of individual performance, a fact well demonstrated by Hayes (1953), Sidman (1952), and Estes (1960), who have shown that the average curve of a group does not necessarily have the same form as those of individual members of a heterogeneous group. Since individual

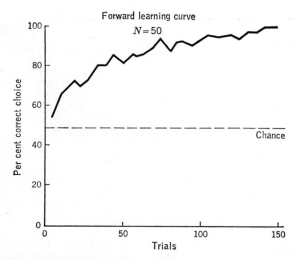

Figure 5-2. Average discrimination learning curve of a group of retardates.

discrimination learning functions are usually too irregular to permit accurate assessment of form, a common alternative procedure averages together performances of homogeneous groups.

Wide individual differences in rate of learning can be eliminated by grouping subjects who take the same number of days to achieve criterion. The 50 subjects described above achieved a learning criterion of 20 correct responses in a daily run of 25 trials on 1 of 6 days of training. Those learning on the first day have their performances averaged and plotted to the left in Figure 5-3. Their function, labeled day 1, is a sharply rising and

Figure 5-3. Forward learning curves of subgroups requiring various numbers of training days to reach criterion. The number of subjects in each group appears at top.

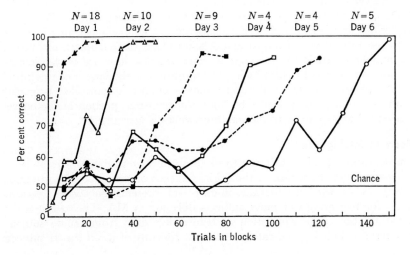

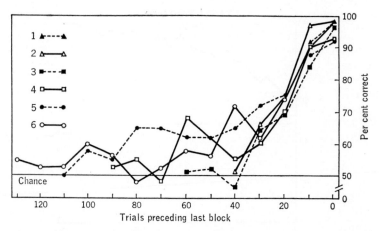

Figure 5-4. The functions of Figure 5-3 have been regrouped prior to averaging for a backward learning curve. The contrast in form of backward and forward learning curves (Figure 5-1) is marked.

negatively accelerated curve. The day-2 group may be classified similarly, but as we move out to days 3, 4, 5, and 6, a new form emerges. The learning curves become more and more ogival in shape. The slow learners appear to stay close to chance performance for varying numbers of trials, but once performance starts to improve, it moves relatively fast.

Backward learning curves.   Furthermore, the final rates of all groups are quite similar. This is more easily seen in Figure 5-4 which moves all the functions in Figure 5-3 to the right so that the *last* point of every function has the same abscissa value, the next-to-last point has the adjacent abscissa value, and so on. Averaging together plots of this kind yields *backward learning curves,* a procedure invented by Hayes (1953) to bring out the shapes of group curves in the vicinity of criterion. Statistically, these backward curves are not different in slope.

Our first clue about the nature of underlying processes comes, then, from Figures 5-3 and 5-4. The difference between fast and slow learning is not so much the rate at which improvement takes place, *once it starts,* but rather the number of trials for learning to start. At this juncture we anticipate our later arguments by introducing the surmise that the length of the initial flat chance-level stages of the performance curves is controlled primarily by an attention process, while the final, sharply rising portion of the curves is largely indicative of instrumental discriminative learning.

Effects of intelligence

The relevance of this conjecture to the problem of retardation is established by showing that the length of the initial flat part of the ogive (the attention phase) varies with intelligence. Figure 5-5 presents backward learning curves for two groups of naïve subjects differing in MA. The task is still a color-form object discrimination as before, but data from failing subjects have been included to indicate the relative difficulty of it. Of the 31 subjects in the MA 4–6 year group, 20 learned the discrimination with the median subject taking 2 days (50 trials). The backward learning curve of this group is given the abscissa locus of the median subject. At the lower-MA level of 2–4 years, 21 of 40 subjects achieved criterion with a median score of 9 days. The backward learning curve of this group is shown at the right. Both groups of nonlearners have their average performances plotted for 10 days of practice.

Simple inspection shows that the difference between the higher- and lower-MA groups lies entirely in the length of the initial chance plateau. The final rates of approach to criterion are the same.

The MA 2–4 group (learners and nonlearners) had about the same average CA (140 months) as the MA 4–6 group (147 months). The mean IQ of the MA 2–4 group was 30, as compared with 41 for the higher-MA group.

The overall picture emerging from analyses of the shapes of discrimination learning curves is one of discontinuity, in the sense that performance is improving either rapidly or not at all. An apparent discontinuity of this sort could be produced by two continuous processes, with the rate of the

Figure 5-5. Effects of intelligence on discrimination learning are shown in the average performances of four groups classified by mental age and achievement. Backward curves are plotted for the two groups of learners.

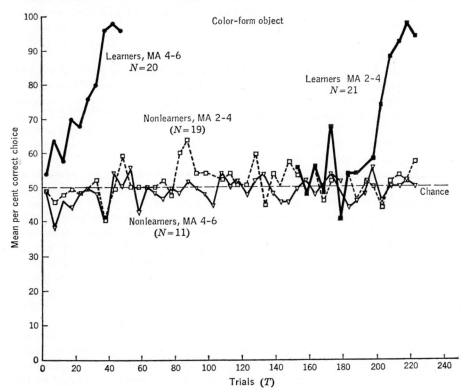

second dependent upon the level of the first. The tentative identification of the process underlying the initial phase as attentive in nature leads us to look next at a general class of input variables that presumably exercise some control over attention—stimulus factors.

Stimulus factors

Differences in number or kind of stimulus dimensions clearly affect acquisition of visual discriminations. Figure 5-6 presents backward learning curves of retardates, MA 4–6, for a variety of stimulus conditions. At the far left, a group of eight naïve subjects learned to discriminate multidimensional stimulus objects in a median of 25 trials (1 day). Examples of multidimensionally different stimuli (junk) are an aluminum pot cover versus a green plastic soap dish and a toy hat versus a tobacco can. None of the eight naïve subjects failed; none took more than 3 days to learn. A great many experienced subjects have been run on this problem, and it is a rare subject who fails.

Junk discrimination is considerably easier than discrimination of objects differing in both color and form. The color-form object functions from Figure 5-5 are recopied for comparison.

Having only form as a relevant aspect of two objects yields the middlemost backward learning curve of Figure 5-6. Of 18 subjects, 11 learned to distinguish pairs of objects, such as a triangle versus a circle, in a median number of 100 trials. These were experienced subjects who had previously been trained on an easier discrimination. For this reason, the difficulty of the object-form problem and, also, the object-color problem may be underestimated.

At the far right of Figure 5-6 is the backward learning curve of subjects who were given the task of learning a color discrimination. Two objects differing only in color, such as a red square versus a green square, are most difficult to discriminate. A minority of 5 out of a total of 20 subjects learned this problem in the 10 days allotted. Since the median subject failed, abscissa locus for the backward learning curve is determinate only to the extent of falling to the right of 250 trials.

Somewhere between the object-form and the object-color problem in terms of difficulty comes the pattern-color-form discrimination. The three-dimensional objects used for the color-form object discrimination were presented as flat, two-dimensional patterns (e.g., red triangle versus yellow cross). This seemingly minor change in the nature of the cues resulted in a large difference in performance. A minority of 8 out of 20 subjects learned to solve this problem, which calls for a placement of the backward learning curve in Figure 5-6 somewhere between 250 trials and the color function.

Despite the wide range in difficulty among these five problems, the slopes of the backward learning curves do not vary widely, a fact to be claimed by the attention theory which follows. In summary, Figure 5-6 leads to the following inferences: (1) The *number* of relevant stimulus dimensions controls speed of discrimination learning, supported by the rank ordering in difficulty of the junk, color-form object, and object-form (or -color) conditions; (2) the *kind* of relevant dimension also exercises control, supported by the

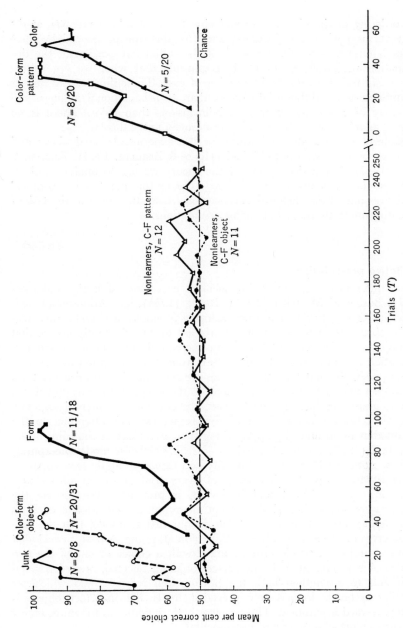

Figure 5-6. Backward learning curves for the discrimination of several kinds of stimuli. Average performance levels of nonlearners stay close to chance.

rank ordering of the object-form and object-color conditions as well as the object versus pattern comparisons; and (3) the control exerted by these factors is largely upon the duration of the initial flat portion of the discrimination performance curves. It is possible that what we are calling kind of cue may turn out to be number of cues. Three-dimensional objects may present more differential aspects than two-dimensional analogs, and form may be made up of more subdimensions than color. There is no evidence as yet on this point, and it is not crucial to the theory.

Details of method and procedure for the experiments cited above and later have been previously published (House & Zeaman, 1960a; Zeaman & House, 1962), but a description of the theory we use to analyze and re-order the data has not been published. Up to this point our theoretical conjectures have been sketched only vaguely, so we turn now to the task of explicating more precisely our major assumptions.

THEORY

Qualitative presentation

Several quantitative discrimination theories, e.g., those of Burke and Estes (1957), Bush and Mosteller (1951), Restle (1955), and Atkinson (1958), predict either negatively accelerated learning functions or ogival forms lacking the abrupt transitions seen in Figures 5-3 to 5-6. These all assume that the subject samples relevant stimuli on every trial. The shapes of our discrimination functions suggest a departure from this assumption by allowing for the possibility that the relevant cues are not attended to on every trial. The subject may have to *learn* to attend to the relevant stimulus dimension.

Thus, instead of having only to learn the correct instrumental response, the subject must learn a chain of two responses: (1) attending to the relevant dimension and (2) approaching the correct cue of that dimension.

Wyckoff (1952) has constructed an *observing-response* model incorporating these notions which we shall modify and extend to apply to our experimental situations. At the beginning of every trial, a variety of stimulus dimensions, both relevant and irrelevant, is presented. We assume the subject's attention is limited so that not all stimuli are effective as cues. As a simplifying assumption, we postulate in our first submodel that the subject observes or attends to only one dimension at a time. A trial is concluded when the subject responds instrumentally with a choice of one of the two stimulus objects presented. If the correct object is selected, reward is given which acts to strengthen both the instrumental response and whichever observing response immediately preceded it. If the incorrect object is selected, reward is withheld. This weakens both responses in the immediately preceding chain, observing and instrumental.

A diagram may facilitate exposition. At the top of Figure 5-7 a somewhat wall-eyed subject is shown viewing a simultaneous presentation of two stimulus objects differing in color and form. At the moment of choice, the subject may be observing either the relevant stimulus dimension S (which in the diagram is form) or an irrelevant dimension S' (color or position, in the example). If the relevant observing response O_1 is made, the specific values or cues of the form dimension, triangle s_1 and circle s_1', are seen. If attention is focused on the irrelevant color dimension O_2, the yellow and blue elements (s_2 and s_2') of this dimension become effective.

Immediately following O_1 the subject makes one of two instrumental responses, approaching the positive cue—R_1—or approaching the negative cue—R_1'; following O_2 an approach is made to one of the cues of the irrelevant dimension. None of these responses is directly observable, neither the instrumental approach responses nor the observing responses. The only observable responses in the system are the overt picking up of the correct (baited) stimulus object R_c or the choosing of the incorrect object R_c'. The theory predicts the probabilities of these observable responses.

The bottom half of Figure 5-7 pictures the subject attending to the form dimension. The theory allows the possibility that only one of the specific

Figure 5-7. A diagram of some of the events of the theory. At top, a yellow triangle and blue circle are presented simultaneously in a form discrimination problem. At bottom, the arrangement of stimuli on another trial is shown with candy following the relevant form cue. Approach to an irrelevant component gets reinforced randomly on half the trials.

The circle inside the subject's head represents the transformation by O_1 of the form dimension S to the effective cue s_1 (circle). Theoretically, the observation of the triangle could be substituted with no difference in outcome.

Other aspects of the diagram are described in the text.

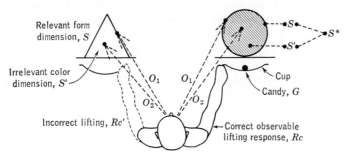

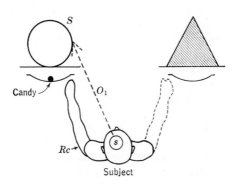

cues (circle) of the relevant dimension might be seen, as would certainly be true if the stimulus objects were presented successively rather than simultaneously. In this event, the subjects can then either approach the circle R_1 or avoid it R_1'. At present, for the two-choice experiment, no distinction is made between approaching the circle or avoiding the triangle.

The diagram portrays the irrelevant color and position cues as inconsistently related to the candy reinforcement. For the simpler models of the theory, only a single dimension is relevant, and all others are randomly associated with reward. For more complex models the number of relevant dimensions and the degree of relevance are made parameters of the system.

The set of all dimensions both relevant and irrelevant, present at the moment before choice, is designated S^* in Figure 5-7. The competing observing responses O_1 and O_2 are elicited by S^* or some subset of S^*. Appropriate transfer experiments could be designed to reveal which aspects of S^* elicit the observing responses. For the present, we simply assume that whatever elicits O_i is present on every trial.

The diagram does not make clear that while *dimensional* aspects of stimuli elicit attention, it is the result of attention, *specific cues,* that elicits the instrumental responses. But the distinction between dimensions and cues is central to the theory and deserves preliminary elaboration.

Dimensions are broad classes of cues having a common discriminative property. Dimensions have the lower informational content of a stimulus display, cues the higher. Consider color and form as the instances of dimensions given in the diagram. If the subject attends to color, he will see that yellow and blue are the specific cues present. If he observes form, a circle and triangle become effective cues. Changing the colors to red and green or the forms to square and cross does not disturb the observing responses because the dimensions of form and color are still intact. All colors have the common property of being colored, and it is this common property which the observing response transforms to specific cues. The precise physical description and mechanism of reception of the color dimensional property are in principle not insoluble problems in psychophysical and physiological psychology. As we shall demonstrate later, dimensional properties are also discoverable in the context of discrimination learning experiments, especially by the experimental operations of *intradimensional shifts.* If, for example, training a subject to attend to color when blue and yellow are positive and negative cues leads to positive transfer when red and green are substituted in an intradimensional-shift test, the inference of a color dimension is supported. As a corollary, knowledge of the existence of a dimension permits the demonstration of the negative transfer of *extradimensional shift.* To illustrate, changing from form relevant to position relevant, or vice versa, will lead to negative transfer to the extent that form and position are different dimensions.

It should be clear that stimulus dimensions are major constructs of the present theory. Things tentatively identified as dimensions can be manipulated physically to test a number of theoretical predictions, the accuracy of which serves as an indicator of the truth of the theory in general and of the identification in particular. Thus, discovery of dimensions is part of the business of confirming the theory, and both are quite programmatic. Some instances of dimensions for the retardate population, as posited by the present authors, are form, color, position, brightness, and size.

A few remarks about response specification will complete this brief qualitative description of the theory. For the simpler models, all responses are mutually exclusive (competing) and exhaustive (one must occur). The number of possible observing responses can vary from 1 to n, but only one is assumed to occur immediately before the moment of choice. This assumption identifies our *one-look* model. *Two-look* models can also be built when this assumption is relaxed, and the possibilities of generalization to an *N*-look model are considered. A simple case of an *N*-look model may be obtained merely by redefining O_i. If some set of dimensions is *always* observed at the same time, as a unit, and the same values always presented together by the experimenter, the predictions of the model with reference to this multiple look would be the same as those for a simple one-look O_i.

The two-choice experimental situation requires the inference of just two competing instrumental responses, only one of which occurs at the moment of choice. The theory can be generalized to apply to experiments with more choices without great difficulty, but we have not chosen to explore such models yet, since all our data are from two-choice experiments.

A final line of generalization which we have considered is in the area of schedules of partial reinforcement. The methods for introducing the now traditional parameter (probability of reinforcement of some reference response) are the same as those used by Estes and Straughan (1954) and Bush and Mosteller (1955).

Quantitative aspects of theory

Mathematical description of the theory is aided by construction of the probability tree in Figure 5-8. Reading the tree from left to right, we see that each trial begins with presentation of S^*, which elicits just one of the n competing observing responses O_i with probabilities $Po(i)$. The observing response, whichever occurs, exposes the specific cues of the dimension observed. These in turn elicit one of two instrumental approach responses with conditional probabilities $Pr_{(i)}$ and $1 - Pr_{(i)}$. Given the occurrence of the relevant observing O_1, reinforcement G always follows approach to the positive cue, with a standard 100 per cent schedule. Given any of the irrelevant observing responses, the rules of experimentation ensure that the probability of reinforcement is one-half regardless of what instrumental reaching response is made.

The tree shows $4n - 2$ possible alternative sequences that may comprise a trial. The next step in theory construction associates with each outcome a rule for changing the probabilities dependent upon the different outcomes.

Direct reinforcement. If a trial ends in reinforcement, the probabilities of both responses occurring on that trial (observing and instrumental) undergo increments proportional to their complements. The constants of proportionality θ may differ for the instrumental and observing responses. The change in probability may be expressed in equation form:

$$\Delta \text{ Prob.} = +\theta(1 - \text{Prob.})$$

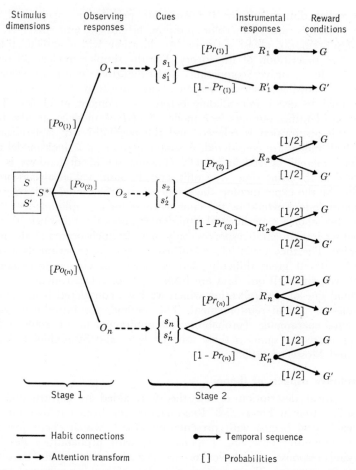

Stimulus dimensions	Observing responses	Cues	Instrumental responses	Reward conditions

Figure 5-8. Probability tree of the basic model. The branches represent all the possible events that can theoretically occur on a single trial. The probability of occurrence of each branch is drawn in brackets.

The set of relevant and irrelevant stimulus dimensions is denoted S^*. Other notation is defined in the text.

Direct extinction. For a trial ending in nonreinforcement, probabilities of both responses in the chain occurring on that trial undergo decrements proportional to their magnitudes. The constants of proportionality θ are set equal to those of acquisition, as a first approximation. In equation form,

$$\Delta \text{ Prob.} = -\theta(\text{Prob.})$$

Indirect reinforcement. When a trial ends in extinction, the probabilities of all the nonelicited observing responses gain an increment, each one getting a fraction of the probability lost by the directly extinguished observing response. These fractions are such as to preserve the relative strengths of the nonelicited O_i. The fractions can be expressed in symbolic terms as $Po_{(i)}/1 - Po_{(j-)}$, if we let $Po_{(j-)}$ be the probability of the directly extinguished observing response and $Po_{(i)}$ be the probability of any one of the remaining, nonelicited observing responses.

For the conditional probabilities of the instrumental response, any loss in the probability of R_i by extinction is accompanied by an equal gain in the probability of R_i', since the two probabilities are complements.

Indirect extinction. The analogous rule holds here. Direct gains in attention to one dimension are spontaneously accompanied by changes in the strengths of other observing responses—each in proportion to its relative strength. Rules of this kind are necessary to conserve probability in a competing response system.

Summary of rules for probability change. The rules described above can be redescribed in operator form to facilitate tabular summary of their application. The acquisition operator Q_A is defined by the equation

$$Q_A(\text{Prob.}) = (\text{Prob.}) + \theta(1 - \text{Prob.})$$

and the extinction operator Q_E by

$$Q_E(\text{Prob.}) = (\text{Prob.}) - \theta(\text{Prob.})$$

The indirect acquisition operator Q_{aj} is defined by

$$Q_{aj}(Po_{(i)}) = Po_{(i)} + \frac{\theta_o Po_{(i)} Po_{(j-)}}{1 - Po_{(j-)}}$$

and the indirect extinction operator Q_e by

$$Q_e(Po_{(i)}) = Po_{(i)} - \frac{\theta_o Po_{(i)}(1 - Po_{(j+)})}{1 - Po_{(j+)}} = Po_{(i)} - \theta_o Po_{(i)}$$

where $Po_{(j+)}$ is the probability of the directly reinforced observing response. Note that Q_e turns out to be identical to Q_E. The occasions for application of the operators together with the probabilities of application are summarized in Table 5-1.

Entries have not been tabulated for sequences beginning with observing responses between O_2 and O_n in the probability tree, since these would not differ from those of O_2 and O_n. Q_I denotes the identity operator. The probability of each sequence has been included to help show the derivation of stat-children and expected operators.

Probability of a correct overt response. From the probability tree of Figure 5-8 an equation can be derived for the probability P of Rc, the correct overt response of choosing the stimulus object associated with the positive cue. Summing up the probability products of all branches leading to G yields the basic equation:

$$P = Po_{(1)}Pr_{(1)} + \tfrac{1}{2}(1 - Po_{(1)}) \tag{5-1}$$

P is the dependent variable of the system, and Eq. (5-1) relates it to the probability of observing the relevant dimension and the conditional probability of approaching the positive cue given observation of the relevant dimension.

The problem of approximations

The theory so far consists of (1) Eq. (5-1) which relates the observable dependent variable P to probabilities of two unobservable responses and (2) rules for changing probabilities of these inferred responses on each trial, for a single subject. This is not enough for empirical tests of the theory. Our data are usually in the form of learning curves relating number of training trials T to percentage of correct responses Rc of a group of subjects, but the theory says nothing about these variables yet.

If for a large group of identical subjects, we know all the starting probabilities in the tree (Figure 5-8) and the other parameter values (θs and n), we can compute directly the mean probability $\bar{P}_1$ of the group on trial 1 and, using standard methods, the expected value $\bar{P}_2$ for trial 2.

$$\begin{aligned}
\bar{P}_2 = {} & (Po_{(1)}Pr_{(1)})[Q_APo_{(1)}Q_APr_{(1)} + \tfrac{1}{2}(1 - Q_APo_{(1)})] \\
& + [Po_{(1)}(1 - Pr_{(1)})][Q_EPo_{(1)}Q_APr_{(1)} + \tfrac{1}{2}(1 - Q_EPo_{(1)})] \\
& + (1 - Po_{(1)})[Pr_{(1)}\tfrac{1}{2}(Q_ePo_{(1)} + Q_aPo_{(1)}) \\
& \qquad\qquad\qquad\qquad + \tfrac{1}{2}(1 - \tfrac{1}{2}(Q_ePo_{(1)} - Q_aPo_{(1)}))]
\end{aligned}$$

The result is a theoretical learning curve for two trials for a group of

TABLE 5-1

Operators applied to four probabilities given the various sequences of events that can occur on a trial

Sequence of events	Probability of sequence	Operators applied to			
		$Po_{(1)}$	$Po_{(2)}$	$Po_{(n)}$	$Pr_{(1)}$
O_1R_1G	$Po_{(1)}Pr_{(1)}$	Q_A	Q_e	Q_e	Q_A
$O_1R_1'G'$	$Po_{(1)}(1 - Pr_{(1)})$	Q_E	Q_{a1}	Q_{a1}	Q_A
O_2R_2G	$Po_{(2)}Pr_{(2)}\tfrac{1}{2}$	Q_e	Q_A	Q_e	Q_I
O_2R_2G'	$Po_{(2)}Pr_{(2)}\tfrac{1}{2}$	Q_{a2}	Q_E	Q_{a2}	Q_I
$O_2R_2'G$	$Po_{(2)}(1 - Pr_{(2)})\tfrac{1}{2}$	Q_e	Q_A	Q_e	Q_I
$O_2R_2'G'$	$Po_{(2)}(1 - Pr_{(2)})\tfrac{1}{2}$	Q_{a2}	Q_E	Q_{a2}	Q_I
O_nR_nG	$Po_{(n)}Pr_{(n)}\tfrac{1}{2}$	Q_e	Q_e	Q_A	Q_I
O_nR_nG'	$Po_{(n)}Pr_{(n)}\tfrac{1}{2}$	Q_{an}	Q_{an}	Q_E	Q_I
$O_nR_n'G$	$Po_{(n)}(1 - Pr_{(n)})\tfrac{1}{2}$	Q_e	Q_e	Q_A	Q_I
$O_nR_n'G'$	$Po_{(n)}(1 - Pr_{(n)})\tfrac{1}{2}$	Q_{an}	Q_{an}	Q_E	Q_I

identical subjects with *equal* irrelevant observing response probabilities. When one tries to compute P_3, P_4, . . . , P_{100}, however, the work rapidly becomes prohibitive. While it may not be impossible in principle to find an explicit solution for the desired function $P_{(T)} = f(T)$ for this system, the methods are not known to us. For this reason, we make use of statistical approximation procedures—stat-children and, also, a kind of expected operator approximation.

Stat-children. Bush and Mosteller (1955) have described in detail a "Monte Carlo" method for getting approximate solutions of stochastic models. We employ these methods to run stat-children. A stat-child is a statistical creature that obeys the rules of a probability model. If a response is to be elicited with a given probability, the stat-child consults a table of random numbers in its head to translate that probability into a yes-no decision. For our model, computation of the behavior of stat-children requires (1) the operators listed in Table 5-1; (2) a table of random numbers to convert the probabilities of column 2 in Table 5-1 to yes-no decisions on application of the operators; (3) a set of starting probabilities, θ values and a value of n; and (4) Eq. (5-1).

Populations of stat-children are conveniently run on high-speed digital computers because of the tedious nature of the computations required. Major results include the proportions of stat-children making the correct overt response on each trial for populations having various starting probabilities and parameter values. These proportions serve as estimates of $P_{(T)}$.

Expected operator approximation of $Po_{(1,T)}$. If each of the operators listed under $Po_{(1)}$ in Table 5-1 is weighted by the probability of its application (second column) and applied to $\bar{P}o_{(1,T)}$, the sum of these weighted operations yields an expected operator approximation of $\bar{P}o_{(1,T+1)}$. Using the relation

$$\Delta \bar{P}o_{(1,T)} = \overline{QPo}_{(1,T)} - \bar{P}o_{(1,T)}$$

we then write an expression for the expected change in the mean probability of a relevant observing response.

$$\Delta \bar{P}o_{(1)} = \bar{P}o_{(1)}\bar{P}r_{(1)}\theta_o(1 - \bar{P}o_{(1)}) + \bar{P}o_{(1)}(1 - \bar{P}r_{(1)})(-\theta_o\bar{P}o_{(1)})$$

$$+ \bar{P}o_{(2)}\tfrac{1}{2}(-\theta_o\bar{P}o_{(1)}) + \bar{P}o_{(2)}\tfrac{1}{2}\left(\theta_o\bar{P}o_{(2)}\frac{\bar{P}o_{(1)}}{1 - \bar{P}o_{(2)}}\right)$$

$$+ \cdots + \bar{P}o_{(n)}\tfrac{1}{2}(-\theta_o\bar{P}o_{(1)}) + \bar{P}o_{(n)}\tfrac{1}{2}\left(\theta_o\bar{P}o_{(n)}\frac{\bar{P}o_{(1)}}{1 - \bar{P}o_{(n)}}\right) \cdots$$

which simplifies to

$$\Delta \bar{P}o_{(1)} = \frac{\theta_o}{2}\bar{P}o_{(1)}\left(2\bar{P}r_{(1)} - 1 - n + \sum_{i=2}^{n}\frac{1}{1 - \bar{P}o_{(i)}}\right) \qquad (5\text{-}2)$$

Applying the expected operator $\bar{Q}$ to a mean probability of a group of subjects with different probability values is not the usual way of obtaining an expected mean and the result may be a quite biased estimate of $\bar{P}o_{(1,T)}$. Calculation of the expected operator for our system in the usual way leads to fearsome complexities of the kind Bush and Mosteller (1955) have shown for simpler models with subject-controlled events. The accuracy of the approximation achieved by our present method can be assessed to some extent by comparing results with mean stat-child performance.

Approximation of the expected change in mean probability of irrelevant observing responses. The same logic used to compute $\Delta \bar{P}o_{(1)}$ can be used to approximate $\Delta \bar{P}o_{(i)}$ $(i = 2, 3, \ldots, n)$. Let $\bar{P}o_{(j)}$ be any particular irrelevant $\bar{P}o_{(i)}$ chosen as reference. The expected change in the mean probability of observing the jth irrelevant dimension is

$$\Delta \bar{P}o_{(j)} = \frac{\theta_o}{2} \bar{P}o_{(j)} \left[\frac{1 + \bar{P}o_{(1)}(1 - 2\,\bar{P}r_{(1)})}{1 - \bar{P}o_{(1)}} - n + \sum_{\substack{i=2 \\ i \neq j}}^{n} \frac{1}{1 - \bar{P}o_{(i)}} \right] \quad (5\text{-}3)$$

Approximation of the expected change in relevant instrumental response probability. We reason as before to get

$$\Delta \bar{P}r_{(1)} = \bar{P}o_{(1)}\bar{P}r_{(1)}\theta_r(1 - \bar{P}r_{(1)}) + \bar{P}o_{(1)}(1 - \bar{P}r_{(1)})\theta_r(1 - \bar{P}r_{(1)})$$
$$= \bar{P}o_{(1)}\theta_r(1 - \bar{P}r_{(1)}) \quad (5\text{-}4)$$

Expected change in the mean probability of a correct response. If Eq. (5-1) holds for the individual subject, then

$$\bar{P} = \bar{P}o_{(1)}\bar{P}r_{(1)} + \tfrac{1}{2}(1 - \bar{P}o_{(1)}) \quad (5\text{-}5)$$

does not hold exactly for a group, but it does yield an approximation. This, in effect, adds an approximation on top of an approximation, but it permits us to write the corresponding difference equation

$$\Delta \bar{P} = \bar{P}o_{(1)}\,\Delta \bar{P}r_{(1)} + \bar{P}r_{(1)}\,\Delta \bar{P}o_{(1)} + \Delta \bar{P}o_{(1)}\,\Delta \bar{P}r_{(1)} - \frac{\Delta \bar{P}o_{(1)}}{2} \quad (5\text{-}6)$$

Into Eq. (5-6) are then substituted values of $\Delta \bar{P}o_{(1)}$ and $\Delta \bar{P}r_{(1)}$ computed by means of Eqs. (5-2) to (5-4).

Starting from assumed initial conditions $\bar{P}o_{(i)}$ and $\bar{P}r_{(1)}$, Eq. (5-6) can be stepped along trial by trial to give an approximation of $\bar{P}_{(T)}$ for various values of parameters θ_o, θ_r, and n.

Explicit solutions for any of the nonlinear difference equations presented here are not known, so we have used a digital computer again for trial-by-trial calculations. These calculations use less machine time than the corresponding stat-child computations.

There is little danger of misinterpreting these approximations to an expected mean curve if it is recognized that $P_{(T+1)}$ equals exactly the expected mean of a group of subjects if all have the same values—$\bar{P}o_{(i,T)}$ and $\bar{P}r_{(i,T)}$—on the preceding trial, T, *and* if all receive the average Δs on trial T. Such approximations can provide useful information about the properties of the system, even though they may be unable to describe the behavior of groups of subjects varying widely in $Po_{(i,T)}$ and $Pr_{(i,T)}$.

Theoretical effects of parameters

Initial $Po_{(1)}$ and n. The probability of attending to the relevant stimulus dimension at the very beginning of training ($Po_{(1,0)}$) may vary, and Figure 5-9 shows the theoretical effects on group discrimination learning curves. Each function represents the mean probability of correct choice R_c for 20 stat-children. The total number of dimensions n appears as a parameter. For $n = 3$ (one relevant dimension and two irrelevant) the effect of initial probability of a relevant observing response is to change the shape of the mean performance curves from a fast rising, negatively accelerated function (when $Po_{(1,0)} = .5$), to a slower rising, ogival function (when $Po_{(1,0)} = .001$). For $n = 11$, the forms of the functions remain roughly the same, but the

Figure 5-9. Mean discrimination curves for eight groups of 20 stat-children. Two families of functions are generated by the n parameter: solid line is for $n = 3$, dashed for $n = 11$. Within each family a separate curve is plotted for different values of $Po_{(1,0)}$. For all functions, the fixed parameters are $Pr_{(1,0)} = .5$, $\theta_o = \theta_r = .3$, and all starting probabilities for irrelevant observing responses are equal within a condition.

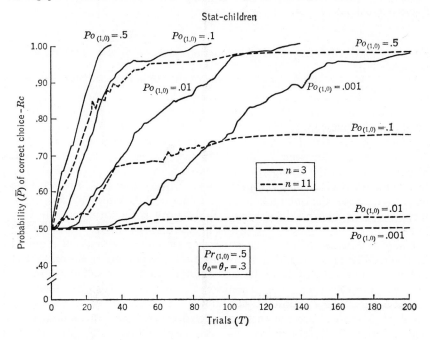

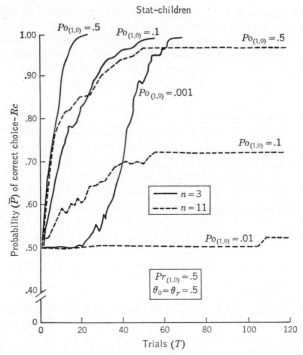

Figure 5-10. Theoretical discrimination learning curves corresponding to those of Figure 5-9, but with $\theta = .5$.

rates are markedly attenuated. All functions are asymptotic at unity, given enough trials.

Comparisons of all the curves in Figure 5-9 show clearly that the two parameters $Po_{(1,0)}$ and n interact strongly. The larger the value of n, the greater the tendency of a low initial $Po_{(1)}$ to retard the rate of improvement of performance with training.

Effects of θ. *Equal θ values.* The effects of variation in θ (when $\theta_o = \theta_r = \theta$) can be seen in the differences among Figures 5-9 to 5-11. These result from the change in θ from .3 (Figure 5-9) to .5 (Figure 5-10) to .7 (Figure 5-11). All three parameters, $Po_{(1,0)}$, n, and θ, interact. One way to describe the interaction is as follows: The effect of $Po_{(1,0)}$ on performance is controlled by n, and this control is, in turn, magnified by low θ values.

Unequal θ values. Equal θs are merely a simplification and not required by theory. Figure 5-12 holds the instrumental-rate parameter θ_r constant at .5 and allows θ_o to vary from .05 to .95. Other parameter values are shown in the figure. Reversing the procedure, Figure 5-13 holds the observing-response parameter θ_o constant and allows θ_r to vary. Note that the curves for $\theta_o = .95$ and .7 are not in the expected order. This is a random error and indicates that stat-children, like ordinary children, sometimes misbe-

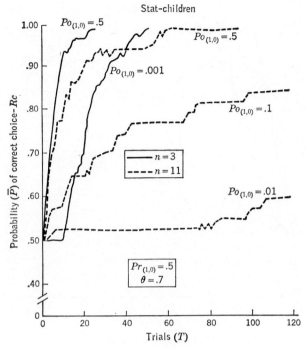

Figure 5-11. θ value equal to .7.

Figure 5-12. Effects of variation in the observing-response parameter θ_o.

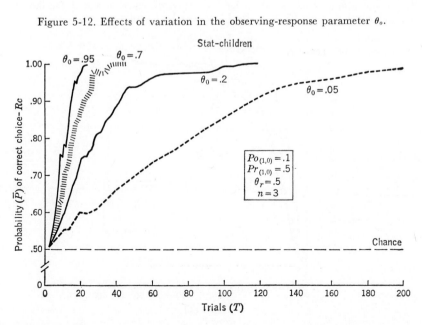

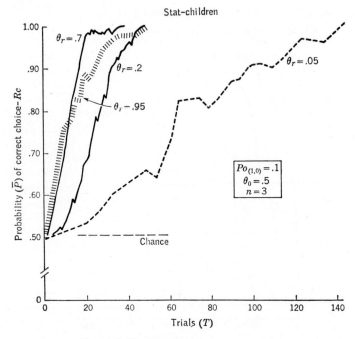

Figure 5-13. Changing the parameter θ_r.

Figure 5-14. Effects on stat-children performance of unequal ratios of irrelevant observing-response probabilities, with other parameters constant.

$Po_{(2,0)}$ and $Po_{(3,0)}$ equal .6 and .3 for the 2:1 ratio, equal .8 and .1 for the 8:1 ratio, and equal .85 and .05, respectively, for the 17:1 ratio.

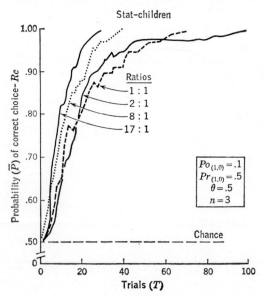

have. Correcting such errors requires the mean of a larger number of subjects.

Unequal irrelevant $Po_{(i,0)}$. For previous theoretical curves, values of irrelevant observing-response probabilities have all been equal within a condition. If, for example, there were three dimensions, with the relevant dimension having a starting probability of .1 of being observed, then the two irrelevant observing-response probabilities—$Po_{(2,0)}$ and $Po_{(3,0)}$—would be equal at .45. This condition is plotted in Figure 5-14 with other parameters as indicated. If the ratio of $Po_{(2,0)}$ to $Po_{(3,0)}$ is changed to 8:1, holding everything else constant, Figure 5-14 shows the rate of learning to be enhanced. This result may seem surprising. One might expect that the competition of a relatively strong irrelevant observing response would

Figure 5-15. Reversal of a discrimination for three groups of 20 stat-children with various θ values. $Pr_{(1,0)}$ for all groups has been set at zero.

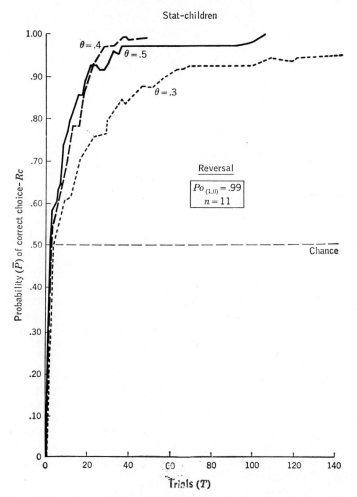

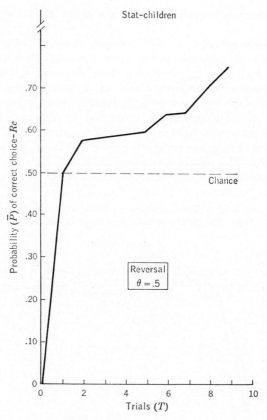

Figure 5-16. First 10 trials of the $\theta = .5$ function of Figure 5-15 replotted with an expanded abscissa.

interfere with the growth of the relevant observing response. But the theory predicts the opposite. Increasing the ratio to 17 : 1 makes the learning even faster. This interesting prediction of the model is testable with carefully arranged transfer paradigms.

$Pr_{(1,0)}$ **and reversals.** Under experimental conditions of original learning, the initial instrumental probability of approaching the positive cue, $Pr_{(1,0)}$, is at the chance value of .5, since the experimenter usually designates the positive cue randomly. There exists, however, a common transfer operation—simple discrimination reversal—that brings $Pr_{(1,0)}$ down to zero or approximately so, depending upon the strength of prereversal learning. Too large a number of families of reversal learning curves can be plotted for the various combinations of parameter values, so one set has been selected for its unusual properties and eventual relation to data. Figure 5-15 presents reversal learning curves for $n = 11$ and three values of θ. Initial probability of observing the relevant dimension is always high for reversals following learning to a stringent criterion, so $Po_{(1,0)}$ has been set at .99 in Figure 5-15.

All the functions in Figure 5-15 rise quickly from the initial probability near zero at the start of reversal, reaching chance level in a trial or two after which the curves decelerate sharply. Although it may be difficult to see in Figure 5-15, these functions tend to flatten somewhat in the middle. More precisely, they begin with negative acceleration, change to positive, then revert again to negative. This tendency we have tentatively labeled a "reversal midplateau," perhaps a questionable label because the plateau is not always flat. Figure 5-16 is a replot of the first 10 trials of the $\theta = .5$ function with an expanded abscissa that accentuates the curvatures in question.

The cause of the reversal midplateau is the extinction of the relevant observing response. The development of this inattention is shown graphically in Figure 5-17, a plot of the expected operator approximations of $\bar{P}_{(T)}$ along with $\bar{P}o_{(1,T)}$ and $\bar{P}r_{(1,T)}$ for the parameters indicated. Note the rapid extinction of the relevant observing response during the early trials as the subject picks up the once positive, but now negative, stimulus.

The midplateau is strongly controlled by θ and n and to some extent

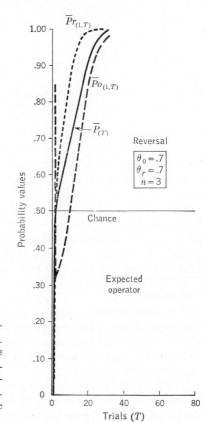

Figure 5-17. Expected operator approximation of theoretical reversal learning $\bar{P}_T$. Also plotted are the theoretical determinants of $\bar{P}_T$ as well as the probabilities of a relevant observing response and correct instrumental response ($\bar{P}o_{(1,T)}$ and $\bar{P}r_{(1,T)}$, respectively). Starting values are those of Figure 5-15.

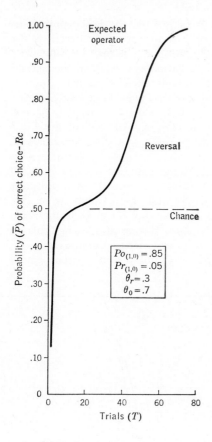

Figure 5-18. Expected operator approximation of a theoretical reversal function with parameter values that accentuate the reversal midplateau.

by starting probabilities. High values of θ_o together with low values of θ_r amplify the effect, as do large values of n. Figure 5-18 shows an extreme case.

The presence or absence of this unusual effect should be of assistance in the problem of parameter estimation, since only certain combinations of parameters predict it. Furthermore, we do not know of any other quantitative theories which predict this phenomenon, so its occurrence in data should have special probative value for the theory.

Variability

For each trial the computer program prints out a mean and standard deviation of the individual probabilities of a correct response for a group of stat-children as well as a series of zeros and ones indicating a correct or incorrect response for each stat-child. Figure 5-19 shows the relation of these three measures.

The function labeled *zero-one* represents the proportion of stat-children making the correct response. It is, of course, much more irregular than the mean probability curve, having an additional source of random variation. It corresponds, in this respect, more closely to raw data. Such correspondence, while desirable, makes comparison of trends difficult. Trial-by-trial variability of percentage correct response for retardate performance is often great enough to require averaging percentages over blocks of trials to reduce random variability and uncover trends. When this is done, we appropriately compare the data with the mean probability curve of stat-children.

The random variability of mean stat-children functions can be reduced by taking larger and larger samples. Figure 5-20 allows an estimate of the order of magnitude of reduction in random error by comparing the

Figure 5-19. Three measures of stat-child performance: mean probability $\overline{P}_{(T)}$ of a group of 30, the standard deviation of $\overline{P}_{(T)}$ values of the group, and the proportion of stat-children making the correct choice (*zero-one* function). A different group of 30 was used for making the zero-one calculations.

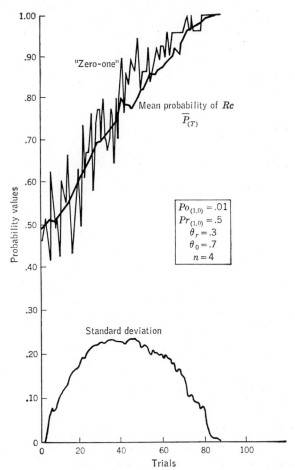

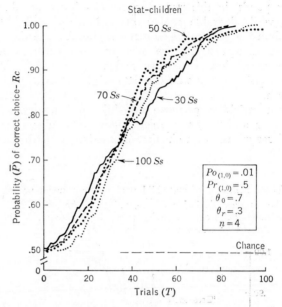

Figure 5-20. Mean *P* functions for groups of 30, 50, 70, and 100 stat-children under the parameter conditions indicated.

mean probability functions of four groups of 30, 50, 70, and 100 stat-children. The maximum difference between the 30 and 100 cases is less than .10 for these arbitrarily selected parameter values. Since we are not yet at the stage of precise parameter estimation, we have not run large numbers of stat-children under each of the various parameter conditions.

Backward curves for stat-children

Theoretical effects of parameters, up to this point, have been shown using standard forward learning curves. It is also possible to program a computer for *backward* stat-children functions as well. We begin by showing the influence of differences in starting probabilities of observing the relevant stimulus dimension. For three widely different values of $Po_{(1,0)}$, Figure 5-21 graphs backward learning curves for three groups of stat-children reaching criterion. The position of the functions on the abscissa is that of the median subject. Note that the three functions have almost identical forms and, with the exception of lateral displacement, are almost equivalent. The contrast with forward learning curves (Figure 5-9) is marked.

The effects on backward curves of two other parameters, θ and n, appear in Figure 5-22. Four parameter conditions are presented for $n = 3$ and 11 and $\theta = .3$ and .7. From left to right, the first two functions are backward curves for all the stat-children reaching criterion of $P_{(T)} = .99$ on the first day with $\theta = .3$. Only a single stat-child of a group of 20 under the $n = 11$ condition achieved criterion, and its $P_{(T)}$ function is plotted as the solid line. When the number of dimensions was reduced to three, the number of stat-children reaching criterion increased to five. The backward curve of these five is shown next as the dotted line. The final portions of these functions overlap.

The next pair of curves differs from the first only in the value of θ, which has been changed to .7. A total of 6 subjects reaches criterion in the first day under the $n = 11$ condition, while 15 achieve criterion under the $n = 3$ condition. These two functions differ only slightly, and not at all in the final portions; but both differ from the $\theta = .3$ functions in final rates of approach to asymptote.

The two pairs of functions at the right in Figure 5-22 represent the same parameter conditions as the first two pairs, but these are backward curves for stat-children reaching criterion on the second day of training (trials 26 to 50). The same conclusions can be drawn from these plots. For backward curves, the parameters, $Po_{(1,0)}$ and n, affect lateral placement of backward functions but not the final slopes. The θ parameter, on the other hand, is directly related to final slopes. Other relations of parameters to backward learning curves will be presented when needed later in relation to data presentation.

Figure 5-21. Backward discrimination learning curves for three groups of stat-children varying in initial probability of attending to the relevant dimension.

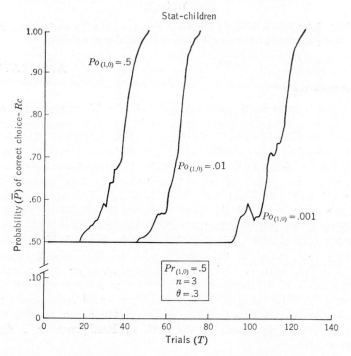

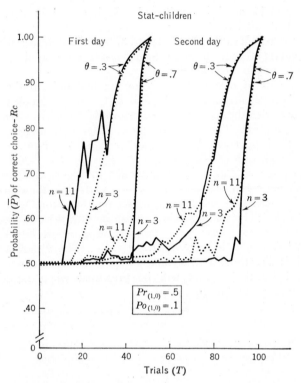

Figure 5-22. Joint effects of the parameters θ and n on mean performance of stat-children reaching criterion on either the first or second day of training.

APPLICATIONS

Original learning

The learning curves in Figures 5-3 and 5-4 of subjects separated on the basis of trials to criterion appear to differ in length of initial chance-level plateau rather than in slope of final approach to asymptote. This is taken as an encouraging sign that backward learning curves may be computed without doing violence to the forms of individual learning curves.

Differences in number of trials to criterion, such as those shown in Figures 5-3 and 5-4, could have been produced by temporary random differences in attention of the kind exhibited by groups of stat-children with identical starting parameter values. However, the wide range of intelligence among these subjects makes it likely that individual parameter differences contributed to the results, with brighter subjects appearing among the fast learners and duller subjects affecting mostly the slow learning curves. If so, there is no evidence that subjects differed in rate of learning, θ; differences in $Po_{(1,0)}$ and/or n could have produced the distribution of curves shown. More direct evidence can be obtained by comparing groups separated on the basis of intelligence as is done in the next section.

Intelligence

In Figure 5-5 it may be seen that subjects separated according to intelligence produce backward learning curves which differ in lateral position but not in final rate of approach to asymptote. While the effects of intelligence on performance level are statistically reliable (House & Zeaman, 1960a), statistics provide no standard method for deciding which of the parameters vary with intelligence. From the similar final rates we infer that there were negligible differences in θ among the subjects. Families of curves such as those shown in Figure 5-5 could be produced by variation in $Po_{(1,0)}$ or n or some combination of the two factors. A bit of rational argument is needed to determine which is the most likely source of differences.

Suppose that our retardates tend initially to attend to certain easy dimensions, such as position, to the exclusion of almost all others. This would make $Po_{(1,0)}$ very low for color-form discriminations and account for the results. If, to pursue the contrary argument, we suppose that the parameter n is responsible for the results, we must then assume that our high-MA group attends to *fewer* dimensions than the lower-MA group. This assumption violates our intuitive notion that brighter subjects are able to discriminate more aspects of the surround than are duller subjects. We conclude that low-MA subjects have lower initial probabilities of observing color and form than high-MA subjects. Further consequences of assuming that subjects of low developmental level attend to fewer (and easier) dimensions are elaborated later in a general discussion of the relationships of theoretical parameters to retardation.

Stimulus factors

If the trouble with retardates' discrimination learning lies in their initial inattention to the stimulus dimensions we happen to choose as relevant, then logically the effects of low intelligence could be minimized by selecting relevant stimuli having high initial attention value. *Position* would certainly be a case in point, and it is true that retardates have little trouble learning position discriminations; in trainables with MAs in the 2–4 year range, position discriminations are learned with fewer than three errors on the average (House & Zeaman, 1959). Multidimensional object discrimination represents another instance, and the fast learning of this problem (Figure 5-6) shows "junk" to have high attention value also.

In general, the discrimination difficulty scale, for combinations of color and form as well as object and pattern, established in Figure 5-6 is interpreted to reflect differences in $Po_{(i,0)}$ for the various dimensions. It could, of course, be true that dimensions not likely to be noticed might also be those hard to learn, in which case easy dimensions would have not only high Pos but high θs as well. The shapes of the functions in Figure 5-6 weigh against this possibility, since, regardless of difficulty, the final rates of approach to asymptote (controlled mostly by θ) do not vary appreciably.

Other stimulus factors will be considered in a later section.

Transfer operations

The *attention hypothesis* (that retardates suffer from low initial probability of observing certain relevant dimensions rather than from poor ability to learn which of two observed cues is correct) is to us a hopeful and exciting notion because it leads so quickly to a search for experimental operations that may change $Po_{(1,0)}$ and hence accelerate discriminations of subjects who might otherwise seem to be natively and irreversibly poor discriminators.

Many transfer operations have been discovered that do control $Po_{(1,0)}$. Perhaps the most dramatic is object-to-pattern transfer (House & Zeaman, 1960b). Color-form pattern discriminations are difficult (see Figure 5-6), while color-form object discriminations are easy. When the easy object discrimination was used to focus attention on the relevant color-form dimensions, we found that attention then transferred strongly to the difficult pattern problem.

Object-to-pattern transfer. Three matched groups of retardates (MA 2–6 years) were employed in this experiment: (1) The P-1 group was trained to discriminate between two-dimensional patterns, such as a red cross and blue triangle. (2) The O-1:P-1 group learned two problems: first a color-form object discrimination (O-1), such as a three-dimensional red cross versus a three-dimensional blue triangle, and second a pattern discrimination (P-1) with the same positive and negative color-form cues— a flat red cross versus a flat blue triangle. (3) Group O-2:P-1 also learned two problems, an object discrimination followed by a pattern, except that in this case the positive and negative cues of the object discrimination were different colors and forms from those of the pattern discrimination; e.g., green square versus black circle in the object discrimination shifted to red cross versus blue triangle in the pattern.

Figure 5-23 presents the results of this experiment in the form of backward learning curves for the three groups. Of the 19 subjects in the P-1 group, only 4 learned within the 500 trials allowed; and their backward learning curve is shown at the far right. In the O-1:P-1 group, 13 of the 19 subjects achieved criterion on the original object discrimination (O-1) and then were placed on the corresponding pattern discrimination (P-1). All 13 learned the pattern with the backward learning curve shown at the far left.

In the O-2:P-1 group, 14 of the 22 subjects learned the object discrimination (O-2) and were then shifted to the pattern problem (P-1). Of this group of 14 subjects, 10 learned the pattern problem. Their backward learning curve is the middlemost function in Figure 5-23.

What do these findings mean theoretically? In the O-1:P-1 condition, the objects and patterns not only have the same relevant color-form dimension (making $Po_{(1,0)}$ high for subjects as they enter P-1), but the specific cues of the relevant color-form dimension are also largely the same for object and pattern (making $Pr_{(1,0)}$ high also for the second problem). With transfer of both instrumental and observing responses, there is little learning left to do under the pattern discrimination of this group to bring P to criterion [see Eq. (5-1)].

In the O-2:P-1 condition we should expect transfer of the relevant observing response but not the correct instrumental response R_1. This follows from the dimensional nature of attention and the greater specificity of approach-avoidance tendencies. Changing the specific color-form characteristics but keeping color-form relevant allows $Po_{(1,0)}$ to remain high, while $Pr_{(1,0)}$ goes to the chance level of one-half as the subject faces new positive and negative cues without having been trained previously to approach or to avoid them. Equation (5-1) tells us that this group must start at a chance level of performance (because $Pr_{(1,0)} = .5$), and Figures 5-9 to 5-11 show that the high value of $Po_{(1,0)}$ will tend to allow for rapid improvement in performance.

The relative locations and shapes of the curves in Figure 5-23 are theoretically accountable allowing variations of $Po_{(1,0)}$ and $Pr_{(1,0)}$ in the predicted directions. No precise parameter estimations have been made for the data, but even these semiquantitative predictions are better than those which follow from other discrimination theories.

From both the theoretical and applied points of view a dramatic aspect of this experiment was that a discrimination which could not be taught by prolonged differential reinforcement could be taught by harnessing some of the dynamics of attention.

Object-to-pattern transfer is a special case of a more general class of experimental operations that achieves high starting probabilities of attention

Figure 5-23. Object-to-pattern transfer. Backward learning curves of a pattern group (far right) and two object-to-pattern transfer groups (at the left) show large transfer effects attributable to attention.

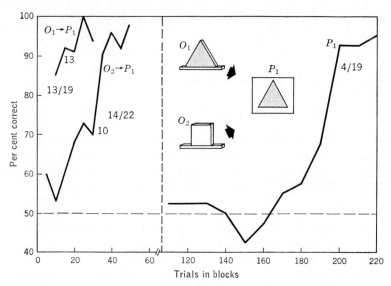

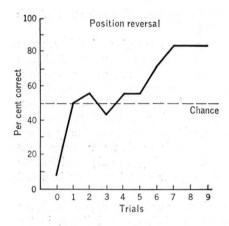

Figure 5-24. Position reversal data for a group of 24 retardates.

to the relevant dimension—the class of intradimensional shifts. Other instances of intradimensional shifts will be described presently.

Reversal. Another more usual method of achieving high $Po_{(1,0)}$ is that of discrimination reversal, or switching the roles of the positive and negative cues. Associating reinforcement with the previously negative stimulus object does two things theoretically: it leaves $Po_{(1,0)}$ undisturbed, and high, if the prereversal learning nears completion; but it reduces the instrumental response probability $Pr_{(1,0)}$ to the complement of its prereversal level, that is, to a value approaching zero after a well-learned original discrimination.

Thus, there should result a positive transfer tendency to the reversal problem from the carry-over of a high $Po_{(1,0)}$, and a negative transfer tendency from the low $Pr_{(1,0)}$. The net result or balance of the two effects is dependent upon specific parameter values, chiefly θ_o and θ_r. The system is therefore capable of predicting either an overall positive, negative, or zero transfer on the reversal problem, assuming different rate constants. From this, it can be seen that until we arrive at the stage of borrowing parameters fixed in earlier experimentation, no critical test of attention theory can be made by comparing speed of reversal learning with that of original learning or other transfer conditions.

Fortunately, among the many possible predictions made by the theory about reversal learning, there are some unusual ones made about the shapes of reversal curves. Certain combinations of parameters yield reversal functions featuring a midplateau as shown in Figures 5-16 and 5-18. It is sufficient for our present purposes to demonstrate that such unusual curve shapes do occur under some experimental conditions of reversal learning.

Figure 5-24 is a forward learning curve for the reversal of a position discrimination for a group of trainables (MA2–6). A section of positive acceleration in the middle of this function is clear. The criterion of learning required by this particular study (Zeaman & House, 1962) was less stringent than usual—six successive correct responses. Data are available, however, from a position reversal problem in which a more severe criterion was adopted (House & Zeaman, 1959)—ten successive correct responses—

and the reversal learning curve for this condition is shown in Figure 5-25. Note that with the more stringent criterion the positive acceleration is less apparent.

Having shown that the criterion stringency exercises some control over the midplateau, we ask whether this control can be explained theoretically. Figure 5-26 shows that it can. Plotted are theoretical reversal functions with fixed parameters $\theta = .7$, $n = 5$, $Pr_{(1,0)} = 0$; the parameter $Po_{(1,0)}$ is varied with values .99 for the upper curves and .5 for the lower. Solid lines are means of 20 stat-children; dotted lines represent the expected operator approximation. Reducing the value of $Po_{(1,0)}$ makes the midplateau more pronounced. This effect is discernible in both the expected operator and the stat-child plots, even though there are sizable discrepancies in magnitude between the two approximations.

A step in the logic has been omitted. To complete the theoretical analysis of the differences between Figures 5-25 and 5-26, we need to say why it is reasonable to assume that differences in the learning criterion should produce differences in $Po_{(1,0)}$. The reasoning is not involved. A more stringent criterion for original learning tends to make both the relevant observing response and the correct instrumental response stronger at the conclusion of the original learning problem. But $Pr_{(1,T)}$ approaches unity faster than $Po_{(1,T)}$ for all cases of equal θs and $n > 2$. For this reason, overlearning trials will likely be acting to bring $Po_{(1,T)}$ toward unity after $Pr_{(1,T)} = 1.0$. Therefore, a stringent criterion will tend to make $Po_{(1,0)}$ closer to 1 to start reversal, while a weaker criterion makes $Po_{(1,0)} < 1.0$.

No systematic attempt has yet been made to find the best parameter combinations for these empirical reversal functions. If equal θs are assumed, then $\theta = .7$ is the right order of magnitude for n values near 5. However, to achieve the degree of positive acceleration exhibited by Figure 5-25 would require unequal θs with $\theta_o > \theta_r$.

Another indication that reversal midplateaus occur under other experimental conditions is given in Figure 5-27. In this study (Clack & Zeaman 1960), original learning and reversal problems are solved by a group of re-

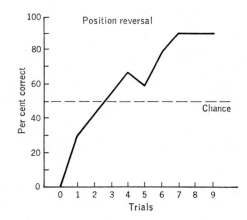

Figure 5-25. Position reversal data for a group of 16 trainable retardates required to reach a more stringent criterion of original learning than the subjects whose data are plotted in Figure 5-24.

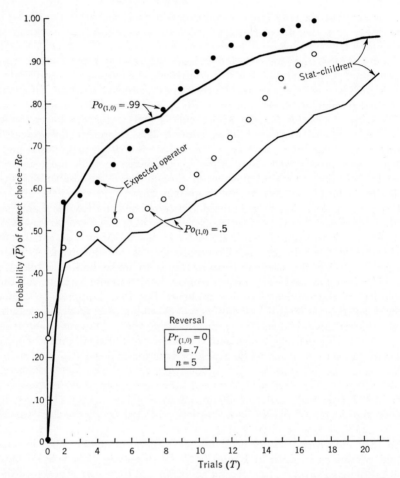

Figure 5-26. Effects of different levels of original learning on theoretical reversal functions. Starting reversal with a well-learned observing response $(Po_{(1,0)} = .99)$ tends to produce less of a midplateau than starting with a relatively weak observing response $(Po_{(1,0)} = .5)$.

tardates and a group of normal children matched for **MA** (2–4 years). Random schedules are employed in this position discrimination experiment. Candy rewards are available on 75 per cent of the trials in one position and 25 per cent in the other. During reversal, the position previously receiving 75 per cent reinforcement now gets 25 per cent. The midplateau is strikingly clear in the reversal function of the normal group. Positive acceleration is also present in the retardate curve, but the initial sharp rise from trial 0 of reversal is obscured by retention loss during a month's gap in training for this group.

We have not yet presented the submodel of the theory which handles schedules of reinforcement, but Figure 5-27 clearly sets a requirement for such a model. It must predict reversal midplateaus for some parameter combinations. A discussion of this point is left for a later section.

Intradimensional and extradimensional shifts. Two transfer operations providing strong but differential control of initial observing response probabilities are intradimensional and extradimensional shifts. For an intradimensional shift, the subject is given, after original learning, a new pair of irrelevant dimension to relevant. From color relevant, we might shift to original learning. Repeating an example given earlier, if blue and yellow were the relevant cues during training, red and green might be the new cues during intradimensional color shift. If, as we have assumed, attention operates on entire dimensions, there should be no loss in probability of observing the new cues. The instrumental approach probabilities, however, go to chance level since the new positive stimulus is designated randomly. Consequently, at the start of intradimensional shift, $Po_{(1,0)}$ should be high, and $Pr_{(1,0)}$ at .5. Most of the learning to be done after intradimensional shift is, therefore, instrumental.

In contrast, the operation of extradimensional shift changes a previously irrelevant dimension to relevant. From color relevant, we might shift to form. The result is, of course, a low $Po_{(1,0)}$ and a chance level $Pr_{(1,0)}$. Table 5-2 summarizes the conditions of starting probabilities for five different problems. The question marks in the table designate probabilities that vary from problem to problem. "High" and "low" approximate unity and zero, respectively, depending upon the performance criterion adopted for pretransfer learning. The oddity problem is discussed later.

Figure 5-27. Original learning and reversal of a position discrimination problem with 75 per cent (random) reinforcement of the correct response and 25 per cent reinforcement of the incorrect response. Both retarded and normal subjects were run. Performance is measured as the group mean percentage choice of the more reinforced position. Of interest is the evidence of a midplateau in the reversal functions.

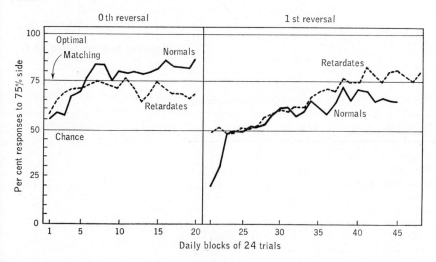

A study has been done comparing performances of matched groups of retardates on intradimensional shift, extradimensional shift, and reversal problems (Zeaman & House, 1962) following a high degree of overlearning. From Table 5-2, some predictions can be made about the relative difficulty of these three problems. If starting probabilities are the only factors differentiating the problems (our working hypothesis), both extradimensional shift and reversal problems should be more difficult than intradimensional shift. Strictly speaking, other comparisons are indeterminate without a knowledge of parameter values. However, with the high degree of overlearning used in the experiment, reversal should be facilitated and extradimensional shift retarded. A reasonable guess, then, is that the problems should rank themselves in order of increasing difficulty: intradimensional shift, reversal, and extradimensional shift.

The expected shapes of the individual discrimination learning curves can also be deduced for the three conditions. Both the intradimensional shift and reversal curves should begin to rise immediately with negative acceleration; the extradimensional shift curve should have an initial tendency to remain at chance, followed by a period of positive acceleration.

In the experiment in which we compared performance on these three problems (Zeaman & House, 1962), three matched groups in the MA 6–8 range were given original training in discrimination of objects differing in only one dimension, either color or form. If form was relevant, then two values of the irrelevant color dimension were varied every trial in random association with the positive and negative cues. This means that the positive stimulus might be either a green square or a red square, for instance, and the negative stimulus either a red triangle or a green triangle.

Following an original learning problem with form relevant for some subjects and color relevant for others, the three groups were transferred to a reversal, an intradimensional-shift, or an extradimensional-shift condition. Table 5-3 illustrates a set of possible stimulus arrangements for the first

TABLE 5-2

Starting probabilities of O_1 and R_1

Problems	Starting probabilities	
	Relevant observing response $(Po_{(1,0)})$	Correct instrumental response $(Pr_{(1,0)})$
Original learning	?	.5
Reversal	High	Low
Intradimensional shift	High	.5
Extradimensional shift	Low	.5
Oddity	?	High

three trials of the four problems for subjects learning originally a form-relevant discrimination.

The data from the experiment are presented in Figure 5-28 in the form of backward learning curves. The median subject in both the intradimensional-shift and reversal conditions reached criterion within the first day's allotment of 25 trials, while the median subject of the extradimensional-shift group took 3 days to learn. Trials have been blocked in fives to achieve enough stability to see the major trends in the data. Differences among the three conditions are statistically significant, and in the expected direction. The forms of the functions also agree roughly with theoretical predictions. Figure 5-29 graphs the performances of three groups of stat-children with parameters appropriate for the three experimental conditions. There are not a lot of completely free parameters here. Since all the subjects were brought to a strong criterion of original learning, the starting probabilities are restricted in their range. $Po_{(1,0)}$ must approach unity for the intradimensional-shift and reversal conditions, which implies that $Po_{(1,0)}$ must be near zero for the extradimensional-shift group. The rules of experimentation fix $Pr_{(1,0)}$ at .5 for the intra- and extradimensional shifts, and at 0 for reversal (given a P near one at the end of original learning). The irrelevant observing-response probabilities are both necessarily very small at the start of reversal and intradimensional shift, whereas one of the irrelevant observing-response probabilities must be very high in the extra-dimensional-shift condition. In Figure 5-29 we have used $Po_{(2,0)} = .98$ and $Po_{(3,0)} = Po_{(1,0)} = .01$. This was a slight mistake; we should have had $Po_{(2,0)} = .99$ and the other two probabilities at .005 to be consistent with the other two curves. Reducing $Po_{(1,0)}$ to .005 might have shifted the extra-dimensional-shift curve to the right.

There is nothing in the data to tell us how many dimensions are operat-

TABLE 5-3

A sample of stimulus arrangements for original learning and three transfer problems on several trials

Trial no.	Original learning		Reversal		Intradimensional shift		Extradimensional shift	
1	(+) Green square	(−) Red circle	(+) Green circle	(−) Red square	(+) Red triangle	(−) Green T	(−) Green square	(+) Red circle
2	(−) Green circle	(+) Red square	(−) Red square	(+) Green circle	(+) Green triangle	(−) Red T	(+) Red square	(−) Green circle
3	(−) Red circle	(+) Green square	(−) Green square	(+) Red circle	(−) Red T	(+) Green triangle	(−) Green circle	(+) Red square

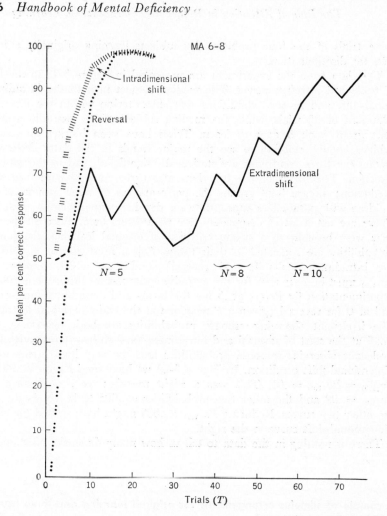

Figure 5-28. Backward learning curves for three groups of retardates in the intra-dimensional-shift, reversal, and extradimensional-shift conditions. Mean percentages of correct choices are plotted for blocks of five trials. Broken lines connect the initial block with the starting level for each condition.

The number of subjects contributing data to various sections of the extradimensional-shift group function diminishes from 10 to 5.

ing, nor are there yet any strong rational grounds for fixing the range of the parameter n, so we have tried out a number of different values of n in combination with values of θ. Three dimensions and $\theta = .3$ give a rough approximation of the data as may be seen by comparing Figures 5-28 and 5-29. We have shown earlier that the slopes of the later portions of the discrimination learning curves are largely controlled by the θ parameter. The slopes displayed in Figure 5-28 are roughly accommodated by θs of the magnitude .3. This may be an underestimation of θ since methods for obtaining empirical backward curves result in less steep functions than methods used with stat-children. This difference arises from the necessity for measuring criterion performance over blocks of trials for empirical data.

The correspondence of theory and data given by a comparison of Figures 5-28 and 5-29 is encouraging. The points of largest discrepancy occur in the extradimensional-shift curve, especially in the early portions. The few unusually high points occurring here may be random fluctuations because the points are based on relatively few measurements. Although ten subjects contributed to the extradimensional curve, only five had data extending

Figure 5-29. Theoretical curves for intradimensional-shift, reversal, and extradimensional-shift problems.

Performances of three groups of 20 stat-children are plotted as backward learning curves except for the first two points of each function which come from forward learning curve calculations. The lateral positioning of the curves is that of the median subject in each group. Parameter values common to all three curves are indicated as are the distinctive parameters for each condition.

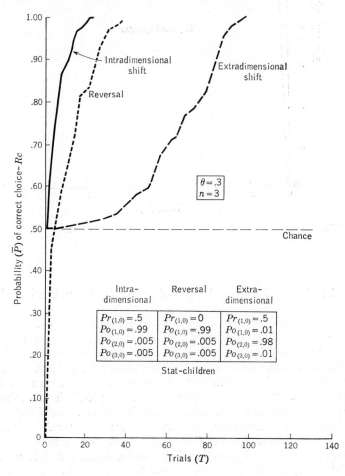

Intradimensional shift

Reversal

Extradimensional shift

$\theta = .3$
$n = 3$

Chance

	Intra-dimensional	Reversal	Extra-dimensional
	$Pr_{(1,0)} = .5$	$Pr_{(1,0)} = 0$	$Pr_{(1,0)} = .5$
	$Po_{(1,0)} = .99$	$Po_{(1,0)} = .99$	$Po_{(1,0)} = .01$
	$Po_{(2,0)} = .005$	$Po_{(2,0)} = .005$	$Po_{(2,0)} = .98$
	$Po_{(3,0)} = .005$	$Po_{(3,0)} = .005$	$Po_{(3,0)} = .01$

Stat-children

Probability ($\bar{P}$) of correct choice- Rc

Trials (T)

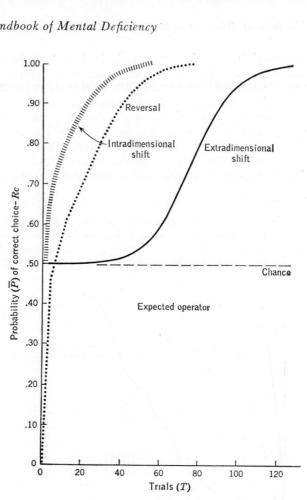

Figure 5-30. Expected operator approximations for the three transfer conditions. Parameter combinations are the same as those of Figure 5-29.

backward 3 days (75 trials). As a result, the first five points include data from only five subjects.

Figure 5-30 displays the expected operator curves with the same parameter combinations as those of the stat-children in Figure 5-29. While the two sets of functions in Figures 5-29 and 5-30 are by no means identical, the formal and quantitative similarities are great enough to accept each as an approximation of the other for the particular parameters needed here.

A question of interest not answered by Figure 5-28 is the relation of original learning and extradimensional shift. It will be recalled that some of the subjects in the extradimensional condition are transferred to a form and some to a color discrimination. The original learning of both these single cue problems is slower than that of the extradimensional-shift conditions. While intuitively the extradimensional shift may seem to be a negative transfer condition, we have shown earlier that such an intuition does not necessarily agree with the theory. Having a single, strong, competing irrelevant observing response may be theoretically facilitating (cf. Figure 5-14). If, in fact, the two irrelevant observing responses were of equal strength at .495 instead of having one strong cue at .98 and one at .01 for the extradimensional-shift stat-children (Figure 5-29), the extradimensional curve would have been shifted 25 trials to the right and would have had a longer chance portion.

The superiority of intradimensional shifts over extradimensional shifts has been demonstrated in variants of the present design by Kurtz (1955) and Eckstrand and Wickens (1954) with college students, and by Bensberg (1958) with retardates. In summary, it seems conservative to remark that attention theory can handle many aspects of the data from these three transfer operations—intradimensional shift, reversal, and extradimensional shift—as well as from original learning. And no obvious disconfirming evidence has turned up.

Other factors controlling attention

Investigations of stimulus variables of greater complexity than those previously mentioned have led us to infer that some of these factors may also exert control of initial attention—$Po_{(1,0)}$. Stimulus novelty is one striking factor.

Novelty. It has been shown in an illustrative experiment that the introduction of one novel stimulus in place of one of the familiar stimuli can bring about sudden and unexpected learning of discriminations apparently too difficult for some of our subjects (Zeaman, House, & Orlando, 1958). These results were not attributable to simple preference for or aversion to novel or familiar stimuli since both novel positive *and* novel negative cues produced facilitation. Novelty and familiarity appear to be discriminable aspects of stimuli. Theoretically, novelty enhances $Po_{(1,0)}$.

This is not to say that novelty cannot also be a preferred aspect in some contexts, and thus raise $Pr_{(1,0)}$ above chance. Such an effect appeared unexpectedly in an experiment designed to discover the relative effects of reward and nonreward in the discrimination learning of the moderately retarded (House & Zeaman, 1958b). A technique was employed of presenting a *single* stimulus, either positive or negative, on the first trial of a junk-object discrimination problem. On the second and subsequent trials both positive and negative stimuli appeared in the standard two-choice, simultaneous procedure. After being forced on the first trial to choose the *negative* stimulus without reinforcement, subjects then strongly preferred, on the second trial, the *positive* (and novel) stimulus. For the converse operation, after an initial forced choice of the positive stimulus with reinforcement, the children preferred the negative (and novel) stimulus on the following trial. The results appear in Figure 5-31. Each of 14 subjects was tested with the above procedures on 30 different junk discrimination problems for each of the two conditions: (1) positive (as labeled in Figure 5-31), i.e., forced initially to choose the single positive stimulus with reinforcement, and (2) negative, i.e., forced to choose the negative stimulus with-

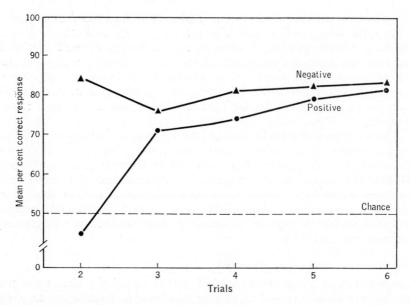

Figure 5-31. Discrimination learning curves for the positive and negative conditions. The funnel shape of the two functions is interpreted as the result of a tendency to attend to and approach novel stimuli.

out reinforcement. Results are most easily explained as a tendency on trial 2 to approach the novel stimulus, regardless of whether the familiar stimulus had been rewarded or not rewarded on the first trial. Similar findings of attraction to a novel stimulus have been reported in primate subjects (e.g., Harlow & Hicks, 1957).

The conclusion presented with our introduction of this assemblage of data can be repeated: Novelty is not only a discriminable aspect of stimuli exercising strong control over attention *Po*, but it also may be a preferred aspect, theoretically acting on *Pr*.

The effects of novelty present us with a paradox, resolvable only by assuming attention to be a central process. The reasoning is straightforward. A stimulus cannot be judged novel except in relation to a prior series or background of nonnovel (familiar) stimuli. But such a judgment must require that the subject have some trace, record, or engram of previous (familiar) stimuli to contrast with the present novel cue. If seeing novelty requires some record of previous stimulation, then the previous stimulation must have gotten past at least the peripheral stages of sensory reception. We are forced to conclude that subjects who fail discriminations because of inattention are nevertheless storing stimulus information somewhere. Attention is, therefore, a central process.

Reward as a cue controlling attention. Candy has high attention value for our subjects but cannot act as a cue since it follows rather than precedes discriminative behavior. Shepp (1960) has presented evidence that anticipatory responses—candy expectations—may precede choice and provide distinctive cue feedback.

In one experiment Shepp used two kinds of candy—a miniature marshmallow and a Hershey chocolate Kiss—with trainable subjects (MA 2–4). One group (successive-D) of 16 subjects learned a successive junk discrimination with one kind of candy always on the left and the other always on the right. In a typical problem, if two identical soap dishes were present, the subject would find a marshmallow on the left, nothing on the right; if two pot covers were present, the subject would find a Hershey Kiss on the right, nothing on the left. As shown in Figure 5-32, this group learned considerably faster than the successive-R group (16 subjects) which had marshmallows and Hershey Kisses placed randomly left or right. According to Shepp's analysis, position cues act as part of a relevant stimulus compound, i.e., soap dish, left, and pot cover, right. When the kind of candy is perfectly correlated with position, distinctive anticipatory responses add differential cues to the compounds, i.e., marshmallow and soap dish, left, and Hershey Kiss and pot cover, right. The high attention value of these implicit candy expectations is shown by the superiority of the successive-D over the successive-R group.

Two other matched groups were run on a simultaneous junk problem, 16 under the experimental condition of candy-position correlation (simultaneous-D) and 16 under a control condition with a single kind of candy

Figure 5-32. Cumulative percentages of subjects at criterion under five of Shepp's experimental conditions. Differences among the conditions provide evidence for inferring that rewards may serve as strong cues.

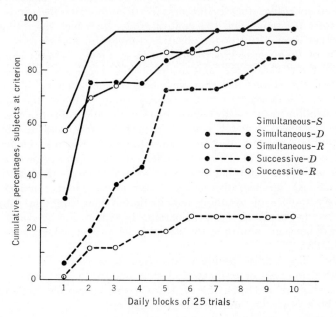

(simultaneous-S). Data were also available with 58 comparable subjects under another control condition with random selections of candy (simultaneous-R). For these simultaneous problems, the correlation of kind of candy with position adds distinct anticipatory cues which are irrelevant, hence detrimental to learning. Significant differences in favor of the two control conditions appear during the first daily block of 25 trials and then tend to disappear, providing some further confirmation of theoretical expectations.

This experiment has been replicated by Shepp using more difficult discriminanda (color-form object) with even clearer results, again in the expected directions. As evidence that rewards act as potent cues and controllers of attention, these findings are clearly reliable, but still largely indirect and inferential. More evidence of the cue power of rewards comes from another experiment by Shepp in which distinctive candies were used experimentally as *both* cues and reinforcements.

On one wedge a colored M & M candy was mounted, on the other a miniature marshmallow was encased in clear plastic. The experimenter selected one of these as the positive stimulus, the other as negative. Under the positive stimulus, a candy (either a marshmallow or M & M) was hidden, and under the negative stimulus, there was, of course, nothing. This task can be classified as a candy-object discrimination with candy reinforcement.

Shepp ran three groups of 13 children (MA 2–5): (1) group PC in which there was a positive correlation between discriminanda and incentives, that is, the positive stimulus and the incentive were the same kind of candy; (2) group NC having a negative correlation between discriminanda and incentive, that is, the negative stimulus and the candy used as reward were the same; and (3) control group, for which the incentive was unlike either the positive or the negative stimulus in color or form.

Results of these three groups are shown in Figure 5-33. It can be seen that when the reward is the same as the positive cue, learning is particularly fast. When the reward matches the negative cue, learning is slow. Both comparisons are in relation to the control group in which the candy cues bear no relation to the candy reinforcements. For the subject at the moment of choice to make a match between a present candy and an absent one (the incentive) appears to require some mechanism of anticipation which makes incentives a source of cues available in some form prior to choice.

While anticipatory mechanisms (such as S-S connections or anticipatory goal reactions) are extratheoretical as far as our present model goes, a major consequence of assuming anticipation is that attention theory then applies to the feedback of anticipation. Incentive cues become another stimulus dimension competing for attention with other, more direct, sources of stimulation.

Oddity. The oddity problem has often been employed to study discriminative processes of primates and children, and it is of especial interest in the context of attention theory, since it can be readily analyzed as requiring both observing and instrumental habits.

To describe a variant of the oddity problem we have used, let A, B, C,

D, E, and F represent different stimuli. A typical trial sequence with three simultaneously presented stimuli might be

Trial 1. A^+ B B
Trial 2.   C C D^+
Trial 3. E^+ F F

with the plus indicating the rewarded choice. The odd stimulus is always correct, and since the odd one never appears in the central position, the problem becomes a two-choice discrimination as the subject learns never to select the center stimulus.

The instrumental component of the oddity habit may be specified as "approach the odd stimulus." The exercise of this habit is, of course, contingent upon the subject's seeing in what respect the stimuli differ. If the odd stimulus differs from the other two along a single dimension, the subject cannot solve the problem unless he observes the single relevant dimension. The interesting feature of the instrumental oddity habit, according to our analysis, is that once learned, it can transfer to any new situation in which oddity is present. In other words, the oddity habit permits the subject to perform correctly on any oddity problem with no training provided that the relevant dimension (or dimensions) is observed.

In terms of the theory, $Pr_{(1,0)}$ approaches unity and $Po_{(1,0)}$ is under the control of the particular dimension selected (see Table 5-2). The usefulness

Figure 5-33. Performances of Shepp's group PC (labeled *positive*) featuring a positive correlation between discriminanda and incentives, group NC (labeled *negative*) representing the corresponding negative correlation, and the control group (labeled *neutral*).

The logic tying these results to the cue value of reward is presented in the text.

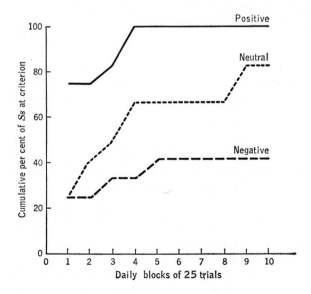

of an oddity habit for attention theory is that it allows us to measure more or less directly the initial attention value $(Po_{(1,0)})$ of new dimensions, uncomplicated by the necessity of teaching a correct instrumental habit $(Pr_{(1,0)})$ at the same time.

The major difficulty lies in teaching the oddity habit to low-level retardates. When training begins with mixed sets of objects, as illustrated above, with oddity the only cue, only 20 per cent (MA 3–4) are able to learn within 1,000 trials. A stimulus reversal method increases percentage learning to 50 per cent. The reversal method consists in presenting ABB (position randomized) until A is chosen six trials in succession, then shifting to BAA until the subject learns to choose B. A and B alternate as the odd, correct cue during a series of reversals until the subject begins to reverse with zero errors, indicating a use of the oddity cue. At this stage, most subjects can perform correctly when mixed sets of objects are introduced. Although the reversal method is the most effective we have tried, percentage learning is still disappointingly small. It is hoped that better ways can be found for training the oddity habit.

Other stimulus dimensions. It will be noted that among the postulated stimulus dimensions are some for which the physical basis for sensory reception is not obvious. We do not reject for a priori reasons stimulus aspects such as relationships—same-different, larger than, brighter than, etc.—if these can be shown to follow the laws of the model. Another example of a somewhat subtle dimension is that of temporal duration. Orlando (1960) presented evidence that efficient performance on a fixed-interval operant schedule in retardates required the ability to discriminate temporal intervals. Another stimulus aspect, variability, was postulated to be a cue in a study by House, Orlando, and Zeaman (1957), as subjects showed evidence of learning to approach or avoid the stimulus which changed from trial to trial. These examples serve to point up the variety of stimulus properties that may function as dimensions.

EXTENSIONS OF THE THEORY

Partial reinforcement submodel

The π parameters. The theory has so far dealt only with the simplest reward schedule of 100 per cent reinforcement for response to the positive stimulus, 0 per cent reinforcement for response to the negative. Consideration is given now to other schedules.

Let π_1 and π_2 be random probabilities of reinforcement associated with the two physical stimuli serving as discriminanda. π_1 is associated with the *positive* cue, π_2 with the *negative* cue, where positive means the more frequently reinforced cue. By convention, then $\pi_1 \gtrless \pi_2$.

The basic equation relating probability of the correct overt response (choice of the more reinforced cue) to theoretical instrumental and observing probabilities [Eq. (5-1)] does not change, nor do the rules of probability change as summarized in operator form in Table 5-1. What does change in this submodel is the probability of application of the various operators. Table 5-4 is a modification of Table 5-1 including the new parameters π_1 and π_2.

The expected operator methods we have employed earlier can be used again for purposes of approximation. The expected change in mean probability of a relevant observing response is

$$\Delta \bar{P}o_{(1)} = \frac{\theta_o}{2} \bar{P}o_{(1)} \left[(\pi_1 - \pi_2)(2\bar{P}r_{(1)} - 1) \right.$$

$$\left. - (2 - \pi_1 - \pi_2)\left(n - \sum_{i=2}^{n} \frac{1}{1 - \bar{P}o_{(i)}} \right) \right] \quad (5\text{-}7)$$

The corresponding equation for an irrelevant observing response, $Po_{(j)}$, is

$$\Delta \bar{P}o_{(j)} = \frac{\theta_o}{2} \bar{P}o_{(j)} \left\{ \frac{\bar{P}o_{(1)}}{1 - \bar{P}o_{(1)}} \left[(1 - 2\bar{P}r_{(1)})(\pi_1 - \pi_2) + (2 - \pi_1 - \pi_2) \right] \right.$$

$$\left. - (2 - \pi_1 - \pi_2)\left(n - \sum_{\substack{i=2 \\ i \neq j}}^{n} \frac{1}{1 - \bar{P}o_{(i)}} \right) \right\} \quad (5\text{-}8)$$

And for an approximation of the expected change in mean probability of the correct instrumental response, we write

$$\Delta \bar{P}r_{(1)} = \theta_o \bar{P}o_{(1)}[\bar{P}r_{(1)}(\pi_1 + \pi_2 - 2) + 1 - \pi_2] \quad (5\text{-}9)$$

TABLE 5-4

Operators applied to four probabilities given the various sequences of events that can occur on a trial in experiments with schedules of partial reinforcement

Sequence of events	Probability of sequence	Operators applied to			
		$Po_{(1)}$	$Po_{(2)}$	$Po_{(n)}$	$Pr_{(1)}$
O_1R_1G	$Po_{(1)}Pr_{(1)}\pi_1$	Q_A	Q_e	Q_e	Q_A
O_1R_1G'	$Po_{(1)}Pr_{(1)}(1 - \pi_1)$	Q_E	Q_{a1}	Q_{a1}	Q_E
$O_1R_1'G$	$Po_{(1)}(1 - Pr_{(1)})\pi_2$	Q_A	Q_e	Q_e	Q_E
$O_1R_1'G'$	$Po_{(1)}(1 - Pr_{(1)})(1 - \pi_2)$	Q_E	Q_{a1}	Q_{a1}	Q_A
O_2R_2G	$Po_{(2)}Pr_{(2)}(\pi_1 + \pi_2)/2$	Q_e	Q_A	Q_e	Q_I
O_2R_2G'	$Po_{(2)}Pr_{(2)}(\pi_1 + \pi_2)/2$	Q_{a2}	Q_E	Q_{a2}	Q_I
$O_2R_2'G$	$Po_{(2)}(1 - Pr_{(2)})(\pi_1 + \pi_2)/2$	Q_e	Q_A	Q_e	Q_I
$O_2R_2'G'$	$Po_{(2)}(1 - Pr_{(2)})(\pi_1 + \pi_2)/2$	Q_{a2}	Q_E	Q_{a2}	Q_I
O_nR_nG	$Po_{(n)}Pr_{(n)}(\pi_1 + \pi_2)/2$	Q_e	Q_e	Q_A	Q_I
O_nR_nG'	$Po_{(n)}Pr_{(n)}(\pi_1 + \pi_2)/2$	Q_{an}	Q_{an}	Q_E	Q_I
$O_nR_n'G$	$Po_{(n)}(1 - Pr_{(n)})(\pi_1 + \pi_2)/2$	Q_e	Q_e	Q_A	Q_I
$O_nR_n'G'$	$Po_{(n)}(1 - Pr_{(n)})(\pi_1 + \pi_2)/2$	Q_{an}	Q_{an}	Q_E	Q_I

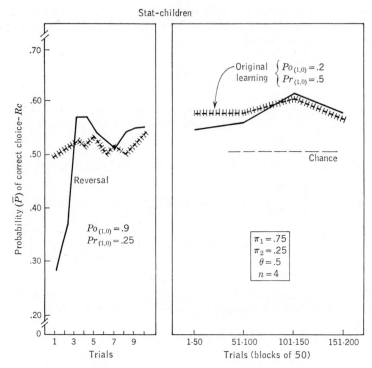

Figure 5-34. Theoretical learning and reversal curves with schedules of partial reinforcement. Mean probabilities of correct choice of groups of 20 stat-children are plotted at the left for the first 10 trials of original learning and reversal.

At the right, the same stat-children are run for 200 trials and their data plotted as means of blocks of 50 trials.

Values of $P_{O(1)}$ and $P_{r(1)}$, computed by means of Eqs. (5-7) to 5-9), can then be substituted into Eq. (5-6) to predict $\bar{P}$, the expected change in mean probability of a correct observable response.

Stat-children under partial reinforcement.   We have not yet computed stat-children functions for a wide variety of conditions including the schedule parameters π_1 and π_2. Examples of those which have been computed are plotted in Figure 5-34 with $\pi_1 = .75$ and $\pi_2 = .25$. Values of θ and n are of the order of magnitude of those used earlier for regular reinforcement, and starting probabilities are those that might be appropriate for original learning and reversal.

These parameter values turn out to be obviously incorrect for the group experimental data shown in Figure 5-27, although a few common properties are shared. Chief among these is the fact that both appear to be approaching slowly some intermediate asymptote less than unity. The experimental data for groups are closer in level to a *matching solution* of 75 per cent than the stat-children groups, but it will be shown in the next section that the apparently stable level of group response during 200 trials with partial reinforcement is under the control of another parameter, the number of relevant dimensions.

Number of relevant dimensions and degree of relevance: the $\pi\rho$ model

A new parameter, ρ.   For purposes of simplicity, consideration has been restricted to single relevant dimensions, even though it is quite likely that more than one relevant dimension may be present experimentally. Not only may the number of relevant cues vary, but the degree of relevance of each may also be a variable. To handle these possibilities, we introduce a new parameter ρ to represent degree of relevance.

Let ρ_j be the probability that the cues of the jth dimension are associated with (i.e., in the same place as) those of the reference dimension S_1. As an illustration, suppose S_1 is a form dimension represented experimentally by a square s_1 as a positive cue, and a circle s_1' as negative. Also, let S_j be any other dimension (say color) which also splits up into two cues, blue s_j and red s_j'.

If $\rho_j = .6$, then the probability that s_j is associated with s_1 is .6. In terms of the example, the probability that the square s_1 is also blue s_j is .6. It follows from this that the probability of the square being red is .4, as is the probability of the circle being blue.

Restating schematically, the arrows indicate probabilities of association:

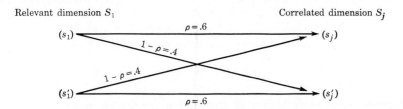

Relevant dimension S_1 ..... Correlated dimension S_j

(s_1) ..... (s_j) $\rho = .6$ $1 - \rho = .4$ $1 - \rho = .4$ (s_1') ..... (s_j') $\rho = .6$

To interpret this model experimentally, we arrange for these associations to hold.

Any number of dimensions may be correlated with the reference dimension, and for convenience we designate the number of relevant dimensions n_r and the number of irrelevant dimensions n_i. Thus, the sum of n_r and n_i equals n, the total number of dimensions.

Table of operators for the $\pi\rho$ model.   To achieve generality the new parameter is incorporated into the partial reinforcement or π model to yield the $\pi\rho$ model. The rules of probability changes for this model are given in Table 5-5. The operators remain the same as before, but the probabilities of applying them differ, and, furthermore, the necessity arises of calculating the probabilities of the instrumental responses to the cues of the correlated dimensions $(Pr_{(j)})$, since these no longer remain at chance.

Basic equation.   Unlike the π model, the $\pi\rho$ model requires a new basic equation for computation of P.

$$P = Po_{(1)}Pr_{(j)} + \sum_{i=2}^{n} Po_{(i)}Pr_{(i)}\rho_{(i)} + \sum_{i=2}^{n} Po_{(i)}(1 - Pr_{(i)})(1 - \rho_{(i)}) \quad (5\text{-}10)$$

A verbal translation of this equation is as follows: the correct (reference) stimulus will be lifted if the subject looks at the correct dimension and approaches the correct cue, *or* if he looks at one of the nonreference dimensions and approaches one of the cues s_i which is associated with the correct stimulus, *or* if he looks at one of the nonreference dimensions and approaches the other cue s_i' which is associated with the correct stimulus.

The reference dimension is any dimension perfectly correlated with reinforcement, and all the others are nonreference dimensions. The nonreference dimensions are *relevant* if their ρ values are 1.0, *irrelevant* if their ρ values are .5, and *partially relevant* or *correlated* if their ρ values lie between .5 and 1.0.

Equation (5-10) can be simplified to

$$P = Po_{(1)}Pr_{(1)} + \sum_{i=2}^{n} Po_{(i)}[Pr_{(i)}(2\rho_{(i)} - 1) + (1 - \rho_{(i)})] \qquad (5\text{-}11)$$

which reduces to Eq. (5-1) when all $\rho_{(i)}$ are equal to .5.

Stat-children functions. Equation (5-11) is used in conjunction with the table of operators to compute stat-children functions. Figure 5-35 shows the effects of variation in number of relevant dimensions n_r for three groups of 20 stat-children. It is evident from these functions that increasing the number of relevant dimensions raises the level of group performance. The theory agrees in this respect with data presented earlier (Figure 5-6) showing that two cues (color and form) resulted in greater learning than either alone. The relative ease of multidimensional (junk) stimulus learning

TABLE 5-5

Operators and probabilities of application for the $\pi\rho$ model

Sequence of events	Probability of sequence	Operators applied to				
		$Po_{(1)}$	$Po_{(j)}$	$Po_{(n)}$	$Pr_{(1)}$	$Pr_{(j)}$
O_1R_1G	$Po_{(1)}Pr_{(1)}\pi_1$	Q_A	Q_e	Q_e	Q_A	Q_I
O_1R_1G'	$Po_{(1)}Pr_{(1)}(1 - \pi_1)$	Q_E	Q_{a1}	Q_{a1}	Q_E	Q_I
$O_1R_1'G$	$Po_{(1)}(1 - Pr_{(1)})\pi_2$	Q_A	Q_e	Q_e	Q_E	Q_I
$O_1R_1'G'$	$Po_{(1)}(1 - Pr_{(1)})(1 - \pi_2)$	Q_E	Q_{a1}	Q_{a1}	Q_A	Q_I
O_jR_jG	$Po_{(j)}Pr_{(j)}[\rho_j\pi_1 + (1 - \rho_j)\pi_2]$	Q_e	Q_A	Q_e	Q_I	Q_A
O_jR_jG'	$Po_{(j)}Pr_{(j)}[1 - \rho_j\pi_1 - (1 - \rho_j)\pi_2]$	Q_{aj}	Q_E	Q_{aj}	Q_I	Q_E
$O_jR_j'G$	$Po_{(j)}(1 - Pr_{(j)})[\rho_j\pi_2 + (1 - \rho_j)\pi_1]$	Q_e	Q_A	Q_e	Q_I	Q_E
$O_jR_j'G'$	$Po_{(j)}(1 - Pr_{(j)})[1 - \rho_j\pi_2 - (1 - \rho_j)\pi_1]$	Q_{aj}	Q_E	Q_{aj}	Q_I	Q_A
O_nR_nG	$Po_{(n)}Pr_{(n)}(\pi_1 + \pi_2)/2$	Q_e	Q_e	Q_A	Q_I	Q_I
O_nR_nG'	$Po_{(n)}Pr_{(n)}(\pi_1 + \pi_2)/2$	Q_{an}	Q_{an}	Q_E	Q_I	Q_I
$O_nR_n'G$	$Po_{(n)}(1 - Pr_{(n)})(\pi_1 + \pi_2)/2$	Q_e	Q_e	Q_A	Q_I	Q_I
$O_nR_n'G'$	$Po_{(n)}(1 - Pr_{(n)})(\pi_1 + \pi_2)/2$	Q_{an}	Q_{an}	Q_E	Q_I	Q_I

is another empirical finding consistent with this property of the $\pi\rho$ model.

Inclusion of the π parameter results in the functions plotted in Figure 5-36. The effects of schedules are seen to be under the control of the number of relevant dimensions. Increasing n_r from 1 to 4 elevates the level of performance to about 75 per cent for the group function, within 200 trials. The empirical data on position discrimination presented earlier (Figure 5-27) are more similar to the 4-relevant dimension stat-child function than the curve for one relevant dimension. The implication is that position may be multidimensional in nature—a not unintuitive proposition.

If we increase the ρ value of a correlated dimension from .50 to .75, it seems to have no marked effect detectable with means of 20 stat-children with the parameters used in Figure 5-36, while increasing ρ value from .75 to 1.0 (and thus making two relevant dimensions) has a marked effect. We have as yet no retardate data to test this interesting and easily testable prediction. But corroborative evidence has been found with rats by Jeeves and North (1956) and by Babb (1956). Both studies showed that increasing correlation between irrelevant and relevant dimensions from .50 to .70 or .75 did not produce any differences in learning speed.

One important question is whether or not a distinction should be made between irrelevant stimuli which vary and those which remain constant. For example, if form were relevant, *variable* colors, such as red and green, might be paired at random with the correct or incorrect form cues. Conversely, the color of the correct and incorrect form cues might be the same,

Figure 5-35. Theoretical effects of increasing the number of relevant dimensions. Average performance levels of three groups of 20 stat-children improve as the number of relevant dimensions increases from one to three.

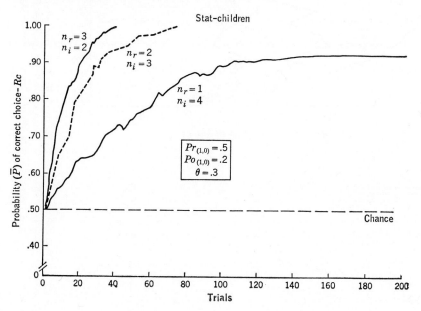

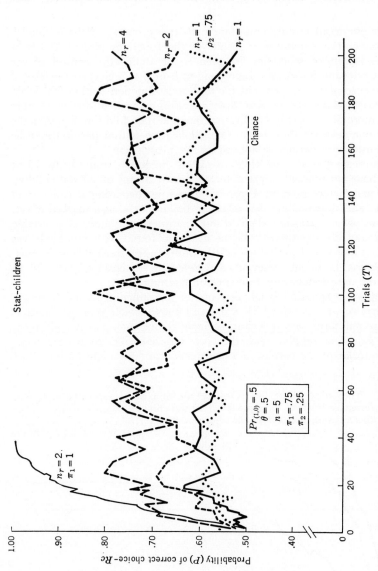

Figure 5-36. The joint effects of schedules of reward and number of relevant dimensions on stat-child performance. All groups were run on a 75-25 schedule with the exception of the fastest learning group which had a 100-0 schedule. Stat-children represented by the dotted function had one relevant and another partially relevant ($\rho_2 = .75$).

always red for example, for a *constant* irrelevant cue. Theoretically, no distinction is made between these two conditions; in both cases, ρ is presumed to be equal to .5. Extratheoretical considerations, however, might suggest that variable cues have more attention value, in which case we should expect variable irrelevant cues to retard learning in comparison with constant irrelevant cues. Evidence is available from rat studies indicating that variability may or may not retard learning depending upon the relative strength of relevant and irrelevant dimensions. Three studies have compared variable black-white irrelevant cues with constant brightness as an irrelevant dimension. Variability did not interfere when bars–no bars was the relevant dimension (Jeeves & North, 1956), but did retard learning when chains–no chains (Babb, 1956) or upright-inverted triangles (Wortz & Bitterman, 1953) were relevant. Elam and Bitterman (1953) found that learning a thick-thin stripe discrimination was not hindered by variable presentation of a horizontal or vertical display. But when this training was followed by an extradimensional-shift condition with horizontal-vertical stripes relevant, variability along the previously trained thick-thin dimension was detrimental in comparison with a constant condition.

Expected operator functions. The expected operator equations have been worked out for this model as before, but the results are cumbersome in form. They are omitted for space considerations.

Two-look model

Without abandoning our central theoretical notion that attention is a limited capacity, we may try to relax our assumption that the subject looks at only a single dimension at the moment of choice. Let us start with the new assumption that a maximum of two dimensions may be simultaneously attended to. To simplify further, we restrict the number of dimensions considered to just two, and let $\pi_1 = 1.0$ and $\pi_2 = 0$.

Paradigms of the possibilities on any trial are given in Figure 5-37. The subject observes either one of the two dimensions, or *both* $(0_{(1+2)})$, in which case four possibilities arise. There is the probability ρ that the two cue compounds $s_1 s_2$ (on one side) and $s_1' s_2'$ (on the other) will result from $0_{(1+2)}$, and there is the complementary probability $(1 - \rho)$ that the other two cue compounds will be made available. Associated with each of the four cue compounds must be an instrumental approach response with conditional probabilities as diagrammed.

The basic equation for such a model is

$$P = P_{0(1)}Pr_{(1)} + P_{0(2)}Pr_{(2)}\rho_2 + P_{0(2)}(1 - Pr_{(2)})(1 - \rho_2)$$
$$+ P_{0(1+2)}Pr_{(1+2)}\rho_2 + P_{0(1+2)}Pr_{(1+2')}(1 - \rho_2)$$

Operator tables and expected operator functions are not sufficiently different from the other models to warrant presentation. Generalization to an N-look model offers no particular difficulty other than a great deal of bookkeeping if we accept as our goal the generation of stat-children functions. We have as yet no stat-children run on this model.

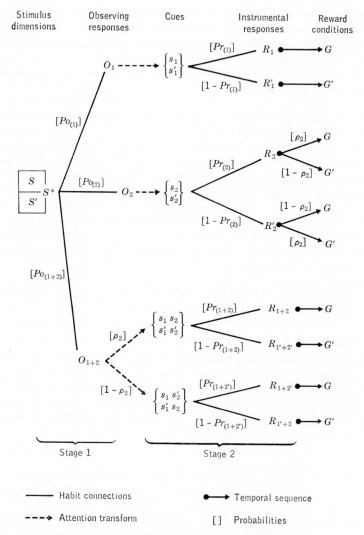

Figure 5-37. Probability tree for the *two-look* model.

Some limitations of the theory

The theory is not intended to give a complete account of discrimination learning. Rather it is an attempt to derive consequences of a few basic assumptions. Restated qualitatively, these are (1) attention is limited to only one (or, at most a few) of the many possible stimulus dimensions available to the subject at the moment of choice; (2) subjects may learn to attend to or disregard stimulus aspects as a result of differential reinforcement; and (3) cues for instrumental learning are those aspects of the stimulus which are being attended to. We have already given a detailed account of many of the empirical effects these assumptions can handle. We now turn to a brief discussion of some of the phenomena which the present formulation is not equipped to handle.

New perceptual learning. The theory is not one of perceptual learning in the sense of acquisition of *new* perceptual responses. Each subject is assumed to have a set of dimensions with varying probabilities of being observed. But no description is given of how the subject gets these dimensions to begin with, or how the number available changes with age. Thus, the theory is to be distinguished from those which have as a goal the explanation of perceptual development, such as Hebb's neurophysiological account (1949) of how organisms learn to perceive or Werner's (1948) hypothetical levels of perceptual organization. Such theories attempt to account for the level of perceptual development which the present model takes as given. The view of perceptual learning most congenial to the observing-response model is that of Gibson and Gibson (1955) and Gibson (1959). They emphasize the wealth of information in the complexity of energies and patterns of energies stimulating the sense organs. Perceptual learning is regarded as a process of discovering new properties of the world by discriminating new variables in the stimulus flux. Perceptual development, then, becomes a matter of differentiating sensory input, rather than a process of reorganizing or reinterpreting sensory information. The notion that organisms learn to discriminate new variables may be roughly equivalent to our supposition that more intelligent subjects observe a greater number of dimensions.

Generalization. Our theory says nothing specifically about stimulus generalization, and experimentally, we have minimized the problem of generalization by using as discriminanda stimulus properties which if seen are easily distinguished by our subjects. Squares versus circles, red versus green, and left versus right are examples. It is obviously not necessary to experiment in this way. Cues closer together on some continuum might be chosen, and then we should expect the traditional finding that speed of discrimination learning is inversely related to the stimulus distance between discriminanda. Many theories of discrimination, e.g., those of Hull (1943), Spence (1937), Burke and Estes (1957), and Bush and Mosteller (1951), can deduce this finding by postulating gradients of stimulus generalization and rules for their interaction.

Such gradients have been demonstrated with retardates. Smith (1960), for instance, trained a lever-pulling response in a go–no go free operant situation using a light of a given wavelength as the positive stimulus versus no light as the negative stimulus. During extinction, the wavelength of the light was varied. After an initial tendency to respond equally strongly to the test wavelengths (which differed from the training wavelength), the retardates showed a generalization gradient by distributing their responses according to a decreasing function of distance from the training stimulus. The function obtained bore a relation to the normal human discriminability function.

Information on stimulus generalization gradients from such experiments may be used to write additional postulates for attention theory to handle generalization effects. This is left as an important line of future theoretical development. Whatever the new generalization postulates, one consequence can already be predicted: Changes in cues of dimensions observed with probabilities close to zero will lead to flat generalization gradients and undisturbed discriminations.

Relationship to other theories

Continuity-noncontinuity theories. Some properties of our model bear on the continuity-noncontinuity controversy without corresponding closely to either position. According to Krechevsky's (1938) version of noncontinuity theory, the organism selects a certain set of discriminanda to which he reacts, i.e., entertains a hypothesis. While paying attention to some particular set of stimuli, the animal learns only about that set. If he is attending to some irrelevant set of stimuli, he eventually gives up the "hypothesis" and adopts another. He learns nothing about the relevant cues until such time as he has adopted the relevant hypothesis. This account has some similarity to our one-look observing-response (OR) model in that the subject learns only about dimensions he is attending to. One difference between OR and hypothesis is that a hypothesis is assumed to hold over a block of trials, while OR theory postulates that over a block of trials several dimensions may be observed, one per trial, corresponding to their probabilities of being observed. Another difference is that ORs are presumed to follow the same laws, such as acquisition and extinction, as any other response, while hypotheses are cognitive states, not necessarily bound by the laws of habit.

Spence (1945), a continuity theorist, described discrimination learning as the gradual growth of differential excitatory tendencies in reaction to the positive and negative cues resulting from rewards and nonrewards. He assumed that excitatory strength was added to every stimulus property which impinged on the sense organs of the animal in close temporal contiguity with response and reward. His theory was intended to apply, however, when the organism was certain to be exposed to the relevant cues on every trial. He made the qualification that in many discrimination situations, performance might be influenced by the necessity for the animal to learn to orient toward relevant aspects of the surround. Orienting responses and ORs follow similar laws of acquisition and extinction, but they differ in degree of selectivity. The orienting response is defined peripherally and has the function of merely ensuring that receptors are stimulated by the relevant stimulus. The OR makes a further selection among the stimulus dimensions impinging upon the sensorium, thereby limiting instrumental learning to a single dimension. Results of experiments designed to test Spence's theory versus Krechevsky's hypothesis theory are not critical for the OR model, which can predict results compatible with either position, depending upon experimental conditions.

Acquired distinctiveness and similarity of cues. The observing-response model may also be seen to belong to a class of theories employing the concepts of acquired distinctiveness and similarity of cues. There is considerable evidence that the positive and negative transfer effects from which these concepts are inferred are present in rats (Lawrence, 1949, 1950) as well as humans (Goss, 1955, 1961). Most of the theories which have been advanced to account for these transfer effects have consisted of extensions or modifications of the continuity position, in the form of inferred mediating responses elicited by the discriminative stimuli. Two types of mediating responses have been postulated—those which act by adding distinctive or similar cues to those already present (e.g., verbal labels) and those which exercise a selective effect on the environment (e.g., orienting response, observing response).

Response-produced cues. Many of the effects considered by the present model have been attributed to response-produced cues, i.e., those added to the stimulus situation by mediating responses. Goss (1955, 1961) has reviewed these theories and the experimental evidence. Kendler and Kendler (1959, 1960) have incorporated verbal mediation into a theory of child development. They maintain that Spence's one-stage discrimination theory is adequate to account for all behavior of nonverbal or preverbal organisms. They present evidence that the superiority of reversal over extradimensional shift occurs only in older children (5–7 years) who learned the original problem quickly, but not in younger subjects (3–5 years). The improvement in reversal performance with age is attributed to the process of language development and the increasing control of verbal mediating responses on behavior.

Observing-response theory does not exclude response-produced cues as stimulus variables affecting behavior. As a part of the total sensory input, these stimuli may be observed or not observed in the same manner as those arising from external stimulation. We have made no assumptions that response-produced cues are particularly potent as compared with other cues. Verbal mediating responses are of obvious importance in accounting for human behavior, not only as a device for adding cues, but as a method for more direct control of behavior by means of complex responses attached to verbal cues during previous training history. For the experimental data presented in this chapter, verbal mediation as a factor cannot be ruled out. A discussion of whether or not *all* the data presented can be accounted for by Spence's theory plus the assumption of verbal mediation is not within the scope of this paper.

Selective mechanisms. Among theorists who have posited that organisms select particular aspects of the stimulus situation to respond to, while ignoring others, are Reid (1953), Lawrence (1949, 1950), and Goodwin and Lawrence (1955). Reid proposed that as animals learn to make the correct response they are also learning a response of *discriminating*, i.e., "learning to respond to a set of stimuli of which the specific stimulus is a member." As evidence, Reid analyzed the performance of rats on a discrimination reversal problem, showing that overlearning trials on the original problem increased speed of reversal.

Goodwin and Lawrence (1955) postulated a dual process—one of identification or reaction to a dimension and one of instrumental learning. They assumed that the identification process could be learned and extinguished. Evidence to support their view came from a study in which rats were given a series of extradimensional shifts, black-white and high-low hurdles alternating as relevant cues. The rats were able to retain an old habit (e.g., black-white) while being trained on a new discrimination (e.g., high-low hurdles) in spite of the fact that during hurdle training, black and white were being randomly reinforced. Goodwin and Lawrence inferred that the rats had quickly extinguished the identification response to the black-white dimension, so that the random rewards and nonrewards were ineffective. The properties of the identification response are quite similar to those of the observing response.

Some other writers who have postulated selective mechanisms can be classified as probability theorists and are discussed in the next section.

Wyckoff. Our models are based on ideas similar to those of a number of theorists, but especially Wyckoff. Wyckoff (1952) defines the observing response as any response which results in exposure to the relevant cues and relates discriminative performance to the product of two probabilities, that of making the observing response and that of making the correct instrumental response [cf. Eq. (5-1)]. He discusses the general properties of any theory in which the frequency of effective instrumental training trials depends upon the probability of observing the relevant cue, and in which (to complete a circular dependency) the increase in probability of observing is a function of the strength of the instrumental habit.

In a later paper, Wyckoff (1954) adds the assumption to his model that the growth of the observing response is a function of the secondary reinforcing power of the discriminative stimuli. An electronic model was constructed which operated according to the postulates of the system to generate learning curves for original learning, reversal, and extradimensional shift.

While, in general, Wyckoff's model has many similar properties to the present theory, a number of points of divergence should be noted. (1) Wyckoff's specification of the observing response differs from ours in not being dimensional in nature. (2) The mechanism for strengthening the observing response is secondary reinforcement in Wyckoff's model, while we assume that the same rewards and nonrewards act on both instrumental and observing responses. (3) We use different operators from Wyckoff's as rules of probability changes. (4) The various extensions of our basic model incorporating the parameters π and ρ and two-looks are not Wyckoffian.

Stochastic models. From Estes (1959) and Bush and Mosteller (1955) we have borrowed our operators, some rules of notation, and methods of getting approximations. The discrimination models of Burke and Estes (1957) and Bush and Mosteller (1951) are, however, quite different from ours in that these theorists do not conceive of discrimination as requiring a chain of two responses.

Atkinson and Restle. An observing-response model based on different assumptions has been developed by Atkinson (1958). The organism is assumed to make either an observing response, in which case he sees *only* the relevant stimulus, or a nonobserving response, which exposes him to *both* the relevant and irrelevant cues. The relevant cues, therefore, begin to be conditioned from the beginning of training, and as trials increase, attention is narrowed so that only relevant cues are sampled. Restle's (1955) discrimination theory achieves somewhat the same effect by assuming that as learning progresses, relevant cues are sampled on every trial and gradually become conditioned. Irrelevant cues, on the other hand, become adapted so that they no longer have any effect on behavior. Bourne and Restle (1959) applied this theory to the problem of the effect on performance of varying numbers of relevant and irrelevant dimensions. Their predicted effects were in the same direction as those predicted by the present model. However, for purposes of describing retardate learning, both Atkinson's and Restle's models have the disadvantage of assuming that learning of the instrumental response begins on the very first trial. Our data suggest strongly that an adequate model must allow for the possibility that instrumental learning is completely absent under some circumstances for a number of trials.

Attention theory and retardation

A major goal in the development of this attention model is to provide a framework for analysis of apparent learning deficits in retardates. In this section we discuss the relationships between parameters of the model and intelligence.

Invariance of θ. One conclusion drawn was that learning rate θ is not a particularly important source of variance in discrimination learning of retardates. We were led to this conclusion by examination of the slopes of the backward learning curves—the most sensitive index of rate differences. With MAs ranging from 2 to 8 years, the final portions of backward curves were not distinguishably different. We have further shown that even in slow learners, abrupt mastery of problems may be obtained by changing stimulus aspects or training procedures. Ruling out learning rate as a factor varying with intelligence may appear to violate intuitive assumptions about the nature of intelligence, since standard definitions have long included the ability to learn as a criterion. However, this conclusion is not unprecedented. Both Woodrow (1946) and McPherson (1948, 1958) have stressed the predominantly negative results which have arisen from attempts to demonstrate a relationship between learning rate and intelligence.

Role of $Po_{(1,0)}$. A low Po for the relevant dimension, we have argued, is a major cause of the retardate's poor performance. That is, the color-form dimensions used in our experiments happened to have low probabilities of being observed by subjects of low mental age. But a low Po for color or form must mean (other factors constant) a correspondingly higher probability of observing some other (easier) dimension, since all Pos must sum to unity. A curious consequence of this state of affairs is the prediction that for certain "easy" dimensions, lower-MA children would learn to discriminate faster than higher-MA children. This odd prediction is not without some experimental support. Weir and Stevenson (1959) report that 9-year-old normal subjects did significantly worse than 5-year-olds on a simple discrimination task using animal pictures as stimuli.

The n parameter. Comments of the older subjects in the Weir and Stevenson experiment indicated that they were looking for something more complicated than the simple solution. Theoretically, this might be interpreted as reflecting individual differences in the n parameter. Older and brighter subjects see more dimensions. While a larger n parameter could conceivably mean faster learning if the experimenter were to use many simultaneously relevant dimensions, it usually implies that the subject will see more *irrelevant* dimensions and learn more slowly because of the common practice of using a limited number of relevant dimensions (i.e., "hard" problems). This implication of poorer performance by brighter subjects appears paradoxical in view of the positive correlation we find between intelligence and ability to solve color-form discrimination problems.

How can we assume that subjects of higher developmental level (1) see more (irrelevant) dimensions, (2) have, therefore, more irrelevant observing responses to extinguish than less intelligent subjects, (3) learn and extinguish (in the sense of θ) at the same rate as lower-level subjects, and then predict *superior* performance for the brighter subjects?

A possible resolution of this paradox may be derived from the theoretical fact that the *relative* strengths of irrelevant observing responses are also determinants of performance (see Figure 5-14). A large number of irrelevant dimensions may not retard discrimination appreciably if a few of the irrelevant dimensions have high initial Pos, while the others are low. We speculate that intelligent subjects may have learned for specific stimulus situations S^*s to restrict attention largely to those aspects which have paid off in the past. The less intelligent subjects are regarded as distributing attention more evenly over their (fewer) observable dimensions.

We contrast children who are capable of discriminating many aspects of the situation, ignoring (relatively) all but those aspects likely to be associated with reinforcement, with children who are able to distinguish only a few aspects but attend to all about equally. The less intelligent subjects might earn the label "distractible" even though they have fewer dimensions to distract them. The answer to the paradox, we believe, lies in the distribution of probabilities of distracting dimensions $Po_{(i)}$ not simply in the number n_i of irrelevant dimensions.

Some implications for training

If our analysis of retardation and attention is correct, the secret of successful training of moderately retarded children lies in the engineering of their attention. In training tasks which require discrimination, one should seek ways of increasing the attention value of the relevant cues. Such methods may include manipulation of the stimulus situation so as to increase noticeability of the relevant dimensions or the use of transfer operations, such as the object-to-pattern sequence described earlier.

It is of interest to note that some traditional methods for training retarded children are derivable from the present theory. Montessori (1912) is a case in point. While her theoretical principles may be questionable, it is presumed that her techniques were adopted because they were found to work. Montessori advocated the use of three-dimensional cutouts in teaching form discriminations, such as letters and numbers. In explicating her principles of brevity, simplicity, and objectivity, she cautioned teachers not to present or draw attention to irrelevant details and described ways of making the relevant aspects of the material as prominent as possible. She recommended an easy-to-hard sequence of training, saying that "one should proceed from few stimuli strongly contrasting, to many stimuli in gradual differentiation always more fine and imperceptible" (1912, p. 184).

Strauss and Lehtinen (1947) emphasize the elimination of distracting details in describing their techniques for training brain-injured children. They suggest covering windows or having students sit facing a blank wall. Reading material is often enclosed within a cover which exposes only a small area at a time. Such techniques might, in terms of attention theory, serve to reduce the n parameter. Many of the training methods described by Strauss and Lehtinen can be analyzed as ways of directing attention to relevant cues. In counting, for example, the child may be required to place each object on a peg as he gives the number. This method not only maintains attention but produces more distinct feedback cues from the counting act. The work of Fernald (1943) in remedial techniques abounds in examples of ways of controlling attention. Her procedure of requiring the child to trace the letter as he repeats it aloud ensures that the relevant form dimension is being attended to as the verbal response is learned. The easy-to-hard sequence of beginning with large letters for early training before attempting to teach letters of ordinary printed size is also compatible with the principles of the present theory.

Thus, we see that successful teachers have made use both of stimulus arrangements which increase attention value of relevant cues and of transfer designs which progress from stronger to weaker cues.

A few stimulus factors in controlling attention have been indicated by the present research. We have shown that three-dimensional displays make later pattern learning easier. Novelty is another attention-getting aspect. Recent work has pointed to yet another important factor—the spatial contiguity of cue and incentive. Marked facilitation of pattern learning was obtained in trainable retardates when the pattern was repeated on the inside of the candy container, so that the candy was found directly on top of an exact copy of the discriminative color-form stimulus. Use of this method reduced failure rate from 100 per cent (for subjects of MA 2–4 using the standard method of pattern presentation) to zero. Similar results have been obtained by Jarvik (1956) with chimpanzees. One possible explanation is that spatial contiguity of the candy and pattern increases the probability that the subject will observe the pattern. Or it may be that the close temporal contiguity of observing the pattern and obtaining the reward is the facilitating factor. Whatever the explanation, the effect is a strong one, deserving of further exploration.

We have discussed earlier some specific transfer effects, such as intradimensional shift. There is also a kind of generalized transfer termed *learning set* by Harlow (1959), which is characterized by gradual improvement in discrimination performance over a long series of different problems. Learning-set acquisition has been shown to vary with intelligence by Kaufman and Peterson (1958), Ellis (1958), and Girardeau (1959). In a typical experiment, the stimuli differ multidimensionally, and the same dimensions are not necessarily relevant from one problem to the next. In terms of the attention model, learning set could result from extinction of observing responses to the class of dimensions which are never relevant and the acquisition of strong tendencies to observe those dimensions which are frequently relevant.

A contrasting kind of general interproblem transfer has been observed, which we have called *failure set* (Zeaman & House, 1960). Trainable subjects suffering prolonged failure on a problem which proved to be insoluble (conditional reaction) were found then to be unable to solve the simplest (junk) problem, although they had previously been able to do so. Failure set receives a ready (although as yet untested) theoretical interpretation as owing to extinction of the observing response to broad classes of visual stimuli, such as those associated with the experimental situation. In the absence of any differential reinforcement for observing particular dimensions, the Pos for all dimensions should approach equality. Subjects have not only lowered Pos for the relevant dimension, but equal ratios of strength of irrelevant dimensions, a particularly unfavorable condition. Whether or not this explanation is correct, the occurrence of failure sets is taken as a strong argument for adoption of easy-to-hard sequences. If we compare the effect of extradimensional shift with that of prolonged failure, the implication is that even learning the wrong things may be preferable to learning nothing. Even though extradimensional shift gives negative transfer as compared with intradimensional shift, such training is not as damaging as prolonged failure.

CONCLUDING REMARKS

A theory has been developed in this chapter that the visual discrimination learning of moderately retarded children requires the acquisition of a chain of two responses: (1) attending to the relevant stimulus dimension and (2) approaching the correct cue of that dimension. The difficulty that retardates have in discrimination learning is related to limitations in the first, or attention, phase of this dual process rather than the second.

A small collection of stochastic models organized by these general notions has been applied to a series of discrimination experiments with lower-level retardates including original learning, reversals, the effects of intelligence, stimulus factors, schedules, and transfer operations.

While the domain of empirical relevance of the theory is given in part by a description of the experimental procedures we have used in studying two-choice visual discriminations, we know of no reasons why the theory might not be found to hold for retardate learning of greater complexity and in other sensory modalities. Nor is it unlikely that the theory may hold for nonretarded subjects of comparable developmental levels.

REFERENCES

ATKINSON, R. C. A Markov model for discrimination learning. *Psychometrika*, 1958, 23, 309–322.

BABB, H. Proportional reinforcement of irrelevant stimuli and transfer value. *J. comp. physiol. Psychol.,* 1956, 49, 586–589.

BENSBERG, G. J., JR. Concept learning in mental defectives as a function of appropriate and inappropriate "attention sets." *J. educ. Psychol.,* 1958, 49, 137–143.

BOURNE, L. E., JR., & RESTLE, F. Mathematical theory of concept identification. *Psychol. Rev.,* 1959, 66, 278–296.

BURKE, C. J., & ESTES, W. K. A component model for stimulus variables in discrimination learning. *Psychometrika,* 1957, 22, 133–145.

BUSH, R. R., & MOSTELLER, F. A model for stimulus generalization and discrimination. *Psychol. Rev.,* 1951, 58, 413–423.

BUSH, R. R., & MOSTELLER, F. *Stochastic models for learning.* New York: Wiley, 1955.

CLACK, D., & ZEAMAN, D. Comparison of probability learning in retardate and normal children of low mental age. In D. Zeaman et al., *Learning and transfer in mental defectives.* Progress rep. No. 2, NIMH USPHS, 1960. Res. Grant M-1099 to Univer. of Connecticut. Pp. 177–190.

ECKSTRAND, G. A., & WICKENS, D. D. Transfer of perceptual set. *J. exper. Psychol.,* 1954, 47, 274–278.

ELAM, C. G., & BITTERMAN, M. E. The effect of an irrelevant relation on discriminative learning. *Amer. J. Psychol.,* 1953, 66, 242–250.

ELLIS, N. R. Object-quality discrimination learning sets in mental defectives. *J. comp. physiol. Psychol.,* 1958, 51, 79–81.

ESTES, W. K. The statistical approach to learning theory. In S. Koch (Ed.), *Psychology: a study of a science.* Vol. 2. New York: McGraw-Hill, 1959. Pp. 383–491.

ESTES, W. K. Learning theory and the new "mental chemistry." *Psychol. Rev.,* 1960, 67, 207–223.

ESTES, W. K., & STRAUGHAN, J. H. Analysis of a verbal conditioning situation in terms of statistical learning theory. *J. exper. Psychol.,* 1954, 47, 225–234.

FERNALD, G. M. *Remedial techniques in basic school subjects.* New York: McGraw-Hill, 1943.

GIBSON, J. J. Perception as a function of stimulation. In S. Koch (Ed.), *Psychology: a study of a science.* Vol. 1. New York: McGraw-Hill, 1959.

GIBSON, J. J., & GIBSON, E. J. Perceptual learning: differentiation or enrichment. *Psychol. Rev.,* 1955, 62, 32–41.

GIRARDEAU, F. L. The formation of discrimination learning sets in mongoloid and normal children. *J. comp. physiol. Psychol.,* 1959, 52, 566–570.

GOODWIN, W. R., & LAWRENCE, D. H. The functional independence of two discrimination habits associated with a constant stimulus situation. *J. comp. physiol. Psychol.,* 1955, 48, 437–443.

GOSS, A. E. A stimulus-response analysis of the interaction of cue-producing and instrumental responses. *Psychol. Rev.,* 1955, 62, 20–32.

GOSS, A. E. Verbal mediating responses and concept formation. *Psychol. Rev.,* 1961, 68, 248–274.

HARLOW, H. F. Learning set and error factor theory. In S. Koch (Ed.), *Psychology: a study of a science.* Vol. 2. New York: McGraw-Hill, 1959. Pp. 492–537.

HARLOW, H. F., & HICKS, L. H. Discrimination learning theory: uniprocess vs. duoprocess. *Psychol. Rev.,* 1957, 64, 104–109.

HAYES, K. J. The backward curve: a method for the study of learning. *Psychol. Rev.,* 1953, 60, 269–275.

HEBB, D. O. *The organization of behavior.* New York: Wiley, 1949.

HOUSE, B. J., ORLANDO, R., & ZEAMAN, D. Role of positive and negative cues in the discrimination learning of mental defectives. *Percept. mot. Skills,* 1957, 7, 73–79.

HOUSE, B. J., & ZEAMAN, D. A comparison of discrimination learning in normal and mentally defective children. *Child Develpm.,* 1958, 29, 411–416. (a)

HOUSE, B. J., & ZEAMAN, D. Reward and nonreward in the discrimination learning of imbeciles. *J. comp. physiol. Psychol.,* 1958, 51, 614–618. (b)

HOUSE, B. J., & ZEAMAN, D. Position discrimination and reversals in low-grade retardates. *J. comp. physiol. Psychol.,* 1959, 52, 564–565.

HOUSE, B. J., & ZEAMAN, D. Visual discrimination learning and intelligence in defectives of low mental age. *Amer. J. ment. Defic.,* 1960, 65, 51–58. (a)

HOUSE, B. J., & ZEAMAN, D. Transfer of a discrimination from objects to patterns. *J. exper. Psychol.,* 1960, 59, 298–302. (b)

HOUSE, B. J., & ZEAMAN, D. Reversal and nonreversal shifts in discrimination learning of retardates. *J. exper. Psychol.,* 1962, 63, 444–451.

HULL, C. L. *Principles of behavior.* New York: Appleton-Century-Crofts, 1943.

JARVIK, M. E. Simple color discrimination in chimpanzees: effect of varying contiguity between cue and incentive. *J. comp. physiol. Psychol.,* 1956, 49, 492–495.

JEEVES, M. A., & NORTH, A. J. Irrelevant or partially correlated stimuli in discrimination learning. *J. exper. Psychol.,* 1956, 52, 90–94.

KAUFMAN, M. E., & PETERSON, W. M. Acquisition of a learning set by normal and mentally retarded children. *J. comp. physiol. Psychol.,* 1958, 51, 619–621.

KENDLER, T. S., & KENDLER, H. H. Reversal and nonreversal shifts in kindergarten children. *J. exper. Psychol.,* 1959, 58, 56–60.

KENDLER, T. S., KENDLER, H. H., & WELLS, D. Reversal and nonreversal shifts in nursery school children. *J. comp. physiol. Psychol.,* 1960, 53, 83–88.

KRECHEVSKY, I. A study of the continuity of the problem-solving process. *Psychol. Rev.,* 1938, 45, 107–133.

KURTZ, K. H. Discrimination of complex stimuli. *J. exper. Psychol.,* 1955, 50, 283–292.

LAWRENCE, D. H. Acquired distinctiveness of cues. I. Transfer between discriminations on the basis of familiarity with the stimulus. *J. exper. Psychol.,* 1949, 39, 770–784.

LAWRENCE, D. H. Acquired distinctiveness of cues. II. Selective association in a constant stimulus situation. *J. exper. Psychol.,* 1950, 40, 175–188.

MCPHERSON, M. W. A survey of experimental studies in learning in individuals who achieve subnormal ratings on standardized psychometric measures. *Amer. J. ment. Defic.,* 1948, 52, 232–254.

MCPHERSON, M. W. Learning and mental deficiency. *Amer. J. ment. Defic.,* 1958, 62, 870–877.

MONTESSORI, M. *The Montessori method.* New York: Frederick A. Stokes Co., 1912.

ORLANDO, R. Component behaviors in free-operant temporal discrimination. In D. Zeaman et al., *Learning and transfer in mental defectives.* Progress rep. No. 2, NIMH USPHS, 1960. Res. Grant M-1099 to Univer. of Connecticut. Pp. 177–190.

REID, L. S. The development of noncontinuity behavior through continuity learning. *J. exper. Psychol.,* 1953, 46, 107–112.

RESTLE, F. A theory of discrimination learning. *Psychol. Rev.,* 1955, 62, 11–20.

SHEPP, B. Role of distinctive incentives in simultaneous and successive discrimination with retardates. In D. Zeaman et al., *Learning and transfer in mental defectives.* Progress rep. No. 2, NIMH USPHS, 1960. Res. Grant M-1099 to Univer. of Connecticut. Pp. 141–151.

SIDMAN, M. A note on functional relations obtained from group data. *Psychol. Bull.,* 1952, 49, 263–269.

SMITH, J. Discrimination learning and stimulus generalization in mental defectives. In D. Zeaman et al., *Learning and transfer in mental defectives.* Progress rep. No. 2, NIMH USPHS, 1960. Res. Grant M-1099 to Univer. of Connecticut. Pp. 152–168.

SPENCE, K. W. The differential response in animals to stimuli varying within a single dimension. *Psychol. Rev.,* 1937, 44, 430–444.

SPENCE, K. W. An experimental test of the continuity and non-continuity theories of discrimination learning. *J. exper. Psychol.,* 1945, 35, 253–266.

STEVENSON, H. W., & ISCOE, I. Transposition in the feebleminded. *J. exper. Psychol.,* 1955, 49, 11–15.

STRAUSS, A. A., & LEHTINEN, L. E. *Psychopathology and education of the brain-injured child.* New York: Grune & Stratton, 1947.

WEIR, M. W., & STEVENSON, H. W. The effect of verbalization in children's learning as a function of chronological age. *Child Develpm.,* 1959, 30, 143–149.

WERNER, H. *Comparative psychology of mental development.* (rev. ed.) Chicago: Follet, 1948.

WOODROW, H. The ability to learn. *Psychol. Rev.,* 1946, 53, 147–158.

WORTZ, E. C., & BITTERMAN, M. E. On the effect of an irrelevant relation. *Amer. J. Psychol.,* 1953, 66, 491–493.

WYCKOFF, L. B., JR. The role of observing responses in discrimination learning. Part I. *Psychol. Rev.,* 1952, 59, 431–442.

WYCKOFF, L. B., JR. A mathematical model and an electronic model for learning. *Psychol. Rev.,* 1954, 61, 89–97.

ZEAMAN, D., & HOUSE, B. J. Approach and avoidance in the discrimination learning of retardates. In D. Zeaman et al., *Learning and transfer in mental defectives.* Progress rep. No. 2, NIMH USPHS, 1960. Res. Grant M-1099 to Univer. of Connecticut. Pp. 32–70.

ZEAMAN, D., & HOUSE, B. J. Reversals as a function of distinct versus identical responses. Paper read at Eastern Psychol. Ass., Atlantic City, April, 1962.

ZEAMAN, D., HOUSE, B. J., & ORLANDO, R. Use of special training conditions in visual discrimination learning with imbeciles. *Amer. J. ment. Defic.,* 1958, 63, 453–459.

6

INTELLIGENCE AND BRAIN DAMAGE

Brendan A. Maher

Introduction. Our purpose in this chapter is to discuss the general nature of the concept of intelligence with a view to examining some organic implications. For the sake of convenience the chapter is organized into two sections. The first of these deals with certain conceptual issues, while the second deals with questions relative to intelligence and organic damage. Space limitations preclude a thorough examination of all the issues which will be raised, but hope is to present what appear to be some central problems at the present time.[1]

PRELIMINARY CONCEPTUAL ASPECTS

Necessity for the concept

Our first consideration is whether there is any need for a concept of intelligence at all. We shall approach this problem by examining some behavioral phenomena which invoke the concept of intelligence as an explanatory vehicle.

Intelligence is sometimes conceived of as a limiting factor which determines the maximum value which certain responses may reach, regardless of further increases in all other variables known to improve performance. Let us take the case of an individual who has been exposed to experiences

[1] Earlier versions of this chapter were read and criticized by Jean Burton, Irving Gottesman, Donal Jones, Barbara Maher, and Walter Mischel. The errors that remain are the fault of the writer. Work on this manuscript was facilitated by previous research support from the National Science Foundation, Grant No. G 3852/6433. Assistance with the manuscript was given by Patricia Hall.

among his peers. They achieve a certain mean level of performance of a given response, while our subject's performance falls below that mean. Past observation has shown that performance may often be improved by increasing motivation, by manipulating rewards for the performance, by increasing the number of training trials, by extinguishing competing responses, and so forth. We therefore manipulate all the variables and find that the performance of our subject does not improve. Thus we conclude that the subject's performance is incapable of further improvement and infer that the difference between his performance and that of his peers is due to some absolute limiting factor. If the responses in which we are interested are those which fall under our particular definition of intelligence, we state that the limiting factor is low intelligence. Provided that we have, in fact, exhausted all the possible manipulations of the variables under our control, it seems difficult not to make this inference.

The example given above is descriptive of a comparatively extreme case, namely, where the performance of the subject did not improve at all. A more frequent situation is that in which the subject shows continuing improvements in performance, but gains less per trial (or per reinforcement or other motivational unit) than most of his peers do. The ceiling is therefore one which relates to *rate* of improvement rather than to asymptotic performance.

By invoking explanations of this kind we are implying that certain other propositions are valid for our subjects. One of these is that the subject will exhibit low improvement rates for other responses which we may try to establish. This low intelligence is regarded as a trans-situational variable which will retard the acquisition of responses in a wide range of circumstances. How wide a range depends upon whether the user of the concept conceives of a unitary intelligence or several intelligences.

A second implication is that we have eliminated the possibility that motivational deficiencies are responsible for the poor performance which was observed. For this assumption to be justified we need a measure of the subject's motivations which is independent of the performance in which he is engaged.

Thirdly we assume, implicitly, that the low acquisition rate is not a consequence of lack of previous opportunity to acquire responses which are prerequisites to this new acquisition. We could not conclude, for instance, that our subject was of low intelligence because of failure to acquire responses if the relevant stimulation were given in a foreign language. It should be noted that we are implying no lack of *opportunity*. If the subject has not learned the prerequisite responses in spite of exposure to conditions in which his peers did learn them, then we should still conclude that low intelligence was the determining factor.

Essentially parallel implications arise when we state that a subject is of superior intelligence. Here again we assume that factors of motivation and past experience are similar to those of his peers and that his more rapid acquisition rate is evidence of higher intelligence. Where differences between individuals' performance cannot be traced to motivational or experimental factors, the explanation then hinges upon structural variations.

Structural differences between organisms may arise either through the effect of the environment operating on existing structure, or because of predetermined structural characteristics the nature of which are subsumed under the study of genetics. Environmental influences may be of the more obvious kind, such as intake of toxic substances, dietary deficiencies, and the like. It is also possible that they may arise as a consequence of stimuli which were not generally considered to affect structure. Instances of these, both empirical and hypothetical, are to be found in the work of Hebb (1949) and Rosenzweig et al. (1960). In this respect the concept of intelligence implies structural differences between individuals which limit the extent to which their behavior is modifiable by a particular environmental event.

Summary. Intelligence is, thus, a concept which is invoked to account for the apparent failure of all individuals to modify their behavior equally in the face of similar environmental influences. The source of this difference is presumed to be structural factors in the individual, genetic influences upon structure being regarded as major variables, but structural changes arising from certain types of experience and from postnatal accidents are also recognized. Intelligence is generally regarded as a ceiling factor which sets the upper limits on an individual's response or on his rate of gain from experience.

This upper-limit aspect of the concept has been formalized in the notion of intelligence as *capacity*. It may be profitable therefore to examine the capacity model in our study of the issues involved in the concept itself.

The concept of capacity

Definitions of intelligence, and of mental deficiency, frequently have recourse to the term capacity. In many ways this has been unfortunate because of the connotations which adhere to the concept of capacity. When we say that a water tank has a capacity of 20 gallons, our statement may be verified empirically in two ways. We may actually fill it with measured gallons of water and observe how much it holds, or we may simply measure its interior dimensions and calculate the volume without ever putting water in it. Provided that our measuring instruments agree with established standards, both observations should coincide. In the latter procedure we have measured the capacity by using stable structural characteristics of the tank, not by sampling its water-holding "behavior." In the same way we may measure the capacity of a battery by making calculations from its structural characteristics. We do not have to exhaust it in order to calculate its capacity to generate current.

Examining the concept of capacity further we find that we can compare two tanks in terms of their capacity and conclude that one of them has more or less capacity to hold water than the other. This difference can be expressed in gallon units. When we come to apply this concept to the measurement of intelligence, certain problems arise. It is axiomatic in psychology that any given response is determined by a complex of variables all of which happen to be operating at the time the response is made. In order for any other response to have occurred, one or more of these determining variables would have to have had a different value. When we say that a subject was functioning below capacity, we mean that if the determining variables had been altered, his response would have been more adequate, by some prior criterion of adequacy. If we say that a subject is operating at capacity, we mean that no alteration in the determining variables can be made which would lead to greater adequacy of this subject's responses.

The water-tank analogy still applies if the observation is made that a metal tank holds less water in cold weather than in hot weather, expansion having increased the volume in the latter case. Thus the capacity of the tank is dependent upon temperature variables; when we state what the capacity is, we must add a temperature subscript. Neither capacity is more *true* than the other. Possibly we may want to decide that the "true" capacity of our tank is the maximum volume which it could ever attain; this might be the volume produced by expansion just before the metal began to melt. One consequence of this would be that true capacity would have little practical value, as it would be poorly predictive of the average capacity. If we manipulate conditions so that our human subject reaches an asymptotic level of performance following which any further manipulation produces disorganization, we should have the analogous measure of capacity.

The statement that an individual is functioning below capacity thus has two meanings. One of these refers to relationship between demand and performance. A subject who performs all items on an intelligence test with such accuracy and speed that he exceeds the requirements for a perfect score is clearly operating *below* capacity at that point. Presumably if there had been more items on the test, he could have done them correctly also without going over the time limit. The test as it was given did not make use of his full capacity. The other meaning of the statement is that two samples of his behavior were discrepant and that in one of the two samples the determining conditions were more favorable than in the other.

When intelligence is defined in capacity terms, there is an implication that one of the determining conditions has a finite value which limits the maximum product of all the conditions operating together. Thus in practice capacity is used with the assumption that, for any given individual, there is a point of performance which cannot be improved by further increases in environmental conditions. Beyond this point, increasing practice, motivation, etc., will not be followed by a change in performance. The limiting variable is, as we have seen before, a subject variable, and presumably it is also basically a function of organic factors, including, in particular, those involving the central nervous system.

The possibility of quantifying the capacity limit in this way depends upon the creation of optimal environmental conditions during measurement. Where this is possible, the obtained value suffers from the practical disability that it is, by definition, not the value which would be obtained under more typical conditions. Where our aim is to predict the behavior of the subject in his natural habitat, then a capacity measure of this kind could be quite misleading. However, when we are in a position to take measures of optimum performance and average performance of the same responses, we may get an estimate of the range within which environmental factors are determining behavior.

Determining this range from responses made within the confines of a single testing situation presents special problems. We must assume, during one testing session, that the test-environment variables are the same for all subtests. Thus the differential effects of environment upon test performance must necessarily be those created by past environments. For such an estimate to be made, the test should include at least one subtest which is particularly insensitive to the effects of previous environments. The performance of the subject on this subtest would never be lower than his performance on any other subtest. Jastak (1949) has advanced this argument with his remark that "there is in every psychometric record an ability through which a person's latent intellectual power may be adequately approximated. It is the ability which yields the highest score. . . ."

If we are assuming some kind of unitary capacity, we are compelled to expect that the same subtest will produce the highest score on repeated administrations of the test to the same person. If we define this capacity as being measurable in the same way in all people, we are likewise compelled to predict that the same subtest will produce the highest score when the test is given to anyone.

This latter conclusion is patently at odds with the facts. In order to reconcile the notion of capacity with the fluctuation observed on test score in repeated administrations, and between different individuals, we are compelled to adopt the assumption that there are several capacities, each of which is defined by a particular kind of subtest in a scale. A subject's performance on each subtest may or may not be close to his capacity for performance of the kind that the subtest measures. There is no way to estimate this unless we repeat the subtest with some improvement in environmental conditions between the two administrations.

In brief, the only way in which we can validate the statement, "*S* is functioning below capacity," is to demonstrate that variables can be manipulated so as to bring about an improvement in the level of functioning. This is clearly predictive validity, i.e., the validation of a statement about responsiveness of a subject to treatment. The statement cannot be validated by any consideration of the relationship between levels of functioning for different kinds of responses. Thus, while it may be useful to apply the concept of capacity to intelligent behavior when we are talking about fluctuations observed in the same response measures on repeated observations, it is difficult to apply it logically to samples of different kinds of responses taken at the same time. It will also be clear that statements to the effect that a particular subject is operating "above capacity" are intrinsically contradictory.

Criticisms of the concept

We have examined in broad outline the kind of behavioral phenomena which lead to the development of a concept of intelligence; we have discussed the limitations of the capacity model when used in conjunction with behavioral measures. However, some students of behavior have suggested that there is no necessity for a concept such as that of intelligence and have specific objections to it.

As we have seen, the concept of intelligence rests upon the observation that there are individual differences in response to the same environmental conditions, but that such differences can also arise because of other factors, especially motivational ones. Within the confines of a single set of observations, such as in a formal intelligence test, there is no sure way to decide whether or not these other factors were adversely affecting performance. In order to assess the effect of these factors, it is necessary to have independent measures of their values uninfluenced by intelligence. Where we may be considering the possible effects of test-taking motivation, this requirement seems to be impossible to meet. As Liverant (1960) has pointed out, the intelligence model does not permit identification of non-intellective variables, and he notes the frequent failures of prediction made from test performance to nontest situations such as school achievement, peer interaction, and the like. Considering this, and other aspects of the concept, he suggests that the term intelligence be relegated to a descriptive function rather than an explanatory one. Variables which would be used to explain (predict) the occurrence of intelligent behavior might then be drawn from more coherent theories of behavior, particularly modern learning theories.

Most modern learning theories eschew consideration of individual differences in performance, being concerned instead with formulating general propositions about the determinants of behavior regardless of any idiosyncratic characteristics of the organism which is behaving. An extreme development of the learning theory position might lead to the echoing of the Watsonian dictum that given complete control over the environment, it would be possible to bring any subject to any level of performance on any task. Ignoring for the moment the problem that any failure to do this in a particular case can be attributed ex post facto to a failure to have controlled the environment correctly, we still face the possibility that the environmental conditions necessary to produce the response in one subject are not the same as those required to produce it in another. In a word, one subject takes more trials, more reinforcements, and must be in a greater state of need than another in order to operate at the same level.

From a practical point of view it may be feasible to disregard this difference as being irrelevant, once the response has been produced. From a scientific point of view it cannot be disregarded. It is important to know why specified values of environmental conditions do not produce response acquisition in different subjects at the same rate. When environmental differences have already been excluded, the differences must be structural ones within the organism. When we know the relationship between such environmental factors and structural changes and between the structural changes and behavior, we may still conclude with a possible statement of environment-subsequent behavior relations which may be formulated independently of the nature of the mediating structural change. This is, in essence, the logical position of the psychology of the "empty" organism. We may, for example, obtain data which suggest that exposure to a wide range of stimuli in infancy leads to a more rapid rate of learning subsequent stimulus-response relations than when no such exposure has been made available. We may also find that early exposure to these stimuli is followed by detectable changes in some physiological system. The empty-organism theorist may remark that this is interesting but irrelevant provided he knows the nature of the relationship between the two psychological variables. Thus, the question of structural limitations upon behavior is dismissed.

Unfortunately this position is much too simple. In the first place it is far from clear that environmental variables which bring about measurable physiological change in the organism do so without limit. Knowledge of the characteristics of the mediating physiological systems may contribute significantly to the formulation of adequate S-R laws. In the second place *we can only assume that an organism is "empty" when we know that it is full but intact.* If the structural deficiency in a given organism is plainly apparent to the environmentalist, he naturally assumes that the typical laws of learning will have to be modified to permit prediction of the progress of learning in the subject. Even the most extreme environmentalist would not expect a blind subject to learn a response which depended upon visual discrimination, nor would he expect a subject whose hand was amputated to learn some task involving finger prehension. The examples appear too ludicrous to cite. But provided that there are no obvious sensory defects and no obvious motor defects, the assumption is often made implicitly that there could be no other site at which physiological anomaly could require modification of predictions about the behavior of the individual in question. When the prediction is not confirmed by events, it is customary to invoke some unknown experiences in the past environment to account for the discrepancy. The possibility that structural anomalies may have partly determined the observed response is usually disregarded.

One effect of this is that the obvious significance of drugs and lesions upon learned behavior has posed a serious problem for those learning theorists who remain stoutly aphysiological. Either one can ignore these data and confine one's psychology deliberately to the study of *some* of the variables which determine behavior, i.e., those which are related to the concept of reinforcement, or one can decide to extend the meaning of the word environment to include variables which have an uncertain relationship to reinforcement. Another effect of the former attitude is that the possibility of behavior being changed by direct manipulation of physiological systems is also disregarded.

In summary then, our hypothetical extreme environmentalist may respond to the problem of the relationship between physiological systems and behavior in any or all of the following ways: (1) We do not need to know the nature of the underlying physiological mechanisms because we have been able to establish laws relating reinforcement variables to behavior without recourse to this knowledge. (2) We are concerned with the establishment of laws governing the behavior of an *average* organism and do not hope to predict the behavior of deviant organisms.

It may well be that the tendency to use the concept of intelligence sometimes as a psychological one and sometimes as a biological one has generated the confusion which continues to surround it. The practicing clinical psychologist, dealing with deviant individuals for the most part, must draw his concepts from whatever disciplines may be most pertinent to the problems which face him. His patients are neither average nor empty. If their behavior is sometimes circumscribed by structural limitations, he must bear this in mind and utilize whatever biological concepts are most helpful in making accurate predictions. The notion of intelligence as involving biologically derived influences upon the interaction between environmental and behavioral change may well be useful in spite of its tenuous status as a purely psychological construct.

MEASUREMENT AND VALIDITY

In this section we shall consider some problems which arise when instruments are devised to measure intelligence. Our main concern will be with the problems of validity and prediction from tests of intelligence and their use in the prediction of organic damage.

Definitions

Systematic examination of the concept of intelligence brings up the question of definition and measurement of the concept itself. There are several problems involved in definition, the first of which might be regarded as that of differential definition. Here the question is simply what responses we shall call intelligent in order to distinguish them from other behavioral phenomena which might be variously defined as *anxiety, motivational, emotional,* and so forth. A definition of this kind will consist of a list of characteristics which a selected unit of behavior must exhibit in order to be included as an example of intelligent behavior. Unfortunately, as Marx (1951) has noted, while the definition of the concept *dog,* to take a concrete instance, may be reduced to a series of pointing operations (or pointing to specific instances of dogs), this is much less easily done with psychological concepts. Psychological concepts are most frequently based upon observations of *relationship* between objects and events, not upon the invariant aspects of a particular class of object.

Operational definitions. One position which may be taken is that the concept is defined by the operations which measure it. Thus the concept of intelligence may be defined by the items which are included in an intelligence test together with the criteria for scoring responses. An articulate account of the implications of this position has been provided by Spiker and McCandless (1954). It is commonly described as the *operational definition,* although Spiker and McCandless have preferred the term *empiricist* meaning *criterion.* This position has been attacked by several writers in the field. Israel and Goldstein (1944) claimed that it would be logically impossible for the operationist to ever get started on the problem of measurement. Likewise, Stoddard commented: "Some persons think it irrelevant or misleading to define intelligence; they say 'Intelligence is whatever the tests measure.' This may be a good cliché now, but how could it be helpful to persons starting out to build tests? At that time a test measures nothing. What does the test constructor put into his tests and why?" (1943, p. 3). Stoddard's criticism is valid enough as far as it goes. The test constructor obviously has some kind of definition in mind when he goes about devising a test of intelligence. While the definition may be implicit or explicit at that point, it becomes explicit and operational once the test has been standardized. In this way the pretest definition has been modified and made operational. Whenever subsequent generalizations are made about intelligence based upon measurements which utilized a particular test, then the definition of intelligence is that provided by the test.

The decision concerning the operations which will be used to measure and thus define intelligence are not open to challenge on any a priori basis. A definition of this kind may be criticized on the grounds that the measuring instrument does not predict anything at all, or that it does not predict the behaviors which the critic defines as intelligent, or that it does not correlate with another test which he uses to define intelligence. But it is irrelevant to state that any test is not a measure of "true intelligence" unless the concept of true intelligence has already been operationally defined in a way which commands some general agreement. In this latter event we have an agreement that the phrase true intelligence shall be defined by some standard operations. We have not made a metaphysical discovery.

Preoperational definitions. Tests of intelligence have most frequently been devised for some practical social purpose. The original Binet-Simon Scale was intended to identify those children who would have difficulty in making normal progress through the Paris school system. Insofar as school achievement was the criterion, then school achievement was the definition of intelligence which preceded the test construction. A test which would predict this perfectly could be called a test of *scholastic aptitude* or *intelligence* depending upon which term the tester preferred to use. It is interesting to note, in this connection, that Hull categorized the early Binet scales as instances of scholastic aptitude testing, recognizing at the same time "that if a test is to be of any particular value it must enable us to forecast a *particular* aptitude or group of aptitudes rather than measure some hypothetical or semi-metaphysical faculty" (Hull, 1928, p. 19).

While the criteria for deciding to keep a particular item in a test may be clear enough, the hypothesis which led to the construction of the items is not always evident. It may be profitable to examine some hypotheses which have guided psychologists who work in this field. Because of the overwhelming importance which has been attached to his scales, the hypothesis of Wechsler (1958) may be examined with some special care. "Intelligence, operationally defined,[2] is the aggregate or global capacity of the individual to act purposefully, to think rationally and to deal effectively with his environment" (Wechsler, 1958, p. 7). Wechsler then proceeds to point out that (1) the final products of intelligent behavior are a function of the pattern of combination of several abilities, as well as their number or quality, (2) that "factors other than intellectual ability, for example, those of drive or incentive, are involved in intelligent behavior,"

[2] The phrase "operationally defined" has been added to the earlier definition (Wechsler, 1944) with which it is otherwise identical. This change is rather curious as the definition given is not, of course, in operational terms at all.

and (3) that while different kinds of intelligent behavior may require different degrees of intellectual ability, an excess of any ability may add but little to the effectiveness of behavior as a whole.

The foregoing may, perhaps, be summarized to mean that a distinction must be made between *intellectual ability* and *intelligent behavior*. The former, in Wechsler's eyes, is a necessary but not sufficient condition for the occurrence of the latter. The fact that a person who, by implicit definition, possesses much intellectual ability (e.g., a mathematician) may sometimes appear to be below average in his production of intelligent behavior is cited as an example of the lack of a perfect correlation between the two.

This means, necessarily, that the responses which indicate intellectual ability are not the same as those which define intelligent behavior. A quote may serve to make the point clear. "The unusual reasoning abilities of the mathematician are more highly correlated with the thing that we ultimately measure as intelligence than sheer memory is, but the possession of this ability (reasoning ability) is no guarantee that behavior as a whole will be very intelligent in the sense defined above" (Wechsler, 1958, p. 7). From this it would follow that measures of something to be called reasoning ability are good measures of intelligence, but not so good as predictors of intelligent behavior. Up to this point, the position of Wechsler is comparatively clear. It can be summarized even more tersely than we have so far by stating that certain classes of behavior, mainly "reasoning behavior," define intellectual ability. They are less than perfectly correlated with the tendency to act purposefully and deal effectively with the environment—these latter being the criteria by which we define intelligent behavior.

However, having made this distinction, Wechsler proceeds to confuse the issue. The point can, once again, best be illustrated by a quotation.

> Our measurements of electricity consist of quantitative records of its chemical, thermal and magnetic effects. But these effects are not identical with the "stuff" which produced them. We do not know what the ultimate nature of the "stuff" is which constitutes intelligence but, as in the case of electricity, we know it by the "things" which it enables us to do—such as making appropriate associations between events, drawing correct inferences from propositions, understanding the meaning of words, solving mathematical problems or building bridges (Wechsler, 1958, p. 8).

It is apparent that Wechsler is drawing a distinction between the ultimate nature of the "stuff" of intelligence and the effects by which we measure it. The distinction is the same as that which metaphysicians made between noumena and phenomena and is the kind of distinction which scientists have generally abandoned as meaningless, or at least unprofitable to pursue.

In this chapter, we shall not develop this question, but shall instead take the position that as there is, by definition, no way to know what the ultimate nature of any event is, our energies may best be bent to discovering empirical relationships between measurable phenomena. Indeed the major significance of metaphysical intrusions of this kind is their capacity to cloud the issues which arise in measuring intelligent behavior. However, we may perhaps characterize the theoretical position of Wechsler as involving a basic distinction between certain kinds of behavior, mainly those called reasoning, and other kinds which are concerned with effective adaptation to the environment. These two classes of behavior are likely to be correlated in individuals but less than perfectly. The first class of behaviors defines intellectual ability; the second defines general intelligence. As the operations which define one are distinguishable in some respects from those which define the other, they stand as two separate concepts although with some overlap in meaning.

Turning to another source of definitions we may examine the position taken by Cyril Burt, especially as summarized by him some years ago (Burt, 1955). Intelligence he defines as an *innate, general, cognitive ability*. While the significance of the term innate may be left to later discussion, it is instructive at this point to consider the other two terms. Cognition is a rather ill-defined concept in modern psychology, and in order to use the term with meaning, it is necessary to define what are, and what are not, cognitive activities. Burt does not present a detailed catalog of cognitive activities but concludes that the basic definition of cognitive involves a contrast between the capacity "for adapting, guiding or directing mental activities, by means of discriminative and integrative processes," which is cognition, and the capacity for "responding promptly, actively and energetically," which is not cognition (Burt, 1955, p. 166). It is not clear how one is to conclude that a "mental activity" has been guided apart from the observation of some overt responses, but perhaps it would be congruent with Burt's position to suggest that cognitive capacity is being adduced to account for the differences between individuals with regard to the adaptiveness of their behavior. Where Burt appears to differ from Wechsler is that he seems to be confining the term cognitive (or intelligent) to those adaptive behaviors which occur as a consequence of discriminative and integrative processes (which presumably involve what Wechsler has called reasoning). Wechsler, as we have seen, makes a distinction between reasoning capacity and adaptive behavior, the latter not being isomorphic with the former.

Space does not permit a detailed examination of the history of the concept of intelligence. For our present purposes it may suffice to note from the previous paragraphs that a recurring issue in the current definitions of intelligence is whether it ought to refer to some adaptive or goal-reaching behavior, or whether it should refer to behaviors which meet certain formal criteria such as those which characterize deductive or inductive reasoning. This, of course, vastly oversimplifies the problem. Furthermore it may give the impression that a dichotomy exists between the two kinds of activity. This is far from being the case, and the differences between theoreticians are mainly in terms of emphasis. However this difference in emphasis is particularly germane to the problem of the validity of any given intelligence test and the problem of validity requires some examination here.

Validity

Content validity. If we define intelligence arbitrarily as, let us say, the ability to produce correct solutions to problems in syllogistic reasoning, the only validity of any significance for a test of this ability is *content validity*. Provided that the test contains only syllogistic problems and that it includes syllogisms derived randomly from a larger population of such items, no further evidence of validity is either required or possible. Such a test can then be used to establish empirically the magnitude of the relationships between the scores it generates and other response measures. The fact that a particular empirical finding indicates a small or no relationship between test scores and other response measures is not relevant to the question of the validity of the test as a test of syllogistic reasoning. It is, naturally, both possible and probable that scores on such a test will not correlate perfectly with scores on another, different sample of syllogistic problems but that they will be subject to the usual extraneous sources of variability such as test-taking attitudes, etc. The point to be made here is not that the test is measuring only ability to solve syllogisms, but that there is no other measure which can provide "purer" validity than the test itself.

This problem has been discussed by Spiker and McCandless who point out that the question of whether or not a particular test is a *true* measure of intelligence presupposes a meaningful concept of true intelligence. This question has led many worker, they suggest, "to attempt to discover the 'underlying nature of intelligence.' It is rarely clear from their writings what is the 'nature' of the 'nature' they expect to find" (Spiker & McCandless, 1954). Thus the question of the validity of intelligence tests which are constructed from some a priori definition of intelligence is ultimately irrelevant. Should it turn out that scores derived from such a test predict nothing else about the subject, it might be abandoned as being of no practical or scientific value, but it is not therefore *invalid*.[3]

Predictive validity. Validity, as applied to tests of intelligence, possesses a second meaning. If we have already defined intelligence by responses or behavior patterns which are hard to observe other than in the natural social habitat of the individual, the purpose of test construction is that of providing an economical predictor. When we have defined intelligence in terms of adaptive or purposeful behavior, then the direct observation of adaptive sequences of response in the individual becomes lengthy and impractical. Consequently the function of a test is to provide a cheaper and easier method of predicting such behavior, even at the possible cost of some minor loss of accuracy. The essence of this argument was advanced succinctly by Hull (1928). "It is necessity for economizing time and energy that has given rise to short-cut methods of predicting aptitudes. This central fact must never be lost sight of. *A method of prognosis which is not at the same time reasonably quick and reasonably inexpensive has*

---

[3] Since this chapter was first prepared, an excellent analysis of the confusion surrounding definitions of validity has been provided by Ebel (1961).

no excuse for existence." (The italics are Hull's.) The validity of such tests is estimated in terms of the accuracy of predictions made from the test to the ultimate behavioral criterion. It is called *predictive validity.* In order, however, to calculate this validity empirically, it is necessary to take direct measures (laborious and expensive though this be) of the behavioral criteria and to compute the appropriate correlations. These direct measures, of course, rest in the last analysis upon the defense of face validity. If, for example, a given test of intelligence is validated against a criterion of teachers' judgments of intelligence, it is pointless to then claim that the test is a "purer" measure than are the teachers' judgments. When the test predicts such judgments with a high degree of accuracy and it is easier to give the test than to go through the process of getting teachers' judgments, the test justifies its own existence. If it is more difficult to give the test than to get an estimate from the teacher, the greater value of the test then depends upon its greater stability.

Concurrent validity. New tests are commonly correlated with other, older tests and the obtained correlations reported as though they represented some kind of validity. If the purpose of the new test were to predict performance on the older test, then this correlation would indeed be a measure of predictive validity.[4] Here, however, the justification of the new test would depend upon its being easier and less expensive to administer. If it did not possess these advantages, it would be difficult to see what purposes its construction had served. Nevertheless, this kind of validation (commonly referred to as *concurrent validity*) is reported as a matter of course. An illustration of a table of concurrent validities of the W-B I is given below.

TABLE 6-1

Illustrations of the concurrent validities of the Wechsler-Bellevue (W-B I)

Test	Subjects	N	Validity coefficient
Stanford-Binet, 1937	College freshmen	112	.62
Stanford-Binet, 1937	Mental patients	227	.89
AGCT	Veterans	100	.83
Army Alpha	Adult female nurses	92	.74
Raven's Progressive Matrices	Adolescent deaf	41	.55
Morgan Mental Ability	College freshmen	125	.62

(Adapted from Wechsler, 1958)

Trait validity. Recently the problem of validity has been attacked with the assistance of the notion of *trait validity,* the status of which is examined

[4] Campbell (1960) has pointed out the essential logical similarity of predictive and concurrent validities, and suggests the term *practical validity* to include both cases. A discussion of the problem in detail is available in Loevinger (1957).

carefully by Campbell (1960). Trait validity is computed by calculating the correlations between two measures, neither of which has the status of an ultimate criterion, both of which possess some face validity, but which employ different measuring methods, e.g., test versus rating. "Both are regarded as fallible measures, often with known imperfections such as halo effects for the ratings and response sets for the tests. Validation, when it occurs, is symmetrical and equalitarian. The presumptive validity of both measures is increased by agreement" (Campbell, 1960). Cumulative trait validation of this kind will result in the progressive gathering of information as to the extent to which the method of measurement has affected the score obtained. If, for example, we measure the ability to reason syllogistically by means of a series of written problems and then by means of similar problems presented orally and, after observing the usual counterbalancing requirements, find a low correlation between performance on the two tests, we might conclude that the methods themselves had introduced measurable variance which was irrelevant to the trait which we had called syllogistic reasoning ability.

The crucial difficulty which arises in this kind of validity is that we may be led to conclude that syllogistic reasoning ability is multifactored and then proceed to describe the structure of the ability in complex terms. Campbell and Fiske (1959) have pointed out clearly that the measurement of method factors in the correlations of test scores requires that we measure the trait by more than one method and that we use each method to measure more than one trait.

Before closing our discussion of trait validity, we should emphasize that the computation of this kind of validity has value for scientific purposes, but per se has no immediate value for practical predictions.

Concurrence with formal assumptions. When tests of intelligence are being constructed, the test constructor frequently uses additional criteria to guide him in the final selection of test items. One of the most important of these is the extent to which the test produces scores which agree with the assumption that mental ability follows a growth curve; another is the extent to which the test scores follow an approximate Gaussian distribution when applied to a random sample of the population. These statistical criteria are used to guarantee that the test accords with certain general propositions about intelligence, which are (1) that intelligence increases with increasing age, up to a point after which it may begin to decline, and (2) that intelligence is distributed *normally* in the total population, much as height and weight are. In the last resort these propositions are in the nature of postulates. When tests are constructed, those items which fail to produce scores which meet these criteria are abandoned. Thus test measurements inevitably confirm the postulates. The postulates in question may be plausible ones.[5] However, we must recognize the fact that even if a test meets these statistical criteria this in itself is not evidence of the test's independent validity.

[5] Their plausibility has been questioned by Richmond (1953), Heim (1954), and Lewis (1957).

Validity and mental retardation

Validity and etiology. Bearing in mind the foregoing comments on validity, we may now consider the relationship of the concept of validity to the problems of mental retardation.

The judgment that a person is mentally retarded is made on the basis of long observation of behavior, or upon the presence of evidence of such obvious physical damage or gross developmental deviation early in life that the future development of normal behavior seems highly improbable. As behavior observation represents the criterion measure itself, it is irrelevant to ask whether or not the observation is valid. We may want to inquire whether or not the observer had enough experience of normal behavior to make the comparative judgment; we may want to make sure that the behavior was observed in many different situations and over a long period of time; but we cannot dispute the validity of the behavioral criterion. What constitutes mentally retarded behavior depends to a large extent upon the society which happens to be making the judgment. An individual who does not create a problem for others in his social environment and who manages to become self-supporting is usually not defined as mentally retarded no matter what his test IQ may be. Mental retardation is primarily a socially defined phenomenon, and it is in large part meaningless to speak of mental retardation without this criterion in mind.

Formal tests of intelligence are not universally good predictors of the future social efficiency of subjects whose test scores indicate retardation. The studies of Anderson and Fearing (1923), Fairbank (1933), Baller (1936), Muench (1944), Kennedy (1948), and Charles (1953) suggest the extent of this unreliability. Indeed, as Masland, Sarason, and Gladwin (1958) have pointed out, when children thus identified as retarded leave school, the majority cease to be defined as retarded, having presumably made a satisfactory adjustment. Anyone who has worked professionally within an institution for the mentally retarded will be aware that one of the significant factors which are taken into account when deciding to discharge a patient is the nature of the social environment to which he will return—not evidence of improved intellectual functioning.

In the light of this, then, we may ask why intelligence tests are given to individuals whose behavior is clearly that which is called retarded. We give tests under these circumstances not to confirm the behavioral phenomena but (1) to guarantee that the behavior of the individual is being compared against a larger standard sample than would be available to the experience of any single observer, and (2) to offer an etiological hypothesis. Of these reasons, the first is self-explanatory and usually comes into play when the "diagnosis" of mental retardation has been made by a parent or teacher who may have atypical standards for defining normal behavior.

Test results can provide hypotheses about the behavioral observation in two ways. One of these occurs when the test-produced IQ is within the normal range even though the daily behavior of the individual resembles that of a mentally retarded subject. In effect the test results are suggesting that the daily behavior of the subject is primarily dependent upon some variables, such as motivational deficit, educational deprivation, etc., which can be modified. Or the total score may provide an IQ within the range of mental retardation but also provide other evidences from the test which suggest the presence of a particular etiological variable. An example of this is the popular inference that certain kinds of test behaviors indicate *brain damage*. Note that the test is not disconfirming the general diagnosis of retardation, but is circumscribing the etiological explanation of the behavior.

What is the practical value of this? Insofar as the methods which are used to help the person who is diagnosed as suffering from educational deficit, cultural impoverishment, simple retardation, or brain damage differ, then the etiological hypothesis serves as a guide to the appropriate treatment. Etiological hypotheses, apart from their academic interest, are useful chiefly as indices of the probable response of the subject to a given kind of treatment. It will now become clear that the validity of an intelligence test when used in this way depends upon its correlations (1) with other evidences of etiology and (2) with responsiveness to various kinds of treatment.

When test scores or data are used to generate etiological hypotheses, a rather critical issue is raised. This issue is related to the multiple causation of behavior. A subject may give a wrong answer to a test question as a consequence of many different variables operating at the time. He may not be able to understand the language in which the question is put, either because it is foreign to him, because the vocabulary is unfamiliar, or because he has a sensory defect such as a hearing loss. None of these variables may be operating, but he may give a wrong answer because that happens to be the answer which his environment has established as the correct one. He may be uninterested in the test because he has learned to avoid academic-type tasks. He may be afraid of the test and find that he does not seem to be able to think. The variables influencing his behavior may be any or all of these. All of them will operate to produce a score of zero on that particular item, and thus all will be regarded as equivalent.

If the test is to be useful in detecting and distinguishing between the influence of these variables, it must contain items or subjects which are differentially sensitive to them. Putting it another way, if all the items are equally likely to be answered incorrectly by an anxious subject or by a poorly educated subject, the test will not be able to distinguish between the two. Likewise, if the test is to be used to distinguish brain-damaged and non-brain-damaged subjects, there must be tests which are differentially sensitive to the two conditions. Constructing a test which would meet these requirements might be undertaken in either of two ways. The first would consist in the inclusion of items which are not necessarily related to any formal concept of intelligence but which have been shown empirically to be correlated with the etiological variable which it is desired to detect. Selecting such items requires some prior knowledge about the etiological variable itself, e.g., a theory of *anxiety* or an articulated body of knowledge about the consequences of brain injury. Such items would not be defining intelligence. They would be defining anxiety, neural integration, or some related concept.

Data obtained from a test constructed in this way might provide evidence that anxiety, for example, was at an unusually high level in a particular subject and that his performance on tests of reasoning, memory, etc., might be presumed to have been affected adversely by this. This latter inference would be more strongly supported if we could show that his actual performance on items involving reasoning, memory, and so forth was directly characterized by responses which were indicative of anxiety. In order to be able to make such inferences, we need empirical laws governing the effects of anxiety as an independent variable, and reasoning as a dependent variable. Similar laws would be needed to permit inferences about brain damage, educational deprivation, and other independent variables. These would be largely in the form of statements about the determinants of different kinds of wrong response to the same items. Thus our second method of test construction would involve the inclusion of items which are a priori definitive of intelligence and the accumulation of scoring procedures which permit etiological inferences to be made from the pattern and/or content of errors.

For accurate inferences to be drawn, it is necessary not only that the relationship between the etiological factor and the response be empirically established, but that it be a relationship not also found between the response and some other etiological factor. This latter consideration is most important because clinical diagnosis from responses, unfortunately, nearly always involves trying to deduce causes by inspecting effects. Complex as this problem is, it is complicated even further by the fact that many of the etiological variables which have been mentioned operate together as *tied variables*. An extreme instance of this is to be found in many cases of cerebral palsy where the motor handicap is likely to be exacerbated by the anxieties generated by having the motor handicap in the first place. The diagnostic distinction between motor handicap and anxiety-produced incompetence then becomes difficult if not impossible to make.

Validity and treatment. The logic which underlies the validity of tests as predictors of responsiveness to treatment is somewhat simpler. Provided that the treatment variable is sufficiently clearly defined and those behaviors which constitute improvement or cure have also been defined, the question of whether or not a subject improved is a matter of empirical verification. Treatments may be classified as *rational* or *nonrational*. Rational treatments are those which have been devised on the basis of knowledge about the etiology and determinants of the behavior in question. Nonrational treatments are those which appear to improve the behavior, but the mechanism which mediates this improvement is unclear or unknown. Bearing this in mind we see that a test may have validity as an indicator of treatment if (1) it has etiological validity where the etiology is reliably connected to a rational therapy, or (2) it has an empirically verified relationship with the outcome of any therapy, rational or nonrational. It will be clear that it would be impossible for a test to be a valid indicator of therapy under the first condition without at the same time fitting the requirements of the second condition. However, it is quite possible for a test to possess predictive validity of response to treatment without thereby demonstrating the validity of the underlying etiological hypothesis. The relationship between a test score and some etiological state of the patient requires direct demonstration and cannot be confidently inferred from the relationship between the test score and the response to a treatment derived rationally from the etiological hypothesis.

INTELLIGENCE AND ORGANIC PATHOLOGY

Of all the etiological hypotheses offered to account for the clinical cases of mental retardation, perhaps the most common and crucial is that the patient is suffering from organic damage, usually to the central nervous system. Organic damage is generally regarded as an alternative explanation to either environmental deprivation or genetically determined retardation. The practicing clinician is continually faced with the problem of differential diagnosis which this distinction implies. He may be required to decide, on the basis of tests, whether the behavior of the patient is to be attributed to subcultural factors or to organic factors. If the former possibility is eliminated on the basis of test inferences, he may be required to decide whether or not the organic anomaly is to be attributed to genetic determinants or to variables which operated to injure the organic integrity of the patient after conception. If the latter appears to be the case, he may attempt to judge whether or not the injury took place *in utero* or whether it is to be attributed to mechanical assault during or after delivery.

Ignoring some of these refinements, we might summarize the position of the diagnostician as involving three broad possible categories: subcultural, genetic anomaly, or postconception damage. Having made this distinction, it should be remarked that it may have little relevance for the treatment of the patient. Once again turning to Masland, Sarason, and Gladwin (1958) we find them commenting as follows:

> Only in the most extreme cases of organic disorder can we say that psychological and environmental factors are not relevant to treatment and development, while there are equally few retarded individuals in whom we can be certain that *no* biological factors (broadly conceived) are affecting their intellectual performance. The concept accepted in psychotherapy of treating the total person is equally or more important in the case of the subnormal individual. Acceptance of this concept practically forbids us to make diagnoses which will label deficits as due exclusively to biology or to learning.

While it may have little relevance for the treatment of the patient now afflicted, it may have very great relevance for the development of techniques of prevention. At the present time this is tantamount to saying that the major value of this kind of differential diagnosis is as a basis for research rather than as a basis for institutional decisions. Once again, the situation has been well put by Masland et al. in their contention that research demands that separate determining variables be isolated and their effects studied individually, even though they may most usually occur together in one patient.

The concept of brain damage as it is currently used in clinical psychology has two broad meanings. The first of these is the literal meaning, whereby when a clinician states that a patient is brain-damaged he means that if we were in a position to observe the physical condition of the patient's brain, we should find evidence of damage to it. He bases this statement upon the fact that the patient's behavior strongly resembles that of previous patients in whom damage to the brain had been verified independently. The second meaning is that the patient's behavior is patterned in a way which does not resemble that produced by any known combination of environmental variables, leaving the hypothesis of brain damage as the only alternative available.

Behavior and brain pathology

The literature of physiological psychology is replete with reports of changes in behavior following specific brain lesions. The vast majority of these reports deal with changes in preoperatively learned behavior in animals consequent upon the lesion, or of changes in the rate of acquisitions of new behaviors. As long as all the necessary controls have been provided, it is reasonable to regard the change in behavior as an effect of the lesion. It would be much less reasonable to reverse the inferential procedure and conclude that all animals who exhibit behavior the same as that of a postoperative animal must therefore be suffering from a similar lesion. For a specific response to be used as an indicator of brain injury, it is necessary that we know the probability that it might occur when there is no lesion present. When our inferential procedure involves going from behavior as a datum to the prediction of tissue pathology, it is necessary that we have collected a sample of subjects who have exhibited the behavior and then proceeded to verify their neurological status. Alternatively we must know the identity and probability of occurrence of those nonneurological determinants of the behavior within the environment in which our subject has been living.

Many studies which have used groups of subjects known to have brain injury compare selected responses of this group with those of a nondamaged control, matched on all other variables as far as possible. In more sophisticated studies, additional controls are provided for the variables which may be tied to brain damage, i.e., hospitalization, previous military experience, physical injury, and so forth. When this is done we obtain a statement of the observed frequencies of the critical response in all groups, which will permit us to make future probability estimates in clinical use. The caution must be observed, however, that these estimates are only appropriate for new patients who are within the limits of the population characteristics of the experimental groups. It is inappropriate to use data gathered from a group of young brain-damaged soldiers (compared with a group of young, non-brain-damaged soldiers) to arrive at probability estimates for use with a group of mentally retarded children. The crux of the problem here is that of the *base rate* for the occurrence of the critical response in the clinical population with which we are dealing. The fact that the critical response did not occur in any healthy young soldier does not justify the conclusion that it could not occur in any non-brain-damaged mental retardate. A thorough account of the issues involved is given by Meehl and Rosen (1955).

A comprehensive survey of studies of test validity and brain injury would be impossible in this chapter. Excellent surveys are already available in the literature (e.g., Yates, 1954; Klebanoff et al., 1954). However, the general state of knowledge has been aptly described by Rosvold with his comment that "Recent studies with respect to the effect of brain damage upon general intelligence, though more rigorous than in the past, are no more in agreement than were earlier studies, some of which claimed deterioration in intelligence, others not" (1959, p. 434). The discrepancies demand resolution, and it may be of value to consider the various methodological tactics available to the psychologist who is investigating in this area.

Research methods in brain pathology

The *post hoc* **study.** The basic design here involves the selection of a group of subjects who are known to have brain injury and comparing their responses on some standardized task with those of other groups who are not brain-damaged. The choice of subjects requires a selection criterion that is itself extremely valid and not likely to produce false positives or negatives. By definition the logical criterion would be that the investigator or one of his colleagues has made the brain lesion. This is possible when the subjects were patients in neurosurgery, or when there has been direct observation of accidental injury, as in a gunshot wound which penetrated the brain. However, in practice many groups are selected on the basis of diagnostic signs, some of which have less-than-perfect correlation with brain damage. Thus electroencephalography is sometimes used as the criterion, although the validity of EEG indicators is far from satisfactory itself. When any one criterion measure is not perfect, as in this case, the probability of an incorrect diagnosis may be reduced by requiring the presence of several such signs in combination. The probability that the subject has brain damage can, and should, be calculated by computing the probabilities of accurate diagnosis from empirically derived data on the validity of the signs used.

An additional problem which arises in studies which employ diagnostic signs of brain injury as the criterion for its existence is that the experimenter naturally excludes those cases where the diagnostic criteria are equivocal. Unfortunately, in clinical use it is precisely those cases which give equivocal neurological signs which lead the neurologist to ask the clinical psychologist for aid in diagnosis. Thus we have the interesting paradox that psychometric tests are most likely to be used to diagnose brain injury in the kind of patient who was automatically excluded from the original validity study! Another possibility, although not always available, is autopsy verification. When it is available, it is usually confined to the brain-injured group, and less readily obtained from the control group. This brings us directly to the second problem in this method; namely, that while it is difficult to be sure that the brain-damaged group is in fact brain-damaged, it is even more difficult to be sure that the control group is not brain-damaged. There is rarely any way of looking at the brain of a control subject, and thus we select him on the grounds that he shows none of the diagnostic signs of brain damage. Proper estimation of the probability that the controls do not have brain damage depends upon knowledge of the proportion of false negatives produced by the diagnostic criteria.

The *post-hoc* method is used when there are no data upon the subject before the brain damage occurred. The estimation of postdamage changes in behavior requires the assumption that, but for the brain damage, the behavior of the experimental group would be the same as that of the control group. This assumption, in turn, requires that the control group and the experimental group be matched on all other variables which might determine the critical response. Usually this is done as a matter of course, the obvious variables including those such as age, sex, education, socioeconomic status, and so forth. As brain-damaged patients are usually found in a medical setting, there are several other variables which may be tied to that of brain damage, e.g., hospitalization, poor employment record, military service, or some other hazardous occupation. As these variables may influence the critical response, quite independently of the effects of brain damage, the control group should, strictly speaking, be matched on them also.

The *post-hoc* method is the one most commonly used in reported studies of brain damage and intelligence. Instances of it abound in the literature, and they will not be summarized here. However, for a typical example of this method we might turn to a report by Balthazar and Morrison (1961). They were studying the efficiency of certain Wechsler signs in localizing the site of damage. Here we find that the "criteria for selection were (1) unequivocal evidence of organic brain damage in their medical history and general medical examination, (2) valid Wechslers, and (3) three or more electroencephalographic reports." Within a group of patients selected by these criteria, three further groups were selected on the basis of EEG indications of the predominant lateral location of the damage. The authors point out, "the term 'predominant' served to qualify classifications because no controls existed for diffuse or bilateral damage which could have caused mild disturbances in the contralateral hemisphere." Their data indicate that "the Wechsler verbal and performance subscales are of diagnostic value in the discrimination of left, right and indeterminate hemispheric disturbances. However, clear-cut limitations in this study were evident in that the electroencephalogram was considered to be an intermediate rather than final criterion." The statistics pertinent to their data indicate that the Wechsler criteria were 25 per cent better than chance for the population used, bearing in mind the base rate in this population.

In passing we may note that as no nonorganic controls were used in this study, it is impossible to decide how many of them would have produced Wechsler scale profiles indicative of brain damage in one or the other hemisphere. Thus the signs may help us decide somewhat better than chance what the EEG record will look like, provided that we know the patient is organic in the first place. It is difficult to see what therapeutic decisions could be differentially affected by this localization; if the decisions were to be affected it would seem wise, in the interests of the patient, to use the criterion measure (EEG) before making them.

The evaluation of a *post-hoc* study requires that we consider the purposes which it might serve. If the study is intended to add to our knowledge of the relationship between gross brain injury and some aspect of intelligence, then it is necessary that we be sure that the subjects are brain-injured. If our diagnosis of brain injury is, let us say, exclusively based upon EEG records, then we have established a relationship between test behavior and EEG records. The brain injury is an inference to account for the EEG data. In view of the tendency of the EEG technique to provide anomalous records with no other evidence of pathology, its inferential worth must be regarded with caution.

Unless the diagnosis of brain damage includes some localization of the site of the damage to the brain, it adds little to the state of knowledge of specific brain functioning. This aspect of such studies has been remarked by Yates (1954), Klebanoff et al. (1954), and again by Fitzhugh, Fitzhugh, and Reitan (1961). Where precise determination of the site and nature of the lesion is possible—as in autopsy—then studies of this kind may contribute considerably to our knowledge of brain functioning and its relationship to the classes of response which are elicited by intelligence tests.

If the experiment is intended to validate certain psychometric test responses, or signs, as measures of a neurological condition, then we must ask two questions. Is it less easy to use the diagnostic criterion than it is to use the test? A full-scale administration of the Wechsler-Bellevue or WAIS may take in the region of 2 hours to give and score. As it can never, by definition, be more valid than the diagnostic criterion used to validate it, it must be much easier to administer than EEG if we are to justify using it instead of EEG with the concomitant loss in accuracy. Secondly we may want to know what use will be made of the diagnosis. If therapeutic decisions are unaffected by the diagnosis of brain injury, it seems pertinent to inquire about the purpose of the procedure.

The pretest and posttest study. The second method available to investigators of the consequences of brain damage in the human subject is the same as that which is commonly used by physiologists in animal experimentation. Some measurement of the critical response is made in the intact subject; the lesion then occurs and postoperative measures are made of the critical response. Control groups are used here chiefly to determine the effect of the repeated testing per se upon the critical response. Changes in the response measures of the operative group are then attributed to the lesion. When this method is used with animals, certain advantages accrue to the experimenter. He can control the preoperative acquisition of the critical response, and if necessary determine the magnitude or probability of it before operating upon the animal. Thus he knows not only what the preoperative status of the response was, but what environmental variables had determined its occurrence. Secondly, he can control the site and nature of the lesion, both by the methods used in placing the lesion and by post-mortem histological control. Knowing the nature of the variables which determined the response preoperatively, he is then in a position to observe whether or not there is a general decrement in the response, or whether the decrement is selectively determined by some but not other of the environmental variables.

Clearly it is difficult to use this method with human subjects. Patients on whom neurosurgery is about to be performed are generally already suffering from some brain pathology. The outstanding exception to this is the psychiatric patient on whom psychosurgical procedures are employed, and for obvious reasons it is difficult to use the responses of such patients to indicate the relationship of brain injury to normal behavior. Almost the only practical procedure available is to use accidental brain injury; this requires that we have preliminary test data on a large number of subjects and then wait for accidents to happen. At the present time, the most available population for such studies is in military service where intelligence testing at entry is routine and where occupational conditions involve some probability that there will be accidents. A good example of this method is to be found in the work of Williams, Lubin, and Gieseking (1959). Using a military population who had been subject to intelligence testing upon induction and had subsequently suffered organic damage to the brain, they were able to obtain a measure of deficit in test performances compared with test-retest performances of military non-brain-injured hospital patients and nonhospitalized soldiers. The tied variables of hospitalization and military service were thus controlled, and the groups adequately matched on premorbid test scores. From this, one of the few studies of its type,[6] the authors concluded that the "verbal tests (Reading and Vocabulary, Arithmetical Reasoning and Clerical Speed) were significantly more sensitive to brain-injury than the spatial tests (Pattern Analysis and Mechanical Aptitude) but the differences were so small as to be of no practical significance." The decrement in performance of the brain-injured group was significant beyond the .01 level of confidence for all tests.

Their conclusions compel the inference that an analysis of the "scatter" of scores among the various tests would have no validity as an indicator of brain damage, but that brain injury does lead to a deficit in overall performance on this kind of test. Certain aspects of their design are not covered in their report, notably the length of the time interval which elapsed between the administration of the two tests. Further they comment that they were compelled to utilize a group of brain-injured subjects who "had diffuse rather than focal brain damage, and the amount of brain tissue involved varied considerably"; their report does not specify the confidence which could be attached to the criteria used to make the diagnoses. Never-

[6] Earlier studies using the pretest and posttest design are reported by Canter (1951) and Weinstein and Teuber (1957).

theless this study may be regarded as an outstanding illustration of some of the possibilities of this method.

Before leaving this description of the pretest-posttest design, we should note that any study of the effect of brain damage upon test behavior makes an important contribution to our knowledge of brain functioning as a determinant of test behavior. However, we cannot use the postdamage responses as a diagnostic sign of brain damage in an unknown population until we have cross-validated them with a separate study. We need to know the base rate for test-retest decrement in an unselected population before we can begin to use this decrement for diagnostic purposes. Excellence of design and execution of an experiment of this kind does not justify the immediate application of its findings in a clinical situation until the problems of optimal discrimination cutoff points and the population base rates have been resolved.[7]

Scatter analysis. An analysis of the differences between subtest scores on the part of a given subject has long formed part of the traditional diagnostic procedures of the psychometrician. Here the measure of interest is not obtained from looking at absolute values of performances, but at the ratios between performances on one test or group of tests and another. Scatter analysis is, strictly speaking, not a particular type of experimental tactic. It refers instead to the response characteristics which are under scrutiny. The research procedures which were used to gather the pertinent data are usually some variant of the two major kinds described in the preceding paragraphs. However, we shall treat it separately here, partly because of its great popularity both as a research activity and as a clinical diagnostic tool and partly because when it is used in connection with the investigation of brain damage it implies a particular theory about brain functioning. A typical proposition is that variable X (schizophrenia, brain damage, or some other independent variable) has the power to change the response made by a subject on a test which ostensibly measures intelligence. These variables are thought of as depressing the subject's performance (never improving it) and are also regarded as pathological or in some way deviant. A further assumption is that they affect the subtests in some selective fashion so that some scores are depressed more than others. In essence this kind of assumption is similar to that behind the notion of *capacity,* but usually comes with the pessimistic implication that the variables which depress the scores are not easily manipulated. Thus while a patient is said to be functioning below capacity under some circumstances, another patient may be said to have suffered *deterioration* under others. The crucial difference is the extent to which the decrement is thought to be remediable.

From the standpoint of clinicians who use scatter analysis to diagnose the condition of brain tissue, damage to the brain has certain nonspecific effects, i.e., effects which do not depend upon the location or nature of the damage. However these effects are relatively response-specific, that is, they are det-

---

[7] For a full account of the problem of the discrimination power of diagnostic signs, the reader is referred to the paper by Meehl and Rosen (1955) already cited earlier in the chapter.

rimental to production of some kinds of response much more so than to
others. This particular position may be considered in several ways. Firstly,
we may examine the state of empirical validities of scatter analysis in relation to clinical diagnosis. Here the current state of the evidence has been
summarized by Cronbach with his comment apropos of the Wechsler scales
that "this type of analysis is no longer depended upon because empirical
checks show that pattern analysis has little validity" (1960, p. 192). Previous
assessments of the evidence include those of Yates (1954) who concludes
from a consideration of various ratio scores derived from the scatter of subtests on the Wechsler that "it seems clear that indices of deterioration are
of little clinical use in their present form." There seems to be no point in
reiterating the problem of *post-hoc* validities, except to point out that they
apply to the majority of scatter studies in the literature. What may be worth
remarking is the tenacity with which some practitioners cling to diagnostic
procedures of no demonstrable validity to produce reports which appear to
have little effect upon the patient's future.

A second aspect of the scatter analysis approach is its implications for a
general theory of brain functioning. The theory in its present form seems
to consist of several postulates.

(1) Any brain injury sufficiently gross to affect test performance at all is
likely to affect the solving of new problems (developing of new responses)
more than the production of responses learned previously. Thus Cronbach
comments, "The performance test has special importance in the clinic.
Performance tests generally depend less on habit and more on ability to
attack a new problem. They are therefore quicker to reveal the effects of
therapeutic treatment. In cross-sectional studies of aging, for example, nonlanguage tests begin to decline in the 20's, whereas verbal ability holds
almost constant until the mid-40's" (1960, pp. 205–296).

(2) The same quotation also indicates the second implicit postulate,
namely, that brain damage produces certain general changes in test performance whether it is associated with aging or occurs in a younger person,
whether it involved loss of tissue or the presence of pathological tissue, and
whether we are observing the patient immediately after the damage or considerably later.

Empirical investigations. As we have already seen, Williams et al. (1959)
report that what differences they found between postinjury performance on
verbal tests and nonverbal tests were so small as to be of no practical significance. Weinstein and Teuber (1957) report that there is a loss in verbal
and vocabulary scores in patients 10 years after lesions which involved the
left parietal-temporal areas, but no loss for patients where focal lesions were
placed elsewhere. Data reported by Hamlin and Kinder (1961) from
patients who had undergone bilateral topectomy 10 years previously suggest
that the manner of presenting a verbal test influences the appearance of
deficit. Nonoral presentation, under conditions which were thought to reduce peripheral distraction, was accompanied by the greatest difference
between operates and controls. The subjects used in this study, both operates and controls, were hospitalized schizophrenics, a fact which makes it
difficult to generalize the results to any nonpsychotic population. Ross

(1958) reports postinjury data on test performances of brain-damaged soldiers and concludes that test performance deteriorates generally. He does not report any selective decrement in particular varieties of test item.

In a very thorough analysis of patients suffering from temporal lobe epilepsy, Milner (1956) obtained test data both before and after unilateral partial temporal lobectomy. She concluded that performance on the Wechsler-Bellevue Scale is not permanently affected although there was a temporary postoperative decrement in verbal subtest performance in her left-temporal group. Lesions associated with epileptic seizures themselves produced a variety of deficiencies in performance on tests depending upon locations of the lesion. All in all there is some tendency to find that lesions in the dominant hemisphere produce more marked disabilities than do lesions in the nondominant hemisphere. However, the question of whether or not these disabilities are more pronounced in some kinds of subtest than others is far from clear. Thus Reitan (1955) reports that dominant hemisphere lesions produce deficits in performance subtests. Heilbrun (1956) finds that performance test scores are not selectively related to the hemispheric location of lesions. In general we may repeat Rosvold's conclusion: "Recent studies with respect to the effect of brain damage on general intelligence, though more rigorous than in the past, are no more in agreement than were earlier studies, some of which claimed deterioration in intelligence, others not. Equally lacking in agreement are the conclusions as to whether these effects may be localized and whether they are specific to one or another modality" (1959, p. 434).

Brain pathology in children

The foregoing pages have been addressed to the problems of research in brain damage, considered in relation to changes in adult behavior. Some comment should be made with regard to the problem of brain damage in children, since this is the more important question for the clinician dealing with the mentally retarded.

In the great majority of cases, the issue of brain damage in a child committed to an institution for the retarded is whether or not the child received brain damage at a very early stage of existence. In the very nature of things, this kind of problem is not suited to investigation with the pretest-posttest design. The closest approximation to this which we might hope to make is by searching for cases of identical twins, one of whom is retarded and the other of normal or superior intelligence and where these differences are evident early in life. Practical considerations make this kind of research very difficult although not impossible. The uninjured twin would be assumed to define the preinjury level of response, and the retarded twin would represent the postinjury level of response.

Graham and Berman (1961) conclude a thorough survey of the literature dealing with behavioral tests of brain damage in children with the following comments:

Measurement difficulties lie less in the ability of investigators to devise ingenious techniques than in stubborn problems in defining a brain-

injured group. Longitudinal studies under way should help clarify some of the controversial questions. They may be particularly valuable in determining whether or not undetected brain injury at birth contributes to a variety of later defects, including the frequently described clinical syndrome of hyperactivity, distractibility and impulsivity. Follow-up studies of other types of brain injury are also needed.

There are no studies showing that the pattern of impairment on behavioral tests differs in well-documented cases of brain injury from that found in uninjured children of the same chronological age. It remains an important and virtually untested question whether or not injury early in life has a pattern of impairment similar to that seen in older children and adults [italics added].[8]

Generalizing findings gained from pretest-posttest studies on adults to populations of mentally retarded children seems most dangerous. Among the broad statements which we can make with some confidence about the development of the central nervous system is that it is not complete during the childhood years. Consequently the comparison of the effects of brain injury in the neonate with the effects of the same injury in the fully grown adult is of questionable validity. This in turn means that the problem of brain injury in the mentally retarded child is, for the most part, dependent for solution upon the *post-hoc* research method.

All in all, at the present time it appears that advances in neuropsychology are more likely to come from controlled laboratory investigations than from the search for relationships between tissue damage and performance on tests devised for other purposes. Until effective therapies for tissue damage have been discovered, the clinical utility of these latter relationships seems to be doubtful.

Summary. In this chapter we have suggested that there is a need for a concept relating to the differences between individuals in rate of acquisition of responses under similar learning conditions. Such a concept necessarily implies the existence of structural differences between individuals and is incompatible with a psychology of the empty organism.

We have also argued that some current conceptions of intelligence are clouded with quasi-metaphysical problems created by the notion of real abilities and the true nature of intelligence divorced from coherent theories of biology and behavior.

Attempts to apply tests constructed within such current concepts of intelligence to the detection of biological phenomena such as brain damage have been largely unsuccessful. The logical and methodological reasons for this were explored. While possible advances might be made using longitudinal and twin studies, the view is offered that the solution of clinical problems related to brain damage will best be furthered by the development of the experimental science of neuropsychology.

[8] Since this manuscript was prepared, Hayes (1962) has offered an interesting discussion of the possibility that early brain damage may affect motivational development later in life.

REFERENCES

ANDERSON, V. V., & FEARING, F. M. *A study of the careers of 322 feeble-minded persons.* New York: National Committee of Mental Hygiene, 1923.

BALLER, W. R. A study of the present social status of a group of adults who, when they were in elementary school were classified as mentally deficient. *Genet. Psychol. Monogr.*, 1936, 18, 165–244.

BALTHAZAR, E. E., & MORRISON, D. H. The use of Wechsler intelligence scales as diagnostic indicators of predominant left-right and indeterminate unilateral brain damage. *J. clin. Psychol.*, 1961, 17, 161–165.

BURT, C. The evidence for the concept of intelligence. *Brit. J. Educ. Psychol.*, 1955, 25, 158–177.

CAMPBELL, D. T. Recommendations for APA test standards regarding construct, trait or discriminant validity. *Amer. Psychologist*, 1960, 15, 546–553.

CAMPBELL, D. T., & FISKE, D. W. Convergent and discriminant validation by the multi-trait–multi-method matrix. *Psychol. Bull.*, 1959, 56, 81–105.

CANTER, A. H. Direct and indirect measures of psychological deficit in multiple sclerosis. *J. gen. Psychol.*, 1951, 44, 27–50.

CHARLES, D. C. Ability and accomplishment of persons earlier judged mentally deficient. *Genet. Psychol. Monogr.*, 1953, 47, 3–71.

CRONBACH, L. J. *Essentials of psychological testing.* New York: Harper, 1960.

EBEL, R. L. Must all tests be valid? *American Psychologist*, 1961, 16, 640–647.

FAIRBANK, R. The subnormal child; seventeen years after. *Ment. Hyg., N.Y.*, 1933, 17, 177–208.

FITZHUGH, KATHLEEN B., FITZHUGH, L. C., & REITAN, R. M. Psychological deficits in relation to acuteness of brain dysfunction. *J. consult. Psychol.*, 1961, 25, 61–66.

GRAHAM, FRANCES K., & BERMAN, PHYLLIS W. Current status of behavior tests for brain damage in infants and pre-school children. *Amer. J. Orthopsychiat.*, 1961, 31, 713–727.

HAMLIN, R. M., & KINDER, ELAINE F. Vocabulary deficit in brain operated schizophrenics. *J. consult. Psychol.*, 1961, 25, 239–244.

HAYES, K. J. Genes, drive and intellect. *Psychol. Rep.*, 1962, 10, 299–342.

HEBB, D. O. *The organization of behavior.* New York: Wiley, 1949.

HEILBRUN, A. B. Psychological test performance as a function of lateral localization of cerebral lesions. *J. comp. Psychol.*, 1956, 49, 10–14.

HEIM, A. *The appraisal of intelligence.* London: Methuen, 1954.

HULL, C. L. *Aptitude testing.* Tarrytown-on-Hudson, N.Y.: World, 1928.

ISRAEL, H. E., & GOLDSTEIN, B. Operationism in psychology. *Psychol. Rev.*, 1944, 51, 177–188.

JASTAK, J. A rigorous criterion of feeblemindedness. *J. abnorm. soc. Psychol.*, 1949, 44, 367–378.

KENNEDY, R. J. A. *The social adjustment of morons in a Connecticut city.* Hartford: Southbury Training Schools, 1948.

KLEBANOFF, S. C., SINGER, J. L., & WILENSKY, H. Psychological consequences of brain lesions. *Psychol. Bull.*, 1954, 51, 1–41.

LEWIS, D. G. The normal distribution of intelligence: a critique. *Brit. J. Psychol.*, 1957, 48, 98–104.

LIVERANT, S. Intelligence: a concept in need of re-examination. *J. consult. Psychol.*, 1960, 24, 101–110.

LOEVINGER, JANE. Objective tests as instruments of psychological theory. *Psychol. Rep.*, 1957, 3, 635–694. (Monogr. Suppl. 9)

MARX, M. H. The general nature of theory construction. In M. Marx (Ed.), *Psychological theory.* New York: Macmillan, 1951.

MASLAND, R. L., SARASON, S. B., & GLADWIN, T. *Mental subnormality.* New York: Basic Books, 1958.

MEEHL, D. E., & ROSEN, A. Antecedent probability and the efficiency of psychometric signs, patterns or cutting scores. *Psychol. Bull.*, 1955, 52, 194–216.

MILNER, BRENDA. Psychological defects produced by temporal lobe excision. *Res. Publ. Ass. Res. nerv. ment. Dis.*, 1956, 36, 244–257.

MUENCH, G. A. A follow up of mental defectives after 18 years. *J. abnorm. soc. Psychol.*, 1944, 39, 407–418.

REITAN, R. M. Certain differential effects of left and right cerebral lesions in human adults. *J. Comp. physiol. Psychol.*, 1955, 48, 474–477.

RICHMOND, W. K. Educational measurement: its scope and limitations: a critque. *Brit. J. Psychol.*, 1953, 44, 221–231.

ROSENZWEIG, M. R., KRECH, D., & BENNETT, E. L. A search for relations between brain chemistry and behavior. *Psychol. Bull.*, 1960, 57, 476–492.

ROSS, A. O. Brain injury and intellectual performance. *J. consult. Psychol.*, 1958, 22, 151–152.

ROSVOLD, H. E. Physiological psychology. *Ann. Rev. Psychol.*, 1959, 10, 415–454.

SPIKER, C. C., & MCCANDLESS, B. R. The concept of intelligence and the philosophy of science. *Psychol. Rev.*, 1954, 61, 255–266.

STODDARD, G. D. *The meaning of intelligence.* New York: Macmillan, 1943.

WECHSLER, D. *The measurement of adult intelligence.* Baltimore: Williams & Wilkins, 1944.

WECHSLER, D. *The measurement and appraisal of adult intelligence.* Baltimore: Williams & Wilkins, 1958.

WEINSTEIN, S., & TEUBER, H. L. Effects of penetrating brain injury on intelligence test scores. *Science,* 1957, 125, 1036–1037.

WILLIAMS, H. L., LUBIN, A., & GIESEKING, C. F. Direct measurement of cognitive deficit in brain-injured patients. *J. consult. Psychol.*, 1959, 23, 300–305.

YATES, A. J. The validity of some psychological tests of brain damage. *Psychol. Bull.*, 1954, 51, 359–379.

7

GENETIC ASPECTS OF
INTELLIGENT BEHAVIOR[1]

Irving I. Gottesman

The science of genetics has made and is continuing to make significant contributions to our knowledge about mental deficiency. Nonetheless it is possible to cite discussions of this problem area which either minimize or ignore the genetic aspects of human behavior. Breakthroughs in the field of cytological genetics (Lejeune & Turpin, 1961), including the discovery of the basis for mongolism (Lejeune, Turpin, & Gautier, 1959) together with advances in biochemical genetics (Knox, 1961), such as finding a test for the heterozygous carriers of the recessive gene for phenylketonuria (Hsia, Driscoll, Troll, & Knox, 1956; Wang, Morton, & Waisman, 1961), demand that serious students of the bases of intelligent behavior have some familiarity with the overlapping area between psychology and genetics (Fuller & Thompson, 1960).

This chapter discusses and demonstrates the relevance of human genetics to considerations of human intelligence. After presenting the dialectics of *heredity* and *environment,* general and specific theoretical constructs and principles in genetics are illustrated. Perhaps least familiar to behavioral scientists are the sections on polygenic inheritance of quantitative variation and the one on heritability. Under the broad section dealing with the inheritance of intelligent behavior in animals, studies which have selected

[1] This chapter was originally conceived as a collaborative effort with Brendan A. Maher. I benefited greatly from his writing experience and shepherding. Early versions of the manuscript were read and commented upon by Gordon W. Allport, Sheldon C. Reed, and W. R. Thompson. My task was made considerably less difficult by the publication of *Behavior Genetics* by John L. Fuller and W. R. Thompson. Preparation of this chapter was aided in part by grant M5384 from the National Institutes of Mental Health.

specific mammalian behaviors and bred for them as well as studies which compare pure strains within a species on these adaptive responses are critically reviewed. The final section discusses the inheritance of intelligence in man. Included are examples of the data gathered from pedigree, correlational, and twin studies. After comparing the conflicting results of animal and human research, the advances in cytological genetics relevant to mental deficiency are presented. The chapter concludes with an exposition of some theories on the genetic transmission of intelligence, together with some cautions about eugenic applications of genetic knowledge.

Genes exert their influence on behavior through their effects at the molecular level of organization. Enzymes, hormones, and neurons may be considered as the sequence of complex path markers between the genes and intelligent behavior. A failure to demonstrate this type of reduction for many clearly heritable differences in human behavior should be no more embarrassing to the behavior geneticist than the lack of knowledge concerning the organic basis of learning is to workers in that area of psychology. It may even be that measures of behavior are the only reliable indicators of certain kinds of inherited organic characters (Fuller, 1957a).

GENETICS IN PSYCHOLOGY: CONCEPTUAL CONSIDERATIONS

The dialectics of heredity and environment

Although it is axiomatic that the phenotypic expression of a trait is dependent on both hereditary and environmental agents, much heat and little light have been generated by attempts to answer the question, "How much of intelligence is due to heredity and how much to environment?" Since neither agent alone can produce the phenotype, the question is meaningless. However, the variation between individuals on a measure of intelligence is capable of being partitioned into heritable and nonheritable components once the environment has been specified. For some traits the observed variation may be almost entirely due to one of these components. Two answerable questions should be posed in the nature-nurture issue: How much of the variability observed within a group of individuals in a specified environment on a particular measure of intelligence is attributable to hereditary differences among them, and how modifiable by systematic environmental changes is the phenotypic intelligence of each genotype? It is mandatory to keep in mind that the answers to these questions may change according to age, sex, culture, or subculture and may be different not only for various traits but also for two different ways of assessing the same trait. Extensive treatment of the many data gathered to appraise the nature-nurture issue may be found in Woodworth (1941), Fuller (1954), Tyler (1956), and Anastasi (1958).

For our purposes the best way to conceptualize the contribution of heredity to intelligence is to think of heredity as determining a norm of reaction (Dobzhansky, 1955) or as fixing a reaction range. Within this framework a genotype determines an indefinite but circumscribed assortment of phenotypes, each of which corresponds to one of the possible environments to which the genotype may be exposed. Fuller has said:

"Heredity is the capacity to utilize an environment in a particular way" (1954, p. 5). Figure 7-1 illustrates schematically the concept of reaction range as applied either to four different individuals or to four classes of individuals. For each of the four curves to apply to individuals, it would require the carrier of a given genotype to be exposed to as wide a range of environments as appeared to lead to a change in the phenotypic expression of intelligence. This is a practical impossibility with humans but may be approached with highly inbred strains of mammals (Thompson, 1954). Allen (1961) pointed out that the most probable phenotype of some genotypes may be an extreme one. These genotypes would produce normal individuals only in unusual environments, if at all. Curve A in Figure 7-1 represents the possible distribution of the IQs of a group of mongoloids. This curve would be interpreted to mean that even in the most favorable of environments the probability of a mongoloid's IQ rising significantly is negligible. As soon as some biochemical intervention becomes feasible for this genetic defect, the curve will have to be modified in an upward direction; this would be analogous to the introduction of insulin as a treatment for diabetes mellitus. The centering of scores around IQ 25 in curve A together with its low slope is an extrapolation from such reports as Penrose's (1954) for a substantial sample of mongoloids who had a mean IQ of 23 with a standard deviation of 7.9. A type A curve with a natural habitat mean under 70 would characterize the the majority of the various types of mental deficiency known to be associated with dominant or recessive gene inheritance as well as the emerging types shown to be associated with chromosomal aberrations (Moorhead, Mellman, & Wenar, 1961; Shaw & Chu, 1961). This model accounts for a substantial minority of the general

Figure 7-1. Scheme of the reaction range concept for four hypothesized genotypes. *Note:* Marked deviation from the natural habitat has a low probability of occurrence. R.R. signifies reaction range in phenotypic IQ.

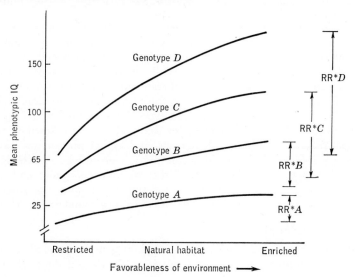

category, mental deficiency. Several of the specific subtypes will be discussed in the next section on genetic principles.

A type B curve represents one of the curves which could be drawn to describe the phenotypical reaction range for the vast majority of defectives labeled aclinical or *garden variety* (Sarason, 1953). The individuals in this category are assumed to differ only quantitatively from those with normal intelligence. A detailed discussion of the basis for this assumption will be presented in the section on theories of the inheritance of intelligence. Notice that the two major differences between A and B are that the latter has a wider reaction range, that is, environmental factors can alter the expression of innate intellectual potential more readily, and B rises more sharply with an enriched environment. This rate change is inferred in large part from experimental results with animals which showed that those bred for dullness on mazes improved their performances greatly after exposure to an enriched environment but showed little decrement from their natural performances after exposure to a restricted environment (Cooper & Zubek, 1958).

Within the broad range of continuous variation in measured IQ two aspects of the environment, *favorableness* and *commonness*, are important to the concept of reaction range. By this we mean to imply that each genotype has its own more or less natural habitat. In regard to the character intelligence, the natural habitat would include an adequate diet, freedom from gross organic defects, exposure to our system of compulsory education, and being reared in a home by one's own parents. Among the obvious factors in an unnatural habitat would be foster parent or orphanage rearing, no formal education, and intensive tutoring. If a genotype determines an IQ of 100 in the most common environments, some uncommon situations could either raise the phenotypic expression to 130 or lower it to 70 depending upon the additional dimension of favorableness. A type C curve is intended to represent the group of individuals whose inferred genotypic IQ is 100, while a type D curve describes the hypothetical distribution of phenotypic scores for a group of superior genotypes.

It should be obvious to the reader that each curve in Figure 7-1 is centered about an inferred genotype. We can never know the innate intellectual potential since only the phenotype can be measured. The curves then are a posteriori constructions. While there is no absolute answer to what is an individual's true intellectual endowment, there is a most probable answer. If the natural habitat obtains, the phenotypic expression of intelligence most probably reflects the genotype. The mutability of IQ is an established fact. A useful shibboleth for the reader is the following: Similar genotypes may have different phenotypes, and similar phenotypes may have different genotypes. This should mean that theorists who choose to focus on genetic factors in intelligence will treat stimulus conditions and life history variables as boundary delimiters for the manifestation of intellectual levels and vice versa for theorists who focus on environmental factors.

Some genetic principles

Although the range and complexity of modern genetics preclude clear and accurate condensation, an attempt is made to define and illustrate some of the terms and mechanisms pertinent to this chapter. Comprehensive treatments of human genetics are available in Stern (1960) as well as in Neel and Schull (1954). One of the better brief expositions directed to an audience of psychologists may be found in Fuller and Thompson (1960). It is likely that the reluctance of many psychologists to embrace genetics arises from the failure of the single-gene models of classical Mendelian theory to appear applicable to behavior. An unfamiliarity with such modern advances as the accounting for quantitative variation, selection experiments with mammals for specific behaviors, and improvements in twin-study methodology could have perpetuated this reluctance.

An overview of the major terms used in connection with descriptions of *nonenvironmental* contributions to behavior should clarify some of the confusion which arises from their incorrect use. Figure 7-2 is Cattell's (1950) diagram showing the relationships among the four components of biologically based behavior. Gene-based qualities biologically acquired from the parents are called hereditary. Some of the genes in the individual germ cell at the moment of conception, however, are not exactly like those in either parent and are not inherited in the sense used above. These changed genes are traced to either spontaneous mutations or other mutagenic agents and become part of the hereditary component for the *next* generation. The hereditary component together with the changes traced to mutations make up the term innate. Sometimes the word inborn is used interchangeably with innate. With these definitions in mind, it should not be paradoxical to say that a characteristic can be genetic but not inherited. The term congenital usually refers to something present at birth. Within the framework of our diagram it means the preceding components plus changes acquired between conception and the completion of the birth process. Finally, the term constitutional is defined by the preceding components plus any postnatal alterations of the body. The constitutional component, then, comprises all that is physiological or somatic in the determination of the individual and changes over time.

Figure 7-2. Schematic definitions of nonenvironmental contributions to intelligence. (*From Cattell, 1950.*)

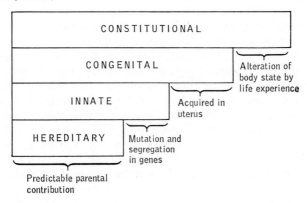

Chromosomes and genes.   The basic units of heredity are the genes. Estimates of the number of genes in a human cell run from no less than 2,000 to no more than 50,000 (Stern, 1960). This is not the place to present the evidence for existence of genes, but it is broadening to read Russian accounts of the inadequacy of the evidence (Turbin, 1959). Genes have been described chemically as desoxyribose nucleic acid (DNA) segments composed of perhaps several hundred molecular subunits. Work on lower organisms suggests that each DNA molecule carries several genes plus some inert or uncoded material (Demerec, 1961). The construct of a gene has been elaborated into that of a clearly differentiated locus which preserves its identity, produces a specific effect, and is capable of duplicating itself. Although the complexity of the gene to behavior pathway has been referred to above, it bears repetition. A gene never directly produces a given trait; Muller (1956) has described it as setting a chain reaction into motion.

All genes are organized into chromosomes which, under the microscope, are seen to occupy the nucleus of each cell. Man has 23 pairs of chromosomes but so do some other nonhuman mammals (Chu & Bender, 1961). Each member of the chromosome pair is homologous to the other; the genes are arranged linearly along the chromosome and are also homologous and paired, each member of a pair being either identical with its partner or differing in some important way. These different forms of genes occupying the same locus are termed alleles. Each nucleus of a male cell contains 22 matched pairs plus an X and a Y chromosome. In the female the twenty-third pair is also matched but contains two X chromosomes. The X and Y chromosomes are collectively called sex chromosomes, with the remaining pairs labeled autosomes. When a photomicrograph of a chromosome complement is enlarged and the individual chromosomes are cut out, arranged in pairs, and grouped according to lengths, arm ratios, and other morphological features, we have what is known as a karyotype. Examples of normal and abnormal karyotypes are shown in Figures 7-6 to 7-9. The numbers which appear below each pair of chromosomes are used to identify a particular pair, and it may be provisionally stated that the pair identified by a number in one individual corresponds to a similarly numbered pair in another individual.

In essence, Mendel reasoned from his experiments with peas that single characters behaved as if determined by paired particles (genes). During the production of sex cells or gametes, meiosis or reduction division takes place so that the chromosome number is halved to 23 single chromosomes. When the two gametes unite in fertilization to form the zygote, 23 pairs are reestablished. Since the process of selection within pairs of chromosomes is entirely random, combinations occur in the offspring which are unlike those in either parent. The number of possible types of gametes is 2^n, where n is the number of pairs of chromosomes. For the human being this amounts to over eight million distinct types of sex cells. If the allele occupying a locus on one member of a chromosome pair is the same as its counterpart, the individual is said to be a homozygote for the gene pair under consideration; if they are different, he is said to be a heterozygote. An individual may be both homozygous and heterozygous for different loci on one pair of chromosomes.

Dominant and recessive genes with examples from mental deficiency. A *major* gene is one which in general determines a character by itself and contrasts with the effects of *polygenes* which have quantitatively equivalent cumulative effects. As far as we now know, both are physically and chemically identical, and both are equally subject to the same rules of segregation. Major gene effects usually involve readily discernible phenotypic discontinuities and are the basis for the classical ratios obtained in the original Mendelian framework. Very few of the assumed single gene abnormalities have frequencies higher than 1 in 5,000, and the vast majority are rarer than 1 in 20,000. With the notable exceptions of Rh and ABO incompatibility, major gene effects which occur with a frequency of from 5 to 50 per cent appear to be neutral in their effects on viability.

If all the offspring of a group of Huntington's chorea patients are followed for their lifetimes, it will be found that half of them develop the disease. Descendants of the nonaffected individuals will have normal children, but the affected offspring will produce children half of whom will eventually show the chorea. The choreic marries a normal person and gives his gene for chorea to one-half of his offspring and his normal gene at that locus to the other half. The children who get the chorea gene from the father and the normal gene from the mother will develop the disease because the pathological gene dominates the function of this locus. When one such allele produces a character, it is termed a dominant and denoted by a capital letter, H. The unexpressed partner is termed a recessive and denoted by a lowercase letter, h. All persons heterozygous, Hh, will manifest Huntington's chorea; all homozygotes, hh, will be normal (HH homozygotes are unknown, the combination probably being lethal). Unfortunately, the average age of onset of this disease is about 36 (Pearson & Kley, 1957) so that the chorea may be perpetuated unknowingly. Although the general incidence of Huntington's chorea is only about 1 in 20,000 and the expected incidence in the offspring of a victim, 1 in 2, individual families will often be found who have all of their two or three children affected. This is a grim reminder that probability theory is fallible at the level of individual prediction.

Another rare defect inherited as a dominant is multiple neurofibromatosis with an incidence of about 4 in 10,000 (Crowe, Schull, & Neel, 1956). About 10 to 30 per cent of the affected persons are mentally defective. This disease illustrates the concept of penetrance. When a dominant gene fails to manifest itself in individuals known to be carrying the gene, the phenomenon is referred to as incomplete penetrance. Observed departure from the expected incidence of 50 per cent in the offspring of affected persons has led to the conclusion that neurofibromatosis is a dominant disease with at least 90 per cent penetrance. The incomplete expression of a dominant gene or of homozygous recessives may be due to a suppressing effect of modifiers which may be either other genes or environmental variables. A further complication to neat Mendelian ratios of 1:1 for these rare dominant diseases is the production of new mutations which will, of course, show no familial pattern for the disease. It has been estimated (Crowe et al.) that half of the observed cases of neurofibromatosis are new mutations. In epiloia or tuberose sclerosis, another form of mental defect inherited as a dominant, with an incidence of about 1 in 30,000, one case in four is thought to be a fresh mutation (Penrose, 1954).

Phenylketonuria (PKU) is an inborn error of metabolism known to be inherited when an individual is homozygous for the recessive genes involved. Allen (1958) has traced the fascinating pattern of the discovery of the disease, its biochemical nature, its genetic basis and mode of transmission, its specific treatment, and possible prevention. Very rarely are the persons homozygous for these genes above the imbecile level, and they very rarely propagate. It thus follows for this pathological recessively inherited disease that the homozygotes will be the offspring of two normal parents who will be carriers for the gene. The expectation for the incidence of, for example, pp individuals from $Pp \times Pp$ matings is one in four, the other offspring being PP (normal) and two Pp (carriers) for a sibship of four children. By looking at all data available on 266 families of PKU affected individuals, Jervis (1954) found close to the expected 25 per cent incidence after correcting for the different size sibships and the advantage of starting with a proband (primary case from which the family investigation began). In rare recessive conditions like this, we expect to find an increased incidence of cousin marriages among the parents of the affected. The rarer the allele, the less chance of meeting it in a random partner, compared with the one in eight chance of meeting it in a first cousin, a figure fixed by their common descent. By taking the square root of the incidence of known pp individuals, we arrive at an estimate of the p gene frequency. In the United States, Jervis estimated the incidence of PKU at about 1 in 25,000 which leads to a gene frequency of 1 in 158. The incidence of the heterozygous carriers is $2 \times \frac{1}{158} \times (1 - \frac{1}{158})$ or about 1 in 80 in the population at large. More recent surveys suggest a PKU incidence of 1 in 10,000 newborn children. To return to the effect of consanguineous marriages on the incidence of PKU, we can calculate that since the expectation of disease for any child from carrier parents is one-fourth, the expectation for the child of a heterozygote who has married an unaffected first cousin is $\frac{1}{4} \times \frac{1}{8}$ or $\frac{1}{32}$. If the person known to be a carrier married an individual not a relative, the expectation for their child is $\frac{1}{4} \times \frac{1}{80}$ or $\frac{1}{320}$. In the three studies summarized by Jervis, the incidence of consanguineous marriages ranged from 5 to 17 per cent with an average of 8 per cent.

With the discovery of a phenylalanine tolerance test that would identify the heterozygous carrier for PKU (Hsia et al., 1956), the gene could no longer be considered as a strict recessive. Expressing itself in any manner when not homozygous necessitates classifying it among those genes now called incompletely recessive. So far there has been no report that the carriers for PKU have lowered intelligence. Microcephaly is another rare disease inherited in the recessive fashion. A noteworthy decrease in the intelligence of parents of affected individuals has led to the speculation (Book, Schut, & Reed, 1953) that the heterozygous form of the gene may express itself as moderate intellectual impairment and account for 0.5 to

1 per cent of the population. It has an estimated gene frequency between $\frac{1}{162}$ and $\frac{1}{230}$.

Table 7-1 is reproduced from Stern (1960) and shows the frequencies of affected and carrier individuals under conditions of random mating for various possibilities of single factor recessive inheritance. The important thing to note from this table is that the ratio of carriers to affected rises remarkably as the disease becomes more rare. It is quite probable, after allowing for yet-to-be-discovered incompletely recessive genes, that recessive genes in the gene pool contribute significantly to the lower and middle grades of mental deficiency.

Three conditions are usually accepted as the necessary and sufficient ones for identifying a disease dependent on major gene substitutions: (1) statistical agreement with Mendelian expectancies for familial incidence and population frequencies, (2) complete concordance in identical twins, and (3) either an elevated rate of consanguineous marriages for rare autosomal recessive diseases or an appropriate pedigree for dominant transmission (David & Snyder, 1954).

Polygenic inheritance and quantitative variation. Major gene models cannot handle the continuous variation observed in such traits as intelligence, human height, or hair color. Even positing more than two alleles at a single locus could not account for the ranges observed since two parents could not contribute more than four alleles to that locus in their children, resulting in four genotypes. Observations in large families show more than four discriminably different phenotypes for these kinds of traits.

Intermediate gradations of a trait such as intelligence, when measured in large, culturally homogeneous samples by IQ tests, will fit a normal distribution quite well within the range of plus and minus three standard deviations (roughly 50 to 150). When a character is determined by the combined action of a large number of randomly assorted influences working together, a bell-shaped or Gaussian curve is the result. The genetic hypothesis which fits the observed distribution of IQ scores is that biological factors based on polygenic effects are operating. Other hypotheses are also

TABLE 7-1

Frequencies of affected and carrier subjects for major recessive gene inheritance under random mating (from Stern, 1960)

Affected frequency (q^2)	Carrier frequency ($2pq$)	Ratio of carriers to affected ($2p/q$)
1 in 10	1 in 2.3	4.3:1
1 in 100	1 in 5.6	18:1
1 in 1,000	1 in 16	61:1
1 in 10,000	1 in 51	198:1
1 in 100,000	1 in 159	630:1
1 in 1,000,000	1 in 501	1,998:1

possible which stress the additive effects of random environmental factors leading to the same sort of distribution. Only the first hypothesis is stressed in our presentation. Proof of the existence of polygenic systems rests on work with purebred and selectively bred mammals and lower organisms. Fuller and Thompson (1960) have performed a great service to psychologists in revealing how the work of such men as Mather (1949) and Wright (1952) on quantitative inheritance with agricultural problems is applicable to behavior. Psychologists who have resisted the usefulness of animal experimentation to human behavior may be expected to be even more resistant to letting fruit flies, grains, and bread molds in through the same door as the rat and mouse.

The importance of polygenic or multifactorial inheritance for describing the 75 per cent of all defectives classified as familial is recognized by many workers in the field (Allen, 1958; Burt, 1958; Burt & Howard, 1956). All suggest that the etiology of this form of retardation is to be sought in the same factors that determine normal intelligence. Polygenic inheritance together with the concept of reaction range described above should form a productive base from which research into the alleviation of retardation may proceed.

An illustration of the principles of polygenic inheritance may be seen in the explanatory power of a simple two-loci model. A serious attempt to fit the facts to the theory will be made in a later section of this chapter. First let us assume that intelligence, as measured in some objective fashion, is controlled by two independent loci, each with one or the other of two alleles, A^1 and A^2 at one locus and B^1 and B^2 at the other. Our hypothetical parents would be from two pure lines homozygous as follows: $A^1A^1B^1B^1$ and $A^2A^2B^2B^2$. We shall call the former the dull parent and the latter, the bright one. The higher intelligence of the brighter parent is considered to be associated with the additive action of A^2 and B^2 alleles, and we further assume, in this simplified model, that the substitution of any 2- for any 1-type allele leads to equal enhancement of the phenotypically measured IQ. It follows that an A^1A^2 combination will be intermediate in intelligence to A^1A^1 and A^2A^2.

We move now to the first generation children who can only have the genotype $A^1A^2B^1B^2$ since each can only receive one kind of gamete from each parent for each of the two loci. Independent assortment in the gametes produced by the first generation (usually denoted F_1) will lead to the formation of four different kinds—A^1B^1, A^1B^2, A^2B^1, and A^2B^2. When these combine at fertilization in all the possible different ways, the offspring in this second generation fall into five different phenotypic classes defined by having zero to four intelligence enhancing alleles:

		$A^1A^1B^2B^2$		
	$A^1A^1B^1B^2$	$A^1A^2B^1B^2$	$A^1A^2B^2B^2$	
$A^1A^1B^1B^1$	$A^1A^2B^1B^1$	$A^2A^2B^1B^1$	$A^2A^2B^1B^2$	$A^2A^2B^2B^2$
Class 0	Class 1	Class 2	Class 3	Class 4

This simple two-locus model, with a limited number of assumptions, accounts for five phenotypic classes which we could label, left to right, retarded, dull normal, average, bright average, and superior. Of course this is artificial since there is a continuous distribution of discriminable phenotypes for intelligence; i.e., an IQ score of 81 is different from one of 80 or 82. However, by increasing the posited number of loci, we rapidly approach the standard Gaussian curve since we are really dealing with the expansion of the binomial expression $(\frac{1}{2} + \frac{1}{2})^{2n}$ where n equals the number of loci. Remembering that this model, up to now, makes no provision for environmental contributions to variation, we can point out that such a provision with, at the most, 12 loci or gene pairs posited, can easily fit the observed distributions of IQ. Theoretically then, we are forced to deal with the effects of a minute number of the total possible 50,000 genes. The array of genotypes above in each class illustrates a point we have emphasized, namely, the same phenotype may have different genotypes. Notice now the effects on intelligence of the next generation when certain of the F_2 genotypes mate and reproduce. Take two average people, $A^1A^1B^2B^2$ and $A^2A^2B^1B^1$, both of whom are in our Class 2, and calculate the intelligence of their children. All will be average, but none will have either parent's genotype. Take two other average people, $A^2A^2B^1B^1$ and $A^1A^2B^1B^2$, and we get quite different results. While the first only produces A^2B^1 gametes, the other produces four possibilities—as in F_1 above. The children of this couple will have three phenotypes: dull normal, average, and bright average in the ratio 1:2:1. Interested readers can pursue the consequences of dominance and unequal gene frequencies on the resulting distribution.

As measurement of behavioral phenotypes improves in precision, whether for intelligence, normal personality, mental illness, or motor behavior, we may expect to find more and better use made of the polygenic model. A constant embarrassment to psychology when measuring human behavior is the problem of scaling. Hirsch (1959b) and Fuller and Thompson (1960) have broached this topic in regard to behavior genetics, but it can only be mentioned in passing as one of the major stumbling blocks to progress in the area.

It may be well to summarize some of the key points about polygenic systems in general. We can do no better than quote Fuller and Thompson:

It is important to bear in mind that the transmission of polygenes follows the ordinary rules of Mendelian genetics. The methods of quantitative genetics are statistical, but the statistics are derived from the laws of segregation and recombination, dominance, epistasis, sex and autosomal linkage, just as in classical genetics. The failure to isolate the effects of individual polygenes stems from the fact that there are many of them affecting each character; hence each has a small individual contribution to variance. In a statistical sense at least, one plus allele can substitute in some measure for any other plus allele. This apparent physiological equivalence is probably spurious. Each gene may influence a different metabolic pathway in a network arrangement, but if the critical point is the number of open paths rather than their chemical nature, the phenotypic effect would be simply a function of gene number. No major physiological discontinuity is evident between major genes and polygenes, and many major genes have been shown to have quantitative effects in addition to their obvious qualitative action (1960, p. 59).

Threshold effects. Related to the theory of polygenic determination of observed variation in a trait is the construct of a critical threshold. Let us take, for example, the dichotomy of institutionalized retarded versus noninstitutionalized retarded. It may be that the number of intelligence-enhancing genes must not exceed a certain critical value for a given retarded individual to become institutionalized. If, for example, we posited a four-pair system, the genotypes with two or less enhancing genes would be classified as institutionalized, and those with four or more would not; those with three could go either way depending on other factors since the genotype only fixes the modal point of the population. Such a dichotomy would mask the underlying continuous distribution of intelligence and may do the same for psychosis. An experiment on the inheritance of audiogenic seizure susceptibility in mice (Fuller, Easler, & Smith, 1950), which many not be too far afield in the light of the incidence of seizures among the retarded, serves to illustrate the combining of the polygenic model with the threshold construct. Mice of a purebred strain which were 100 per cent susceptible to seizures after their first exposure to a ringing bell were bred to another pure strain that had almost no mice susceptible under the same conditions. Their F_1 hybrids are represented by the middle curve in Figure 7-3. The horizontal axis represents two parameters of the experiment, (hypothetical) number of seizure-susceptible genes and degree of environmental stress. In Figure 7-3 the threshold has been drawn for a moderate stress condition which almost completely separates the parent strains and leads to seizures in 75 per cent of the F_1.

Figure 7-3. The multiple factor–critical threshold theory. (*Adapted from Fuller, 1954.*)

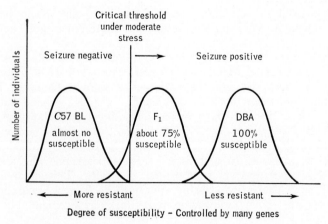

This combined model would lead to the prediction that increasing or decreasing the stress and/or the number of seizure genes in an F_1 mouse would increase or decrease, respectively, the number of F_1 having seizures without having much effect on the incidence in the parent strains. The first part of the prediction concerning stress has been confirmed. Fruitfulness of this combined model for theory in mental retardation depends on the degree of validity of making seizure susceptibility in mice analogous to *institutional susceptibility* in the genotype represented by the familial group of retarded. Suffice it to say that some apparent dichotomies in adaptive behavior which would first lead the genetically oriented psychologist to the positing of classical Mendelian mechanisms may be masking an underlying polygenic effect of the type outlined here.

Heritability. Interindividual or phenotypic (P) *variance* in adaptive behavior in a well-controlled environment can be partitioned into components due to genotype G, plus that due to microenvironment E, plus that due to their interaction I.

$$\sigma_P^2 = \sigma_G^2 + \sigma_E^2 + \sigma_I^2 \tag{7-1}$$

When the interaction term is zero, the relationship of the genetic and environmental components to the phenotypic variance becomes additive and interpretable in a straightforward fashion. Only in animal behavior experiments can the interaction term be made to approach zero. The research worker on human behavior assumes this variance is small relative to the other two components or includes it with environmental variance or computes a range of values together with a confidence interval for any ultimate ratio of genetic to environmental variances (Cattell, 1960). By experimentally and statistically eliminating systematic environmental effects so as only to contend with random effects, we can focus on the contribution of the genotype to the observed variation in either animal or human studies. With these specifications in mind, we shall write a simplified version of Eq. (7-1) above for clarity of exposition.

$$\sigma_P^2 = \sigma_G^2 + \sigma_E^2 \tag{7-2}$$

Heritability, denoted by h^2, is defined as the proportion of trait variance in a specified population for a specified trait which is determined by variation of genotype in that population. It is the ratio of genetic to phenotypic variance from Eq. (7-2).

$$h^2 = \frac{\sigma_G^2}{\sigma_P^2} = \frac{\sigma_G^2}{\sigma_G^2 + \sigma_E^2} \tag{7-3}$$

Phenotypic variance is conventionally set equal to unity so that h^2 can be read as either a proportion or a percentage of the total. An examination of Eq. (7-3) reveals several important properties of the concept of heritability as it will apply to human intelligence. We should not be surprised if the value obtained changes with the age, sex, or social class of the subjects, with a verbal versus performance test of general intelligence, with each factor in a factored test, with increasing homogeneity of our sample, or with any variable which may modify any of the three terms in Eq. (7-2).

Although this potential variability precludes any single statement about *the* heritability of intelligence, h^2 serves as a ready means for comparing results obtained from different samples and for different measures of intelligence. In animal selection studies, the determination of h^2 is of paramount importance since it will determine the success of selection. Another important value of h^2 for all studies of intelligent behavior rests on its properties as a measurement of the accuracy with which the genotype can be determined from our knowledge of the phenotype of an individual or of a group of individuals (Lerner, 1950). Since we should like to estimate the intellectual potential or endowment of an individual, we must look at either his performance or that of his relatives. In both cases heritability of intelligence enters as a variable. If h^2 for any trait is zero, the phenotype tells us nothing about the genetic makeup of the individual. Equation (7-3) above should suggest some immediate ways of either lowering or raising the heritability of intelligence. One of many possibilities would be the relaxation of environmental controls, thereby increasing σ_E^2 and the denominator of Eq. (7-3), and by so doing lowering the previous value of h^2 (Fuller & Thompson, 1960, p. 65).

The most useful method of obtaining a heritability estimate utilizes the ratio of the observed correlation between relatives to the correlation calculated on the basis of their genetic communality. The latter is easily obtained from the principles of segregation and recombination. For example, identical twins have a genetic correlation of 1.0, fraternal twins and sibs, .5, parent-child, .5, uncle-nephew, .25, and first cousins, .125. Each correlation represents the most probable proportion of genes derived from their common antecedents. Unfortunately this type of h^2 estimate when calculated empirically is often inflated since nongenetic variables common to families, such as social status, are confounded with the overlap in their genotypes.

Holzinger (1929) derived a coefficient of heritability H' for use in the classical method of twin comparisons which is not the same as h^2. His coefficient gives the proportion of variance produced by genetic differences *within* families, while h^2 gives an estimate of the effects of heredity *between* families in the general population. Both estimates are important for a full understanding of the factors involved. Heritability based on the twin method is the one most often found in the literature and underestimates the effects of genetic factors in the general population. In a random-mating population half of the genetic variance is due to variations of individuals within families, and half is due to variations between families (Li, 1955, p. 39). Equation (7-4) gives the most useful form of H'.

$$H' = \frac{\sigma_{DZ}^2 - \sigma_{MZ}^2}{\sigma_{DZ}^2} \qquad (7-4)$$

Both the fraternal (DZ) and identical (MZ) twin variances refer to within-pair variances. Only Cattell (1960) has proposed a general program for the estimation of the relative importance of nature and nurture within and beween families. References in the literature to nature-nurture ratios are nothing more than the ratio σ_G^2/σ_E^2 from Eq. (7-2) above. Any practical application of Cattell's proposal is beyond the resources of current investigators, but it can serve as an illustration of the intricacies of research on the effects of human heredity.

Inheritance of intelligent behavior in animals

No treatment of the bases of intelligent behavior would be complete without a discussion of the excellent work carried out with animals. While we are keenly aware of the dangers of extrapolation to human intelligence, the great advantages inherent in animal experimentation on adaptive behavior make possible a sharp focusing upon the many variables that are involved.

Selection studies. Animal studies on the inheritance of adaptive behaviors have proceeded along two main lines, the first being the selective breeding of animals that display the desired behavior followed by the breeding of those among their offspring who show more of the behavior than average, and the second being the comparison of pure strains, breeds, or lines. Passing mention must be made of an advance in experimental behavior genetics possible at the level of *Drosophila* which permits chromosome-to-behavior correlations (Hirsch, 1959a, 1959b; Hirsch & Tryon, 1956). Work by Tryon begun in 1927 and continuing in part over more than three decades exemplifies the method of selection. His purpose was to breed a pure line of maze-bright rats and one of maze-dull rats. Briefly, his procedure consisted in running an unselected *parent* sample of 142 albino rats for 19 trials through a 17-blind T maze and recording the total number of entrances into blind alleys as each animal's (intelligence) score. The brightest were then bred together and likewise for the dull. Thereafter, the breeding program consisted in mating the brightest rats within each of the brightest litters, the dullest within each of the dullest (Tryon, 1940). Gradually the phenotypic performances of the two lines separated, and by F_7 there was practically no overlap in their error scores. There were negligible effects of selective breeding for maze brightness and dullness after the seventh generation. Figure 7-4 shows vividly the effects of the selection process. Heron (1935, 1941) was able to achieve similar results.

These data show that rat intelligence as operationally defined in terms of maze performance is genetically based. In order to test the polygenic mode of transmission of the genetic factors, Tryon crossed the bright strain with the dull to obtain their F_1 and mated these to get an F_2. If the lines were nearly isogenic for the brights and dulls, the F_1 would show a homogeneous median performance and the F_2 should vary widely over the entire range. Since the F_2 did not vary more than the F_1 and the latter did not give a homogeneous performance, the polygenic theory was not verified. Since Tryon did not use close inbreeding such as brother-sister matings within a single line, the parents of F_1 were not pure strains and invalidated the subsequent genetic analysis (Thompson, 1954). A further test of the polygenic theory of adaptive behavior awaited the use of isogenic animals in addition to selection for the operationally defined intelligence unconfounded by other variables.

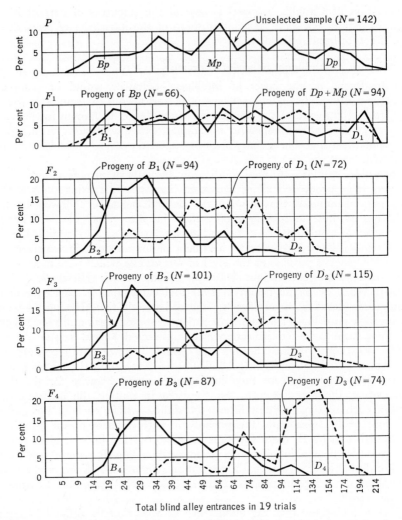

Figure 7-4. Selective breeding for maze-learning ability in nine generations of rats. (*After Tryon, 1942.*)

Tryon was by no means content to equate maze brightness with general rat intelligence but proceeded to examine the psychological nature of the trait. The brights and dulls were found to differ on a number of other traits. The results showed that the brights were more adjusted emotionally in the maze-learning situation, whereas their response to handling was labeled neurotic; exactly the reverse was found for the dulls. The data for these judgments were ratings for hiding, avoidance, escape reactions to handling, and reactions to new objects. These and other findings led Tryon to conclude that maze learning was specific and did not reflect a general capacity to learn. At his suggestion Searle (1949) proceeded to analyze intensively the total organization of the behavior of the two groups of rats.

Searle obtained 30 measures of learning, emotionality, activity, and other behaviors from nine different apparatuses for 10 bright, 10 dull, and 15 rats of a median strain. For example, in the open field (an 8-foot-diameter circular area with a 12-inch wall) he measured defecations, urinations, rearings, washings, and total distance traveled in 2 minutes. For measures of learning on five different apparatuses the dulls were either equal to or

Figure 7-4 (*Continued*)

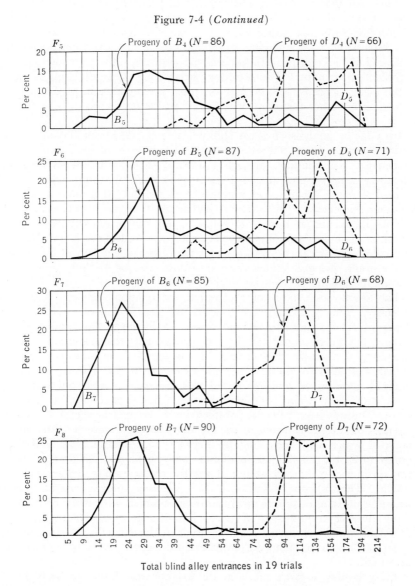

Total blind alley entrances in 19 trials

better than the brights on three. An overview of this experiment is perhaps best obtained from the author's general summary (1949, p. 323):

No evidence was found that a difference exists between Brights and Dulls in the learning capacity *per se*. A detailed study of the behavior profiles indicated that Brights are characteristically food-driven, economical of distance, low in motivation to escape from water, and timid in response to open spaces. Dulls are relatively disinterested in food, average or better in water motivation, and timid of mechanical apparatus features. It is concluded that brightness and dullness in the original Tryon Maze may be accounted for in large part by such motivational and emotional patterns. Although indications exist that the two strains may also be differentiated with reference to certain basic "cognitive" tendencies, the procedures followed in this experiment were not sufficiently analytical to indicate their nature. The need for further study is evident, both to relate the factors identified to the maze-learning performance in particular, and to discover other factors which may be present.

In a factor analysis of maze ability (Wherry, 1941) for Tryon's bright and dull strains, three components emerged and were named forward-going tendencies, food pointing, and goal gradients. Further analysis revealed that the three factors were utilized differently by the two strains over time. It seemed that the brights were insightful and the dulls depended upon food pointing. Krechevsky (1932, 1933) had found that the brights made more use of spatial cues (right or left), while the dulls preferred visual cues (light or dark). The entire family of experiments reviewed above is paralleled by and culminated in attempts to discover the physiological basis of intelligence in the bright and dull strains. Success in this endeavor would be a large step toward the linking of behavior to the genes.

The results and status of the search for relations between brain biochemistry and behavior were summarized by Rosenzweig, Krech, and Bennett (1960). Our review will draw heavily upon this summary. The general hypothesis under test in their program is that variation in brain chemistry is a major determinant of the variation in adaptive behavior among normal individuals. Only the results with the descendants of the original maze-bright and maze-dull rats will be reported although their work with other strains is essential to the complete exposition of their program. The adaptive behaviors studied were the spatial versus visual preferences of the rat in problem solving plus the error scores in three mazes, none of which had been used by Tryon or Searle. Initially the Berkeley group measured cholinesterase (ChE) activity on the assumption that it was an index to the availability of the transmitter substance, acetylcholine (ACh). They reasoned that since ACh is importantly involved in neural transmission in the central nervous system, animals with more of it should show steadier transmission of nerve impulses and tend to manage new problems more effectively than animals with less efficient transmission systems. ChE rather than ACh was assayed since it could be more readily measured.

Early in the research program the brights were found to be higher in

ChE activity than the dulls. Subsequently it was found that the brights were superior to the dulls on the three new mazes. The higher the ChE activity, the better was the learning; but in a cross between the two strains, the higher the ChE activity, the worse was the learning. In order to resolve this paradox they made a new assumption about the relation between ChE and ACh. They assumed that the two were under separate genetic controls so that ChE was not a good indicator of ACh and retained the basic assumption that the ACh transmission system, therefore ChE, was intimately involved in learning ability. Their current hypothesis is the following: "learning capacity is related to the levels of both ACh and ChE, such that, within limits, the greater amount of ACh functioning at the synapse, the greater the efficiency of transmission and, consequently, the greater the learning ability" (Rosenzweig et al., 1960, p. 486). Support for this hypothesis came from the finding that the brights had a 14 per cent greater concentration of ACh in their brains than the dulls as well as a 10 per cent greater concentration of ChE. The authors concluded from their work that the original selection for maze ability led to general results for adaptive behavior even though the other behavioral tests were all varieties of mazes.

Comparisons of pure strains. The other main line of investigation of the inheritance of adaptive behaviors is the comparison of pure strains, breeds, or lines. It is exemplified by the work of the Bar Harbor group under Scott and Fuller with dog breeds and the work of Thompson with rats and mice. Thompson (1954) attempted to correct the deficiencies of the selection experiments by achieving a high degree of homozygosity with inbreeding and by eliminating the confounding effect of emotional and motivational variables on operationally defined intelligence. To accomplish the latter he used the nonmechanical Hebb-Williams maze. It consists of a square enclosure with a starting box in one corner and a food box diagonally opposite. Different length barriers can be placed in different positions to make up a series of problems so that the maze is somewhat analogous to a human intelligence test. Each animal is given pretest training to eliminate emotional reactions to handling or to the maze and to eliminate differences in food motivation. Any rat which is not adapted during pretesting is not used. Results for the first six generations on a series of 24 short problems showed a marked separation between the emergent bright and dull strains as early as F_3. In the following generation there were only two cases of overlap between the brights and the dulls. At the time of the study the two lines were not as homozygous as desired. So far this is the only work which shows clear genetic differences in learning capacity which exist independently of emotional and motivational variables.

A great deal of experimentation has been conducted over the years in the Jackson Laboratories at Bar Harbor on the social and intellectual behavior of highly inbred dog breeds. Incorporating the experiences of those who had gone before them, Fuller and Scott (1954) set up their experiments to magnify the genetic differences among five behavioral types of dog breeds. Their five pure breeds were basenjis, beagles, cocker spaniels, Shetland sheep dogs, and wire-haired fox terriers. All were tested for numerous behaviors under favorable conditions during the first year of life. Only the results which relate to learning ability will be reported. Evidence for hereditary differences in capacity to perform in a variety of situations was found in each of the three experiments. For leash control training, which involves emotional training, the breeds fell into three groups based on the number of demerits: a high group of basenjis and sheep dogs, a middle group of beagles and basenji-cocker hybrids, and a low group of cockers and terriers. The discrimination-delayed response series of tests required the dogs to learn to associate a swinging panel with an open corridor leading to food. Beagles and terriers were the superior performers. On the final test, spatial orientation, the animal was required to choose the one correct path to a food reward, from a choice of three, by depending upon visual cues. Terriers and basenjis performed the worst. Tetrachoric correlation coefficients between the three tests were low or negative. This can be interpreted to mean that no single factor of intelligence or docility can account for their distributions.

Certain conclusions seem to be warranted in regard to adaptive behavior in infrahuman mammals; they are based upon the work cited above and upon other experiments of the Bar Harbor group (e.g., Scott & Charles, 1953; Anastasi, Fuller, Scott, & Schmitt, 1955). Genetic effects on behavior are specific. It is easier to obtain clear-cut genetic differences when a single type of motivation is used and when a response topography is divided into its apparent elements for separate scoring. With the possible exception of the Thompson (1954) study, the evidence indicates that it is easy to find performance differences which can be attributed to motivational, emotional, and peripheral processes but difficult to find evidence of genetically based differences in the more purely central nervous processes (Scott & Charles, 1953). Even under homogeneous environments and maximum homozygosity, there is substantial within- and between-breed variability. And finally, any test of performance shows some hereditary effects.

We shall conclude this section with the results of an experiment which exposed known genotypes to radical systematic changes in the environment of the rat and measured the effects on adaptive behavior. Cooper and Zubek (1958) used the F_{13} of both the bright and dull lines of Thompson's McGill rats as their subjects. Table 7-2 gives the mean error scores for the brights and dulls on the first 12 problems of the Hebb-Williams maze under three environmental conditions. The normal environment consisted in the natural habitat for a laboratory rat. The subgroup of brights and dulls

TABLE 7-2

Maze error scores for bright and dull rats reared under three different conditions

Strain	Environment		
	Enriched	Natural	Restricted
Brights	111.2	117.0	169.7
	(N = 12)	(N = 11)	(N = 13)
Dulls	119.7	164.0	169.5
	(N = 9)	(N = 11)	(N = 9)

reared in an enriched environment after weaning had access to such objects as ramps, swings, polished balls, slides, tunnels, barriers, and teeter-totters; and their cages faced a decorated wall. Only a food box and water pan in an otherwise bare cage formed the restricted environment for the two groups reared under that condition.

An enriched early environment led to a considerable improvement in the performance of the dulls but had little or no effect upon the brights. The dulls reduced their errors by about 27 per cent. A restricted early environment increased the errors of the brights by about 44 per cent but had little or no effect upon the dulls. Notice that with an enriched environment the dulls were equal to the brights under the latter's normal or natural habitat and that the restricted brights equaled the natural dulls. These data fit in very nicely with the earlier exposition of the reaction range. Cooper and Zubek discussed their findings in terms of Hebbian theory (Hebb, 1949). Extrapolating to the human case, it may be that eventual manipulation of the intelligence phenotype will be only a question of economics. Within the range of intelligence accounted for by a polygenic system, a great expenditure of effort may replace the effects of intelligence-enhancing genes.

Inheritance of intelligent behavior in man

In their efforts to establish the role played by heredity in the expression of intelligence in man, geneticists and psychologists have been primarily limited to looking at data from families as found in Western civilization. For purposes of presentation, we may divide these data into more convenient categories—pedigree studies, correlational- and mating-type studies, and twin studies.

Pedigree studies. The first of these, pedigree studies, as originally construed by Galton (1869), are primarily of historical interest to the study of intelligence since they could not separate heredity from environment. It is now recognized that parents pass on their culture and societal status or prestige (or lack thereof) as well as their genes. While Galton recognized that he was dealing with a quantitative variable and devised a rating scale to analyze his pedigrees of hereditary genius, the unrepresentativeness of the families plus the dependence upon reputation for data limits us to the conclusion that ability appears to be transmitted from parents to offspring. Other examples of the pedigree method are of historical interest too, such as Dugdale's (1877) description of the Jukes and Goddard's (1913) of the Kallikaks. The eugenic fervor of some pedigree studies of feeblemindedness plus a misguided confidence in simple recessive inheritance as the cause of this class of retarded may partially determine some present-day attitudes of mistrust toward genetic explanations (Dunn, 1962). From the point of view of prediction rather than explanation, the pedigree method allows us to establish empirical risk figures for a quantitative variable. This would show, for example, the probability of different degrees of relatives being retarded given the fact that a parent or sibling was retarded. A good example of the risk methodology is that of Kallmann (1953) for the psychoses. We may expect similar arrays for mental deficiency when the extensive study of 296 families of defective propositi with an average of 158 persons per family is completed (Reed, Reed, & Palm, 1954; Higgins et al., 1961).

Correlational- and mating-type studies. Following the introduction of the correlation coefficient for the analysis of quantitative data by Pearson (1904) and such extensions as those of Fisher (1918), the resemblances between parents and children and between siblings could be computed. An extensive literature has developed from just the calculation of such correlation coefficients. Seldom have the interpretations of the coefficients been above reproach. By itself, a correlation coefficient between the IQ scores of relatives does not indicate the importance of heredity any more than of environment in determining the magnitude of the resemblance. Extensive discussions of the significance of the correlations between *traits* (Thompson, 1957; Fuller & Thompson, 1960) reveal that they may arise from genic, chromosomal, gametic, or environmental communalities. By substituting *relatives* for *traits* much of their exposition is relevant in the current context. A correlation between brothers' IQs could arise from their having some similar genes; from different genes with the same physiological effects; from cross-homogamy in the parents, e.g., high verbal capacity in the mother and high mathematical capacity in the father transmitted differentially to the offspring but both leading to superior total test performance; or from sharing the same family and cultural environment. Certain mechanical factors such as the homogeneity of the sample can raise or lower the correlation in a particular study also. The interpretation of a correlation coefficient from a genetic viewpoint is not as hopeless as it may sound when additional information is appraised concurrently. By comparing an array of correlation coefficients derived from samples of varying but known (on the average) genetic dependency, after the control of systematic environmental effects, we can obtain a working estimate of the contribution of heredity to IQ variation. Kallmann's (1946) twin-family method illustrates one strategy for the interpretation of an array of correlation coefficients. The correlation between IQs of six different sibship groups reared under comparable environmental conditions is computed for identical twins, fraternal same-sex twins, fraternal opposite-sex twins, full siblings, half siblings, and step siblings. The identical twins would be expected to have the highest correlation followed by fraternal twins and full siblings with tied ranks. Half siblings with only one parent in common should have a correlation between that of the ordinary siblings and the unrelated step siblings if genetic factors are important. If such an array from substantial samples in each category could be obtained, the supporters of purely environmental causation of intelligence would be forced to demonstrate that a consistent increase in IQ correlations could be found in association with particular environmental circumstances in the absence of consanguinity.

Some of the data which bear on this topic will be presented, but extensive summaries can be found in some of the texts already mentioned. Neither before nor after the now classical study of familial resemblance in intelligence by Conrad and Jones (1940) has any significant data appeared to counter their findings. This study serves as a model of thoroughness in the collection, analysis, and interpretation of data. They tested a large, representative, rural

New England sample of 997 persons in 269 family groups. The correlations between siblings and between parents and siblings were both .49. It was noteworthy that the correlation between parents was .52 which demon- strated the extent of homogamy and the danger of assuming random mating for behavioral traits. Conrad and Jones concluded that their theories of environmental influence on intelligence received no positive support and that one of the genetic models, that of Fisher, succeeded moderately well with their data.

While it is a little premature to present the correlations obtained between twins, the array of correlations offered by Burt (1955, 1958) for substantial samples of different degrees of sibship among London school children sup- ports the importance of genetic factors. Table 7-3 gives his findings. Final assessment refers to those results obtained by submitting the initial marks for criticism or correction to teachers and then adjusting the marks where necessary by supplementary tests of an individual and nonverbal type (Burt & Howard, 1957). Correlations most discrepant with the body of literature have been reported by Cattell and Willson (1938). By using a supposedly culture-free test, correcting for age, for attenuation, for scatter, and for skewness, they found an *r* of .91 between parents and children and an *r* of .77 between siblings. While the use of numerous corrections may perhaps

TABLE 7-3

Correlations for mental and scholastic measures between twins, siblings, and foster children reared together and apart (after Burt, 1958)

	Identical twins reared together N = 83	Identical twins reared apart N = 21	Non-identical twins reared together N = 172	Siblings reared together N = 853	Siblings reared apart N = 131	Un-related children reared together N = 287
Mental "intelligence"						
Group test	.944	.771	.542	.515	.441	.281
Individual test	.921	.843	.526	.491	.463	.252
Final assessment	.925	.876	.551	.538	.517	.269
Scholastic						
General attainments	.898	.681	.831	.814	.526	.535
Reading and spelling	.944	.647	.915	.853	.490	.548
Arithmetic	.862	.723	.748	.769	.563	.476

Note: Sample sizes are derived from Burt (1955) and assume that twin data are based on pairs.

be statistically defensible, they could conceivably result in statistical artifacts rather than purer measures of the trait. Other studies (Hildreth, 1925) demonstrated that group homogeneity rather than level of intelligence accounted for the differences between groups with respect to sibling correlations. The sib correlation in an average but homogeneous sample was .27 but in an average but heterogeneous sample was .63.

Roberts (1952) plotted the distributions of the IQs of 562 sibs of high-grade and low-grade mental defectives. Figure 7-5 reveals that the mean IQ of the sibs of the low grades was about 20 points higher than that of the sibs of the high grades. The distribution for the sibs of the low-grade defectives was actually quite similar to that found in the general population. These data offer strong support for the proposition that two different genetic mechanisms underlie the gross phenomenon of mental deficiency—major genes associated with low-grade retardation and polygenes associated with high-grade retardation.

Adopted children have been studied to provide evidence for the bases of intelligent behavior with the rationale that if heredity has something to do with IQ, adopted children should be less similar to their adoptive parents than the biological children of a control parent group. Woodworth (1941) and Anastasi (1958) summarized the extensive literature. One of the major criticisms of these kinds of studies was that some of them relied on an intellectual assessment of a child before age 5 when IQ tests are notoriously unreliable (Bayley, 1955). A further source of error was the conscious or unconscious effort of many adoption agencies to place the child with parents similar to the known characteristics of its biological parents. The studies of Burks (1928) and Leahy (1935) are among the better conducted ones in this area. Burks administered the Stanford-Binet to 214 foster children and their foster parents, as well as to 105 control children and their parents who had been matched on most of the relevant variables with the experimental group. Only children who had been placed in the foster home before 1 year of age were included. At the time of testing, the children ranged in age from 5 to 14. Leahy's study was similar but had better matching and used the Otis Self-Administering Test for the parents. The findings with regard to correlations between parent and child IQ are given in Table 7-4.

Both volumes of the *Thirty-ninth Yearbook* are pertinent to an awareness

Figure 7-5. Frequency distributions of the IQs of sibs of feebleminded and imbeciles of the IQ range 30–68. (*After Roberts, 1952.*)

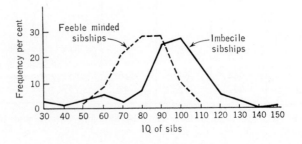

of the wide range of experiments that can be and have been conducted to explore the "nature and nurture" of intelligence.

While the casual observation that like tends to beget like does not permit conclusions about the relative importance of heredity and environment, the data obtained from the observation of the percentage of offspring from the mating of two retarded parents or a normal with a retarded yield practical information for prediction and spur the search for causality. A follow-up study of Terman's gifted children (Terman & Oden, 1947) group which had a mean IQ of 151 showed that the average IQ of their offspring was 128; the spouses of the gifted group were not as intelligent as their mates. Penrose (1954) and Halperin (1945) took as their starting point institutionalized defectives and then examined the mental status of their parents. Penrose found that 37.1 per cent of the parents of *aclinical aments* were of borderline or lower levels of intelligence and that 15.1 per cent of the parents of aclinical aments were defective themselves. Halperin's findings are given in Table 7-5. Note that of 252 children from matings of individuals in the IQ range 70 to 85, 28 per cent of the offspring

TABLE 7-4

Burks and Leahy results for parent ✕ child resemblances in intelligence

	Foster group		Control group	
	Parents ✕ adopted *r*		Parents ✕ own children *r*	
	Burks	Leahy	Burks	Leahy
Fa MA (Burks) or Otis score (Leahy)	.07	.19	.45	.51
Mo MA (Burks) or Otis score (Leahy)	.19	.24	.46	.51

TABLE 7-5

Offspring of various types of parents ascertained by their having had a mentally defective child (from Halperin, 1945)

Parents	Number	Children		
		Average or above (%)	Inferior (%) IQ 70–85	Defective (%) IQ 50–70
Average ✕ average	18	72	5	22
Average ✕ inferior	59	64	33	3
Inferior ✕ inferior	252	28	57	15
Inferior ✕ defective	89	10	55	35
Defective ✕ defective	141	4	39	57

were of average IQ or above. This suggests the importance of polygenic factors which, despite the child's exposure to an obviously inferior environment, allowed these children to perform at an intellectual level above that of their parents and siblings. Reed (1955) in commenting upon a paper by Skodak and Skeels (1949) pointed out that while the 11 children placed for adoption of 11 retarded mothers with a mean IQ of 63 had an average of 94 themselves, the 3 lowest children scored 66, 74, and 87. Reed emphasized the fact that the foster parents were adopting individuals rather than an average. The controversy over the placement for adoption of the children of the mentally defective is just one of the many side issues which arise when examining theories of intelligent behavior.

We shall conclude this section with one of the most sophisticated efforts to support the polygenic theory of intelligence by observing parent-child resemblances in intelligence. Burt (1955) tested a random sample of 954 London school children and at least one of their parents.

On the basis of the measurements, the children were divided into three groups—bright, average, and dull—in the proportions 1:2:1; and a similar classification was adopted for the parents. The percentages we should expect for the bivariate distribution, based on the triple assumption of random mating, Mendelian segregation, and no tendency to dominance, are shown below. . . . It will be seen that the observed proportions agree tolerably well with the hypothetical; and . . . the divergences themselves are very much what we would expect (pp. 172–173) (see Table 7-6).

Burt proceeded through other steps allowing for unreliability, random environmental conditions, dominance, and assortative mating and concluded at that time that for his sample 75 per cent, at least, of the

TABLE 7-6

Bivariate distributions of intelligence for parents and their children (from Burt, 1955)

Parents	Theoretical frequencies				Observed frequencies			
	Children				Children			
	Bright	Average	Dull	Total	Bright	Average	Dull	Total
Bright	12.5	12.5	0.0	25.0	10.8	12.3	1.9	25.0
Average	12.5	25.0	12.5	50.0	13.4	26.5	10.1	50.0
Dull	0.0	12.5	12.5	25.0	0.8	11.2	13.0	25.0
Total	25.0	5).0	25.0	100.0	25.0	50.0	25.0	100.0

measurable variance of intelligence was attributable to differences in genetic constitution, and less than 25 per cent to environmental conditions. In Burt's article as well as those by others attempting to attribute so much of the observed variation to heredity and so much to environment, it is not made explicit, as it must be, that systematic environmental effects have been eliminated and that microenvironmental effects are what are being referred to (Fuller & Thompson, 1960, p. 63).

Twin studies. Galton (1875) called attention to the uniqueness of twins and suggested their usefulness in the appraisal of the hereditary contribution to intelligence. Since monozygotic (MZ) twins have identical genotypes, any dissimilarity between pairs must be due to the action of agents in the environment, either postnatal or intrauterine; dizygotic (DZ) twins, while no more alike genetically than ordinary same-sex siblings, have certain environmental similarities in common such as birth rank and maternal age, thereby providing a measure of environmental control not otherwise possible. When both types of twins are studied in a particular population, a method is provided for the evaluation of the effect of different environments on the same genotype or the expression of different genotypes under the same environment. Another strategy which has not been sufficiently utilized is the intensive study of similar and dissimilar MZ pairs (Rosenthal, 1959).

When dealing with major gene disorders such as phenylketonuria, the phenotypes of MZ twins should be concordant while the phenotypes of DZ twins may be discordant. The difference in concordance rates can be used as a measure of heritability for major gene mg effects similar in interpretation to H' of Eq. (7-4) above. If environment has little effect on genotype, CMZ will be near 100 per cent with a smaller value for CDZ.

$$H'_{mg} = \frac{\text{CMZ}\% - \text{CDZ}\%}{100 - \text{CDZ}\%} \tag{7-5}$$

For an infectious disease with no known genetic differences in resistance, such as measles, both concordances would be near 100 per cent and the heritability would be zero. Equation (7-4) for H' is the one used when the variable under consideration, intelligence within $\pm$ three standard deviations of the mean, is a continuous one.

There are a number of limitations and criticisms of the twin method. Some are statistical including the assumption of equivalent environments for the two classes, and others are biological. With the introduction of increased knowledge about blood grouping (Smith & Penrose, 1955), the difficulty of zygosity diagnosis is no longer a handicap. Before attempting to evaluate the results of twin studies, the student should familiarize himself with the papers by Price (1950), Allen (1955), and Kallmann (1959). The results of twin studies conducted before 1950 should be viewed with caution, while those conducted since should be evaluated in the light of the criteria now accepted. Even though accurate evidence for the effects of limitations of the twin method is lacking, Price was willing to conclude: "In all probability the net effect of most twin studies has been underestimation of the significance of heredity in the medical and behavior sciences" (p. 293).

Correlation coefficients between MZ and DZ twin pairs on any of the standard tests of general intelligence, such as the Stanford-Binet, give routinely replicable results. The findings of Newman, Freeman, and Holzinger (1937) are typical. For their sample of 50 pairs each of MZ and same-sex DZ adolescent twins the intraclass correlations for the 1916 Binet IQs were .91 and .64, respectively, and .92 and .62 for an Otis test. H' from these two tests was .69 and .84, respectively, for the proportion of within-family variance accounted for. Carter (1940) reviewed over 130 studies that dealt with aspects of twins and the inheritance of intelligence. Only three studies have compared the IQs of identical twins separated early in life and reared in environments at least more different from those of fraternals reared together. Newman, Freeman, and Holzinger (1937) found an MZ r of .67 for 19 pairs, Burt (1955) an r of .88 for 21 pairs, and Shields (1958; Shields & Slater, 1961) an r of .77 on a nonverbal test for a remarkably large sample of 40 pairs of identical twins reared apart. Shields collected his sample by requesting cooperation on a BBC television program. In the sample of 19 pairs of MZ twins reared apart, there was a correlation of .79 between discrepancy in educational advantage and discrepancy in Binet IQ. All these data afford us an insight into the effects of different environments on the same genotype and suggest that the reaction range for average individuals under average conditions is not more than 12 IQ points in each direction and most probably less. The mean difference in Binet IQ for the 19 pairs reared apart was close to 8 points compared to about 5 points for the 50 pairs reared together. All three of the rs between MZ reared apart are higher than those reported for same-sex DZ twins reared together.

Most of the recent attempts to utilize the twin method in the study of intelligence have not been content with the assessment of general intelligence or g but have used such factored tests as Thurstone's Primary Mental Abilities (PMA) or tests of special ability such as the subscales of a Wechsler test. The studies (Thurstone et al., 1953; Blewett, 1954; Vandenberg, 1962) are among the soundest ever conducted on twins with respect to the criteria for such studies. Regretfully, none of these studies analyzed their data separately for males and females. It is possible that one or more components of intelligence are highly heritable for one sex and not for the other. At any rate, studies examining other than general intelligence shed some light on the structure of measured intelligence as well as demonstrate differential heritability for the components. Blewett's findings from 26 pairs each of MZ and DZ adolescent twins are given in Table 7-7. He found no support for his hypothesis that variation in the second-order factor score from the PMA would be determined by hereditary agents to a greater degree than any of the scores which contributed to it. It is difficult to reconcile the low H' for PMA total score which should be comparable to the value found for such tests as the Stanford-Binet. Thurstone et al. (1953) reported their findings with the PMA in the form of χ^2 for frequencies of *large* differences between a sample of 48 MZ and 55 DZ pairs of about the same age as those in Blewett's sample. Although space, verbal, and fluency factors showed marked heritability, in that order, neither number nor reasoning discriminated between the two kinds of twins. In addition to the specificity of *H'* to which we have already alluded, part of the discrepancy between the above two studies may be attributed to the fact that Blewett's sample consisted of equal numbers of male and female twins in each category, while the Thurstone et al. study had three times as many female MZ pairs as male MZ pairs. The Thurstones (1955) have graciously made all their original data for 35 psychological tests available for different kinds of analyses. Vandenberg (1962) presented his PMA findings for 45 MZ and 37 DZ pairs of adolescents in yet a different fashion. His DZ sample had almost twice as many females as males. The sex-difference literature is replete (Anastasi, 1958) with instances of female superiority in various linguistic aspects and male superiority in spatial aptitude. Stafford (1961) has suggested that the aptitude for visualizing space may be a sex-linked recessive trait. Among the results for many cognitive-type tests, Vandenberg reported *H'* values of .46 for WISC Digits and .54 for WISC Vocabulary. Eysenck and Prell (1951), using the twin method, reported an *H'* of .68 for intelligence based on a combined score from Wechsler-Bellevue Similarities and Digit Symbol. As witnessed by correlations of .38 to .54 between the reasoning factor of the PMA and the other factors and .84 with *g* (Bischof, 1954), the general intelligence or *g* construct may be an indicator of facility with symbols above all else. It may be disconcerting to note at this point that Guilford (1959) put forth a model of the structure of intellect with no less than 120 factors. Evidence from the vast majority of twin studies reviewed presents solid support for the position of importance attributed to genetic or biological strata. The degree of importance is, however, a function of the prevailing internal and external milieu. A few studies using mentally

TABLE 7-7

The inheritance of primary factors of mental abilities and of second-order general intelligence (after Blewett, 1954)

PMA factor	MZ *r* N = 26 prs	DZ *r* N = 26 prs	*H'*
Verbal	.726	.145	.680
Space	.630	.248	.508
Number	.489	.449	.073
Reason	.708	.188	.640
Fluency	.734	.257	.642
Total A*	.583	.369	.339
Total B†	.754	.394	.594

* PMA total score from formula $V + S + 2N + 2R + W$.
† PMA total score calculated on the basis of the square of Thurstone's second-order factor loadings.

retarded twins all lend further support to the general thesis of this chapter, but they used rather coarse groupings for their categories of retardation. Rosanoff, Handy, and Plesset (1937) reported a concordance rate of 91 per cent for MZ twins and 61 per cent for same-sex DZ pairs institutionalized for mental deficiency. The total sample consisted of 366 pairs. For those cases uncomplicated by such factors as psychosis, epilepsy, delinquency, and behavior problems (73 MZ pairs, 45 same-sex DZ pairs), 73 per cent of the MZ twins were concordant for retardation and within five IQ points of each other compared with 29 per cent of the same-sex DZ twin pairs. Juda, as reported by Shields and Slater (1961), studied all the twin pairs attending special schools in Munich. She excluded cases where the defect was caused by a known birth injury or other possible exogenous causes and found 100 per cent concordance for her sample of 60 MZ pairs, and 58 per cent for 129 DZ pairs. Kallmann (1959) reported corroborating data for the importance of genetic factors in intelligence both from his study of a large sample of senescent twins and from Baroff's study of retarded twins.

It seems to us that theorizing about bases of intelligent behavior would be given a firmer footing if a number of studies were to be conducted with the twin method on the parameters of such behaviors as are fairly universally accepted signs of learning. Among these would be included the various aspects of respondent and operant conditioning. Kanaiev (1938) made an intensive study of the salivary reflex in one pair of MZ twins and some supplementary observations for one additional pair of MZ and one of DZ twins. He reported that the mean difference in the number of drops of saliva to an unconditioned stimulus, food, was .42 for the two MZ pairs and 1.29 for the DZ pair for 20 trials. With respect to acquisition, the conditioned response in the MZ pair of twins "was identical to such a degree that with both girls the reflex was established on the same day and even after the same number of stimulations (thirty-six). The children even gave the same number of drops of saliva" (p. 182). While by no means definitive, such a study is suggestive of the kinds of data that could be collected profitably.

Animal and human studies compared. An obvious discrepancy exists between findings from animal studies and those from human studies on the inheritance of intelligence; it is difficult to find a factor analogous to g in the adaptive behavior of animals. Fuller (1957b) suggested a number of possible reasons for this: (1) The intellectual level of animals may be so low that hereditary differences in motivational and emotional traits are easier to demonstrate. (2) General intelligence may be an artifact produced by assortative mating between individuals both high or low in diverse abilities. (3) Psychologists may not have been clever enough to discover g in animals. (4) The evolutionary uniqueness of man's cerebral cortex may have led to g.

The last point is worth pursuing further. Beach (1958) has suggested with respect to sexual behavior that evolutionary changes in the direction of increasing corticalization seem to be associated with increasing complexity and modifiability of an individual's sexual pattern. He emphasized the evolution of the "uses" of hormones, i.e., evolution of reaction patterns.

Harlow (1958) endorsed the view that all learning and thinking resulted from the single operation of the inhibition of inappropriate responses or response tendencies. Although he has found a greater degree of intellectual communality among the primates, he does not feel that there is any evidence of a break in learning capabilities between primate and nonprimate forms. Selective breeding for bright and dull apes might bring important data to this problem area. General intelligence in man may be the function of an extensive formal language development. Nissen (1958), however, reasoned that language did not introduce any really new psychological process, but only served as an instrumental means for increasing the efficiency of processes already present in nonhuman animals. It might be argued, finally, that such efficiency is the basis for *g* in man and hence to be expected from an evolutionary point of view. With regard to such abnormalities as the mental deficiencies, Allen (1957) has proposed as a working hypothesis that the "recent" evolutionary advances in man's nervous system have led to extreme, nonadaptive variations which will eventually stabilize by natural selection.

Advances in cytological genetics. Improvement in cytological techniques led to the discovery that the true number of chromosomes in man was 46 rather than 48 (Tjio & Levan, 1956). The study of chromosomal abnormalities in man is still more recent and was ushered in by the remarkable discovery of trisomism in cases of mongolism (Lejeune, Turpin, & Gautier, 1959). It has since been established rather conclusively that mongolism is associated with an extra chromosome at pair number 21 for a karyotype with 47 chromosomes. Figure 7-8 is a typical mongolian karyotype. Although most of the work in cytogenetics is too technical for other than a few remarks in this chapter, and the rate of discovery precludes a really timely summary, the reader would benefit from the excellent summaries of Ford (1960) and Lejeune and Turpin (1961). The present account leans heavily upon these sources.

Mongolism has baffled science ever since its clinical description by Langdon Down in 1866. The clinical data, stereotypy of the features, and concordance of MZ twins suggested an obvious dominant gene. However, this was contradicted by the frequency of the condition, which was at least 100 times greater than other known mutation rates. The incidence of mongolism is about 1 in 700 births, and about 10 per cent of the population of institutions for the mentally defective have been so diagnosed. Another weakness to the dominant gene hypothesis was the observation that such polygenic concomitants as degrees of mongoloid features were observed in relatives of the propositus and even in *normals*. Environmental agents were implicated by the finding that older women were more likely to have mongolian offspring and by the observation that many mothers had been irradiated during pregnancy. The finding of 47 chromosomes by Lejeune et al. together with the discovery of *partial trisomy* by Shaw and Chu (1961) in the mothers of affected children explains all the conflicting evidence. The latter finding raises the possibility of exploring the consequences on the intelligence phenotype of different degrees of triplication of chromosome 21.

Among the most exciting outcomes of this particular discovery is the clue to the gene content of chromosome 21 and the possibility of chemical correction of the defect. Consistent observations on 15 mongols and 16 controls led to the hypothesis (Lejeune & Turpin, 1961) that mongols suffer from a disturbance of tryptophan metabolism and are probably affected by a low amount of brain serotonin. It could be that the genic overdosage leads to overconcentration of some enzymes which exaggerates some normal reactions thereby inhibiting necessary action in other enzyme pathways. One view of gene action (Knox, 1961) holds that the primary product of a mutated gene will be qualitatively altered in structure, while the other enzymes will be qualitatively normal but changed in quantity. Radiation probably increases the probability of autosomal nondisjunction manifested by the extra chromosome (Uchida & Curtis, 1961).

Other instances of an extra autosome in positions other than number 21 are coming into the literature, and almost all of these individuals manifest mental retardation (Therman, Patau, Smith, & DeMars, 1961) but are not mongols. Numerical aberrations of the sex chromosomes have been reported by an increasing number of investigators. It seems that most of the abnormal combinations reduce the phenotypic intelligence of the carrier. Whereas the normal male has 44 autosomes, an X and a Y, and the normal female has the same number of autosomes, and 2 X's, the individuals referred to here are of such types as XXY, XXXY, XXXXY, XXX, and XO.

Another discovery in this rapidly evolving field was that of karyotypes with one less autosome than normal for a total of 45. The missing chromosome becomes translocated to the arm of another chromosome. Moorhead et al. (1961) examined a family of two adults and six children psychologically and cytologically. The karyotypes of the normal father, normal daughter, mongoloid daughter, and 45-chromosome son are reproduced in Figures 7-6 to 7-9. The mother and four children had 45 chromosomes, the father and one child had a normal complement, and one child had the usual mongoloid karyotype with trisomism for number 21. Although the mother had a tested IQ of 93 (verbal scale of W-B I), the four children with 45 chromosomes were all retarded (untestable, IQ 38, IQ 68, and IQ 70). The most striking feature of the children's retardation was the failure of speech development. Moorhead et al. take care to point out that a causal explanation relating the translocation to speech and mental development remains to be proved. The research possibilities of this method of karyotypal analysis using peripheral blood are obvious and important to new insights about the etiology not only of mental retardation but also of mental and physical illness.

The majority of evidence accumulated so far with respect to chromosomal aberrations suggests that practically all parts of chromosomes are capable of affecting measured intelligence and that any upset in the general genic balance has harmful effects on both physical and mental traits. It must be stressed however that the particular anomaly may not affect the intelligence genotype qua intelligence but may manifest itself as a lowered phenotypic intelligence via the influence on motivational and emotional traits or on sensory and receptor channels.

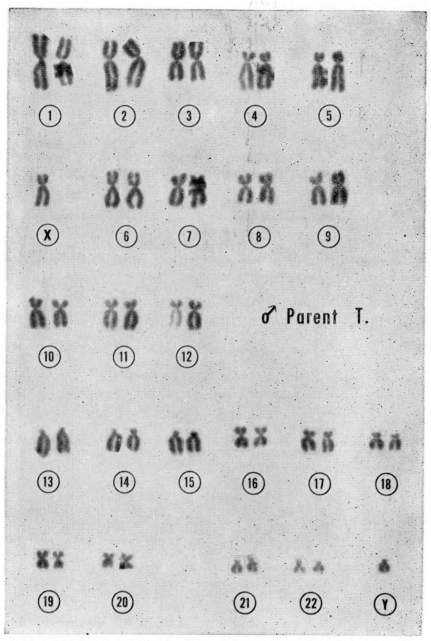

Figure 7-6. Karyotype of the father of T. family: 46 chromosomes, normal intelligence. Approximate enlargement 1,400×. (*Courtesy of P. S. Moorhead.*)

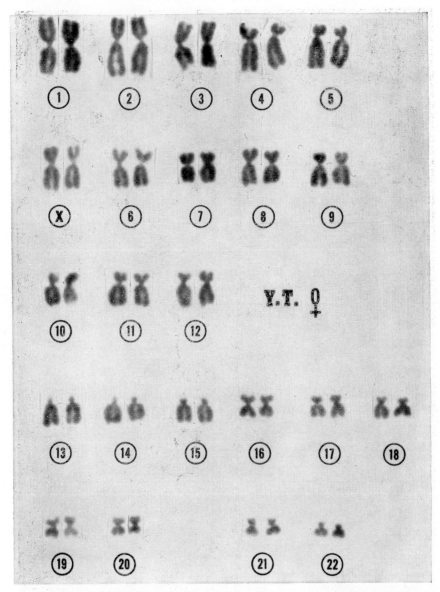

Figure 7-7. Karyotype of the child, Y. T., female: 46 chromosomes, normal intelligence. Approximate enlargement 1,700×. (*Courtesy of P. S. Moorhead.*)

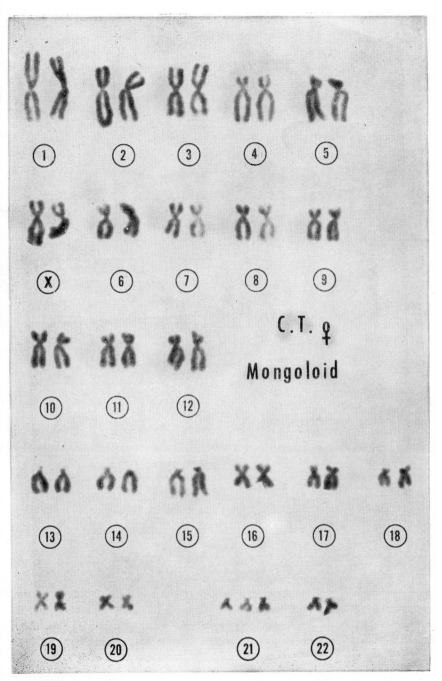

Figure 7-8. Karyotype of the infant, C. T., female: 47 chromosomes, trisomic for number 21, typical mongoloid. Approximate enlargement 1,700×. (*Courtesy of P. S. Moorhead.*)

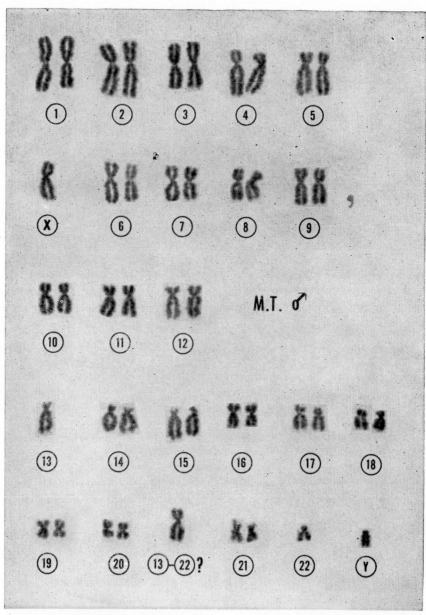

Figure 7-9. Karyotype of the child, M. T., male: 45 chromosomes, including the translocation chromosome, mentally defective. Approximate enlargement 2,000X. (*Courtesy of P. S. Moorhead.*)

Some theories on the genetic transmission of intelligence

On the grounds that it is better to have partial and approximate theories of the genetic transmission of intelligence than none at all, we shall present a few of the suggestions put forward to account for variation in measured general intelligence or IQ as usually measured by a total score on a Binet or Wechsler test. We are keenly aware of the shortcomings in supporting the theories without adequate data from studies on humans. The models to be presented require familiarity with the section on polygenic inheritance. Only the range of IQs which empirically plot as continuous variation are included in the derivations. Burt and Howard (1956, 1957) have presented and defended a general model of polygenic inheritance of intelligence for n pairs of genes. After allowing for assortative mating and incomplete dominance, their predicted correlations between relatives agreed quite well with their observed correlations. Their use of Fisher's formulae was similar to that already reported by Conrad and Jones (1940).

Hurst (1932) attempted to build a model of the genetic transmission of intelligence based on ratings of intelligence for 212 European royal families (parents and offspring) studied by Woods and on his own sample of 194 English families. The Woods ratings were based upon the adjectives used by historians to describe the members of royal families (some from the eleventh century) and hence suffer from unknown error. What heuristic value there is in his model however is rather independent of his data. The theory involves a major pair of genes, Nn, and five pairs of polygenes, Aa, Bb, Cc, Dd, and Ee. N is dominant and leads to normality or mediocrity in any genotype carrying it regardless of the polygenes. For those nn genotypes, however, the A, B, etc., genes act as intelligence-enhancing units while a, b, etc., alleles act as unit decreasers since they replace the dominant allele without contributing to the phenotypic intelligence. That the theory fits the Hurst data should not be surprising since the data were used to derive the theory; no independent test of the theory has been carried out (Conrad & Jones, 1940). If each dominant allele among the five pairs of polygenes added 20 IQ points to the phenotypic measure of intelligence, the model would account for a range from 0 to 200. The genotypes of the two extremes would be nn, aa, bb, cc, dd, ee, and NN, AA, BB, CC, DD, EE. As we shall see shortly any simple polygenic model can explain the appearance of offspring deviant from both parents in either direction if we assume the parents are heterozygous at the various loci. Among their criticisms of Hurst's model, Conrad and Jones (1940) pointed out that it is unknown whether it would lead to a normal distribution of intelligence in a population at genetic equilibrium.

Another theory has been proposed by Pickford (1949) which posits a polygenic system of 10 pairs of genes. As evidence to support his model he cited the fact that the expansion of $(\frac{1}{2} + \frac{1}{2})^{20}$ gave a very good fit to the distribution of IQs obtained in the *standardization* population of the 1937 Binet revision. The model covers the range $\pm$ 4.5 standard deviations. Pickford rejected a five-pair model because the entire empirical range would not have been accounted for. While we do not quarrel with the assumption and repeated observation of more or less normal distributions for general intelligence, fitting curves to a specifically non-random sample of IQs seems a mistake. Terman and Merrill (1937) said that their goal was to construct a sample representative of children from the census distribution for occupational grades of fathers. The lowest two grades were greatly underrepresented with 16 per cent of the total sample rather than the required 30.8 per cent; this suggests that the number of re-tarded children should have been greater than that observed. No children in institutions were tested for the 1937 standardization group. The whole point of this departure is that a model of polygenic intelligence need only account for the patently continuous range 50 to 150, and it would be a temporarily significant enterprise. Both Penrose (1954) and Roberts (1952) interpreted their findings to mean that polygenic factors are not operating below IQ 50.

Let us see what a five-pair polygenic model, assuming random mating and no dominance, will reveal. Let us take the genotype for the intelligence of both parents to be $A^1A^2B^1B^2C^1C^2D^1D^2E^1E^2$ and assign it an index of 100. Let each additional allele with superscript 2 enhance the phenotypic measure of intelligence by 10 points and each allele with superscript 1 have a neutral effect upon the phenotype. The usual rules of segregation apply so that, e.g., the locus A^1A^2 gives rise to two kinds of gametes. Relative frequencies of the various genotypes from the matings of the completely heterozygous parents are given by the expansion of the binomial $(\frac{1}{2} + \frac{1}{2})^{10}$. The relative frequencies reveal the expected proportion of genotypes for each of 11 phenotypes having from 0 to 10 intelligence-enhancing genes. This is illustrated in Table 7-8 together with the phenotypic IQs for each genotype. The total number of genotypes in this five-pair model is 3^5 or 243. A plot of the frequencies from Table 7-8 would not, of course, lead to a smooth curve but to a step-like histogram. By invoking further assump-tions, such as additional phenotypic variability from microenvironmental variability, the curve becomes smoother. Beyond that, however, the assump-

TABLE 7-8

Theoretical predictions of IQ from a five-pair polygenic model

Number of enhancing genes	Relative frequency of genotypes	Phenotypic IQ
0	1	50
1	10	60
2	45	70
3	120	80
4	210	90
5	252	100
6	210	110
7	120	120
8	45	130
9	10	140
10	1	150

tions necessary lead to other than a simple polygenic model. This next step in theorizing is necessary and must account for the dominance implied by the regression effect, for probable unequal gene frequencies, for other than an additive effect of genes, and for assortative mating. Stern (1960) reminded us that if a trait such as intelligence were controlled by the same genotype in all individuals, i.e., *species specific,* such as upright loco-motion, all phenotypic variations would be caused by variations in the environment. By positing five systematic environmental factors acting additively, we should end up with the same model as the one above. There is little doubt that the normal frequency distribution of intelligence pheno-types is the resultant of both genetic and environmental variability.

There is nothing sacred about the figure *five* used above, and the fact that five of the primary mental abilities account for almost all the variance of *g* should not be construed to imply an endorsement of congruence between psychological and genetic elements. We have already discussed the com-plexity of the path between traits and genes and the likelihood that any gene has multiple phenotypic effects, i.e., may be part of more than one polygenic system. Royce (1957) in an attempt to relate factor analysis to genetics presented an interesting model which did imply a congruence between the two elements. All evidence appears to support the idea that factor analysis does not automatically yield a genetic analysis (Fuller & Thompson, 1960, p. 340).

It is difficult to discuss the transmission of genes without raising in many readers' minds the possibility of control over mating with the hope of increasing the proportion of intelligent genotypes and of decreasing the proportion of genotypes leading to low intelligence. To those who would infer some general eugenic principles from what we have discussed in this chapter, we can only insist on the utmost of caution. The issues involved in eugenics are only partly based on a knowledge of genetics, the others being social, axiological, moral, economic, and political. We agree with Neel (1954) that the preservation and improvement of those genetic attributes of man that have resulted in his favored evolutionary position are important but that premature attempts to apply our fragmentary knowledge in any dogmatic fashion would be extremely complex. The reader interested in the genetic facts related to eugenics is urged to note the fallacy of labeling genes as harmful or deleterious rather than their effects (Snyder, 1954); the implications for selection are enormous. Muller's (1961) eugenic suggestions are certainly provocative but should not be read in-dependently of the comments of his peers. Dunn (1962), reviewing the crosscurrents in the history of human genetics, reminds us that all scientists face a dilemma because of their desire to advance sound knowledge and also to make it serve its essential social function. While increasing knowledge will not of itself resolve this dilemma, the resolution will certainly not come without it.

REFERENCES

ALLEN, G. Comments on the analysis of twin samples. *Acta genet. Med. et Gemelli,* 1955, 4, 143–160.

ALLEN, G. Genetic aspects of mental disorder. In *The nature and transmission of the genetic and cultural characteristics of human populations.* New York: Milbank Foundation, 1957. Pp. 112–121.

ALLEN, G. Patterns of discovery in the genetics of mental deficiency. *Amer. J. ment. Defic.,* 1958, 62, 840–849.

ALLEN, G. Intellectual potential and heredity. *Science,* 1961, 133, 378–379.

ANASTASI, ANNE. *Differential psychology.* (3rd ed.) New York: Macmillan, 1958.

ANASTASI, ANNE, FULLER, J. L., SCOTT, J. P., & SCHMITT, J. R. A factor analysis of the performance of dogs on certain learning tests. *Zoologica,* 1955, 40, 33–46.

BAYLEY, NANCY. On the growth of intelligence. *Amer. Psychologist,* 1955, 10, 805–818.

BEACH, F. A. Evolutionary aspects of psychoendocrinology. In Anne Roe & G. G. Simpson (Eds.), *Behavior and evolution.* New Haven: Yale, 1958. Pp. 81–102.

BISCHOF, L. J. *Intelligence: statistical concepts of its nature.* New York: Doubleday, 1954.

BLEWETT, D. B. An experimental study of the inheritance of intelligence. *J. ment. Sci.,* 1954, 100, 922–933.

BOOK, J. A., SCHUT, J. W., & REED, S. C. A clinical and genetic study of microcephaly. *Amer. J. ment. Defic.,* 1953, 57, 637–660.

BURKS, BARBARA S. The relative influence of nature and nurture upon mental development: a comparative study of foster parent–foster child resemblance and true parent–true child resemblance. *Yearb. nat. Soc. Study Educ.,* 1928. 27, Part I. Pp. 219–316.

BURT, C. The evidence for the concept of intelligence. *Brit. J. educ. Psychol.,* 1955, 25, 158–177.

BURT, C. The inheritance of mental ability. *Amer. Psychologist,* 1958, 13, 1–15.

BURT, C., & HOWARD, M. The multifactorial theory of inheritance and its application to intelligence. *Brit. J. statist. Psychol.,* 1956, 9, 95–131.

BURT, C., & HOWARD, M. Heredity and intelligence: a reply to criticisms. *Brit. J. statist. Psychol.,* 1957, 10, 33–63.

CARTER, H. D. Ten years of research on twins: contributions to the nature-nurture problem. *Yearb. nat. Soc. Stud. Educ.,* 1940, 39, Part I. Pp. 235–255.

CATTELL, R. B. *Personality.* New York: McGraw-Hill, 1950.

CATTELL, R. B. The multiple abstract variance analysis equations and solutions: for nature-nurture research on continuous variables. *Psychol. Rev.,* 1960, 67, 353–372.

CATTELL, R. B., STICE, G. F., & KRISTY, N. F. A first approximation to nature-nurture ratios for eleven primary personality factors in objective tests. *J. abnorm. soc. Psychol.,* 1957, 54, 143–160.

CATTELL, R. B., & WILLSON, J. C. Contributions concerning mental inheritance. I. Of intelligence. *Brit. J. educ. Psychol.,* 1938, 8, 129–149.

CHU, E. H. Y., & BENDER, M. A. Chromosome cytology and evolution in primates. *Science,* 1961, 133, 1399–1405.

CONRAD, H. S., & JONES, H. E. A second study of family resemblances in intelligence: environmental and genetic implications of parent-child and sibling correlations in the total sample. *Yearb. nat. Soc. Stud. Educ.,* 1940, 39, Part II. Pp. 97–141.

COOPER, R. M., & ZUBEK, J. P. Effects of enriched and restricted early environments on the learning ability of bright and dull rats. *Canad. J. Psychol.,* 1958, 12, 159–164.

CROWE, F. W., SCHULL, W. J., & NEEL, J. V. *Multiple neurofibromatosis.* Springfield, Ill.: Charles C Thomas, 1956.

DAVID, P. R., & SNYDER, L. H. Principles of human genetics. In D. Hooker & C. C.

Hare (Eds.), *Genetics and the inheritance of integrated neurological and psychiatric patterns.* Baltimore: Williams & Wilkins, 1954. Pp. 3–22.

DEMEREC, M.   The nature of the gene. *Amer. J. human Genet.,* 1961, 13, 122–127.

DOBZHANSKY, T.   *Evolution, genetics and man.* New York: Wiley, 1955.

DUGDALE, R. L.   *The Jukes: a study in crime, pauperism, disease, and heredity.* New York: Putnam, 1877.

DUNN, L. C.   Cross currents in the history of human genetics. *Amer. J. human Genet.,* 1962, 14, 1–13.

EYSENCK, H. J., & PRELL, D. B.   The inheritance of neuroticism. *J. ment. Sci.,* 1951, 97, 441–465.

FISHER, R. A.   The correlation between relatives on the supposition of Mendelian inheritance. *Trans. Roy. Soc. Edin.,* 1918, 52, 399–433.

FORD, C. E.   Human cytogenetics: its present place and future possibilities. *Amer. J. human Genet.,* 1960, 12, 104–117.

FULLER, J. L.   *Nature and nurture: a modern synthesis.* New York: Doubleday, 1954.

FULLER, J. L.   The genetic base: pathways between genes and behavioral characteristics. In *The nature and transmission of the genetic and cultural characteristics of human populations.* New York: Milbank Foundation, 1957(a). Pp. 101–111.

FULLER, J. L.   Comparative studies in behavioral genetics. *Acta genet. statist. Med.,* 1957(b), 7, 403–407.

FULLER, J. L., EASLER, C., & SMITH, M. E.   Inheritance of audiogenic seizure susceptibility in the mouse. *Genetics,* 1950, 35, 622–632.

FULLER, J. L., & SCOTT, J. P.   Heredity and learning ability in infrahuman mammals. *Eugenics Quart.,* 1954, 1, 28–43.

FULLER, J. L., & THOMPSON, W. R.   *Behavior genetics.* New York: Wiley, 1960.

GALTON, F.   *Hereditary genius: an inquiry into its laws and consequences.* London: Macmillan, 1869.

GALTON, F.   The history of twins as a criterion of the relative powers of nature and nurture. *Fraser's Magazine,* 1875, 12, 566–576.

GODDARD, H. H.   *The Kallikak family: a study in the heredity of feeblemindedness.* New York: Macmillan, 1913.

GUILFORD, J. P.   Three faces of intellect. *Amer. Psychologist,* 1959, 14, 469–479.

HALL, C. S.   The genetics of behavior. In S. S. Stevens (Ed.), *Handbook of experimental psychology.* New York: Wiley, 1951. Pp. 304–329.

HALPERIN, S. L.   A clinico-genetical study of mental defect. *Amer. J. ment. Defic.,* 1945, 50, 8–26.

HARLOW, H. F.   The evolution of learning. In Anne Roe & G. G. Simpson (Eds.), *Behavior and evolution.* New Haven: Yale, 1958. Pp. 269–290.

HEBB, D. O.   *The organization of behavior.* New York: Wiley, 1949.

HERON, W. T.   The inheritance of maze learning ability in rats. *J. comp. Psychol.,* 1935, 19, 77–89.

HERON, W. T.   The inheritance of brightness and dullness in maze learning ability in the rat. *J. genet. Psychol.,* 1941, 59, 41–49.

HIGGINS, J. V., REED, E. W., & REED, S. C.   An analysis of 1016 families for whom intelligence test scores are available for both parents and children. Paper read at Sec. int. Conf. human genet., Rome, September, 1961.

HILDRETH, G. H.   The resemblance of siblings in intelligence and achievement. *Teachers College, Columbia Univer., Cont. to Educ.,* 1925, 186, 1–65.

HIRSCH, J.   Studies in experimental behavior genetics. II. Individual differences in geotaxis as a function of chromosome variations in synthesized *Drosophila* populations. *J. comp. physiol. Psychol.,* 1959(a), 52, 304–308.

HIRSCH, J.   Individual differences in behavior and their genetic basis. Paper read at A.A.A.S. Sympos. on Roots of Behav., 1959(b).

HIRSCH, J., & TRYON, R. C.   Mass screening and reliable individual measurement in the experimental behavior genetics of lower organisms. *Psychol. Bull.*, 1956, 53, 402–410.

HOLZINGER, K. J.   The relative effect of nature and nurture influences on twin differences. *J. educ. Psychol.*, 1929, 20, 241–248.

HSIA, D. Y., DRISCOLL, K. W., TROLL, W., & KNOX, W. E.   Detection by phenylalanine tolerance tests of heterozygous carriers of phenylketonuria. *Nature*, 1956, 178, 1239–1240.

HURST, C. C.   A genetic formula for the inheritance of intelligence in man. *Proc. Roy. Soc. Lond.*, 1932, 112 (Series B), 80–97.

JERVIS, G. A.   Phenylketonuria. In D. Hooker & C. C. Hare (Eds.), *Genetics and the inheritance of integrated neurological and psychiatric patterns.* Baltimore: Williams & Wilkins, 1954. Pp. 259–282.

JUDA, A.   Neue Psychiatrisch-genealogische Untersuchungen an Hilfsschulzwillingen und ihren Familien. *Z. ges. Neurol. Psychiat.*, 1939, 166, 365–452. Cited by J. Shields & E. Slater, Heredity and psychological abnormality. In H. J. Eysenck (Ed.), *Handbook of abnormal psychology.* New York: Basic Books, 1961. P. 327.

KALLMANN, F. J.   The genetic theory of schizophrenia. *Am. J. Psychiat.*, 1946, 103, 309–322.

KALLMANN, F. J.   *Heredity in health and mental disorder.* New York: Norton, 1953.

KALLMANN, F. J.   Psychogenetic studies of twins. In S. Koch (Ed.), *Psychology: a study of a science.* Vol. 3. New York: McGraw-Hill, 1959. Pp. 328–362.

KANAIEV, I.   Physiology of the brain in twins. *Charact. & Pers.*, 1938, 6, 177–187.

KNOX, W. E.   Biochemical genetics. *Amer. J. human Genet.*, 1961, 13, 185–192.

KRECHEVSKY, I.   Hypotheses vs. "chance" in the presolution period in sensory discrimination learning. *Univer. Calif. Publ. Psychol.*, 1932, 6, 27–44.

KRECHEVSKY, I.   The hereditary nature of "hypotheses." *J. comp. Psychol.*, 1933, 16, 99–116.

LEAHY, A. M.   Nature-nurture and intelligence. *Genet. Psychol. Monogr.*, 1935, 17, 236–308.

LEJEUNE, J., & TURPIN, R.   Chromosomal aberrations in man. *Amer. J. human Genet.*, 1961, 13, 175–184.

LEJEUNE, J., TURPIN, R., & GAUTIER, M.   Le mongolisme, premier example d'aberration autosomique humaine. *Ann. Genetique,* 1959, 2, 41–49.

LERNER, I. M.   *Population genetics and animal improvement.* London: Cambridge, 1950.

LI, C. C.   *Population genetics.* Chicago: Univer. of Chicago Press, 1955.

MASLAND, R. L., SARASON, S. B., & GLADWIN, T.   *Mental subnormality.* New York: Basic Books, 1958.

MATHER, K.   *Biometrical genetics.* New York: Dover, 1949.

MILLER, O. J., BREG, W. R., SCHMICKEL, R. D., & TRETTER, W.   An XXXXY sex chromosome complement in a chromatin-three-positive man. *Program, Amer. Soc. human Genet.*, May, 1961. (Abstract)

MOORHEAD, P. S., MELLMAN, W. J., & WENAR, C.   A familial chromosome translocation associated with speech and mental retardation. *Amer. J. human Genet.*, 1961, 13, 32–46.

MULLER, H. J.   Genetic principles in human populations. *Amer. J. Psychiat.*, 1956, 113, 481–491.

MULLER, H. J.   Should we weaken or strengthen our genetic heritage? *Daedalus,* 1961, 90, 432–451.

NEEL, J. V. The clinical applications of genetics. In D. Hooker & C. C. Hare (Eds.), *Genetics and the inheritance of integrated neurological and psychiatric patterns.* Baltimore: Williams & Wilkins, 1954. Pp. 386–399.

NEEL, J. V., & SCHULL, W. J. *Human heredity.* Chicago: Univer. of Chicago Press, 1954.

NEWMAN, H. H., FREEMAN, F. N., & HOLZINGER, K. J. *Twins: a study of heredity and environment.* Chicago: Univer. of Chicago Press, 1937.

NISSEN, H. W. Axes of behavioral comparison. In Anne Roe & G. G. Simpson (Eds.), *Behavior and evolution.* New Haven: Yale, 1958. Pp. 183–205.

PEARSON, J. S., & KLEY, IRENE B. On the application of genetic expectancies as age-specific base rates in the study of human behavior disorders. *Psychol. Bull.,* 1957, 54, 406–420.

PEARSON, K. On the laws of inheritance in man. II. On the inheritance of the mental and moral characters in man, and its comparison with the inheritance of the physical characters. *Biometrika,* 1904, 3, 131–190.

PENROSE, L. S. *The biology of mental defect.* (rev. ed.) London: Sidgwick & Jackson, 1954.

PICKFORD, R. W. The genetics of intelligence. *J. Psychol.,* 1949, 28, 129–145.

PRICE, B. Primary biases in twin studies. *Amer. J. human Genet.,* 1950, 2, 293–352.

REED, S. C. *Counseling in medical genetics.* Philadelphia: Saunders, 1955.

REED, S. C., REED, E. W., & PALM, J. D. Fertility and intelligence among families of the mentally deficient. *Eugenics Quart.,* 1954, 1, 44–52.

ROBERTS, J. A. F. The genetics of mental deficiency. *Eugenics Rev.,* 1952, 44, 71–83.

ROSANOFF, A. J., HANDY, L. M., & PLESSET, I. R. The etiology of mental deficiency with special reference to its occurrence in twins. *Psychol. Monogr.,* 1937, 216, 1–137.

ROSENTHAL, D. Some factors associated with concordance and discordance with respect to schizophrenia in monozygotic twins. *J. nerv. ment. Dis.,* 1959, 129, 1–10.

ROSENZWEIG, M. R., KRECH, D., & BENNETT, E. L. A search for relations between brain chemistry and behavior. *Psychol. Bull.,* 1960, 57, 476–492.

ROYCE, J. R. Factor theory and genetics. *Educ. psychol. Measmt.,* 1957, 17, 361–376.

SARASON, S. B. *Psychological problems in mental deficiency.* (2nd ed.) New York: Harper, 1953.

SEARLE, L. V. The organization of hereditary maze-brightness and maze-dullness. *Genet. Psychol. Monogr.,* 1949, 39, 279–325.

SCOTT, J. P., & CHARLES, MARGARET S. Some problems of heredity and social behavior. *J. gen. Psychol.,* 1953, 48, 209–230.

SCOTT, J. P., & FULLER, J. L. Research on genetics and social behavior. *J. Hered.,* 1951, 42, 191–197.

SHAW, MARGERY W., & CHU, E. H. Y. Chromosome analysis of a mother of two

SHIELDS, J. Twins brought up apart. *Eugenics Rev.,* 1958, 50, 115–123. mongols. *Program, Amer. Soc. human Genet.,* May, 1961. (Abstract)

SHIELDS, J., & SLATER, E. Heredity and psychological abnormality. In H. J. Eysenck (Ed.), *Handbook of abnormal psychology.* New York: Basic Books, 1961. Pp. 298–343.

SKODAK, M., & SKEELS, H. M. A final follow-up study of one hundred adopted children. *J. genet. Psychol.,* 1949, 75, 85–125.

SMITH, SHEILA M., & PENROSE, L. S. Monozygotic and dizygotic twin diagnosis. *Ann. human Genet.,* 1955, 19, 273–289.

SNYDER, L. H.. The effects of selection and domestication on man. *J. nat. Cancer Inst.*, 1954, 15, 759–769.

STAFFORD, R. E. Evidence for the sex-linked inheritance of the aptitude for spatial visualization. *Program, Amer. Soc. human Genet.*, May, 1961. (Abstract)

STERN, C. *Principles of human genetics.* (2nd ed.) San Francisco: Freeman, 1960.

TERMAN, L. M., & MERRILL, MAUD A. *Measuring intelligence.* Boston: Houghton Mifflin, 1937.

TERMAN, L. M., & ODEN, M. H. *The gifted child grows up.* Stanford: Stanford, 1947.

THERMAN, E., PATAU, K., SMITH, D. W., & DEMARS, R. I. The D trisomy syndrome and XO gonadal dysgenesis in two sisters. *Amer. J. human Genet.*, 1961, 13, 193–204.

THOMPSON, W. R. The inheritance and development of intelligence. In D. Hooker & C. C. Hare (Eds.), *Genetics and the inheritance of integrated neurological and psychiatric patterns.* Baltimore: Williams & Wilkins, 1954. Pp. 209–231.

THOMPSON, W. R. Traits, factors, and genes. *Eugenics Quart.*, 1957, 4, 8–16.

THURSTONE, T. G., THURSTONE, L.L., & STRANDSKOV, H. H. *A psychological study of twins.* Chapel Hill: Univ. of North Carolina, Psychometric Lab., No. 4, 1953.

THURSTONE, T. G., THURSTONE, L. L., & STRANDSKOV, H. H. *A psychological study of twins.* Chapel Hill: Univer. of North Carolina, Psychometric Lab., No. 12, 1955.

TJIO, J. H., & LEVAN, A. The chromosome number of man. *Hereditas*, 1956, 42, 1–6.

TRYON, R. C. Genetic differences in maze-learning ability in rats. *Yearb. nat. Soc. Stud. Educ.*, 1940, 39, Part I. Pp. 111–119.

TRYON, R. C. Individual differences. In F.A. Moss (Ed.), *Comparative Psychology.* Englewood Cliffs, N.J.: Prentice-Hall, 1942. Ch. 12.

TURBIN, N. V. Philosophical problems in contemporary genetics. In *The central nervous system and behavior.* (Trans. from the Russian medical literature.) Bethesda: Russian Scientific Trans. Program., N.I.H., 1959. Pp. 944–972.

TYLER, LEONA E. *The psychology of human differences.* (2nd ed.) New York: Appleton-Century, 1956.

UCHIDA, IRENE A., & CURTIS, ELIZABETH J. A possible association between maternal radiation and mongolism. *Program, Amer. Soc. human Genet.*, May, 1961. (Abstract)

VANDENBERG, S. G. The hereditary abilities study: hereditary components in a psychological test battery. *Amer. J. human Genet.*, 1962, 14, 220–237.

WANG, H. L., MORTON, N. E., & WAISMAN, H. A. Increased reliability for the determination of the carrier state in phenylketonuria. *Amer. J. human Genet.*, 1961, 13, 255–261.

WHERRY, R. J. Determination of the specific components of maze-ability for Tryon's bright and dull rats by means of factorial analysis. *J. comp. Psychol.*, 1941, 32, 237–252.

WOODWORTH, R. S. *Heredity and environment.* New York: Soc. Sci. Research Council, 1941.

WRIGHT, S. The genetics of quantitative variability. In E. C. R. Reeve & C. H. Waddington (Eds.), *Quantitative Inheritance.* London: H. M. Stationery Office, 1952. Pp. 5–41.

8

THE APPLICATION OF PIAGET'S THEORY TO RESEARCH IN MENTAL DEFICIENCY

Mary Woodward

INTRODUCTION

Piaget's theory deals with the process of intellectual development. The object of the theory is to trace the evolution of abstract thinking from its origins in the sensorimotor behavior of infancy through the intermediate forms. This has been done by observation of the behavior of infants and by study of the concepts that older children have about various aspects of reality. Piaget's interest lies in the kind of psychological operation that leads to a result rather than in the fact of success or failure alone, and the aim of the investigation is to interpret the behavior and not merely to make an inventory of items of behavior that appear at successive ages. Consequently, the theory provides a conceptual framework from which to study the behavior of intellectually subnormal individuals.

The techniques that have been devised to investigate cognitive processes are quite distinctive, and they have brought to light new facets of the thinking of normal children; they provide a similar opportunity in the field of mental deficiency. The theory postulates a sequence of intellectual developments. Since the important feature is the order of the steps and not the age at which they are attained, this approach can be applied to individuals whose rate of development is extremely slow. It offers the means of placing them on an ordinal scale (of development from birth onward) so that age comparisons can be avoided. The type of manipulations of objects and the type of thinking shown in problem solving are more important than particular responses. This is useful in view of the prevalence of sensory and motor defects in mental deficiency: comparable results can be obtained for physically handicapped and nonhandicapped individuals.

Piaget's views have provoked considerable controversy, some of which arises from misconceptions about his theory rather than from conflicting experimental evidence. Much of this controversy centers around the earlier work for which a different method was used. It is the later work and the theory arising from it that can most usefully be applied to research in mental deficiency; thus the later work will be dealt with most fully in this chapter.

PIAGET'S THEORY OF INTELLECTUAL DEVELOPMENT

General outline of theory. The behavior pattern or schema is adopted as the unit of analysis; the child's responses in certain defined stimulus situations are classified according to their similarity. Apart from the reflex schemata which are given at birth, learning enters into the formation of all the schemata described. The analysis is at the behavioral level: it deals with the generalization and modification of responses in relation to objects and the process by which complex schemata are progressively organized out of simpler ones. The theory does not enter into detailed neurological considerations nor postulate how the process of neural organization occurs. Thus, in its interest in the process, it has a somewhat different emphasis from that of learning theories; and, similarly, it differs from factorial studies of the structure of intelligence.

The biological terms assimilation and accommodation are used in a functional sense. In a manner analogous to the assimilation of food by the organism, schemata of action and thinking that have been developed in relation to one object are evoked by new objects, which are thereby assimilated to those schemata; accommodation of schemata occurs when they are modified in the face of environmental situations. Berlyne (1957) has likened assimilation to generalization and discrimination in learning theory terminology and accommodation to the differentiation of responses. Adaptive behavior and the acquisition of new schemata result when assimilation and accommodation are in equilibrium.

This involves a total reorganization of schemata when some that were previously independent are coordinated and others are differentiated and recombined. Hence, distinct stages rather than continuous development are postulated; the stages are characterized by different types of behavior and thinking, which succeed one another in the same order in the development of most children.

The various types of thinking have been analyzed in terms of the logical operations involved. More recently an attempt has been made to express the theory in the language of cybernetics. Piaget (1953c) points out that exponents of cybernetics use symbolic logic in the same way as he does for describing intellectual operations. Secondly both make use of the concept of equilibrium: there is a parallel between homeostasis and feedback on the one hand and the process of progressive equilibrium that characterizes the development of intelligence on the other.

Schemata are extended, modified, and coordinated through the child's exploratory behavior with physical objects. Hence, an important role in the development of intelligence is attributed to experience in the form of the child's own activities. Thus Piaget is equally opposed to theories which regard the organism as a passive receptor of environmental stimuli and to maturational theories which neglect the role of experience. Despite this, the system is sometimes interpreted as a maturational theory. This appears to be because a sequence of developmental stages is postulated. A constant order of developmental events could, however, arise equally well from the child's interactions with objects; i.e., it can be postulated that behavior patterns of type A, when coordinated, differentiated, and recombined through activities with objects, can give rise only to behavior patterns of type B; these in turn can develop only into those of type C, and so on. In other words, the learning that is possible with the behavior pattern of one stage determines the type of behavior pattern of the next stage.

An important role is also attributed to the child's social interactions. Adults influence the development of concepts and reasoning when they affirm or deny a child's statements.

Both maturation and experience influence the child's rate of progress through the sequence, and it is likely that there will be differences in the average age of the attainment of a given stage in different social and cultural environments (Piaget, 1960).

The four main stages are (1) the sensorimotor stage (birth to about 1½ years); (2) the preoperational stage, subdivided into the preconceptual (1½ to about 4 years) and the intuitive (about 4 to 7 years); (3) the stage of concrete operations (about 7 to 11 years); and (4) the stage of abstract operations (about 11 years onward). In the following outline of this sequence, the earlier stages are dealt with in more detail for two reasons. New developments are more numerous in the first few years than later, and it is the early stages that are most relevant to the study of mental deficiency.

Techniques and method. The results of Piaget's studies and those of other workers who perform related experiments cannot be considered apart from his method of investigation, which has not always been closely followed in replicating his work. Since Piaget is interested in the process of development, he has devised techniques which are aimed at discovering the type of thinking used by children when they tackle a problem. Thus he records not merely the result but how the child arrived at it. For both successful solutions and failures, he notes the method the child uses and explores further by varying certain aspects of the problem.

The techniques used obviously vary with the age of children being studied. With preverbal infants Piaget, like other investigators of infant behavior, has observed the child's spontaneous movements, manipulations of toys, and responses to problems. The experimental situations are determined by the object of the investigation. One study of infant behavior (Piaget, 1953a) was concerned with the origins of intelligent behavior, and it examined the infant's method of dealing with simple problems. (This is referred to in this chapter as sensorimotor intelligence.) Other observations of infant behavior (Piaget, 1955) arose from an interest in determining the process by which the child develops a belief in the permanence of objects and takes into account in his behavior an awareness of the spatial relations between objects, the causal agents that make them move, and the temporal sequence of events when they move. Finally (Piaget, 1951), another set of observations was directed at tracing the development of imitation in infants.

Some aspects of behavior and some of the problems studied by Piaget have been the object of other investigations of infants; e.g., see Shirley (1931), Buhler (1930), and Gesell (1940). Piaget's observations have been more intensive. For example, when a toy is placed out of the child's reach on a cushion within his reach, Piaget did not merely record whether the child did or did not pull the cushion toward him and take the toy once; further investigations were carried out in order to check whether the child's main interest was in the cushion or the toy. Hence, the problem was varied by overlapping two cushions and placing the toy on the farther one; it was then noted whether the child pulled only the first cushion or pulled the second one when the toy did not move toward him with the first. All interpretations of children's behavior are based on careful observations and checks of this sort.

The method also differs from other studies of infants in that almost daily observations were made. This clearly limits the number of children who can be studied, and Piaget, in fact, observed his own three children.

With children aged 3 or 4 years and over, Piaget used larger groups drawn from schools and nursery schools. The earlier work was concerned with the nature of children's speech (as an egocentric monologue or communication, Piaget, 1926), with their concepts of physical causality (Piaget, 1930), the world (Piaget, 1928), and with the development of reasoning (Piaget, 1928). In these early studies a verbal questioning method was mainly used. For example, the child was asked where shadows come from, what makes clouds move, and so on. Much of the later work has been carried out in collaboration with Inhelder, and it has included the investigation of children's concepts of number (Piaget, 1952), space (Piaget & Inhelder, 1956), movement (Piaget, 1946), and geometry (Piaget, Inhelder & Szeminska, 1960), of their ability to classify (Piaget & Inhelder, 1959), and of logical thinking in adolescents (Inhelder & Piaget, 1958). In these studies an entirely different method has been used involving concrete material which the child can handle and observe. For example, in the study of number concepts with children of 4 to 7 years, experiments were devised that would elucidate how far children understood numbers as a series, as constant in quantity, and so on. With children of 3 to 9 years Piaget and Inhelder (1956) investigated concepts of space by various means, e.g., in children's copies of geometrical figures, in their copies of spatial orders, and in the use of external reference points. A further study by Piaget, Inhelder, and Szeminska (1960) followed this lead with children up to 11 years. This included, among others, experiments designed to study the child's spontaneous measurement of one dimension and his understanding of the invariance of areas and volumes and the measurement of them. Inhelder and Piaget (1958) devised ingenious methods in order to study the thinking of adolescents, e.g., their understanding of proportion, of systematic combinations, and of the operation of varying only one factor at a time. A recent investigation (Piaget & Inhelder, 1959) has studied children's understanding of classes by means of sorting tasks. An example of a problem used in studying concepts of number is that the child is instructed to put in order a series of sticks that are graded in length; questions are then asked about ordinal position. A problem from concepts of geometry is that a tower of bricks of assorted sizes is presented, and the child is supplied with sticks of varying length and given the problem of building a tower of the same height on a lower table (the sizes of the bricks are such that a solution cannot be achieved by matching bricks one for one).

An important point of Piaget's method is that the child is allowed repeated opportunities to correct his first statement on the basis of further experience. If a child who has just paired 10 counters opposite another set of 10 counters states that there are more in the longer row when one is spread out, the counters are repeatedly placed opposite and spread out again with the question about equality being asked each time. He is also given repeated opportunities to check whether or not his statements are correct. If he thinks that one ball of clay weighs more than an identical ball when it is stretched into the shape of a sausage, he is allowed to place both the ball and the sausage on scales and see what happens. The problem is then given again, with one of two balls being modeled into a different shape.

Further details of the techniques used by Piaget and Inhelder can be found in their various publications, and further examples will be used in the following outline of the main steps of development.

Piaget does not give any details concerning the representativeness of his samples, nor of the average ages and scatter for the development of each stage. Thus the sequential aspects of his theory can be applied to mental deficiency; but until normative data are available, age comparisons cannot validly be made. The ages which he quotes in illustrative examples vary somewhat; the ages quoted for the beginning and end of each stage in the following outline are those suggested by Piaget as average ages, but they are obviously only approximate.

Sensorimotor stage (birth to approximately 1½ years). There is a sequence of six substages, whose characteristics, with examples of the type of behavior classified at each, are given below:

1. The first substage (lasting from birth to about 4 weeks) is that of the use and extension of separate reflex activities. For example, the child learns to suck, and to suck his thumb if by chance it touches his lips.

From substage 2 onward, all schemata are acquired. In the account of their acquisition, the concept of the circular reaction is used: A movement that by chance produced a certain effect is repeated, and again followed by the effect, so that it is once more repeated, and so on.

2. The second substage (1 month to 4 or 5 months) is the stage of the first learned schemata, the primary circular reactions. The child makes repetitive movements, such as opening and closing his fist, playing with his fingers, moving his hand about while looking at it. These behavior patterns are distinguished from those of the next substage in that they

are centered around themselves, not on producing an effect on objects. During this substage reflex activities are integrated with higher activities, resulting in coordinations between independent schemata, e.g., between vision and hearing near the beginning and between grasping and vision at the end of the substage.

3. The behavior patterns, secondary circular reactions, classified at the third substage (4 or 5 to 8 or 9 months) are centered on the result produced in the external environment; the child rediscovers and repeats chance-made movements which produce on objects an effect that he sees or hears. The behavior pattern is then evoked by similar objects. Examples are shaking a rattle, banging toys, and making hanging objects swing without variation in the effect.

4. At substage 4 (8 or 9 months to 11 or 12 months) existing behavior patterns, developed during substage 3, are coordinated and applied to new situations. An example of new adaptive behavior is that the child is able to remove an obstacle, such as an adult's hand, that prevents him from taking a toy. This is more complex behavior than that of secondary circular reactions in that one behavior pattern (striking objects) is subordinated to another (grasping a toy), or in other words one activity (the means) is performed in order to carry out another (the goal).

5. At substage 5 (11 to 12 months to about 18 months) new means are discovered for new situations; the child obtains a toy that is out of reach by pulling an extension of it (the support on which it stands, or the string attached to it). When success depends on first moving objects to other positions than those in the immediate perceptual situation, the solution is achieved only by trial and error. For example, if a long stick is placed horizontally behind vertical bars at right angles to them, the child tugs at it without turning it around. He discovers the correct position for success by chance. Manipulations (tertiary circular reactions) are more varied in their effects and are apparently aimed at exploring the object; the child drops objects from various heights and observes the effect; he bangs objects on various surfaces, apparently comparing the sound; he rolls objects, spins them, and splashes them, while watching intently.

6. At the last substage (about 18 months onward) new means are applied at once to new situations through anticipation of the future position of an object before moving it instead of finding out the effect after trying it in position, as at substage 5. With the stick and bar problem the child at once rotates the stick through 90 degrees and pulls it through the bars. Using a stick in order to obtain a toy which is out of the child's reach is also a behavior pattern of substage 6.

Piaget (1953a) has analyzed the development through these substages in terms of the concepts of assimilation and accommodation. It is not possible in a short space to give a full account of this. The second substage which includes the first learned schemata is given in detail.

Assimilation, according to Piaget, has three aspects of repetition, generalization, and recognition; these can be illustrated at the level of reflexes. The existence of a function gives rise to a need to use it. Hence, the use of a reflex leads to a need for repetition; for example, when a few minutes after birth, before the first meal, the child's hand elicits the sucking reflex, he goes on sucking it. Generalizing assimilation occurs when the child extends his sucking to other objects; and assimilation by recognition occurs when, in a state of hunger, the child rejects objects for sucking other than the nipple. Accommodation of the reflex to external events occurs when the child becomes increasingly adept at taking hold of the nipple efficiently and eventually in finding it again after losing it.

During substage 1, when the child's thumb falls out of his mouth, his head moves in a searching manner; but the movements of his hands are not coordinated with the head movements. This coordination occurs during substage 2, when the child learns to direct his thumb to his mouth. This is an example of the circular reaction, which is regarded as an active coordination of assimilation and accommodation. Assimilation is in the repetition of the activity of sucking; and the accommodation occurs when the child learns to use contact of fingers with covers, face, lips, etc., as signals that direct his hand to his mouth. The active element in the learning is that the child discovers the relations in the course of his searching.

The active element is illustrated by Piaget's interpretation of the series of coordinations that lead to grasping on sight. At the beginning of substage 2, the child (of 4 to 5 weeks) independently looks at objects and independently grasps them. These independent schemata develop through learning within themselves. Through assimilation the child learns to grasp objects when they touch the back and side of his hand instead of the palm only; and circular reactions involving movements of fingers and hands are formed. At some time the child's sucking activities lead him to catch sight of his hand as it falls from his mouth, and by chance he looks at his hand while it is moving. He then watches his hand while it is carrying out various activities, moving about, opening and closing its fist, and so on. Thereby, visual schemata are assimilated to manual schemata, but the converse is not true; the child as yet cannot keep his hand in his visual field though he tries to follow it with his eyes. However, arising from his assumption of the need to exercise a function, Piaget infers that the child's visual interests make him continue activities that prolong interesting spectacles, in this case his moving hand; and his kinaesthetic and motor interests lead him to make manual activities last. In the course of these activities he discovers that by moving his hand in a certain way, e.g., more slowly, he can keep this interesting moving object in view. In this way two independent schemata are coordinated. The child assimilates to visual activities the movements of his hands, and he assimilates the visual image to his manual activities so that he is moving with his hand the image that he sees and reciprocally he looks at the movement he produces. This Piaget terms reciprocal assimilation.

Either before or after this coordination, the sucking and grasping schemata are reciprocally coordinated when the child grasps objects (still only on chance tactile contact) and takes them to his mouth and reciprocally grasps objects that are placed in his mouth. There is thus progressive organization, with three schemata—vision, sucking, and hand movement—now being coordinated with one another.

In the course of looking at his moving hand, the child at some time sees objects in it, and also at some time he is looking at his hand when it is grasping an object with which it has come into tactile contact. The activities of the child's hands are assimilated with his visual schema, and then, with the next step, moving his hand to the object he sees when his hand and the object come into the same visual field, the child is assimilating the sight of his hand to the visual-motor schema involved in looking at grasping. With the final step, an extension of the previous one, when the child grasps the object he sees regardless of the position of his hands, reciprocal assimilation is complete in that the child also brings to his eyes, not to his mouth, objects that he grasps. The accommodation which is simultaneously taking place involves the adjustment of the child's hand to objects being grasped, including the gradual opposition of the thumb and modifications of the movements of hands and arms and mouth to various kinds of objects. Piaget does not go into detail about this process which has received more attention from other investigators who have paid less attention to the coordination of vision and grasping.

With the end of substage 2 when the child can grasp objects on sight, the object is assimilated to several schemata simultaneously (vision, grasping, and sucking); and it is to that extent externalized in relation to the child. It is after this that secondary circular reactions are formed. Accommodation of schemata occurs through their differentiation; for example, in trying to grasp a hanging object, the child accidentally swings it, sees the effect, and repeats the movement that produced the effect. This response is then evoked by other objects; i.e., the objects are assimilated to this schema.

This analysis of behavior is continued in terms of assimilation and accommodation to the higher levels, each schema being progressively more organized. The early schemata are not superseded but are integrated in the more complex ones of later stages.

An example quoted by Piaget of the application of a behavior pattern developed during substage 3 to a new situation (thereby constituting substage 4 behavior) is when the action of striking hanging objects to make them swing is used to knock down an obstacle which prevented the child from grasping a toy. (There are, of course, individual variations in the particular behavior pattern from which this response is developed.) Finding a novel means for the solution to a new situation involves the reorganization of schemata and their differentiation and combination in different ways. The same process is implied both at substage 5 when the child discovers the solution by trial and error and at substage 6 when the solution is immediate. In both cases, the accommodation to the situation is attributed to the cumulative assimilation of a series of attempts and not to a sudden reconstruction unrelated to previous learning, as in the gestalt analysis. At both substages, when an obstacle is encountered, earlier schemata, developed in analogous situations, are aroused through reciprocal assimilation. For example, when the child is given a chain in a partially opened matchbox with the slit too narrow for him to insert his finger and remove the chain, schemata connected with opening and closing boxes and with putting his hand through small openings will be aroused. At the substage 5 level the activities appropriate to these other situations will be tried out in action, and the necessary combination of schemata will be achieved in this way; at the substage 6 level the reorganization of schemata takes place on the representative plane before the action (the correct one in the situation) takes place. (Piaget observed a child who was given the matchbox problem who opened and closed her mouth while looking at the slit, and he interpreted this to mean that she was making an analogy by assimilation between the slit in the box and other openings and that this led her to the solution of enlarging the slit.)

Piaget discusses the implications of representative as opposed to sensorimotor schemata in connection with the development of a concept of permanent objects and of imitation, and his analysis of it will be taken up again after these developments have been described.

Construction of the objective world

Parallel with the development of sensorimotor intelligence the child is increasingly taking into account in his actions certain features of the objective world. Piaget studied both aspects in the same infants. Toys were hidden while the child was looking in order to investigate the child's belief in the permanence of objects. When studying the child's awareness of spatial relations between objects and causal relations between events, the child's manipulations of objects and responses to events were observed. It was concluded that these aspects are interrelated and that they are classifiable in stages which are related to the development of sensorimotor intelligence as follows:

During substages 1 and 2 (up to 4 or 5 months), the child makes no response when objects go out of his perceptual field, nor does his behavior take account of spatial relations or causality. During substage 3 (4 or 5 to 8 or 9 months), after he has begun to grasp objects on sight and manipulate them, the child's response when he drops a toy shows the beginning of permanence in that he follows the line of fall; and he also recovers half-hidden objects. When he pulls a string and makes a toy swing, he is uniting in space two objects which he sees. With regard to causality, the child behaves as though events depended on his own actions; for example, if the investigator, not visible to the child, makes a toy swing while the child is making some movement, such as arching his back, the child, while looking at the toy, continues his movement even when it stops swinging, apparently in an attempt to make it swing again.

During substage 4 (8 or 9 to 11 or 12 months) the child searches for a toy if it is hidden briefly under one cover; but if he then sees it hidden in another place, he searches where he first found it. Behavior relevant to the spatial field is that the child looks at an object which he alternately holds at different distances, and that he turns an object round and round and examines it visually. The child's actions suggest that he is beginning to be aware that there are causal agents outside himself; for example, when a child's mother stopped singing, he pressed her lips.

At substage 5 (11 or 12 months to about 18 months) the child searches in different places for objects hidden briefly; and his activities indicate an interest in the spatial interrelations of objects, as when he repeatedly puts small objects in and out of large containers. Causes are recognized in the child's direct perceptual field but not outside it. For example, the child lets an object slide down a slope of its own accord, not continuing to push it, and he uses one object to make another move.

During the sixth substage (18 months onward) the child searches for a long period for objects hidden more deeply, thus having achieved a belief (in action) in the permanence of objects. He behaves as though he can represent to himself the spatial relations between objects as they would be if he moved them and not as they are in the immediate perceptual field (as for example with the stick and bars problem mentioned earlier). He also looks for external agents, and so assumes an unperceived cause in the presence of a perceived effect and represents to himself the future effects of a certain action. For example, if his pram moves, he looks for an external agent; and when he sees someone's foot near it, he ceases to look and appears satisfied.

Development in the temporal field cannot be inferred directly from behavior but only from interpretations of behavior in other fields. A subjective world without permanent objects, without groups of objects displaced in space, and without causality between events cannot give rise to awareness of a temporal series unrelated to the action of the subject. But the development of the fourth sensorimotor substage forces the child to begin to arrange some events in order; this is generalized at the fifth substage to the whole perceptual field, but not to events which are not linked to the present. With the sixth substage the child is able to evoke memories not linked to direct perception.

The development of imitation

Piaget's observations of the imitative behavior of infants similarly led him to distinguish stages. No imitation was found to occur during sensorimotor substages 1 and 2. With the development of the secondary circular reactions of substage 3, the child imitated his own sounds when made by someone else but not new sounds; and he imitated movements if they were already part of his repertoire and if he could see the part of his body he was moving. At substage 4, children imitated new sounds that were similar to their own and imitated movements again only if they were part of their repertoire, but now even if they could not see the parts of their bodies they were moving. During substage 5, they imitated new models when their own movements were not visible to them (for example touching features). Up to this point the children who were studied imitated actions only if they had just seen them, but at substage 6 they imitated actions seen sometime previously.

The symbolic and preconceptual stage (1½ to 4 years). For the first half of the sensorimotor stage the child acts as though to him the existence of objects and their spatial relations and movements depended on his own actions and perceptions with presumably little differentiation between himself and the objective world. The main development of the sensorimotor stage is a progressive change in the child from this point of view to the one which takes account in action of certain features of the objective world. Piaget's interpretation is that the infant at about the age of 18 months becomes conscious of himself in a world of permanent objects that are separate from him and have causal effects on one another when they move and among which he, spatially, is merely another object. In action, he takes account of the future positions of objects; and he can imitate actions seen previously. Simultaneously with these developments, symbolic activity appears in imaginative play and in the systematic acquisition of language. This leads Piaget to conclude that the attainment of sensorimotor substage 6 is one of the major turning points in the child's development, which is marked by the appearance of a general *symbolic function*.

Piaget's account of the child's transition from perceptual and motor behavior to the verbal plane depends on his theory of the development of the mental image, and this appears to be as follows. The behavior of substage 6 means that the child is able to represent to himself objects and events which he is not directly perceiving, in other words, that he has formed representative schemata. It is suggested that the mental image is the means of recall. Mental images are then available to be linked in imaginative play with a different perceived object, and in the acquisition of language with the verbal label that has been associated with the real object.

Piaget describes the mental image as internal imitation, which develops in the same way as external imitation. This he regards as interiorized action, and mental images are internal imitations of previously performed actions. Both types of imitation result from the accommodation of sensorimotor schemata. During the sensorimotor period, when the child imitates a new model, the perceived movement activates an analogous schema (assimilation), which is then modified in action to reproduce the new details (accommodation). External imitation thus occurs when schemata are activated by a perceived action, and internal imitation (or the mental image) occurs when sensorimotor schemata that are developed in the course of perceptual activities (which are also partly motor) are similarly activated and modified.

The mental image represents the object, and representation is further developed in language and symbolic play. Since the learning of verbal labels is a long process, the child will need to invent symbols for his needs. Hence imaginative play is dominant during the 2- to 4-year period.

Piaget suggests that the verbal labels which children of 2 to 4 years learn are midway between the individual and the general, and he accordingly refers to them as *preconcepts;* for example, the child of this age appears to be unsure whether there is one moon or several and to be uncertain whether a second snail he sees on a long walk is the first one or an individual of a class. The ability to deal correctly with classes and subclasses involves concrete-operational thinking, as does arranging objects in a series. However, partial solutions can be achieved by making use of certain perceptual features of objects; when this occurs, the child has reached the intuitive stage.

The stage of intuitive thinking (approximately 4 to 7 years). Piaget found that some problems, which apparently needed for success the type of thinking which he has called concrete-operational, could also be solved in a trial and error manner by the use of perceptual configurations, though reliance on the latter led the child to make incorrect inferences. For example, if given the problem of making equal in number two unequal groups of counters (say 8 and 18), the child using concrete-operational thinking succeeds through an understanding of the principle involved by putting to each group half the difference between them. The least adequate method of dealing with this problem is to move over to the smaller group a few counters at random and to aim to make equal the areas covered by the counters; the solution is achieved only by chance. An advance on this is to move counters from one group to the other in a trial and error manner until identical patterns are achieved on both sides. This leads to a correct result, but the limitations of the thinking of children who can only use the last method are revealed when the spatial pattern is disarranged. They think that the group covering the larger area has more counters in it.

It is the type of thinking shown in the last two methods which Piaget has termed intuitive, and he classifies it as a separate stage, during which the child's thinking is confined to what he directly perceives at any given moment, not taking account of changes from one moment to another. At the level of thinking, this is analogous to the behavior of the infant whose actions are limited to objects in his perceptual field. But the child who attained a concept of the permanent object at about 18 months does not, at the age of 5 or 6 years, believe in the numerical constancy of a number of objects. The same results were found with continuous quantities as with elements; the amount of liquid was thought to vary with the shape of the container. Piaget attributes this to the failure of the child to take account of two factors at once, so that he concentrates on the difference either in height or in cross section of two glasses. With the counters problem he considers only the difference in the area covered and not the difference in the spaces between the counters. The child centers on one aspect of the perceptual situation at a time.

These features were also observed in the development of spatial concepts; for example, when shown a model of three mountains of different colors and instructed to arrange pieces of cardboard to represent the view as it would be if seen from various viewpoints, the child at the intuitive stage produced a copy of the model as it was from the position he was actually in. He was unable to disregard his own viewpoint and imagine what the left-right and fore-aft relations of the mountains would be from other viewpoints. Thus Piaget considers that children show in spatial concepts the same egocentricity which characterizes their speech.

When children of this level do take account of successive changes of position, they assimilate them to their own actions; they fail to distinguish between physical processes which they observe and the effects of their own actions. If a weight is put on one arm of a horizontal bar, the child at the beginning of the intuitive stage uses his hand in order to make the bar level and expects it to remain horizontal when he releases it. Another concept, that of reversibility, is used to explain this. The child's actions and thinking are not reversible; he does not reverse the effect of a weight on one arm of the balance by putting any weight on the other side, let alone

an equal weight at an equal distance from the center. In numerical operations, having split 10 into two groups of 6 and 4 counters, he does not
realize, without doing it and counting, that 6 and 4 if put together again
will make 10. During the intuitive stage the child can manage increasingly
difficult problems that involve copying elements in a certain order, e.g.,
colored beads on a string, provided he is required to copy them in the same
order as the model. He is, however, unable to copy a row of beads in the
reverse order when the bead at the extreme right of the model is at the
extreme left of the copy.

However, there is progressive organization and coordination throughout
the intuitive period in the direction of attending to two aspects at once.
For example, the child eventually believes that the quantity of water
remains the same when it is poured into a different glass if the difference
in height and cross section is sufficiently large. Each distortion when
carried to the extreme in this way makes the child look at relations he
had previously ignored. Successive experience of contradictions between
his beliefs and what happens eventually makes the child begin to take
account of other points of view and of two factors at once, though this
process is not complete and is not generalized to other situations. When
this happens, the child has reached the level of concrete-operational thinking.

The stage of concrete operations (approximately 7 to 11 years). The
child showing the kind of thinking which Piaget classifies as the stage of
concrete operations is no longer tied to perceptual configurations; he
can make correct inferences about concrete material. For example, he
can solve the problem of the unequal groups by the method of halving
the difference between the two groups; he conceives of quantities as
constant in amount or number, can copy a row of elements in the reverse
order, and not only can put a series of sticks in order of length, but is
able to insert a second set, realizing that each stick has only one place
in the series.

The measurement of length by the use of units is classified as concrete-
operational thinking, though development through the intuitive stage
moves from visual comparison of a model of a tower and one the child
is building to the use of his own hands, to the use of a stick equal to the
model, and then to the use of a stick longer than the model on which a
mark is made at the appropriate point. Later, at the concrete-operational
stage, children can make use of a stick shorter than the length being
measured; this activity involves a belief in the constancy of a length and
an ability to take account of successive changes of position when the stick is
stepped along the model.

The child's behavior when he tackles the problems by which various
concepts were studied indicates that he is now (after the age of about
7 years) considering simultaneously various aspects of the perceptual situation and taking account of successive changes which he has seen, so that
he is no longer tied either to the immediate perceptual situation or to his
own viewpoint. Piaget interprets this development as an equilibrium
between the assimilation of objects and their relations to the subject's
actions and the accommodation of the subject's schemata of thinking.

These are modified to conform to objective reality in the physical world. The child thus has now achieved in thinking what he achieved in action at the end of the sensorimotor period.

There are, however, limitations to concrete-operational thinking; when a child of 7 to 10 years is given, in the form of verbal statements alone, the same type of problem that he successfully dealt with using concrete material, he is unable to reason correctly. For example, the child at this stage can make correct inferences of the $A = B = C$ type when concrete material is involved; if blocks of identical shape and size, A and B, are shown to be of equal weight on scales, and C of the same shape and size is similarly shown to be equal in weight to B, the child reasons that A and C will also make the pans of the balance level.

But given verbal statements, the child is no longer able to make the correct inferences with the $A = B = C$ problem. Piaget, therefore, believes that a new organization of thinking is involved when children can deal with verbal statements alone.

The stage of abstract operations (11 years onward). Piaget distinguishes, as a separate type of thinking, that by which the child is able to reason by hypothesis—to accept any data, even if they are absurd, as hypothetical, and to reason correctly from them. This type of thinking is revealed by verbal problems and by the methods children use in tackling more complex problems involving concrete material. For example, children solve the problem of making a horizontal arm balance with unequal weights; they also show an understanding of inverse proportion in other problems, as in producing the same-sized shadow with rings of different diameter which can be placed at different distances from a source of light and then projected on a screen. Children at this stage also tackle systematically problems which involve combinations, as in the problem of finding out which combination of chemicals in five glasses gives a liquid of a particular color.

Abstract operations are said to be involved in the conservation of volume, whereas only concrete operations are involved in the conservation of quantity and of weight. When children were given the task of building model houses of the same volume (i.e., with the same number of rooms when one brick represents one room) on bases of varying areas, success was rarely achieved under the age of 11 years.

Similarly, although an understanding of the measurement of length is achieved by younger children showing concrete-operational thinking, an understanding of the measurement of area and volume occurs among older children. For example, before the abstract level children think that the effect of doubling the length of the sides of a square will be to double the area.

Piaget suggests that another state of equilibrium occurs at the age of about 15 years. This is shown in behavior when the child not only systematically arrives at a correct solution of these problems but seeks to verify his solution and checks it.

At the abstract level, as at others, great importance is attached to the role of action, particularly in the development of spatial concepts. The contents of the operational systems arise from a series of abstractions from the subject's actions in relation to the objective world and not from abstractions from perceived objects alone. But the process of abstraction can be encouraged or delayed by the conditions in which various groups of objects are met; number is understood before spatial measurement (of area and volume) because groups of separate elements suggest the repetition of a unit more readily than linear continuity in two dimensions.

Abstract-operational thinking is further distinguished from the concrete variety in that the latter directly operates on objects, whereas the former reflects on the concrete operations, that is, it operates on operations, so that this is a second-order grouping of operations.

Summary of Piaget's theory. Piaget postulates that intellectual development occurs in stages and that the stages succeed one another in a sequence which is the same for most children, though the ages at which different children attain each stage may vary widely. Factors which influence this variation in age are the maturation of the nervous system, the child's experience of physical objects, and his social interactions.

During the early part of the sensorimotor period, the child is restricted in action to objects and relations between them that are perceptually present; at the end of this stage he takes account in his actions of objects and their spatial, causal, and temporal relations when he does not directly perceive them. This makes possible the symbol in various forms, particularly in imaginative play and in acquisition of language. During the intuitive period the child gradually makes use of the perceptual appearances of things in order to solve certain problems, but he is restricted in his thinking to the immediate perceptual situation; at the concrete-operational stage he takes account in his thinking of objects and their objective spatial, causal, and temporal relations. But he is limited in performing these operations to concrete material. When abstract operations develop, he can carry out these operations with verbal statements alone; and he thus develops mathematical and verbal concepts that have no concrete form.

EXPERIMENTAL INVESTIGATIONS OF PIAGET'S THEORIES

Relevant hypotheses. The main point about the hypothesis of a sequence of development is that the steps in it occur in the same order in the development of most children; there is no assumption that the steps occur at particular ages or that the development of successive stages is uninfluenced by social and cultural experiences.

Piaget's critics have sometimes quoted experimental results which are not strictly relevant as evidence against his theory, such as findings of different average ages from those suggested by Piaget for the attainment of a particular concept, or results which indicate the influence of experience in its development.

The relevant evidence for and against Piaget's theory of intellectual development bears on the following hypotheses: (1) that children's responses to the problems devised by Piaget can be classified into the categories of thinking which he described; (2) that the order he suggests for the succession of the different types of thinking is the same in the development of most children; and (3) that the different types of thinking constitute stages of development.

Methodological considerations. Since it is Piaget's later work based on the method of using concrete material which is mainly useful for research in mental deficiency, the early studies will not be considered in detail. Piaget (1953b) has agreed with critics that some of his early investigations were too verbal in nature, and a study by Nass (1956) of children's concepts of physical causality has indicated that the form of the question influences the result.

McCarthy (1954), however, reports that she found a high consistency between different scorers who classified children's spontaneous speech in the categories described by Piaget in his study of the egocentric and socialized aspects of children's speech. Much of the repetition of Piaget's earlier work is concerned with this question, which gave rise to controversy. McCarthy (1954), who reviews these studies, feels that the discrepancies in the proportion of egocentric speech reported by various investigators can be accounted for by differences in the definition and interpretation of Piaget's terms, by differences in the situation in which speech was recorded (egocentric speech was more common in free play and child-child situations than in child-adult ones), and by differences in the personalities of the individual children.

The following review covers studies which repeat Piaget's later work when the child was given concrete material to handle. Some investigators have not followed the technique closely or have given insufficient details of their method so that it is uncertain whether or not they have done so. This must obviously be borne in mind when their results are compared with Piaget's. The present writer's experience is that a minimum time of 15 minutes is required for each experiment; for some half an hour or longer is necessary. Beard (1957), who repeated 98 of Piaget's experiments and spent 5 hours with each subject, appears to have given only one trial. Hyde (1959) also reports that she did not give repeated trials because the opportunities for learning from them confuse the issue. The point of the method, however, is to vary the problem so as to give the child experiences which contradict his belief in order to find out whether he can resolve the inconsistencies. Estes' (1956) method (in a study of number concepts) bears so little resemblance to Piaget's that it has not been included in this review.

The present writer has found that a subject may use a more advanced type of thinking on later trials than on earlier ones after experience with the problem. This has also been reported by Lovell and Ogilvie (1960). On the other hand, a subject may at first appear to have achieved concrete-operational thinking, but further investigation reveals that this was not so. A wrong classification can be made if the subject is allowed to count with a number concept problem such as that of the one-to-one correspondence and numerical equivalence of two rows of counters. The operational response is to know, when one row of counters is spread out and made longer than the other, that there is still the same number in both rows because the elements were previously placed in a one-to-one correspondence. Subjects who need to count before they know are not using this available information; and when they affirm equality after counting, they are presumably saying no more than that their counting of each row ended with the same verbal label. The inability of such subjects to infer equivalence from the fact of the previous correspondence has been demonstrated by using more elements beyond their counting limit.

The validity of types of thinking. Mainly in connection with the study of concepts of number and space, the types of responses observed by Piaget with Swiss children have been found among other groups by Peel (1959), Lovell and Ogilvie (1960), Beard (1957), Churchill (1958), and Page (1959) for English children of 4 to 7 years and by Woodward (1962) for intellectually subnormal adults and children. Hyde (1959), who investigated number concepts among European, Arab, Indian, and Somali children living in Aden, found responses made in English and Arabic which were almost a direct translation of the responses in French reported by Piaget. Not surprisingly, responses of a given type (e.g., intuitive) have been more varied than the examples quoted by Piaget. English children appear to make more use of counting at the intuitive level than Swiss children do; this may result from the difference in the age of starting school in the two countries. With problems described by Inhelder and Piaget in *The Growth of Logical Thinking*, Lovell (1961) observed similar responses in English subjects aged 8 to 18 years.

The hypothesis of a sequence. It was pointed out above that the finding of a particular type of thinking in children who are younger than the ages quoted by Piaget is not evidence against the sequence; similarly to find several stages present in one narrow age group does not question the validity of the sequence. The relevant point is whether children who show a type of thinking which is supposed to develop at a later age have passed through the earlier stages before reaching the advanced one.

The validity of the postulated sequence can be examined by three methods: (1) by longitudinal studies, (2) by a study of age trends within one social group, and (3) by giving all the problems from a particular sequence to the same children, in order to compare their order of difficulty with that found by Piaget. (This method is, however, not possible when the stages in the sequence consist in alternative responses to the same problem as in the number problem of unequal groups previously described.)

Longitudinal studies have not as yet been published. Churchill (1958), however, examined the same 16 children after an interval of 3 months during which half this group had classroom experiences designed to encourage the development of number concepts, the rest acting as controls. Most of the experimental group were at the beginning of the intuitive stage at the first testing and at the intermediate intuitive or at the concrete-operational stage on the second occasion. She states that the sequence does not always occur in Piaget's order, though she appears to mean by this that the second stage was bypassed, not that the order was reversed.

The trend with age in the incidence of three stages (two intuitive and one concrete-operational) in the conservation of substance among children reported by Lovell and Ogilvie (1960) supports the sequence of development suggested by Piaget. Using a method of analysis based on Guttmann's scaling method, Peel (1959) confirmed the sequence of stages proposed by Piaget and Inhelder for the development of spatial concepts in children's drawings; and Page's (1959) results support their findings on the tactile recognition of shapes. Lovell (1959) also found, like Peel and Page, that children draw and identify by tactile perception rounded shapes before forms such as the square and rhombus with long straight sides and few corners. Contrary to Piaget and Inhelder, he found that partly angular and partly curved forms were produced and identified as easily as rounded forms, and he questions the Piaget and Inhelder thesis that the child's first concepts of space are topological in nature. Hyde (1959), who gave tests derived from Piaget's study of number concepts to four national groups in Aden, found trends with age within each community supporting Piaget's sequence. Hyde also obtained data on the conservation of substance, weight, and volume in the same children, though 98 of her 144 subjects were at the lowest stage on all three of these; so they were insufficiently advanced in any one for the validity of Piaget's sequence from the conservation of substance to that of weight to that of volume to be examined. Of the rest, the results of 21 subjects supported this sequence, and those of 25 did not. As pointed out earlier, Hyde did not follow Piaget's method and did not allow the children to verify their statements on weight and volume. Inhelder (1944), who did follow this method, obtained results with mildly subnormal subjects which did support this sequence, with a few exceptions.

Lovell (1961), repeating 10 of the experiments described by Inhelder and Piaget (1958), who classified responses as intuitive, concrete-operational, and abstract-operational, found age trends in a group of 200 which confirmed the suggested sequence for all experiments.

The hypothesis of stages of development. It is more difficult to verify experimentally the hypothesis of stages. Some of Piaget's own argument rests on his logical analysis of the psychological operations; it is suggested that new logical operations are involved at each main stage (Piaget, 1953b; Inhelder & Piaget, 1958). An evaluation of the logical aspect can only be made by a logician. Parsons (1960) has made an extensive critical review of the book in which the most detailed logical analysis of children's problem solving is made.

Other arguments put forward for the existence of stages are based on evidence of the integration in a higher stage of functions that were independent in a lower one, and of minimal anticipations in a lower stage of the functions of a higher one. Distinctions can be made between (1) stages in the development of a particular aspect of a concept, for example, the conservation of quantity in the development of number concepts; (2) stages in all aspects of a concept, such as number; and (3) general stages of thinking affecting all concepts. The last implies that the child will show the same type of thinking in all fields. Piaget, however, does not suggest that the child develops a given type of thinking simultaneously for all concepts; Inhelder (1960) points out that the child finds it more difficult to structure one aspect of reality than another and that children and adults too, though capable of a higher type of thinking, may relapse to an earlier form under stress. (They also do this, of course, when influenced by prejudice and other strong emotional attitudes.) Despite this, however, the views advanced by Piaget lead us to expect that the child at some point, having allowed for time lags for certain concepts, will show the same type of thinking for several concepts.

Few published studies have yet appeared which compare results for several concepts with the same children. Lovell and Ogilvie (1960) found that some children who showed a nonoperational response with one type of material showed a concrete operational type of thinking with another; children who did not believe in the conservation of substance when balls of clay were used did so with elastic bands. Hyde (1959), who only partially followed Piaget's method, found that some of her subjects showed concrete-operational thinking for some aspects of number concepts and intuitive thinking for others. The present writer (Woodward, 1961) has found that while some subnormal subjects showed concrete-operational thinking for four problems involving number concepts, or intuitive thinking for all four problems, others gave concrete-operational responses to some problems and intuitive responses to others. The intuitive responses, how-ever, showed indications of incipient concrete-operational thinking; and these subjects appeared to be in a transitional state between the two levels. There was considerable inconsistency of results as between the two intuitive substages. Also with subnormal subjects, Inhelder (1944) found, on the whole, consistency of thinking for three problems; but there were some inconsistent subjects who tended to be hesitant or inhibited.

Lovell (1961) found high consistencies in the type of thinking shown by the same subject for various combinations of four experiments among the ten which he repeated from the Inhelder and Piaget (1958) study of logical thinking. These problems are of a type which might be used as experimental illustrations in science lessons, but only four of the experiments had been taught in one type of school; and school instruction did not affect the results. A high degree of consistency in the type of thinking was found among subjects who had been taught some experiments and not others. Children who had been shown the experiment at school did not necessarily solve the problem and thus show abstract thinking. In an example which is quoted, the subject had no notion of proportion and could not solve the problem. Lovell concluded that instruction is most useful when the child has reached or almost reached the appropriate level of thinking for an understanding of the problem; otherwise the facts are learned by rote and tend to be forgotten.

SUMMARY AND EVALUATION

Compared with the volume of work produced by Piaget and his colleagues, there is as yet very little from other sources bearing on his theory, and in some of this the technique has been only partially applied. Nevertheless, the studies carried out so far support Piaget in the contention that the different types of thinking are distinct categories. Children in other national groups respond in the same way as those observed by Piaget when they are presented with the same problem. Similarly, the studies which present data on Piaget's sequences are on the whole confirmatory; the exceptions were Lovell (1959), who disagreed with Piaget and Inhelder on the development of spatial concepts, and Hyde (1959), who found that some children believe in the constancy of volume and not in the substance or weight. No conclusion can, however, be drawn about the validity of this sequence until further experiments have been carried out, following Piaget's method, and preferably using the techniques for investigating the conservation of volume described previously.

Studies of various concepts in the same children are as yet too few for any definite conclusion to be drawn on the generality of the type of thinking. Lovell (1961) found high consistencies at the more advanced levels of thinking, but inconsistency appears quite common, as between the intuitive and concrete-operational types of thinking. This unevenness may reflect differential experience. Hyde (1959) found age variations in the attainment of number concepts between different socioeconomic and cultural groups, and the results of Churchill's (1958) study suggest that appropriate experiences accelerate the development of number concepts. Thus a hypothesis for further research is that children with inconsistent results will, if given appropriate experiences, show improvement in the less advanced aspects and thereby attain for these aspects the more advanced type of thinking which they show for other concepts, whereas children at the lower level for all aspects will show no rapid improvement from experience. If this hypothesis were confirmed, then Piaget's theory of general stages in the development of thinking could take account of such discrepancies; the new structures involved in a more advanced type of thinking in some concepts would be available for transfer to other concepts, provided the necessary experiences were given.

Even if many children are unevenly developed in terms of Piaget's stages and if some aspects of his sequence are modified as the result of further research, his work must still be regarded as a major contribution to child psychology; it has opened up new areas of research. His techniques and methods of analysis have brought to light new facts about children's thinking, and this in itself provides a tool for research. Secondly, he has brought order into the field of infant development, which otherwise is an accumulated mass of isolated facts or at best a chronology of specific items of behavior. In classifying these specific items of behavior into groups, and in approaching the study of infant behavior from the point of view of the process by which the child constructs a formless world of sensations into a meaningful world of objects, Piaget has made a theoretical contribution of the highest order. Equally important is his analysis of the process by which the thinking of older children is freed from subjective perceptual influences and from the necessity of being tied to concrete objects.

The question of the role of social and cultural factors in this process must be raised at this point. Are the types of thinking universal? Or are they specific to the culture in which they have been found? In the former case, social and cultural factors would only affect the rate of development through the sequence; there is already some evidence of variations in this respect. The sequence which ends in the development of hypothetico-deductive thinking has been found in Western industrial society, which needs scientific thinking. Will none of these stages, therefore, be found in primitive societies? Or will only the early part of the sequence be found in them? Since the sensorimotor stage is, according to Piaget, dependent upon experience with objects of some sort, it might be expected that this stage would be found in all societies. Yet experience with objects in infancy is also subject to social influences. Piaget has pointed out the role of adults in the development of verbal concepts and reasoning, but he has not mentioned that adults provide the objects and thereby influence what opportunities children have to learn from manipulating them. More remote social factors may also be relevant in that different cultures vary in the kind of toys which are customarily given to children. The relatively poorer results on performance tasks of children who are given no toys have been demonstrated by the study of Nissen et al. (1935) of children in a primitive African village.

Thus Piaget's scheme might profitably be investigated under different social conditions. In fact his work can stimulate as much research as did the acquirement in psychology of a tool for measuring intelligence. It can give rise to longitudinal studies, to investigations of the role of social deprivation and stimulation, emotional disturbance, patterns of rearing, and so on. Not least in these extensions is the study of the intellectually subnormal.

APPLICATIONS TO RESEARCH IN MENTAL DEFICIENCY

The study of cognitive functions. The first obvious application to mental deficiency of Piaget's techniques and methods of interpretation is to the study of the cognitive processes of subnormal individuals. Their concepts of number, time, geometry, space, movement, etc., may be investigated in this manner. For older children and more backward adults problems for which normal children show intuitive or concrete-operational thinking are appropriate, for example, those in concepts of number (Piaget, 1952) and space (Piaget & Inhelder, 1956); for less backward adults, problems whose solution involves concrete or abstract operations are applicable, for example, those described by Piaget, Inhelder, and Szeminska (1960) and by Inhelder and Piaget (1958). For the very backward or for younger children, the techniques of the sensorimotor stage are suitable (Piaget, 1953a, 1955).

The present writer (Woodward, 1959) has observed a group of 147 idiots and young imbeciles in the light of Piaget's stages of sensorimotor development. All subjects failed to reach the lower limit of the Revised Stanford-Binet Intelligence Scale. They were classified by the problems they solved in terms of the stages of sensorimotor intelligence. All the problems of all stages were administered to 65 of the subjects, and 60 of these solved all the problems of stages lower than that at which they classified. This suggests that the sequence of sensorimotor development which Piaget observed in normal infants also occurs in low-grade mental defectives. When the stage of sensorimotor intelligence, based on problem solving, was compared with the stage reached in the development of a concept of permanent objects, 87 per cent of the total group of 147 were at the same stage for both aspects. Hand movements and manipulations of toys were readily classifiable as primary, secondary, derived secondary, and tertiary circular reactions, which should occur at stages 2, 3, 4, and 5, respectively. Only 43 per cent of the subjects in stages 1 to 5 showed this correspondence, but in all but six of the noncorresponding cases, the discrepancy was one way round: manipulations were at a lower stage than problem solving. Behavior disturbance was significantly more common among subjects with discrepant results.

By this method questions can be expressed in a meaningful form; for example, has this child attained a belief in the permanence of objects, or is he limited in action to those objects perceptually present to him? Has this adult an understanding of numbers as forming a series, and does he regard a number as invariant, or is he tied to perceptual appearances in his thinking?

This alone can bring to light new facts about the cognitive processes of mental defectives. Further investigation is possible by comparing the type of thinking shown by the same individuals for various concepts so that it can be asked whether a population which has a high incidence of cerebral abnormality shows a different pattern of development from that of normal children. The present writer (Woodward, 1962) has found with a group of 90 child and adult subjects that mental defectives tend to produce lower-stage responses for copying geometrical figures by drawing than they do for number concepts and for other problems involving spatial concepts. Comparisons can also be made between backward individuals who are stable and those who are emotionally disturbed, between those who have been socially deprived and those with normal social experiences, and also between those with and without sensory or motor disabilities.

This approach can also be applied to the long-term study of cerebral function; psychological findings in these terms can be subsequently compared with post-mortem data on brain pathology.

The advantage of a system of classification which is based on the type of behavior or thinking is that the material used, and even the task, can be varied to suit problems of administration presented by individuals with multiple or severe physical handicaps or with psychotic features in their behavior. What is important is that the task should be designed to elicit one or two types of thinking; the particular form of the task or the material does not matter. This becomes useful for the study of the lower grades of mental deficiency, among which motor and sensory disabilities are common, and when interest in material may be fleeting.

Least modification is probably required for the deaf, provided that the instructions can be conveyed by gesture or a demonstration.

Since performances are not timed, the slowness of those with a motor disability is no handicap, but modifications are required when the handicap is so severe that the intention indicated by the movements is unclear. The present writer has extended the use of Piaget's techniques to the physically handicapped for the sensorimotor period, but not yet for higher stages. For the former it is useful with the problem of presenting a toy out of the child's reach, at the end of a piece of string, or with that of hiding an object under a cover, to present the string and the cover alone so that the investigator can find out whether movements in the direction of the cover or string occur only when the child has seen an object hidden or placed on the string. Material for problems in the later stages could no doubt be made larger so that fine motor movements are avoided, or the investigator could move material as directed by the subject.

A method of investigating the concept of permanent objects of blind children is to remove an object from the subject's tactile field, assuming that this is analogous to removing an object from the visual field of a sighted individual. Whether the problems of later stages can be modified for blind subjects so that they elicit the same type of thinking is a matter for further research.

Much of the psychological research in mental deficiency has necessarily been carried out with stable subjects because of the limited cooperation of emotionally disturbed individuals, but the inclusion of such individuals is necessary for some investigations. The estimation of the intellectual ability of autistic children remains one of the thorniest psychological problems in this field. Apart from its clinical importance, the distinction between autistic children of normal intelligence and autistic mentally defective children is essential for the satisfactory investigation of the hypothesis of psychogenic mental deficiency. This hypothesis suggests that early adverse experience produces severe intellectual deficiency. Unfavorable experiences may, however, produce behavior disorders so severe that no contact can be made with the child, in which event no estimate of his intelligence can be made by standard tests for which his cooperation is necessary. There are probably children like this in mental deficiency hospitals, but mental deficiency cannot be assumed. This creates a problem for a study such as that of Bourne (1955), who postulated psychogenic causation for some cases of extreme deficiency at the imbecile level. He found that in a group of 154 consecutive admissions to the Fountain Hospital, London, 16 showed no clinical signs of organic involvement. They were significantly differentiated from the rest of the group by a higher incidence of early adverse experiences. But on examining the psychological reports in 15 of the 16 children who were examined, the present writer has found that only four children in the group have ever been sufficiently cooperative for a complete test to be given. These results and those of five incomplete tests indicate that only six children in the group were definitely or probably below the 50 IQ level; also, two were definitely above this level and one was probably so; the remaining six were completely inaccessible, and no estimate was possible.

The whole question of the duration of the long-term effects of adverse environments on cognitive development is at present unsettled. Pinneau (1955) has criticized the methodology in Spitz's work. Clarke, Clarke, and Reiman (1958), who found IQ increases in subnormal adults (above imbecile level) significantly related to living in extremely unfavorable environments before admission, have concluded that the effects of adverse experiences are not necessarily irreversible. Their group consisted of individuals of limited potentiality who were further retarded by adverse environments. Whether children of average or higher intelligence can become imbeciles, solely through adverse psychological experiences, without the intervention of injury or disease, is uncertain. As mentioned above, the investigation of this question involves differentiating levels of ability among children with severe behavior disorders, since early adverse experiences are related to behavior disorders in mentally defective children, as in normal children (Woodward, 1960). There is a possibility that Piaget's approach might be used to tackle this problem.

Again as yet only at the sensorimotor level has it been found possible to study children with limited interests by means of Piaget's method. Since the type of manipulation and not the score of many specific responses is used for the classification of behavior into the substages, it does not matter if the child takes only a little of the material offered. With problems (string, stick, hiding) an uncooperative child can be motivated to tackle the problem if an object in which he has shown interest is used. Even if he is only interested in playing with the light switch, this can be covered up and his searching behavior observed. The technique obviously cannot be used for extremely withdrawn or inhibited children who show no interest in toys or other objects at all, but it is successful with some of those who refuse to respond to other methods.

For the distinction between different levels of ability in autistic children, the use of the sensorimotor stages is useful only for children up to about 2 years. Beyond the sensorimotor period, the child's cooperation is needed for Piaget's method. It is possible, however, for further research to extend to older children and to higher levels of development the technique of using a toy in which the child is interested. This is placed in a problem situation so that the child has to solve the problem in order to obtain the object. The children could then be classified in terms of Piaget's sequence if the problems could be so devised that the solution depends upon the use of his various types of thinking.

An example of the use of Piaget's approach for determining whether or not particular behavior is abnormal has been described by the present writer (Woodward, 1959). This example also illustrates the manner in which Piaget's system has theoretical significance in the interpretation of the behavior of mentally defective individuals. In the section of this chapter in which the sensorimotor stage is described, the primary circular reactions of substage 2 were defined as repetitions by the child of movements of his own body made in the first instance by chance; examples of this type of behavior pattern are that the child holds his hand in front of his face and looks at it or watches his moving hand, twiddles his fingers and looks, and so on. Idiots also commonly show this type of behavior, which is often regarded as bizarre. The hand movements, however, are the same as those of the infant of 2 or 3 months, and the bizarre quality is due to the much greater size of the idiot and to the discrepancy between his size and his behavior. It was concluded that these mannerisms originated, as in the infant, in the course of coordinating vision and grasping. Thus, Piaget's approach offers an explanation of the origins of certain maneristic behavior. Following this lead, the suggestion was also put forward that other mannerisms (shaking hands about, banging on a table) are continuations in the absence of objects of behavior patterns developed in the first place in relation to objects (shaking them and banging them). Subsequent observations have confirmed this explanation.

Some of the idiots observed in this study showed other behavior of the sensorimotor substages 2 and 3. Their behavior with their hands was, therefore, consistent with their sensorimotor development; and those hand movements cannot, therefore, be regarded as abnormal or indicative of psychotic features in an idiot. Some idiots, however, whose problem-solving and object-concept behavior was at the fifth or sixth sensorimotor substage also displayed these hand mannerisms (and they can be observed, of course, among more advanced children). In these cases, the behavior is not consistent with sensorimotor development, and it may therefore be regarded as abnormal; the children at the more advanced substages with these mannerisms tended to show signs of behavior disturbance, such as visual avoidance, rejecting a social approach, and crying when brought to a strange room. Piaget's approach thus offers a means of distinguishing normal and abnormal manneristic behavior among idiots, and this can be useful when a study on psychosis in mental deficiency is extended to the lowest grades.

Application to the problem of measurement. The value of a sequence of development is that it carries the assumption that the individual who has reached a certain point in it has passed through the steps placed earlier in the sequence, but has not yet attained those placed after it. Thus, it is possible to classify individuals by the point they have reached in the sequence and, consequently, to place them in respect to their intellectual development in a rank order.

This possibility offers a partial solution to the problem of measurement in an extremely deviant group; it enables a satisfactory differentiation of intellectual status to be made among individuals who lie outside the limits within which accurate differentiation can be made in terms of standard deviation units. The lower limit is probably -3 or -3.5 SD (Scarr, 1953) so that imbeciles and idiots lie outside this limit. Scarr (1953) examined the applicability to low IQs of the Roberts-Mellone corrections, which are adjustments to make revised Stanford-Binet IQs comparable in terms of standard deviation units. She found that below a certain point (about 40 IQ) the corrected IQ ceased to predict closely a subsequent IQ. Thus the IQs of imbeciles and idiots of different ages or their results from different tests are not comparable on an equal-interval scale.

In some research problems involving individuals with IQs under 50, this difficulty can be overcome by matching experimental and control groups for both age and IQ on the same test. This, however, excludes from the study physically handicapped subjects who require a different test and the emotionally disturbed who only partially cooperate on a formal test; it also excludes those for whom no test is available because they fail to reach the lower limit of a scale appropriate to their chronological age (e.g., blind mental defectives under 8 years, young imbeciles, and all idiots). In addition, it is not possible to match satisfactorily two subnormal groups of different ages, for example, adults with children, or two groups of younger and older children. In default of any more adequate measure, the mental age, discarded in clinical practice, has to be used for matching groups for research, again excluding individuals with emotional or physical handicaps or speech defects. This method of matching implicitly places the individual on a scale of functions that develop at successive ages, but it is derived from scales devised to place the individual by the extent of his deviation from the average of his age group. This being so, it might be preferable to use a method which is explicitly based on the development of successive functions with increasing age and for which there is some evidence that the functions do represent a sequence of development. The use of Piaget's sequence would mean that pairs would be matched by the point reached in the sequence without reference to age. With the modification of techniques as suggested above, matched groups could be made of stable and emotionally disturbed subjects, as well as matched groups with various types of physical handicaps. Children with a given type of thinking, e.g., the intuitive, could be compared in other aspects, such as learning ability, with adults who show the same type of thinking.

Piaget's method might also be usefully applied to matching mental defectives with normal children so that some of the problems involved in matching them for mental age scores might be avoided. One of these problems is the different composition of the mental age score, especially when it is based on both verbal and performance items. This applies particularly when institutionalized mental defectives are matched with normal children living at home. Lyle (1959) found that imbecile children living in hospitals were markedly retarded in verbal ability, relative to their performance ability, compared with imbecile children living at home and that both groups were relatively retarded in verbal ability when compared with normal children.

Other extensions and concluding comments. As well as applying Piaget's scheme as outlined in the preceding section, it is of theoretical interest to relate other aspects of behavior to the different types of thinking distinguished by Piaget. For example, the present writer and colleagues (unpublished study) are comparing the locomotor, language, and social behavior of mentally defective children classified into the sensorimotor stages. It would also be useful to compare the performance on learning tasks of individuals classified by their type of thinking or by the pattern of types of thinking if they are at various stages for different concepts. It would be interesting as well to determine the verbal ability of individuals so classified and to investigate to what extent the development of logical thinking, as Piaget defines it, is dependent upon verbal development.

Piaget's approach of examining the method the subject uses rather than success or failure with the problem can also be applied to other tasks. In the experience of the writer this can direct the investigator's attention to aspects of behavior that would not otherwise have been recorded. This in turn has given rise to hypotheses for further investigation that might not otherwise have been thought of.

Inhelder (1944) suggested that the Piaget stages could be used as a new means of classifying different grades of mental deficiency; those who reached the stage of concrete operations, when their development is complete, would constitute a mildly subnormal group, corresponding to the present feeble-minded or moron category; those who finally reach only the intuitive and preconceptual stages would constitute two intermediate groups; and those who did not advance beyond the sensorimotor stage would form the grade with the most severe deficiency. Such a classification is possible with adults who have completed their development; its application to children implies the prediction of a future end result. This requires the longitudinal study of subnormal children in different environments.

These are some suggestions about ways in which Piaget's theory of intellectual development can be applied to the study of mental deficiency. As yet little research based on this approach has been carried out. As this becomes more extensive, the picture of the subnormal that emerges will gradually be filled in and amplified.

REFERENCES

BEARD, RUTH M. An investigation of concept formation among infant school children. Unpublished doctoral thesis, Univer. of London, 1957.

BERLYNE, D. E. Recent developments in Piaget's work. *Brit. J. Educ. Psychol.,* 1957, 27, 1–12.

BOURNE, H. Protophrenia: a study of perverted rearing and mental dwarfism. *Lancet,* December, 1955, 1156–1163.

BUHLER, CHARLOTTE. *The first year of life.* New York: John Day, 1930.

CHURCHILL, EILEEN M. The number concepts of the young child. *Res. Stud.,* 1958, No. 17, 34–49.

CLARKE, A. B. D., CLARKE, ANN M., & REIMAN, SUSANNE. Cognitive and social changes in the feebleminded—three further studies. *Brit. J. Psychol.,* 1958, 49, 144–157.

ESTES, BETSY W. Some mathematical and logical concepts in children. *J. Genet. Psychol.,* 88, 1956, 219–222.

GESELL, A. *The first five years of life.* New York: Harper, 1948.

HYDE, DORIS M. An investigation of Piaget's theories of the development of the concept of number. Unpublished doctoral thesis, Univer. of London, 1959.

INHELDER, B. *Le diagnostic du raisonement cher les Débiles Mentaux. Neuchateli Delachaue Niestlé,* 1944.

INHELDER, B. In J. M. Tanner & B. Inhelder (Eds.), *Discussions on child development.* London: Tavistock Publications, 1960. Part II. P. 125.

INHELDER, B., & PIAGET, J. *The growth of logical thinking from childhood to adolescence.* A. Parsons & S. Milgram (Trans.) London: Routledge, 1958.

LOVELL, K. A follow-up study of some aspects of the work of Piaget and Inhelder on the child's conception of space. *Brit. J. Educ. Psychol.,* 1959, 29, 104–117.

LOVELL, K. A follow-up study of Inhelder and Piaget's "The growth of logical thinking." *Brit. J. Psychol.,* 1961, 52, 143–153.

LOVELL, K., & OGILVIE, E. A study of the conservation of substance in the junior school child. *Brit. J. Educ. Psychol.,* 1960, 30, 109–118.

LYLE, J. The effect of an institution environment upon the verbal development of imbecile children. I. Verbal intelligence. *J. ment. Def. Res.,* 1959, 3, 122–128.

MCCARTHY, DOROTHEA. Language development. In L. Carmichael (Ed.), *Manual of child psychology.* New York: Wiley, 1954.

NASS, M. L. The effects of three variables on children's concepts of physical causality. *J. abnorm. soc. Psychol.*, 1956, 53, 191–196.

NISSEN, H. W., MACHOVER, S., & KINDER, E. F. A study of performance tests given to a group of native African negro children. *Brit. J. Psychol.*, 1935, 25, 308–355.

PAGE, E. I. Haptic perception. *Educ. Rev.*, 1959, 11, 115–124.

PARSONS, C. Inhelder and Piaget's "The growth of logical thinking." II. A logician's viewpoint. *Brit. J. Psychol.*, 1960, 51, 75–84.

PEEL, E. A. Experimental examination of some of Piaget's schemata concerning the child's perception and thinking, and a discussion of their educational significance. *Brit. J. Educ. Psychol.*, 1959, 29, 89–103.

PIAGET, J. The language and thought of the child. M. Warden (Trans.) London: Routledge, 1926.

PIAGET, J. *The child's conception of the world.* J. Thomlinson & A. Thomlinson (Trans.) London: Routledge, 1928.

PIAGET, J. Judgment and reasoning in the child. M. Warden (Trans.) London: Routledge, 1928.

PIAGET, J. *The child's conception of physical causality.* M. Gabain (Trans.) London: Routledge, 1930.

PIAGET, J. *Les notions de mouvement et de vitesse chez l'enfant.* Paris: Presses Universitaires de France, 1946.

PIAGET, J. *Play, dreams and imitation in childhood.* C. Gattegno & F. M. Hodgson (Trans.) London: Heinemann, 1951.

PIAGET, J. *The child's conception of number.* C. Gattegno & F. M. Hodgson (Trans.) London: Routledge, 1952.

PIAGET, J. *The origins of intelligence in the child.* M. Cook (Trans.) London: Routledge, 1953(a).

PIAGET, J. *Logic and psychology.* Manchester: Manchester Univer. Press, 1953(b).

PIAGET, J. Structures operationnelles et cybernetique. *L'Annee Psychologique,* 1953, 53, 379–388 (c).

PIAGET, J. *The construction of reality in the child.* M. Cook (Trans.) London: Routledge, 1955.

PIAGET, J. The general problems of the psychobiological development of the child. In J. M. Tanner, & B. Inhelder (Eds.), *Discussions on child development.* London: Tavistock Publications, 1960. Pp. 3–27.

PIAGET, J., & INHELDER, B. *The child's conception of space.* F. J. Langdon & J. L. Lunzer (Trans.) London: Routledge, 1956.

PIAGET, J., & INHELDER, B. *La genese des structures logique elementaires: classifications et seriations.* Neuchatel: Delachaux et Niestle, 1959.

PIAGET, J., INHELDER, B., & SZEMINSKA, A. *The child's conception of geometry.* E. A. Lunzer (Trans.) London: Routledge, 1960.

PINNEAU, S. R. The infantile disorders of hospitalism and anaclitic depression. *Psychol. Bull.*, 1955, 52, 429–452.

SCARR, ELIZABETH H. Changes in Terman-Merrill I.Q.'s with dull children. *Brit. J. Statist. Psychol.*, 1953, 6, 71–76.

SHIRLEY, MARY M. *The first two years.* Univer. of Minnesota Press, 1931.

WOODWARD, MARY. The behaviour of idiots interpreted by Piaget's theory of sensori-motor development. *Brit. J. Educ. Psychol.*, 1959, 29, 60–71.

WOODWARD, MARY. Early experiences and later social responses of severely subnormal children. *Brit. J. Med. Psychol.*, 1960, 33, 123–132.

WOODWARD, MARY. Concepts of number in the mentally subnormal studied by Piaget's method. *J. Child Psychol. and Psychiat.*, 1961, 2, 249–259.

WOODWARD, MARY. Concepts of space in the mentally subnormal studied by Piaget's method. *Brit. J. Soc. Clin. Psychol.*, 1962, 1, 25–37.

9

SOCIAL PSYCHOLOGIES
OF MENTAL DEFICIENCY[1]

Samuel Guskin

The plural *social psychologies* in the title is meant to suggest (1) a lack of agreed-upon definitions of the realm of social psychology, (2) an unwillingness on this writer's part to limit himself to any one social psychological approach, and (3) an unwillingness to cover all the material in mental deficiency which other readers might feel is a part of *the* social psychology of mental deficiency. This chapter does not treat such topics as social adjustment, rehabilitation, or social competence. There is also very little to be found here in the way of studies of social behavior which, while using defective subjects, do not otherwise deal with problems relevant to mental deficiency.

What, then, is the content of this chapter? The focus here is twofold: (1) on the social stimulus properties of the defective, i.e., how he is conceived of, judged, and reacted to by others; and (2) on the social determinants of the defective's behavior, i.e., how his behavior is influenced by aspects of the social situation in which he is placed and by the behavior of others toward him. The emphasis is on the study of variables which can be manipulated in either natural or laboratory settings rather than upon correlates of ability. The phenomena selected for treatment meet the following criteria: (1) relevance to mental deficiency; (2) relevance to broader

[1] This paper was written while the author was engaged in full-time research on the social aspects of mental deficiency supported by Research Grant M-2529, National Institute of Mental Health, United States Public Health Service.

The writer would like to thank Phyllis Guskin, Martin Miller, and Lawrence S. Wrightsman, Jr., for critically reading the manuscript from the points of view of layman (and wife), graduate fellow in mental deficiency, and social psychologist, respectively.

325

problems of social psychology; and (3) emphasis on examining relationships among variables rather than seeking solutions to applied problems. The chapter will include sections on (1) conformity and deviation in groups, (2) social roles, (3) social stereotypes, (4) person perception, (5) institutional effects, (6) family reactions, (7) social development, and (8) comparisons with normal social behavior.

THE SUBNORMAL DEVIATE IN THE GROUP

Many experimental studies of small group behavior have dealt with conformity pressures, and several are concerned with the question of how groups react to a markedly deviant member. A number of these studies have been reviewed by Festinger (1950, 1954), whose theoretical approach has stimulated much of the research in this area. In his "Theory of Social Comparison Processes," Festinger postulates that an important determinant of group behavior is the individual's striving for self-evaluation. Since there are so few objective or physical bases for evaluation, persons are forced to compare themselves with one another. Thus they seek out others who are *comparable,* i.e., persons who are sufficiently similar to themselves to enable accurate self-evaluation. Persons who differ considerably from themselves are avoided since noncomparability is unsatisfying. Much group behavior is, then, concerned with associating with and becoming even more similar to those who are relatively similar to oneself and changing or avoiding those who are different. Deviates are pressured by their own and others' needs for self-evaluation to move toward modal group behavior or, if too deviant, to leave the group.

Most of the research testing hypotheses derived from this theory has involved persons deviating in opinion rather than in ability. As Festinger (1954) points out, the situation differs somewhat for ability since (1) rather than attempting to approximate one another's behavior, group members try to be slightly better than one another; (2) the ability deviate may not be able to modify his behavior in the direction of the group norm; and (3) the presence of persons performing subnormally does not suggest that one is inaccurate as it does with deviating opinions. Nevertheless, the theory has obvious implications for the behavior of groups which include mentally subnormal members. Thus, Reynolds (1960) has suggested the importance of Festinger's hypotheses for the study of children who are deviant in ability. He emphasizes the implication that "if [ability deviates] are confined to groups of incomparables [i.e., those of normal ability], we may expect them to be imprecise in evaluation of themselves, relatively unsatisfied in social contacts, and, in the case of low ability deviates, chronically frustrated and rejected" (Reynolds, 1960, p. 247). What evidence is there to support these hypotheses?

There have been several sociometric studies which deal with the relationship between intelligence and popularity. Dentler and Mackler (1962) review this literature and report a consistent positive association between ability and status measures with correlations ranging from .25 to .50, indicating that the less intelligent person is seen as less popular. Among the studies reviewed were those on institutionalized defectives by Clampitt and Charles (1956), Hays (1951), McDaniel (1960), Marden and Farber (1961), and Sutherland, Butler, Gibson, and Graham (1954) as well as those on noninstitutionalized retardates by Johnson (1950) and Turner (1958). Dentler and Mackler are so convinced by the consistency of the evidence that they suggest ending all research limited to this question and as an alternative propose investigating changes in sociometric status as a function of experience variables.

If we interpret the above sociometric findings in terms of Reynolds's conclusions from Festinger's theory, we can assume that differences in ability result in observably deviant behavior on attributes valued by group members and that low sociometric status indicates dislike and the desire that the person be removed from the group. Johnson's study bears on the first question. After obtaining estimates of those classmates most and least liked, Johnson had subjects indicate the reasons for negative choices. He found that they rarely mentioned academic weakness as a reason for not liking retarded class members, but instead their comments focused on antisocial behavior; words such as rough, mean, bullies, fights, poor sport, and cheats were frequent. Thus it seems that it is not ability deviation to which other group members are reacting. Johnson believes that this antisocial behavior is the result of academic failure, a sort of compensatory response. Another interpretation would be that children who fail and are put back find themselves in a group which they do not value and hence do not attempt to conform to the norms of social behavior for that group.

The second assumption in interpreting the sociometric findings is that low sociometric status indicates hostility and the desire that the person be ejected from the group. Sociometric measures often ask the rater to choose the person least liked, and this is interpreted as a measure of *rejection*. Miller (1956), however, had children rate each of their classmates on a five-point scale ranging from 1—"want that person as a friend very much" through 3—"doesn't matter whether that person is your friend" to 5—"don't want that person as a friend." Although the less intelligent children (PMA IQ 60–80) were rated less favorably than the rest on social acceptance, 33 of the 40 children in this group had mean ratings by others of better than 3.0 (indifference), and none had a mean rating poorer than 3.3. Miller interprets this finding as *mild acceptance* rather than *rejection*. Miller also reports data on estimated social status in the group. His data indicate no difference between dull and normal children in their own estimated popularity. Thus, the implication of low self-acceptance resulting from rejection is not supported at all by Miller's data. Of course, it may be that low self-acceptance is not likely to be divulged in this direct a manner.

While Festinger's theory need not imply a hostile response to those deviating markedly in ability, it definitely indicates that there should be a reduction of comparisons and communication with the subnormal deviate. A study performed as part of the Parsons Language Research Project by Rosenberg, Spradlin, and Mabel (1961) seems highly relevant to our discussion. Institutionalized defectives were selected on the basis of high or low language ability scores, and each individual was paired with another

who had low ability in one series of sessions, and with a defective who had
high ability in another series. When the quantity of verbalization was
examined as a function of the level of ability of each person and the
person he was paired with, it was found that lows spoke only to low-ability
defectives, and highs spoke only to highs. Thus, under these conditions
there is almost no communication between persons noncomparable in ability.

The above studies were concerned with positive or negative evaluation of
members deviating in ability and the extent of interaction with them.
Festinger's hypotheses can be looked at from another direction. Instead of
fixing the defective in a deviant position, one may give him freedom to
conform more or less to group norms. Does he choose to follow the group
consensus on issues or doesn't he? Festinger's theory suggests that in situations where group decisions and individual evaluations differ from one
another, brighter persons will feel less pressure to conform to the group
decision because of the unidirectional drive upward with regard to ability.
First Lucito (1959) and then Hottel (1960) compared dull school children
with brighter children in a situation requiring judgment of the size of lines.
Half of the judgments could be made accurately by all subjects individually.
In a group situation, each subject was led to believe that all five of the
remaining group members agreed on a particular response, and then he
had to make his estimate publicly. On half of the trials using discriminable
lines, the group's decision was the incorrect one. In both studies it was
found that the duller pupils showed more frequent conformity to the group
decisions than did brighter subjects, both under ambiguous stimulus conditions and when the group chose the wrong discriminable line.

Lucito's interpretation is that as a result of previous experiences bright
children see themselves as successful in interpreting objective reality and
as definers of social reality for others, whereas dull children have more
frequently failed at interpreting objective reality and have looked to others
to define social reality for them. This is consistent with Festinger's notion
that social comparisons are a substitute for unavailable objective comparisons. Lucito also reports that in his preliminary experimentation he noted
that brighter subjects were more task-oriented whereas duller subjects were
more concerned with social acceptance. These findings and interpretations
resemble closely the work of Cromwell and his associates, reported elsewhere in this volume, particularly the concept of locus of control, which
Hottel (1960) suggests as a source of individual variability in conformity
situations.

While Festinger's theory conforms quite well to both naïve observations
and research findings, an approach by Dentler and Erikson (1959) deviates
markedly from the expectations of both the layman and the social psychologist (but will not be rejected for noncomformity in this analysis). They
propose that the deviate has certain positive functions in groups, that other
group members often create a special role to be filled by deviates, and that
groups will frequently resist the removal of such deviant members, even
though they are disliked. The presence of a person functioning as a deviant
member serves to indicate to others in the group the group's standards, the
punishments which may be encountered upon deviation, and the bound-

aries of acceptance in the group. Furthermore, the presence of a person clearly more deviant than themselves reduces somewhat the pressure on others. In short, Dentler and Erikson believe that a clearly defined group structure requires deviates as much as it requires leaders. As demonstrations of the operation of these principles, they cite two studies in which they have been involved, one with Quaker workcamp groups and the other with GI groups, in which highly deviant members were supported, or at least not ejected, despite obviously disturbing or aberrant behavior. Many studies attempting to examine the relationships among group members employ sociograms which indicate the preferences of group members for one another. Those who are mutually preferred are placed toward the center; those who are least preferred appear outside the ring of mutual choices. These persons are usually termed isolates. Dentler and Erikson suggest that sociograms of this sort are misleading, that in actuality the deviates in such situations are not outsiders but are clearly a significant reference point for the group and should instead be placed within the ring of mutual choices, to show that they are protected and fostered by the group.

The theoretical approaches of Festinger and Dentler and Erikson might be briefly compared. Festinger's theory seems to be most useful for the group situation in which communication and movement are feasible, with members being free to move in or out of the group and to become more or less similar to other members. Under such conditions, members will tend to associate with those similar to themselves; they will attempt to change themselves and others to increase similarity; and highly dissimilar persons will leave or be pressured out of the group if they do not conform. Dentler and Erikson's approach fits the situation in which the barriers are greater between group and not-group or outgroup, as a result of either cohesive forces deriving from within the group or pressures upon the group from without. Under such conditions, rather than ejecting the deviant member, he is "put in a corner" for all to learn from or put in the middle for all to protect.

What sort of further research in the field of retardation is suggested by these two approaches? Research might be directed to test the following hypotheses stemming from Festinger's theory:

1. *When given a choice of joining and remaining in groups varying in ability distributions, the subnormal individual will prefer a group which has a modal ability slightly below his own but a range including superior individuals.* This sort of study would go beyond the sociometric one in giving a person experiences in different groups and requiring him to make decisions concerning a whole group. When choosing friends individually, the general preference for brighter individuals would probably hold up. Here the concern is with finding groups which offer the individual maximum satisfaction. It is assumed that two factors would operate: (1) the value of the group would be enhanced by the presence of high status, bright individuals; (2) the satisfactions offered by the group would be maximized by the presence of individuals who are comparable but slightly lower in ability so as to satisfy the "drive upward" with regard to ability in our society.

2. *The subnormal individual will conform to group decisions only when (a) he is clearly recognized as a group member and accepts the membership, (b) he sees the other group members as more capable than himself of making the particular decision, and (c) he is concerned with the goal toward which the group is moving.* This, then, goes beyond the finding of Hottel and Lucito—that the retardate is more likely to conform—and suggests that this finding was a function of the fact that the retardates were not outsiders in the experiment, that they viewed the other members as more capable than themselves, and that they were offered rewards for successful group performance. The superior retardate in the special class, the outsider on the playground, and the uninterested child in the normal classroom might not be expected to conform to their respective groups' decisions.

3. *When a new group is organized to perform some activity together, attempts will be made by the group to aid a member who is doing poorly; but if conspicuously poor performance continues, such a member will be avoided or ignored, and the others will tend to compare their own performance with the performance of those of comparable ability.* This should hold in a noncompetitive situation where rewards result from one's own performance but where members are free to assist one another.

Dentler and Erikson's approach would lead to the following hypotheses:

1. *If group members are given the choice of retaining or removing a member with subnormal ability, they are more likely to retain him if (a) he defines himself clearly as subnormal, (b) he seeks assistance from other group members to protect him from a common enemy or to help him toward a common goal, and (c) if the group has some means of demonstrating the inappropriateness of his behavior to other members.* This follows from Dentler and Erikson's proposition that the deviant group member functions as a clarifier of group norms and goals and as a means of indicating to other members their own closeness to the norm.

2. *When a deviate is removed from the group, the group will shift its judgments of other members and will attribute to one of them some of the unfavorable characteristics previously attributed to the deviate.* This is consistent not only with Dentler and Erikson's notions concerning the importance of the deviate but also with judgment principles of greater generality (see, e.g., Helson, 1947).

SOCIAL ROLES

In the previous section, it was hypothesized that groups create special roles for deviant members. This suggests that groups treat deviates differently from other members, and such treatment results in their exhibiting special behavior. This pattern of behavior unique to deviates who have experienced these special relationships may be called the role of the deviate. It does not refer to the determinants of deviation nor to the attributes defining deviation but to the resultants of social response to deviation. More generally, roles may be defined as socially determined patterns of behavior peculiar to persons in specific positions or social situations. Role expectations are the patterns of beliefs, anticipations, etc., held by persons in a given social group with regard to individuals occupying a particular position or in a particular situation.

Given the above definition of social role, can it be said that there is a social role which could be called *mental defective?* Dexter (1956, 1958, 1960) suggests that this is the case and that much of the defective's behavior may be determined by the expectations of others and their treatment of him. The first step in inquiring into a social role is to define the designating properties of the role.

Defining properties of the defective role. The social role called mental defective can be designated in the following ways: (1) a person not permitted to take part in the normal school curriculum because of limited intelligence; (2) a person committed to an institution for the feebleminded, mentally defective, or mentally retarded; (3) a person publicly labeled mentally retarded, mentally defective, feebleminded, moron, imbecile, or idiot. These designations are not technical or legal definitions but are, rather, ways in which the defective may be socially discriminated from other persons. The empirical questions to be asked here are (1) whether people see these terms and definitions as related to one another and as different in meaning from terms such as "mentally ill," and (2) whether most people discriminate separate groups of defectives such as educables and trainables.

Role concepts, i.e., expectations about the behavior of defective persons. Assuming that people understand one or more definitions of a defective person, the next empirical question concerns what expectations people have about the behavior of defectives. These expectations might be hypothesized to include (1) inability to hold a job, (2) inability to take care of personal needs, (3) inability to control sexual and aggressive impulses, and (4) unusual behavior. Role concepts can be investigated by presenting naïve judges with designating qualities and asking them to describe what such persons are like, what they can do, how they respond in particular situations, etc.

Complementary roles. Another method of investigating role concepts is to note how others behave in the presence of persons designated as mentally defective. Thus, protective behaviors may be seen as indicators of expected helplessness. Put in another way, to have any validity and usefulness, the role concept "helplessness" should be able to predict protective behavior as a complementary role. The more general empirical question here is how persons behave in an interaction situation with a retarded individual. There is also the related question of how people think they ought to behave in the presence of a defective. An example of complementary role behavior is reported by Rosenberg (1959). (See also Spradlin & Rosenberg, 1959.) College students were instructed to interview a series of institutionalized children. Unknown to the students, the children were selected on the basis of verbal ability, and the questions asked by the interviewers were categorized into those requiring only agreement or disagreement (binary questions) and those to which any number of different replies might be given. Thus, in finding out the child's age, the latter approach would be to ask, "How old are you?" whereas the binary approach would be, "Are you eight years old? Nine? Seven?" The author hypothesized that students would ask fewer binary questions of the group with higher ability and that the number of binary questions would increase over time for those interviewing children of lower ability. Rosenberg interprets this situation in terms of the reinforcement of adult behavior by the retarded child and believes its significance lies in the possibility that such shifts in adult behavior result in poor learning situations for the retarded child. If the adult exposes the retarded child to oversimplified verbal stimuli, this may limit the child's capacity to learn more complex verbal behavior. Translating the above terminology to that of role theory, one arrives at the following: The interviewer has defined the child as defective and has altered his behavior to that felt appropriate to interaction with such a child; he has assumed the role of questioner of a defective child. His role behavior may cause the child to behave less adequately than he would otherwise; i.e., the complementary role may lead to defective behavior which is role-determined rather than ability-determined.

In the normal life circumstances of the defective, certain complementary roles are particularly likely to influence his behavior. Among the more obvious roles are parent, teacher, attendant, and fellow classmate. The complementary role behaviors of the first three would probably include protection and control as important elements, and the fourth might show avoidance. It would seem important to test these and related hypotheses about persons interacting with mental defectives.

Role behaviors of the defective. It has been implied above that complementary role behaviors might be learned from previous interactions with defectives or from expectations learned elsewhere. Furthermore, these complementary behaviors might be expected to influence the behavior of the defective. As examples, one could hypothesize nonachievement orientation, dependency behaviors, and rebelliousness as patterns of behavior determined by previous and present interactions with people who have role concepts of the defective emphasizing inability, helplessness, and lack of control, respectively. Such hypotheses suggest that the presence in others of a role concept of the defective is probably detrimental to the deviate's personality and social adjustment. This point of view has been particularly emphasized in a series of articles by Dexter (1956, 1958, 1960), who argues that society has created the defective by its unnecessary academic demands and that it has further fostered in him some apparently inappropriate behaviors by having certain expectations about him and by treating him in a different manner from others. An opposing position might also be argued, namely, that without the role concept "defective," the retarded individual might be labeled a delinquent or something equally unfavorable which would be more disturbing to him. In other words, the role concept "defective" probably leads to certain privileges as well as punishments, including the absence of demands for self-support and protection, and the acceptance of certain unusual behaviors contrary to norms for nondefective individuals. Dexter (1956) makes this point in comparing the defective role with the *sick role* (Parsons & Fox, 1952). As far as the empirics of this argument are concerned, it comes down to a question of what effects a knowledge of the person's defect has upon the behavior of those interacting with him and what influence these behaviors have upon the defective's own responses. More specifically, the following may be hypothesized:

1. Adults instructed that a child is defective will tend to assist the child more in play, give the child easier tasks, and be less critical of his performance.

2. A mentally defective individual will perform a task less adequately when an adult present is more concerned with his needs for protection and assistance than he would with uninvolved adults.

3. Given an experimental situation in which a normal and a subnormal person work together at learning and performing a task, if the task is defined as requiring ability and the subnormal individual is defined as defective, (a) the normal person will tend to take on the retarded subject's task as well as his own, (b) the retarded person will not learn the task as well, but (c) the retarded subject will be judged favorably by the normal person.

4. If one were able to identify social groups (nations, communities, subcultures) where different conceptions were held with regard to the obviously defective, deviates in groups which expect childlike behavior from them should develop fewer adult skills and be more protected by adults, those in groups expecting delinquent behavior should show more "acting out" behavior, and those in groups having no special conception of mental defect should be judged least favorably.

5. Parents and parent surrogates who normally orient their relationship with their children in terms of protectiveness and assistance of helpless children or control and manipulation of irresponsible children should adapt more readily to having a defective child than those parents oriented toward educating the child for adult achievement. However, the latter children may eventually show more adultlike behavior.

STEREOTYPES, ATTITUDES, AND STEREOTYPING

Stereotypes are akin to role concepts, role concepts having been defined as expectations about the way persons in a particular position or social situation will behave. A stereotype might be defined as a conception or set of associations concerning a group or class of persons. The term stereotype is usually reserved for traits or attributes of a group, and role concepts usually focus on behaviors expected of the class of persons. Few definitions of stereotypes are willing, however, to stop with the notion of a set of associations to a group or class name. Among the properties frequently held to be essential to a definition of stereotype are the high degree of consensus among persons in their judgments of the group, the unfavorableness of the associations, and the inaccuracy and distortive properties of the conception. These are not properties which can be defined into a set of associations simply because they are responses to a group name. They are empirical questions which may be asked of any set of judgments. For this reason, the analysis of the stereotype of the defective will be divided into three parts: (1) the

content of the stereotype and the degree of agreement concerning these
associations, (2) the favorableness of the stereotype, and (3) its distortive
properties.

The content of the stereotype of the defective. The content of the
stereotype refers to those verbal responses given most frequently to the
group name or those responses given differentially to this group name as
opposed to others. Table 9-1 presents one empirical definition of the stereotype of the defective. The data were collected for the writer in interviews
of 50 persons in the Nashville, Tennessee, area, selected on a quota basis
so as to assure broad coverage with regard to socioeconomic status, sex, and
age. There was no attempt to approximate the population proportions in
age and social class. Each subject was asked to rate the "average 18-year-
old boy who has just finished high school" on a series of five-point rating
scales (e.g., the subject could choose either "very quiet, fairly quiet, can't
answer, fairly talkative, or very talkative"). Then he was asked to go
through the same set of adjective choices for "an 18-year-old boy who has
just returned home to live after being in a state training school for the
feebleminded or mentally defective." The items in Table 9-1 are listed in
the order in which they discriminate the average and defective boys. In this

TABLE 9-1

Content of the "defective" stereotype ($N = 50$ **)**

Term applied to defective		Number of interviewees selecting term to apply to the					
More often	Less often	Defective			Average		
(1)	(2)	(1)	(?)	(2)	(1)	(?)	(2)
Quiet	Talkative	44	2	4	4	2	44
Timid	Confident	43	2	5	7	0	43
Unintelligent	Bright	37	1	12	3	1	46
Abnormal	Normal	34	0	16	2	0	48
Strange	Ordinary	42	2	6	11	1	38
Helpless	Capable	36	1	13	6	3	41
Clumsy	Skillful	40	3	7	12	3	35
Unpleasant	Likable	20	3	27	1	0	49
Unfriendly	Friendly	19	3	28	0	0	50
Lazy	Ambitious	18	14	18	8	0	42
Irresponsible	Reliable	38	1	11	18	1	31
Sloppy	Neat	27	6	17	8	4	38
Careless	Careful	34	3	13	16	4	30
Nervous	Calm	40	0	10	20	7	23
Dissatisfied	Happy	24	1	25	11	1	38
Quick-tempered	Self-controlled	28	7	15	18	2	30
Inconsiderate	Good-natured	15	7	28	14	2	34

table, the ratings "very _____" and "fairly _____" have been combined to simplify the presentation. With the exception of the last scale all differences are statistically significant (at the .01 level or better). There appears to be considerable agreement that the defective 18-year-old boy is less assertive, less capable, and less normal than the average 18-year-old. While the defective is not rated favorably on moral and social traits, these are not the most discriminating items. If the extent of intersubject agreement were considered a measure of the strength of the stereotype, that of the defective would be very strong; but excess meanings attributed to this strength disappear rapidly when one notices the greater "strength" of the stereotype of the "average 18-year-old boy."

Another way of getting at the nature of the stereotype of the defective is to ask whether such a conception is related to those of other groups or even whether this group can be discriminated at all from certain other groups. One method of investigating this problem is to have subjects rate several groups on the same set of traits. Another method would require subjects to compare groups directly, stating how similar they appear to one another. Table 9-2 presents data from a study of this type. The judges were 35 college students who were asked to rate the degree of similarity of 10 boys to one another on a seven-point rating scale, comparing them one pair at a time. Each boy was defined by a label and a descriptive phrase, e.g., *mentally subnormal* boy, i.e., one who can't manage in normal school classes. Only the labels are included in Table 9-2, and only the comparisons with the subnormal boy are presented. The three categories on each end of the scale have been collapsed for simplicity of presentation. It appears that even a college population does not discriminate well the defective from the mentally ill, and a substantial proportion of this group see the subnormal as similar to the emotionally disturbed and the delinquent. On the other hand, physical abnormality and social subnormality are not frequently associated with mental subnormality.

It should be noted that in selecting groups to be compared, attributes to

TABLE 9-2

Judged similarity of mentally subnormal to other sorts of boys (N = 35)

Other sort	Mentally subnormal judged as		
	Similar	?	Different
Mentally ill	28	2	5
Emotionally disturbed	20	4	11
Delinquent	18	3	14
Worker's son	8	6	21
Crippled	7	3	25
Tubercular	8	4	23
Doctor's son	2	5	28
Athlete	2	2	31
Average	1	1	33

be rated, and judges to make the ratings, one is devising a set of hypotheses, whether explicitly stated or not.

Before leaving this section on the content of stereotypes, a topic on which only the above preliminary studies seem to be available, certain studies of misconceptions might be briefly mentioned. Traditionally, the notion of stereotype has been entangled with that of inaccurate conceptions. Since associations to group names are not usually stated in testable terms and since in any case appropriate sampling and measurement procedures are rarely available to evaluate the "true" characteristics of members of a group, the question of accuracy seems unanswerable (that of distortion will be considered later). If one is concerned with the need for dissemination of accurate information, it would be more appropriate to obtain answers to academic-type questions concerning facts well agreed upon by professionals. Studies attempting this approach are reported by Mahoney and Pangrac (1960), who found that college seniors were more accurate than freshmen, and Winthrop and Taylor (1957), who found that only two out of nine false beliefs were accepted by as many as a third of their respondents.

Data selected from one other study seem relevant to the question of stereotypes of the defective. Bartlett, Quay, and Wrightsman (1960) administered 175 statements to 99 attendants at an institution for defectives in the preliminary stage of attitude scale construction. Among their items were a number which dealt with attributes of the defective. These have been selected from the larger pool and presented in Table 9-3 along with the mean rating given, where a rating of 0 means disagree, 1 means can't decide, and 2 means agree. Only ratings below 0.50 or above 1.50 can be said to show a great amount of consensus, and the responses in these cases all deny the stated negative attributes.

The favorableness of the defective stereotype. While the data in Table 9-3 indicate that the stereotype is not extremely unfavorable, those in Tables 9-1 and 9-2 certainly indicate that most of the attributes applied to the defective are of an adverse nature and that he is seen as far more similar to the delinquent than to the average person. Certainly people in the field of mental deficiency have been led to believe that the public holds an adverse view of the defective. The apparently unfavorable stereotype has led to several studies which attempt to improve the public's attitude toward defectives.

Cleland and Chambers (1959) and Cleland and Cochran (1961) investigated the effects of institutional tours upon the attitudes and opinions of high school and college groups. While they report changes under specific conditions for certain items, their best controlled analysis seems to indicate no superiority of change over a control group which read a brief statement about the institution. Donaldson (1959) compared employers with and without experience with mentally retarded employees and found no differences related to experience. (Interestingly, he did find differential effects of using different labels.) Quay, Bartlett, Wrightsman, and Catron (1961) attempted, with little success, to manipulate attendants' attitudes using three different persuasive techniques.

Perhaps one of the reasons for the lack of shifts in these studies is the relative favorableness and realism of subjects' initial responses to these questionnaires. To be sure, the stereotype is not favorable, but is it unrealistically unfavorable? For example, in their study of attendants, Quay et al. (1961) ask whether attendants' attitudes should be open to ready manipulation when they have been in close contact with defectives for so long. Bartlett et al. (1960) suggest that in such studies, if changes in questionnaire responses do occur, they may not reflect changes in attitudes but a greater awareness of what they are expected to say, a greater tendency to respond in a socially desirable manner. Bartlett's solution to this problem is to use a forced-choice technique where subjects must select one of two items equal in social desirability but differing in the extent to which they measure the attitude of concern.

Distortive properties of the defective stereotype. The extent of agreement on stereotypic content and the degree of unfavorableness of the stereotype have frequently been interpreted as signs of a strong stereotype. Strength in turn has often been interpreted as a tendency to depend on the stereotype rather than on objective evidence when the two conflict. As this writer has pointed out elsewhere (Guskin, 1958), measures of intersubject agreement on content and favorableness are inappropriate measures of

TABLE 9-3

Attitude item preference indices ($N = $ 99 attendants)

Item	Mean preference
Retarded people are just like animals.	0.08
Mentally retarded people are no better than criminals.	0.12
Mentally retarded people are crazy.	0.24
Retarded people who are not locked up are dangerous.	0.29
The retarded can't learn right from wrong.	0.38
Retarded people can't ever be trusted.	0.53
Retarded people like to be dirty.	0.54
Mentally retarded people are mean.	0.60
The mentally retarded are born stubborn.	0.63
Mentally retarded people are dangerous.	0.75
Mentally retarded people don't try to outsmart you.	0.79
Mentally retarded people are not stubborn.	0.92
Most retarded people would steal if they had the chance.	0.93
Retarded people can be trusted.	0.97
Mentally retarded people are not dangerous.	1.03
Mentally retarded people will listen to reason.	1.04
Most retarded people wouldn't steal.	1.09
Retarded people don't like to be dirty.	1.24
Mentally retarded people are not mean.	1.29
Mentally retarded people try to outsmart you.	1.31
The retarded can learn right from wrong.	1.53
Mentally retarded people are not crazy.	1.60

stereotype strength as strength is frequently interpreted. A strong stereotype is often interpreted as one which is highly resistant to contrary information, one which greatly exaggerates the similarities among group members, or one which exaggerates the differences between members of different groups. An appropriate way to measure the strength or distortive power of a stereotype is to examine how differently an individual is judged after subjects are given added information concerning the individual's group membership. This procedure has been applied by the writer in a study of the defective stereotype.

In this study of the defective stereotype, subjects are presented stories describing a person's life situation and certain aspects of his personal history. On the basis of this information, the subject is to form an impression of this person, describe him in a paragraph or so, and rate him on a set of five-point attribute scales. The critical manipulation in the experiment consists in the presence or absence of information labeling the person in the story as defective. If a distortive stereotype exists, subjects judging the person with the defective label should describe him as more nearly similar to the conception of the defective group than subjects judging without the defective label. A *judged subnormality* index was developed which included the items which best discriminated between judgments of the average and the defective 18-year-old boy in the two samples. In an initial attempt to study this phenomenon, the author found no reliable effects of the label which may have been due to either the lack of distortion, the inappropriateness of the stimulus materials, or the high degree of individual judge variability relative to the magnitude of the distortion. In a second study, the materials were altered somewhat by strengthening the salience of the label and by modifying the stories so that the central figures were not so clearly definable as either normal or defective. The sample was also increased in size. There was a highly significant label effect in this second study, and the findings held up both for a group of 40 college students taking a paper-and-pencil group version and for 50 members of the general public responding individually in an interview format.

This effect of the label may be referred to as stereotypy and distortion. Might not an alternative view hold that judges' behavior demonstrates a realistic acceptance and use of relevant information provided by the experimenter? After all, knowledge that a person has been in an institution for defectives seems highly relevant to judgments of intelligence, skill, and competence.

Whether one views the above findings in terms of stereotypes and their distortive effects or in terms of integrating information obtained from various sources, the following further hypotheses are suggested:

1. Associations to "mentally retarded," "mentally defective," and "feeble-minded" include abnormality, inadequacy, and helplessness.

2. These terms are seen as very similar to "mentally ill" and "emotionally disturbed," as somewhat related to "delinquent," but as unrelated to "physically ill" and very different from "average."

3. The preceding associations are widely held, i.e., by a majority of persons in most unsophisticated groups.

4. Associations to "defective," etc., while highly unfavorable relative to associations to "average," are less unfavorable than they might be; e.g., they are more favorable than similar associations to "delinquent."

5. Information defining a described person as feebleminded may or may not influence judgments of his subnormality, depending upon other information available about the individual.

In conclusion it should be restated that the content of the associations, the degree of consensus about them, how favorable they are, and to what degree they influence individual instances of subnormality must be independently investigated and cannot be summarized in a single statement regarding the strength of the stereotype.

THE STIMULUS PROPERTIES OF MENTALLY DEFECTIVE INDIVIDUALS

In contrast to the study of preconceptions or stereotypes concerning defectives, one can examine the way in which observed defective individuals are judged by other persons. Such studies can determine the extent to which individual defectives are responded to differently from the hypothetical defective (the stereotype), the extent to which individual defectives are discriminated from one another, and the degree to which knowledge of the child's defect biases judgment of the child. Although there are no reported studies of this sort with defectives, there is an extensive literature on interpersonal perception which bears on this question. Studies of the accuracy of naïve personality judgements indicate that much accuracy can be accounted for by stereotypic responding, i.e., by attribution of common traits to all members of a group (see, e.g., Cline & Richards, 1960). Studies of impression formation have shown that certain predisposing information considerably influences later judgments of persons (see, e.g., Kelley, 1950). Taken together, the literature suggests the importance of expectations and stereotypes in judging individuals' attributes. The present writer has performed two studies to examine the influence of expectations concerning mental defect upon the way individual defectives are judged.

In one study, 42 college students were shown a film in which two defective children, a boy and a girl both aged about 10 with IQs close to 45, were separately observed playing. Each child was observed twice, once without the benefit of sound, with the child shown playing with a dart gun, and once with sound, allowing the observer to overhear a conversation between the child and a nursery school teacher known to the child. One-half of the observers were initially given the written information that both children were in special classes for mentally retarded children in the public schools, and the other half were only told that they were school children. After each of the four observation sequences, judges were asked to rate the child just observed on a series of five-point scales, and from these ratings a judged subnormality score was obtained. The findings are indicated in Table 9-4, where the difference between the first and second judgments is ignored on the left half of the table, and the difference between label and control conditions is ignored on the right half. The findings may be summarized as follows: (1) The boy was judged to be more subnormal when the label was presented, but the two children were not judged differently in the control condition; (2) the boy was seen as more subnormal at first but no different from the girl on the second observation; (3) the girl was judged to be more subnormal following the second observation. The differences in reactions to the two children can be partly explained by the boy's obvious behavioral symptoms, which included holding his head to one side and speech difficulties. The girl showed few, if any, signs of physical abnormality, thus the initially more unfavorable reaction to the boy. The content of his speech indicated a higher level of intelligence than initially apparent, whereas for the girl, the content indicated a lower level of functioning. What is not so easily explicable is the interaction of label with child, i.e., why the boy is seen as more defective when labeled retarded, while the girl is not. If one assumes an assimilation of judgments of the child to that of the stereotype of the group, one would expect a greater shift in the case of the less obviously defective child. The most conservative interpretation of the findings seems to be that information concerning defect is used by these judges only when the child himself also presents cues to his abnormality. The cues themselves are cautiously interpreted when the label is absent.

Another observational study by this writer (Guskin, 1962) suggests that such moderately defective children are judged to be less subnormal when observers have been warned of their speech difficulties. The label "speech defect" seems to have the effect of isolating some of the major cues from their usual properties as signs of mental defect.

Further research will be concerned with further specification of the observer expectations and child characteristics which result in variations in judged subnormality of defective children. Among the hypotheses to be considered are:

1. Labels which are related to specific signs of abnormality such as "speech defect" and "cerebral palsied" will reduce judged subnormality since they bring with them less unfavorable associations and are still able to explain away the apparent disturbance.

TABLE 9-4

Judged subnormality of two defective children

Child	Label conditions		Judgment conditions	
	Control ($N = 21$)	"Retarded" ($N = 21$)	First ($N = 42$)	Second ($N = 42$)
"Mary"	16.07	16.00	14.85 **	17.21
		*	**	
"Ralph"	16.19 ?	18.64	17.85	16.97

Note: "?" indicates that the differences between the adjacent pair of means are significant only at the .10 level. "*" indicates the .05 level, and "**" the .02 level or beyond.

2. The "mental defect" label will increase judged subnormality when the defective appears unusual if the signs are not already intellective ones such as inadequate verbal content.

3. While judgments of subnormality should increase under the above conditions, judgements of the likableness or pleasantness of the defective person should also increase when the label is present. That is, without the label, abnormal behavior may be interpreted in moral terms whereas with the label the behavior is explained without requiring moral categories.

BEHAVIOR AS A FUNCTION OF THE INSTITUTIONAL SOCIAL ENVIRONMENT

Psychiatrists and sociologists have been giving considerable attention recently to the influence of social factors in the field of mental illness, with particular emphasis on social variables operating in the mental hospital and the potentialities for their therapeutic manipulation. Among the types of things that have been done are changing the administrative structure of the hospital, providing special therapeutic training for ward aides, facilitating social experiences for patients, and analyzing communication patterns in the mental institution (see, e.g., Belknap, 1956; Greenblatt, Levinson, & Williams, 1957; Stanton & Schwartz, 1954). Perry (1954) has recently suggested applying a similar approach to mental deficiency. Perhaps the clearest exposition of the special problems created by institutional living is that of Goffman (1957), who points out that in any residential facility which has a large number of persons living all day long within the same four walls under a central authority the inmate is likely to experience certain "mortifications of the self." Among the potentially degrading experiences are the removal of personal clothing and possessions, the restrictions on privacy, the assignment of unpleasant tasks, the reduction of independence of movement and decision, the restriction of communication with the outside world, and the clearly designated inferior status to the staff and to those outside. Most of these experiences are the result of the system of authority and order, essential if all the personal needs of a large number of people are to be handled by a small staff in an economical way. Edgerton and Sabagh (1962), in applying Goffman's conceptions to the mental deficiency institution, suggest that the mortifications for the high-level defective may be fewer within the institution than in the outside environment, that certain *aggrandizements* of the self are available in the hospital. Such aggrandizements include the presence of clearly inferior low grades with whom they can compare themselves favorably, their far greater social success within the institution, the rewards they receive from personnel when they conform to institutional demands, and mutual support for face-saving rationales concerning their presence there. The analysis resembles the argument presented by Johnson and Kirk (1950) for special classes in the public schools for the retarded since these children are isolated and rejected in the regular classes. Both discussions are supported by the previously summarized data showing the consistent relationship between IQ and sociometric status both inside and outside the institution. The defective is likely to find himself in a more favorable social position when the mean IQ of fellow group members is sharply decreased.

The notion that the residential institution has many properties which make it particularly suitable for its inmates or patients has, of course, been presented before. Thus, Goffman points out that the mode of operation of the *total institution* is usually supported by an official rationale. As an example, note the following statement concerning institutions for the defective: "The steady routine, constant repetition, kindly discipline, and ordered group life which the institution provides are powerful forces in developing regular habits of the right kind" (Davies, 1959, p. 106). By changing the tone of the terms slightly, one could have: The inflexible routine, unending repetition, ever-present discipline, and lack of freedom and privacy which the institution demands are powerful forces in developing habits of the kind required for effective management of an impersonally oriented institution. While the choice of wording in the above statements is a problem of rhetoric and not the presentation of alternative testable theorems, there are empirical questions concerning institutions which the social psychologist may investigate, such as: (1) Whom does society place in institutions, and what factors determine such placement? (2) What are the special characteristics of those persons in the institution who most directly control and manipulate the defective's behavior? (3) What are the differential effects of institutional and noninstitutional environments upon the behavior of the defective?

Institutional populations. Examining a few recent studies should be sufficient to give some picture of the factors determining placement in institutions for the defective. Goldstein (1959) reports that the lower-grade younger group is comprising a growing proportion of the institutional population. Saenger (1960), while finding that intelligence level is a major determinant of commitment in New York City, also reports that the defective's coming from a broken home, having gotten into trouble (particularly sexual), coming from a family of low socioeconomic status, and having incompetent parents were also important determinants, especially among higher-level defectives. A study in California (Sabagh, Dingman, Tarjan, & Wright, 1959) and Hobbs's (1961) preliminary study in Tennessee also support the notion that such social factors are often critical. Taken together, the above findings seem to indicate that although there is a trend toward thinking of the institution as a place for the severely defective with multiple disabilities, many of the persons now in institutions are there because they cause problems in the community, whether the problem is deviation in ability, deviation in social behavior, or lack of guardianship. This implies that experiments using institutionalized defectives as subjects may be studying factors very different from intellectual deficit.

Attendants in institutions. Belknap (1956), in his study of a state mental hospital, indicates that ward attendants have the major responsibility for controlling the everyday life of the patients, although the importance of their role is not written into the formal therapeutic structure of the hospital. Gilbert and Levinson (1956) found that aides were very high in authoritarianism and were oriented toward custodial rather than humanistic or therapeutic treatment. Cleland and Peck (1959), studying differences between those attendants who stay and those who leave in a hospital for defectives, found those who remained to be more authoritarian. Quay et al. (1961), in their previously mentioned study of changes in attendant attitude, discuss the possibility that this authoritarian attitude might be the reason why their lectures were more effective than more democratic procedures such as discussion sessions. These studies suggest that attendants fit quite well the demands of the total institution as decribed by Goffman.

The effects of the institutional environment. There have been numerous research reports dealing with the deleterious effects of institutional life on normal infants, many of which have been summarized by Bowlby (1951) and Yarrow (1961). Recent studies with defectives include one by Lyle (1959) which reports superior language development among imbecile children reared in private homes as opposed to institutions and another report by Tizard (1960; Tizard & Lyle, 1961) which demonstrates a sharp improvement in verbal and social behavior of a group of children transferred to a nursery-school-type facility from a large institution when compared with a control group who remained. Another study (Dentler & Mackler, 1961a,b) examines changes in social behavior following institutionalization among a group of higher-level defectives. It was found that while brighter children were initially more popular, this popularity showed a sharp decline when a second sociometric measure was obtained a month later. While these findings may be interpreted in other terms, Dentler and Mackler believe the data suggest that in the long run socialization pressures in the institution may lead to a decline in level of intelligence, language ability, and social skills.

A series of experiments on the effectiveness of social reinforcement are relevant here. These studies ask whether social support results in a greater increment in performance for institutionalized feebleminded children than for other children. The underlying assumptions are that institutionalization results in social deprivation and that social deprivation leads to a higher motivation to seek social reinforcement. Zigler, Hodgden, and Stevenson (1958) found that institutionalized feebleminded subjects spent more time at a repetitive motor task under social support conditions (where verbal rewards such as "That's fine" were given) than under control conditions, whereas normal subjects did not respond differentially to social reinforcement and control conditions. However, later studies (Stevenson & Cruse, 1961; Stevenson & Fahel, 1961) have failed to substantiate these findings. While institutionalization influences the results in these studies, it is the non-institutionalized subjects who tend to respond more favorably to social reinforcement. An interesting finding has been that institutionalized subjects usually continue longer at repetitive tasks under all conditions. This might reflect the more general tendency of institutionalized subjects to accept instructions and unpleasant situations, a required adaptive mechanism in many institutions. In general, then, one wonders whether differential social deprivation or differential societal instruction is responsible for many of the findings.

Finally, a study by Abel (1941) showed that institutionalized defective adolescent girls tended more often to expect punishment to follow misdeeds than did the matched noninstitutionalized controls. This is consistent with Goffman's picture of the excessive control to be found in institutions.

The analyses in this section suggest a variety of modifications in the institutional setting. Some hypotheses concerning the effects of modifications include:

1. Decreasing the efficiency of institutional control by increasing the number of choices and errors open to the patient in his daily routine will improve his capabilities for independent performance in these everyday situations.

2. Training and selecting attendants to tolerate administrative disorganization and inefficiency but to expect the patients to independently solve their problems will result in superior performance on such tasks in the long run.

3. Modifying the size and organization of groups in institutions to approximate that of the family will increase the variety and number of interactions engaged in by the individual defective and the complexity of his behavior.

Such hypotheses could be tested on a small scale as Tizard (1953) and Tizard and Lyle (1961) have done. It should be recognized that the level of defect of the patient has not been specified. The decreased control and increased complexity and independence demanded of the patient in the above situations should always be relative to the present level of performance. If over a period of time, some increase in the behavioral complexity shown has occurred, a still greater freedom from control could be attempted.

THE FAMILY OF THE DEFECTIVE

The defective is born into the natural group called the family and, unless institutionalized, remains a member of that natural group until he dies. Among the questions raised by this fact are (1) what changes in the behavior and development of other family members result from the presence of a defective member, (2) what are the feelings of other family members toward the defective, and (3) how does the behavior of other family members influence the defective's behavior and development?

Effects on adjustment of family members; family crisis. One way of examining the influence of the defective on the family is to view the family as a unit which is operating at some state of equilibrium, a given level of adjustment, or some degree of adequacy, defined, perhaps, by the feelings of satisfaction of the individual family members with themselves and with one another. The recognition or presence of a defective member may then operate to alter the equilibrium or decrease the level of adjustment or adequacy. The family members may then take some actions to quickly restore the initial level of adjustment, or the readjustment may occur slowly or not at all. This sort of analysis of family reaction to the "crisis" has been applied to other disruptions by sociologists of the family (e.g., Hill, 1949). Farber (1959) has taken a somewhat different approach in evaluating the effects of the defective and has termed his adjustment variables *marital integration* and *sibling role tension*. Farber first developed a measure of marital integration which is based on (1) the favorableness of parents' descriptions of each other's personality attributes and (2) the extent to which husband and wife rank order certain family values similarly. The measure correlates with interviewers' judgments and the parents' own estimates of their satisfaction with the marriage (Farber, 1957). This measure was then administered, along with many other questions, to large samples of parents belonging to various associations for parents of the retarded. The published studies report the relationship between marital integration and such variables as sex and age of the defective child, religion of the parents, social status of the family, and whether or not the child was institutionalized (Farber, 1959, 1960; Farber, Jenne, & Toigo, 1960). The relationship between these variables and the reported adjustment of the other children in the family is also examined.

Among the difficulties with this sort of study is that the underlying notion implies a longitudinal study in which the family is observed over a period of time before the onset, during it, and over the long period of adjustment which follows. Farber (1959), for example, is interested in the way the presence of the defective upsets the normal marriage "careers" of the parents, i.e., the usual changing sequence of roles from parent of helpless infant to parent of independent adult. If one cannot examine the problem longitudinally, the alternative would seem to be comparisons with matched parents of normal children. Since Farber does not present these comparisons, it is difficult to interpret his findings in terms of the special problems caused by the presence of a defective child.

A smaller and less theoretically oriented study of family problems resulting from the presence of a retarded family member is presented by Tizard and Grad (1961). Among the interesting points made in the report are the importance of purely physical and situational problems and the diversity of adjustments which occur in a variety of situations.

Parent attitudes toward the defective child. Although there are many reports which discuss parental acceptance or rejection of their retarded child, they tend to be summaries of caseworkers' experiences and often are concerned with evaluating the adequacy of parents' feelings and actions. An alternative approach might be to specify the conditions which lead to varying attitudes toward the child. One theoretical framework which could apply here is Festinger's theory of cognitive dissonance (Festinger, 1957). One application of this theory (Festinger, 1961) hypothesizes that an object toward which an individual has taken instrumental steps, even if unmotivated at the time, will in itself take on value. The parent who works hard to care for her defective child may therefore come to value the child very much. Another approach might involve the concept of role. For example, Tizard and Grad (1961) suggest that in many families the defective takes on an important role which would normally be unfilled, such as companion for an elderly mother.

Empirical studies of parent attitudes include one by Fredericks (1957), who found that mentally retarded children were reacted to less favorably than were physically handicapped and nonhandicapped children when parents' attitudes were measured by Shoben's Parent Attitude Survey. Thurston (1959, 1960) has developed a sentence completion instrument for evaluating parent reactions to handicapped children. Worchel and Worchel (1961) had parents rate their retarded child, their other children, "most children," and the ideal child on 40 traits. The retarded child was judged less favorably than the ideal and their normal siblings, but there was little difference in mean judged favorableness between the retarded child and "most children." The studies by Saenger (1960) and Hobbs (1961) mentioned previously show little, if any, influence of parental attitudes toward the defective child upon whether or not the child was institutionalized.

Parent-child relationships. Related to the above sections are studies of child training practices. The measures used are usually derived from questionnaires administered to the parents. The most popular measures in this field seem to be Shoben's (1949) Parent Attitude Survey and the Parent Attitude Research Instrument (PARI) (Schaeffer & Bell, 1958).

In the study by Fredericks (1957), mentioned earlier, mothers of normal, physically handicapped, and mentally retarded children were matched on socioeconomic status and education. The greatest differences between groups were on the ignoring and dominating scales where the parents of retarded children scored less "favorably." Klebanoff (1957) compared 15 mothers of schizophrenics, 26 of normals, and a combined group of 15 mothers of brain-injured and retarded children, using the PARI scales. No differences were found between the two abnormal groups, but both differed from parents of normal children on overpossessiveness. This finding, if it is substantiated, is an important one since a great deal has been written recently about studies indicating differences between parents of schizophrenics and those of normals, and the emphasis has been on the parent-child relationship as a *determinant* of schizophrenia. This study implies that such parental differences are at least as much a reaction to the child's behavior as they are a determinant. Furthermore, it suggests that the empirical literature on parents of schizophrenics (e.g., Kohn & Clausen, 1956; Farina, 1960) might be highly applicable to parents of defectives.

Further research. The most appropriate research here would seem to require observations of parent-child interactions, using systematic time sampling and observational categories, as Bishop (1951) has done with normal children. Such research could answer the following questions: Do parents of defectives show more protective behavior than parents of normal children? Are defective children less responsive to their mothers' commands? This sort of research would be even more productive if the situation could be controlled and manipulated in such a way as to make certain interactive behaviors likely. For example, the situation could be so structured that the child's preferred activity and the parent's preferred activity conflict with one another. The empirical question would be whether the parent or child wins out more frequently where the child is defective versus where he is normal. Or, the question could be, does the parent of the defective child more often use physical controlling techniques, whereas the parent of the normal child more often uses verbal manipulations? Another situation might have the child doing a task which the parent knows he can complete but which takes him a seemingly endless period of time to do. Will the mother help the child? Will her assistance reduce or increase his interest in the task and his eventual competence at the task? How will these results differ from those obtained with normal children engaged in tasks difficult for them? Studies can, then, attempt to manipulate situational structure and more or less directly the behavior of either the parent or child. The resulting interaction can then be systematically observed and categorized and the findings compared with similar data collected with normal groups.

DEVELOPMENTAL SOCIAL PSYCHOLOGICAL APPROACHES

Certain studies of defectives have examined social behavior which had previously been shown to vary with chronological age among normal children. Capobianco and Cole (1960) investigated the play behavior of trainable and educable, institutionalized and noninstitutionalized children using observational categories developed by Parten (1932). Trainable children showed significantly more solitary play and less associative play than did the educables, and this difference between the two levels of defect in degree of social participation was different for institutionalized and noninstitutionalized groups and for male and female groups.

Abel (1941), using procedures similar to those of Piaget (1932), investigated the developmental level of children's conceptions of morality as a function of intelligence, rebelliousness, and institutionalization among adolescent defective girls. The more intelligent, rebellious, and less institutionalized, the more objective and less oriented toward punishment were their interpretations of events.

The studies of Lucito (1959) and Hottel (1960) mentioned previously are relevant here since their finding of increasing independence with increasing intelligence in social conformity situations is in agreement with previous findings of increasing independence with increasing chronological age.

NORMAL SOCIAL PSYCHOLOGICAL PHENOMENA INVESTIGATED AMONG DEFECTIVES

In many studies, authors are not concerned with distinguishing the peculiarities of defective behavior but instead attempt to demonstrate that the usual principles of social behavior operate or that special techniques have been devised to allow measurement of social behavior among defectives. Perhaps the earliest example of an application of a popular social psychological approach to a defective population is Abel's (1938) study of social facilitation, in which it was found that the brighter girls (IQ 70 to 79) improved more in performance on a pencil maze task when another girl was performing the task nearby than did the duller girls (IQ 50 to 59). Among normals it had been found that social facilitation decreased with increasing ability. Abel (1943) was later intrigued with certain patterns of dominance relationships in a population of institutionalized female defectives and developed a laboratory technique for measuring dominance. Albee and Pascal (1951) were interested in competitive behavior, and they devised a clever technique for measuring successful competitiveness among defectives. They related this measure to intelligence and popularity indices.

Tizard (1953) employed experimental manipulations similar to those of Lewin, Lippitt, and White (1939) in studying the relative effectiveness of critical, kindly, and indifferent supervision in a sheltered workshop situation. While there was little difference between critical and kindly leadership, the indifferent or laissez-faire atmosphere seemed to result in chaos and inefficiency.

In summary, it would seem that the importance of studies falling into this category lies primarily within content areas removed from the special problems of mental deficiency.

SUMMARY

A variety of theoretical approaches and empirical studies relevant to social psychologies of mental deficiency have been discussed in this chapter. The various sections will be briefly summarized by presenting some of the hypotheses (not findings) and viewpoints which they suggest.

1. In a normal group, the defective is likely to be seen as deviant in ability. The effect of this may be that other group members stop comparing themselves with him and may stop associating with him. Another effect is the greater dependence of the defective upon the competence of others when the situation is skill-oriented. The reactions of and toward the deviate will probably be determined by the visibility and extent of his deviation, the value he places on group membership, and the relevance of his deviation to group values.

2. The behavior of persons interacting with defectives may be seen as a function of their expectations concerning the defective's behavior and the actual behavior shown by the defective in that situation. If many persons have similar expectations (role concepts) concerning the defective's behavior, interactive behavior may be well predicted or explained using the concept of complementary roles. The behavior of the defective, in turn, may be determined to some extent by consistent expectations and behavior on the part of others; i.e., much of the defective's behavior may be fruitfully seen as role performance.

3. Popular attitudes and stereotypes may to some extent influence the way the individual defective is evaluated by others. There is considerable agreement among persons on the subnormal and inadequate attributes of imagined institutionalized defectives, and the labeling of persons as defective does seem to increase judged subnormality if the person judged is not unambiguously normal.

4. Observed defectives present variable cues in respect to their defect. When these cues are minimal, labeling the defective as such seems to have little effect on judgments of subnormality. Furthermore, even when the cues are obvious, their effect may be made minimal by the use of alternative labels, such as "speech defect." The implication is that there is a considerable resistance to judging a person as subnormal.

5. The residential institution seems to function primarily as an efficient custodial apparatus with little attention to the normal social and personality needs of the patients. Institutionalization is frequently a result of social misbehavior, attendants tend to be autocratically oriented, and early residence in large institutions seems to result in language and social deficits.

6. The presence of a defective in the family may lead to disruption in family relationships, unfavorable attitudes toward the defective member, and modifications in the parents' child-rearing practices.

7. Many differences in social behavior between normals and defectives are similar to differences between older and younger children.

8. Many social psychological phenomena observable and measurable among normals may also be studied and found among defectives.

None of the above statements are intended as facts, i.e., descriptions of reliably obtained findings. They are approaches and hypotheses which it is hoped will stimulate further thinking and research. Hopefully, future reviews of the social psychology of mental deficiency will have available a large body of empirical data to put flesh on this skeleton of theory, orientation, and preliminary findings.

REFERENCES

ABEL, THEODORA M. The influence of social facilitation on motor performance at different levels of intelligence. *Amer. J. Psychol.,* 1938, 51, 379–389.

ABEL, THEODORA M. Moral judgments among subnormals. *J. abnorm. soc. Psychol.,* 1941, 36, 378–392.

ABEL, THEODORA M. Dominant behavior of institutionalized subnormal Negro girls: an experimental study. *Amer. J. ment. Defic.,* 1943, 47, 429–436·

ALBEE, G. W., & PASCAL, G. R. A study of competitive behavior in mental defectives. *Amer. J. ment. Defic.,* 1951, 55, 576–581.

BARTLETT, C. J., QUAY, LORENE C., & WRIGHTSMAN, L. S., JR. A comparison of two methods of attitude measurement: Likert-type and forced-choice. *Educ. psychol. Measmt.,* 1960, 20, 699–704.

BELKNAP, I. *Human problems of a state mental hospital.* New York: McGraw-Hill, 1956.

BISHOP, BARBARA M. Mother-child interaction and the social behavior of children. *Psychol. Monogr.,* 1951, 65, No. 11 (Whole No. 328).

BOWLBY, J. *Maternal care and child health.* Geneva: World Health Organization, 1951.

CAPOBIANCO, R. J., & COLE, DOROTHY A. Social behavior of mentally retarded children. *Amer. J. ment. Defic.,* 1960, 64, 638–651.

CLAMPITT, R. R., & CHARLES, D. C. Sociometric status and supervisory evaluation of institutionalized mentally deficient children. *J. soc. Psychol.,* 1956, 44, 223–231.

CLELAND, C. C., & CHAMBERS, W. R. Experimental modification of attitudes as a function of an institutional tour. *Amer. J. ment. Defic.,* 1959, 64, 124–130.

CLELAND, C. C., & COCHRAN, IRENE L. The effect of institutional tours on attitudes of high school seniors. *Amer. J. ment. Defic.,* 1961, 65, 473–481.

CLELAND, C. C., & PECK, R. F. Psychological determinants of tenure in institutional personnel. *Amer. J. ment. Defic.,* 1959, 63, 876–888.

CLINE, V. B., & RICHARDS, J. M., JR. Accuracy of interpersonal perception—a general trait? *J. abnorm. soc. Psychol.,* 1960, 60, 1–7.

DAVIES, S. P. *The mentally retarded in society.* New York: Columbia, 1959.

DENTLER, R. A., & ERIKSON, K. The functions of deviance in groups. *Soc. Prob.*, 1959, 7, 98–107.

DENTLER, R. A., & MACKLER, B. The socialization of institutional retarded children. *J. Hlth. Human Behav.*, 1961, 2(4), 243–252. (a)

DENTLER, R. A., & MACKLER, B. Effects on sociometric status of institutional pressure to adjust among retarded children. Unpublished manuscript, Bureau of Child Research, Univer. of Kansas, 1961. (b)

DENTLER, R. A., & MACKLER, B. Ability and sociometric status among normal and retarded children: a review of the literature. *Psychol. Bull.*, 1962, 59, 273–283.

DEXTER, L. A. Towards a sociology of the mentally defective. *Amer. J. ment. Defic.*, 1956, 61, 10–16.

DEXTER, L. A. A social theory of mental deficiency. *Amer. J. ment. Defic.*, 1958, 62, 920–928.

DEXTER, L. A. Research on problems of mental subnormality. *Amer. J. ment. Defic.*, 1960, 64, 834–838.

DONALDSON, H. C. Industrial attitudes toward the placement of mentally deficient workers as functions of experience and stereotypes. Unpublished Master's thesis, Vanderbilt Univer., Nashville, Tenn., 1959.

EDGERTON, R. B., & SABAGH, G. From mortification to aggrandizement: changing self-conception in the careers of the mentally retarded. *Psychiat.*, 1962, 25, 263–272.

FARBER, B. An index of marital integration. *Sociometry*, 1957, 20, 117–134.

FARBER, B. Effects of a severely mentally retarded child on family integration. *Monogr. Soc. Res. Child Develpm.*, 1959, 24, No. 2.

FARBER, B. Family organization and crisis: maintenance of integration in families with a severely mentally retarded child. *Monogr. Soc. Res. Child Develpm.*, 1960, 25, No. 1.

FARBER, B., JENNE, W. C., & TOIGO, R. Family crisis and the decision to institutionalize the retarded child. *Res. Monogr. Counc. except. Child.*, 1960, No. 1, (Series A).

FARINA, A. Patterns of role dominance and conflict in parents of schizophrenic patients. *J. abnorm. soc. Psychol.*, 1960, 61, 31–38.

FESTINGER, L. Informal social communication. *Psychol. Rev.*, 1950, 57, 271–282.

FESTINGER, L. A theory of social comparison processes. *Human Relat.*, 1954, 7, 117–140.

FESTINGER, L. *A theory of cognitive dissonance.* New York: Harper & Row, 1957.

FESTINGER, L. The psychological effects of insufficient rewards. *Amer. Psychol.*, 1961, 16, 1–11.

FREDERICKS, MARILEE U. A comparative study of expressed parent attitudes: mothers of mentally retarded and orthopedically handicapped vs. mothers of non-handicapped children. Unpublished doctoral dissertation, Univer. of Oregon, 1957.

GILBERT, DORIS C., & LEVINSON, D. Ideology, personality, and institutional policy in the mental hospital. *J. abnorm. soc. Psychol.*, 1956, 53, 263–271.

GOFFMAN, E. On the characteristics of total institutions. In *Symp. on preventive and social psychiatry.* Washington, D.C.: U.S. Govt. Printing Office, 1957.

GOLDSTEIN, H. Population trends in U.S. public institutions for the mentally deficient. *Amer. J. ment. Defic.*, 1959, 63, 599–604.

GREENBLATT, M., LEVINSON, D. J., & WILLIAMS, R. H. (Eds.). *The patient and the mental hospital.* New York: Free Press, 1957.

GUSKIN, S. L. The measurement of social stereotypes. Unpublished doctoral dissertation, Univer. of N.C., 1958.

GUSKIN, S. L. The perception of subnormality in mentally defective children. *Amer. J. ment. Defic.*, 1962, 67, 53–60.

HAYS, W. Mental level and friend selection among institutionalized defective girls. *Amer. J. ment. Defic.*, 1951, 56, 198–203.

HELSON, H. Adaptation level as frame of reference for predictions of psychophysical data. *Amer. J. Psychol.*, 1947, 60, 1–29.

HILL, R. *Families under stress.* New York: Harper, 1949.

HOBBS, MARY T. Differences between institutionalized and non-institutionalized mentally retarded subjects. Unpublished research report. George Peabody College for Teachers, 1961.

HOTTEL, J. V. The influence of age and intelligence on independence-conformity behavior of children. Unpublished doctoral dissertation, George Peabody College for Teachers, 1960.

JOHNSON, G. O. A study of the social position of mentally handicapped children in the regular grades. *Amer. J. ment. Defic.*, 1950, 55, 60–89.

JOHNSON, G. O., & KIRK, S. A. Are mentally handicapped children segregated in the regular grades? *J. except. Child.*, 1950, 17, 65–68.

KELLEY, H. H. The warm-cold variable in first impressions of persons. *J. Pers.*, 1950, 18, 431–439.

KLEBANOFF, L. B. Attitudes of mothers of schizophrenics, brain-injured and retarded, and normal children. Unpublished doctoral dissertation, Boston Univer., 1957.

KOHN, M. L., & CLAUSEN, J. A. Parental authority behavior and schizophrenia. *Amer. J. Orthopsychiat.*, 1956, 26, 297–313.

LEWIN, K., LIPPITT, R., & WHITE, R. K. Patterns of aggressive behavior in experimentally created social climates. *J. soc. Psychol.*, 1939, 10, 271–299.

LUCITO, L. J. A comparison of independence-conformity behavior of intellectually bright and dull children. Unpublished doctoral dissertation, Univer. of Ill., 1959.

LYLE, J. G. The effect of an institution environment upon the verbal development of imbecile children. 1. Verbal intelligence. *J. ment. defic. Res.*, 1959, 3, 122–128.

MCDANIEL, J. Group action in the rehabilitation of the mentally retarded. *Group Psychother.*, 1960, 13, 5–14.

MAHONEY, S. C., & PANGRAC, I. Misconceptions of college students about mental deficiency. *Amer. J. ment. Defic.*, 1960, 64, 671–678.

MARDEN, P., & FARBER, B. High-brow versus low-grade status among institutionalized mentally retarded boys. *Soc. prob.*, 1961, 8, No. 4.

MILLER, R. V. Social status and socioempathic differences among mentally superior, mentally typical, and mentally retarded children. *Except. Child.*, 1956, 23, 114–119.

PARSONS, T., & FOX, RENEE. Illness, therapy, and the modern urban American family. *J. soc. Issues*, 1952, 8, No. 4, 31–43.

PARTEN, M. B. Social participation among pre-school children. *J. abnorm. soc. Psychol.*, 1932, 27, 243–269.

PERRY, S. E. Some theoretical problems of mental deficiency and their action implications. *Psychiatry*, 1954, 17, 45–73.

PIAGET, J. *The moral judgment of the child.* New York: Harcourt, Brace, 1932.

QUAY, LORENE C., BARTLETT, C. J., WRIGHTSMAN, L. S., JR., & CATRON, D. Attitude change in attendant employees. *J. soc. Psychol.*, 1961, 55, 27–31.

REYNOLDS, M. C. The social psychology of exceptional children. III. In terms of the interaction of exceptional children with other persons. *Except. Child.*, 1960, 26, 243–247.

ROSENBERG, S. Interpersonal processes in the perpetuation and reduction of language retardation: some speculations and some data. Paper read at Amer. Ass. ment. Defic., Milwaukee, May, 1959.

ROSENBERG, S., SPRADLIN, J. E., & MABEL, S. Interaction among retarded children as a function of their relative language skills. *J. abnorm. soc. Psychol.*, 1961, 63, 402–410.

SABAGH, G., DINGMAN, H. F., TARJAN, G., & WRIGHT, S. W. Social class and ethnic status of patients admitted to a state hospital for the retarded. *Pacif. Sociol. Rev.*, 1959, 2, 76–80.

SAENGER, G. *Factors influencing the institutionalization of mentally retarded individuals in New York City.* Albany: New York State Interdepartmental Health Resources Board, January, 1960.

SCHAEFFER, E. S., & BELL, R. Q. Development of a parental attitude research instrument. *Child Develpm.*, 1958, 29, 339–361.

SHOBEN, E. J. The assessment of parental attitudes in relation to child adjustment. *Genet. Psychol. Monogr.*, 1949, 39, 101–148.

SPRADLIN, J. E., & ROSENBERG, S. Complexity of adult verbal behavior in a dyadic situation with retarded children. Working paper No. 18, Parsons Research Project, Bureau of Child Research, Univer. of Kansas, November, 1959.

STANTON, A., & SCHWARTZ, M. *The mental hospital.* New York: Basic Books, 1954.

STEVENSON, H. W., & CRUSE, D. B. The effectiveness of social reinforcement with normal and feebleminded children. *J. Pers.*, 1961, 29, 124–125.

STEVENSON, H. W., & FAHEL, LELIA S. The effect of social reinforcement on the performance of institutionalized and noninstitutionalized normal and feebleminded children. *J. Pers.*, 1961, 29, 136–147.

SUTHERLAND, J. S., BUTLER, A. J., GIBSON, D., & GRAHAM, D. M. A sociometric study of institutionalized mental defectives. *Amer. J. ment. Defic.*, 1954, 59, 266–271.

THURSTON, J. R. A procedure for evaluating parental attitudes towards the handicapped. *Amer. J. ment. Defic.*, 1959, 64, 148–155.

THURSTON, J. R. Attitudes and emotional reactions of parents of institutionalized cerebral palsied retarded patients. *Amer. J. ment. Defic.*, 1960, 65, 227–235.

TIZARD, J. The effects of different types of supervision on the behavior of mental defectives in a sheltered workshop. *Amer. J. ment. Defic.*, 1953, 58, 143–161.

TIZARD, J. Residential care of mentally handicapped children. *Brit. Med. J.*, 1960, 1, 1041–1046.

TIZARD, J., & GRAD, JACQUELINE C. *The mentally handicapped and their families.* (Maudsley Monogr. No. 7) London: Oxford, 1961.

TIZARD, J., & LYLE, J. *The Brooklands study of residential care for mentally handicapped children.* London: Maudsley Hospital, 1961.

TURNER, MILDRED W. A comparison of the social status of mentally retarded children enrolled in special classes. Unpublished doctoral dissertation, Univer. Indiana, 1958.

WINTHROP, H., & TAYLOR, H. An inquiry concerning the prevalence of popular misconceptions relating to mental deficiency. *Amer. J. ment. Defic.*, 1957, 62, 344–348.

WORCHEL, TILLIE L., & WORCHEL, P. The parental concept of the mentally retarded child. *Amer. J. ment. Defic.*, 1961, 65, 782–788.

YARROW, L. J. Maternal deprivation: toward an empirical and conceptual reevaluation. *Psychol. Bull.*, 1961, 58, 459–490.

ZIGLER, E. F., HODGDEN, L., & STEVENSON, H. W. The effect of support on the performance of normal and feebleminded children. *J. Pers.*, 1958, 26, 106–122.

10

PSYCHOLOGICAL STUDIES
OF MENTAL DEFICIENCY
IN THE SOVIET UNION

A. R. Luria

The two papers which follow these introductory notes represent some theoretical and experimental approaches to mental deficiency which are the basis of a series of works of Soviet psychologists and neurologists.

The idea of the dynamic approach to the study of feebleminded children and the application of some qualitative experimental methods for the investigation of this very complicated group is the basic idea of all Soviet psychologists engaged in this field. It was the late professor L. S. Vygotsky, the founder of the scientific study of the defective child in the U.S.S.R., who introduced this approach and whose ideas are still the leading ones in Soviet neuropsychological studies.

Dynamic Approach to the Mental Development
of the Abnormal Child[1]

I

Child psychiatry, just as the science which is engaged in the education of abnormal children, is now confronted with a fundamental task; it must learn to *qualify the basic defect* and still more to approximate to the analysis of *its underlying mechanisms*.

Any more or less marked advance in the accomplishment of this task will enable us to diagnose the defect with much greater exactitude, to

[1] Reprinted from *Journal of Mental Deficiency Research,* Volume 2, Part 2, December, 1958. (Received June 18, 1958.)

discern between externally similar but in essence profoundly different states, to place the therapy of these diseases on a scientific basis, and finally to find proper methods and ways for corrective training and education of abnormal children.

There is no doubt that child psychiatry, like special pedagogics dealing with abnormal children, both being very young branches of science, has attained notable successes during the last decades.

Considerable headway has been made in the clinical description of certain forms of anomalous development; one of the indisputable achievements of modern psychiatry is its special study of such forms as primary mental deficiency, anomalies in development resulting from traumas, inflammatory processes, or other retarding factors, as well as anomalies connected with partial defects (local lesions of the brain). Another achievement is the now widespread description of cases of anomalous mental development connected with reactions of the child to complex life situations; the valuable contribution to the study of this problem made by a number of scientists engaged in dynamic psychology and psychosomatics is beyond doubt.

However, it is quite clear that many fundamental problems of child psychiatry still remain unsolved and that the future decisive successes of this young branch of science will be connected with the analysis of *the causes which are responsible for the emergence of this or another form of anomalous development, as well as with the study of the underlying initial defect.*

There is no need to trace here the entire intricate course of anomalous development formed under the influence of mental conflicts and difficult situations (in recent years these facts have already been repeatedly discussed in European and American literature); here we shall dwell on the analysis of *some forms of anomalous development arising as a result of organic disturbances in the activity of the central or peripheral nervous apparatus.* In this field Soviet researchers (physicians and psychologists) have applied some special methods and attained certain results which clarify the nature of anomalous development and its neurophysiological mechanisms.

In the present communications we shall dwell on two fundamental problems. We shall try first to show the extensive systemic consequences which may be called forth by particular defects arising at early stages of the child's development; then we shall try to show that the study of the neurodynamic mechanisms which characterize various forms of anomalous development may furnish essential material to the researcher.

II

In the theory of the abnormal child there often still persist erroneous conceptions which lag far behind the level of modern scientific knowledge and greatly hamper the practical work of educating abnormal children. These conceptions consist in a naïve, extremely simplified *symptomatic approach* to the defect exhibited by the child; they disregard the complexity of the child's mental development and stop the genuinely scientific analysis of the symptoms just when such analysis should be started; this often leads to errors which impede the proper comprehension of the causes of anomalous development and do not allow us to find adequate ways for its correction.

The narrow-mindedness of the naïve symptomatic approach is equally manifested in the analysis of general disturbances observed in the child's development and in the interpretation of its particular defects.

When describing backward school children or children with considerably retarded mental development, many psychologists and teachers up to now have drawn the flat conclusion that such cases of subnormal development, or "dullness," are always accounted for by inborn mental deficiency, often by a hereditary deterioration of "mental abilities," and that the derangement of "general ability" (in the terminology of the British authors), which is observed in these cases, is of a primary and irreversible character. On the other hand, when describing particular defects often observed in children, such as derangements in writing, reading, and arithmetical operations, or defects in the child's character, psychologists and psychiatrists not infrequently confine themselves to the statement that these defects are due to the underdevelopment of "special abilities," and refer to such phenomena of particular disturbances as *dyslexia* and *dysgraphia,* but do not attempt to disclose the very essence of these disturbances and to trace the considerably more extensive consequences which they may entail.

This naïve symptomatic approach, which is, unfortunately, not uncommon in the analysis of the abnormal child, lags far behind both the conceptions of modern psychology and the views firmly established in the neurological and psychiatric clinic.

Already more than a quarter of a century ago the outstanding Russian psychologist L. S. Vygotsky expressed the idea that the principal mental functions, such as complex perception or intelligent memorization, voluntary attention or logical thinking, do not represent inborn properties of personality. By a series of important observations and experiments, subsequently carried on by his collaborators and pupils, he showed that all these complex processes are formed in the course of the child's development and that they are accounted for by the methods and means of organization of activity which arise and are adopted by the child in the course of its manipulations with real objects and in its intercourse with adults, rather than by inborn capacities (which are, of course, of great importance as well).

The mother shows the child a cup and pointing to it says: "This is a cup." With the help of this gesture and these words she singles out the given object from other objects, renders this stimulus more powerful and essential, and attaches to it, according to our terminology, a new "signaling sense." Then the child begins to reproduce the mother's gesture and to repeat the same word; thus it organizes its own perception. Such perceptive processes are formed in the child in a social way: intelligent perception and voluntary attention result from the intercourse of the child; the function which was previously divided between two persons gradually turns into an internal psychological method of organization of the child's own activity.

Subsequent investigations carried out by A. N. Leontiev, A. V. Zaporozhetz, and P. Y. Galperin, of Moscow University, show that other mental processes, like active memorization, voluntary action, and abstract thinking, are formed in a similar way.

What for many decades have been regarded as inborn properties of the human mind, or as inborn "abilities," actually pass through a long process of formation. As shown by the above-mentioned investigations, such faculties as active memorization or logical thinking are derived from the extensive material activity which is adopted by the child in the process of its intercourse; later this activity gradually diminishes, becomes curtailed, relies more and more on external and internal speech, and finally turns into these mental functions which seem so simple, but in reality have their own long and intricate story of development. Also similar is the course of development of those faculties which were usually considered manifestations of inborn "special gifts," such as a good ear for music. *What were erroneously regarded in psychology as inborn and elementary "properties" of the mind actually represent complex functional systems* formed during the long process of the child's development; therefore we should commit a great mistake if we overlooked this, if we naïvely assumed that active attention and insight are inborn properties of the child's mind which can be interpreted as direct manifestations of natural general ability.

There is no doubt that many natural inclinations constitute a very important prerequisite for the development of these complex systemic functions, and when they become deranged, the entire further development of the child assumes an abnormal character. However, it would be the height of carelessness to ignore this entire course of development, to disregard the highly complicated methods and means with the help of which the child, during its intercourse with adults, forms its complex system of functions, and to interpret any retardation of mental development or any defects in behavior as a direct manifestation of innate dullness, or of an inborn deficiency of abstract thinking. Such assertions would hardly differ much from the judgments of Molière's physician who felt that the soporific action of opium was a result of its inherent "soporific force" and explained derangements in speech by saying that the patient's tongue did not move properly.

It is quite natural that this concept of the nature of complex mental abilities, regarded by us as a result of intricate development, impels us radically to change our attitude toward anomalous development in children and toward the tasks which confront us in the diagnosis of children with these or other forms of mental anomalies.

The peculiar features of abnormal children are no longer interpreted as direct manifestations of some general deficiency; they are regarded as a result of complex and anomalous development, accounted for by the fact that a definite link indispensable to the normal development of mental activity becomes deranged owing to an early (more often intrauterine) disease and sometimes to an inborn defect. This deranged or defective link which is responsible for the anomalous development of the child may relate to various stages of its formation and be highly diverse in nature. In some cases it is the elementary nervous processes which constitute this defective link; the disorganization of the force, equilibrium, and mobility of these nervous processes may from the very onset greatly impede the further development of the activity of the child. In other cases this defective link, hindering the further mental development of the child, is formed by a certain defect in a particular mental function, for example, in the visual or auditory analysis of the signals perceived; in these cases a particular defect may entail considerable systemic consequences and markedly retard the general mental development of the child. Finally, in still other cases a retardation of the development of cognitive processes and of the higher psychological systems may be caused by defects in the intercourse of the child with adults, as well as by defects in training. Indeed, the formation of complex mental activity always requires strict consistency and a succession of individual operations; sometimes, if only a single link of training is missed, if a certain stage in the development of the necessary operation is not properly worked out, the entire process of further development becomes retarded, and the formation of higher mental functions assumes an abnormal character.

It is quite clear that such an approach to abnormal childhood complicates, and at the same time enriches, the course of clinical and psychophysiological analysis of the child. In the place of the naïve symptomatological approach, which unjustifiably ascribes intellectual defects to the underdevelopment of certain "primary abilities," a new approach arises and takes definite shape; it consists in the qualification of symptoms, that is, in a more precise ascertainment of the structure of the defect under observation and in the analysis of the various causes which are responsible for the retardation and distortion of the mental development of the child.

About thirty years ago Kurt Goldstein expressed the idea that in any analysis of a syndrome it is, above all, necessary to disclose the *basic disturbance* which entails a number of *secondary symptoms* arising from it and which requires no special explanation. This proposition remains true also for the analysis of any abnormal child, being even more complicated on account of the systemic development of mental processes. Any researcher who does not confine his research to a mere ascertainment of the defect in the abnormal child must always attempt to reveal the basic, primary disturbance and deduce from it the secondary systemic consequences which, in the course of the mental development of the child, may assume quite an extensive character.

A researcher proceeding from such a causal-dynamic approach must be ready to face the fact that serious, sometimes fundamental, changes in development may be called forth by disturbances of very particular and seemingly insignificant functions, if these particular functions are of great importance for the further formation of the complex mental activity of the child. *The effect produced by an early disturbance of a certain function depends primarily on the role played by this function in the general mental development of the child,* as well as on *the period of development during which the given disturbance occurred.* Therefore, as stated by L. S. Vygotsky, one and the same localization of a lesion may evoke quite different consequences, depending on whether the lesion occurred in early childhood or at a mature age. In the first case, along with the derangement of a particular function (for example, hearing) there takes place a derangement of a whole system of functions created on its basis. In the second case, when the formation of all these complex processes has already been fully completed, this primary disturbance may remain a particular defect which is more or less easily compensated by the already developed speech and intellect of the adult. In all cases only such causal-dynamic analysis, which thoroughly considers the structure of the syndrome and discloses its basic source, can comply with the principal task—and overstep the limits of formal description of the defect to impart to the diagnostics of anomalous development a truly scientific character.

This genetic and systemic analysis of defects in abnormal children may contribute to the proper solution of the problem concerning the nature of the anomaly under observation and the correlation between particular and general disturbances; it may facilitate the highly complicated task of the differential diagnosis of various externally similar, but in essence profoundly different, disturbances. Finally, it may help the physician correctly to formulate the prognosis of the given disturbance and, what is most important, to find proper methods of therapy as well as appropriate corrective pedagogical methods which prove to differ considerably, depending on the nature of the anomalous development of the child.

Thus, our task can be quite clearly formulated. When approximating to the clinical and psychophysiological analysis of the abnormal child, we must put before ourselves the following question: *What is the nature of the psychophysiological structure of the defect,* and *precisely what constitutes the basic (sometimes inconsiderable by itself) disturbance* arising even at the earliest stages of development? On the other hand, we must realize *how this disturbance influenced the further mental development of the child,* what its effect was on the formation of mental processes conditioned by it.

It is quite natural that the above-mentioned task should render the clinical investigation of the abnormal child much more complicated; it requires decisive renunciation of the simplified descriptive symptomatological approach which disregards the many-sided development of the child; it presupposes the application of special, sometimes experimental, psychological and physiological methods of investigation which disclose the nature of the basic defect and of its systemic consequences. But will not this new approach be of benefit to the accomplishment of our principal humane task—to reveal the essence of anomalous development and to find adequate means of compensating the defect?

III

We shall begin our analysis of systemic anomalies of development with cases in which a relatively insignificant defect causes considerable changes in the entire mental development; only then shall we pass to those various forms where the anomalous development of the child is due to causes which bear a more general character and require special physiological investigation.

Let us first dwell on *defective hearing;* owing to the frequency of this defect, the analysis of its influence on the general mental development of the child may present considerable interest.

Defective hearing, in its grave and mild forms, is well known to otologists and teachers of ordinary schools; the specific nature of this defect is beyond any doubt.

However, two facts arrest our attention at once: they are connected with the peculiarities of general intellectual development as well as development of speech in children with defective hearing.

Statistical data collected by Sir Cyril Burt and relating to British children show that whereas in ordinary schools the number of children with severe defects of hearing does not exceed 1 per cent and the number of children with slight defects of hearing amounts to 4 per cent, in schools for mentally backward children the respective figures are 6 per cent and 18 per cent.[2] This means that almost one-quarter of all the children who cannot attend ordinary schools and are compelled to enter schools for backward children suffer from these or other defects of hearing.

The second fact relates to the development of speech in children with defective hearing. Experience shows that if this defect arises at a mature age, in practice it does not lead to any gross derangements of speech; but as shown by investigations carried out at the Moscow Institute of Defectology, even a relatively inconsiderable derangement of hearing, even a decline in its intensity by 20 to 25 decibels, if it occurs at a very early stage of development, is almost invariably accompanied by a serious defect of speech.

How should the two facts be interpreted? Do they mean that each of these phenomena has its own particular cause and that while in the first group of children, the defect of hearing is accompanied by organic mental deficiency, in the second group, along with the derangement of hearing, there are additional defects of speech of the aphasic or alalic type caused by the presence of a special local lesion in the cerebral cortex? If this supposition is correct, then it is quite reasonable that children of the first group should attend schools for the feebleminded and that children of the second group should be treated as those who suffer from residual phenomena of severe cerebral lesions.

However, such a conclusion, which is typical of the simplified symptomatological approach, is profoundly wrong.

Thorough observations carried out by a number of Soviet psychologists, physicians, and teachers (R. M. Boskis, T. A. Vlasova, L. V. Nieman, and others) have shown that derangements of speech and retardation of intellectual development in children suffering from defects of hearing since early childhood are *inevitable systemic consequences of the auditory defect* and need not be explained by any other additional causes.

It is a well-known fact that the development of speech, as well as of intellectual activity, takes place in the child in the process of its intercourse with the adult: the child first accumulates a rather extensive "passive" vocabulary and only then begins to speak, adjusting its speech to the system of phonemes and of their combinations adopted from the adult. Active

[2] C. Burt. *The Backward Child*. London, 1951.

articulations are formed by the child on the basis of differentiated perception of the speech of others or, using physiological terminology, are afferented by the child's auditory perception. A habitual conversation seldom proceeds at high intensities of sound; the intensity of sound is particularly low in the articulation of certain unaccented vowels, as well as suffixes and inflexions which are often pronounced very faintly or almost omitted.

In order to be able clearly to perceive oral speech and to form the necessary system of language, the child must, naturally, possess a keen, irreproachable ear. Therefore, a relatively slight deterioration of the sense of hearing, which in the adult is easily compensated by his guessing, owing to his good knowledge of the language, and which thus remains practically imperceptible, proves to be fatal to speech formation if it occurs in early childhood. In this case the child perceives only insufficiently differentiated sounds which do not group into distinct systems of phonemes; the child does not discern the phonetic cues (sometimes very delicate), which are of signaling importance; the words which the child does perceive prove to be greatly distorted and inarticulate; words having a like phonetic contour (for example, "whiskers" and "whispers") are mixed up; thus, the necessary system of language is not assimilated.

Early disturbances of hearing entail one more consequence: the deranged formation of a strictly differentiated phonemic system inevitably causes a retardation in the development of active articulated speech. Not being afferented by this distinct auditory system, the child's own speech may for a long time remain at the level of babbling, or it assumes an inarticulate character which is a natural consequence of the hearing defect, and the explanation of which should not be sought for in any additional local lesion affecting the speech areas of the cerebral cortex. In this case *a relatively inconsiderable, purely peripheral defect leads to extensive functional consequences.*

The secondary disturbance evoked by defective hearing is not confined to external defects of speech but manifests a number of additional symptoms.

A thorough study of the mental development of children with hearing defects has been carried out for a number of years in special schools created for such children in the Soviet Union. This study has shown that in the course of training a considerable majority of such children exhibit distinct phenomena of *agrammatism* and that special efforts are required to overcome it. For a considerable length of time these children confuse the case inflexions, omit the prefixes and suffixes, and reveal, in their speech, elements of the "telegraphic style" which is so familiar to researchers dealing with the clinic of motor aphasias.

However, it would be erroneous to ascribe such agrammatism of these children to any additional factors or, as was often the practice, to interpret these cases as a combined manifestation of hearing defects and motor (or sensory) aphasia. The impossibility of clearly discerning all the phonetic elements of speech, which particularly manifests itself in the impeded perception of indistinctly articulated suffixes and inflexions, hinders the mastery of the grammatical system of the language and at the same time makes it difficult to learn the abstract meanings expressed in the linguistic combinations of words. This is why a child with hearing defects for a long time exhibits phenomena of aggrammatism and has great difficulties in mastering the categories of quality, number, tense, and passage of the action to an object, which in inflected languages (such as Russian and German) are expressed by special grammatical forms.

Thus, from a primary, limited defect, which, however, hampers the normal intercourse of the child and thereby retards its normal development, there arise distinct secondary consequences; as a result, a child suffering from an inconsiderable and purely peripheral defect begins to show a highly peculiar, anomalous development which leads both to a retardation of speech and to substantial disturbances in intellectual activity.

However, to confuse such a child with an aphasic or with a real feeble-minded, oligophrenic child and to place it in a clinic or school for the feebleminded would be to commit a fatal mistake. Secondary defects arising in such a child prove to be quite surmountable, but this requires a number of specially organized measures. To eliminate the defect of the child it is not sufficient to seat the child in the front row of desks or to supply it with a sound-intensifying device; it is necessary to work out a special system of corrective training which must be based on conscious learning of those grammatical forms of the language which normal children have practically mastered before they enter school. Such systematic corrective influence on the secondary defects must have the attention of the teacher and physician; precisely this system of corrective measures directed against the systemic consequences of the primary defect, rather than against the defect itself, can fully restore the normal thinking and speech of the child.

This is why special schools for children with defective hearing have been established in the Soviet Union; the system of training in these schools is aimed at conscious learning of the grammatical system of the language as well as of the system of notions which is connected with it. And this is why the fundamental pedagogical principle—to act upon the systemic consequence produced by the primary defect rather than upon the defect itself (which yields to influences with difficulty)—proves its value in the practice of work with these children.

IV

Up to now we have dealt with cases clearly showing that a relatively inconsiderable, particular defect may evoke essential changes in the general mental development of the child, which often gives grounds for erroneously regarding them as inborn deficiencies of mental development.

Now we should like to approach the same question from the opposite direction and to dwell on cases in which the causal-genetic analysis of mechanisms responsible for the given defect may help to explain the nature of the obscure defect and to determine proper methods for its compensation.

In school practice, children are frequently encountered who have keen vision and hearing and who make relatively good progress in other disciplines, but who exhibit great difficulties in mastering *writing* and *reading*. They make dozens of incomprehensible mistakes in dictation so that their writing is often deciphered with great difficulty. Usually these children give no cause for regarding them as mentally backward, and teachers and psychologists used to refer to their difficulties as an underdevelopment of the special ability for writing and reading or to defects of a "special factor" which was designated by different letters (*s*, special, or *p*, partial) but whose nature remained to a considerable degree obscure.

However, these cases of dysgraphia or dyslexia prove to be particularly accessible to analysis if we interpret them as secondary, systemic disorders and are able to break them down into component elements so as to disclose the underlying primary defect; of great importance is the fact that if this is done these cases will likewise become accessible to corrective training.

What is, then, the cause of this disturbance which, at first sight, seems so astonishing? To answer this question it is necessary, first of all, to understand the psychophysiological structure of the process of writing (of reading) and to know precisely in which of its links this process may become deranged; otherwise, we shall be unable to analyze it and shall be compelled to explain the phenomena of dysgraphia and dyslexia in a tautological way as the "underdevelopment of the ability for writing or reading."

In all languages having phonetic transcription (such are, for example, the Russian and German languages and, with the exception of some conventional forms of spelling, also the English and French languages) the process of writing does not represent an act of direct graphic representation of notions (as is the case with the Chinese language); it presupposes the preliminary acts of separation of sounds from the living speech, decomposition of the fluent sequence of its phonation into individual phonetic elements, and designation of these elements by respective letters. The complexity of this process is best proved by the strained efforts which a little child exerts when trying to master it; the child not only listens attentively to the words offered, but reinforces the sound analysis by his own articulation, carefully repeating separate sounds and singling them out from the general flow of sounds. In the course of one of our researches it was demonstrated that *if such repetition is excluded, as when the pupil is compelled to write the dictation with his mouth open, the number of mistakes in his dictation increases sixfold.*

From the point of view of modern phonology this process of separating individual sounds from the living language and designating them by letters is quite clear. *It consists in the transformation of certain unstable variants of the pronounced sounds into distinct and stable phonemes;* in other words, it consists in the act of inhibiting those properties which are inessential to speech sounds (intensity, pitch, timbre, etc.) and marking out those essential (or phonemic) properties whose modification immediately changes the meaning of the word (for example, "ball" and "pall," "dome" and "tome"), and without which it is impossible to make speech distinct and articulate. To perform all this work, which precedes the act of writing, it is insufficient to possess a keen ear: a human being must not only discern diverse and delicate nuances of the sounds, but also mark out in them the essential properties, separate these from the inessential ones, and relate the sounds possessing essential properties to that stable group whose phonation, irrespective of the intensity and timbre of pronunciation, is invariably designated by the letters "d" or "t," "b" or "p," etc. This complicated work, which physiologically may be denoted, in accordance with Pavlov's term, the process of "differentiation of sounds" based on the phonemic properties of the language (for example, based on such properties as the voicefulness and voicelessness essential to these sounds), requires a number of auxiliary means. The decisive role in this work belongs to the processes of excitation and inhibition in the *auditory analyzer* (in particular, in the cortex of the left temporal lobe), but the articulatory or *kinesthetic* analysis which adds new subsidiary means facilitating the accomplishment of the task of differentiation between related sounds may also be of considerable help.

Only when the required sounds are quite distinctly separated and their sequence firmly preserved does the next stage come into play—the very act of writing, during which the auditory phoneme is converted into a visual symbol, and this receives graphical expression in a motor act.

What happens to the act of writing if a link of this complex process becomes deranged? In this case we shall witness a process very similar in nature to that which has already been described above; a minor derangement will bring about sizable secondary consequences, and the entire functional system will become disturbed owing to this, even though minor, primary defect.

In order to get the clearest possible idea of the concrete consequences which a particular disturbance may entail, we shall have to digress for a few minutes from the sphere of abnormal childhood and turn to the analysis of the question: How does an already developed process of writing disintegrate when this or some other particular defect arises in an adult? Such analysis of more elementary stages of development, through the investigation of disturbances arising in more perfect and already fully developed forms, proves to be sometimes very helpful.

During World War II we were in a position to analyze a considerable number (amounting to many hundreds) of cases of bullet and shell-splinter wounds in the brain; they were supplemented by numerous cases of operatively verified local lesions of the brain by tumors. The results of these observations found a partial reflection in special researches.[3]

The observations showed that derangements in the act of writing were particularly often met with in cases of wounds in the left (predominating) hemisphere; they accompanied, as particular symptoms, those phenomena of aphasia which inevitably arose when the wound (or tumor) destroyed also this or some other section of the so-called "speech zones" of the cerebral cortex. However, the nature of the derangement of writing (just as that of speech) proved to be absolutely dissimilar in different cases and was obviously dependent on which link of this complex process was in each case deranged.

If the wound destroyed the brain tissue in the area of the posterior part of the superior temporal convolution in the left hemisphere, the patients

[3] A. R. Luria. *Traumatic Aphasia.* Moscow, 1947; *Recovery of Cerebral Functions after Wounds.* Moscow, 1947; *Essays on the Psychophysiology of the Act of Writing.* Moscow, 1950.

exhibited pronounced phenomena of disturbances of the auditory cortex. These disturbances did not necessarily lead to a decline in the hearing acuity (the keenness of hearing in many cases remained fully preserved); of essential importance was the fact that the activity of the temporal cortex, which is the central part of the auditory analyzer, proved to be disturbed: the process of excitation in it became so diffuse and the processes of inhibition so weakened that the cortex could no longer cope with the complex task of singling out the necessary phonemic cues and of differentiating some related phonemes (and in more serious cases also phonemes of remote likeness). As a result, the overwhelming majority of patients with such wounds could not discern the so-called correlating (or oppositional) phonemes (which are distinguished only by one property, for example, by voicefulness or voicelessness) and wrongly repeated them pronouncing "b-p" as "b-b" or "p-p" and "d-t" as "d-d" or "t-t"; naturally, they likewise confused these sounds in their spelling, feeling that there was a certain difference between them, but being unable to qualify it and to relate the sounds to definite groups. This disturbance (which could be also observed in the course of elaboration of more elementary sound differentiations)[4] led to the manifestation of complete helplessness in the separation of the required sounds from complexes of consonants (for example, in the word "strike"). The phonation of words containing more or less complex combinations of sounds assumed the character of inarticulate noises.

All this, naturally, led to a marked derangement of writing which manifested itself in the inability to separate individual sounds from their complexes, in omitting certain sounds, in their displacement, sometimes in their anticipation or perseveration. I shall not dwell here on the fact that all these derangements of writing were developed as a particular symptom of sensory aphasia which was accounted for by the same primary disturbance of the analyzing and synthesizing activity of the auditory cortex.

Derangements of writing of a similar character could develop in cases when the wound destroyed other areas of the cortex located within the central parts of the *kinesthetic analyzer,* which plays an important role in the regulation of complex motor processes. However, these derangements greatly differed in nature from those which have just been described, and the underlying primary mechanisms called forth marked differences in the structure of the symptoms.

Lesions of the kinesthetic parts of the cortex in the left hemisphere invariably caused substantial derangements in the differentiation of kinesthetic impulses; the planning of movements proved to be disturbed, the motor impulses lost their strictly established directions and became diffused, excitation did not take the proper course at once and spread to inadequate groups of muscles. Owing to this, the act of proper coordination of movements greatly suffered, and there arose the phenomena of "afferent motor apraxia" which manifested themselves in both the derangement of the delicate movements of the arm and (what is particularly important) the delicate movements of the articulatory apparatus. A patient with such a lesion lost the

[4] This has been carried out in the researches of the Institute of Neurology of the U.S.S.R. Academy of Medical Sciences.

ability to differentiate the pronunciation of the necessary sounds and confused those sounds which are closed as regards their articulation (for example, substituting "m" or "p" for the labial "b" and "d" or "l" for the linguopalatal "n").

This quite peculiar derangement of articulemes (when sounds were confused because of the likeness of their pronunciation and not their acoustic properties) led, in its turn, to a peculiar derangement of writing. A patient deprived of distinct articulatory means, necessary for the separation of individual sounds from speech, was unable to write down these sounds properly; such derangements of writing, caused by this primary defect and expressed in the confusion of closed articulemes, made it possible to ascertain logically the nature of their underlying primary defect.

We are in a position to advance our investigation of defects in writing somewhat further. If the lesion affects one more area of the cerebral cortex and destroys the central parts of the visual-spatial analyzer situated within the parieto-occipital parts of the cerebral hemispheres, the ensuing changes in the behavior of the patient will be of a different nature. Being deprived of strict spatial differentiation of excitation, the patient will confuse the right and left sides, will be unable to coordinate properly the movements of the hand, and will confuse the disposition of the cardinal geographical points; these principal disorders will inevitably be reflected in his writing. In this case the analysis of the sound composition of speech will remain unchanged, but the handwriting will be substantially deranged: the patient will be unable to differentiate the direction of the strokes when tracing the contours of a letter, preserving only elements of the letter, but not its spatial orientation and synthesis, so that it will become quite unrecognizable.

We shall not continue our analysis by dwelling on cases in which derangements in the act of writing are caused not by limited local disorders but by a *defect of the general neurodynamics*. These are defects connected with the weakness of the inhibitory process, owing to which the child is unable to inhibit its direct impulses, and each excitation at once reaches its motor end deranging the normal *order* of tracing letters and imparting to the act of writing an impulsive character. In these cases, as shown by our experience, the defects in the child's writing can be easily eliminated by placing the child in a condition of constant control which inhibits the impulsive character of his reactions.

From the above analysis it is quite clear that *a primary derangement of any particular link may inevitably lead to the disintegration of the whole system* and that genuine analysis of the nature of derangements in this system is possible only *if we disclose this primary disorder, as well as the systemic consequences which it entails*.

There is no need to emphasize that such analysis of the symptom considerably oversteps the bounds of mere references to a derangement of the ability for writing and brings us close to scientific diagnosis of the given derangement.

We have deliberately cited a few examples of such analysis borrowed from the clinic of local cerebral lesions in the adult. These examples enable us to solve with particular exactness the problem arising before us in the clinic of abnormal childhood; the only difference is that in conditions of anomalous development these defects may manifest themselves with still greater intensity and if the defect arises early enough, it may bring about severe disturbances in the entire mental development of the child.[5] A child with central lesions or underdevelopment of corresponding cortical systems, accompanied by disturbances of the auditory, kinesthetic, or spatial analyzing and synthesizing activity, just as a child with serious defects of general neurodynamics, will inevitably exhibit marked derangements in the mastery of the process of writing, but in different cases these derangements have different foundations, are components of different syndromes, and bear a different character.

We have dwelt only on the causal-dynamic analysis of phenomena of dysgraphia (and of the related phenomena of dyslexia); however, we could with equal success apply this analysis to the phenomena of disorders of speech and derangements of motor processes or, what is of particular interest, to various forms of anomalous behavior (for example resulting from early encephalitis). In all such cases the approach to the symptom under observation in respect to a secondary consequence of a definite primary defect, a consequence which has taken shape in the course of development, proves to be effective and makes it possible not only to understand the structure of the derangement better, but also to approximate the scientific analysis of the anomalous development as a whole.

V

Our exposition of the way which we consider most effective in the analysis of anomalous development of children would not be complete if we did not dwell on the *practical results* of the systemic or, in other words, causal-dynamic approach to the phenomena under investigation.

The formal symptomatological approach, describing only those defects of the abnormal child which most of all arrest our attention, and attempting to explain them by an underdevelopment of certain inborn (general and special) abilities, not only lags far behind the level of modern scientific knowledge but also proves to be practically inefficient. Being unable to reveal the primary cause of the derangement and to interpret the symptoms under observation as its systemic consequences, it is useless in finding any proper, scientifically grounded methods for its compensation.

Indeed, what is the practical use of a mere assertion that the given child exhibits general intellectual deficiency, or suffers from primary derangements of the ability to write and to read which is expressed as inborn dysgraphia and dyslexia?

At best, such an assertion does not lead to any distinct results nor does it open any definite ways for correcting the defect. At worst, it leads to an erroneous approach and to such recommendations which cannot be of any practical help in devising corrective work for the abnormal child. What

[5] We had the opportunity to observe it when specially analyzing a case of underdevelopment of speech in twins. A. R. Luria and Y. C. Yudovich. *Speech and Development of Mental Processes in the Child.* Moscow, 1956.

could be practically achieved if we placed a child who does not speak and suffers defects of hearing in a school for feebleminded or alalic children and if we attempted to teach him according to a program designed for such children? Could we attain any sizable results if, upon establishing a derangement of writing in a child with a primary defect of the auditory or kinesthetic analysis or synthesis, we began (as, unfortunately, is often the case) to have such a child copy letters, thereby compelling him to perform absolutely unnecessary work?

The causal-dynamic analysis of the abnormal child, aimed at disclosing its primary defect and deducing from it the secondary systemic consequences, simultaneously enables us to find adequate means of compensating this defect and, in the case of adults, adequate ways of corrective training. This corrective training—in cases of organic lesions of the peripheral and central apparatus—must be only to an inconsiderable degree aimed at the direct elimination of the primary cause underlying the anomalous development. Primary defects of hearing, just as a primary derangement of the auditory or kinesthetic analysis and synthesis, can be eliminated only to a small extent, and the effect of treatment (such as administration of stimulating substances) is usually of limited use.

However, corrective training directed against the *systemic consequences of this defect* and, as a rule, consisting in a *functional readjustment of the deranged system* may produce a tremendous, decisive effect and to a considerable degree restore the deranged (or underdeveloped) function.

It would be senseless to direct all efforts exclusively to the elimination of severe defects of hearing; but children with such defects can successfully cope with the normal program of general 10-year education (though in a somewhat longer period) if special attention is paid to the compensation of those secondary difficulties in their mastery of the grammatical system of speech and the forms of abstract thinking, which arise as a result of their primary defects.

Nor would it be reasonable to attempt directly to eliminate the defects of the form of sound and kinesthetic analysis and synthesis which suffered as a result of a cerebral lesion; but a series of rational methods aimed at the readjustment of the functional system may lead to complete elimination of the secondary defects caused by the primary derangement.

I cannot forget a well-known engineer and designer who, having been wounded in the temporal area, preserved his abilities as a designer, but fully lost the ability of writing; he was brought to our clinic after unsuccessful attempts to restore his ability to write with the help of protracted exercises in copying texts. After an adequate four months' course of training in sound analysis based on the intact visual and articulatory analysis, this patient, like many others, left our clinic with a fairly well restored writing ability. Similar positive results were obtained in cases when the derangement of the kinesthetic analysis of articulations was supported by the auditory and visual oral analysis of speech.

A special clinic of speech disorders in Moscow created at the Institute of Defectology of the Academy of Pedagogical Sciences and headed by R. E. Levina has worked out an elaborate system of such corrective training of alalic children and convincingly proved the effectiveness of those practical methods which are engendered by a correct theoretical analysis of the symptom.

There is no doubt that a thoughtful approach to the analysis of the defect and the ability to disclose its real nature will be of great practical use and provide a scientific foundation for the corrective training of abnormal children, which is the most humane branch of our medical and pedagogical sciences.

Experimental Study of the Higher Nervous Activity of the Abnormal Child[6]

I

In the preceding section we made an attempt to advance some important theoretical principles of child psychopathology and dwelt on the proposition that general derangements in the mental development of the child may be caused by relatively limited particular defects. We also tried to show that the analysis of anomalous development may be highly efficient if it succeeds in approaching the mental ability of the child as a secondary consequence of such a particular primary defect.

There is no doubt, however, that cases in which the mental development of the child has assumed an abnormal character due to a limited, strictly localized defect by no means cover all the forms which are known in child psychopathology. There are more frequent cases when children exhibit no particular defects in vision or audition, in writing or reading, but manifest gross and much more general derangements in their intellectual development or in their behavior. Clinical investigations of such children are full of records showing certain derangements of their ability to concentrate; they are easily distractible, impulsive, disinhibited, inert, and sluggish. All these symptoms indicate a tendency to early fatigue, susceptibility to asthenia, and, finally, general retardation of mental development, not accompanied by any marked particular defects. Some of these children can attend normal schools, but they do not remain there for a long time, not being able to cope with the general program; they require special medical measures, and if given special help, can show good progress in their studies; other children reveal distinct symptoms of mental backwardness and must attend special schools for the feebleminded.

However, the following question naturally arises: Must we confine our research to the external clinical description of such children, or should we, in accordance with our general principle, go further and set ourselves the task of *qualifying* their disturbances? Should we attempt to *disclose the changes which underlie the anomalous development* and to express the disturbances in more profound pathophysiological units?

We contest the viewpoint—incompatible with modern medicine—which

[6] Reprinted from *Journal of Mental Deficiency Research*, Volume 3, Part 1, June, 1959. (Received Oct. 7, 1958.)

is inclined to deduce peculiarities of development from different inborn abilities. The assertion of some authors that a considerable part of the population is hereditarily "subnormal," or exhibits traits of "constitutional psychopathy," can be hardly regarded as a worthy contribution to science.

Thorough investigations carried out by Soviet specialists in the field of child psychiatry (Sukhareva, Osipova, Pevzner, and others) give firm grounds for stating that the overwhelming majority of children who cannot attend ordinary schools suffered in their early, or intrauterine, childhood from severe organic lesions (traumas or inflammatory processes, infections or metabolic disorders) which adversely affected their subsequent development. Therefore, the pathological state of disinhibition, sluggishness, and exhaustibility, as well as the retardation of mental development hindering normal studies, in a considerable number (and even overwhelming majority) of cases results from pathological processes endured long before; these processes have modified the cerebral substratum and inevitably lead to the defective development of the child.

If in these cases we are actually confronted not with various forms of normal development but with sick children whose nervous processes, as a result of lesions endured in the past, have assumed certain pathological peculiarities, then, naturally, the following questions arise: How can we characterize these peculiarities of the nervous processes, and can we study the pathologically changed nervous activity of these children? Only by answering these questions shall we be able to make a substantial step forward, to pass from the external description of deviations in behavior to the study of the *neurophysiological mechanisms* which are responsible for anomalous development.

The achievements of modern normal and pathological neurophysiology and, above all, the classical investigations of I. P. Pavlov, which during the last two decades have been extensively applied to man, make it possible to accomplish this task; they arm us not only with a system of notions, which can express the principal deviations in the dynamics of human nervous processes, but also (and this is particularly important) with experimental methods by means of which these peculiarities can be objectively ascertained.

Let us dwell for a short while on the physiological symptoms indicating both the normal development of the higher nervous processes and derangements in their dynamics in pathological cases; in our further exposition we shall have to deal with these symptoms repeatedly.

Any nervous processes, which, as we know, are reducible to the basic processes of excitation and inhibition, may manifest a definite *strength* expressed in the rapidity with which new connections are formed, as well as in the stability and concentration of these processes; normally the strength of the basic nervous processes is sufficient to effect a relatively quick coupling of the new connections, to inhibit inadequate reactions, and to keep up the elaborated systems of connections for a long time without yielding to the influence of other external stimuli or to the influence of the on-coming exhaustion. As is known, in pathological states of the brain the strength of the basic nervous processes may markedly suffer; their concentrated character gives way to a diffused, generalized irradiation of excitation; the nerve cell quickly falls into a state of transmarginal inhibition; its reactions to strong stimuli become weaker, while its responses to weak stimuli assume a paradoxically strong character. It is likewise well known that in such cases any extraneous stimulus may easily disrupt the already established system of connections; even slight fatigue may evoke appreciable disturbances in the normal course of the nervous processes.

Further, any higher nervous activity consisting of the excitatory and inhibitory processes may be characterized by a different degree of *equilibrium* between these processes. Normally this equilibrium reaches a very high level. Because of this we do not react to a negative, inhibitory stimulus with an impulsive response, or to a positive signal requiring a rapid reaction with a delayed or disappearing response. But, pathological states of the brain very often lead to a *disturbance of the equilibrium* between the two nervous processes. In some cases this disturbance is expressed in the predominance of excitation over inhibition; then the ability to abstain from premature responses is elaborated with great difficulty, and inhibitory signals frequently begin to evoke involuntary impulsive reactions. In other cases this disturbance is expressed in the predominance of elementary inhibition; then sluggishness and torpidity arise in the higher nervous activity, new positive reactions are elaborated slowly, and in the presence of a certain complicating factor entirely disappear. Although in normal subjects the predominance of this or another process is a symptom of temperament, under pathological states of the brain (as we shall see later) the disequilibrium between both nervous processes may assume strongly pronounced abnormal forms.

Finally, any higher nervous activity possesses a third property which until recently has not received sufficient attention. Nervous processes may differ in their *mobility*. Normally this mobility is manifested in the fact that a human being is able *to inhibit certain systems of connections rapidly and pass to others;* this faculty of the nervous system (genetically connected with the physiological property of *lability* which was investigated by the outstanding Russian physiologist Wedensky) is one of the most important faculties and ensures successful adaptation to quickly changing natural conditions. Under pathological states of the brain this faculty may particularly deteriorate. When this occurs the patient is no longer able to inhibit quickly the connections that were once established and to pass easily from certain systems of connections to new ones. The well-known fact of *preservation* may be interpreted as an external manifestation of the *inertness of the nervous processes* which, as shown by investigations, is one of the most essential symptoms of the onset of a pathological state in the brain. Later we shall see how important these features are for the diagnostics of pathological states of the higher nervous activity of the child.

However, we should commit a serious mistake if we did not make another important step in our reasoning. The characteristic properties of the basic nervous processes—their strength, equilibrium, and mobility—as well as changes which take place under pathological states, are quite sufficient to qualify the peculiarities of the higher nervous activity in animals, but they are by no means sufficient to qualify the peculiarities of the higher nervous activity in man. The behavior of man, which always bears a reflex character, in the broad sense of these words (each action being invariably a response to certain conditions arising in his interrelation with the outer world), is at the same time a *conscious* and *voluntary* nature. This, first of all, means that a human being responds with this or another action to the *verbal instructions* of the people with whom he is associated; he orients himself in the surrounding reality with the help of language, through which he systematizes his impressions, realizes his own actions, and, what is particularly important, subordinates his behavior to verbally formulated intentions. Along with the system of direct signals of reality, man is constantly influenced by language and speech. The "second signaling system" consists of words, which embody and express our social experience, and of connections between them. The second signaling system possesses the properties of abstraction and special generalization and constitutes the foundation of our thinking; it forms a component part of the mental reality in which man lives. At the same time it is a powerful means of *regulating his behavior;* there is hardly anybody who knows it better than the physician or teacher engaged in the treatment and instruction of children.

This essential feature of man's behavior makes it necessary to introduce an important additional factor in the study of the principal indicators of human higher nervous activity. In order to express the specific properties of the human higher nervous processes in units which are peculiar to man, we must not confine ourselves to the characteristics of general strength, equilibrium, and mobility of the nervous processes; we must also ascertain specially the specific features which characterize the dynamics of his speech processes (or processes developing at the level of the second signaling system) and, above all, establish *to what extent these speech processes organize the course of his more elementary reaction,* and to what degree the *connections of his second signaling system are able to regulate the acts of his behavior.*

Precisely this *physiological characteristic of the processes of regulation of behavior,* or in a broader sense, the interaction of the two signaling systems, will serve us as a fundamental indicator in the study of the normal and pathologically modified behavior of the child. Therein we expect to find the basic "units" which will allow us to make a proper step toward a more precise qualification of various forms of abnormal development.

II

The simplest way of studying the specific features of the higher nervous processes in the child and the role of speech in the regulation of its actions is the method—well known in psychology—of recording *motor reactions arising as a result of verbal instruction.*

We give the child the following simplest instruction: "When a light appears, press the balloon." Thereby we actually try to solve two problems: firstly, we are able to find out whether a most elementary temporary connection can be established in the child in this way (i.e., whether the flash of an electric bulb assumes a new signaling property); secondly, we get the opportunity to ascertain the degree of stability and mobility of the connection which has been evoked by the verbal instruction. By performing this experiment more or less protractedly, presenting the child with extraneous stimuli, using signals of different strength, and observing the intensity and quickness of the motor reactions, we are able to judge the relative strength of the induced nervous processes.

By asking the child to perform a somewhat more complicated task, for example to press the balloon in response to a red signal (positive reaction) and to abstain from this movement in response to a green signal (inhibitory reaction), we are in a position to observe both the strength of its active inhibition and the degree of equilibrium between the excitatory and inhibitory processes: a child with a predominance of excitation over inhibition will easily replace the abstention from reactions by impulsive pressures, while a child highly susceptible to inhibition will often miss the required positive reactions, exhibit reactions of an ever-diminishing intensity, and, finally, cease to react to positive signals altogether.

By observing the ease with which the transition from positive to inhibitory reactions is effected, when a given instruction is replaced by a reverse one, or by a new instruction, and by noting both the speed and the correctness of the reactions, we shall be able to judge the mobility of the nervous processes.

Finally, by finding out to what degree the child realizes its incorrect reactions and how it endeavors to rectify them, by reinforcing the speech signals and by applying a number of additional methods, we shall be able to establish the role played by the child's own speech in the regulation of its motor processes.

Does this seemingly very simple task always prove to be so easy and within the powers of a normal child? Experience shows that this is far from being the case. A thorough study of the evolution of motor reactions in children of different ages may provide very instructive material for the genetic investigation of the higher nervous activity of children.

If we attempt to offer such a task to a 2-year-old child by a direct order to press the balloon, or by saying: "When light appears, press the balloon," we shall immediately witness marked difficulties experienced by the child. A child of this age, as a rule, is not yet in a position to make at once the relatively complex connection which figures in the two parts of the verbal instruction; the child reacts to each fragment separately: on hearing the first part of the instruction—"when light appears . . ."—it begins to look for the light, while to the second part—"press the balloon"—it reacts by affecting an immediate pressure, without waiting for the appearance of the conditioned signal. This means that the movements of a child of this age are not yet properly regulated by verbal instruction; they begin before the appearance of the signal and sometimes are even discontinued with the actual presentation of the stimulus (the latter proves to distract the attention of the child and therefore often acts as an inhibitory agent). Even if we succeed in obtaining the necessary motor response to the signal, there arises another difficulty: once evoked, the motor impulse proves to be so inert that the child goes on pressing the balloon endlessly even in the absence of the signal, thus manifesting a series of uncoordinated reactions not subordinated to the verbal instruction. This feature is so characteristic of a little child that if we make an attempt to reinforce the inhibitory part of the verbal instruction by stressing additionally that the child must be attentive and should not press the balloon before the light appears, the required effect will not be achieved; on the contrary, this will evoke even more intense and irradiated pressing (Figure 10-1).

Thus whereas in the more elementary systems (sucking, grasping) the nervous processes of a normal child of this age are already adequately concentrated, *it is still impossible to evoke in such a child with the help of verbal instruction, stable, coordinated motor reactions.* Each attempt to do so is greatly impeded by the *high diffuseness of the child's nervous processes.*

Only at the age of 3–3½ years do appreciable changes in the higher nervous processes of a child occur; in conditions of the same experiment a child at this age will demonstrate only single "intersignal" reactions. However, if we somewhat complicate the task by asking the child to press the balloon in response to a red signal and not to press it in response to a green signal, we shall clearly see that the verbal regulation of such an act will prove impossible to the child; a child of this age will very soon begin to produce uncontrolled motor reactions in response to any signal, both positive and inhibitory. It is characteristic that here, too, no additional verbal instruction yields any stable effect; while continuing to produce many inappropriate or intersignal reactions, the child, as a rule, will try to convince the experimenter that it acts properly and presses the balloon only in response to the red signals. There is another characteristic fact: if we strongly reinforce the inhibitory instruction and once more tell the child not to press the balloon in response to green signals, the wave of inhibition, which arises in the child, spreads to all subsequent reactions, and then, following the inhibitory (green) signal, no positive (red) signals will evoke any reactions either.

Figure 10-1. Motor reactions in children of 2–2½ years.

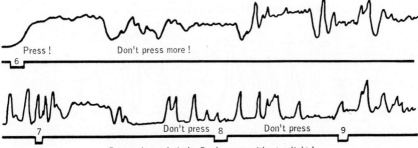

Press!   Don't press more!

6

7   Don't press   8   Don't press   9

Press when a light!   Don't press without a light!

This means that even at this age the higher nervous processes of the child continue to manifest a marked diffuseness, the child easily yields to the influence of direct stimuli, and the verbal regulation of its motor processes is impeded. Only with the help of certain methods aimed at strengthening the influence of verbal instruction (for example, by a transition to a repeated verbal reinforcement of the positive and inhibitory signals by the child (cf. Figure 10-2) or by special methods on which we shall dwell later) is it possible to ensure the necessary concentration of the nervous processes and to obtain distinct and coordinated motor reactions. However, it is interesting to note that even these coordinated motor reactions of a child of this age are still very unstable: the child has only to fall ill with a comparatively mild form of influenza or dyspepsia, and even the prodromal stage of the disease manifests itself in the weakening of the inhibitory processes and in the emergence of impulsive reactions to inhibitory signals.

Only at the age of 5–5½ years does this diffuseness of the nervous processes disappear, and the verbal system begin firmly to regulate the motor reactions of the child. But even at this age a comparatively slight complication of the experimental conditions, for example, a transition to

Figure 10-2. Organization of motor reactions in a child of 3½ years by means of its own speech.

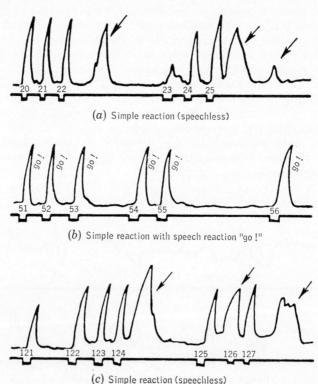

(*a*) Simple reaction (speechless)

(*b*) Simple reaction with speech reaction "go !"

(*c*) Simple reaction (speechless)

complex forms of interchange of positive and inhibitory reactions or to shorter signals in more rapid succession, may result in the reappearance of symptoms of disequilibrium and diffuseness of the nervous processes.

III

There arises the following essential question: Is it not possible to make use of this simplest mode of investigation of the child's voluntary behavior and to turn it into a means of analyzing pathologically modified higher nervous activity? Will not this experience reflect in a more accessible form the changes which arise in the dynamics of the nervous processes of an abnormal child? Shall we not be able to disclose in this way the physiological mechanisms which underlie the pathological behavior of the child?

We shall begin our analysis with the data obtained from the investigation of children with the *cerebro-asthenic syndrome,* and we shall then show how different are the data which we obtain from the investigation of feeble-minded children.

At the beginning of this article we briefly characterized such children who are quite often met with in school. These are children who at an early age suffered from traumas of the head, inflammatory processes, arachnitis, severe general infections, and sometimes early dyspepsias with resulting protracted dystrophic disorders. In the first few years after the second world war and German occupation the number of such children was particularly great.

In many of these children gross intellectual derangements can hardly be established: they can read relatively well, they can count and are sufficiently quick-witted. Their principal defect lies in the extreme instability of their connections, in the utter fragility of their behavior.

As a rule, these children display high distractibility; the mere appearance of a stranger during the experiment is sufficient to change the results. Sometimes they prove unable to solve a task which is immeasurably easier than one which has just been accomplished. They soon tire; after 5 to 7 minutes of studies their efficiency drastically declines, and they begin to make mistakes which were not observed earlier. Sometimes they demonstrate paradoxically violent reactions to insignificant factors, thus revealing symptoms of the "excitatory weakness" which is always characteristic of the syndrome of cerebral asthenia. Usually they take their defects to heart and react strongly to them, sometimes trying to conceal their failure in school studies, or stating that they will do their best to overcome it in the next school year.

Is it possible with the help of the above-described simple method of investigation to solve our principal task—to define more exactly the physiological mechanisms which are responsible for the syndrome just mentioned? Can we elaborate experimental methods which facilitate the diagnosis of this defect? The experiments carried out in recent years in my laboratory by E. D. Homskaya enable us to answer this question.

If we take a child aged from 9 to 12, a typical representative of the group displaying distinct traits of pathological excitability, and offer a simple task—to press the balloon in response to each red signal, but to abstain from this movement in response to each green signal (or to a signal of some other color)—we shall observe a picture sharply differing from that which is displayed by a normal child of the same age.

Already when the signals are presented at a relatively low frequency, the child usually begins to manifest a weakness of its inhibitory processes and sometimes produces impulsive reactions even to inhibitory signals, reactions that are little susceptible to inhibition. If we complicate the conditions of the experiment and begin to present shorter signals, or if we

Figure 10-3. Organization of motor reactions in a cerebro-asthenic child by means of its own speech.

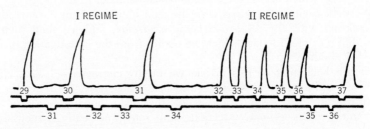

(A) Normal child (sib)

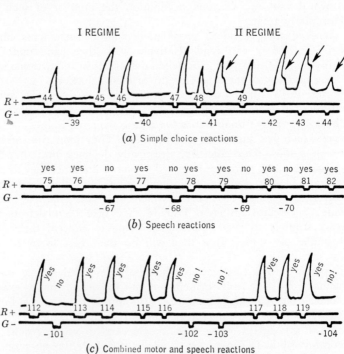

(a) Simple choice reactions

(b) Speech reactions

(c) Combined motor and speech reactions

(B) Cerebro-asthenic child (9 years)

present these signals at a higher frequency (thereby making greater demands of the inhibitory process), this picture assumes a still more pronounced character; the overwhelming majority of the inhibitory signals begin to evoke disinhibited impulsive reactions (Figure 10-3*a*). Exact measurement of the latent periods of these reactions makes it possible to disclose some mechanisms of this defect. It proves that when certain positive signals are repeatedly presented, the level of excitability steadily rises and shortens the latent period of the reaction to an ever-increasing degree; as a result, there arise conditions which break the inhibition and call forth impulsive reactions to the inhibitory signal (Figure 10-4*a*). It is characteristic that the child itself is well aware of the erroneousness of its impulsive reactions and accompanies almost all inappropriate reactions by the exclamation: "Oh, it's wrong! . . ." but in spite of that, repeats the same mistake at the presentation of the next inhibitory stimulus.

We, therefore, have good grounds for stating that *the weakness of the nervous processes in these cases develops against a background of high excitability in a person with particularly deteriorated inhibitory process* and that despite this neurodynamic derangement, the verbal system of the child *remains relatively intact.* The child recognizes the mistakes com-

Figure 10-4. Reaction times of motor reactions in a child with cerebro-asthenic syndrome: (*a*) motor reactions without speech; (*b*) motor reactions combined with the child's own speech (go! go!).

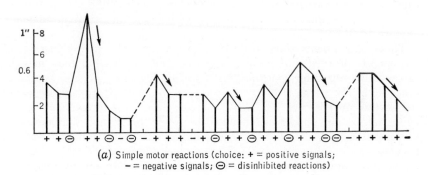

(*a*) Simple motor reactions (choice: + = positive signals; − = negative signals; ⊖ = disinhibited reactions)

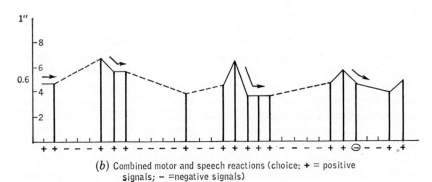

(*b*) Combined motor and speech reactions (choice: + = positive signals; − =negative signals)

mitted perfectly but is unable to regulate the excessively heightened excitation.

If a drastic derangement of the general neurodynamics accompanied by a relatively intact second signaling system really constitutes the principal symptom of this group of cerebro-asthenic states, then is it not possible *to compensate the defects of the neurodynamics peculiar to the given child with the support of relatively intact speech* and thus to ensure the necessary regulation of the motor reactions? The solution of this question would arm us with a new essential basic symptom in the diagnosis of various pathological states of cerebral activity.

In order to solve this question we must, first of all, find out what are the physiological characteristics of the child's speech activity and resort to its compensatory role only if the strength, equilibrium, and mobility of speech activity are higher than those of direct motor reactions.

The most effective method in this respect is very simple: for this purpose it is sufficient to cancel the motor reactions of the child by asking him to react to each signal with appropriate *words*—to pronounce the word "press" in response to each positive signal and the words "don't press" in response to each inhibitory signal. Experiments performed on numerous children with the cerebro-asthenic syndrome demonstrate that a child who makes many impulsive motor reactions to inhibitory signals when the conditions of the experiment are relatively complicated will, *under the same experimental conditions,* make no mistakes, but will be able to pass rapidly from a positive verbal response to an inhibitory one at the presentation of corresponding stimuli, if asked to give verbal and not manual responses (Figure 10-3*b*).

These experiments show that, if in these cases the neurodynamics of the speech processes are relatively intact (Figure 10-3*c*), they may be successfully utilized for *compensating the neurodynamic defects in the motor processes of the child.*

For this purpose we *combine the motor and verbal reactions of the child;* we ask the child to pronounce the word "press" and simultaneously to press the balloon at the presentation of the positive signal and, in response to the inhibitory signal, to pronounce the words "don't press" and at the same time to abstain from the act of pressing. In this way we bring the verbal response closer to the motor reaction and utilize the relatively intact speech of the child for the regulation of its motor reactions.

Experiments showed that in a considerable number of children with the cerebro-asthenic syndrome this method produced a marked effect. Whereas in the case of silent motor reactions the child under certain conditions effected from 60 to 70 per cent of impulsive disinhibited pressures of the balloon, in the case of combined verbal and motor responses such movements were not observed at all, or were reduced 10 to 15 per cent; a subsequent return to silent motor reactions again resulted in a predominance of the excitatory processes and in the reappearance of inappropriate and uncontrolled impulsive reactions. Here, too, exact measurements of the latent periods enable us to approximate to the analysis of the mechanisms which underlie this influence of speech; they show that the latent periods in this experiment become longer, that the general growth of excitability stops, and that speech acts in a regulative way raising the tone of the inhibitory processes and modifying the dynamics of excitability in the cortical apparatus (Figure 10-4*b*).

Similar results may be obtained in those children with the cerebro-asthenic syndrome in whom the weakness of the excitatory processes is associated with a distinct predominance of elementary forms of inhibition and who are well known as children with a torpid form of this syndrome.

Any more or less marked complication of the experimental conditions leads in such children to the disappearance of reactions to positive stimuli and, in the end, to the disappearance of motor reactions in general; the mechanism of this process consists in the steady increase of the latent periods, which testifies to a considerable exhaustion of the excitatory processes.

As in the case of the excitable children, inhibited children also will give correct verbal responses even in experimental conditions which lead to the inhibition of motor reactions; the combination of verbal and motor reactions tones up the activity of the child, and correct motor reactions, reinforced by relatively normal speech, persist even in these more complicated experimental conditions. The mechanism of this compensatory influence of speech, apparently, consists in the heightened tone of the excitatory processes. In the case of combined verbal and motor reactions the latent periods are greatly shortened, their growth being discontinued.

This shows that there exists a group of children with the cerebro-asthenic syndrome, whose principal defect consists in their weakened basic nervous processes, as well as in the violation of the normal equilibrium between these processes, and in whom a marked compensatory effect may be achieved with the help of the regulating role of their relatively normal verbal system. How this compensatory influence of speech manifests itself depends on the nature of the disequilibrium between the basic nervous processes and on the kind of nervous mechanisms underlying the neurodynamic defect under observation.

We have dwelt on a numerous group of children with the syndrome of cerebral asthenia, who exhibit derangements in behavior bearing a general, diffuse character, and whose relatively normal speech processes make it possible to find proper means for compensating their functional defect.

Our physiological analysis of the symptom proves to be equally effective when the lesion, evoked by an inflammatory process or trauma, is not of diffuse, but of *local* character; in such cases there develops a limited *local asthenia* of certain cortical functions, and precisely the same methods enable us to reveal the specific pathology of these or other functional systems.

For example, if the pathological process has deranged the normal activity of the cortical parts of the *auditory analyzer,* the child is still able to produce distinct reactions to optic signals, but will display an appreciable derangement of reactions to acoustic signals. In such cases the inclusion of verbal reactions in the experiment leads to the compensation of the neurodynamic defects.

The disturbance of the cortical parts of the kinesthetic (motor) analyzer allows us to examine phenomena of functional cerebral asthenia of a different kind. While producing relatively accurate differentiated reactions under any of the just-described conditions, such a child begins to reveal marked derangements as soon as we pass to an experiment in which it is necessary to differentiate between two movements differing in strength (for example, to press the balloon with force in response to the red signal and without force in response to the green signal). In this case, too, the inclusion of verbal responses (the words "hard" and "gently") proves to be a factor regulating the deranged work of the damaged motor analyzer. In cases of very gross lesions of the motor parts of the cortex such compensation with the help of speech remains unfeasible.

The disturbance of cortical neurodynamics, therefore, in both its diffuse and local forms, is of great clinical importance, as is the possibility of compensating for these dynamic disorders by the inclusion of the relatively more normal speech into the functional system.

IV

We have described the results of investigations carried out on children with the cerebro-asthenic syndrome, in whom the pathological process entailed a considerable derangement of the dynamics of the higher nervous processes, but left relatively intact their most complex forms connected with the second signaling system.

Can we expect that similar investigations will enable us to analyze another, essentially different group of children, feebleminded or oligophrenic children, in whom severe cerebral lesions endured in early (more often, intrauterine) childhood engendered profound derangements of the processes of abstraction and conceptual thinking, and who cannot attend ordinary schools owing to serious defects in their entire intellectual development?

Cannot we assume that the above-mentioned methods will allow us to mark out the specific features of this form of childhood anomaly and disclose its underlying neurophysiological mechanisms?

Investigations carried out in recent years jointly with a group of our collaborators (M. S. Pevzner, V. I. Lubovsky, A. I. Mescheriakov, E. N. Martsinovskaya), as well as by a number of Soviet physiologists, showed that the dynamics of the higher nervous processes in oligophrenic children are really characterized by certain gross derangements and that these peculiar features essentially distinguish this group of children from the above-described children with the cerebro-asthenic syndrome.

Just as in the children described above, and to a still greater degree, the *strength* of the nervous processes in oligophrenics proves to be markedly lower; this finds expression not only in the fact that the overwhelming majority of oligophrenic children rapidly develop a pronounced state of fatigue, but also in their impaired formation of complex systems of connections and in their still more impaired retention of these connections. It is sufficient sometimes to give such children an instruction containing two or several components (for example, simultaneously to put out the tongue and to close the eyes, or to press the balloon in response to red and green signals and to abstain from this action in response to white and blue signals), and it becomes quite clear that the accomplishment of this task is beyond their powers. Each connection established in this way, owing to negative induction, inhibits the neighboring connection, and the entire functional system evoked by this instruction collapses.

In oligophrenics, just as in the above-described children, the equilibrium between the two nervous processes may be greatly deranged; this is why we often meet highly excitable and highly inhibited oligophrenics.

However, their characteristic feature is *the severely disturbed mobility of their nervous processes* and, what is of importance, that all the above-mentioned changes are not confined to the most elementary forms of the higher nervous activity, but considerably extend *to the complex connections of the second signaling system*. These changes make even the speech processes much more defective than the simpler forms of behavior which have been mentioned earlier; they profoundly disturb the regulatory function of speech, the normal state of which has been stressed when analyzing the above-described syndrome of cerebral asthenia.

We can prove this by a series of very simple experiments which, however, yield quite conclusive results in oligophrenic children.

If we ask a child suffering from a severe form of oligophrenia to press the balloon in response to each order or to each conditioned signal, we shall see that its motor reactions are easily separated from the signal and the child begins to produce a number of inert, perseverated movements (Figure 10-5*a*).

We can observe the symptoms of this inertia also in children with milder forms of oligophrenia.

If we ask such a child to press the balloon at the appearance of a red

Figure 10-5. Motor reactions in oligophrenic child: (*a*) inertness in simple reactions (14 years old); (*b*) inertness—returning to the first (reverted) system after a pause (12 years old).

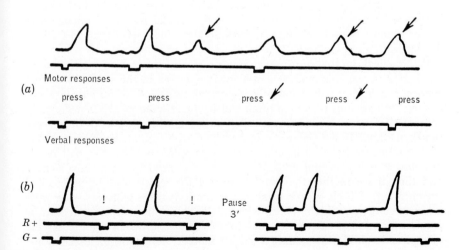

signal and to abstain from pressing it in response to a green signal, it will easily comply with this task; with similar ease will the child fulfill after that another task—to act in a reverse way, i.e., to press the balloon in response to a green light and not to press it at the presentation of a red signal. However, if in the course of the experiment a strong bell is heard, acting on the child as an external inhibiting agent, the new, reshaped system will disintegrate and give way to the old, inert connection. The same will be observed if upon reshaping the connection we interrupt the experiment for 2 or 3 minutes and after a short interval resume it again. In this case we clearly see that the newly established second connection has disappeared and that the child has returned to the previous, well-established connection, again pressing the balloon in response to a red signal and abstaining from it in response to a green signal (Figure 10-5*b*).

Sometimes the inertness of the more stable, old connection is manifested also in the fact that it reappears in the child's verbal system, thereby inhibiting the new, less stable verbal connection.

If we go on with our experiment and replace the just-mentioned instruction by a new one, asking the oligophrenic child to press the balloon in response to a long (optic or acoustic) signal and to abstain from pressing it in response to a similar short signal, this inertia will assume a still more pronounced character; we shall see that the child, properly fulfilling the instruction, when asked what action it performs, will stubbornly answer that it presses the balloon in response to a red signal and abstains from pressing it in response to a green signal, though these colors no longer figure in the experiment and quite a different factor has been imparted a signaling property. This experiment clearly shows that in these cases *pathological inertia may manifest itself with particular force in the verbal system,* whose neurodynamics lag far behind the dynamics of the motor processes. Sometimes this inertia in the verbal system proves to be so considerable that the child under investigation, having successfully reversed the practical system of reactions, still retains the previously established inert stereotype in the verbal system; the child, for example, claims that it "pressed when the light was on for long and did not press when it was on for a short time," although in fact the child long ago began to fulfill a diametrically opposite task.

Pathological inertia of the nervous processes which are manifested in direct motor reactions and to a still greater degree in the system of verbal connections leads to the clinically important fact of *dissociation of speech and motor reactions* or, as we often call it, *dissociation of the two signaling systems.* This can be experimentally induced with the help of a very simple method. If we elaborate, in an oligophrenic child, a reaction to one of the just-mentioned instructions (for example, to press the balloon in response to a long signal and not to press it in response to a short signal) and then if we modify the usual course of the experiment by a repeated presentation of both signals in strict alternation, there will very soon arise an inert stereotypy in the child, which will replace the correct reactions by a mere alternation of positive and inhibitory reactions. In these cases the oligophrenic child will exhibit a simple motor "stereotypy of alternation," at the same time, however, continuing as inertly to state that it fulfills the given instruction quite properly.

It is characteristic that this may inertly repeat itself even when the child is offered a very simple task—to react to definite words pronounced by the experimenter (for example, "tree," "boy," "horse," "table") with one of the two following attributes—"alive," or "not alive." As shown by the observations of A. I. Mescheriakov, in these cases, too, it suffices to pronounce the names of the given objects several times, strictly alternating the animate and inanimate ones, and the oligophrenic child begins to react to them not with meaningful responses, but with a stereotypy alternation of the attributes "alive" and "not alive," divorced from the stimulus words spoken by the experimenter.

This *pathological inertia of once established verbal connections* and the simultaneously arising *pathological dissociation of the two signaling systems* constitute a specific feature of the higher nervous activity in oligophrenic children; it leads to the gravest defects in their mental processes and determines the extreme difficulties with which their training is connected. Not without reason one of the oldest Soviet defectologists once complained that some children with grave forms of oligophrenia, who firmly memorized the rules: "After a full stop the word must begin with a capital letter; when there is a question mark, the voice should be raised," at the next lesson in arithmetic read the text of the problem as follows. "Mary had two apples. Full stop. After a full stop the word must begin with a capital letter. Peter had one apple. Full stop. After a full stop the word must begin with a capital letter. How many apples had Mary and Peter together? Question mark. When there is a question mark, the voice should be raised! . . ." It is quite clear that this pathological inertia, which is the most characteristic feature of the higher nervous activity in an oligophrenic child, creates considerable additional difficulties for the teacher.

However, the pathological inertia of the higher nervous processes in an oligophrenic child, which tells with particular force upon the verbal system, not only prevents the child from fulfilling the given task in a conscious way. Its still more pernicious effect consists in the fact that it *prevents the child from any creative, intellectual activity.*

To illustrate this, we must modify the usual methods of our experiment.

This time we do not give the child any preliminary verbal instruction which fully discloses the action to be performed. We accompany each presentation of a signal by an additional verbal order, saying the word "press!" after the presentation of each red (or protracted) signal, and "don't press!" after each green (or short) signal; thus we shall leave the elaboration of a respective connection to the child itself.

Experiments based on the application of this method (widely known in the U.S.S.R. as the "method of verbal reinforcement" elaborated by Professor A. G. Ivanov-Smolensky) show that already a child aged from 5 to 6 rapidly generalizes the order it receives by formulating a rule. "It is necessary to press when the signal is red (or long) and not to press when it is green (or short)!" Subsequently the child intermediates the presentation of each signal by such verbally formulated rules. When the experimenter passes to a new system of signals, the child immediately resorts to its active speech, trying with the help of verbal suppositions to orient itself in the new situation and to find a solution for the new task.

Naturally, such use of speech as an orienting factor imparts a specific character to the formation of a new connection, highly accelerating its elaboration, making the newly established connection mobile and generalized.

Is such an active participation of the child's own speech in the elaboration of new connections possible in the case of oligophrenics?

Practice shows that such an active, orienting role of speech is evident in oligophrenic children only in the most elementary problems, and usually, only in the first experiments. By elaborating with the help of the method just described a positive reaction to a red signal and an inhibitory reaction to a green signal, we quite soon obtain in the oligophrenic child a generalized rule: "it is necessary to press when there is a red light, and not to press when the light is green." However, as soon as we pass to our subsequent experiments, especially to the more complicated ones, in which the child must inhibit the previously coupled connections and orient itself in a new situation, the picture essentially changes: the previous verbal formulation, owing to the inertia of processes in the verbal system, persists, and speech, far from helping the child to orient itself in the new situation, even hinders the transition from its previous experience to the elaboration of new connections.

This is particularly manifest in cases when we expect the child to perform the more complex forms of analysis and synthesis, for example, when we positively reinforce each protracted yellow signal and negatively reinforce each short yellow signal: there the child must inhibit the property of color which has lost its significance and mark out the property of duration which has assumed a signaling character. This task, easily solved by a normal child with the help of the active abstracting and generalizing function of speech, sometimes creates insurmountable difficulties for an oligophrenic child. The speech of the latter, which is inert and whose function of abstraction and generalization is incomplete, is not properly included in the analysis of the new situation; often it stubbornly retains the previous stereotypy which has already lost its significance; sometimes instead of establishing a new elective connection, it crudely generalizes the order of the experimenter, as a result of which after the reinforcement of the positive signal by the order "press!" the child begins in a generalized way to press the balloon in response to all signals, and after the order "don't press!" accompanying the negative signal, ceases to press the balloon altogether or it presses the balloon without any signal after certain periods of time (Figures 10-5 and 10-6).

Naturally, under these conditions, when active speech no longer participates in the formation of temporary connections, the elaboration of new temporary connections in oligophrenic children assumes a mechanical and protracted character; in numerous cases we could observe how such connections were elaborated in oligophrenic children only gradually, after 70 or 80 combinations, how they were easily destroyed after the discontinuance of constant reinforcement (Figure 106a), after a short interval, or under the influence of any extraneous stimulus acting as an external inhibiting agent (Figure 10-6*b*). Most interesting in these experiments is the fact that even after the elaboration of a relatively stable connection the child cannot realize and verbally formulate the connections practically established by it long ago.

Can we expect in these conditions to compensate the profound defect of formation of temporary connections in an oligophrenic child by the same method which has been succesfully applied when compensating the defect of excitatory and inhibitory processes in children with the cerebro-asthenic syndrome?

The very fact of the pathological inertness of the verbal system, which was repeatedly stressed as a characteristic feature of the higher nervous processes in oligophrenic children, makes us profoundly doubt such a possibility.

Experiments carried out with this aim fully answer this question. They showed, first of all, that in a number of cases even a mere attempt to switch the oligophrenic child over from motor reactions to verbal responses proved to be very difficult; while exhibiting a well-established system of motor reactions, the oligophrenic child, owing to the pathological inertness of the nervous processes, readily returns in these conditions to the stereo-typed system of verbal responses.

It is quite easy to understand that the combination of inert motor re-actions with still more inert verbal responses presents in these cases a very complicated task, and that these two links often inhibit each other by way of negative induction. It is likewise easy to understand that the combination of motor and verbal reactions, creating additional difficulties for oligophrenic children, does not compensate, but, on the contrary, still more aggravates the defects which had been evident in the usual experiment carried out in silence (Figure 10-7*a*). Characteristic also is the fact that when (in spite

Figure 10-6. Instability of inhibition in an oligophrenic child 10 years old: (*a*) exhaustion of inhibitory processes after cessation of reinforcement; (*b*) the same after an extra stimulus (loud bell).

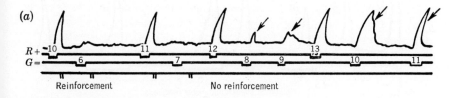

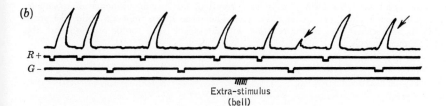

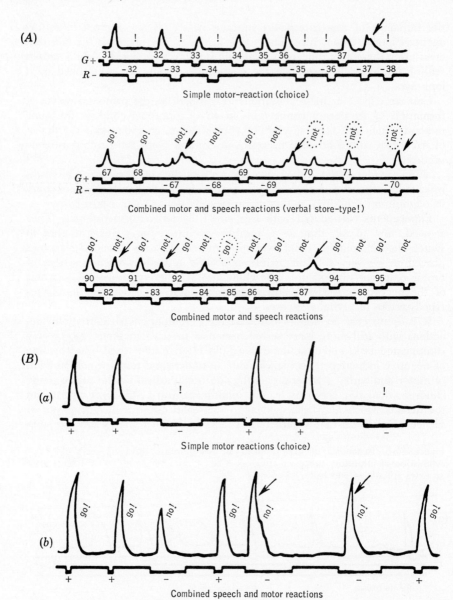

Figure 10-7. Deficit of organization of motor reactions by means of speech in oligophrenic children: (*A*) Disinhibition as a result of nonspecific influence of speech in a feebleminded child (10 years old). (*B*) The same in an imbecile child (14 years old) in both cases: (*a*) motor reaction without speech; (*b*) motor reaction with the child's own speech.

of all these difficulties) we succeed in combining the motor and verbal reactions of the oligophrenic child, the verbal reactions do not produce any
regulatory effect, owing to the weakness of the complex, elective connections
which lie behind the oligophrenic's words, in which therefore a direct impulsive role clearly predominates. While repeating the order "don't press!"
in a loud voice, the child simultaneously makes an impulsive movement of
pressing the balloon which is not inhibited, but intensified, by this nonspecific, exciting influence of the verbal response (Figure 10-7*b*).

It is clear that our experimental research was of double benefit: firstly, it
actually helped us to mark out the principal features of the physiology of
the higher nervous activity in oligophrenic children, and secondly, having
disclosed the basic mechanisms of these disturbances, it enabled us to
facilitate the differential diagnosis between oligophrenics and the cerebro-
asthenic syndrome, which in children often present considerable difficulties.

The experimental study of the abnormal child, which reveals the specific
features of its higher nervous processes, is still at its initial stage of development. Countless special researches still await us ahead.

However, it is obvious that this objective analysis of physiological
mechanisms underlying clinical symptoms opens up great new possibilities.
By marking out the principal symptoms of pathological disturbances, by
studying their physiological mechanisms, we earnestly try to make a new,
substantial advance toward a scientifically grounded psychopathology of
childhood and its related pedagogics. Our experience, the results of which
have been presented here, gives us grounds for believing that studies uniting
clinical medicine, psychology, and physiology, which have demonstrated
their effectiveness in other problems of medicine, may ensure further advances in the study of the abnormal child—this important and particularly
humane branch of knowledge.

PART II

11

LEARNING:
VERBAL, PERCEPTUAL - MOTOR,
AND CLASSICAL CONDITIONING[1]

Ronald S. Lipman

Jensen's (1960) observation that individual difference variables have been neglected in the search for laws of learning seems less accurate now than it was a few years ago, particularly with regard to intellectual variables. Since McPherson's (1958) review of the 14 studies, published in the decade between 1948 and 1958, which investigated learning of retarded Ss, there has been a marked increase in research in this area, the main focus of which has been on comparing the performance of retarded and normal Ss on different learning tasks. The basic aim of these comparisons is, of course, to identify the learning deficits which characterize the retarded. However, as Hilgard (1951) has stressed, learning per se is a permissible inference from performance only when such factors as motivation, fatigue, drug effects, and maturational changes have been controlled. Since Zigler (1962) has indicated that differing histories of social deprivation in retarded and normal Ss may result in differences in motivation, inferences about learning drawn from performance differences are highly tenuous.

Caution is also necessary in generalizing from the results of particular studies in view of the heterogeneity of the retarded population (exogenous versus endogenous; institutionalized versus noninstitutionalized) and the real possibility of interaction between different intelligence levels and task difficulty. The general finding that no single g factor will account for the variance across different learning tasks (Hovland, 1951, p. 635) or, for that matter, within a subarea such as classical conditioning should also be noted.

Denny (1963) has suggested a useful approach for identifying learning

[1] The writer is indebted to Herman H. Spitz, Belver C. Griffith, Philip Siegmann, and Leonard Blackman for their assistance in the preparation of this chapter.

391

deficits in the retarded population.[2] A possible low-IQ–low-MA deficit becomes discernible when equal-CA retardates and normals are compared; comparing equal-MA groups casts light on a possible low-IQ deficit. Of the two potential deficits, the low-IQ deficit is the more serious since it implies that a still larger deficit would be found if the normals also had the MA advantage. Denny cogently argues for the use of both normal controls. The reviewer concurs with this position and will emphasize those studies which have employed normal controls. Unfortunately, agreement is lacking regarding the question of whether IQ, MA, or both variables should covary with learning (House & Zeaman, 1960; Stolurow, 1960). A detailed discussion of this question is provided by Johnson and Blake (1960).

While cautions are necessary in interpreting and generalizing from our data, sufficient research has been done to enable us to draw some qualified conclusions and to suggest some tentative hypotheses regarding learning deficits. However, the identification of deficits in particular learning areas provides only a starting point toward understanding retardation. The more important task, the task that has hardly begun in this field, is the identification of the basic capacities which determine task performance. In this regard, the present review will raise more questions than it answers. There seems little doubt, however, that these questions are central to understanding behavioral inadequacy.

The present review will focus on the following areas: (1) verbal learning, (2) perceptual-motor learning, and (3) classical conditioning. An emphasis will be given to verbal learning since most intelligence tests weigh verbal factors heavily and, in keeping with the conceptualization of IQ tests as aptitude measures, a prediction of deficits in this particular area seems closely tied to theory. It also seems clear that verbal demands made by the academic environment are mainly responsible for the emergence of retardation as a cultural problem and, furthermore, that remedial techniques would prove particularly welcome in this area.

VERBAL LEARNING

Paired-associate learning

The two most general paradigms in the study of verbal learning are paired-associate learning and serial learning. The latter is conceptualized as a special category of the former. Studies which have employed normal CA controls will be considered first, followed by normal MA controls, and then by studies which have employed only a retarded sample.

[2] In keeping with the practice of investigators whose studies are reviewed in this chapter, retardation is operationally defined by an IQ score below 80 derived from a standardized individually administered IQ test. The reviewer is aware, however, that many authorities would prefer a lower cut-off point and additional criteria before applying the label retarded. The terms retarded and deficient are used interchangeably and the severe, moderate, and mild classification refer, respectively, to the IQ range below 25, between 25 and 49, and between 50 and 79. When the designation "organic" is employed, the reader can assume the presence of demonstrated CNS damage.

Equal-CA comparisons. Lott (1958) administered a list of seven pairs of common pictured objects to 69 Ss from a public junior high school. Three IQ groups, 46 to 77, 91 to 108, and 120 to 134, were matched for sex and age. The stimulus card was presented, and S was given up to 8 seconds to respond before E presented the S-R combination (correction procedure). Different randomizations of the list were presented until S achieved the criterion of four successive correct anticipations. Following criterion performance, a modified stimulus series, e.g., bus substituted for auto, was presented as a test of stimulus generalization. One week later, 12 Ss randomly selected from each IQ group relearned the original list to a criterion of one perfect recitation. One month later, the remaining 33 Ss, 11 from each group, also relearned this list.

Although none of the tests of these comparisons proved reliable, it should be noted that the task proved extremely easy to learn with the highest-IQ group achieving criterion in 5.3 trials and the lowest-IQ group achieving criterion in 7.5 trials.

Lott employed an x^2 analysis of these data. However, since in each instance the performance of the three IQ groups was ordered from best in the highest-IQ group to poorest in the lowest-IQ group, the reviewer felt that t tests between extreme IQ groups were in order. A reliable difference was found on original learning and on the short-term retention test but not on the long-term retention test. This short-term retention advantage of the higher-IQ group agrees with studies cited by Pryer (1960) which indicates a short-term retention advantage for faster learners on verbal learning tasks.

This study suggests that educable retardates are not severely penalized relative to equal-CA normals when the materials to be associated are highly familiar pictures; and, furthermore, no long-term retention deficit, as postulated by Stolurow (1960) and Mowrer (1960), was evidenced. There are data (Karwoski, Gramlich, & Arnott, 1944) to indicate that the kinds of associations elicited by pictures differ from those elicited by words; and, since serial-learning studies using words have indicated a sizable learning deficit, it would be worthwhile to replicate the Lott (1958) study using words rather than pictured objects.

A second study (Akutagwa & Benoit, 1959) also employed equal CA Ss and common pictured nouns as stimulus and response members. The lower-IQ Ss in this study cannot be considered markedly deficient since their IQs ranged from 70 to 89. A normal IQ group, 90 to 110, was matched at two age ranges, 8 to 10 and 11 to 13, with the lower-IQ Ss. Three lists were administered to all Ss in the following order: a high association value list (e.g., "horse-cow"), a low association value list ("wagon-owl"), and a high interference list which employed the same stimulus members as list I with a new response ("horse-baby"). Each of the 3 eight-pair lists was presented six times, with items appearing in different random orders. A 4-second stimulus exposure was followed by an S-R exposure, with a 1-minute interlist rest interval. A superiority of the combined older Ss was reported on each list (a computational error seems to be involved on list II), but no reliable difference was found on any list between the combined lower-IQ and the combined higher-IQ *S*s. This finding is not surprising, however, since there was approximately a 1-year MA difference between IQ groups and a 2½-year MA difference between age groups.

Berkson and Cantor (1960) compared equal-CA groups that differed more widely in mean IQ (70 versus 99). Three 6-item lists consisting of various combinations of numbers, colors, and pictures of common objects were employed as stimulus and response items. Half the *S*s from each group were randomly assigned to an E group and the other half to a C group in order to evaluate mediation as well as "direct" learning. List I consisted of odd-numbered stimuli (1 to 11) for the E group and even-numbered stimuli (2 to 12) for the C group. The same common objects served as response members. Lists II and III were identical for both groups. List II had list-I common objects as stimuli and colors as responses. List III had list I *odd* numbers as stimuli and list II colors as responses. Thus for the E group, a common object should serve to mediate the association, on list III, between the odd numbers and the color responses.

Over the three lists, an increasing superiority in performance was found for the higher-IQ group. No reliable performance differences were found on list I. On list II the retarded *S*s made more errors, and on list III they made more errors and also required more trials to reach the criterion of five successive correct anticipations. Although a significant mediation effect was found, this effect did not interact with intellectual level. Before ruling out the possibility of differential facility in using trained verbal mediators, however, it would be of interest to experimentally manipulate the strength of the verbal mediator by employing lower levels of overlearning, i.e., fewer than five successive correct anticipations as the learning criterion.

The writers attribute the increasing superiority of the higher-IQ group to a *learning-to-learn* effect. This effect does seem to be involved since list II, which contains less meaningful response members than list I and should, therefore, be more difficult (e.g., see the study by Cieutat, Stockwell, & Noble, 1958), was actually learned in fewer trials.

The paucity of studies which have examined paired-associate learning in equal-CA groups is obvious. Clearly, studies which examine lower-IQ *S*s within the retarded range as well as studies which employ words rather than pictures are needed. The problem, of course, is that the investigator will quickly face the dilemma of not finding lower-IQ *S*s who are capable of reading. That retarded *S*s of the same MA as normals are severely handicapped in their reading facility is indicated, although rather incidentally, in a study by Cassel (1957) which will be reviewed in a later section.

Equal-MA comparisons.　The only study (Johnson & Blake, 1960) that compared equal-MA *S*s employed an E group—C group design arranged to cast light on learning and transfer effects. Within the retarded and normal samples, E and C groups were matched for MA, CA, and IQ. List I, consisting of three pairs of low association value nonsense syllables, was presented to the mildly retarded and normal E groups for 36 trials. Stimulus items were presented for 2 seconds (anticipation method) followed by a 2-second S-R exposure and a 35- to 45-second intertrial rest. List II, in which the medial vowel of the stimulus members was changed (e.g., "Kej-Kaj") while the response members were held constant from list I, was administered to both E and C groups with the same time constants as list I, but for 54 trials.

The normal Ss (combined groups) correctly anticipated more syllables than the retarded Ss (combined groups) on the list they were exposed to first ($P < .05$). With regard to transfer, although the slopes of the learning curves of both E groups differed significantly from the corresponding slopes of the C groups, the mean displacement of the normal E group was significantly higher (better performance) than the normal C group, while no significant displacement was found between retarded E and C groups. When the 54 trials on list II were divided into thirds, it was found that the normal E group performed significantly better than the normal C group over the first two-thirds of the task. The retarded E group surpassed the retarded C group on only the first third of the task. A comparison of E minus C scores in the normal and retarded groups was not significant. This latter finding, however, reflects the significantly higher performance of the normal C group relative to the retarded C group and the ceiling on the task which the normal E group achieved by about trial 23. It would be interesting to repeat this experiment with a longer list of paired syllables to minimize the ceiling effect.

Although the Johnson and Blake study certainly suggests stronger transfer in normal Ss, their particular design did not control for a possible learning-to-learn effect (McGeoch & Irion, 1952). The experimental Ss learned two lists, whereas the control Ss were exposed only to list II. If learning-to-learn occurs faster in normal Ss, as suggested by the Berkson and Cantor (1960) study, the superiority of the normal E group relative to the normal C group, coupled with the finding of no difference between the retarded E and C groups, might be attributable to this factor rather than to transfer per se. To control for this possibility, the C groups might have been given a dissimilar list of nonsense pairs and then, after rest, exposed to list II.

These paired-associate studies suggest that a basic equal-MA deficit is characteristic of the performance of even mildly retarded Ss when the verbal material is low in meaningfulness. Moreover, the relatively sparse data available on transfer and learning-to-learn effects suggest that the superiority of normal Ss as evidenced on initial learning would tend to be greater after learning similar kinds of lists. In this connection, it would be of considerable interest to determine how the performance of retarded Ss compared with that of normal Ss when this learning-to-learn effect had reached an asymptote in these groups.

On familiar pictured material, a small equal-CA deficit is suggested when very bright normal Ss are employed as controls; but, when more "average" normals are employed, no deficit is indicated. When somewhat less meaningful pictured material (colors and numbers) is employed, an equal-CA deficit is suggested even with average-IQ controls (this latter suggestion may be confounded by differences in learning-to-learn effects). Quite obviously, the difficulty (meaningfulness) dimension is an important parameter of the IQ-paired-associate learning relationship. The more difficult the task, the greater the performance deficit becomes in the retarded. Further studies in this area are clearly indicated.

Serial verbal learning

Serial learning represents a special category of paired-associate learning in which each item (except for the first and last) serves as both a stimulus and a response member. This special characteristic of serial learning tends to maximize the presence of interference effects.

Equal-CA comparisons. The three studies reviewed in this section employed relatively older retardates (older than the normal controls) who were lower in both MA and IQ. These three studies (Barnett, Ellis, & Pryer, 1960b; Ellis, Pryer, Distefano, & Pryer, 1960; Pryer, 1960) employed the same basic procedure. The serial list, consisting of 10 highly familiar nouns, was presented at a 2-second rate with a 20-second intertrial interval to a criterion of one errorless anticipation.

In one study (Ellis et al., 1960), 84 institutionalized retardates, 72 institutionalized delinquent girls, and 144 high school students served as Ss. Three IQ groups were formed: subnormal (40 to 89), normal (90 to 109), and superior (110 to 139). A significant decrease in trials to criterion was found between adjacent IQ groups with the magnitude of this difference being most pronounced between the subnormal and normal groups. The correlation between trials to criterion and IQ was reliable only in the subnormal group. It was —.49. This study clearly indicates a marked equal-CA deficit in serial learning even with lightly familiar verbal material. Although all IQ groups evidenced the typical bow-shaped serial position curve, the degree of bowness was more pronounced in the lower-IQ ranges.

Barnett, Ellis, and Pryer (1960b) compared 46 institutionalized retardates (mean IQ = 50) with 47 normal Ss (mean IQ = 129) and plotted the number of errors at each ordinal position in the serial list as a percentage of the total number of errors in learning the list. This plot was made in order to cast light upon the McCrary-Hunter hypothesis that the distribution of percentage of errors remains invariant, regardless of ability differences. Results indicated a significant difference in the error distribution of normal and retarded Ss with the retarded Ss making relatively more errors at position II and the normal Ss making relatively more errors at position V. This finding is in keeping with a study by Noble and Fuchs (1959), who found that fast learners (defined by an independent learning task) made *relatively* more errors in the center positions of a serial list, whereas slow learners made *relatively* more errors at the extremes.

In the third study in this series (Pryer, 1960), 75 mildly retarded institutionalized Ss and 75 normal high school students were tested. The higher-IQ Ss performed at a reliably $(P < .01)$ higher level, and the r between IQ and trials to criterion was —.61. Pryer also investigated retroactive inhibition (RI) by interpolating a different 10-item list of nouns either 30 seconds, 5 minutes, 30 minutes, or 2 hours after original learning (OL) and having S relearn the OL list to the same criterion 24 hours later. A C group learned the OL list and 24 hours later relearned this list. The interpolated list (IL) produced a significant amount of interference, but the time variable did not differentially affect the amount of RI. When an adjustment was made for differences in OL, no significant interaction between RI and IQ level was found. The interaction term, however, approached significance with the retarded *S*s tending to show *less* RI. This tendency may possibly be attributable to more overlearning of certain of the units of the IL list by the retarded *S*s since learning continued until *all* the items were correctly anticipated.

Finally, it should be noted that Ellis, Pryer, and Barnett (1960b), using the data obtained from their previous studies, found support for Hull's postulate that individual differences in learning can be handled by employing different constants in the same learning equation. An exponential function provided a good fit to performance curves which plotted the probability of correct response as a function of the number of previous reinforcements in normal and retarded *S*s. Although these functions suggest different learning rates, this seems to be the result of a "ceiling" effect. Needless to say, our task of understanding retardation would be greatly simplified if qualitative differences in performance did not obtain and the learning of retardates and normals could be adequately described by the same equations.

The evidence on serial verbal learning indicates a pronounced equal-CA deficit. In this connection, the disparity between these results and the results of equal-CA paired-associate studies is striking. However, there are many differences between these studies; the retarded *S*s in the serial learning experiments were lower in IQ, the materials were words rather than pictures, and the retarded *S*s were institutionalized rather than noninstitutionalized.

Equal-MA comparisons. Cassel (1957) compared equal-MA mildly retarded familial and organic *S*s with normal *S*s. The MA match was based on the Chicago Non-Verbal Test, and the retarded *S*s were, on the average, about 11 years older than the normals. Stimuli were highly familiar words. Two 3-word practice lists were employed, followed by an original learning (OL) list of six words. At this point, half the *S*s in each group sorted cards, while the remaining *S*s learned an interpolated (IL) list. All *S*s then relearned the OL list. The criterion for learning was one perfect recitation by the anticipation method, and items were exposed for 2 seconds with a 2-second intertrial rest. The typical RI effect was found in groups exposed to the IL list ($P < .001$). Although the normal *S*s learned the practice lists faster than the retardates ($P < .05$), no other differences were found on the OL list, the IL list, or on the relearning of the OL list. The results of this study must be viewed with considerable caution, however, since Cassel had to eliminate approximately 100 retarded *S*s who were unable to read the words on these lists. All the normal *S*s, on the other hand, were able to qualify for the experimental sample. Cassel's failure to find an interaction between IQ level and RI is congruent with the findings by Pryer (1960).

Johnson and Blake (1960) compared equal-MA noninstitutionalized mildly retarded *S*s with normals. Six fairly low association value nonsense syllables were presented 1 second apart by the anticipation method to a criterion of two successive repetitions. One week after OL, *S*s were asked to underline the syllables they had previously learned. These syllables were imbedded in a larger, 72-item, list. After completing this task Ss immediately relearned the OL list to the same criterion. This procedure was repeated again the following week. No reliable differences were found between groups on any of the learning or relearning measures, although the normal Ss evidenced better recognition in terms of selecting more OL items from the 72-item list both the first and the second week after OL. Saving scores differentiated the groups on week 1 but not on week 2. Recall scores were not reliably different.

With regard to original learning, the paired-associate and serial learning studies by Johnson and Blake (1960) are clearly incongruent despite the fact that both investigations employed low association value nonsense syllables and approximately the same level of MA (10-year versus 9-year) groups. Two major points of difference, however, should be stressed, namely, institutionalized retardates and a more widely distributed practice schedule obtained in the paired-associate study. With regard to the institutionalization variable, Badt (1958) and Lyle (1959) have demonstrated that verbal skills are adversely affected by institutional settings. Perhaps more important than the institutionalization variable was the *massed* interitem interval (1 second) in the serial learning study. Although there is disagreement regarding the effect of different practice schedules on serial verbal learning (McGeoch & Irion, 1952, pp. 138–193; Osgood, 1953, pp. 515–520), Underwood and Shulz (1960, p. 298) present data which suggest that normal Ss frequently use verbal mediators in learning nonsense syllables. Since much research (Ellis, Pryer, Distefano, & Pryer, 1960; Griffith & Spitz, 1958; Griffith, Spitz, & Lipman, 1959; Luria, 1932; Luria, 1959; O'Connor & Hermelin, 1959) suggests that retardates do not employ verbal mediators as efficiently as normal Ss, and since it seems reasonable to assume that the extremely massed schedule in the serial task would prevent the use of mediators, it is likely that the mediational (assumed) advantage of the normals in the paired-associate task was not operative in the serial learning task. It is suggested, therefore, that the serial learning task of Johnson and Blake be replicated with the inclusion of an institutionalized group and at the same time that equal-MA groups of normals and institutionalized and noninstitutionalized retardates be tested under a more widely distributed practice schedule. It would also be interesting to question Ss after the experiment with regard to their possible use of mediators. The reviewer would predict reliable differences in the reported use of mediators by the normal Ss under spaced presentation, particularly in comparison with the institutionalized retardates. It is anticipated that better performance will be found in groups who report the more extensive use of verbal mediators.

Still another possible explanation for the divergent findings of the two studies by Johnson and Blake stems from the stimulus trace theory of serial learning elaborated by Hull and his associates (Hull, Hovland, Ross, Hall, Perkins, & Fitch, 1940). Inhibitory effects are said to be maximized under massed practice schedules but to dissipate more quickly than excitatory tendencies with rest. Assuming that normal Ss are characterized by stronger memory trace processes and hence develop relatively stronger inhibition effects, massed practice would *differentially* impair performance in normal Ss. The fact that the normals evidenced reliably better recognition scores suggests perhaps that, when inhibition has dissipated, the higher habit strength of the normals is now reflected in performance. This speculation is, of course, tenuous but could be tested by manipulating the time interval between successive syllable exposures.

In summary, studies of the equal-MA performance of retardates and normals in serial verbal learning do not indicate a learning deficit, although the reviewer would guess that a deficit would be evidenced were certain features of these experiments to be changed.

Retarded Ss only. Six studies will be reviewed in this section. Two studies (Barnett, Ellis, & Pryer, 1960a; Mitchell, 1952) examine the performance of organic and familial Ss and will be considered first.

Mitchell (1952) employed matched (CA and IQ) groups of mildly retarded institutionalized female Ss screened for normal hearing and intelligible speech. The organic Ss (there was also an undifferentiated group which will not be discussed) consisted of mongoloids, cretins, and postencephalitic and birth-trauma cases. The familial group consisted of Ss with a history of deficiency in the family and no record of organic impairment.

The serial list of nine low association value nonsense syllables was presented orally at a 3-second rate for 20 trials, with S attempting to recall syllables at the termination of each trial. Although there were no reliable differences in learning between the groups, an examination of recall scores over trials strongly suggests that there was also no learning. Ten minutes after "learning," recall was tested by E's saying syllable 1 (and S responding, or not responding), then syllable 2, and so on. Mean recall was .4 with the upper limit being 8. The series was then presented in reverse order for 20 trials. Over this series there clearly was learning in the familial group, who performed at a significantly higher level than the organic Ss. IQ scores were correlated with list-I performance and with the transfer scores obtained by subtracting list I- from list-II performance. The Pearson rs of .53 and .36, respectively, undoubtedly overestimate the covariation of IQ with these measures since, as Mitchell indicates, a few extreme scores were weighted disproportionately.

The second study to examine the possibility of serial learning differences between equal-MA organic and familial retardates (Barnett, Ellis, & Pryer, 1960a) also found superior performance in the familial group. This study employed familiar nouns and the same procedure as described earlier (see Pryer, 1960). Moreover, the selection procedure was very carefully and explicitly stated. In the interest of establishing uniformity in future studies, their selection criteria are presented. Familial Ss were selected as follows: (1) defective intelligence, (2) a family history of retardation, (3) no known developmental incident which might have contributed to organic impairment, and (4) no visible organic signs. Brain-injured Ss were selected on the following basis: (1) defective intelligence, (2) parents and siblings of normal intelligence, (3) a known incident in S's developmental history which seemed likely to have caused organic impairment, and (4) no physical defect which would interfere with task performance.

These two studies provide strong evidence for a serial learning deficit in organic retardates as compared with familial Ss of roughly the same MA, IQ, and CA. The reader will note, however, that Cassel (1957) found no difference between equated organic and familial Ss on a paired-associate task. The reviewer suggests that Cassel's use of a nonverbal IQ test and/or his screening procedures were responsible for this difference.

Three studies (McCulloch, Reswick, & Roy, 1955; McCulloch, Reswick, & Weismann, 1955; Sloan & Berg, 1957), employing a common procedure, investigated the relationship between MA and total, grasp, and gain scores derived from the serial verbal learning of monosyllabic words. Eight lists, sequentially increasing in length from two to nine words, were presented orally with each list being presented five times and with S being allowed 3 seconds per word to reproduce the list.

These studies indicate that within the retarded population, MA is an important parameter of serial verbal learning. McCulloch, Reswick, and Roy (1955) found that an MA-9 group performed significantly better than an MA-6 group in total score, grasp (trial-1 performance on the various lists), and gain (five times trial-1 performance minus total score). McCulloch, Reswick, and Weismann (1955) and Sloan and Berg (1957) report, respectively, rs of .54 and .62 between MA (S-B) and total score, rs of .40 and .44 between MA and grasp, and rs of .34 and .23 between MA and gain.

These authors stress the fact that grasp and gain scores are not strongly related and that MA does not correlate with learning ability (gain) to any very meaningful extent. The stress on the use of gain scores can be traced to an article by Woodrow (1946), who pointed out that learning is typically defined as a *change* in performance with practice, so that in relating brightness measures to learning, a measure of change (gain) should be employed. When learning is equated with gain, Woodrow points out that the available evidence does not support a significant relationship between intelligence and learning. It would seem that gain scores are not worthwhile measures both from a statistical and from a logical point of view. First, reliability of trial-1 performance is certainly questionable (Hovland, 1951), and difference scores tend to be less reliable than the scores from which they were derived. In the McCulloch, Reswick, and Weismann (1955) study the estimated reliability of the gain measure was +.68, whereas in the Sloan and Berg study (1957) it was only +.22. Second, very different functions can have the same initial and terminal values, so that gain scores convey very little information regarding the complete course of learning. Third, if a function is negatively accelerated, and this seems to be true of most learning tasks, Ss who start with an initial advantage are strongly penalized by a decreasing rate of improvement with trials. For example, if one examines the serial learning data plotted by Ellis, Pryer, and Barnett (1960b) (see Chapter 3 by Cantor), it seems evident, despite the fact the normal Ss start at a higher level and reach an asymptote at a higher level, that the retarded Ss have the *rate* advantage. This is also true of other studies in the perceptual-motor area (Holman, 1933). Hence, if gain scores were taken seriously, it could be concluded that retarded Ss learn faster than equal-CA normals, despite the obvious contradiction that the normal Ss perform at a reliably higher level at all stages of performance! Fourth, on certain tasks there is very little room for improvement so that, again, Ss with higher trial-1 performance would be strongly penalized by the "ceiling" on possible improvement. Finally, the logic of the gain score implies that trial-1 performance reflects only ability and that new learning does not occur. This assumption seems highly improbable particularly in verbal learning tasks where S is being exposed to nonsense syllables.

This section can be conveniently summarized by noting the fairly high correlation between MA and serial learning in the retarded population and the handicap of organic Ss relative to familial Ss.

PERCEPTUAL-MOTOR LEARNING

The general literature on the relationship between CA and perceptual-motor learning indicates increasing proficiency with age on such tasks as the pursuit rotor (Ammons, Alprin, & Ammons, 1955), digit-symbol substitution, and mirror drawing (Pyle, 1925). Selected studies in this area are reviewed by McGeoch and Irion (1952) and Hovland (1951).

Maze learning studies

Hilgard (1951, p. 536) has indicated that the motor aspects of maze learning are typically subordinate to the verbal learning of serial choices. Maze learning is, however, reviewed here under the general rubric of perceptual-motor learning.

Only three studies have examined maze learning in retardates. An early study by DeSanctis (1931) employed 12 moderately retarded Ss, 9 approximately equal-MA preschool normals, and 11 school-age normals of roughly equal CA. The paper and pencil maze was used. Although statistical analyses were not made, DeSanctis reports that the younger normals learned the maze by a trial-and-error procedure, whereas both the older normals and the retardates mainly employed a strategy of "general orientation," i.e., sizing up the maze visually before starting. Only one retarded S (an idiot) did not learn the maze. Although the retardates were somewhat slower than the equal-CA normals, DeSanctis concluded that the performance of the retardates was more similar to that of the older normals than to that of the younger normals. Thus, there is evidence of an equal-MA superiority of the retarded Ss and little or no evidence to support an equal-CA deficit on an exposed maze.

Sloan and Berg (1957) tested 32 mildly and moderately retarded institutionalized Ss on an exposed maze and found no significant correlation between MA and time improvement scores or on time scores for the final trial of maze performance. Unfortunately, the authors did not assess the correlation between IQ, CA, and performance measures. Assuming a high correlation between MA and IQ in the Sloan and Berg sample, it would seem that performance on the exposed maze is not related to measures of intelligence provided the CA or possibly MA is roughly above 4 years. The DeSanctis study (1931) and studies cited by McGeoch and Irion

(1952, pp. 523–524) suggest that CA (emotional and muscular maturity) is an important parameter of maze learning independent of the CA-MA correlation.

When we turn to the most recent study by Ellis, Pryer, Distefano, and Pryer (1960), which tested a large sample of normal and retarded *S*s (the retarded *S*s were, on the average, older than the normals but lower in MA) on a concealed maze, a marked equal-CA deficit was evidenced. The normal *S*s required less than half the number of trials to learn the maze when compared with the retardates. This finding is particularly impressive in view of the fact that 22 *S*s, mainly below IQ 60, were eliminated from the experiment on the basis of their inability to learn a practice maze. The test maze traced by *S* was an eight choice-point, high-relief maze screened from his view. A learning criterion of not more than two errors on two successive trials and/or 100 trials was employed. *S*s were permitted to retrace out of cul-de-sacs and were given a 20-second rest after each trial. The mean performance scores of the different IQ groups are presented in Figure 11-1. It can be seen that the sharpest break in performance occurred between the IQ intervals of 60 to 79 and 80 to 89, i.e., between the upper range of deficiency and the lower range of "normal" intelligence. A plot of performance over trials in the different IQ groups suggested a common family of curves with different constants.

Figure 11-1. IQ and mean trials to criterion for retarded and normal *S*s on a shielded-maze task. (*Ellis, Pryer, Distefano, & Pryer, Amer. J. ment. Defic.,* 1960.)

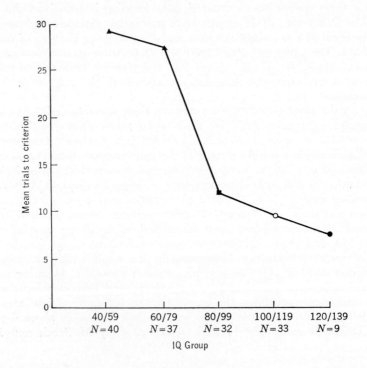

Denny (1963) has suggested that the dramatic inconsistency in findings among the studies which have employed the exposed and concealed maze is attributable to the important role played by verbal mediators in the successful performance on the shielded maze. The efficient use of verbal mediators, when *S* has not been specifically trained in their use, does not seem characteristic of retarded *S*s. That "verbalizers" have a strong performance advantage in learning a concealed maze is clearly indicated in studies reported by Hovland (1951, p. 629).

Within the retarded population, no reliable difference was found in the shielded-maze performance of 21 organic and 31 familial *S*s (Barnett, Ellis, & Pryer, 1960a).

In summary, on the open-maze task retarded *S*s have an equal-MA advantage when compared with fairly young normals (below CA 6 years) and evidence little or no deficit in equal-CA comparisons. On the shielded-maze task a pronounced equal-CA deficit is indicated which parallels the findings in the area of serial verbal learning. No data are available on the shielded maze to evaluate a possible equal-MA deficit, although the presence of this deficit would seem indicated in view of the importance of verbal mediation for successful task performance.

Rotary pursuit studies

The pursuit rotor, because of its motivating characteristics, high reliability, and the potentially wide range in scores from initial to final performance, has been extensively employed to investigate perceptual-motor learning.

Equal-CA comparisons. Two studies (Ellis, Pryer, & Barnett, 1960a; Jones & Ellis, 1962) compared the performance of older, but lower MA, institutionalized retardates with normals. The first study (Ellis, Pryer, & Barnett, 1960a) employed 80 mildly retarded and 80 normal *S*s under a 20-second work, 20-second rest schedule for 20 trials, 5-minute rest, and an additional 20 trials with the same work and rest intervals. Half the *S*s in both groups were given 10 additional trials 1 day later, while the remaining *S*s received 10 additional trials 28 days later. The normal *S*s performed at a reliably higher level over the 20 prerest and the 20 postrest trials. They also demonstrated larger reminiscence scores (last prerest score minus first postrest score), which bordered on significance ($P < .06$), and a considerably larger warm-up effect (first postrest trial minus the third postrest trial); they also retained *relatively* more over the retention trials ($P < .01$). The authors stress the theoretical importance of the relatively greater gains made by the normal *S*s after rest (and the longer retention intervals) and postulate that this difference may be attributed to a greater buildup of reactive inhibition (I_R) (Hull, 1943, pp. 277–302) in the normals during acquisition. The subsequent dissipation of I_R during rest would, of course, be reflected in better postrest performance in the normal *S*s as compared with the retardates. An alternative explanation is suggested by the work of Lipman and Spitz (1961). These authors found that the Hullian analog of satiation differences in rotary pursuit performance was the rate at which I_R *dissipated* during rest, with low satiaters showing a faster rate of I_R dissipation. Since retardates are lower satiaters, on the average, than equal-

CA normals, the reviewer would postulate that the basic difference between retarded and normal Ss is in the rate of I_R dissipation rather than in the rate of I_R buildup. The theoretical difference between these positions could be tested in a number of ways. One experiment, for example, might compare the performance of equated groups under three different work and rest schedules; (1) a spaced schedule in which I_R would not be a performance parameter (20-second work, 40-second rest), (2) a *pure* massed schedule (7-minute continuous work) where I_R dissipation would be minimized since no rest is given, and (3) a relatively massed schedule (20-second work, 10-second rest) which has been found to reflect satiation differences (Lipman & Spitz, 1961). The Ellis et al. (1960a) postulate would predict a reliable interaction between the performance of retarded and normal Ss under the pure massed schedule and the spaced schedule. The reviewer, on the other hand, would not predict an interaction effect between these schedules and IQ level. Both positions would predict an interaction between the relatively massed schedule (20-second work, 10-second rest), the spaced schedule, and IQ level, with the normals being relatively more penalized under the massed schedule.

Perhaps a more sensitive test of the two formulations would be provided by comparing the equivalent trial performance of equated CA groups under a well-spaced schedule with the reminiscence performance of retardates and normals when switched from a pure massed schedule to a well-spaced schedule after a rest interval, which permitted some but not all I_R to dissipate. We should again have the different interaction predictions with regard to prerest performance, but in this experiment the reviewer predicts that the retardates would close the performance gap between the massed and the spaced groups *more quickly* than would the normals. Ellis et al., if I understand their position correctly, would predict just the reverse: that the normal Ss would evidence the larger reminiscence gain (assuming they build in more I_R and that there are no group differences in the rate of I_R dissipation) and would close the prerest performance gap relatively more quickly under the postrest schedule than would the retarded Ss.

A second study (Jones & Ellis, 1962), which also employed older but lower-MA mildly retarded Ss, was designed to test the hypothesis that normal Ss build in more I_R than do retarded Ss. However, this study is not relevant to the prior discussion since a *pure* massed schedule was not employed, and positive results would support either interpretation. The 80 normal and 80 retarded Ss were randomly assigned (from each group) to either a massed (20-second work, 10-second rest) or a spaced (20-second work, 30-second rest) schedule. After 30 trials all Ss received a 5-minute rest and a postrest block of 20 trials. An examination of Figure 11-2 shows that the performance curves for all groups were typical for the rotary pursuit. Over trials 11 to 30 the normals performed at a significantly higher level than the retardates ($P < .01$), and Ss under the distributed practice schedule surpassed the massed practice Ss ($P < .01$). The predicted interaction between schedule and population approached significance. The normal Ss showed larger reminiscence gains over both schedules, but no reliable interaction between schedule and IQ level was found. Over the 20 postrest trials normals again surpassed the retardates, and a significant interaction between groups and schedules was evidenced. The triple-order interaction (trials $\times$ population $\times$ schedule) which would have more strongly suggested differences in the rate of I_R buildup (or dissipation) was not reliable. In summary, the studies by Ellis, Pryer, and Barnett (1960a) and Jones and Ellis (1962) clearly indicate an equal-CA deficit in retardates with regard to both acquisition and *relative* retention of rotary-pursuit skills. However, the reviewer cannot agree with Jones and Ellis in assuming that this deficit may be mainly motivational with associative components playing only a minor role. For one thing, if normals do develop I_R more quickly than do retardates, other things being equal, this would result in a relative performance *advantage* in the retarded population. Since it is also apparent that the normal Ss have a reliable performance advantage under the spaced schedule, where I_R is minimized, the reviewer would postulate that the underlying basis for the deficit is associative ($_sH_R$). The possibility remains, however, that retarded Ss may be relatively less handicapped under massed practice schedules, although the Jones and Ellis data provide, at best, only minimal support for this hypothesis.

Equal-MA comparisons.   Although no studies have directly examined the rotary-pursuit performance of equal-MA groups, Denny (1963) used the data obtained by Ellis and Sloan (1957) on $\overline{\text{MA}}$ 6.3 and $\overline{\text{MA}}$ 9.4 retarded Ss and compared their performance with that of the third-grade normals tested by Ammons, Alprin, and Ammons (1955). He concluded that these data were very similar and did not support an equal-MA deficit. Although

Figure 11-2. Rotary-pursuit performance of mentally defective and normal Ss under massed and distributed practice schedules. (*Jones & Ellis, J. exp. Psychol.,* 1962.)

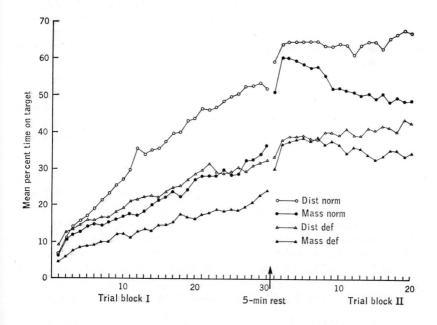

the performance of these groups was roughly equivalent, Denny's assumption that the practice schedules were *comparable* is questionable. In the Ammons et al. study, *S*s were run for 3 minutes, given a 5-minute rest, and then put back on a pure massed schedule; whereas the Ellis and Sloan schedule consisted of twenty 20-second trials with 20-second intertrial rests. The postrest performance of the normal *S*s showed a slightly falling performance curve, whereas the retarded *S*s evidenced a negatively accelerated curve over trials. It is suggested, therefore, that the possibility of an equal-MA deficit should remain an empirical question at this time.

Retarded *S*s only. Three studies (Barnett & Cantor, 1957; Ellis & Sloan, 1957; Ellis & Distefano, 1959) examined rotary-pursuit performance in retarded groups. The results of these studies indicate that retarded *S*s evidence typical pursuit-rotor effects: negatively accelerated acquisition curves, gains following rest, and more efficient performance under spaced practice than under massed practice schedules. The performance of retardates was also shown to be significantly influenced by verbal praise (Ellis & Distefano, 1959).

The studies by Barnett and Cantor (1957) and Ellis and Sloan (1957) do not agree with respect to the MA performance correlation in the retarded population. The former study found no reliable association between MA and a 1-minute performance score of 52 institutionalized retardates following twenty 1-minute trials on a 30-rpm rotor. The latter study reports a correlation of .43 between MA and total time-on-target with CA statistically controlled. The 88 institutionalized retardates in this latter study were more heterogeneous with respect to MA (2.4 to 10.8 years *versus* 5.7 to 10.2 years), and their performance over a wider range of trials was related to MA. Furthermore, the pursuit-rotor turntable turned at 60 rpm in the Ellis and Sloan experiment. Any one, or some combination, of these factors may have caused the difference in the results of these studies. The reviewer would speculate that the more difficult nature of the task in the Ellis and Sloan study is probably the main reason for the discrepancy. An MA $\times$ task difficulty interaction could, of course, be checked empirically.

Finally, Barnett, Ellis, and Pryer (1960a) examined the rotor performance of 24 organic and 37 familial *S*s who were roughly equated for MA and CA. Their criteria for selecting *S*s have been detailed in the section headed "Serial Verbal Learning." *S*s received twenty 20-second trials with 20-second intertrial rests. No reliable differences were found between the groups.

Mirror drawing

Equal-CA comparisons. Reynolds and Stacey (1955) tested 108 mildly retarded institutionalized *S*s and 60 normals approximately equal in CA on a mirror-drawing task in which *S* was required to connect 60 small circles contained within the borders of a six-pointed star. All *S*s received two trials with the nonpreferred hand. In the E group these trials were separated by 10 trials with the preferred hand, while in the C group they were separated by an equivalent rest interval. The *r* of —.54 between trial-1 time scores and IQ indicates an initial equal-CA deficit. The retarded *S*s, however, in both the E and the C groups, gained more from practice as evidenced by the —.50 correlation between IQ and the gain in seconds required for task completion from trial 1 to trial 2. Whether or not this gain was sufficient to overcome their initial absolute disadvantage was not tested. An inspection of the time scores revealed that the normal Ss, on the average, still required less time on trial 2. A projection of the different rates of gain suggests, of course, that given sufficient practice, the retarded Ss would have closed the performance gap. This projection is in keeping with the results of Holman (1933), who found that retarded Ss given extended practice on a ball-and-slot task were able to overcome an initial performance disadvantage relative to equal-CA normals.

Retarded Ss only. Ellis, Barnett, and Pryer (1957) tested a large ($N = 170$) and representative sample of institutionalized retardates using a five-pointed star. With a 20-minute limit for tracing the star, a biserial r of .46 was found between MA and the pass-fail dichotomy. The 93 Ss in the pass group were given 10 massed practice trials, and total errors (instances in which S traced outside the boundary of the star) were found to be significantly correlated ($r = .27; P < .01$) with MA. These investigators, however, were not able to replicate the Reynolds and Stacey (1955) finding of a significant correlation between IQ and time to trace the star on trial 1. Time to trace all stars was also not reliably associated with MA and CA. Denny (1963) attributes this discrepancy to a basic procedural difference in the two studies. He suggests that time is a more accurate reflection of proficiency when S is required to touch circles than it is when S is required to stay within the pathway of the star.

A comparison of 24 organic and 41 familial Ss on the task discussed above revealed no reliable difference in performance over the 10 trials employed (Barnett, Ellis, & Pryer, 1960a).

In summary, an equal-CA deficit is indicated on the mirror-drawing task. There is some suggestion, however, that with *extended* practice this deficit might be overcome. There is no evidence to bear out the possibility of an equal-MA deficit. In the main, the findings on the rotary pursuit and mirror-drawing tasks are very similar.

Assembly, card-sorting, and coding tasks

Equal-MA comparisons. Johnson and Blake (1960) compared equal-MA normals and noninstitutionalized retardates on a puzzle assembly task. The study was designed to provide a measure of transfer. The 18 Ss in each of the E and C groups were shown how to disassemble and reassemble a five-part puzzle and were then timed on 10 reassembly trials. Total time was recorded, and on following days the C groups repeated this same procedure four additional times. The E groups, on the other hand, were shown how to efficiently arrange the parts of the original puzzle and three unique puzzles, on the following days, before reassembling them for 10 timed trials. On the final day of the experiment, all Ss were required to reassemble the original puzzle as well as a unique puzzle.

Both C groups required reliably less time than their counterparts on the final trial of the original assembly task. Both E groups required significantly less time than the respective C groups on the final unique assembly task. It is of interest that the retarded C group surpassed the normal C group on the final administration of the original assembly task but performed at a significantly lower level on the unique assembly task. Within the E groups, no reliable performance difference was found on the original assembly task; but the retarded E group surpassed the normal E group on the final unique assembly task.

These data suggest an equal-MA advantage in the retarded group *provided* sufficient practice is given on those components of the task which make for efficient performance. However, the superior performance of the normal C group, relative to the retarded C group, on the unpracticed unique assembly task suggests either more indirect positive transfer and/or a more flexible task orientation in the normal Ss.

An equal-MA advantage for retarded Ss was also found by Johnson and Blake (1960) on a card-sorting task in which S was required to sort 32 cards containing four meaningless designs into four boxes similarly labeled.

In a third study, Johnson and Blake (1960) compared the letter-coding performance of 80 equal-MA normals with that of 80 institutionalized retardates. An E group–C group design was employed to cast light upon proactive and retroactive inhibition. Both groups received two administrations of the original coding task (OT). In the E groups, these administrations were separated by an interpolated task (IT), in which S had to assign the same set of numerals (1 to 9) differentially to the same letters employed in the OT. The retarded Ss assigned reliably more numbers to the appropriate letters on the OT. They also demonstrated reliably less proactive and retroactive inhibition. These findings suggest that *perhaps* the normal Ss had adopted a different strategy in approaching this task as compared with the retardates. One hypothesis would be that the normal Ss attempted to memorize the specific digit-letter associations and thus showed more interference when prior associations were no longer correct in the task. In this connection, if a recall task had been employed after OT I, IT, and OT II, it would have been possible to determine the associations formed in the different groups. At any rate, the results of the Johnson and Blake studies, for the most part, indicate an equal-MA advantage for retardates on such perceptual-motor tasks as card sorting, letter coding, and object assembly.

Form-board, athletic, and miscellaneous tasks

Equal-CA comparisons. The first study in this series to employ a normal control group was that of Holman (1933). Eighteen normals and thirty-three equal-CA retardates were tested on a ball-and-slot task in which S was required to tip a small glass-covered box so that a ball on the top platform fell into a specific slot on the bottom of the box. Ss were given 800 trials per week over a 4-week period, and the number of balls correctly placed was tabulated. The normal Ss maintained a reliable performance advantage over the first week of practice, but the retarded Ss began closing this gap, so that by the third and fourth weeks there were no reliable differences between the groups. This suggests that with sufficient practice, even on a somewhat difficult perceptual-motor task, retarded Ss may reach the same performance asymptote as normals. In view of this finding, it would seem profitable to extend the practice sessions on other perceptual-motor tasks, such as the pursuit rotor and mirror drawing, to determine whether similar findings might obtain here as well.

In what appears to be a "pure" work task (block turning), Boldt (1953) tested 60 mildly and moderately retarded Ss and 60 college students under a massed and a spaced work schedule. The college Ss were faster under both practice schedules; interaction, presumably, was not significant (statistics are alluded to but not presented); and the spaced groups worked at a faster rate than the massed groups. The presumed failure to find a reliable interaction between IQ level and schedule does not support the Jones and Ellis (1962) hypothesis that normal Ss build in more I_R than retardates, nor does it support the alternative hypothesis of the reviewer that retarded Ss dissipate I_R more quickly than normals. However, Boldt's report of the study is rather sketchy; and it is difficult to gauge the validity of these results. For one thing, motivational instructions are not presented. It also seems likely that the much more varied age range in the retarded sample introduces an unevaluated source of variability. In view of the general literature on work tasks, the reviewer would speculate that the results of this study may only reflect the fact that the older Ss in the retarded sample were handicapped in their speed of motor response.

Retarded Ss only. Congruent with Holman's (1933) finding on the beneficial effect of extended practice with retarded Ss, Tizard and Loos (1954) have shown that with sufficient demonstrations, coaxing, and practice, a "fair" percentage (three out of eight) of moderately retarded Ss score above the 50th percentile on the Minnesota Spatial Relations Test. Within a more applied setting, Clarke and Hermelin (1955) have also demonstrated that moderately retarded adults with long histories of institutionalization and probably organic involvement can reliably perform such vocational tasks as wire cutting, soldering colored wires to matching terminals, and assembling bicycle pumps which required nine sequentially ordered operations. Interestingly enough, while these Ss were able to cut wires as efficiently as well-practiced Ss with a 40 IQ point advantage, they were unable to learn the more abstract operations required by the Wechsler Block Design Test.

A series of studies (Brace, 1948; Johnson, 1919; Kuhlman, 1904) have examined performance on athletic tasks in the retarded population (target throwing, ball bouncing, etc.). The general conclusion to be drawn from these studies, which were not well controlled, is that both performance level and improvement in performance with practice are only slightly, if at all, related to IQ. Brace, in the most sophisticated approach to this problem, has shown that when physical ability measures (balance, agility, etc.) are statistically removed from the IQ-learning task correlation, little or no variance remains.

Despite the apparent importance of the task-difficulty dimension, as suggested by the divergent results of verbal learning studies when familiar pictured objects and nonsense syllables were employed as well as by the rotary-pursuit studies where rpm (30 versus 60) seemed to be a significant parameter of the MA-performance relationship, only one study, excluding massed versus spaced schedules, has *directly* examined this variable. Annet (1957) tested 72 institutionalized retardates ranging in age from 16 to 21 years. *S*s were subdivided into three IQ groups: 60 and over, 40 to 59, and 39 or less. The task was to remove the white pegs from one form board and insert them into another form board. *E* varied the white pegs on the source board in the following four ways: all white pegs, an equal number of white and black pegs, four times the number of black to white pegs, and eight times the number of black to white pegs. In information-theory terms, this corresponds to 0, 1, 2, and 3 bits, respectively. Task order was counterbalanced with time as the dependent variable. Although the design of the study precluded the statistical analysis of interaction effects, there is a strong suggestion that IQ groups were most alike in performance under the least difficult arrangement (0 bits) and least alike under the most difficult arrangement (3 bits). The lower-IQ *S*s performed at a reliably lower level, over the combined conditions, than did the higher-IQ *S*s. Twelve *S*s, from each of the three IQ groups, were then given extended practice (1,200 trials) at this task; and, although the lower-IQ *S*s improved more than the other groups, they still did not reach the performance level of the higher-IQ *S*s. The author suggested that this discrepancy might be attributable to the organic impairment and/or the low MA of the imbecile group. In this connection, Ordahl and Ordahl (1915) found that an MA-6 group of retarded *S*s who were given ten 1-minute trials in a task which consisted in learning to associate different colors with the keys they controlled, over a 6-day period, were unable to perform the task with the keys and colors covered. An MA-8 and an MA-10 group, in contrast, were capable of learning the task, with the brighter *S*s having the initial and final performance advantage. In this same vein, it should be noted that Ellis and Sloan (1957) found that an MA-3.6 group was unable to learn the rotary-pursuit task. These findings add weight to the generally held view that MA level determines the complexity of tasks that can be learned.

Because of the gaps which exist with regard to relevant normal control groups, it is difficult to summarize the learning deficits of retardates in the area of perceptual-motor learning. On the pursuit-rotor and the mirror-drawing tasks there is an equal-CA deficit. However, there is some evidence to suggest, with regard to the mirror-drawing task, that with extended practice the retarded *S*s would be able to overcome this performance handicap. With extended practice on a ball-and-slot task this situation obtained.

There are no data directly relevant to a possible equal-MA deficit on the rotary-pursuit or mirror-drawing tasks. However, on such tasks as puzzle assembly, digit-symbol substitution, and card-sorting an equal-MA advantage was found in the older retarded *S*s.

Task difficulty seems to be an important parameter of the intelligence-performance relationship, as does amount of practice. MA level seems to determine the upper limit of task complexity that can be mastered. However, provided the task is within the ability range of the *S*, *sufficient* practice might overcome initial performance disadvantages. Both the difficulty dimension and the practice dimension are worthy variables for future study.

CLASSICAL CONDITIONING

The classical-conditioning paradigm, more so than most other learning paradigms, is fraught with the possibility of artifacts and is definitely not an area in which the inexperienced investigator is likely to obtain valid data. Hilgard and Marquis (1940) and Hilgard (1951) have indicated many of the problems with regard to providing the necessary controls for sensitization and pseudoconditioning effects. In addition, apparatus and recording problems, environmental control problems (noise, temperature, etc.), and controls for temporal conditioning, when they themselves are not being studied, all present serious difficulties for the experimenter. Moreover, instructional sets and more subtle "self-instructional" sets (how *S* interprets the task) have been shown to influence the course of conditioning (Hilgard & Marquis, 1940). On this latter point, Woodworth (1938, p. 110) has suggested that certain types of conditioning may represent a "game" which *S* plays with *E*. At any rate, Pavlov's basic assumption that conditioning reflects underlying brain processes cannot be unconditionally accepted even with regard to the most involuntary conditioned responses (CRs) (Hilgard & Marquis, 1940, p. 34).

Since many of the studies reviewed here are not published in the English language, the writer has made extensive use of secondary sources. Another point which should be stressed is that the Russian literature in this area is extremely difficult to evaluate since IQ and MA scores are not sufficiently detailed to permit evaluation of control features. No attempt will be made to review the important contributions of Professor A. R. Luria. The reader is referred to his chapter (10) in the present text. The usual organization of materials will not be attempted in this section, but rather a rough chronology of studies will be presented, organized in terms of their usage of appetitive or aversive unconditioned stimuli (UCS).

Appetitive UCS

The first study to investigate the acquisition and extinction of the CR to a positive UCS (candy and honey) in retarded and normal children was done by a Russian experimenter, Krasnogorski, in 1913. This study was reviewed by Mateer (1917), Burnham (1924), and Razran (1933). Unfortunately, Krasnogorski did not report the number, age, or ability level of his *S*s. How *S*s were handled in the experimental situation is also not indicated (Mateer, 1917). The conditioned stimuli (CS) were auditory and tactual, and their presentation was followed, 10 seconds later, by the UCS. The CR (swallowing and mouth movements) was recorded by running a tambor from between the jaw and hyoid bone to a kymograph. *S*s were blindfolded during the experiment.

The CR took longer to establish in the retarded group and was much more difficult to extinguish. Delayed CRs were hard to establish in mildly and moderately retarded *S*s, and almost impossible in the severely defective.

Conditioned inhibition was similarly very difficult to establish and extremely fragile. With severely and moderately retarded children, differential response to mechanical, thermal, and tactual stimuli could not be established.

Florence Mateer, who has the historical distinction of being the first American to do a classical-conditioning study, modified Krasnogorski's procedure and tested 50 normal children and 14 retarded children (of these retarded *S*s, 7 were employed in the pilot phase of Mateer's study before a finalized procedure was determined and the remaining 7 received the same treatment as the normals) for CR acquisition, retention, extinction, and reconditioning. The procedure Mateer employed was to place a bandage over *S*'s eyes (CS) and on the eleventh second to put candy in *S*'s mouth (UCS) and then remove the bandage after 20 seconds, wait 3 minutes (invariable) during which *E* and *S* played games, and then repeat the sequence. The CR (mouth and throat movements which occurred during the 10-second CS-UCS interval) was recorded kymographically, and the experiment was continued until two successive CRs occurred. Reconditioning to the same criterion was repeated 24 hours later whereupon extinction trials were given until the CR failed to occur on two successive trials. At this point, the CS and UCS were again paired until conditioning was reestablished.

Mateer's results are somewhat difficult to interpret, even when the primitive nature of her instrumentation and her failure to control for temporal conditioning are overlooked, since only seven retarded *S*s received the same treatment as the normals, and these *S*s were not matched for MA or CA. The CA match, of the two, was the closer although the normal *S*s were younger, on the average. Despite the normal *S*'s requiring roughly the same number of trials to CR acquisition as the retarded *S*s, the .82 correlation between CA (1 to 5 years) and trial to criterion in the normal sample suggests that an equal-CA comparison would have revealed an equal-CA deficit. Razran (1933), who reviewed both the Krasnogorski and Mateer studies, offered much the same *low degree of confidence* conclusion. With regard to the acquisition of salivary and motor food CRs, he states, "Other things being equal, the more intelligent the child the more readily it forms the CR" (p. 100). Razran also offered this same tentative conclusion with regard to equal-MA comparisons. The reviewer, however, was unable to find the evidence to support this viewpoint unless reference was being made to the severely defective and the lower-IQ *S*s within the moderately retarded IQ range where conditioning was extremely slow.

The CR was retained, with almost no loss, in all *S*s over the 24-hour interval. The most dramatic difference between the groups was in the number of trials required to obtain extinction. Denny (1963) found a highly reliable difference between the normal ($\overline{7.4}$; range = 3 to 12 trials) and retarded ($\overline{12.3}$; range = 8 to 16 trials) data ($P < .001$). Both an equal-CA deficit and an equal-MA deficit are indicated by these extinction data. To quote Mateer, "If we place any defective boy or girl in the unselected group in the place where he would belong by virtue of his age, sex and mentality . . . he will be outside the range of variations of the unselected (normal) group in the number of trials he needs to develop unlearning" (p. 205).

Hilgard and Marquis (1940), it should be noted, have classified the responses of mouth opening and swallowing among the more voluntary CRs. Razran (1933), however, also cites a study by Chuchmarev, who found a fairly high correlation between school achievement and the acquisition and extinction of the *salivary* response in seven sixth-grade children. Thus, there is some additional presumptive evidence to suggest that the generality of the findings of the Krasnogorski and Mateer studies are not limited to only the more voluntary CRs.

While these findings seem reasonably clear, their interpretation seems anything but clear. Thus, they might be considered to reflect differences in central nervous system (CNS) functioning, attentional deficits in the retarded population (Zeaman & House, 1959), weakened verbal control of motor response in retardates (Luria, 1959; Luria & Vinogradova, 1959), or lowered contingencies of reward expectations as a result of developmental histories of deprivation (Stevenson & Zigler, 1958).

Aversive UCS

The first study (Osipova, 1926, as reported by Razran, 1933) to examine the acquisition of a CR (finger withdrawal) to an aversive UCS (electric shock) employed 58 retarded males, 67 normal boys, and 75 normal girls who were approximately equal in CA to the retarded Ss. A bell signaled the approach, which followed 2 to 3 seconds later, of the electric shock, and a 15- to 45-second rest (control for temporal conditioning) occurred between trials. There were no sex differences within the normal group. The retarded Ss formed stable CRs to the shock significantly faster than the equal-CA normals (5.5 trials versus 11 trials). Moreover, whereas all 58 retarded Ss acquired the finger withdrawal CR, approximately 25 per cent of the normals did not condition. Thus, the results of the Osipova study are in direct contradiction to the prior findings of conditionability with a positive UCS; namely, the retarded Ss evidence an equal-CA superiority. This finding, however, must be interpreted in light of the rather well-known (Denny, 1963; Hilgard & Marquis, 1940) fact that normal Ss frequently interpret finger-withdrawal conditioning as a test of "guts" so that the significance of this result is not entirely clear. Osipova's results are also inconsistent with those of Goldenfoun (Razran, 1933, pp. 88–89) and of Marinesco and Kreindler (1933). However, these latter studies each employed only four retarded Ss, and they were in the severely and moderately retarded range. The Marinesco and Kreindler study employed strong shock to the palm or bottom of the foot as the UCS and limb withdrawal as the CR. Conditioning was difficult to establish, generalized in nature, and very unstable. These observations are congruent with those of Goldenfoun, who worked with the patellar reflex. Hilgard and Marquis (1940) have commented, however, that when successful patellar conditioning is obtained "it appears that voluntary habitual facilitation is an important factor . . ." (p. 35).

In this country, Melhado (1949) tested pupillary conditioning in 14 adult retardates, 14 retarded children (mildly, moderately, and severely retarded being about equally represented), and 6 normal adults (5 of these *S*s were college students). A tactile stimulus (CS) was applied to *S*'s right ankle 0.5 second prior to a 1.0-second light flash (UCS). A 2-second rest was given, and this pattern was repeated for 12 trials with a 15-second rest following trial 12. This sequence was repeated three times, and on trial 36 the CS was presented alone followed by a 1-minute rest and then four additional administrations of this same sequence until 180 trials were given. These 180 trials included five conditioning test trials. Those *S*s who conditioned (evidenced pupillary contraction to the CS when presented alone) were then tested for *irradiation* by presenting the CS to four points between the original focal point and the knee. Melhado's results are more in keeping with those of Goldenfoun and Marinesco and Kreindler as opposed to Osipova. The reviewer tested the number of trials to the first appearance of the CR in the normal (who were older) and mildly retarded group and found a significant difference favoring the normals. Whereas all normal and mildly retarded *S*s evidenced the CR, two *S*s from both the moderate and severe range failed to condition. The CR was found to generalize to points further removed from the original point of conditioning to a greater extent in the retarded than in the normal group. The less impaired retardates performed most like the normals. Definite cautions, however, are needed in accepting Melhado's findings since there were no controls for sensitization, pseudoconditioning, or temporal conditioning. Moreover, *E* worked alone in an experimental room that was not soundproofed, in which the apparatus was noisy; and further, *E* had considerable difficulty in keeping *S* in the experimental task. More doubt is cast upon the validity of Melhado's findings in light of a study by Hilgard, Dutton, and Helmick (1949), which convincingly demonstrated the extreme difficulty of obtaining reliable pupillary conditioning with light as the UCS, even under "ideal" conditions of instrumentation and control.

Another rather crudely instrumented study (Berger, 1954) examined inhibition of the eyelid reflex in 61 institutionalized retardates (classified as organic, familial, and psychogenic) and 20 normal *S*s. The retarded groups were roughly equal in MA and CA and of about the same CA as the normals. *E* rated *S*'s eyeblink response, elicited by an object striking a glass plate positioned in front of *S*'s eye, as either "absent," "partially inhibited," or "totally inhibited." All retarded groups required significantly more trials than the normal group to totally inhibit the response. Organic *S*s required reliably more trials to partially inhibit the response as compared with familial *S*s. Thus, again, we find the equal-CA inhibition (extinction) deficit and the suggestion that this deficit is particularly pronounced in the organic subgroup. That organicity may indeed represent an important population parameter within the classical conditioning paradigm is strongly suggested in a recent study by Franks and Franks (1960). These authors employed 17 organic and 52 nonorganic retardates, roughly equal in CA and IQ, and 80 *S*s of normal IQ and approximately the same CA as the defective *S*s. This study has the distinctive merit of being the only investigation reviewed so far in this section in which satisfactory controls for pseudoconditioning, sensitization, and temporal conditioning, as well as sophisticated instrumentation and the use of a specially constructed soundproofed laboratory (at Maudsley Hospital, London), all obtained. Their basic procedure was to present the CS (a pure tone) for 800 milliseconds with UCS (an air puff) overlapping the last 500 milliseconds of the CS. A *variable* 25-second rest was given between trials. Eighteen CS presentations were interspersed among 30 paired CS-UCS presentations. The CR was recorded by a photoelectric cell. Ten extinction trials followed the acquisition period. The results of this study are presented in Figure 11-3, and as can be seen there, the course of CR acquisition and extinction was very similar in the normal and nonorganic retarded groups. The organic *S*s, in contrast, conditioned reliably more slowly than the other groups. They also did not evidence the regular decrease in the strength of the CR that characterized the performance of the normals and the nonorganic retardates under the extinction procedure. Within both the retarded and normal samples, no reliable association was found between IQ and conditioning or extinction. Franks and Franks concluded that "acquisition and extinction of conditioned eyelid responses in the mental defective is not related to intelligence level as measured by tests but to the presence or absence of CNS deficit" (p. 5). Since Franks (1958) had previously indicated that no general factor of conditioning had been established, they cautioned against generalizing this finding beyond eyelid conditioning.

Cromwell, Palk, and Foshee (1961) have also examined eyelid condition-

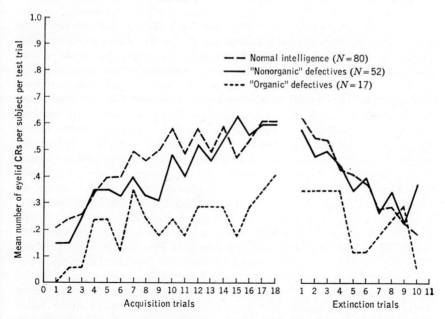

Figure 11-3. Acquisition and extinction of the eyelid response in organic and nonorganic retardates as compared with normal controls. (*Franks & Franks, Proc. London Conf. Sci. Study ment. Defic.*, 1960.)

ing. They employed 61 randomly selected institutionalized retardates who varied widely in CA, MA, and IQ. The experiment was well controlled and well instrumented. Eighty conditioning trials were administered with a buzzer signaling a voluntary eyeblink; and then, after a 3-second delay, an illuminated disc, which S was instructed to watch, was increased in brightness and remained bright for 550 milliseconds (the CS). The air puff (UCS) was given during the 50 milliseconds of the increasing illumination. The main scoring measure was the number of eyeblinks which occurred in the 200- to 500-millisecond interval of the CS and which were not proceeded by eyeblinks in the 0- to 200-millisecond range. As in the Franks and Franks (1960) study, IQ (also CA) was not found to be reliably related to eyelid conditioning. A low (.29) but reliable ($P < .05$) association was found between MA and eyelid conditioning. Since no attempt was made in the Cromwell et al. investigation to identify organic and nonorganic Ss, it is not possible to evaluate the extent to which a likely heavy loading of organic Ss at the lower-MA ranges might be contributing to the MA–eyelid-conditioning relationship. In any event, the results of both studies are in fairly close agreement: For eyelid conditioning they contradict an equal-MA deficit in nonorganic retardates, and with less certainty, an equal-CA deficit in this subgroup. An equal-CA deficit in eyelid conditioning and extinction is indicated in organic retardates.

The final study in this section examined the conditioning and extinction of the galvanic skin response (GSR) to mild electric shock in 8 mongoloid children without CNS damage; in 18 organic Ss, who were classified behaviorally as either "hyperactive," "normoactive," or "hypoactive"; and in 4 normal Ss (Birch & Demb, 1959). Although the conditioning procedure was well controlled and well instrumented, the size and variability (with regard to CA, MA, and IQ) of the retarded subgroups, together with the lack of specification regarding the normative characteristics of the normal controls, make interpretation of the results of this study extremely difficult. The mongoloid Ss, for example, were both younger and lower in IQ than the other retarded subgroups. The normal Ss were reported to condition significantly faster than the retardates, with the nonhyperactive Ss (normoactive and hypoactive) being a possible exception. Within the retarded sample, the hyperactive and mongoloid subgroups did not condition as readily as the nonhyperactive group. Congruent with the Franks and Franks (1960) study and the Cromwell et al. (1961) study, no correlation was found between IQ and GSR conditioning. One rather surprising aspect of the Birch and Demb investigation was their failure to find reliable extinction differences among the groups. On this latter point, Birch and Demb present observational data which suggest a basic difference in the extinction process between the hyperactive organics and the normals and mongoloids. In these latter groups, many of the Ss fell asleep during extinction leading the authors to attribute extinction in these Ss to internal inhibition. The hyperactive Ss, on the other hand, either maintained their previously high activity level or even increased their activity during extinction, leading the authors to postulate that external inhibition was operating to produce extinction in these Ss.

The studies reviewed in this section are very difficult to summarize, and the reviewer would stress the need for better instrumented and controlled studies in this area. Further, it would seem profitable to pay more attention to the etiological classification of retarded Ss. Perhaps the strongest conclusion that can be drawn is that of an equal-CA deficit in CR acquisition and, particularly, in CR extinction in retarded Ss with CNS damage. In this connection, it is the writer's strong impression that the Russian studies have primarily employed organic retardates and that the likelihood of organicity in the severely and moderately retarded ranges in studies which have not attempted etiological classification is high. It also seems likely than an equal-MA deficit in CR acquisition and extinction obtains with CNS-damaged retardates and/or severely retarded Ss. With mildly retarded nonorganic Ss, the reviewer would carefully weigh the Franks and Franks (1960) study, which argues against an equal-CA deficit in eyelid conditioning. How far the results of this study can be generalized is questionable since no general factor of conditionability has yet been found.

In a recent review of psychological research in the Soviet Union, Razran (1961) has reported the use of *interoceptive* conditioning (vascular changes, for example) which proceeds without the S's conscious awareness. He points out that this technique controls for the possibility that classical conditioning may be "wholly a function of cognitive-perceptual expectancies . . ." (p. 97). The reviewer would strongly suggest that future investigators seriously consider the use of interoceptive conditioning as a means of obtaining more clearly interpretable data in this area.

A POINT OF VIEW AND SUGGESTED RESEARCH DIRECTIONS

Since the various areas of learning covered by this review have been summarized on a section-by-section basis, no attempt at recapitulation will be made. The writer will, instead, take a broader look at the area of learning and will draw upon research that falls outside the domain of the present chapter.

The "big-deficit" versus "little-deficits" approach

There is the strong temptation, apparently motivated by closure and parsimony needs, to attribute the learning deficiencies of lower-IQ Ss to the operation of some single variable. The reviewer has labeled this approach the "big-deficit" theory. Thus, for example, long-term retention (Mowrer, 1960; Stolurow, 1960), incidental learning (Denny, 1963), attention (Kuhlmann, 1904), and a dissociation between the verbal and motor "signaling-systems" (Luria, 1959) have been variously nominated as the big deficit. The other pole of the deficit continuum, and the reviewer is somewhat overstating these positions, is the "little-deficits" theory, in which the observed learning deficits in retardates are attributable to the *interaction* of many variables whose combined influence results in lowered learning efficiency. Thus, for example, deficiencies might arise from any combination of the following: poor attention, a "sluggish" brain and nervous system which requires more stimulation before structural connections are affected, stronger proactive and retroactive interference effects, less efficient transfer from similar learning experiences, less incidental learning, poorer short- and long-term retention, inefficient use of verbal mediators, and less efficient categorization of learned materials.

In the reviewer's opinion the little-deficits theory has some very definite conceptual advantages. For one thing, it takes cognizance of the fact that no single *g* factor can adequately account for the variance in different learning tasks or, for that matter, in the variance of scale scores in IQ tests. Thus, the little-deficits theory does not obscure the fact that very different abilities are probably involved in different learning tasks. Moreover, it also does not preclude the likelihood that certain deficits and combinations of deficits are apt to be more basic at different levels of retardation and possibly, also, with different etiological classifications. Hence an attentional deficit which appears to be quite important in the discrimination learning of severely retarded *S*s (Zeaman & House, 1959) may not be at all basic within the mild retardation range. Just as we have found that all-encompassing systems of psychology have given way to the more fruitful "miniature system" (for example, Hull et al., 1940), so too the reviewer would suggest that what is urgently needed is a *systematic* approach to a better understanding of task parameters. As an example, House and Zeaman and their associates at the University of Connecticut have adopted such an approach in the area of discrimination learning. Similar systematically focused research is undoubtedly needed in the learning areas covered by this review. It is unfortunate, therefore, that the *modus operandi* of most investigators in the field of retardation has been to distribute their research efforts rather thinly over the many experimental tasks in the psychologist's repertory.

The long-term retention deficit

The long-term retention deficit has only recently been nominated to the big-deficit list (Mowrer, 1960; Stolurow, 1960). It is predicated on the *assumption* that retarded and normal *S*s learn at the same rate. If, in fact, learning rates are equivalent, then the less efficient performance of retarded *S*s, according to this position, is most likely attributable to a long-term retention deficit. Denny (1963) has reviewed the relevant literature and has suggested that the limited data on retention do not support a long-term retention deficit of any appreciable magnitude. The writer would concur with Denny and, in addition, would point out that in many studies learning rates are *not* the same across IQ levels (for example, Ellis, Pryer, & Barnett, 1960b; Ellis & Sloan, 1959; Holman, 1933; Jones & Ellis, 1962). Moreover, the most widely accepted theory of forgetting, aside from psychoanalytic considerations, stresses the importance of *interference,* i.e., proactive and retroactive inhibition (Osgood, 1953). When studies which have examined these effects are scrutinized (Cassel, 1957; Johnson & Blake, 1960; Pryer, 1960), little or no support is found for the presence of stronger retroaction or proaction in lower-IQ *S*s.

Denny (1963) also rejects the "leaky bucket hypothesis" which has been proposed to underlie an assumed long-term retention deficit.[3] The reviewer is again in agreement with Denny and would cite the classic experiment by Gerard (1953) which seems to indicate that *structural* changes take place when learning occurs. Hebb (1949) also presents evidence along similar lines. A "leaky bucket" concept of forgetting, like the "law of disuse," which it strongly resembles, is not congruent with structural change. Denny proposes that to the extent that a long-term retention deficit may obtain, a "peanut brittle hypothesis" seems more plausible; that is, retarded Ss may not have retained available associates as well-integrated responses to the same extent as normal Ss. As support for the "peanut brittle hypothesis," Denny cites the fact that the verbal associations of retardates are frequently not semantically related and that in the serial verbal learning study of Johnson and Blake (1960) retarded Ss did not perform as well as equal-MA normals on an imbedded nonsense syllable recognition task but did not differ from the normals on the relearning of these syllables. This, of course, suggests that retarded Ss do not "store" their associations in as efficient a fashion as do normal Ss. In this connection, the associative clustering technique (Bousfield & Cohen, 1955), which represents a logical outgrowth of Hebbian theory, might profitably be employed to further explore the organizational aspects of learning and retention across IQ levels. In one of the few studies that compared equal-MA normal, organic, and familial Ss, Osborne (1960) found no reliable overall differences in clustering (successive recall of words from the same semantic category), although the performance curves of the retarded groups showed some irregularities which Osborne interpreted as suggesting inefficient learning habits.

The incidental learning deficit

Denny (1963) has suggested that retarded Ss, characterized by weaker "internal" sets, may not be as effective incidental learners as normals. That is, retardates may require special guidance and motivation to learn effectively, whereas normal Ss may be "naturally" set to learn. Denny has indicated that although no data are presently available to evaluate this hypothesis, an experimental test of the postulate would not be difficult. While the reviewer would agree that this hypothesis merits investigation, and certainly recognizes the very tentative nature of Denny's hypothesis, he cannot help but feel that *both* incidental learning deficiencies and "focused" learning deficiencies will eventually be attributable to more genotypical deficits.

Retardation studies and general theoretical issues

Most of the studies reviewed by the writer have focused on comparing the performance of retardates and normals or on MA and IQ as parameters within the retarded population. While this is a necessary emphasis to further our understanding of retardation, the reviewer would also point out that studies can be designed, at the same time, to cast light upon general theoretical issues. For example, Pryer (1960) not only compared normal and retarded Ss on a serial learning task but he also designed the

[3] The reviewer was unable to determine the source of the "leaky bucket hypothesis."

study to investigate the general problem of the relationship between retention loss and the temporal interval between the OL list and the IL list. The main point here is that there is no a priori reason why we cannot, in the same study, both further our knowledge about retardation and also collect data relevant to general issues in psychology. This latter approach would serve the useful purpose of widening the general audience of scientists who become acquainted with research problems in the area of retardation and, hopefully, would impose a stronger theoretical orientation on future studies.

REFERENCES

AKUTAGWA, D., & BENOIT, E. P. The effect of age and relative brightness on associative learning in children. *Child Develpm.*, 1959, 30, 229–238.

AMMONS, R. B., ALPRIN, S. I., & AMMONS, CAROL H. Rotary pursuit performance as related to sex and age of pre-adult subjects. *J. exp. Psychol.*, 1955, 49, 127–133.

ANNETT, J. The information capacity of young mental defectives in an assembly task. *J. ment. Sci.*, 1957, 103, 621–631.

BADT, MARGIT I. Levels of abstraction in vocabulary definitions of mentally retarded school children. *Amer. J. ment. Defic.*, 1958, 63, 241–246.

BARNETT, C. D., & CANTOR, G. N. Pursuit rotor performance in mental defectives as a function of distribution of practice. *Percept. mot. Skills*, 1957, 7, 191–197.

BARNETT, C. D., ELLIS, N. R., & PRYER, MARGARET W. Learning in familial and brain injured defectives. *Amer. J. ment. Defic.*, 1960, 64, 894–901. (a)

BARNETT, C. D., ELLIS, N. R., & PRYER, MARGARET W. Serial position effects in superior and retarded subjects. *Psychol. Rep.*, 1960, 7, 111–113. (b)

BERGER, A. Inhibition of the eyelid reflex in three etiologic groups of mentally retarded boys as compared with normals. *Train. Sch. Bull.*, 1954, 51, 146–152.

BERKSON, G., & CANTOR, G. N. A study of mediation in mentally retarded and normal school children. *J. educ. Psychol.*, 1960, 51, 82–86.

BIRCH, H. G., & DEMB, H. The formation and extinction of conditioned reflexes in "brain-damaged" and mongoloid children. *J. nerv. ment. Dis.*, 1959, 129, 162–170.

BOLDT, R. F. Motor learning in college students and mental defectives. *Proc. Iowa Acad. Sci.*, 1953, 60, 500–505.

BOUSFIELD, W., & COHEN, B. The occurrence of clustering in the recall of randomly arranged words of different frequencies-of-usage. *J. gen. Psychol.*, 1955, 52, 83–95.

BRACE, D. K. Motor learning of feeble-minded girls. *Res. Quart. Amer. Ass. Hlth*, 1948, 19, 269–275.

BURNHAM, W. H. *The normal mind.* New York: Appleton-Century-Crofts, 1924.

CASSEL, R. H. Serial verbal learning and retroactive inhibition in aments and children. *J. clin. Psychol.*, 1957, 13, 369–372.

CIEUTAT, V., STOCKWELL, F., & NOBLE, C. The interaction of ability and amount of practice with stimulus and response meaningfulness (m,m′) in paired-associate learning. *J. exp. Psychol.*, 1958, 56, 193–202.

CLARKE, A. D., & HERMELIN, B. P. Adult imbeciles: their abilities and trainability. *Lancet*, 1955, 2, 337–339.

CROMWELL, R. L., PALK, B. E., & FOSHEE, J. G. Studies in activity level. V. The relationships among eyelid conditioning, intelligence, activity level, and age. *Amer. J. ment. Defic.*, 1961, 65, 744–748.

DENNY, M. R. Learning. In R. Heber and H. Stevens (Eds.), *Review of research in mental retardation*. Chicago: Univer. of Chicago Press, 1963.

DESANCTIS, S. Visual apprehension in the maze behavior of normal and feeble-minded children. *J. genet. Psychol.*, 1931, 39, 463–467.

ELLIS, N. R., BARNETT, C. D., & PRYER, MARGARET W. Performance of mental defectives on the mirror drawing task. *Percept. mot. Skills*, 1957, 7, 271–274.

ELLIS, N. R., & DISTEFANO, M. K., JR. The effects of verbal urging and praise upon rotary pursuit performance in mental defectives. *Amer. J. ment. Defic.*, 1959, 64, 486–490.

ELLIS, N. R., PRYER, MARGARET W., & BARNETT, C. D. Motor learning and retention in normals and defectives. *Percept. mot. Skills*, 1960, 10, 83–91. (a)

ELLIS, N. R., PRYER, MARGARET W., & BARNETT, C. D. Note on habit formation in normal and retarded subjects. *Psychol. Rep.*, 1960, 6, 385–386. (b)

ELLIS, N. R., PRYER, MARGARET W., DISTEFANO, M. K., JR., & PRYER, R. S. Learning in mentally defective, normal and superior subjects. *Amer. J. ment. Defic.*, 1960, 64, 725–734.

ELLIS, N. R., & SLOAN, W. Rotary pursuit performance as a function of mental age. *Percept. mot. Skills*, 1957, 7, 267–270.

ELLIS, N. R., & SLOAN, W. Oddity learning as a function of mental age. *J. comp. physiol. Psychol.*, 1959, 56, 228–230.

FRANKS, C. M. Some fundamental problems in conditioning. *Acta Psychol.*, 1958, 14, 223–246.

FRANKS, VIOLET, & FRANKS, C. M. Conditioning in defectives and in normals as related to intelligence and mental deficit: the application of a learning theory model to a study of the learning process in the mental defective. *Proc. London Conf. Sci. Study ment. Defic*, July, 1960.

GERARD, R. W. What is memory? *Sci. Amer.*, September, 1953.

GRIFFITH, B. C., & SPITZ, H. H. Some relationships between abstraction and word meaning in retarded adolescents. *Amer. J. ment. Defic.*, 1958, 63, 247–251.

HEBB, D. O. *The organization of behavior*. New York: Wiley, 1949.

HILGARD, E. R. Methods and procedures in the study of learning. In S. S. Stevens (Ed.), *Handbook of experimental psychology*. New York: Wiley, 1951. Pp. 517–567.

HILGARD, E. R., DUTTON, C. E., & HELMICK, J. S. Attempted pupillary conditioning at four stimulus intervals. *J. exp. Psychol.*, 1949, 39, 683–689.

HILGARD, E., & MARQUIS, D. *Conditioning and Learning*. New York: Appleton-Century-Crofts, 1940.

HOLMAN, PORTIA. The relationship between general mental development and manual dexterity. *Brit. J. Psychol.*, 1933, 23, 279–283.

HOUSE, BETTY J., & ZEAMAN, D. Visual discrimination learning and intelligence in defectives of low mental age. *Amer. J. ment. Defic.*, 1960, 65, 51–58.

HOVLAND, C. I. Human learning and retention. In S. S. Stevens (Ed.), *Handbook of experimental psychology*. New York: Wiley, 1951. Pp. 613–689.

HULL, C. *Principles of behavior*. New York: Appleton-Century-Crofts, 1943.

HULL, C. L., HOVLAND, C. I., ROSS, R., HALL, M., PERKINS, D., & FITCH, F. *Mathematico-deductive theory of rote learning*. New Haven: Yale, 1940.

JENSEN, ARTHUR R. Teaching machines and individual differences. *Autom. Teach. Bull.*, 1960, 1, 12–16.

JOHNSON, B. Practice effects in a target test: a comparison of groups of varying intelligence. *Psychol. Rec.*, 1919, 26, 300–316.

JOHNSON, G. O., & BLAKE, KATHRYN A. *Learning performance of retarded and normal children*. Syracuse Univer. Press, 1960.

JONES, W. R., & ELLIS, N. R.   Inhibitory potential in rotary pursuit acquisition by normal and defective subjects. *J. exp. Psychol.*, 1962, 63, 534–537.

KARWOSKI, R. F., GRAMLICH, F. W., & ARNOTT, P.   Psychological studies in semantics: I. Free association reactions to words, drawings and objects. *J. soc. Psychol.*, 1944, 20, 233–247.

KUHLMANN, F.   Experimental studies in mental deficiency. *Amer. J. Psychol.*, 1904, 15, 391–446.

LIPMAN, R. S., & SPITZ, H. H.   The relationship between kinesthetic satiation and inhibition in rotary pursuit performance. *J. exp. Psychol.*, 1961, 62, 468–475.

LOTT, BERNICE S.   Paired associate learning, generalization, and retention as a function of intelligence. *Amer. J. ment. Defic.*, 1958, 63, 481–489.

LURIA, A. R.   *The nature of human conflicts: an objective study of disorganization and control of human behavior.* New York: Grove Press, 1932.

LURIA, A. R.   Experimental study of the higher nervous activity of the abnormal child. *J. ment. Def. Res.*, 1959, 3, 1–22.

LURIA, A. R., & VINOGRADOVA, O. S.   An objective investigation of the dynamics of semantics systems. *Brit. J. Psychol.*, 1959, 50, 89–105.

LYLE, J. G.   The effect of an institution environment upon the verbal development of imbecile children. I. Verbal intelligence. *J. ment. Def. Res.*, 1959, 3, 122–128.

MCCULLOCH, T. L., RESWICK, J., & ROY, I.   Studies of word learning in mental defectives. I. Effects of mental level and age. *Amer. J. ment. Defic.*, 1955, 60, 133–139.

MCCULLOCH, T. L., RESWICK, J., & WEISSMANN, SERENA.   Studies of word learning in mental defectives. II. Relations to scores on digit repetition, the Stanford-Binet, M., and the WISC verbal scale. *Amer. J. ment. Defic.*, 1955, 60, 140–143.

MCGEOCH, J. A., & IRION, A. L.   *The psychology of human learning.* New York: McKay, 1952.

MCPHERSON, MARY W.   Learning and mental deficiency. *Amer. J. ment. Defic.*, 1958, 62, 870–877.

MARINESCO, G., & KREINDLER, A.   Des reflexes conditionells. *J. de Psychol.*, 1933, 30, 855–886.

MATEER, FLORENCE.   *Child behavior: a critical and experimental study of young children by the method of conditioned reflexes.* Boston: Badger, 1917.

MELHADO, J. W.   Irradiation and generalization in aments. Unpublished master's thesis, Univer. of New Hampshire, 1949.

MITCHELL, W. C., JR.   Learning in undifferentiated and familial female mental defectives: a study to differentiate the *bona fide* mental defective from the so-called pseudo-defective. Ann Arbor: Univer. Microfilms, 1952, Publ. No. 4146.

MOWRER, C. H.   Converging trends in the psychology of learning. (1960). Mimeo. paper on library reserve George Peabody Coll. for Teachers.

NOBLE, C. E., & FUCHS, J. E.   Serial errors in human learning: a test of the McCrary-Hunter hypothesis. *Science,* 1959, 129, 570–572.

O'CONNOR, N., & HERMELIN, B.   Discrimination and reversal learning in imbeciles. *J. abnorm. soc. Psychol.*, 1959, 59, 409–413.

ORDAHL, L. E., & ORDAHL, G.   Qualitative differences between levels of intelligence in feeble-minded children. *J. Psycho. Asth., Monogr. Suppl.*, 1915, 1, No. 2, 3–50.

OSBORNE, W. J.   Associative clustering in organic and familial retardates. *Amer. J. ment. Defic.*, 1960, 65, 351–357.

OSGOOD, C. E.   *Method and theory in experimental psychology.* New York: Oxford, 1953.

PRYER, R. S.   Retroactive inhibition in normals and defectives as a function of temporal position of the interpolated task. *Amer. J. ment. Defic.,* 1960, 64, 1004–1015.

PYLE, W. H. *Nature and development of learning capacity.* Baltimore: Warwick and York, 1925.

RAZRAN, G. H. S. Conditioned responses in children: a behavioral and quantitative critical review of experimental studies. *Arch. Psychol.,* 1933, No. 148, 1–120.

RAZRAN, G. H. S. The observable unconscious and the inferable conscious in current Soviet psychophysiology: interoceptive conditioning, semantic conditioning, and the orienting reflex. *Psychol. Rev.,* 1961, 68, 81–147.

REYNOLDS, W. F., & STACEY, C. L. A comparison of normals and subnormals in mirror drawing. *J. genet. Psychol.,* 1955, 87, 301–308.

SLOAN, W., & BERG, I. A comparison of two types of learning in mental defectives. *Amer. J. ment. Defic.,* 1957, 61, 556–566.

STEVENSON, H., & ZIGLER, E. Probability learning in children. *J. exp. Psychol.,* 1958, 56, 185–192.

STOLUROW, L. M. Learning, ability and language in mental retardation research. Paper read at NARC Conf. on ment. Retardation, Los Angeles, 1960.

TIZARD, J., & LOOS, F. M. The learning of a spatial relations test by adult imbeciles. *Amer. J. ment. Defic.,* 1954, 59, 85–90.

UNDERWOOD, B. J., & SHULZ, R. W. *Meaningfulness and verbal learning.* Philadelphia: Lippincott, 1960.

WOODROW, H. The ability to learn. *Psychol. Rev.,* 1946, 53, 147–158.

WOODWORTH, R. S. *Experimental psychology.* New York: Holt, 1938.

ZEAMAN, D., & HOUSE, BETTY J. Discrimination learning in retardates. *Train. Sch. Bull.,* 1959, 56, 62–67.

ZIGLER, E. Rigidity in the feebleminded. In E. Trapp and P. Himelstein (Eds.), *Research readings on the exceptional child.* New York: Appleton-Century-Crofts, 1962.

12

DISCRIMINATION LEARNING

Harold W. Stevenson

During the past decade there has been a rapid growth of interest in studying the learning processes of retarded individuals. A great deal of this interest has centered on discrimination learning. Although other types of problems have been investigated, there are many reasons why discrimination learning has been so frequently selected for study.

When psychologists move into a relatively unexplored area of research, such as learning in retarded individuals, it is not surprising that they should begin by utilizing problems and methods that have already been developed with other types of subjects. The processes involved in learning to discriminate among stimuli and in transferring such discriminations to successive problems have been popular topics for research, primarily with lower animals. Methods have been developed which make it possible for the experimenter to approach the study of retarded individuals with a degree of methodological sophistication that is not available for other areas of learning, such as classroom learning, skill learning, or language learning. Further, the body of data concerning the performance of lower animals and normal children provides a comparative basis for assessing the performance of retarded individuals. Another reason for selecting discrimination problems is that they are relatively simple, and more nearly adequate control over the experimental situation is possible than if more complex problems are used. Finally, theoretical positions have been developed regarding discrimination learning which provide a framework for interpreting the performance of retarded individuals. Regardless of whether such interpretation is valid, these theories offer an organized means of looking at problems which have guided investigators in selecting variables

424

which have a good likelihood of exerting a significant influence on performance.

General procedure

Although the ability to discriminate among stimuli was initially studied as a sensory or perceptual process, the discrimination problem was adopted early by psychologists interested in learning. Most studies follow a fairly constant procedure. Typically, the S is presented with two or more stimuli varying in one or more sensory dimensions. Many different kinds of stimuli have been used, but they have most frequently been geometric forms, pictures, or miscellaneous everyday objects. The stimuli are presented simultaneously, and the S's task is to learn which to select in order to obtain a reward. The apparatus may be fairly elaborate, such as an adaptation of the Wisconsin General Test apparatus, or quite simple. The essential components of the apparatus are a tray containing wells into which rewards can be placed and a movable screen to shield the experimenter as he arranges the stimuli.

One of the stimuli, designated at random, is deemed to be correct, and a choice of this stimulus yields the reward. One of two methods is employed if S makes an incorrect choice. In the correction method the S is allowed to displace the second stimulus, so that every trial ends with a correct response. In the noncorrection method S is given only one choice on each trial, and if the choice is incorrect the trial is terminated and S receives no reward. Positions of the stimuli and other irrelevant cue dimensions are randomized so that only a discrimination between the stimuli can produce consistently correct responses.

Training is usually continued until the correct stimulus is chosen so frequently or so consistently within a limited number of trials that it is improbable to attribute S's performance to chance. Reaching the criterion of learning marks the termination of a series of processes, each of which is critical for successful performance. It is obviously impossible for S to discriminate between the stimuli if he is incapable of attending to the stimuli through either lack of motivation or psychological deficiency. Little improvement in performance is possible until S does attend to the stimuli and begins to discriminate the differences between them. The consequence of reponse must be meaningful to S, for if an incorrect response leads to as satisfactory a consequence as a correct response, there is little basis for a discrimination to become manifest in performance. Finally, S must be able to remember the stimuli which were chosen and the consequences of these choices before any benefit can be derived from previous experience. Thus, although discrimination learning may be a relatively simple type of learning, a broad range of psychological processes are involved, including attention, inhibition, motivation, reinforcement, and memory.

Comparisons of discrimination learning in normal and retarded Ss

There has been an active interest in determining whether normal and retarded children of comparable mental age show equal ability to learn. Since learning ability is one of the commonly used indices of level of mental functioning, there is a basis for assuming that regardless of the IQ of the individual, learning rate should be comparable for groups of Ss of the same MA. At the same time, there are arguments that retarded children have certain deficiencies that should produce poorer learning than would be shown by normal children of comparable MA.

Several studies to be discussed in later sections provide information about this topic, even though this was not the major purpose of the investigations. The studies of Plenderleith (1956), Stevenson and Zigler (1957), O'Connor and Hermelin (1959), and Kass and Stevenson (1961) reveal no differences in learning rate on two-choice discrimination problems between groups of retarded and normal Ss of comparable MA. Two other studies, however, found significant differences between the performance of the two types of Ss. The retarded Ss in Rudel's study (1959) took significantly longer to learn a size discrimination than normal children. Similarly, Stevenson and Iscoe (1955) found that retarded Ss required significantly more trials to learn a two-choice size discrimination than normal Ss of the same MA.

Several other studies have been primarily concerned with comparing the performance of normal and retarded Ss. House and Zeaman (1959) selected normal and retarded children at two mental age levels, 4 and 5 years. Five geometric forms painted five colors formed a pool of 25 stimuli from which two were randomly drawn for each S. No two forms or colors were identical for a particular S. The Ss were given 25 trials a day until they reached a criterion of 20 correct responses out of 25. The two types of Ss in the 5-year mental age range learned with equal ease, but normal Ss with MAs of 4 years learned the discrimination more rapidly than retarded Ss at the same level.

Normal and retarded Ss of the same MA were tested on two tasks by Stevenson (1960). A series of 7 two-choice object discriminations was presented. Each pair of objects appeared in random order until the whole series had been repeated 15 times. The normal and retarded Ss did not differ in their performance. The Ss were then presented a three-choice size discrimination for 50 trials in which the choice of one of three squares was reinforced. Again, there was no significant difference between the number of correct responses made by the normal and retarded Ss.

Ellis and Sloan (1958) compared the performance of normal and retarded children and attempted to determine whether the mental age of the retarded Ss correlated significantly with performance. There was no significant difference between the performance of the normal and retarded children in the 6- and 7-year MA range. The correlation between mental age and number of correct responses made by the retarded Ss was .48. The latter finding was supported in a study by House and Zeaman (1960a). In a two-choice color-form discrimination a correlation of —.55 was found between mental age and log errors made by retarded Ss in learning the discrimination or in completing 250 training trails.

In summary, retarded Ss learned more slowly than normal Ss in three studies, and no differences in learning rate were found in five studies. The basis of the divergent findings is not clear. So many factors differ among the studies, such as level of difficulty of the problem, type of stimuli, mode of stimulus presentation, and type of incentive, that it is impossible to point to any particular variable or groups of variables as the primary contributor to the divergent results. At the present time the possibility that normal and retarded Ss of comparable mental age differ in rate of discrimination learning cannot be discarded.

Probability learning

The question of whether retarded children differ from normal children in their performance on a discrimination task employing partial reinforcement has been investigated in three recent studies. In all the studies different probabilities of reinforcement were associated with each of the choices available to the subject.

The first study (Stevenson & Zigler, 1958) utilized a three-choice position discrimination in which choices of two of the positions never yielded reinforcement and choices of the third yielded reinforcement for different groups of subjects, 33, 66, or 100 per cent of the times this choice was made. The frequency of reinforcement was thus a function of the frequency with which S chose the reinforcing position. Groups of normal and familial retarded children with average MAs between 6.0 and 6.5 years were used.

The hypothesis tested was that performance in this type of task differs, depending upon the degree of success that the child has learned to expect from his everyday experience. Normal children were assumed to have learned to expect a high degree of success, and it was predicted that they would not maximize the frequency with which they chose the reinforcing stimulus when less than 100 per cent reinforcement was available. On the other hand, institutionalized retarded children were assumed to have learned to expect and to settle for lower degrees of success, and it was predicted that they would choose the reinforcing position to a greater degree than would normal children.

When choices of the reinforcing stimulus were consistently reinforced, both normal and retarded Ss learned to select that stimulus quickly and continued to choose it with a high frequency. When 33 to 66 per cent of the choices were reinforced, the retarded Ss chose the reinforcing stimulus more frequently than the normal Ss. The results thus supported the hypothesis relating expectancy of success and frequency of choice of the reinforcing stimulus.

In another study, Metzger (1960) found no significant differences in performance in a probability task between normal and retarded Ss with high MAs (9.2 years) or with low MAs (6.4 years), or between familial and nonfamilial retardates. The task required Ss to predict which of two lights would appear. Each S received 451 trials; one light appeared on 70 per cent of the trials and the other appeared on 30 per cent. Between 65 and 70 per cent of the predictions on the last 150 trials were of the more frequently appearing light, indicating a close match between average frequency of choice and probability of appearance.

Although the general level of performance did not differ among the groups, differences were obtained on measures reflecting stereotyped behavior. Two measures were used in analyzing *S*s' responses, the tendency to alternate responses and the tendency to choose the light which had appeared on the previous trial. A score combining both measures indicated less stereotypy for the high-MA than for the low-MA groups and less stereotypy for the normal than for the retarded *S*s. The question is therefore raised about the meaningfulness of comparing average levels of response when differences occur between the modes of response of the two types of *S*s.

A third study (Clack & Zeaman, 1960) also revealed no significant differences between the performance of normal and retarded children in probability learning. Normal children between 2 and 4 years of age, with retardates matched on MA, were tested in a two-choice discrimination problem. One of two wells with identical covers contained the reinforcement on 75 per cent of the trials and the other well, on 25 per cent of the trials. Training was continued for 20 days with 24 trials a day. Following this, positions were reversed so that the choice which previously yielded the lower frequency of reinforcement now yielded the greater frequency.

During original learning the normal *S*s came closer to maximizing their choices of the more frequently reinforced side than the retarded *S*s, but after the reversal the opposite was found. On the last 360 trials of training, both types of *S*s exceeded matching level, but departed significantly from consistent choice of the more frequently reinforced side. The prediction that prolonged maintenance on random schedules would lead to the gradual adoption of maximizing strategies was not confirmed, nor was the prediction that retardates would maximize to a greater degree than would normal *S*s.

Because of the differences among these studies in type of task, type of reinforcement, and reinforcement schedule, it is impossible to reach any general conclusions concerning probability learning by retarded *S*s. The topic must remain an interesting one for future research.

Conditions affecting rate of discrimination learning

Investigations of variables which have a significant effect on rate of learning by retarded *S*s are potentially very important sources of practical information. It is obvious that retarded children have difficulty in learning. Even though their difficulty may be no greater than that of other individuals with comparable mental ages, their slow rate of learning poses serious problems in their training and education. Several interesting leads concerning significant variables in the learning process have been uncovered in some recent studies.

One of the first problems explored was whether changes could be made in the experimental procedure to produce learning by *S*s who have previously been unable to learn a discrimination. Barnett and Cantor (1957) used 40 *S*s who were unable to surpass a chance level of performance in a problem involving the discrimination of an upright and inverted triangle. Half of the *S*s were presented with a new discrimination problem utilizing a black and a white semicircle. The *S*s first learned the names "black" and "white." They were instructed that the reward would always be found under the same stimulus and were asked where they had found the reward after every correct response. A control group was not given such practice but spent an equal amount of time with the experimenter conversing and naming colors. The Ss were then given 48 trials on a new triangle discrimination. The experimental group made significantly more correct responses than the control group and exceeded a chance level of response. The control group did not improve beyond their earlier level of performance.

A study investigating similar variables has been reported by Zeaman, House, and Orlando (1958). Two groups of Ss were selected on the basis of whether or not they had learned a simple color-form discrimination within a maximum of 100 trials. In a subsequent series of tutorial trials five of the six Ss who had learned the discrimination problem had also learned to name the colors. In contrast, of eight Ss who had failed to learn the discrimination problem only one could learn to name the colors. Ability to learn the name of the relevant stimuli was thus related to discrimination learning ability.

In a second phase of the study Ss who were performing a color-form discrimination poorly after several hundred trials were given training under altered stimulus conditions. One of the two discriminative stimuli was changed for some of the Ss. A new stimulus replaced the previously positive stimulus or the previously negative stimulus. For the 100 trials following the change in stimuli, these Ss did significantly better than the Ss for whom no new stimuli had been introduced. The results are interpreted as supporting the hypothesis that familiarity and novelty can improve discrimination performance by increasing the distinctiveness of the stimuli.

The final phase of the study was essentially a repetition of the Barnett and Cantor study. Subjects who were failing to make a color-form discrimination were switched to a two-choice problem involving two new stimuli. When retraining was given on the original stimuli following mastery of the intervening problem, Ss performed no better than they had at the termination of the original training.

The effect of different incentives on performance has been investigated in two studies. Cantor and Hottel (1955) tested retarded Ss on a two-choice triangle discrimination using either one or four peanuts as a reward for each correct response. Two experimenters were used in testing the Ss. No significant differences were found as a function of the amount of food reward, but there was a significant interaction between incentive condition and experimenter. The number of peanuts had a differential effect upon performance depending upon who tested the Ss. In a related study, Ellis and Pryer (1958) found no differences in rate of learning when correct responses were reinforced with candy or with slips of paper. Incentives differing as little as those used in these studies do not appear to have significant effects on discrimination learning.

The effect of the order in which hard and easy tasks are presented to Ss has been studied by House and Zeaman (1960b). Is it harder to learn a difficult discrimination problem after mastery of an easy or a hard problem? One group of retarded Ss was presented a pattern discrimination; a second group was given up to 250 trials on an object discrimination before learning a pattern discrimination involving stimuli of the same color and form; and a third group was given up to 250 trials on an object discrimination before learning a pattern discrimination employing stimuli of different color and form. The Ss were given 25 trials a day on the pattern discrimination until they reached a criterion of 20 correct out of 25 responses. After 20 days the Ss who had been trained only on the pattern discrimination were still performing at a low level. The groups receiving training on similar objects and patterns showed a rapid rise of correct responses, and those trained on different patterns and objects showed an intermediate level of performance. The difficult pattern discrimination was learned more rapidly following experience with the easier problem.

House and Zeaman (1960c) summarized the variables which they and their associates had found to be significant in determining the rate of discrimination learning. Several studies (House & Zeaman, 1957, 1958a, 1958b), in addition to those which have been discussed, provide the data from which these conclusions were reached. They argue that the deficit shown in discrimination learning by retarded Ss is related to the Ss' failure to keep their attention on the relevant stimulus dimensions involved in the discrimination. Several characteristics of the data obtained with retarded Ss are interpreted to support this view. Ogival curves are found which indicate relatively little improvement during the early phases of performance. Since the eventual approaches to an asymptotic level of response are almost identical regardless of wide differences in the duration of early low portions of the curve, it is assumed that the early poor performance reflects a failure to attend to the relevant cues and that the duration of the early flat portion of the curves is determined by stimulus factors and transfer operations. Among the stimulus factors which play an important role are novelty, number of relevant cues, and the nature of the cues employed. Several aspects of stimuli are believed to have greater attention value, namely, form more than color, three-dimensional stimuli more than two-dimensional stimuli, and large cues more than small cues. The transfer operations which aid learning are training on an easy problem prior to a difficult problem, overtraining, and directing S's attention to the relevant cues.

Transposition

The ability of retarded children to transpose a size discrimination from one set of stimuli to another has been investigated in three studies. The Ss are trained in a size-discrimination problem and are then tested with stimuli which differ from the training stimuli in absolute size but bear the same relationship in area to each other. The question is asked whether Ss will choose the stimulus most like the one reinforced during original training or the one bearing the same relationship to the stimuli in the test set as the correct stimulus had in the training set.

A significant incidence of transposition was found by Stevenson and Iscoe (1955) for Ss trained and tested in a two-choice size discrimination. The incidence of transposition did not vary as pairs of test stimuli increasingly remote in absolute size from the training stimuli were used. Even though the Ss did transpose, only three of the 44 Ss were able to verbalize the basis of their response.

Rudel (1959) compared the ability of groups of normal and retarded children to make absolute responses in a test of generalization after original learning. Normal and mongoloid Ss were reinforced following choices of a single stimulus or choices of the smaller of two stimuli. The mongoloid Ss showed more variability in responses than the normal Ss to eight test stimuli presented simultaneously. In a second study Rudel (1960) tested the hypothesis that normal Ss will make fewer relational responses than brain-damaged or mongoloid Ss in a transposition task. A three-choice discrimination was used, and choices of the stimulus of intermediate size were reinforced. The mongoloid and brain-damaged Ss tended to make more relational responses than the normal Ss, thus supporting the hypothesis.

Discrimination reversal

Most discrimination learning tasks are concluded once S has reached the criterion of learning. In reversal problems, training is continued beyond this point to determine whether learning a discrimination has a significant effect on S's later ability to learn to choose the stimulus which was previously incorrect. Interest in discrimination reversal has its origins in earlier studies with lower animals and in the theories of Luria and Lewin. The first studies have been addressed to the theory of Lewin.

The Lewinian hypothesis that the boundaries within the life space of the retarded child are more rigid than in the normal child was investigated in an early study by Kounin (1941). More recently, Plenderleith (1956) tested the Lewinian hypothesis that the greater functional rigidity of retarded Ss causes them to cling to a fixed habit and have more difficulty in changing response to new situations. The solution of a reversal learning problem requires S to relinquish an old response and to substitute for it a previously antagonistic one. This is predicted to be more difficult for retarded than for normal Ss of the same MA.

In Plenderleith's study normal and retarded Ss of the same MA were presented pairs of pictures. One picture in each pair was randomly deemed to be correct, and S was reinforced with a trinket when it was chosen. Six trials were given on each pair, and new pairs were presented until S reached a criterion of five correct responses after the initial trial on three successive pairs of pictures and could verbalize the solution. Reversal learning was then begun, and the previously incorrect member of each pair was now correct. Other than the change in correct picture, the procedure was the same during reversal and original learning.

The number of problems required by the normal and retarded Ss to reach criterion did not differ. For Ss given reversal training 24 hours after termination of initial learning, no differences between the performance of the normal and retarded Ss were found. For Ss given reversal training after 6 weeks, retarded Ss required more problems to reach criterion than normal Ss. In general, the results are either contrary to or unexplained by the Lewin-Kounin position.

In a second study of discrimination reversal (Stevenson & Zigler, 1957), the *S*'s task was to determine which of the three stimuli varying in size yielded a reward. Half of the *S*s were given 30 overtraining trials beyond the criterion for learning. Following this, the stimulus yielding reinforcement was switched so that now one of the previously incorrect choices was correct. No significant differences were found in original learning among groups of normal children, retarded children, and retarded adults. Further, no significant differences were found in performance on the reversal problem between the normal and retarded *S*s in either the criterion or overtraining groups.

On the assumption that the problems may have been too simple, the experiment was repeated with a different problem and new *S*s. Instead of switching from one stimulus to another, a switch was made from one of the stimuli to one of the positions in which the stimuli were presented. Again, the performance of the normal children, retarded children, and retarded adults did not differ in original learning or in the learning of the second problem. Although the incidence of perseverative responses was higher in the second experiment than in the first, there was no difference in the degree to which the three groups of *S*s chose the previously correct stimulus. These results are not in accord with the predictions derived from Lewinian theory and give no indication that retarded *S*s display rigid behavior more frequently than normal *S*s.

The theoretical position of Luria regarding the relationship between the verbal and motor systems provided the basis for a study of reversal learning by O'Connor and Hermelin (1959). The writers follow Luria's proposal that connections between stimuli not formed through verbal associations are extremely unstable and depend upon constant reinforcement. Retarded children are assumed to be deficient in the ability to form such verbal-motor connections. As a consequence, shifting responses to constantly reinforced stimuli is predicted to be easier for retarded children than for normal children.

Normal and retarded children of the same MA were trained on a problem in which either the smaller or larger of two squares yielded reinforcement and then the source of reinforcement was reversed. In the first problem the two types of *S*s learned with equal rapidity. In line with the hypothesis, the retarded *S*s learned the reversal more readily than the normal children. All but two of the ten normal *S*s correctly verbalized the basis of response, while only one retarded *S* could do this. It was concluded that the results were in line with the position that a verbal association established in accordance with a motor habit reduces mobility of response and retards reversal learning.

It was assumed in a second study that if retarded *S*s were forced to verbalize concerning each response, performance would be disrupted and retarded *S*s would now perform in a manner similar to normal *S*s. Such a procedure was followed with an additional group of retarded *S*s, and it was found that these *S*s required an average of 25.1 trials to learn the discrimination, whereas in the first study the retarded *S*s had required only 11.0 trials to learn the reversal. The results of the O'Connor and Hermelin studies are somewhat difficult to interpret, especially since they are discrepant with those of both Plenderleith and Stevenson and Zigler.

Several other studies have been concerned with variables that influence reversal learning in retarded children. Rosenberg (1961) has shown that rate of reversal learning of brain-injured retardates does not differ as a function of the amount of experience given on the initial task. In this study *S*s were to guess whether a cross or a square would appear on each card to be turned over. Either 100 or 50 cards were used during original learning. The proportion of squares and of crosses was not equal, for there were four times as many cards bearing one symbol as the other. The proportions were then reversed so that the less frequently appearing symbol now appeared more frequently. The *S*s showed significant reversal learning but the amount of original training did not influence performance significantly.

The performance of mongoloid adults in daily reversal problems has been studied by Longnecker and Ferson (1961). Two plastic squares with vertical or horizontal stripes were used as stimuli. The *S*s were reinforced for choices of vertical stripes on even numbered days and for choices of horizontal stripes on odd days, or vice versa. There was a gradual and relatively uniform reduction in errors from the first to the twenty-fourth day, when the *S*s began to manifest one-trial reversal learning. Similarities between the performance of retarded *S*s and that of rats and fish were noted during the early phases of learning, but the superiority of the retardates became manifest during the last half of the trials.

Retarded *S*s were tested in a series of nine position reversals by House and Zeaman (1959b). A left-right discrimination required *S*s to choose, for example, the left stimulus to a criterion of 10 successive correct responses and then the right stimulus to criterion. The number of errors increased from the first to the fourth reversal and then dropped to a low level. Eventually, all but one of the 15 *S*s reached the criterion of one-trial reversal. The form of the curve for reversal learning was comparable to that obtained with rats on a similar problem.

Zeaman and House (1960) investigated the effect of cues which are relevant or irrelevant in original learning to speed of learning reversal and nonreversal shifts. Retarded *S*s were trained in a problem in which, for example, color was a relevant cue and form an irrelevant cue during original learning. The irrelevant cue was present either constantly or randomly during original learning. A simple reversal, a new problem with stimuli from the relevant dimension, or a new problem with stimuli from the irrelevant dimension was then presented. The last of these problems was more difficult to learn than either of the other two. Performance did not differ on the simple reversal or on the second problem employing stimuli from the dimension which was previously relevant. Variability of form as an irrelevant cue resulted in *S*s' having greater difficulty in learning the latter problem when form was a relevant cue, but variability of color during original learning had no significant effect on the later learning.

The last three studies indicate similarities in the performance of retarded *S*s and of lower animals in learning discrimination reversals. These studies, along with others, provide a beginning for a potentially productive venture in comparative psychology. An understanding of the similarities and differences between the significant variables in the learning processes of retarded human *S*s and lower animals should greatly increase the reliability with which generalizations about the learning process can be made.

Learning set

Some of the studies discussed above have investigated the effect of learning one discrimination upon the learning of subsequent discriminations. One group of studies, however, is primarily concerned with the analysis of performance during the learning of relatively long series of discriminations. This research on interproblem learning has been stimulated primarily by the primate research of Harlow on what he has termed *learning set*. Harlow found that when successive discrimination problems were presented to monkeys, each problem tended to be learned somewhat more readily than the preceding problem until, finally, the problems were learned in a minimum number of trials. The decrease in the number of trials required to learn the successive problems indicates that the subjects learn something about how to solve such discrimination problems. They learn how to learn.

The learning-set studies follow a relatively constant procedure. A two-choice discrimination is presented to *S*s either for a constant number of trials or until a criterion of learning has been reached. Following this, another problem employing similar stimuli is presented. This procedure is repeated through a large number of problems or until *S*s reach a criterion of consistently correct response following a maximum of one error per problem.

One of the first questions explored was whether rate of improvement across problems is associated with mental age. Ellis (1958) presented 10 successive object-discrimination problems to two groups of retarded *S*s with average MAs of 5 and 8 years. Marked differences in number of errors required to meet a criterion of 20 successive correct responses on each problem were found between the two MA groups. The *S*s with higher MAs made fewer errors on each of the 10 problems than the *S*s with lower MAs. Of eight *S*s who were unable to learn the original discrimination, all had MAs at or below the 4-year level.

Stevenson and Swartz (1958) also found large differences in the performance of *S*s at three MA levels. A maximum of 24 two-choice object discriminations was presented to normal *S*s with an average MA of 11.9 years and to retarded groups with average MAs of 5.7 and 4.1 years. All the normal *S*s, eight of the retarded *S*s in the higher-MA group, and one retarded *S* in the lower-MA group met the criterion for learning set. A decrease in trials required to solve successive problems was found for all groups, but only the normal and the retarded *S*s with the higher MAs showed a significant increase in frequency of correct responses on trial 2 of each problem.

Wischner and O'Donnell (1961) tested normal and retarded *S*s of similar average MAs in learning-set problems involving the concurrent presentation of a series of five or ten pairs of objects. Each series was repeated until the *S*s learned the problem. At this time a new series was introduced. The greatest improvement in performance occurred between the first and second series. On the first problem the retarded Ss met the criterion for learning earlier than the normal Ss, but the normal Ss surpassed the retarded Ss on the four subsequent series that were presented.

Eight retarded Ss and six normal Ss of comparable CA were given 48 two-choice discrimination problems by Kaufman and Peterson (1958). Three trials were given for each problem, and eight problems were presented each day. Five of the normal Ss and one retarded S reached the criterion of 90 per cent correct responses on the second trial over the 48 problems. When 48 more problems were presented, all Ss except three in the retarded group demonstrated learning set.

A similar tendency for retarded children to show poorer performance than normal children of comparable MA has been reported by Girardeau (1959). The stimuli within a set were highly similar, but there were large between-set differences. Five problems were presented, and the criterion for learning each problem was 11 successive correct responses. The interaction between problems and type of S was significant, reflecting earlier learning by the normal Ss. The retarded Ss showed significant improvement between the first and fifth problems and performed only slightly less adequately on problem five than the normal Ss.

Wischner, Braun, and Patton (1958) tested groups of retarded Ss with average MAs of 5.3, 7.8, and 8.9 years. The Ss were given 12 problems a day with three trials per problem for a maximum of 10 days. Twelve of thirty-two Ss showed little improvement over the 10 days of training, but 9 Ss reached the criterion of learning set in 4 days, 6 in 6 days, and 5 in 10 days. There were no significant differences in CA, MA, or IQ for the Ss who did and did not reach criterion. Further, no significant differences in performance were found among the various MA groups.

The results of these studies indicate that retarded Ss are capable of learning how to learn and that, in general, such learning is more rapid for Ss with high MAs. There is fairly consistent agreement among the studies that when normal and retarded Ss are matched for MA, the retarded Ss show some tendency to learn more slowly, at least during the first few problems of a learning-set series.

An attempt has been made to analyze some of the variables which play significant roles in the formation of learning sets by retarded Ss. De Haan and Wischner (1960) have shown that rate of learning does not differ when the S is required to discriminate between objects or between colored transparencies of these objects.

An extensive study of the effects of initial experience on learning-set problems has been reported by Ellis, Girardeau, and Pryer (1961). Sixteen problems were presented each day with six trials per problem. The correctness of the first trial of each problem was manipulated by E for some of the retarded Ss. The first choice was always correct for half of these Ss, and the first choice was always incorrect for the other half. This procedure had no significant effect on performance. Ten of the thirty retarded Ss in the control group showed little improvement over the trials, but ten reached 98 per cent correct responses by the seventeenth day. The correlation between MA and number of days to reach single-trial learning was not significant for retarded *S*s, though it was —.54 for the normal *S*s. A detailed analysis of errors indicated that stimulus perseveration errors disappeared early in the training of the retarded *S*s, and position errors occurred more frequently in retarded than in normal *S*s.

House (1960) found that when four objects were presented in different combinations on subsequent discrimination problems, the least difficult change was created by retaining the stimulus which had previously been correct and inserting a new negative stimulus on the subsequent problem. Next in difficulty was an old negative stimulus with a new positive stimulus. The introduction of two new stimuli was of intermediate difficulty. The most difficult changes were, in order, changing the previously negative stimulus to the positive stimulus while introducing a new negative stimulus, and changing the previously positive stimulus to the negative stimulus while introducing a new positive stimulus. It was considered that the deficit shown by retarded *S*s in learning-set problems cannot easily be attributed to a failure to suppress negative transfer from previous problems.

CONCLUSIONS

The studies that have been reviewed provide representative demonstrations of experimental investigations of learning by retarded *S*s. The work in the area is heterogeneous and fragmentary, and it is not possible to reach general conclusions. Only a few simple questions can be answered with surety. Retarded *S*s are able to learn discrimination problems of the types presented, and they show evidence of developing learning set; duller *S*s have more difficulty than brighter *S*s in solving problems; and conditions can be arranged so that learning is facilitated. The studies suggest that experimental investigation of the learning processes of retarded *S*s is feasible and that gradually more specific, less obvious, and more useful data will be obtained.

Before it can be concluded that a certain level or type of performance is a result of the intellectual deficit of retarded *S*s, consideration must be given to other characteristics of retarded *S*s associated with their atypical social experiences and environmental histories. The failure to consider such characteristics restricts the types of interpretations and the generalizations that can be made from experimental work.

Usually, comparisons have been made between the performance of institutionalized retarded and noninstitutionalized normal *S*s. It is impossible from these studies to determine the relative effects of institutionalization and retardation on the differences in learning found between the two groups of individuals. The difficulty that retarded *S*s have been found to have, especially during the early phases of learning, may result as much from fear and anxiety over being examined as from a basic learning difficulty or an inability to attend to stimuli.

Incentives varying from beads to candy have been chosen arbitrarily for use in the studies. Actually, in some studies different incentives have been used for the normal and the retarded *S*s. It is likely that a particular type of incentive may have quite a different effect in motivating retarded *S*s and normal *S*s. Praise for correct response, for example, may have different effects on the performance of retarded children who characteristically may not be given adult approval as frequently as normal children. Research is needed to determine the effects of different kinds of incentives on performance and the differences in motivational level that may be created by certain incentives for normal and retarded *S*s.

Recent studies have shown that the scores on tests of anxiety are higher for retarded *S*s than for normal *S*s. Other research has indicated that performance may vary in learning tasks as a function of anxiety level. The question needs to be clarified, therefore, whether the poor performance of retarded *S*s may not be attributed to their high level of anxiety, and whether better performance might not occur if experimental procedures were introduced to relieve their anxiety.

A great many factors other than institutionalization, incentive conditions, and anxiety could be discussed. Perhaps the greatest weakness of present studies is that there has been little attempt to determine whether intellectual level alone is the major contributor to the particular results. Other factors associated with retardation must be considered when drawing conclusions.

Beginnings have been made. There is some promise that future research in this area will yield information of value both for theoretical psychology and for the furtherance of our understanding of how to train and educate retarded individuals.

REFERENCES

BARNETT, C. D., & CANTOR, G. N. Discrimination set in defectives, *Amer. J. ment. Defic.*, 1957, 62, 334–337.

CANTOR, G. N., & HOTTEL, J. V. Discrimination learning in mental defectives as a function of magnitude of food reward and intelligence level. *Amer. J. ment. Defic.*, 1955, 60, 380–384.

CLACK, D., & ZEAMAN, D. Comparison of probability learning in retardate and normal children of low mental age. Progress Rep., NIMH Grant M-1099, 1960.

DE HAAN, H. J., & WISCHNER, G. J. Stereometric objects versus colored transparencies of objects as stimuli in learning set formation by retarded children. Paper read at East. Psychol. Ass., 1960.

ELLIS, N. R. Object-quality discrimination learning sets by mental defectives. *J. comp. physiol. Psychol.*, 1958, 51, 79–81.

ELLIS, N. R., GIRARDEAU, F. L., & PRYER, M. W. Analysis of learning sets in normal and severely defective humans. Unpublished study, George Peabody Coll. for Teachers, 1961.

ELLIS, N. R., & PRYER, M. W. Primary versus secondary reinforcement in simple discrimination learning of mental defectives. *Psychol. Rep.*, 1958, 4, 67–70.

ELLIS, N. R., & SLOAN, W. Oddity learning as a function of mental age. *J. comp. physiol. Psychol.*, 1959, 52, 228–230.

GIRARDEAU, F. L. The formation of discrimination learning sets in mongoloid and normal children. *J. comp. physiol. Psychol.*, 1959, 52, 566–570.

HOUSE, B. J. Learning sets from minimum stimuli in retardates. Progress Rep., NIMH Grant M-1099, 1960.

HOUSE, B. J., ORLANDO, R., & ZEAMAN, D. Role of positive and negative cues in the discrimination learning of mental defectives. *Percept. mot. Skills*, 1957, 7, 73–79.

HOUSE, B. J., & ZEAMAN, D. Reward and nonreward in discrimination learning of imbeciles. *J. comp. physiol. Psychol.*, 1958, 51, 614–618. (a)

HOUSE, B. J., & ZEAMAN, D. Visual discrimination learning in imbeciles. *Amer. J. ment. Defic.*, 1958, 63, 447–452. (b)

HOUSE, B. J., & ZEAMAN, D. A comparison of discrimination learning in normal and mentally defective children. *Child Developm.*, 1959, 29, 411–416. (a)

HOUSE, B. J., & ZEAMAN, D. Position discrimination and reversals in low-grade retardates. *J. comp. physiol. Psychol.*, 1959, 52, 564–565. (b)

HOUSE, B. J., & ZEAMAN, D. Visual discrimination learning and intelligence in defectives of low mental age. *Amer. J. ment. Defic.*, 1960, 65, 51–58. (a)

HOUSE, B. J., & ZEAMAN, D. Transfer of a discrimination from objects to patterns. *J. exp. Psychol.*, 1960, 59, 298–302. (b)

HOUSE, B. J., ZEAMAN, D., et al. Learning and transfer in mental defectives. Progress Rep. NIMH Grant M-1099, 1960. (c)

KASS, N., & STEVENSON, H. W. The effect of pretraining reinforcement conditions on learning by normal and retarded children. *Amer. J. ment. Defic.*, 1961, 66, 76–80.

KAUFMAN, M., & PETERSON, W. Acquisition of a learning set by normal and mentally retarded children. *J. comp. physiol. Psychol.*, 1958, 51, 619–621.

KOUNIN, J. S. Experimental studies of rigidity. I. The measurement of rigidity in normal and feeble-minded persons. *Charact. & Pers.*, 1941, 9, 251–273.

LONGNECKER, E. D., & FERSON, J. Discrimination reversal learning in mongoloids. *Amer. J. ment. Defic.*, 1961, 66, 93–99.

METZGER, R. Probability learning in children and aments. *Amer. J. ment. Defic.*, 1960, 64, 869–874.

O'CONNOR, N., & HERMELIN, B. Discrimination and reversal learning in imbeciles. *J. abnorm. soc. Psychol.*, 1959, 59, 409–413.

PLENDERLEITH, M. Discrimination learning and discrimination reversal learning in normal and feeble-minded children. *J. genet. Psychol.*, 1956, 88, 107–112.

ROSENBERG, S. Probability reversal learning as a function of prior training in brain injured retardates. Unpublished study, Vineland Training School, N.J., 1961.

RUDEL, R. G. The absolute response in tests of generalization in normal and retarded children. *Amer. J. Psychol.*, 1959, 72, 401–408.

RUDEL, R. G. The transposition of intermediate size by brain damaged and mongoloid children. *J. comp. physiol. Psychol.*, 1960, 53, 89–94.

STEVENSON, H. W. Learning of complex problems by normal and retarded Ss. *Amer. J. ment. Defic.*, 1960, 64, 1021–1026.

STEVENSON, H. W., & SWARTZ, J. D. Learning set in children as a function of intellectual level. *J. comp. physiol. Psychol.*, 1958, 51, 755–757.

STEVENSON, H. W., & ZIGLER, E. F. Discrimination learning and rigidity in normal and feeble-minded individuals. *J. Pers.*, 1957, 25, 699–711.

STEVENSON, H. W., & ZIGLER, E. F. Probability learning in children. *J. exp. Psychol.*, 1958, 56, 185–192.

WISCHNER, G. J., BRAUN, H. W., & PATTON, R. A. Acquisition of and long-term retention of an object-quality learning set by retarded children. Paper read at East. Psychol. Ass., Philadelphia, April, 1958.

WISCHNER, G. J., & O'DONNELL, J. P. Concurrent learning set formation in normal and retarded children. Paper read at East. Psychol. Ass., Philadelphia, April, 1961.

ZEAMAN, D., HOUSE, B. J., & ORLANDO, R. Use of special training conditions in visual discrimination learning with imbeciles. *Amer. J. ment. Defic.*, 1958, 65, 453–459.

13

PROBLEM - SOLVING AND CONCEPTUAL BEHAVIOR

Sheldon Rosenberg

Problem-solving and conceptual behavior have for many years ranked high among the factors of intelligence. Some writers have even attempted to define intelligence in terms of problem-solving or conceptual ability. Others have employed problem-solving or conceptual tasks in their attempts to validate the construct of intelligence. The importance of this area to the study of mental deficiency would appear to be obvious. However, a perusal of the literature for the present chapter, which encompassed a period from approximately 1927 through March, 1961, has uncovered a relatively limited number and variety of studies about the basic processes of problem solving and concept formation. There appears to have been a preoccupation with the comparative study of individual differences in abstract behavior to the neglect of areas of practical, if not theoretical, importance.

After an attempt to define some of the basic terms in use in the area of problem-solving and conceptual behavior, the plan of the present chapter is to consider some problems of research methodology and then to review critically the literature on problem solving, concept formation, and abstract and concrete behavior. Only those studies that clearly include mentally deficient Ss have been reviewed in the present chapter. The reader will note the exclusion of topics such as learning set and reversal learning, which are traditionally covered in chapters on learning, but which sometimes appear in general reviews of concept formation (e.g., T. S. Kendler, 1961). A review of the research derived from Piaget's formulations has also been omitted, in view of the presence of a separate chapter dealing with his contributions. The problem of exclusion was particularly difficult, as the subject matter of the present chapter so clearly overlaps certain other areas

439

of learning. Delineation of subareas, therefore, has in more than one instance been arbitrary and done for convenience, rather than on any clearly defensible theoretical or methodological grounds. It will be left to the reader to decide which areas deserve separate treatment in the future and which studies should not have been included at all in this review.

DEFINITIONS

Any attempt to delineate the area of problem-solving behavior with any degree of generality is at best a frustrating task. Wholly operational definitions suffer from undue restriction unless one is prepared to describe all conditions under which the term is used in the research literature. The general preference has been for broad definitions. Johnson (1950) has stressed, among other things, the involvement of complex stimulus situations, varied behavior, and solution processes in problem-solving behavior. Problem solving is defined essentially as solution-oriented behavior by Ray (1955) in his review of complex tasks used in human problem-solving research. According to Ray, problem-solving tasks usually involve a given stimulus situation, a "desired" situation, and a method of solution. The importance of verbal instructions in defining problem situations is clearly implied in his review of tasks, a factor which would prevent the use of many of these instruments with mentally deficient *S*s. Gagné (1959) distinguishes between five stages in problem-solving behavior—presentation of the stimulus situation, concept formation, behavior determination, decision making among alternative solutions, and verification. Duncan (1959) has indicated that writers who attempt to define problem-solving behavior stress the importance of the discovery of the correct solution. Kendler, Glucksberg, and Keston (1961) have emphasized the longer response chains of problem-solving behavior in attempting to distinguish it from conditioning.

Skinner (1953) has offered a definition of problem solving which is general enough to include a variety of phenomena, but closer to the data language than other formulations. According to this view, a problem situation arises when (1) conditions exist which prevent or interfere with the occurrence of responses which are at high strength in an individual, and (2) there are no responses in the behavioral repertoire which will immediately alter the problem situation. Problem solving is the behavior which, through the manipulation of relevant conditions, facilitates the occurrence of the strong responses in question. For example, if candy eating is at high strength in a child and candy is suspended from a ceiling by a string, box stacking may be the problem-solving behavior which permits him to obtain the candy. The chief task for experimentation is to identify the variables which facilitate or interfere with problem-solving behavior. In the area of mental deficiency, this goal would appear to be of particular practical importance.

The observation that problem-solving behavior often involves the strengthening or occurrence of a common response to dissimilar objects or events has led some writers (Gagné, 1959; Johnson, 1950; Taylor & McNemar, 1955) to emphasize the importance of concept formation in problem-solving behavior. Concept-formation tasks themselves have frequently been employed as problem-solving situations (e.g., Duncan, 1959; Kendler, Glucksberg, & Keston, 1961). The inclusion of studies on concept formation and related behavior in the present review, then, would appear to be justified on historical, if not on empirical, grounds. An attempt has been made to define concept formation with reference to the major trends in the general experimental literature in recent years (T. S. Kendler, 1961).

Methodologically, if we conceive of concept formation as the process of strengthening common responses to dissimilar objects or events, as compared with the performance of responses which are in the behavioral repertoire of the individual, it is possible to differentiate between two stages, *abstraction* and *generalization*. We speak of abstraction when a common response is brought under the control of recurrent similarities (absolute or relational) associated with diverse objects or events. The dimension of similarity may be represented by a common physical property of the objects or events; or, where items are totally dissimilar, it may be the result of the prior association of a common (e.g., verbal) response with the objects in question. It is generally assumed by behavior theorists that the laws of discrimination learning operate in instances of abstraction (Buss, 1950; T. S. Kendler, 1961; Skinner, 1953, 1957). The critical test of concept formation is the occurrence of the behavior in question in the presence of objects and events not encountered in abstraction. Here it is assumed that the laws of stimulus and mediated generalization are operating.

Experimentally, it would be possible to center attention upon either stage or both stages of the conceptual process or to concern ourselves with the variables which affect the performance of conceptual behaviors which are at strength in a particular culture. Too, the observation that objects and events can have a number of dimensions of similarity associated with them (e.g., form, color, number, relationship of parts) raises the question of the variables which influence ability to shift behavior (the strengthening or occurrence of responses to a previously irrelevant dimension of similarity). Studies of individual differences, a prime concern of workers in the field of mental deficiency, can be carried out at any level. In this respect, behavioral *deficiencies* might be manifested in (1) failure to abstract, (2) failure to generalize, or (3) the ease of establishment of abstraction or generalization. It should be noted here that terms such as "stage" and "establishment" are not used to imply the existence of discontinuities or emergents but simply for purposes of analysis.

METHODOLOGY

The methodology of research on problem-solving and conceptual behavior will be evident as we review the relevant literature. Individual studies have been grouped into subareas according to such factors as similarity of tasks or similarity of independent or dependent variables. Within each subarea, an attempt has been made to distinguish between two general classes of research design, the experimental and the comparative.

Experimental studies are those in which antecedent environmental conditions are manipulated, while *comparative* denotes those investigations which study the relationship between subject variables (measurable characteristics of Ss such as MA, CA, brain injury, educational status, and length of institutionalization) and behavior. Sometimes an investigator will combine experimental and subject variables in a single study. Although the distinction between experimental and comparative designs is rarely made in the research which follows, it should be clear that when subject variables are studied, it is not possible to talk as if one were attempting to identify the antecedents of behavioral change. One reason is that subject variables are themselves dependent variables which have to be accounted for. In addition, if it were possible to attribute a significant difference between groups to a subject variable, it would be necessary to demonstrate that the groups in question differ *only* with respect to the subject variable under investigation. Any subject variable which correlated with the one in question would be a logical candidate for the status of determinant. From a statistical standpoint, it should also be remembered that Ss cannot be assigned at random to different levels of a subject variable (Edwards, 1960).

PROBLEM SOLVING

The number of studies uncovered in the area of mental deficiency concerned with problem solving per se totals less than 10, the majority of which have appeared in recent years. A smaller group of studies has utilized problem-solving tasks for other purposes. It is interesting to contrast this development with the reference list of approximately 100 items for Duncan's (1959) review of problem-solving research on normal human adults, which covered the period from 1946 through 1957.

As one would anticipate, the earliest research was basically qualitative in nature. Wilson (1931) compared the performance of children at CA 9 and 12 years and IQ 70 to 80 and 110 to 120 in a game in which success was facilitated by application of a common principle. Results were reported in terms of means and percentages, and differences between groups were described qualitatively. The highest level of overall performance appeared in the high-IQ and older Ss. Low-IQ Ss, nevertheless, made similar errors and showed evidence of improvement with practice.

Of primarily historical interest is a group of three studies (Aldrich, 1930; Aldrich & Doll, 1931a, 1931b) in which attempts were made to extend problem-solving techniques from research on the animal level to low-grade defective children (IQ 14 to 35). A single, small group of Ss appears to have been used in all three studies, in a qualitative analysis of individual performance. In addition, there is reason to believe that methodological procedures often varied from S to S. Consequently, the reliability of results derived from such conditions and the generality of conclusions drawn by the authors are highly questionable. Therefore, the present review has been limited to a brief description of each study.

The first (Aldrich, 1930) was an investigation of box stacking in which various lures were suspended from a ceiling. The initial problem required for solution the use of one box; the second, two; and the last, three. The second study (Aldrich & Doll, 1931a) was essentially a detailed report of a replication and extension of the first, with similar methodological difficulties. The paper is important, since it raises the issue of the application of concepts and methods derived from general theoretical and experimental psychology to the study of mental deficiency. Moreover, it suggests the use of mental defectives to evaluate the generality of empirical laws and theoretical formulations derived from research on normal organisms. Unfortunately, general interest in this approach did not appear until some years later. The final study in the series (Aldrich & Doll, 1931b) was concerned with the use of implements to obtain reinforcers under conditions of controlled observation.

A good many years passed before psychologists again showed interest in the study of problem solving among the mentally deficient. This interest, however, has been largely limited to studies of alternation problem-solving behavior. Stolurow and Pascal (1950) attempted to replicate an earlier study of double-alternation behavior in normal children on a group of mental defectives in the CA range 6 to 32 years and MA range 2 years, 1 month to 8 years, 7 months. The mentally deficient sample was roughly matched with the earlier one on MA. The problem for each *S* was to select from two boxes the one containing candy. The pattern of choices for a correct trial was RRLLRRLL, and the learning criterion was three consecutive correct trials. After the criterion had been reached, *S*s were questioned about their basis for solution. The results of interest indicated a positive correlation between double-alternation performance and MA (.83). The *S*s who solved the problem were not all able to identify verbally the basis for correct response.

The need for an estimate of intelligence which was not strongly dependent upon motor and verbal abilities in cerebral-palsied children and the relationship between MA and double-alternation performance observed by Stolurow and Pascal (1950) and others led Pascal and Zax (1955) to explore the possibility of the development of the double-alternation task for this purpose. The sample consisted of 24 *S*s, males and females, in the CA range 7 to 20. A candy reward could always be found in the end doors of a five-door apparatus. The correct trial pattern was two consecutive choices of one end door followed by two consecutive choices of the other end door. The criterion for solution was two consecutive correct trials. Performance was also scored in terms of whether an *S* showed evidence of an *end concept* (i.e., two consecutive trials in which middle doors were never chosen). The *S*s were also rated on a behavior scale of educability and cooperativeness, and an IQ rank was estimated for each.

The product-moment correlation between double-alternation performance and behavior ratings was .64; between double alternation and IQ rank, .43; and between IQ rank and behavior ratings, .57. A biserial *r* between a pass-fail criterion of double-alternation and behavior ratings was .73. All these *r*s were found to be significant. However, the relationship between double-alternation performance and CA was nonsignificant. In general, *S*s who failed double alternation and who showed no evidence of an end concept received the lowest behavior ratings.

Barnett, Ellis, and Pryer (1960) compared familial and brain-injured defectives, equated on mean MA and CA, on the double-alternation task using the Yerkes Multiple Choice apparatus. The measure of performance was the number of responses to a criterion of two consecutive correct sequences. Brain-injured *S*s required significantly more trials to criterion than familials. Analysis of covariance adjusted for differences in MA. These results would indicate that there are other subject variables besides MA that are related to alternation behavior.

Simple alternation problem solving (LRLRLR) in a two-choice reinforcement apparatus has been investigated in two studies by Ringelheim (1960a, 1960b). In the first of these (1960a), the experimental effects of pretraining conditions were evaluated in three groups of mental defectives equated on MA and CA. Simple alternation training was carried to a criterion of six successive reinforced choices. Prior to simple alternation, group I was reinforced for 100 per cent choice of the right door, group II received a randomized left-right reinforcement schedule, and group III received no pretraining. Group I performed at a significantly lower level than group II or III on the simple alternation task. However, differences between group II and III were not significant. In the total sample a low but significant correlation between MA and ability to solve the simple alternation problem was reported; CA was not related to the criterion behavior.

The effect of amount of one-sided pretraining (6 versus 12 trials to criterion) and CA was studied by Ringelheim (1960b) in four groups of mental defectives equated for MA and IQ. However, none of the group differences were found to be significant. The author hypothesized that results were confounded by problems of variability and sampling.

Although the number of studies of alternation problem-solving behavior has been limited, the observed relationship between performance and intellectual ability and the demonstration of the effects of one variety of training conditions should encourage additional research with these tasks.

The remainder of the research uncovered on problem solving in mental defectives has utilized problem-solving tasks in the study of other behavioral phenomena. Johnson and Blake (1960) employed puzzle-assembly tasks to study transfer in mentally deficient and normal children in a combined experimental by subject variable design. Pretraining on a general solution procedure significantly facilitated subsequent performance on a unique puzzle task in both normal and mentally deficient *S*s. However, there was evidence to suggest that positive transfer effects were greater in the mental defectives than in the normals. An explanation for the latter finding was not readily apparent in the data, and additional research is needed to determine its reliability.

The use of a puzzle task as a criterion measure in studies of motivational and personality variables in relationship to task resumption phenomena is exemplified in a study by Miller (1960).

Research on problem solving among defectives has been disappointing. The effects of such variables as methods of training, amount of training, conditions of problem presentation, kind and difficulty of problem-solving task (Duncan, 1959) need to be evaluated if the research in this area is to have implications for educational practices and the broader issues of relevance to behavior theory.

CONCEPT FORMATION

Experimental studies of the concept-formation process as outlined earlier (i.e., involving abstraction and generalization) are virtually nonexistent in the area of mental deficiency. This is surprising from both a practical and a theoretical standpoint. Special educators and clinicians working with the retarded are often heard describing them as being deficient in the area of conceptual behavior. However, the primary research activity has been the comparative study of differences in abstract and concrete behavior. The question of the *source* of observed differences and the environmental variables and conditions of learning which facilitate or interfere with conceptual behavior—data which would supply an empirical base for educational and training programs—has been of little concern. At the same time, behavior theorists are to be criticized for their failure to consider and evaluate the possibility that the basic processes which are assumed to underly complex adult conceptual behavior can be studied in mental defectives. Very few studies have used defective Ss for this purpose. The latter viewpoint has been fostered by a consideration of such factors as the following:

1. Many defectives have impoverished or limited reinforcement histories (a condition which cannot be assumed in normal college students).

2. In many instances the potential for complex learning is limited, a factor which would permit intensive concentration on simple processes.

3. The wide range of age in institutional environments would facilitate the sampling of Ss with varying reinforcement histories.

4. Institutional Ss are readily available for extended training periods.

5. The absence of verbal behavior in some and the low level of development of verbal behavior in others should further suggest the use of defectives as Ss for general studies of behavior, especially with respect to the question of the role of verbal mediators in concept formation. Preverbal normal Ss are not as readily available; moreover, they are limited to a very narrow age range.

Two recent studies (Bensberg, 1958; Martin & Blum, 1961), one experimental and the other comparative, approximate the conditions for concept formation. Bensberg focused attention on both practical and general theoretical problems in a study of the mediation hypothesis and the concept of habit strength in male defectives. The problem was to evaluate the effects of variations in the the relevant dimension of similarity (form or color) and in the number of pretraining trials upon subsequent performance in a task in which only one dimension—form—was relevant.

Sixty male defectives, with a mean IQ of 47.01 and a mean CA of 20.31, were assigned at random to five groups of 12 Ss each. The pretraining materials consisted of stimuli varying in color and form. The task was to establish a response—button pressing—to either form or color as a relevant dimension. Group I (color) and group III (form) were carried to a criterion of one errorless presentation of the stimulus series; groups II (color) and IV (form) were given additional trials. Group V, a control group, performed a neutral task. Color and form tasks were equated empirically for level of difficulty. In the second part of the experiment a paired-associate task was used to test for generalization of pretraining responses, in which form only was the relevant dimension. The colors and forms of the generalization task were different from those used in pretraining. The forms were paired with nonsense syllables, and all groups performed the same task.

Bensberg anticipated that transfer would be negative for the groups pretrained on color and positive for the groups pretrained on form, while overlearning would increase the predicted effect. Statistical analysis indicated that the groups did not differ significantly on the pretraining task and that all predictions made for performance on the transfer task were confirmed except one. The group given additional pretraining on form did not show a significantly higher level of performance on the transfer task than the form group carried to criterion.

Martin and Blum (1961) employed the dimension of oddity in a comparative study of conceptual learning and generalization in normal children, familial defectives, and mongoloids, with groups further differentiated according to sex. The nature of the study and the Ss available did not make it possible to choose or assign Ss at random or to equate groups adequately on any subject variable except sex. Groups differed, then, not only with respect to diagnostic category, but also with respect to mean CA, MA, and IQ.

Stimulus objects were presented three at a time to all Ss. The odd item was varied in size, color, form, or spatial orientation. Two training series were run with correction in which size was the odd dimension, followed by a series of eight tests of generalization. The sequence of odd dimensions in the test series was size, form, spatial orientation, color, color, spatial orientation, form, size. Each test was presented for six noncorrected trials, with candy and social approval as reinforcers.

Descriptive statistics and detailed statistical comparisons of group performance on the training series were, for unspecified reasons, not presented. Nor were measures of variability reported or commented upon for the generalization or learning measures. The sketchy descriptive data presented indicated that the training task was relatively easy for all groups to master, although there was some slight suggestion of differences in favor of normal and familial Ss. The measure of generalization for all eight tests as a whole was the mean number of correct responses on trial 1. An overall measure of learning for the eight trials was also computed in terms of the number of correct responses on trials 2 to 6.

An analysis of variance of the generalization data revealed that group differences alone were significant. However, after adjustment by covariance for group differences in MA, the differences associated with diagnostic category lost significance, while sex differences and the sex by group interaction reached significance. In view of the suspected heterogeneity of groups with respect to CA and IQ, it is questionable whether adjustment for MA alone was sufficient. The results for the generalization series suggested, further, that in normal and familial Ss and in mongoloid boys, there was a tendency for orientation tests to be most difficult and for form tests to be easiest. For the mongoloid girls, form was the most difficult, and color the easiest.

On the overall measure of learning the only significant difference found was between groups, a difference which remained significant after group differences were adjusted for MA. The adjusted group means of the normal and familial Ss did not differ appreciably, but the mean of the mongoloid group was lower than either. The order of difficulty of tests for the normal and familial Ss was, from most to least difficult: orientation, color, size, and form. No consistent pattern emerged for the mongoloids with the exception that the orientation tests tended to be most difficult for both males and females. The similarity between the generalization and learning measures in pattern of difficulty is to be noted.

In general it can be said that while the results which Martin and Blum present suggest a number of sources of interaction, the sampling problem (which the authors indicate they are aware of) would necessitate a replication of the study before the generality of the results can be evaluated. Their study also points up the necessity for evaluating the contribution of as many subject variables as possible, if one is to be able to interpret the results in any meaningful manner. The studies reviewed in this section, however, are of considerable significance in that they represent what appear to be the only attempts to study the process of concept formation in mental defectives.

ABSTRACTION

In the present section an attempt has been made to distinguish between studies of abstraction, in which a common response is *strengthened* in association with dissimilar objects and events, and those studies that are concerned primarily with *assessing* the strength of abstract responses, which are assumed initially to be at some strength in the population under investigation. The former are studies of learning, the latter of performance.

Abstract learning

Relatively few studies of abstraction in mental defectives have involved learning. The earliest one was a comparative study by Whiteside (1934), also reviewed by McPherson (1948), of "selective learning" in normal and mentally deficient children. The mentally defective Ss were selected from an IQ range of 60 to 69, and the normals from an IQ range of 84 to 118. Both groups were selected from institutional populations of low-socio-economic background. The Ss were presented with four different series of five rows of geometric designs and were required to choose the one which would be followed by a buzzer. The correct items in a given series possessed some stimulus characteristic in common. In the "duplico" series, for example, the correct design was one which was enclosed inside itself.

The designs were exposed in rows of five items on a revolving drum, and the criterion for learning was 30 consecutive correct choices. It was assumed that an *S* was responding to a common stimulus characteristic if he identified it spontaneously during the learning trials. An additional test involving new designs but the same common characteristic was presented to *S*s who failed to verbalize spontaneously the relevant dimension.

Differences in favor of the normal children were found in the two series which were considered to be the most difficult in terms of the number of trials to learn and the proportion of *S*s who identified the dimension of similarity. The kinds of materials used by Whiteside and the manner of presentation should suggest a variety of possible studies of the experimental variables involved.

Equally interesting is an early comparative study by Ray (1936) of what was referred to as "generalizing ability" in intellectually dull (IQ 84 and below), average (IQ 92 to 108), and superior (IQ over 116) children. Groups were equated on CA and sex. The *N* of six in each group, however, was relatively small for the many detailed qualitative comparisons made. Unfortunately, statistical tests of significance were not carried out, and the results have to be interpreted with caution. The technique was sufficiently systematic to warrant consideration.

The stimulus materials consisted of 22 series of 20 pairs of meaningful items. One pair appeared at a time in an exposure apparatus. If an *S* pressed the key corresponding to the correct item, the drum was automatically advanced to the next pair. Some of the classes of correct items included were, for example, whole objects, living things, flowers, means of transportation, contentment, and vegetables. A given series was considered learned after one errorless presentation and a verbal identification of the dimension of similarity. Time and errors were also recorded. The following results were the most interesting: (1) The highest frequency of verbal identification of the dimension of similarity occurred in the superior group, the next highest in the average group, and the lowest in the dull group. For the three groups combined, a rank-order correlation of .87 was found between the number of series completed with verbal identification and IQ. (2) Total failures were absent in the superior group, but present to about the same extent in the average- and dull-IQ groups. (3) The superior group tended to take less time and made fewer errors than the other groups as evidenced in rank-order correlations with IQ of .72 and .79, respectively.

A more recent experimental study by Hermelin and O'Connor (1957) attempted to determine whether imbeciles (IQ range 28 to 50) could be trained to respond to common characteristics of objects. An attempt was also made to develop *learning sets* (intertask improvement) in two different sequences of tasks. A sample of 20 male defective children was divided into two groups of 10 *S*s each. The sample was heterogeneous with respect to clinical type. Six series of twelve drawings were presented in pairs, and choice of the correct item was reinforced by candy hidden in a well beneath the drawing. All *S*s received 20 trials on each series. Each *S* was able to name the object depicted in each drawing. The stimulus materials were broken down into two rote series (correct items had nothing in common), two *concrete* series (the reinforced item was either an article of furniture or an animal), and two *abstract* series ("three of a kind," and "more than one"). The distinction between abstract and concrete was defined, it appeared, in terms of anticipated level of difficulty. The order of presentation of the two series was reversed for the two experimental groups as follows: group I: (1) rote series, (2) concrete series, (3) abstract series; group II: (1) abstract series, (2) concrete series, (3) rote series—thus producing a partial counterbalancing for order.

Significantly fewer trials were needed in both groups to reach criterion on the concept series than on the rote series. Learning curves were not presented, but trial-to-trial improvement was described as being *gradual* for rote material and *sharp* for the concept series. It appeared, then, that discrimination learning was facilitated by the presence of discriminanda with common characteristics. As order of presentation of tasks did not appear to influence performance, the data for the two experimental groups were combined to test for learning sets. The measure of transfer was the number of correct responses on trial 2 in each series. Significant transfer effects were found for the two abstract series only. However, since each of the two series was presented in the *same* order within each group, the results are equivocal. Only two *S*s in the entire sample were able to identify verbally the basis for correct responses. Performance was clearly unrelated to the presence of verbal mediators, a finding which raises the question of whether pretraining on verbal mediators would facilitate learning. It is interesting to note in this respect the lower frequency of occurrence of verbal identifications among defective *S*s in the studies by Ray and Whiteside.

For all tasks combined, a positive rank-order correlation of .55 was reported between IQ and trials to criterion. Unfortunately, separate coefficients were not presented for rote and concept materials. No relationship was found between trials to criterion and clinical type.

The methodology of the three studies reviewed here (as is also characteristic of the general experimental literature in this area) implicitly assumes that the abstractions in question are at some strength in the population under study. The abstract learning involves the association of a new response with a common dimension of equivalence. Basic research, it would seem, would be facilitated by the discovery of dimensions of similarity which have not been differentiated in the behavior repertoire of the *S*s under investigation. Systematic control and manipulation of the *irrelevant* dimensions of stimulus materials (e.g., see Rasmussen & Archer, 1961) would further facilitate interpretation of performance in abstraction tasks.

Abstract performance

A group of studies by Griffith and associates represents the only interrelated series of papers on the problem of verbal abstract performance in the literature. In one study Griffith and Spitz (1958) set out to determine "to what extent the ability to abstract a common property from a group of three nouns can be related to the way an *S* defines these nouns." The design of the study was essentially comparative and involved two testing sessions. In the abstraction session *S*s were presented with 24 groups of three nouns (e.g., elephant, mountain, whale) and asked to identify verbally the characteristic each group had in common (e.g., "big"), and in the definition session, each *S* was required to define the 18 words which made up 6 of the 24 groups of 3 words in addition to a number of new words. The two sessions were counterbalanced for order and spaced roughly 24 hours apart. The *S*s were 26 males, mean CA 17 years, 2 months and mean IQ 66.

The results indicated clearly that the proportion of correct abstractions increased significantly if a minimum of two of the words in each triad had been defined in terms of an acceptable abstraction.

A second study in the series (Griffith, Spitz, & Lipman, 1959), was essentially a replication of the first with the addition of two groups of normal children. The results showed the following:

> Although the percentage of abstractions attained generally increased as the number of words defined in common with a possible abstraction increased, the nature of the relationship varied among groups. Retardates and normal 7-yr. *S*s were not very successful in concept attainment unless they had the opportunity to match words on the basis of their eliciting a common immediate associate; i.e., unless they defined at least two words in terms of an acceptable abstraction. Normal 9-yr. *S*s, on the other hand, were relatively successful even when they defined only one word in terms of an abstraction.

There was a suggestion of a higher level of performance in high-IQ defectives than in low-IQ *S*s.

The observation in mental defectives of a sharp increase in the correct identification of a common characteristic in word triads, associated with the ability to define at least two of the words in terms of the common characteristic, raised the question of whether verbal abstraction was dependent upon "defining a threshold number or some constant proportion of the stimulus words in terms of a possible abstraction" (Griffith, 1960). Accordingly, Griffith studied the effects of word group length (three-word and six-word) upon verbal abstraction ability in groups of low- (below 65) and high- (65 and above) IQ defectives. The results confirmed the hypothesis that a constant proportion of words had to be defined in common in both the three- and six-word conditions in the low-IQ groups. The ability to identify verbally the dimension of similarity was related to the ability to define approximately two-thirds of the words in common. The data for the high-IQ groups were not interpretable in terms of either hypothesis. If anything, there was a suggestion that the threshold value for the high-IQ groups was *one* word defined in terms of the common characteristic.

The fourth study on this problem (Lipman & Griffith, 1960) departed from the trend of the first three and attempted to determine the relationship between performance on an adaptation of the Manifest Anxiety Scale for Children (CMAS) and the verbal abstractions task. The chief aim of this study was to evaluate the prediction from Hullian drive theory "that anxiety should facilitate performance in tasks where the correct response tendency is dominant but should produce inferior performance in tasks where incorrect response tendencies are dominant." It was assumed, further, that "there should be few and weak competing responses when S defines all the presented words by a correct abstraction, and strong competing responses when none of the presented words elicit a correct abstraction."

The CMAS was administered to 115 mental defectives, males and females, who had participated in two of the previous studies of verbal abstraction. The results of interest were a negative correlation ($-.51$) between CMAS and verbal abstract performance, and a positive correlation (.69) between IQ and total abstraction score. Sex and age were not found to be related to either anxiety or abstraction. The prediction that increased anxiety should facilitate performance when the correct response was strongest was not confirmed.

The suggestion of a lower level of abstract performance in mental defectives in some of the previous data led to the question of whether strengthening an appropriate association to the individual words in an abstraction set would increase the probability of identifying the dimension of similarity. By the same token, one would expect the opposite effect of strengthening irrelevant associations. These hypotheses were evaluated by Miller and Griffith (1961) in a study which represents perhaps the only attempt in the literature to assess differences in abstract performance strength in defectives and then to identify the experimental variables which may influence observed differences. Forty-two of the Ss who participated in the earlier studies were selected at random from those still available and assigned to four training groups and one untrained group. Groups were matched on IQ, CA, and previous performance on the abstractions task. In the training condition verbal associates were elicited by pictures of nouns under conditions of abstraction-relevant, abstraction-irrelevant, and no reinforcement. The nouns were later arranged into triads of related words and presented as part of a verbal abstractions test, followed at a later date by the definitions test. The untrained group received only the abstractions and definitions tests. The following results were indicated clearly:

> . . . that social reinforcement of relevant or irrelevant associates had no apparent effect on abstraction performance within the Trained group. However, when Trained and Untrained Ss were compared, Trained Ss performed significantly better on the items composed of the nouns used in training, so that elicitation *per se* resulted in improved conceptual performance; however, they performed no better than Untrained Ss on materials not used in training. This finding generally suggests that any improvement in the conceptual behavior of retardates, effected through training, may be limited to the materials used in training.

The validity of the conclusion is highly questionable in the light of the findings of such studies as Johnson and Blake (1960) and Bensberg (1958) of positive transfer to new materials in problem solving and concept formation. Additional research is clearly needed before the question of the effects of training can be fully evaluated. An alternative training procedure would be to set up a paired-associate learning task in which a given abstract term was separately strengthened as a response to each of the words included in a test triad.

If verbal or pictorial instances of classes of abstract terms (e.g., food) are presented in random order as a recall task, Ss tend to recall them in clusters of related items. This phenomenon has been referred to as *associative clustering* in recall. Two studies of verbal abstract performance in this sense have been reported in the literature. Weatherwax and Benoit (1957) compared associative-clustering tendencies in two groups of mentally deficient children, one with and one without demonstrable neurological signs of brain injury. Groups were roughly equivalent in mean MA, CA, and IQ. Each S received six presentations and six recall tests of a series of twelve pictures which were definable in terms of four classes of three items each. Six different random orders of presentation were used.

Data for the effects of number of trials were not presented. On an overall measure both groups clustered significantly above chance, but did not differ between themselves. The results were equivocal, however, in that half of the brain-injured group had participated in a previous teaching project which included situations similar to the associative-clustering task. Data were presented which suggest that the experience influenced clustering.

Osborn (1960) presented brain-injured, familial, and normal Ss, matched on MA, with a longer randomized series of related pictures. In this instance the series was presented three times, in three different random orders, before a recall test was administered. None of the group differences in the measures of clustering used were found to be significant.

Careful attention should be given to the question of the validity of clustering as a measure of verbal abstraction. It may simply be the case, as the work of Jenkins and Russell (1952) suggests, that so-called "related" words are recalled in clusters because of simple S-R associative strength, rather than as the result of elicitation of a common abstract mediator. In the light of Griffith's work, the degree to which clustering is related to the availability of abstract mediators (verbal identification of dimension of similarity) would appear to be a question of considerable importance.

The final study to be reviewed in this section is a comparative investigation by McMurray (1954) of performance on a modified version of the Wisconsin Card Sorting Task (WCST) in brain-injured and non-brain-injured defectives. Subjects in each group were matched for CA, IQ, and sex. The WCST is a measure of nonverbal abstract performance and the ability to shift responses from dependence on one dimension of similarity to another. The task consists of a series of cards containing items varying in color, form, and number. McMurray employed a shortened version of the standard task. Sortings for color were verbally reinforced first, form next, and number last. In the standard version this sequence is repeated a second time. The criterion of successful abstraction prior to shift was five consecutive correct responses. Three stimulus cards containing the essential features of the response deck were placed on a table before *S*, and *S* was instructed that the cards could be sorted according to color, form, or number (another departure from the standard procedure). The results were reported in terms of (1) perseverative errors (sorting a card according to a dimension which was previously correct), (2) total number of cards sorted prior to reaching criterion, and (3) time needed to reach criterion. It was hypothesized that brain-injured *S*s would manifest a higher degree of perseverative errors than non-brain-injured. With the exception of the initial sorting for color, brain-injured *S*s made significantly more perseverative errors, sorted more cards, and took more time to reach criterion than non-brain-injured *S*s.

ABSTRACT AND CONCRETE BEHAVIOR

The Goldstein-Scheerer tests

The study of individual differences in abstract performance was given its greatest impetus by the monograph of Goldstein and Scheerer (1941) and the related work which preceded it. Goldstein and Scheerer postulated the existence of two general response tendencies in behavior, one *abstract* and the other *concrete*. While the dimension of abstract and concrete behavior was clearly a dichotomy, each half of the dichotomy was represented by a continuum. Both response tendencies were supposedly present in normals, but only the concrete in abnormal conditions such as schizophrenia and brain injury.

In brief, the "abstract attitude" is seen in the ability to consciously respond to common properties of otherwise dissimilar objects and events and to shift response from one dimension of similarity to another. The criterion for conscious awareness is the ability to identify verbally the relevant dimension of similarity. The "concrete" individual is unaware of the common properties of objects and events and is, therefore, unable to respond to them. There is a tendency, rather, to respond to each object in a class as if it were unique. The concrete attitude is also seen in an inability to shift from one sorting dimension to another.

Goldstein and Scheerer (1941) maintained, further, that abstract and concrete behavior could best be revealed in a qualitative analysis of individual performance and described a group of tests which were considered to be appropriate for such purposes. While it appeared that an attempt was made to standardize the administration of the tests, this was not extended to the scoring procedures, and because of this, the results of their analysis of individual cases are difficult to interpret. Three of the tests will be described here briefly. Two others, a Stick Test and a Cube Test, are of doubtful validity as measures of abstract and concrete behavior in that they do not involve response to common properties of otherwise dissimilar objects. The three tests of interest include, generally, *active* sorting and shifting and *passive* verbal identification of relevant dimensions of similarity. The Color Sorting Test (CST) includes woolen skeins varying in hue and saturation. In the Object Sorting Test (OST) *S* is presented a variety of real objects varying in material, color, and form. The Color Form Sorting Test (CFST) consists of a set of figures varying in form and color. Some efforts have been made to standardize scoring of the Goldstein-Scheerer tests, notably, Rapaport (1945) and Silverstein (1960); but considerably more research is needed before their use as diagnostic instruments can be justified. One of the chief drawbacks of the tests is the large number of scoring categories in each, which, when comparing groups, increases the probability of making a type-I error of statistical inference (i.e., false rejection of the null hypothesis). More important, however, is the questionable validity of the underlying theory which insists upon a dichotomization of abstract and concrete and the necessity for conscious awareness of relevant conceptual dimensions as the *sine qua non* of abstract behavior (Weatherwax & Benoit, 1957).

The research on abstract and concrete behavior in the area of mental deficiency has been entirely comparative and concerned primarily with the question of whether mental defectives as a group can be characterized as concrete in their conceptual behavior. A sizable number of studies have employed one or the other or a combination of the Goldstein-Scheerer tests, in original or modified form. Other developments of interest to students of individual differences in abstract behavior will be discussed subsequently.

Halpin and Patterson (1954) compared brain-injured and familial mental defectives matched on MA, CA, IQ, sex, educational achievement, and length of institutionalization on the CFST. The results did not suggest a superiority of sorting behavior in the non-brain-injured. Jordan (1956) employed a color-form-size sorting task with a group of cerebral-palsied school children varying in IQ from 27 to 138 and found sorting ability to be more clearly related to MA than to either degree or kind of neurological disability. The interested reader should also consult Strauss and Werner (1942) and Werner and Strauss (1943), who present the results of performance by brain-injured mental defectives on other tasks.

Bolles (1937) compared mental defectives and dements without history of brain injury and normals with comparable MA in their performance on the CST, the CFST, and the OST. The small *N* in each group, coupled with the absence of statistical comparisons, make the reliability of her results questionable. The results were interpreted as supporting the contention that normals perform on a more abstract level than mental defectives or dements. Kounin (1941), in another qualitative study of color-form sorting, confirmed Bolles's observations. The *S*s were a group of older mental defectives (mean CA 41.7), a group of young mental defectives (mean CA 14.5), and a group of normal children (mean CA 6.8) matched on MA. All mental defectives were diagnosed as "functional." The superiority of the normals was observed in their ability to spontaneously sort on the basis of both form and color and in their ability to shift when required from one sorting category to another. There was some suggestion of a lower level of performance in the older as compared with the younger mentally deficient *S*s.

Prothro (1943) compared a group of familial and undifferentiated mental defectives with a group of normals matched on MA on a series of sorting tasks. The ability to shift *voluntarily* was found to be significantly greater in normals.

Two groups of mental defectives, both of which were similar in CA and MA, but who differed in IQ (means 59.32 and 73.64) were compared by Stacey and Portnoy (1951) on the OST. Groups were not found to differ in active sorting ability, but there was evidence of a superiority in the higher-IQ group with respect to ability to identify verbally the basis for *E*'s sortings. In a later study Korstvedt, Stacey, and Reynolds (1954) employed a modification of the CFST in a comparison of normal and mentally deficient adolescents. The sample of mental defectives was further broken down into a moron (mean IQ 60) and a borderline (mean IQ 74) group. The results of primary interest were a significantly greater tendency to sort by both form and color in normals, a significantly greater tendency to sort by neither in defectives, and a significantly greater ability to identify the basis for sorting in normals. Unlike the earlier study, all differences between IQ groups in the mentally deficient sample were found to be nonsignificant.

Halpin (1958) studied the relationship between performance on the CFST and CA and MA in a large sample of mentally deficient boys and girls. Of interest was the observation of a significant positive relationship between shifting ability and both CA and MA. Four groups of non-brain-injured defectives varying in CA from 12.10 to 43.19 were compared by Iscoe and Giller (1959) in their performance on the Rapaport modification of the OST. The hypothesis being tested was that with increasing CA, mental defectives would abstract more on the basis of commonly accepted dimensions of similarity. The results failed to support this hypothesis, but rather, suggested a decrease in common abstractions with age. Unfortunately, mean CA and MA were proportional in the four groups (a fact which the authors do not appear to have noticed), and abstract performance could be related to either.

Lastly, Hughes (1959) compared groups of *S*s equated on MA but differing in IQ (the means being 135, 104, and 72) in their performance on the CFST, the OST, and the similarities subtest of the Wechsler Intellegence Scale for Children. Mentally deficient *S*s were classed as non-brain-injured. Differences in favor of the high-IQ group were found only on the verbal portion of the CFST and on the second part of the OST. All other group differences were nonsignificant.

Verbal abstraction

Another line of development in this area has centered around an attempt to analyze verbal definitions from vocabulary and similarities tests in terms of some inferred level of abstraction. In general, the scoring categories which have been used most frequently, in one form or other, are (1) abstract (e.g., "an apple is a fruit"); (2) functional (e.g., "you eat an apple"); (3) concrete (e.g., "an apple is red"). Abstract (categorical) definitions are those which identify a given item as a member of a particular class of items, functional (use) definitions describe some operation which is performed with the item, and concrete (descriptive) definitions describe some stimulus property of the item.

Stacey and Portnoy (1950) employed nouns from the vocabulary sub-test of the Wechsler Intelligence Scale for Children in two groups of mental defectives, with mean IQs of 58.42 (range 50 to 65) and 70.44 (range 66 to 79). The two groups did not differ in proportion of abstract definitions, but the higher-IQ group gave a significantly greater number of concrete responses and the lower-IQ group, a significantly greater number of functional definitions. Although the authors make no mention of it, it is clear from the tabulated data that a considerably greater proportion of responses in both groups were of the functional variety. Stacey and Portnoy (1951) attempted to test the generality of these results on adult samples with the addition of a dull normal (mean IQ 83.12, range 80 to 90) group and found no significant differences among adult groups. However, when the younger mental defectives were compared with their adult counterparts, the following significant differences emerged: (1) a greater proportion of concrete descriptive responses in the adult group at both IQ levels; (2) a greater proportion of functional responses in the younger groups; and (3) a greater proportion of abstract categorial definitions in both older groups. It was interesting to note, also, that functional definitions occurred more frequently than either of the other varieties in the adult samples.

The results of both studies clearly question the assumption that concrete descriptive responses represent a lower level of abstraction than functional and raise the question for experimental research of the source of CA differences in abstract definitions.

Two studies (Papania, 1954; Badt, 1958) have employed Stanford-Binet vocabulary items. A group of 50 mentally deficient children (Papania, 1954) was chosen at each of five MA levels (6, 7, 8, 9, and 10 years) and matched on IQ (mean IQ was approximately 70 in all groups). As has been observed all too frequently in the course of the present review, however, mean MA and CA were proportional in the five groups. A sample of normal Ss of average IQ in essentially the same CA range as the defectives was also included. The reliability of scoring definitions reached .97. In the mentally deficient samples the proportion of abstract definitions was found to increase generally with increase in MA, while responses scored as concrete tended to decrease with increase in MA. Comparisons with the normal group revealed the following significant differences: (1) fewer abstract definitions in the defectives, (2) more concrete responses in the defectives, and (3) no differences in the proportion of acceptable definitions.

Badt (1958) reports the results of a correlational study of the relationship between vocabulary definitions and CA, MA, IQ, and length of institutionalization in a sample of 60 educable, non-brain-injured mentally deficient children in the IQ range 50 to 75. It is to be noted that Badt's sample covered a wider range of CA and IQ than Papania's. Acceptable (correct) definitions from a vocabulary list of the Stanford-Binet were scored and weighted, with abstract responses given a weight of five; use, three; and descriptive, one. High interscorer agreement was reported.

Each S's "abstraction score" was the total of weighted scores for acceptable definitions.

There is a question which arises here concerning the validity of the weighting procedure. A significant correlation does not tell us what proportion of responses fell into each scoring category. An abstraction score of five, for example, could be the result of a single acceptable definition judged as abstract, or five acceptable definitions judged as descriptive. Or what would be more serious, an S with 10 acceptable descriptive responses would come out with a higher abstraction score than an S with one acceptable abstract definition. These examples may represent extreme cases, but obviously, a measure is needed which is in some way or other independent of the absolute number of acceptable definitions. With these objections in mind, the most important finding seemed to be a relatively high negative correlation between abstraction score and length of institutionalization.

Three groups of Ss, with mean IQs of 57.88, 73.54, and 83.20, and mean CAs of 19.34, 20.55, and 19.68, respectively, were compared in their performance on the similarities subtest of the Wechsler Intelligence Scale (Stacey & Markin, 1951). Responses were scored in terms of the abstract-functional-descriptive trichotomy, with the following results: (1) none of the group differences in proportion of abstract responses was significant, (2) the lowest-IQ group produced a significantly greater proportion of functional responses than the borderline and dull normal groups, and (3) descriptive responses occurred significantly more frequently in the dull normal as compared with the lowest-IQ group. All other group differences were nonsignificant. Hughes (1959), it will be recalled, failed to find differences on the similarities test in groups differing in IQ.

Other studies

The two final studies to be reviewed in this section are of importance in that they represent attempts to develop greater objectivity in the measurement of abstract behavior. Siegel (1957) reports the results of a study using an instrument called the Visual-Verbal Concept Formation Test, where Ss have the dual task of selecting items which have a common stimulus property and of identifying verbally the relevant dimension of similarity. Briefly, the mentally deficient Ss as compared with the normals showed impairment in both the ability to shift the basis of selection from one relevant dimension to another and the ability to verbalize the relevant dimension of similarity. Johnson and Blake (1960) employed analogies tests to assess differences in what was referred to as "reasoning" ability, but which clearly involved ability to identify common properties of dissimilar items. Differences between mentally defective and normal children were nonsignificant.

Discussion

In general, one might be willing to hazard the conclusion that in abstraction tasks using nonverbal stimulus materials, there appears to be some tendency toward poorer performance in mental defectives. In the sphere of verbal abstractions, however, there is little evidence to suggest that abstract definitions occur less frequently in the mentally deficient. A variety of methodological difficulties, however, including a number of statistical prob-

458 *Handbook of Mental Deficiency*

lems related to questions of sampling, variability, multiple comparisons, and appropriateness of a given test for group differences, which were not discussed at any length, have rendered the results of some studies questionable. Too, the question of the reliability of measuring instruments used has not been given a degree of attention in the literature which could be called adequate. Notable, also, by its absence has been any concern with the measurement of abstract performance at lower levels of mental deficiency. This development may be in part a function of the level of difficulty of instructions and other requirements for performance in the traditional abstract-concrete tasks.

For future research purposes it would be constructive to conclude this section with a brief discussion of the major questions to be considered in evaluating any presumed dimension of individual differences. Initially, one would raise the question of intraindividual generality; i.e., how consistent is an S's performance from one abstraction task to another. For example, do Ss who perform well in sorting tasks also give a high proportion of verbal abstractions in vocabulary definitions and take fewer trials to criterion in a discrimination learning situation in which a response is being strengthened to a common property of dissimilar objects? Assuming adequate reliability, if an S's relative position in a distribution changes markedly from one abstraction task to another, the generality (and thus the *importance*) of the postulated dimension would be seriously questioned. Given a certain degree of generality, one might then raise the question of whether the proposed dimension should be considered as an independent factor or as a component of a broader construct, such as intelligence. Thirdly, an attempt would be made to identify the range of environmental conditions under which group differences held. The familiar experimental by subject variable design would be of immeasurable value in evaluating interactions. One would want to know, for example, whether differences between normals and mental defectives hold for all levels of task difficulty. Lastly, an intensive experimental study would be carried out of the antecedent environmental variables which facilitate and interfere with the performance of mental defectives on abstraction tasks.

In a sense, we have been outlining a long-range research program designed to evaluate the validity of the construct, abstract versus concrete behavior. Unfortunately, there appear to have been no sustained attempts in the area of mental deficiency to consider any of the questions raised here. It is impossible to avoid the impression that research to date has been essentially an attempt to *demonstrate* differences which some writers have concluded are reliably present in the populations under analysis. The paucity of experimental research in this area should suggest further the strength of preconceptions concerning the durability of postulated group differences.

CONCLUSIONS

The present review leads to disappointment, in terms of not only the limited number and variety of investigations, but also the neglect of problems of statistical design, terminology, and the logic of formal theoretical and research methodology. The most pressing need at present is perhaps for research pertaining to the effects of a wide variety of environmental variables upon problem solving and concept formation. In this respect, much can be gained from a careful consideration of the literature on learning. By the use of randomized group designs and analysis of covariance, we can overcome some of the major sampling and statistical problems which have plagued comparative research in the area of mental deficiency.

It would be difficult to attempt to characterize the problem-solving and conceptual behavior of mental defectives from the research reported to date with any high degree of reliability. There should be little doubt, however, of the existence of a relationship between problem-solving and/or conceptual behavior and IQ and MA. The relationship, nevertheless, is a very complex one, the details of which will have to be worked out in future research. It is also clear that under certain conditions, some mental defectives are capable of problem solving, abstract learning, abstract performance, and generalization despite evidence of an inability to identify verbally the relevant dimensions of similarity. These results should act as a stimulus for those workers interested in education and training to search for the variables which facilitate and interfere with problem-solving and conceptual behavior.

In the latter respect, the sharp increase in recent years in experimental research on the basic learning processes in mental defectives is also bound to have its effect upon the present area. The beginnings of such interest can be found, for example, in Bensberg, 1958; Hermelin and O'Connor, 1958; Johnson and Blake, 1960; Miller and Griffith, 1960; and Ringelheim, 1960a. We can only hope that the effort in the future will not be as discontinuous as it has been in the past.

REFERENCES

ALDRICH, CECELIA G. Incentive as a factor in problem-solving among idiots. *Train. Sch. Bull.*, 1930, 27, 121–126.

ALDRICH, CECELIA G., & DOLL, E. A. Problem solving among idiots. *J. comp. Psychol.*, 1931, 12, 137–169. (a)

ALDRICH, CECELIA G., & DOLL, E. A. Problem solving among idiots: the use of implements. *J. soc. Psychol.*, 1931, 2, 306–336. (b)

BADT, MARGIT I. Levels of abstraction in vocabulary definitions of mentally retarded children. *Amer. J. ment. Defic.*, 1958, 63, 241–246.

BARNETT, C. D., ELLIS, N. R., & PRYER, MARGARET W. Learning in familial and brain-injured defectives. *Amer. J. ment. Defic.*, 1960, 64, 894–901.

BENSBERG, G. Concept learning in mental defectives as a function of appropriate and inappropriate "attention sets." *J. educ. Psychol.*, 1958, 49, 137–143.

BOLLES, MARY M. The basis of pertinence. *Arch. Psychol., N.Y.*, 1937, No. 212.

BUSS, A. H. A study of concept formation as a function of reinforcement and stimulus generalization. *J. exp. Psychol.*, 1950, 40, 494–503.

DUNCAN, C. P. Recent research on human problem solving. *Psychol. Bull.*, 1959, 56, 397–429.

EDWARDS, A. L. *Experimental design in psychological research.* (Rev. ed.) New York: Holt, 1960.

GAGNÉ, R. M. Problem solving and thinking. *Annu. Rev. Psychol.*, 1959, 10, 147–172.

GOLDSTEIN, K., & SCHEERER, M. Abstract and concrete behavior. An experimental study with special tests. *Psychol. Monogr.*, 1941, 53, No. 2.

GRIFFITH, B. C. The use of verbal mediators in concept formation by retarded subjects at different intelligence levels. *Child Develpm.*, 1960, 31, 633–641.

GRIFFITH, B. C., & SPITZ, H. H. Some relationships between abstraction and word meaning in retarded adolescents. *Amer. J. ment. Defic.*, 1958, 63, 247–251.

GRIFFITH, B. C., SPITZ, H. H., & LIPMAN, R. S. Verbal mediation and concept formation in retarded and normal subjects. *J. exp. Psychol.*, 1959, 58, 247–251.

HALPIN, VIRGINIA C. The performance of mentally retarded children on the Weigl-Goldstein-Scheerer color form sorting test. *Amer. J. ment. Defic.*, 1958, 62, 916–919.

HALPIN, VIRGINIA C., & PATTERSON, RUTH M. The performance of brain-injured children on the Goldstein-Scheerer Tests. *Amer. J. ment. Defic.*, 1954, 59, 91–99.

HERMELIN, BEATE, & O'CONNOR, N. The rote and concept learning of imbeciles. *J. ment. Def. Res.*, 1958, 2, 21–27.

HUGHES, DOROTHY, H. A study of concept formation in a group of superior, average, and mentally retarded children of similar mental age: a comparison of the concept formation of boys and girls whose mental ages are between 9–6 and 10–6, but whose intellectual levels vary from superior to mentally retarded. Unpublished doctoral dissertation, New York Univer., 1959.

ISCOE, I., & GILLER, D. Areas of concept formation in the mentally retarded. *Amer. J. ment. Defic.*, 1959, 63, 112–116.

JENKINS, J. J., & RUSSELL, W. A. Associative clustering during recall. *J. abnorm. soc. Psychol.*, 1952, 47, 818–821.

JOHNSON, D. M. Problem solving and symbolic processes. *Annu. Rev. Psychol.*, 1950, 1, 297–310.

JOHNSON, G. O., & BLAKE, KATHRYN A. *Learning performance of retarded and normal children.* Syracuse Univer. Press, 1960.

JORDAN, J. E. An investigation of the nature of concept formation in cerebral palsied school children. Unpublished doctoral dissertation, Michigan State Univer., 1956.

KENDLER, H. H., GLUCKSBERG, S., & KESTON, R. Perception and mediation in concept learning. *J. exp. Psychol.*, 1961, 61, 186–191.

KENDLER, TRACY S. Concept formation. *Annu. Rev. Psychol.*, 1961, 12, 447–472.

KORSTVEDT, A., STACEY, C. L., & REYNOLDS, W. F. Concept formation of normal and subnormal adolescents on a modification of the Weigl-Goldstein-Scheerer Color Form Sorting Test. *J. clin. Psychol.*, 1954, 10, 88–90.

KOUNIN, J. S. Experimental studies of rigidity. 1. The measurement of rigidity in normal and feeble-minded persons. *Charact. & Pers.*, 1941, 9, 251–272.

LIPMAN, R. S., & GRIFFITH, B. C. Effects of anxiety level on concept formation: a test of drive theory. *Amer. J. ment. Defic.*, 1960, 65, 342–348.

MCMURRAY, J. G. Rigidity in conceptual thinking in exogenous and endogenous mentally retarded children. *J. consult. Psychol.*, 1954, 18, 366–370.

MCPHERSON, MARION W. A survey of experimental studies of learning in individuals who achieve subnormal ratings on standardized psychometric measures. *Amer. J. ment. Defic.*, 1948, 52, 232–254.

MARTIN, W. E., & BLUM, A. Intertest generalization and learning in mentally normal and subnormal children. *J. comp. physiol. Psychol.*, 1961, 54, 28–32.

MILLER, M. B. "Rebelliousness" and repetition-choice of a puzzle task under relative autonomy or control conditions in adolescent retardates. In R. L. Cromwell (Ed.), *Abstracts of Peabody studies in mental retardation,* 1960, 1, No. 74.

MILLER, M. B., & GRIFFITH, B. C. The effects of training verbal associates on the performance of retarded *S*s at a conceptual task. In R. L. Cromwell (Ed.), *Abstracts of Peabody studies in mental retardation,* 1960, 1, No. 65.

OSBORN, W. J. Associative clustering in organic and familial retardates. *Amer. J. ment. Defic.,* 1960, 65, 351–357.

PAPANIA, N. A qualitative analysis of vocabulary responses of institutionalized, mentally retarded children. *J. clin. Psychol.,* 1954, 10, 361–365.

PASCAL, G. R., & ZAX, M. Double alternation performance as a measure of educability in cerebral palsied children. *Amer. J. ment. Defic.,* 1955, 59, 658–665.

PROTHRO, E. T. Egocentricity and abstraction in children and in adult aments. *Amer. J. Psychol.,* 1943, 56, 66–77.

RAPAPORT, D. *Diagnostic psychological testing.* Vol. 1. Chicago: Year Book Publishers, 1945.

RASMUSSEN, ELIZABETH A., & ARCHER, E. J. Concept identification as a function of language pretraining and task complexity. *J. exp. Psychol.,* 1961, 61, 437–441.

RAY, J. J. The generalizing ability of dull, bright, and superior children. *Peabody Coll. Contr. Educ.,* 1936, No. 175.

RAY, W. S. Complex tasks for use in human problem solving research. *Psychol. Bull.,* 1955, 52, 134–149.

RINGELHEIM, D. The relation of set to simple alternation problem solving in mental defectives. In R. L. Cromwell (Ed.), *Abstracts of Peabody studies in mental retardation,* 1960, 1, No. 26. (a)

RINGELHEIM, D. The relation of degree of set and CA to simple alternation problem solving in mental defectives. In R. L. Cromwell (Ed.), *Abstracts of Peabody studies in mental retardation,* 1960, 1, No. 27. (b)

SIEGEL, S. M. Discrimination among mental defective, normal, schizophrenic and brain damaged subjects on the visual-verbal concept formation test. *Amer. J. ment. Defic.,* 1957, 62, 338–343.

SILVERSTEIN, A. B. A cluster analysis of object sorting behavior. *J. consult. Psychol.,* 1960, 24, 98.

SKINNER, B. F. *Science and human behavior,* New York: Macmillan, 1953.

SKINNER, B. F. *Verbal behavior.* New York: Appleton-Century-Crofts, 1957.

STACEY, C. L., & MARKIN, K. E. A study of the differential responses among three groups of subnormals on the similarities sub-test of the Wechsler Intelligence Scale. *Amer. J. ment. Defic.,* 1951, 56, 424–428.

STACEY, C. L., & PORTNOY, B. A study of the differential responses on the vocabulary sub-test of the Wechsler Intelligence Scale for Children. *J. clin. Psychol.,* 1950, 6, 401–403.

STACEY, C. L., & PORTNOY, B. A study of the differential responses on the vocabulary sub-test of the Wechsler-Bellevue Intelligence Scale. *J. clin. Psychol.,* 1951, 7, 144–148. (a)

STACEY, C. L., & PORTNOY, B. A study of concept formation by means of the object sorting test with subnormals. *Amer. J. ment. Defic.,* 1951, 56, 169–173. (b)

STOLUROW, L. M., & PASCAL, G. R. Double alternation behavior in mental defectives. *Amer. Psychologist,* 1950, 5, 273–274.

STRAUSS, A. A., & WERNER, H. Disorders of conceptual thinking in the brain-injured child. *J. nerv. ment. Dis.,* 1942, 96, 153–172.

TAYLOR, D. W., & MCNEMAR, OLGA W. Problem solving and thinking. *Annu. Rev. Psychol.*, 1955, 6, 455–482.

WEATHERWAX, JOY, & BENOIT, E. P. Concrete and abstract thinking in organic and non-organic mentally retarded children. *Amer. J. ment. Defic.*, 1957, 62, 548–553.

WERNER, H., & STRAUSS, A. A. Impairment in thought processes of brain-injured children. *Amer. J. ment. Defic.*, 1943, 47, 291–295.

WHITESIDE, STELLA. Spontaneity of normal and mentally deficient subjects in selective learning. *Proc. Amer. Ass. ment. Def.*, 1934, 39, 344–383.

WILSON, F. T. Errors, difficulty, resourcefulness, and speed in the learning of bright and dull children. *J. educ. Psychol.*, 1931, 22, 229–240.

14

SENSORY PROCESSES AND MENTAL DEFICIENCY

Frank Kodman, Jr.

In the light of changing concepts in psychology, it would be rather foolish to dichotomize the sensoriperceptual continuum. Nevertheless, an attempt will be made to orient the information more toward the sensory event than toward the perceptual event. The reader should bear in mind that throughout this chapter, sensation and perception will not be viewed as dichotomous or discontinuous processes even though the contrary may at times appear to be the case. In addition to conceding that sensation and perception are causally related, one cannot ignore the important role of learning in these areas, nor can one ignore the interdependence of the sensory and motor systems. It is inevitable that some overlap will occur in discussions of sensation and perception in the present text. In most instances, the overlap will be treated from different points of view and should enrich the offering rather than detract from it.

Historically, sensory psychology was the primary interest of the new discipline, *experimental psychology*. Psychophysics developed from this interest and provided the basic methodology. At that time, there was a strong leaning toward physiology with its knowledge of the sensory organs and related nervous structures. Laboratory or experimental psychology received strong impetus from the work of E. H. Weber (1795 to 1878), a physiologist. There followed Weber's law and later the Weber-Fechner law which designated the relationship between the dimensions of the physical stimulus and its psychological correlatives. Fechner, (1801 to 1887), who was basically a physicist, felt that psychophysics applied to sensation and perception would make possible a definition of the dynamics involved in relating mind and matter to each other. With this beginning, experimental psychology made a significant contribution to our knowledge of man. It should be borne in mind, however, that psychophysical methods are most effective when applied to a subject who is particularly sophisticated in making discriminatory responses and lose much of their effectiveness when the subject is unwilling or unable to perform reliably and validly.

Perception is, for the most part, an approximation of the physical stimulus in the environment. Although an exponential number of environmental stimuli reach the sensory receptors, the product does not mirror the environment in exact detail, even in the normal organism. It is generally conceded that the sensory modalities alter the information in some respects and that further modifications in coding and decoding occur in the central nervous system. It might be argued that the latter occurs in a differential manner in the retardate even though his sensory receptors are basically identical to the normal. Retardation in its many forms probably has its greatest influence upon the central processes rather than the peripheral or end-organ functions. The next section will consider sensorineural organization.

SENSORINEURAL ORGANIZATION

In order to relate theoretical considerations of sensorineural organization to the mentally retarded, it is necessary to draw upon existing formulations applied to the normal intact organism. The brief treatment given here will draw heavily upon the work of Hebb (1949), who has cited his own research as well as that of Lashley (1938), Riesen (1947), von Senden (1932), and others in approaching the problem of innate perception and early learning in man and animals.

There is general agreement that sensory input is always superimposed upon an already active cortex. This activity is said to be in opposition to organization or change imposed upon it by sensory events. At birth, the intrinsic organization of cortical activity is said to be dominant; however, as perceptual learning increases, there is probably a decrease in this dominance. Hebb attributes to this phenomenon the slow first learning found in man and the higher species. A function of perceptual learning is to establish a control over association-area activity by sensory events as they acquire new and greater meaning. As the process of primary learning increases, there is greater environmental control over the sensory projection areas of the brain. In the familial retardate, the entire process is undoubtedly slower than in the normal. In the retarded child with congenital brain damage, the function may be influenced by the manner in which certain neurological processes are altered.

Strauss and Lehtinen (1951) describe the behavior of organic and familial mental defectives as characterized by poor motor coordination, short attention span, perseveration, and the inability to discriminate figures. It is important to point out that these characteristics are merely descriptive and are not diagnostic labels. Can these characteristics be attributed, at least in part, to a faulty or attenuated development of the influence or control of association-area activity by sensory events? This might occur as a result of the decreased rate in primary or perceptual learning. Hebb would probably argue that a decrease in sensory control should also retard motor learning since he stresses the role of sensory control in motor learning. It has been said that clumsiness and high sensory accuracy rarely go hand in hand.

According to Hebb, the human infant goes through a period of establishing simple associations followed by conceptual stages. Form perception begins with a primitive sensorily determined unity which is dependent upon patterns of sensory excitation and the innate characteristics of the central nervous system. The perception of simple diagrams as discrete wholes is acquired *slowly* through learning, and perhaps even more slowly in the retardate.

Attention, in the Hebbian framework, refers to a selectivity of response which is influenced by something in addition to the immediately preceding sensory stimulation. Short attention span and hyperactivity are often noted in the severely retarded and the brain-injured. These gross labels are rarely analyzed into their components nor are they readily measurable. When we refer behaviorally to a short attention span, are we talking about visual, auditory, tactile, or motor systems? It appears to this writer that the label should be more specific. The same criticism is applicable to perseveration and rigidity. The writer has attempted to relate sensation and perception in a preliminary manner using Hebb's psychoneurological approach. The reader may readily reject the treatment, and it is his prerogative to do so. There is a related and comprehensive discussion of the development of perception by Strauss and Kephart (1955) entitled *Psychopathology of Perception*.

Sensory pathology offers some insight into the mentally retarded and has both genetic and rehabilitative implications. The results of various investigations are summarized in the following section.

Auditory pathology

At the Fourth Annual Meeting of the American Association on Mental Deficiency held at Columbus, Ohio, on May 19, 1950, Birch and Matthews presented a paper on the measurement of hearing in the mentally retarded. Their research marked a step forward on this problem in the United States and stimulated a host of subsequent inquiries.

Subjective puretone audiometry

The most popular approach has been the use of *subjective* puretone audiometry. The method is referred to as subjective since the response is not verified by objective means. Although the approach works well with normal subjects and represents one of the classical measurements in audiometry and experimental psychology, it is doubtful whether the result can be viewed as an absolute puretone threshold whenever the subject demonstrates poor response integrity. Nevertheless, subjective puretone audiometry serves as a stalwart beginning. Birch and Mathews (1951), Schlanger (1953), Johnson and Farrell (1954), Foale and Patterson (1954), Schlanger and Gottsleben (1956), Kodman et al. (1956), and Siegenthaler and Krzywicki (1959) have called attention to the prevalence of impaired puretone sensitivity in the mentally retarded. The samples were drawn largely from institutions.

The results suggest rather strongly that the prevalence of impaired hearing is considerably *higher* than that found in public school children. Estimates range from 13 to 49 per cent depending upon the hearing loss criteria used. In public school children, the estimates range from 3 to 10 per cent.

Bradley, Evans, and Worthington (1955) tested 56 retardates and compared their test time for two audiometric techniques with their mental ability. They concluded that subjective or standard puretone audiometry required less time to administer and was more reliable than an alternative ear-choice technique. The latter required the subject to localize the ear being stimulated. They also found that test reliability favored subjective audiometry and was more consistently related to mental age. Kodman et al. (1958) placed their retarded subjects into five response groups ranging from those who could localize the ear being stimulated (modified ear-choice technique) to those who were untestable by subjective puretone audiometry. They suggested modifications of the traditional puretone techniques applicable to each of the various groupings.

GSR audiometry

Galvanic skin response audiometry using puretone stimuli has been attempted with samples of retarded subjects. Irwin, Hind, and Aronson (1957) in an exploratory study examined 20 subjects in the Southern Wisconsin Colony and Training School. Four of the subjects had a confirmed history of epilepsy. IQ estimates ranged from 23 to 72 with a median of 50. They reported poor agreement between subjective audiometry and GSR audiometry with the latter showing lower thresholds. The mean conditioned GSR latencies for both hands for all testable subjects were 1.9 seconds. This value agrees closely with the 2.0-second mean latency found by Goldstein, Ludwig, and Naunton (1954) for deaf and aphasic children. In 1959, Kodman, Fein, and Mixson applied GSR puretone audiometry to 31 retardates using two test frequencies, 500 and 2,000 cycles. Meaningful results were obtained with 28 of the cases. IQ estimates ranged from 25 to 64 with a mean of 38.0. The subjects were divided into two groups of 14 each. One group received a 100 per cent reinforcement schedule and the other a 50 per cent reinforcement schedule. Subjective speech audiometry was included to obtain a relative measure of the speech threshold using the standardized Harvard spondaic words (baseball, armchair, etc.). Twenty-eight of the original 31 subjects were testable by various modifications of the conditioning techniques after the acquisition periods were completed. Mean GSR latencies were on the order of 1.0 second, which is considerably shorter than that found in normals. The mean relative speech thresholds were 4.0 decibels lower than the GSR thresholds. Nineteen of the 28 speech thresholds were lower, four were higher, and five were the same. Moss, Moss, and Tizard (1961) evaluated the hearing of 24 retarded children using GSR puretone audiometry. They replicated their study and concluded that GSR audiometry has limited utility with mentally retarded children. They suggested that the children who are not testable by subjective puretone audiometry are probably not testable by the GSR approach. They did report, however, that 95 per cent of their cases gave a UCR to the puretone stimulus in the pretrial period.

The major effort to date has been an attempt to define the *prevalence* of organic hearing loss in the mentally retarded. It is understandable but not wholly defensible that the majority of the studies of the last decade have used subjective puretone audiometry. It is interesting to note that tuning-fork audiometry along with noise makers, the whisper test, and other qualitative measures have not been reported. This does not rule out the common use of these techniques in the examiner's office. It does denote a more cautious and systematic approach to auditory measurement in the retardate. Of the various studies reported above, one does not find two investigations that are identical with respect to their criteria of hearing loss, sample size, audiometric technique, tester sophistication, psychometric classification, etiology of retardation, etc. We note with concern that a great deal of heterogeneity exists on most of the parameters investigated. This argues strongly for a greater uniformity among research designs.

Response integrity (reliability and validity) of subjective puretone audiometry with the more severely retarded child or adult can be seriously questioned. A number of investigators have called attention to the poor response reliability of subjects with mental ages within the 4- and 5-year level and below. Partial success may be obtained with those having an MA of 4 to 5 years. Below this level it is doubtful if the clinical results warrant the effort. The three investigations which recorded the galvanic skin response to puretone stimuli are reflections of the need for an objective approach to the measurement of hearing sensitivity in the retardate. Kodman and his associates apparently had the best success with the GSR method. This may have been due to clinical skill, instrumentation, flexibility of the GSR techniques, or the selection of subjects who, although severely retarded, may have manifested less neurological pathology. The validity of their results was enhanced by the speech thresholds included in the measurements. Correlation coefficients of .74 and .64 were obtained between the puretone GSR thresholds for 500 and 2,000 cycles and the speech thresholds. These coefficients are of the order of magnitude of those reported between subjective puretone thresholds and GSR puretone thresholds using normal subjects.

The author (1958) reviewed the results of seven puretone audiometric studies of the prevalence of hearing loss among the mentally retarded. He argued for a uniformity of hearing loss criteria and predicted that the prevalence of hearing loss among retarded children would exceed that of public school children by a factor of 3 to 4:1. In other words, if the prevalence among school children were 5 per cent, then the prevalence among the retarded would be 15 to 20 per cent provided that valid assessments were made in each population.

If we wish to validate the assessment of hearing loss among the retarded, a battery of hearing tests with known validity should be used. The measurements would be made ideally in a two-room sound-treated laboratory especially designed for auditory measurements. Ruhm and Carhart (1958) and

Whipple and Kodman (1960) have demonstrated the validity of GSR audiometry using speech stimuli with subjects having normal learning ability. The validity of this method has not been established with retarded subjects and remains to be explored. On the other hand, we have no evidence that the method would not be valuable. As a basic approach to determining the degree of hearing loss among the retarded, the author would suggest the following. The measurements should be performed in the proper acoustic environment. Subjective puretone audiometry, GSR puretone audiometry, GSR speech audiometry, and subjective speech audiometry would be performed on each subject. The samples should be large and classified properly according to mental age, chronological age, sex, and etiology of retardation. A cooperative effort in each state would yield sufficient data to verify the degree of organic hearing loss among the mentally retarded population in the United States.

Curiously enough, no studies have been reported concerning the validity of audiometric patterns, type of hearing loss, and etiology of deafness among the retarded. The use of EEG audiometry has yet to be explored using predictive samples. Delayed auditory feedback should have some diagnostic utility. Stimuli other than speech can be used. Although a good beginning has been made in the area of audiometric measurements, much remains to be learned about auditory function in the retardate. The reader may turn to the chapter on perception for additional information. Concerning hearing aids, auditory abilities, receptive aphasia, and functional or nonorganic hearing loss among the retarded, our knowledge is meager. We should look beyond the degree of organic hearing loss in order to uncover the most meaningful information regarding the role of auditory function in mental retardation.

Visual pathology

Although the research related to auditory pathology in the mentally retarded leaves much to be desired, there is even less information in the area of visual pathology. Clarke and Clarke (1958) note the absence of any large-scale study of visual handicaps. Information with which to make comparisons of visual sensitivity with auditory sensitivity is inadequate. We can merely speculate upon the prevalence of impaired visual sensitivity among the mentally retarded. In the previous section, the data suggest that auditory impairment is more prevalent among retardates than among normals. A similar assumption could be made for impaired visual sensitivity but without comparable support.

Lowe (1949) reports frequent pathology of the iris and myopia in one-third of his testable cases. Skeller and Oster (1951) comment on lens opacities and a high percentage of hypermetropia, or farsightedness. Benda (1960) feels that strabismus and refractive errors are more frequent in the young mongoloid than among normal children. Igersheimer and Mautner (1951) have observed a type of cataractous opacity in mongoloids between 8 and 15 years. Kratter (1957) and O'Conner (1957) call for further investigation of the prevalence of color blindness. O'Conner studied color blindness in 144 male imbeciles with results which suggest a greater prevalence than in the normal. Kratter reported that 3.91 per cent of a group of 128 male morons and 7.93 per cent of a group of 63 male imbeciles had red-green blindness. In the normal population, the most common form of color blindness is that of the dichromate who can distinguish only two of the three primaries. He confuses red and green when these hues are equal in brightness.

The high prevalence of biological diseases among the retarded would tend to raise the prevalence of visual pathology and other sensory defects as well. The following conditions or diseases may be contributory according to Heber (1959): congenital rubella, syphilis, toxoplasmosis, postimmunization encephalopathy, prenatal radiation of the mother, mechanical injuries to the child at birth, Tay-Sach's disease, late infantile and juvenile lipoidoses, Neimann-Pick's disease, Wilson's disease, galactosemia, gargoylism, cranio-stenosis, hydrocephalus, primary microcephaly, mongolism, acute infantile diffuse sclerosis, Scholz' disease, and Schilder's disease to mention a partial list.

Other senses

As the review is extended beyond audition and vision, to the "secondary" senses—taste, smell, touch, kinesthesis—a more conspicuous absence of information is found. Clarke and Clarke (1958) support the assumption that "true" mental defectives are subnormal, not only in learning ability, but also in sensory capacities. They call attention to the probable importance of partial handicaps over total handicaps like deafness and blindness. Is partial or distorted information more handicapping than no information? At the present time, we cannot answer this question directly.

Tactile performance

Fink, Green, and Bender (1953), Rosenstein (1957), Satter and Cassel (1955), Gordon (1944), and Benda (1960) have studied tactile responses in the retarded. The consensus is that tactual performance is poor. Rosenstein compared normal, blind, deaf, and aphasic children on tactile perception of rhythmic patterns. He found that the blind and normal improved on repeated trials, while the deaf and the aphasic did not. The latter were nonretarded subjects.

Satter and Cassel studied tactual-kinesthetic localization on six skin areas using three retarded groups—familial, psychogenic, and organics (brain-injured) matched with normals. The brain-injured made the largest errors in localization followed by the psychogenics and the familials. Gordon was concerned with visual and tactile discrimination with mongoloids and normals matched on mental age. The mongoloids were inferior on tactile discrimination and superior to the normals on some visual tests.

Swanson (1957) studied the perception of simultaneous tactual stimulation in retarded children and compared them with normal children. He found no reliable statistical difference on the Face-Hand test. He also reports no difference on homologous stimulation between familials and brain-injured children. Pollack and Gordon (1960) reported that mentally retarded adults and normal children learn to identify simultaneous touches to cheek and hand within 10 trials. In this sample of 124 children consisting of retardates, borderline cases, and dull normals, the Face-Hand test was used with both disturbed and normal children. The performance of the disturbed children was not related to their psychiatric diagnoses.

Mayer-Gross, Slater, and Roth (1960) are of the opinion that the retarded are *insensitive* to visual, acoustic, tactile, or olfactory sensations. Although they have written a comprehensive and scholarly text, their assumption regarding the sensory performance of the retarded is not supported by contemporary research.

Pain sensitivity

This section begins by noting the paucity of experimental evidence relative to pain sensitivity in the retardate. Again a comment by Mayer-Gross, Slater, and Roth seems pertinent. These authors feel that the retarded have a morbid craving for strong sensations, especially pain. Stengel, Oldham, and Ehrenberg (1955) studied the pain reactions of various types of mental patients to 11 different painful and noxious stimuli. Their sample also contained 54 female low-grade defectives and 43 male low-grade defectives. Their results do not support the "reduced pain sensitivity" assumption in idiots and imbeciles.

One notes the conflicting evidence regarding pain sensitivity in the emotionally disturbed patient including the chronic schizophrenic and catatonic. Bender and Schilder as early as 1930 report an elevated threshold to pain in the schizophrenic. Suffice it to say that other research supports conflicting results or an increased sensitivity to pain. A review of the literature on this topic is beyond the scope of this chapter. Experience and set are obviously crucial factors. Individual differences are large, and the valid measurement of the response leaves much to be desired. Researchers are reluctant to impose pain-producing stimuli for obvious reasons. Thus, our experimental knowledge of pain sensitivity in retardates is incomplete.

Gustatory and olfactory sensitivity

Mayer-Gross, Slater, and Roth (1960) view the retardate as impervious to gustatory and olfactory sensations. The author was unable to find a single large-scale study of gustation or olfaction using retarded subjects. The severely retarded child may place inedible substances into his mouth. This act may be indicative of a judgmental or a conceptual error. Conditioning experiments may offer some insight into this problem. At present, our experimental knowledge is inadequate. Our clinical information based on numerous individual observations seems to support the view expressed by Mayer-Gross, Slater, and Roth.

Kinesthetic and static senses

Most of our information regarding vestibular function in the retardate resides in the clinical files of our various institutions and in the case folders of private medical examiners. At present there does not appear to be a summary of this information in the literature. An interinstitutional collation would seem to be a worthwhile undertaking. Kinesthetic data are scarce.

SENSORIMOTOR DEPRIVATION

The importance of sensoriperceptual information to the well-being of the organism has been well substantiated. If a neonate came into the world deprived of its afferent pathways leading to the brain, we could only speculate on the profound effects which would ensue. Experimental sensory deprivation or isolation in the laboratory and organic sensory deprivation (deafness, blindness, etc.) offer some insights.

It has been shown by Bremer (1943) that the cat whose brain has been deprived of major sensory inputs assumes a temporary sleeplike state. The frog whose skin has been removed or anesthetized may lose its muscular tone and go into a coma or even fail to breathe. It can be reactivated by certain sensory stimuli (Pieron, 1952).

The work of Bexton, Heron, and Scott (1954) and Lilly (1956) demonstrates dramatically the behavioral effects of short-term, partial sensory deprivation or more appropriately *sensorimotor deprivation* upon normal subjects. Can we assume that mental retardation operates in a fashion analogous to partial sensory deprivation? Obviously, such a case for sensory inputs cannot be made. On the output side, however, a substantial differential or decrement in response accuracy, response flexibility, and response repertoire is found. Some have argued that psychology should deal with action or behavior and not the central or intervening processes which produce it. This is the old peripheralist versus centralist argument. In the study of mental retardation, the present writer tends to lean hopefully toward a centralist's position as a means of trying to understand mental retardation.

Our knowledge of the world is built up from the raw material which comes by way of the sensory modalities. Sensory input alone is not sufficient. The organism must be capable of integrating the information and learn to use it in an economical manner. On the output side of S-O-R, the product is deficient as far as the mentally retarded are concerned. In fact, evaluation of the output is the primary means by which we define retardation.

Prior to the pioneering efforts of the Abbé de l'Eppe, the deaf were regarded as mentally deficient. This humanitarian was able to demonstrate that the deaf child could hurdle the language barrier if the proper educational methods were used. Deprived of the primary or acoustic feedback information, the deaf are able to utilize visual information augmented by "secondary" or tactile-proprioceptive feedback to learn oral and written language. Itard (1801) faced an almost impossible task when he sought to "educate" the wild boy of Aveyron. This case constitutes a prime example of environmental deprivation. Although the youngster made educational progress, he was finally considered to be feebleminded. Itard's contribution was more than a new attitude toward the retarded; he succeeded in setting a pattern of *educational* therapy from which modern concepts of perceptual training have grown. Had Itard begun his training program when the boy was of preschool age, the outcome might have been more successful.

Sensory defects may retard or limit learning. Honzik (1936) studied the ability of rats to learn a maze after sensory impairment had been experimentally induced. His five groups of animals were ranked in the following order according to their performance. From best to poorest the groups were the normal, the blind, the deaf-blind, the blind-anosmic, and the deaf-blind-anosmic. It is apparent from these data that the extent of sensory defect influenced the degree of learning. One notes the conspicuous absence of a deaf group.

K. S. Lashley and others have shown that the learning of sensory discriminations is causally related to, or dependent upon, specific areas of the brain. The exact boundaries of these areas are open to question. The results have been deduced largely from ablation studies of animals. Sensory discriminations may also be dependent upon accessory areas of the cerebrum. As we ascend the phylogenetic scale from lower mammals to man, it appears that lower animals are less dependent for sensory discrimination upon the specialized centers in the cortex. The lower or midbrain animals suffer less sensory-motor deficit from brain injury. One interpretation is that control of higher learning processes in man is localized in the anterior portions of the frontal lobes. An alternative explanation is that injuries tend to lower attentiveness and motivation and to increase distractibility, thus bringing about a decrement in performance (Munn, 1961).

In addition to labeling deficiencies in threshold and suprathreshold functions and their effects on learning, we should not lose sight of the fact that the summative effect of sensory deficit is one of significantly decreasing the quality and quantity of experiential events. As yet, we have not been able to measure or even estimate the number of experiences encountered by the human within a 60-second period. Psychologists have been confined by necessity to observations covering a limited sample of the temporal sequence of human or animal experience. Conventionally, the position that sensory deprivation (deafness, blindness, etc.) affects psychological function to a marked or moderate degree has been adopted. We have been unable to assign meaningful numbers to the broad reduction and alteration in sensoriperceptual experiences. Largely the concern has been with the gross effects. An *environmental unit of experience* is needed.

In the retarded youngster, the rate of experiential growth is undoubtedly reduced and altered. The ability to benefit from learning in general is impaired. The ability to profit from the experiences of others is reduced. Reality testing suffers. Sensory inputs may arrive at a rate too rapid to be assimilated or decoded. In a manner of speaking, a type of sensory or environmental deprivation prevails. The effects of environmental stimulation and environmental deprivation need further study.

Sensory stimulation

The beneficial effects of auditory stimulation have been studied using various types of music, rhythmic sequences, auditory memory span, speech-in-noise, and noise alone. Weigl (1959) reported impressive results with music as a therapeutic agent. She uses the term "functional" music to denote music that is not used for its aesthetic value but for therapy. She cites an improvement in posture, muscular control, rhythmic coordination, and even speech. Music therapy is said to delay the onset of fatigue, prolong attention span, and lower sensory thresholds. Murphy (1958) found that music promoted relaxation, helped the emotionally disturbed, and promoted more orderliness in the cottages. Sherwin (1953) used music with three nonretarded, autistic children and reported favorable results. They responded with rhythmical motions and an easing of anxiety and seemed to attend well to the auditory stimulation. Music appears to have certain advantages over speech as a form of communication with the retarded and the emotionally disturbed. The qualitative effects of music therapy are difficult to measure, and therefore the results should be viewed as tentative.

Cantor and Girardeau (1959) did not find support for a *marked* sense of rhythm in the mongoloid. Twenty-eight of forty-two mongoloids showed no sense of rhythm. Other investigators and clinicians have ascribed an unusual sense of rhythm to the mongoloid. At present, the data are insufficient to settle the issue.

Keller (1957) studied the relationship of digit span to learning ability in 63 high-grade mentally retarded boys. Replication of the experiment yielded a reliability coefficient of .90. Those subjects with a lower or poorer digit span were poorer in arithmetic, picture arrangement, and block design. He offered no explanation for this finding.

Schlanger (1958) was concerned with speech perception in 24 brain-injured retarded children using ambient noise, continuous noise, and music as a background against which the speech was presented. He found no difference between the background conditions in the discrimination of monosyllabic word pairs. Pascal (1953) presented a disturbing noise stimulus to 22 retardates who ranged in age from 5 years, 11 months to 31 years, 10 months. Mental age ranged from 2 years, 1 month to 7 years, 1 month. He measured reaction time to white light. The thermal noise delivered over headphones significantly speeded up reaction time before adaptation occurred.

Bensberg and Cantor (1957) found that a sample of familials responded faster than a sample of organics on simple and complex discriminative tasks. Gardner and Cromwell (1959) were concerned with the influence of reduced visual stimulation on 24 organic, 24 familial, 22 hypoactive, and 22 hyperactive retardates. All four groups showed less activity under reduced visual stimulation. There was no difference between the organics and the familials. The hyperactives were more strongly influenced than the hypoactives. Hunt and Patterson (1958) used three types of stimuli—visual, visual-auditory, and auditory—with 26 brain-injured retardates matched with an equal number of familial retardates. They found a statistically reliable difference between the two groups in favor of the familials.

The above results are extremely interesting and reflect the importance of environmental stimulation on the subnormal, institutionalized subject. In addition, the studies offer an approach for distinguishing between certain characteristics of various types of retardates with implications for educational training. Overstimulation has not been adequately explored.

Cutaneous localization

Renshaw (1930) investigated errors of cutaneous localization with practice in children and adults. In a first task, the subjects were required to tap four squares in the same order in which they were tapped by the experimenter. In a second task, four squares were lighted in various sequences, and the subject responded to the lighted squares in the order in which they were lit. Renshaw found that older children did better on the lighted task than on the tap task. These results are supported by Werner (1940, 1944). Critchley (1949) was interested in a phenomenon referred to as *tactile inattention*. A patient manifests this phenomenon when he has no profound loss of sensibility but fails to perceive a tactile sensation on one side if stimulated bilaterally and simultaneously. He comments on the relationship between parietal lobe lesions and tactile inattention. Cohn (1951) found that the pattern of rostral or proximal dominance is no longer present in the 6-year-old normal child. He proposes that there is an innate pattern of perception for multiple simultaneously applied, ipsilateral, cutaneous stimuli.

Fink, Green, and Bender (1952, 1953) reported on the effectiveness of the Face-Hand test as a diagnostic sign of organic brain damage. The patient closes his eyes while one cheek and the contralateral hand are simultaneously touched or stroked. The test may be applied to other parts of the body using various sequences of tactile stimulation. Organics make persistent errors while normals and schizophrenics do not. Fink, Green, and Bender also studied retarded subjects and found that they made errors similar to those made by patients with diffuse brain disease and normal children of age 6 or less. The Face-Hand test, when successfully performed, appears to correlate with a mental age of 6–7 years. White (1957) performed a comprehensive investigation of the Face-Hand test with four groups of subjects—normals, mentally retarded, schizophrenics, and nonschizoid patients—over an extended age range. The older mentally retarded subjects tended to make more errors than the older schizophrenic and nonschizophrenic patients. White offers the hypothesis that the mentally retarded group may incur organic brain changes (encephalopathy) at an earlier age than normals.

SENSORY TRAINING

History has noted with distinction the pioneering work of the Abbé de l'Eppe, J. M. G. Itard, and E. Seguin; and although their contributions may not rank in magnitude with Sputnik I as scientific achievements, as humanitarian achievements they have few peers. The early attempts of these men to educate the handicapped were referred to erroneously as *sense training*. A more accurate term would be *perceptual learning* oriented toward educational achievement. The basic principles set forth by the Abbé de l'Eppe, Itard, and Seguin have been altered but not replaced by contemporary clinicians. Considerable advances have been made in educational techniques and in the development of quantitative diagnostic instruments. Rehabilitation programs are flourishing and the graduation of well-trained clinicians is on the increase. Nonetheless, experimental studies of *comparative* educational techniques for the handicapped are almost non-existent.

Gunzburg in his chapter on educational problems in mental deficiency in Clarke and Clarke (1958) mentions the more recent issues in the educational needs of the mentally retarded. He cites the work of Duncan (1942), who points up the teaching of crafts as a means to an end. Duncan combines the teaching of crafts with planned exercises for developing the children's thinking by exposing them to visual and concrete relationships. He claims that transfer of training and the stimulation of intellectual activities occur.

A mass of evidence has been accumulating over the past two decades regarding the need for neurological, psychological, pediatric, educational, psychomotor, and perceptual assessments of each youngster. This is particularly true of the brain-injured, the aphasoid, the retarded, and the emotionally disturbed child. A comprehensive survey of the literature on this topic is beyond the scope of this review. The evidence is strongly in favor of special diagnostic classifications to describe the sensoriperceptual defects, the educational retardation, and the language disorders of the exceptional child. The routine medical examination, the EEG alone, and the conventional intelligence and personality tests are frequently not sensitive enough to identify the basic problems manifested by these children. Worthy of note are the contributions of Orton (1937), Blau (1946), Strauss and Lehtinen (1947) Myklebust (1954), Strauss and Kephart (1955), and Kephart (1960) to the diagnosis of special problems. As we learn more about these children diagnostically and educationally, we should be able to develop special educational techniques for the deaf-blind, the retarded deaf, the retarded psychogenic, the retarded aphasoid, the retarded blind, the retarded cerebral palsied, and the slow learners who have partial sensory impairments.

Tretakoff and Farrell (1958) have developed a curriculum for the retarded blind. Myklebust (1958) has summarized the problems of the deaf child with other handicaps. Jolles (1958) has devised a teaching sequence for the training of visual and motor sequences. Benoit (1957) has discussed the relevance of Hebbian learning theory to educational research on the mentally retarded. Rittmanic (1959) describes an aural rehabilitation program for the institutionalized mentally retarded with impaired hearing. De Leo and Boly (1956) established an educational program for the blind and partially sighted. Insight into normal, blind, deaf, and aphasic children may come from comparative studies of these groups. An example is the interesting study by Rosenstein (1957). These studies are on the increase.

Contemporary emphasis is being placed upon the effects of mental growth through environmental stimulation. Evidence for this point of view may be found in Kephart and Strauss (1940), Kephart (1940), Carmichael (1954), Mundy (1957), and McCandless (1961). One can trace significant stages from Itard to Kephart. The quilt has been woven, but all the stitches are not yet in place. Research does seem to be making a worthwhile contribution.

SUMMARY

This chapter has summarized a number of studies concerned directly or indirectly with the role of sensory processes in mental retardation. Complete coverage of the literature was not intended.

A review of studies dealing with sensory pathology pointed up the need for considerably more definitive information. A sustained effort to define the prevalence of impaired sensory functions has not been made. Hearing loss has been studied but the results do not agree, except for the strong possibility that a much higher prevalence exists among retardates than among normal school children. The use of a battery of hearing tests was recommended with special emphasis on objective measurements. Studies of visual pathology have been concerned largely with end-organ deviations. Inadequate data exist for comparing intersensory impairments. Taste and smell have not been studied to any appreciable degree. Although tactile perception and vestibular functions have been of diagnostic interest to psychologists, psychiatrists, and neurologists, the data are largely idiographic rather than nomothetic. All in all there is a paucity of information regarding sensory pathology in the mentally retarded.

Some interesting questions were raised relating to (1) the development of perceptual learning in the preschool retardate, (2) sensory deprivation as a meaningful frame of reference for viewing mental retardation, (3) the effects of sensory stimulation on activity, and (4) the application of perceptual training techniques for improving the mental age or educational potential of the retarded child. In addition, the value of a comprehensive differential diagnosis using a team approach for the retarded with multiple handicaps was stressed.

It was suggested that an attempt be made to define or devise a unit of environmental experience. This approach would place the emphasis upon experiential information rather than upon the degree of sensory impairment or end-organ pathology. Perceptual learning was offered as a substitute term for sense training. Also, sensorimotor deprivation seemed to be a more appropriate term than sensory deprivation.

Intensive study of the mentally retarded child is proving to be a worthwhile endeavor. Psychologists, psychiatrists, biochemists, geneticists, and neurologists are making important contributions to our understanding of mental retardation. The potential for stimulating mental growth through environmental control cannot be overemphasized at this time.

REFERENCES

BENDA, D. E. *The child with mongolism.* New York: Grune & Stratton, 1960.

BENDER, L., & SCHILDER, P. Unconditioned and conditioned reactions to pain in schizophrenia. *Amer. J. Psychiat.,* 1930, 10, 365–384.

BENOIT, E. P. Relevance of Hebb's theory of the organization of behavior to educational research on the mentally retarded. *Amer. J. ment. Defic.,* 1957, 61, 497–507.

BENSBERG, G. J., & CANTOR, G. N. Reaction time in mental defectives with organic and familial etiology. *Amer. J. ment. Defic.,* 1957, 62, 534–537.

BEXTON, W. H., HERON, W., & SCOTT, T. H. Effects of decreased variation in the sensory environment. *Canad. J. Psychol.*, 1954, 8, 70–76.

BIRCH, J., & MATTHEWS, J. The hearing of mental defectives. *Amer. J. ment. Defic.*, 1951, 55, 384–393.

BLAU, A. *The master hand.* New York: Amer. Orthopsychiat. Ass. Inc., 1946.

BRADLEY, E., EVANS, W. E., & WORTHINGTON, A. M. The relationship between administration time for audiometric testing and the mental ability of mentally deficient children. *Amer. J. ment. Defic.*, 1955, 60, 346–353.

BREMER, F. Etude oscillographique des responses sensorielles de l'aire acoustique corticale chez le chat. *Arch. int. Physiol.*, 1943, 53, 53.

CANTOR, G. N., & GIRARDEAU, F. L. Rhythmic discrimination ability in mongoloid and normal children. *Amer. J. ment. Defic.*, 1959, 63, 621–625.

CARMICHAEL, L. *Manual of child psychology.* London: Chapman & Hall, 1954.

CLARKE, A. M., & CLARKE, A. D. B. *Mental deficiency.* New York: Free Press, 1958.

COHN, R. On certain aspects of the sensory organization of the human brain. II. A study of rostral dominance in children. *Neurology,* 1951, 1, 119–122.

CRITCHLEY, M. The phenomenon of tactile inattention with special reference to parietal lesions. *Brain,* 1949, 72, 538–561.

DE LEO, C., & BOLY, L. F. Some considerations in establishing an educational program for the institutionalized blind and partially sighted mentally subnormal. *Amer. J. ment. Defic.*, 1956, 61, 134–140.

DUNCAN, J. *The education of the ordinary child.* London: Nelson, 1942.

FINK, M., GREEN, M., & BENDER, M. B. The face-hand test as a diagnostic sign of organic mental syndrome. *Neurology,* 1952, 2, 46–58.

FOALE, MARTHA, & PATTERSON, J. W. The hearing of mental defectives. *Amer. J. ment. Defic.*, 1954, 59, 254–258.

GARDNER, W. I., & CROMWELL, R. L. The effect of visual stimulus conditions on activity level. I. Hyperactives vs. hypoactives. II. Organics vs. Familials. *Amer. J. ment. Defic.*, 1959, 63, 1028–1033.

GOLDSTEIN, R., LUDWIG, H., & NAUNTON, R. F. Difficulties in conditioning galvanic skin responses: its possible significance in clinical audiometry. *Acta Otolaryngologica,* 1954, 44, 67–77.

GORDON, A. M. Some aspects of sensory discrimination in mongolism. *Amer. J. ment. Defic.*, 1944, 49, 55–63.

HEBB, D. O. *The organization of behavior: a neuropsychological theory.* New York: Wiley, 1949.

HEBER, R. A manual on terminology and classification in mental retardation. *Amer. J. ment. Defic. Monogr.*, 1959, 64, No. 2.

HONZIK, C. H. The sensory basis of maze learning in rats. *Comp. Psychol. Monogr.*, 1936, 13, No. 64.

HUNT, BETTY, & PATTERSON, RUTH M. Performance of brain injured and familial mentally deficient children on visual and auditory sequences. *Amer. J. ment. Defic.*, 1958, 63, 72–80.

IGERSHEIMER, J., & MAUTNER, H. About changes of the crystalline lens in mongoloids. *Amer. J. ment. Defic.*, 1951, 55, 370–376.

IRWIN, J. V., HIND, J. E., & ARONSON, A. E. Experience with conditioned GSR audiometry in a group of mentally deficient individuals. *Train. Sch. Bull.*, 1957, 54, 26–31.

ITARD, J. M. G. *De l'éducation d'un homme sauvage.* Paris: 1801.

JOHNSON, P., & FARRELL, M. Auditory impairments among resident school children at the Walter E. Fernald State School. *Amer. J. ment. Defic.*, 1954, 58, 640–644.

JOLLES, I. A.   A teaching sequence for the training of visual and motor perception. *Amer. J. ment. Defic.*, 1958, 63, 252–255.

KELLER, J. E.   The relationship of auditory memory span to learning ability in high grade mentally retarded boys. *Amer. J. ment. Defic.*, 1957, 61, 574–580.

KEPHART, N. C.   Influencing the rate of mental growth in retarded children through environmental stimulation. *Yearb. nat. Soc. Stud. Educ.*, 1940, 39, Part II.

KEPHART, N. C.   *The slow learner in the classroom.* Ohio: Charles E. Merrill Books, 1960.

KEPHART, N. C., & STRAUSS, A. A.   A clinical factor influencing variations in IQ. *Amer. J. Orthopsychiat.*, 1940, 10, 343–350.

KODMAN, F.   The incidence of hearing loss in mentally retarded children. *Amer. J. ment. Defic.*, 1958, 62, 675–678.

KODMAN, F., FEIN, A., & MIXSON, A.   Psychogalvanic skin response audiometry with severely mentally retarded children. *Amer. J. ment. Defic.*, 1959, 64, 131–136.

KODMAN, F., POWERS, T. P., WELLER, G. M., & PHILIP, P. P.   An investigation of hearing loss in mentally retarded children and adults. *Amer. J. ment. Defic.*, 1958, 63, 460–463.

KODMAN, F., POWERS, T. R., WELLER, G. M., & PHILIP, P. P.   Puretone audiometry with the mentally retarded. *J. except. Child.*, 1958, 24, 303–305.

KRATTER, F. E.   Color blindness in relation to normal and defective intelligence. *Amer. J. ment. Defic.*, 1957, 62, 436–441.

LASHLEY, K. S.   The mechanism of vision. XV. Preliminary studies of the rat's capacity for detail vision. *J. gen. Psychol.*, 1938, 18, 123–193.

LILLY, J. C.   Mental effects of reduction of ordinary levels of physical stimuli on intact, healthy persons. *Psychiat. Res. Rep.*, 1956, No. 5, 1–28.

LOWE, R.   The eyes in mongolism. *Brit. J. Opthal.*, 1949, 33, 131–174.

MCCANDLESS, B. R.   *Children and adolescents.* New York: Holt, 1961.

MAYER-GROSS, W., SLATER, E., & ROTH, M.   *Clinical psychiatry.* Baltimore: Williams & Wilkins, 1960.

MOSS, J. W., MOSS, M., & TIZARD, J.   Electrodermal response audiometry with mentally defective children. *J. speech hear. Dis.*, 1961, 4, 41–47.

MUNDY, LYDIA.   Environmental influence on intellectual function as measured by intelligence tests. *Brit. J. med. Psychol.*, 1957, 30, 194–201.

MUNN, N. L.   *Psychology: the fundamentals of human adjustment.* Boston: Houghton Mifflin, 1961.

MURPHY, MARY M.   A large scale music therapy program for institutionalized low grade and middle defectives. *Amer. J. ment. Defic.*, 1958, 63, 268–273.

MYKLEBUST, H. R.   *Auditory disorders in children.* New York: Grune & Stratton, 1954.

MYKLEBUST, H. R.   The deaf child with other handicaps. *Amer. Ann. Deaf*, 1958, 103, 496–509.

O'CONNER, N.   Imbecility and color blindness. *Amer. J. ment. Defic.*, 1957, 62, 83–87.

ORTON, S. T.   *Reading, writing and speech problems.* New York: Norton, 1937.

PASCAL, G. R.   The effect of a disturbing noise on the reaction time of mental defectives. *Amer. J. ment. Defic.*, 1953, 57, 691–699.

PIERON, H.   *The sensations: their functions, processes and mechanism.* M. H. Pirene & B. C. Abbott (Trans.). New Haven: Yale, 1952.

POLLACK, M., & GORDON, E.   The face-hand test and non-retarded emotionally disturbed children. *Amer. J. ment. Defic.*, 1960, 64, 758–760.

RENSHAW, S.   The errors of cutaneous localization and the effect of practice on the localizing movement in children and adults. *J. genet. Psychol.*, 1930, 38, 223–238.

RIESEN, A. H. The development of visual perception in man and chimpanzee. *Science*, 1947, 106, 107–108.

RITTMANIC, P. A. Hearing rehabilitation for the institutionalized mentally retarded. *Amer. J. ment. Defic.*, 1959, 63, 778–782.

ROSENSTEIN, J. Tactile perception of rhythmic patterns by normal, blind, deaf and aphasic children. *Amer. Ann. Deaf*, 1957, 102, 399–403.

RUHM, H. B., & CARHART, R. Objective speech audiometry. *J. speech hear. Dis.*, 1958, 1, 169–178.

SATTER, G., & CASSELL, R. H. Tactual-kinesthetic localization in the mentally retarded. *Amer. J. ment. Defic.*, 1955, 59, 652–657.

SCHLANGER, B. B. Speech examination of a group of institutionalized mentally handicapped children. *J. speech hear. Dis.*, 1953, 18, 339–349.

SCHLANGER, B. B. Results of varying presentations to brain-damaged children of an auditory word discrimination test. *Amer. J. ment. Defic.*, 1958, 63, 464–468.

SCHLANGER, B. B., & GOTTSLEBEN, R. H. Testing the hearing of the mentally retarded. *J. speech hear. Dis.*, 1956, 21, 487–493.

SEGUIN, E. *Traitement moral, hygiene et éducation des idoits et des autres enfants arrières*. Paris: J. B. Ballière, 1846.

SENDEN, N. VON. *Raum- und gestaltauffassund bei operierten blindgeborenen vor und nach der operation*. Leipzig: Barth, 1932.

SHERWIN, A. C. Reactions to music of autistic children. *Amer. J. Psychiat.*, 1953, 109, 823–831.

SIEGENTHALER, B. M., & KRZYWICKI, D. F. Incidence and patterns of hearing loss among an adult mentally retarded population. *Amer. J. ment. Defic.*, 1959, 64, 444–449.

SKELLER, E., & OSTER, J. Eye symptoms in mongolism. *Acta Opthalmologica*, 1951, 29, 149–161.

STENGEL, E., OLDHAM, A. J., & EHRENBERG, A. Reactions to pain in various abnormal mental states. *J. ment. Sci.*, 1955, 101, 52–69.

STRAUSS, A. A., & KEPHART, N. C. *Psychopathology and education of the brain-injured child*. New York: Grune & Stratton, 1955. Chap. III.

STRAUSS, A. A., & LEHTINEN, L. E. *Psychopathology and education of the brain-injured child*. New York: Grune & Stratton, 1951.

SWANSON, R. Perception of simultaneous tactual stimulation in defective and normal children. *Amer. J. ment. Defic.*, 1957, 61, 743–752.

TRETAKOFF, M., & FARRELL, M. J. Developing a curriculum for the blind retarded. *Amer. J. ment. Defic.*, 1958, 62, 610–615.

WEIGL, VALLY. Functional music: a therapeutic tool in working with the mentally retarded. *Amer. J. ment. Defic.*, 1959, 63, 672–678.

WERNER, H. Perception of spatial relationship in mentally deficient children *J. genet. Psychol.*, 1940, 57, 93–100.

WERNER, H. Development of visuo-motor performance on the marble board test in mentally retarded children. *J. genet. Psychol.*, 1944, 64, 269–279.

WHIPPLE, C. I., & KODMAN, F. The validity of objective speech audiometry. *J. Laryngol. Otol.*, 1960, 74, 85–89.

WHITE, R. P. Face-hand test responses of psychotic and mentally defective patients. *Arch. neurol. Psychiat.*, 1957, 77, 120–125.

15

PERCEPTUAL PROCESSES

George Spivack

The purpose of this chapter is to review studies dealing with perceptual processes in mental retardates. The goal is not to draw theoretical conclusions, nor point to the significance of any particular study. Theory is considered in other chapters. An attempt will be made, however, not only to review perceptual studies, but also to draw certain conclusions about the status of empirical studies in this area and to point to certain methodological issues of importance when doing perceptual research with retardates. Although this appears as a fairly straightforward task, two issues immediately demand attention: What is to be meant by (1) *perceptual* processes, and (2) *mental retardation*. There has been long and continuing debate on both counts. For the sake of presentation, therefore, the reviewer will arbitrarily delimit these areas without attempting to justify these particular delimitations as the only ones possible.

Over the past two decades, attention paid to perception has dramatically increased. It has been stimulated by issues such as the effects of needs or values on perceptual responses, the potency of stimulus qualities and cognitive attitudes in determining the extent of play of central factors, and more recently the question of what is learned in perceptual learning situations. At times perception has been defined quite narrowly, while at other times it is difficult to see the difference between what are called perceptual responses and responses usually described as reflecting personality functioning. The fact that the term "perception" has been used to refer to varying operations has led some to address themselves to the issue of definition and to caution others regarding some of the dangers inherent in too broad or loose a conceptualization.

480

The position of this reviewer draws upon (but is not identical with) conceptions of Bartley (1958), Hochberg (1956), Solley and Murphy (1960), and Garner, Hake, and Eriksen (1956). A study deals with perception when the subject is "set" to discriminate between definable stimuli and responds within a relatively short time period and/or while the stimuli are present. The response bears a contingent relationship to the stimulus, but there is some experimental control of response characteristics of the subject that have little or no relationship to the stimulus and could equally well appear without it. These criteria imply that stimuli must be present to excite some sense receptor or receptors before perception occurs. The problem of what is a *stimulus* is perennial in psychology (Gibson, 1960); but it is clear, within any definition, that unless the stimulating condition can be defined and measured, it is impossible to assess any relationship that may exist between stimulus and response. The present position also implies that a perceptual "trace" lasts a short time, probably changing into a memory trace, and that there is more assurance that we are dealing with perceptual processes when there is continued presence of the stimulus or when the response is made immediately after its cessation. Moreover, since perception is a process inferred from response indicators, particular attention must be paid to the extent to which the response indicator may embody nonperceptual elements within its total variance.

Because of the preceding criteria, many studies purporting to deal with perceptual processes, or which use the term "perceptual" or "perception" in the title, are not mentioned in the present review. This is not to say that such studies make no contribution to the understanding of mental retardation. The question is whether they shed light on perceptual processes. For example, Rorschach studies have not been included in the present chapter. Perceptual processes *may* contribute to, and therefore become manifest in, responses to ink blots. However, the manner in which the test is presented clouds the issue. The subject is not asked to tell what he sees or to describe the card along some dimension or to tell the difference between one card and another card. In fact, he is told he will be presented with ink blots; and if the subject describes the card (e.g., "I see an ink blot," or "I see red, green, and blue colors"), the responses are classed as pathological or the examiner may question whether he has made his instructions clear. In the main, the task is presented as a conceptual rather than a perceptual one. The subject may *free associate* along dimensions partly or entirely irrelevant to the properties of the stimulus. The relationship between stimulus and response is not defined by the experimenter but chosen by the subject and becomes a *projective* response dimension.

Most of the studies of visual-motor performance are also excluded. In most studies no attempt is made to control or partial out the effects of motor and other nonperceptual response characteristics which affect performance and may be sufficient in themselves to explain individual difference in performance. At best, the response indicator clouds the issue and makes it difficult to assess the extent to which perceptual factors are in operation. The findings of Bortner and Birch (1960) are instructive in this regard. After hemiplegic patients had performed on a modified block-design test, the authors discovered that their subjects, when put in a multiple-choice situation, could choose the correct design in 81 per cent of instances where their reproductions had previously been incorrect. In the remaining instances, they chose an experimentally altered design as often as they did their own incorrect production when asked to choose the "correct" one. They conclude that "it appears to be necessary in discussing perceptual tasks to differentiate the discriminative perceptual function from the perceptual-motor. It should be clear, therefore, that perceptual-motor inadequacy, per se, does not permit the inference of perceptual disturbance" (p. 53).

Other studies are not included in this review because either the conditions of responding or the nature of the response itself allowed for the operation of other cognitive processes (e.g., memory, learning, etc.), making it extremely difficult to know the extent to which perceptual processes came into play.

The approach to the definition of mental retardation has been arbitrary. Studies are included which deal with subjects singled out because of below-average intelligence as measured by a standard IQ test. The IQ criterion was chosen for practical reasons. Heber (1961) has emphasized that such a global measure "is nothing more than the statistical average of . . . a number of widely varying abilities" (p. 10). The research data of published studies do not supply a more refined criterion. Also included will be studies of perceptual processes in individuals with life-long brain injury, when such studies shed light on the relationship between perceptual functioning and retardation. Investigations of adult brain-injured individuals (most of those studied having suffered "localized" war injuries) and studies of older populations (often in VA hospitals) with degenerative diseases are excluded. This is not to say that such neurological deficits do not adversely affect perceptual functioning, nor does it imply that what is learned from such studies may not be instructive for those interested in mental retardation. It seems likely, however, that age of onset of brain injury may very well be pertinent to such issues as the nature and extent of effect. Hebb (1942) has addressed himself to this question, and more recently the work of Belmont and Birch (1960), Birch and Belmont (1960), and Teuber and Rudel (in press) indicates the wisdom of not applying generalizations regarding the effects of brain injury in adults to children, and vice versa.

RESEARCH FINDINGS

Figure-background

Perhaps the most frequently mentioned study of figure-background is that of Werner and Strauss (1940). In an attempt to explain alleged inferior performance of brain-injured (BI) mental retardates, when compared with non-brain-injured (NBI) mental retardates on a marble board test, they raised the hypothesis that the BI *S*s were "struggling against the interference of the background in order to see the marbles as a complete figure" (p. 214). The marble board test requires *S* to copy a design made by *E* with marbles on a board consisting of a 10 by 10 matrix of holes in which marbles can be placed.

To test their hypothesis, Werner and Strauss had their Ss copy five designs on a specially designed board with holes forming a definitely structured background. They expected the background to intrude more upon the performance of the BI Ss than upon that of the NBI Ss. They employed 22BI and 25NBI mild and borderline retarded Ss.[1] They found that in four out of six measures the BI Ss showed significantly greater background intrusion.

In a second study, Werner and Strauss (1941) attempted to corroborate their earlier finding. Nine cards were constructed, each with a different simple object drawn on it and each embedded in fields of lines of various types drawn across the figure and extending beyond it on all sides. These figures were presented with a tachistoscope for 0.20 second, and each S was asked "to tell what he saw." Three groups were used: 30 normals subdivided into three equal-CA groups (7 to 8, 8 to 9, and 9 to 10), 25NBI Ss with mild or borderline retardation, and 25BI Ss equated on MA and IQ with the NBI group. The results showed that 75 per cent of the responses of the BI group were to the background. This was true of only 7 per cent of the responses of the MA-equivalent normals and of 14 per cent of the responses of the NBI group.

Coleman (1960), employing the tachistoscopic method, attempted to show that moderately retarded mongoloid Ss would show behavior similar to that of a BI group having the same level of retardation. Coleman closely followed the procedure of Werner and Strauss, scoring the responses as "foreground," "background," and "mixed." The results showed that 73 per cent of the mongoloid and 80 per cent of the BI Ss reported foreground, while between 7 and 8 per cent of each group reported background. The results are not only inconsistent with those of Werner and Strauss, but they are in sharp contrast with data obtained on BI Ss of normal intelligence (Cruickshank, Bice, & Wallen, 1957; Dolphin & Cruickshank, 1951).

The consideration of method is central to the interpretation of these tachistoscopic studies. S is presented a set of stimuli consisting of what E calls a "figure" and a "background" at brief exposures. Careful examination of the stimuli indicates that what is referred to as background is the *dominant* feature, covering more of the stimulus than the figure. The figure is centrally located, but it is masked by the background. S is asked to tell what he saw. He is not asked to find what the investigator labels as the figure. The question, then, is whether a background response reflects an inability to perceive the figure when briefly exposed, or a more complex decision on the part of S concerning what he should report. Since S was not instructed to report the figure, the fact that he reports the background is not in itself sufficient to come to a conclusion regarding either of these alternatives. An S reporting the background may see the figure, but being less sure of it than the background reports only the latter, or he may

[1] In what follows, rather than specify IQs, degrees of retardation will be designated by the terms borderline (70–84), mild (55–69), moderate (40–54), and severe (20–39), closely following Heber (1959).

report the background in conjunction with the figure. The procedure should require that *S* perceive and report the figure. If this were done, and *S* still reported the background, the next question would be whether this reflected a figure-background problem or the tendency for dominant features of a stimulus complex to "dampen out" less dominant features.

In their 1941 paper, Werner and Strauss also report on multiple-choice test. Using the same sample of *S*s, they presented two standard cards tachistoscopically for 0.50 second. Each standard consisted of a matrix of small circles in which slightly more pronounced circles were embedded in the form of a design. After each presentation, *S* was presented with three cards and asked to choose the one most like the test card. One of the choices was the background of the standard, another the background with a different figure, and the third a different background (less dominant) with the standard figure. *The complete original stimulus was not one of the choices.* They report that significantly more BI *S*s chose the card with only the original background, while NBI *S*s chose the card with the original background and the different figure.

A problem of interpretation of the results again arises, this time complicated by the fact that *S* was asked to decide which one was "most like" the standard. None of the choices was actually correct. *S* had to choose between cards which were all incorrect. The fact that BI *S*s tended to choose the card with background alone may indicate that they responded to the most dominant feature of the stimulus and not in terms of figure and background as defined by *E*. Furthermore, in this instance they were as accurate as the other groups, all forced to choose from three cards, none of which was the complete stimulus as originally presented. A crucial test would have been to present the original card in the set of choices, telling each *S* to pick out the card exactly like the standard in every respect.

Werner and Strauss (1941) also included a tactual task of figure-background in their battery. They asked their *S*s to explore three simple geometric forms with their fingers "until they could draw what is there." In the control condition, the various shaped figures were made of wood, projecting up from a flat lowered background. The test figures were the same forms, composed of raised rubber-headed round tacks, the background consisting of flat enameled thumbtack heads. They report that for the control figures, neither group had difficulty drawing the figures with straight lines. For the test figures, however, 93 per cent of the drawings of the NBI group were straight-line forms in comparison with only 26 per cent of the drawings of the BI group. In contrast, 74 per cent of BI *S*s' drawings "showed only the circles of the background, or the figure with the background" (p. 244), while this was true of only 7 per cent of the NBI *S*s' drawings. Werner and Strauss interpret these results as consistent with their other findings.

Analysis of these findings raises doubts about the interpretation given. Again, *S*'s understanding of the task may not coincide with that of *E*. Further, both figure and background of the test figures consisted of circular forms, not straight edges. Reproducing circles does not in and of itself indicate attention to background. In fact, drawing straight-line figures indicates either a carry-over "set" from the control figures or an abstraction from the actual test figures which were all comprised of circular elements. If the latter were true, it would indicate that the NBI group was more capable of abstraction and not necessarily less prone to figure-background disturbance. A further question can be raised about the apparatus in this study. A potentially contaminating issue is one of the ability of Ss to discriminate between round rubber-headed tacks and round enamel-headed tacks. Inability to discriminate between these reliably could result in a poor reproduction which would be interpreted in terms of figure-background disturbance. Finally, the use of familiar forms has the disadvantage of allowing for differential recognition from past experience.

Research in this area suggests that BI rather than retardation produces responses to background or intrusion of background in perception. The question remains open about whether such performance reflects a basic defect in BI Ss in the capacity to disregard background or the tendency for dominant aspects of complex stimuli to intrude upon or dampen out less dominant features, or whether the research techniques have allowed nonperceptual response characteristics to guide performance. It is of interest that Werner and Strauss (1941) raise the first two possibilities in the discussion of their series of experiments. The possibility of alternative explanations has not been pursued.

The advisability of further work in this area is suggested by two studies. One involved the use of only one S, but the idea conveyed is worth noting. Keller (1954) tested a 13-year-old female with borderline intelligence with a modified Kohs blocks procedure. He had this S draw the block design within a square which included the outlines of the blocks of the stimulus. Although S could draw the necessary lines, each time the stimulus form became dominant, she failed to consider articulating her drawing with the guidelines of the block outlines supplied by E. When the overall design was not a dominant one, the drawing hit the corners of the guidelines correctly and the entire production was perfect. It would appear as though each time a dominant feature was presented, the less dominant requirements were ignored.

The second study is that of Schlanger (1958), who set out to see if background auditory noise would interfere with correct word discrimination in 24BI Ss, most either severely or moderately retarded. Names of objects were read aloud, and S was asked to point to the picture of the object which was on a card along with pictures of three other objects. The task required that S be able to discriminate between similar sounding words (e.g., pin and pen). Schlanger did not find background interference when performance under various background noise conditions was compared with a noise-free condition. It is interesting to note that in this study the "figure" (i.e., word read) was clearly presented to S as the thing for him to attend to. There was no ambiguity. What was background for E was clearly viewed as such by S. Also, the background was not as integral a part of the figure-background configuration as in the studies previously described.

Discrimination

Although a basic perceptual capacity, the ability to discriminate reliably has been studied infrequently in retardates. More often than not, evidence of poor discrimination is viewed as a methodological problem in the design of experiments. Rarely is it treated as a subject for study.

In two studies, Spitz and Blackman felt it necessary to deal with the problem in designing means to investigate other phenomena. In studying the Muller-Lyer illusion (1958), the criterion measure was the difference between settings with the arrow lines and lines with straight-lined ends. This means of controlling for errors of discrimination (and also direction) was warranted, as evidenced by the fact that a retarded group made significantly more errors than normals in the judgments with the straight-lined figure. In a study of visual figural aftereffects (1959) this problem resulted in the loss of a number of Ss. Before examining whether the fixation of an inspection figure would affect the subsequent comparison of two squares comprising the test figure, they had to make sure that at preinspection the two equal squares were seen as equal. Fifty of the eighty-seven retarded Ss perceived them as unequal, a significantly larger proportion than in the normal group. The mean IQ of these 50 Ss was significantly lower than that of the remainder of the retarded group who perceived them as equal.

Both Cantor and Girardeau (1959) and Gordon (1944) have examined discrimination in mongoloid Ss. Noting the frequent clinical comments regarding their good rhythmic discrimination, Cantor and Girardeau studied 44 mongoloids with moderate and mild retardation. A normal control group was used. Each S was given 60 presentations of a metronome beating half the time at a rate of 88 per minute, and half the time at 120 per minute. Following this, S was asked to identify which of the two metronome speeds was presented; Ss were told whether or not they were correct following each trial. Although the mongoloid group did better than chance, their performance was significantly poorer than that of the control group. There was a tendency for discrimination performance to be related to MA in both groups.

Gordon (1944) examined the visual and tactual discrimination of six adult mongoloids, comparing their performance with six normal children of equivalent MA. His visual test "battery" consisted of a test for size, pattern, three-dimensional form, texture, brightness, and color. His tactual group of tasks included one for size, two for form, and one for texture. Gordon obtained a composite visual and composite tactual score for each S by averaging ranks on the various tasks, and then compared his two groups. The normal group did significantly better than the mongoloid group on the tactual but not on the visual battery. Gordon then did a rank-order correlation between discrimination scores and MA, educational achievement, IQ, Vineland Social Maturity, and Arthur Performance scores, discovering no significant relationships.

Considering the large number of tasks given, the varying nature of the tasks themselves, and the fact that one composite score was derived, it is difficult to assess the reliability of Gordon's results. Within modalities, the tasks vary widely in possible response biases and in the qualities of discrimination assessed. Some tasks required much reasoning, while others required simple matching. Little information is given regarding instructions to Ss. Very few Ss were used, and the age disparity between groups raises problems in assuming equivalence of groups despite comparable MA scores.

Merachnik (1960) compared color-discrimination responses of BI and NBI retardates and normal Ss. A multiple-choice matching procedure was used, which required a discrimination between small color saturation differences. Age, sex, and presence or absence of BI were not related to performance. The normals discriminated with significantly greater accuracy than both retarded groups.

In three studies Spivack and Levine (1961) investigated visual discrimination in groups of BI Ss covering a broad IQ range. In the first study, the standard deviation of eight distance settings was the score taken for each S, the standard deviation being the classical index of sensitivity of discrimination. For each trial, S was to adjust a variable bar so that it was as far from a fixation cross as a stationary standard bar. The performance of a male BI group (IQ range 55 to 105) yielded a significantly larger standard deviation than that of the emotionally disturbed and normal control groups. Within the BI group, the standard deviation was significantly related to Wechsler performance IQ ($-.44$).

In the second study the method of constant stimuli was used, employing the three categories "greater than," "equal," and "less than." The procedure employed length of lines as the stimuli, the standard being 2 inches long, and the 11 comparison stimuli ranged between $1\frac{11}{16}$ and $2\frac{5}{16}$ inches. The same male BI group as above was studied along with a female BI group with an equivalent IQ range. The results indicated that both BI groups had a significantly larger standard deviation than their respective normal control groups. The correlations between the standard deviations and IQ in the male and female groups were $-.26$ and $-.25$, respectively. Both BI groups also had significantly larger difference limens than the normals, and the standard deviation and difference limen measures were significantly correlated in the BI groups, though not in the control groups. This correlation raised the issue of whether the poorer discrimination in the BI groups stemmed from an attitudinal factor, known to influence the use of the equal category (Fernberger, 1931) or whether the large difference limens were a consequence of poor discrimination. To assess these alternative explanations, the actual frequencies of use of the equal category in the BI and control groups were compared. The groups did not differ, suggesting that the issue is one of poor discrimination and not a tendency to say "equal" when confronted with a discrimination choice.

In the third study a simple forced-choice procedure was designed, wherein two orange round dots were presented tachistoscopically in succession, with a 1-second interval intervening. One light appeared for 500 milliseconds and the other for 700 milliseconds. S had to judge whether the first or second light was on longer. Data on 200 trials were obtained. In a second (single stimulus) procedure, S was first exposed six times to both orange lights separately, after which each light was presented for 100 trials within a random series of 200 trials. S reported whether the light presented was the "longer" or "shorter" one. Reward and feedback were used in both methods of presentation. Considering the large number of total trials, it was possible to assess whether differential fatigue effects, learning, or response biases might explain group differences in overall discrimination scores. The responses of 10 BI Ss (IQ range 55 to 104) were compared with those of 10 emotionally disturbed Ss (IQ range 77 to 120) and with a normal group.

The results indicated that the BI group, though performing better than chance, did significantly worse than the control groups. The results further indicated that the poorer BI performance could not be ascribed to fatigue effects or differential learning. Although failures tended to disrupt subsequent BI performance in the single stimulus procedure, and thus contributed to poorer performance, this was not true in the forced-choice procedure wherein the BI group still did worse. A rather complete analysis of response biases indicated that they could not be responsible for poorer-BI performance, at least in the forced-choice procedure. In the BI and emotionally disturbed groups, discrimination efficiency was significantly related to IQ.

In general, the findings indicate a discrimination problem in retardates. As IQ decreases from the average into the retarded range, there is a decrease in efficiency of discrimination between different points along a single stimulus dimension.

Recognition

Griffith (1960) examined perceptual recognition as a function of exposure time, retention interval, and IQ. She employed 120 retarded Ss with mild and moderate retardation, not differentiated on the basis of presence or absence of BI. Ten irregular geometric figures were flashed tachistoscopically at 0.01 and 0.50 second. After no delay, a 15-, or 120-second delay, S had to point to the design on a card, which had on it the correct design as well as three similar designs. Both IQ and exposure time significantly affected differences in performance, although no interactions were significant.

Rosenberg (1961) studied the relationship of IQ and exposure time to how competently 40 Ss with mild and moderate retardation could find, "as quickly as possible," a previously or concurrently presented design within a 6 by 6 matrix of designs. No information regarding presence or absence of BI is given. The stimuli were nonsense shapes presented on cards one at a time either for 4 seconds or continuously. In the 4-second condition, the matrix was not exposed to S until he had looked at the stimulus and it had been taken away. After dividing his group into low- and high-IQ subgroups, Rosenberg found that the low-IQ subgroup did significantly worse than the high-IQ subgroup under both exposure conditions. There was no interaction between IQ and exposure conditions. Rosenberg concludes that low IQ reflects itself in inefficient searching behavior.

Two questions may be raised about Rosenberg's results. The comparison matrix is constant, and therefore the reexposure of it on each trial creates a condition for incidental learning of the nonsense figures and their positions. If this learning were to occur, it might reasonably be expected to be different depending upon IQ. A second problem is created by the "speed" set given to the *S*s. *S*s might differentially respond to such pressure as a function of IQ.

The data available suggest that ability to recognize unfamiliar, complex figures following limited exposure to them diminishes as IQ level decreases.

Constancy

Despite the fact that the study of perceptual constancy has a long tradition in psychology, only four studies could be found dealing with constancy in retarded *S*s, and these have been done over the past two or three years. Two of these deal with size constancy in NBI retarded, another with size constancy in a group of BI retarded, and the fourth with shape constancy in an NBI-retarded group.

Jenkin (1960) attempted to determine whether size-distance judgments are mediated by growth in intelligence or are a function of development and independent of intelligence. His NBI-retarded group had a median CA of 15–10 and an MA of 8.2. Three normal control groups at three levels of median CA—8–3, 13–7, and 26–6—were used. The standard, a square 4-inch white card, stood 320 inches away from *S*. Behind the standard was a homogeneous green background. Using the method of limits, comparison stimuli were presented at two different angles from the plane of the standard and at two distances. *S*s were instructed to judge on the basis of real size. The results with normals indicated that with increased age, constancy increased to the point of overconstancy. For all conditions of angle and distance of the comparison stimuli, the retarded group did not differ from their CA-equivalent normal group and achieved greater constancy than their MA-equivalent but younger normal group. The data clearly support the developmental hypothesis.

Leibowitz (in press) hypothesized that size constancy is a function of CA rather than MA. His NBI-retarded and normal group covered adolescent years and went into the twenties. His procedure was similar to Jenkin's, *S*s having to judge, in a method-of-limits procedure, the size of sticks. As with Jenkin, the CA-matched groups performed the same, both tending toward overconstancy.

Jenkin and Morse (1960) compared size-distance judgments of BI retardates, NBI retardates, and normals of adolescent age. Both retarded groups had a median MA of 7–10. They also included an older group of normals to assess age trends. They hypothesized that the BI group would fall short of constancy, performing like younger children. Their procedure was similar to that of the study described above. The results support their hypothesis. The BI group gave size judgments significantly smaller than the NBI retardates and normals. The age trend, suggested by previous studies, was found, the older normals tending to have greater constancy than the younger NBI groups. The authors conclude that since size-constancy judgments depend upon the apprehension and integration of various depth cues, the organics' performance is probably due to impaired ability to integrate the sources of information given, and the tendency "to rely more heavily than other groups upon the proximal stimulus size" (p. 9).

Leibowitz et al. (1959) investigated the relationship between shape-constancy judgments and intelligence "under experimental conditions which produce high variability" (p. 108). The Ss studied were 42 Ford fellows "of superior academic potential," 21 mild and borderline retardates, and 21 "slow learners" from public school remedial classes. Although the experiment in most respects follows traditional lines, the "conditions which produce high variability" place the significance of the findings apart from the usual constancy study. Rather than instruct S to judge on the basis of the real shape of the standard, the instructions requested S to choose from the comparison stimuli the one that "looks the most like" the standard. To follow this instruction, S attempts to ignore the cues that make for constancy, emphasizing the operation of proximal cues. The results showed that the higher-IQ groups responded with less constancy than the lower-IQ groups, demonstrating that the higher the IQ, the greater the ability to assume the set requiring S to ignore cues supporting constancy of shape judgment. They concluded that "the less intelligent subjects are less able to shift from the everyday, non-analytic modes of observation in order to comply with the requirements of the experiment" (p. 111). The authors see this explanation as having the disadvantage of not allowing one "to specify the correlated conditions of the organism," although the ability to assume this "set" has been related to individual differences in "introversion" (Singer, 1950) and intolerance of instability in the perceptual field (Spivack, 1954).

The relevant work with constancy to date suggests that size constancy is a function of CA and not of intelligence. Although the size constancy of BI retardates differs from NBI Ss with the same MA, a question remains about whether this is due to inability to integrate the cues available in making objective judgments, as suggested by Jenkin and Morse, or to a greater need in BI Ss for cue support in making such judgments. Jenkin and Morse limited available cues by employing a homogeneous background, and BI performance may have suffered more from this cue limitation than that of the NBI groups. This issue could be settled by a study which varies the number of cues available and notes whether or not the performance of BI Ss approaches that of NBI Ss as the number of cues made available increases.

Depth

Barnett and Pryer (1958) studied the depth perception judgments of 70 Ss with mild and moderate retardation. The usual depth perception method of adjustment was employed. BI and NBI subgroups, equated for MA and IQ, did not differ in performance. Constant error was not related to MA or IQ, although the standard deviation of scores showed a low relationship ($r = -.25$) with MA and IQ. Unfortunately it is difficult to assess from the report whether or not the standard deviation scores are contaminated by starting position effects. No studies could be found which compared the performance of retarded and normal Ss on depth perception performance.

Cutaneous localization

Single stimulation. Satter and Cassel (1955) studied the ability of retarded Ss to locate where they had just been touched. Both BI and NBI groups had a mean IQ of about 60. The control Ss were assumed to have average intelligence. Each S was touched 10 times in each of six different areas: back of each hand, both insteps, and right and left forehead. S was blindfolded and after each stimulation asked to touch the place he had just touched with a stylus. The scoring was based on how close S came to touching the spot where E had touched him. BI Ss did significantly worse than the normal and NBI Ss. The NBI group performance equaled that of the control group in touch localization at three areas, but NBI Ss performed much worse when touched on the preferred hand and both forehead points. It is difficult to know whether or not, or to what extent, the use of a motor indicator may have contaminated the results.

Double simultaneous stimulation (DSS). There have been four studies with DSS in retarded Ss, all focusing upon the issue of MA and its relationship to various response deficiencies. S is touched simultaneously on two body parts and then is asked to report or in other ways indicate where he had been touched. Studies of adults with cerebral dysfunction and of very young children have indicated that these groups frequently show the phenomena of *extinction* (i.e. the report of only one stimulus) and displacement of one stimulus to another body area. These response deficiencies have also been studied as a function of the body parts touched, especially the face-hand combination. Facial "dominance" seems to be the rule whenever extinction occurs (i.e., the hand is not reported).

Fink, Green, and Bender (1953) studied 57 retardates (MA range 2.0–9.0). No IQs are reported. With S's eyes closed, combinations of cheek, hand, shoulder, thigh, and foot were touched ipsilaterally and contralaterally. Extinction was noted in *all* Ss, with the expected strong face-dominance pattern as found in 3- to 6-year-old normal children and in BI adults. Also noted were perseverations of previously given responses (in 38 per cent of subjects) and displacements (in 46 per cent of the Ss). Of particular interest was the fact that with increased MA, there was a decrease in persistent errors. Since the Ss' errors were not random, and symmetrical stimuli were correctly localized, the authors conclude that errors under other simultaneous conditions cannot be ascribed to inattention or confusion, and "that the face-hand test reflects the same performance ability as the Stanford-Binet test" (p. 48).

Swanson (1956) investigated the extinction phenomenon in a group of BI and a group of NBI Ss covering a broad range of IQs. A normal group was also used. After noting that all could locate single stimuli correctly, 32 trials were run in all combinations of face and hand simultaneous conditions. The data indicated that for the face-hand combination, increase in

MA is the major determinant of decreased errors, with IQ a determinant only under MA of 7 and under contralateral conditions. Swanson concludes that IQ is the critical determinant of group differences under homologous conditions, since both retarded groups exhibited more extinction responses than normals at all MA levels.

White (1957) compared 56 retarded *S*s (CA range 16–30) and 57 retarded *S*s (CA range 45–56) with two CA normal groups equated for CA. After being assured that all *S*s could report single stimuli applied to the hand, he presented a series of face-hand trials, scoring a failure on the "test" when *S* reported only one stimulus instead of both on 10 successive trials. Whereas none of the younger normal and only 5 per cent of the older normal group failed, 43 per cent of the younger and 65 per cent of the older retarded group failed the test. White does not present his data in terms of MA levels.

Pollack and Gordon (1960) studied the DSS-MA relationship in 115 retarded and nonretarded *S*s referred for outpatient treatment because of emotional or behavioral problems. There were 67 *S*s with IQs under 70, 18 with IQs between 70 and 80, and 30 with IQs over 80. The group included 31 schizophrenic *S*s, 21 of these falling into the retarded classification. They used 14 trials, the "test" consisting of various combinations of face-face, hand-hand, and face-hand stimulation. An *S* failed when by the tenth trial he did not report both stimuli. He passed when, within 10 trials and thereafter, he identified both stimuli. Only one *S* with an MA greater than 7.0 failed the test. When equated for MA, there were no statistically significant differences between the retarded and nonretarded emotionally disturbed groups. The pattern of errors was related to MA. At MA of 7 and over, there were no homologous errors and only face-hand errors of the hand-extinction variety. Between MA 5 and 7, displacement errors accompanied the more frequent extinction errors; and below MA 5, displacement errors were more typical than extinction errors. Drawing upon their own data, as well as the work of others with nonretarded groups, Pollack and Gordon conclude that DSS performance is not related to diagnosis or severity of behavioral disorder, but rather to MA alone. Considering the fact that Pollack and Gordon had a broad CA range in each of their MA groups, their data, in conjunction with that of the others, are highly consistent with their contention.

The results of DSS studies are strikingly consistent, indicating dependence on MA for success. The MA of 7.0 stands out as a critical point in face-hand DSS success. Swanson's finding that IQ is a determinant of success under certain circumstances warrants replication since it is the exception to the rule. BI seems to have a more deleterious effect than retardation upon location of single cutaneous stimuli. Why retardates are less efficient than normals in locating single stimuli applied to certain body surface areas and not to others remains an unanswered question.

Illusions

Muller-Lyer illusion. As part of a study of normal development, Pintner **and** Anderson (1916) also studied the performance of 13 feebleminded individuals (MA about 9.0) on the Muller-Lyer illusion. Three "in" and three "out" trials were run, with S adjusting the variable line "to make the two lines look the same" or "look equal." The authors considered the in and out trials separately, noting that between ages 6 and 14 there was a decrease among normals in the amount of illusion. The sample of 14-year-olds performed like the adult normals. On the in trials the feebleminded group is described as functioning more like the 6- to 13-year-olds, while on the out trials they are said to have functioned like older normal groups. No statistical treatment of the data is offered. The results could be explained solely on the basis of starting position effect rather than susceptibility to the illusion.

Spitz and Blackman (1958) studied 24 mild and borderline retarded and 22 normal Ss. The retarded group was not classified on the basis of presence or absence of BI. A method of adjustment procedure was used that controlled for discrimination and directional errors. The retarded and normal groups did not differ significantly on the amount of illusion exhibited.

Jenkins and West (1959) predicted that organic mental defectives would show less Muller-Lyer illusion; this prediction was based on the hypothesis that organicity lowers capacity to integrate or synthesize stimuli in complex situations. In this instance, the integration of stimuli which cause the illusion in normals would be less operative in the BI group. The method of limits was employed. The BI group CA range was 10 to 40 (mean 22), with MA ranged 5 to 11. No IQs are reported. The normal group consisted of high school students and institution employees. The BI group demonstrated less illusion, the F ratio closely approaching the .05 level of significance. The authors conclude that support for the hypothesis is limited. Pertinent to the remarks made earlier relative to the Pintner and Anderson study, Jenkin and West found that the BI group exhibited a significantly larger starting position effect than the normals. Amount of illusion was not related to age in either group, nor was it related to MA within the BI group.

The results would seem to suggest that retardates do not perform differently from those of normal intelligence on the Muller-Lyer illusion. The evidence that BI may affect performance finds limited support.

Ponzo illusion. Only one study has assessed the amount of the Ponzo illusion in retardates. In this illusion, two parallel vertical lines of equal length are not viewed as equal when presented within a matrix of lines that converge to a point slightly to one side of one of the vertical lines. Leibowitz and Heisel (1958) compared the performance of 65 normal children, a group of college students, and a group of 59 NBI-retarded individuals. No IQs are reported. The method of limits was employed. The authors noted an increase in illusion in the normal group as a function of CA up to 7, after which there was no noticeable change. They conclude that there are no noticeable CA or MA trends in the retarded group and that the illusion is greater in the retarded group.

Since the published tables of Leibowitz and Heisel supply the mean amount of illusion obtained at each CA level in the retarded group, this reviewer combined the data of adjacent CA groups to increase the N at each level and calculated a rank-order correlation between CA and illusion means. The obtained rho was .64, indicating that within the retarded group the CA and illusion *means* are significantly related. Since the raw data were not available, the magnitude of the actual relationship remains unknown. A similar analysis of MA was not possible owing to the heavy concentration of retarded Ss in the 6.0 and 7.0 MA categories. This reviewer then attempted to compare the performance of retarded and normal Ss with the same CA. The greatest CA overlap of the two groups was between 9 and 12. No difference in amount of illusion was found within this age range. The data in the tables suggest that the older retardates, those outside the age range of normals studied, may show greater amounts of illusion than the younger Ss of both groups. Too few Ss were tested to assess this statistically.

The data suggest that amount of illusion is a function of CA rather than mental development. The authors' conclusion that the retardates exhibited greater illusion than normals may be questioned.

Size-weight illusion.   The study of the size-weight illusion in retarded Ss began with DeMoor (see Rey, 1929–1930), who noted that some retarded children did not experience the illusion. In 1906, Clarparede (see Rey, 1929–1930) also noted the tendency for such children not to experience this illusion, adding that performance may depend upon the nature of retardation. In this country, Doll (1913) studied presence or absence of the size-weight illusion in a group of 345 Ss ranging from "low idiocy" to "high-grade moronia." No information is given about the group except their MAs, which ranged from 1 to 12. S was handed two blocks of the same weight but different size, with the instructions "tell me which block seems the heavier." Data on presence and absence of the illusion are presented as a function of MA. No statistical treatment of the data is attempted, but inspection suggests that at about an MA of 5 a significant number of Ss experienced the illusion. Since CAs are not given, the relationship between CA, IQ, and performance cannot be assessed.

Rey (1929–1930) studied the amount of this illusion in a heterogeneous experimental group of 42 Ss (CA range 7–15). Some had brain injuries, but for others the diagnosis appeared questionable. Two normal groups of children were studied, one with a CA range 5–6, and the other 7–14. The measure taken was the amount of weight E had to add to the larger of two boxes before S judged it as heavier than the smaller box. Rey notes that the experimental group more often failed to demonstrate the illusion than their CA-equivalent normal controls, but a larger number experienced the illusion than in the 5–6 age normal group. The illusion was weaker in the experimental group than in their CA-equivalent normals, but the amount of illusion was equivalent to that of the younger normal group.

Rey does not treat his data statistically. This reviewer analyzed the data in Rey's tables, and the result indicates that in the experimental group, there was no correlation between IQ or age and amount of illusion. In the normal groups, although there was not a significant relationship between amount of illusion and age, the 5- and 6-year-olds tended to have smaller illusions than the older group.

Ohwaki (1953), primarily interested in the developmental aspects of weight judgments, studied the size-weight illusion in a group of 32 retardates with a broad range of IQ. The group consisted of both BI and NBI Ss. The method of constant stimuli was used; S was to hand E the "heavier" block. The data suggested that at about MA 4 or 5 the illusion became stable. Ohwaki notes, however, that even in his highest-MA group (6.0 to 11.6) only 27 per cent reported the illusion 100 per cent of the time. The correlation between illusion and MA with age partialled out is .31, and the correlation with CA, with MA partialled out, is .25.

Jenkin and West (1958) hypothesized that a group of BI-retarded Ss would demonstrate less illusion than a group of normals. Ss judged whether each of a series of comparison cylinders, when compared with the standard, was lighter than, equal to, or heavier than the standard. The BI group reported significantly less illusion than the control group. In the BI group, MA and IQ were not related to amount of illusion reported. Age was not related to amount of illusion in the normal group, but was correlated .45 in the BI group. The authors feel that this last correlation is probably spurious in view of the other correlations.

It is difficult to summarize the work with the size-weight illusion since all of the studies, with the exception of that of Jenkin and West, employed either heterogeneous or undefined groups. The data of Doll and Ohwaki suggest that MA is an important determinant of performance. The fact that Jenkin and West did not find a correlation between MA and amount of illusion may be because their group did not extend down low enough in MA. The data of Rey and Jenkin and West suggest that IQ is not the critical dimension. Jenkin and West interpret their findings as indicating that BI Ss have a deficiency in the integration of input of visual, tactual, and kinesthetic cues necessary for the creation of the illusion. To date, no study has focused attention on the performance of NBI-retarded Ss.

Aftereffects

The spiral visual aftereffect (SVA). Research with SVA has largely focused upon the issue of brain injury. Only two studies have assessed the performance of retardates, and two more have included retardates within the sample studied.

Mill[2] compared BI and NBI retardates on the report of presence or absence of SVA. Both the BI group with positive EEGs and the NBI group with negative EEGs consisted of Ss with mild and moderate retardation. Both sexes were equally represented in each group. The Price and Deabler (1955) procedure was employed. Each S was exposed to eight trials, four with the spiral turning, to give an aftereffect of expansion, and four to give an aftereffect of contraction. Mill varied the usual procedure by questioning S while the spiral was turning so that before the spiral was stopped and the aftereffect assessed, each S had described the turning spiral in terms of size change or change in distance from S. Eighteen of the forty-seven Ss in the BI group and six of the twenty-five Ss in the NBI group failed to report SVA, a difference significant at between the .05 and .10 levels. It is difficult to assess what effect the specific line of questioning by E may

[2] Personal communication.

have had on the results. Mill notes that some Ss reported the aftereffect as going in the reverse of the expected direction. In such a case, S is using the same label he employed to describe the turning spiral. The question arises about whether such perseverative use of labels was more characteristic of the BI than NBI Ss, thus enhancing the likelihood of failure in the BI group.

Spitz and Lipman (1959) studied the report of presence or absence of SVA in 32 Ss covering a broad range of retardation and in 32 normals. No attempt was made to determine the presence or absence of BI. The spiral was given alternately inward and outward, with exposure time to spinning varied randomly between 2 and 20 seconds (excluding odd numbers). The score was the total number of times SVA was reported. Two interesting results were found. Normal males and retarded females gave significantly more reports of SVA than normal females and retarded males. Nine retarded Ss who never reported SVA and were eliminated from the study proper had significantly lower IQs (mean 49) than the 32 who did report SVA (mean 60).

In two studies, Spivack and Levine (1959, 1961) examined the effect of diffuse BI upon the report of presence or absence of SVA and SVA duration, as a function of duration of exposure to spinning, speed of spinning, and monocular versus binocular viewing. The earlier study employed 24 BI females, and the later study 28 BI males. Most of the Ss in both groups had mild or borderline retardation. Although the major findings derive from comparisons made between BI performance and that of various control groups, both BI groups had retarded as well as nonretarded Ss, making it possible to assess the relationship between IQ and performance. In both studies, IQ was not related to the report of either presence or absence of SVA or to SVA duration.

The findings of Mill and Spivack and Levine taken together suggest that the failure to report SVA is a function of BI and not retardation. The studies of Spivack and Levine also indicate that the significantly longer SVA durations reported by BI Ss are a function of their injury and not their low IQ. These findings relative to the effect of lifelong BI on SVA performance have been corroborated by others (Blau & Schaffer, 1960; Davids, Goldenberg, & Laufer, 1957; Mark, 1955; Truss & Allen, 1959). The findings of Spitz and Lipman are in marked contrast to the findings of others. It is possible that the nine retarded Ss who did not report SVA and who had lower IQs than the remaining retardates did not understand what was expected of them. Mill indicates the necessity of carefully instructing retardates in the task so as to ensure understanding. The interaction of sex and presence of retardation on report of presence or absence of SVA is not so easily reconciled. It is possible that the Spitz and Lipman retarded sample, not differentiated on the basis of BI, may have had significantly more BI Ss in the retarded male than retarded female group. The nature of the interaction suggests however that combining sexes should wash out differences between diagnostic groups. The data of Mills suggest that this does not occur. The finding of sex differences among normals is unique.

Visual and kinesthetic aftereffects. Three studies have examined visual figural aftereffects (VFA) in retarded and BI Ss. Spitz and Blackman

(1959) used two equal-sized squares, one above the other, as the "test" figures. If *S* judged them as equal in size, he was then shown the inspection figures. These figures were circles, one falling within the upper square and the other outside the lower square. After fixating the inspection figures, the aftereffect was noted if, subsequently, the upper square was judged as larger than the bottom one. *S*s were separated into two groups. One group fixated the inspection figure for 1 minute, made a judgment of the test figures, then had another fixation period of 1½ minutes and made a test-figure judgment. A 2-minute rest followed, after which another test-figure judgment was made in order to examine persistence of the aftereffect through time. The second group followed the same procedure, except that the two inspection periods were 2 and 2½ minutes in length, followed by a 4-minute rest and retest. Sixteen BI and 21 NBI mild and borderline retarded males were compared with normals. The dependent variable was the number of times VFA was noted (i.e., the upper square was judged as larger than the lower).

Results indicated that the normals reported VFA significantly more often than did the retardates. Significantly more normals demonstrated VFA after all four inspection periods. The BI and NBI groups did not differ, and in those retarded *S*s who did satiate, the effect dissipated more slowly than in the normals.

In two studies, Spivack and Levine (1959, 1961) have compared the VFAs of female and male BI *S*s with normal and emotionally disturbed controls. In both instances, the BI groups exhibited significantly less VFA than the control groups. Of particular interest here is the fact that amount of VFA was significantly correlated with IQ in retardates in both studies. The correlation was positive in females and negative in males.

Spitz and Lipman (in press) have compared the kinesthetic aftereffect (KFA) performance of mild and borderline retardates with college sophomores. The normal group demonstrated significantly more aftereffect. Mark (1955) reports smaller KFA effects in BI *S*s in comparison with controls, but states that performance was not related to IQ.

The evidence suggests that retardation as well as BI results in less VFA than in normals. Since in the KFA study Spitz and Lipman did not divide their retarded group into BI and NBI subgroups, a relationship between KFA and IQ remains to be demonstrated. One cannot assume that there is individual consistency between VFA and KFA performance, since two recent studies failed to find an intercorrelation between them (Gardner, in press; Spitz & Lipman, 1960). The contrasting VFA-IQ correlations in male and female BI *S*s noted by Spivack and Levine remain unexplained as well as unreplicated.

Figures with reversible perspective

Studies with reversible figures have dealt with three parameters: readiness or capacity to report reversals, rate of change of perspective through time, and pattern of rate of reversal through time.

Spitz and Blackman (1959) compared 16 BI and 21 NBI mild and borderline retardates with normals. They employed the modified Rubin vase figure first described by Harrower (1939). This method measures the amount of support S requires before reporting the alternative perspective. Increasing supports take the form of gradual strengthening of the alternative perspective through modification in the drawing. The BI and NBI groups did not differ significantly in readiness to report a change in perspective, but both needed significantly more support than the normal group. In another study Spitz and Lipman[3] report a longer latency for the first reversal of the Necker cube in a group of 44 retardates when compared with normals.

The most frequently studied parameter of reversible figures is the frequency of reversal over a prescribed time interval. Murray (1954) compared 15 BI and 15 NBI Ss with moderate and mild retardation. He used the Lissajous figure, and S was asked to point whenever the direction of movement changed. The BI group reported a significantly fewer number of reversals over ten 1-minute trial periods. Spitz and Lipman report that over two consecutive 2-minute periods, their retarded group (undifferentiated as to BI) consistently reported fewer Necker reversals. Spivack and Levine (1959) found Necker cube and Schroeder staircase reversal rate over a 1-minute period uncorrelated with IQ in BI females. In another study (Spivak & Levine, 1961) they found a significant positive correlation (.44) in BI males between IQ and number of Necker cube reversals.

Two studies have dealt with the pattern of reversal rate through time. Miller and Spitz (1960) first noted that reversal rate in retardates built up over a 30-second period, describing a negatively accelerated curve. Spitz and Lipman compared their retardates and normals for reversal rate over four consecutive 30-second intervals. After a 2-minute rest period, Ss were given 2 minutes of spaced (30 second—30 second) trials. They discovered that the reversal rate in both groups increased over the initial 2-minute period, dropped after the rest period, and again increased over the four spaced 30-second trials. The curves for both groups in both prerest and postrest periods were negatively accelerated. Of greater interest in the present context was the fact that the retarded group's increase in reversal rate was significantly less rapid initially, dropped less during rest, and again climbed at a slower rate after rest. The authors present these data as evidence of less cortical modifiability in the retarded group. Spivack and Levine (1961) have not obtained negatively accelerated curves for 2-minute observation periods in BI, emotionally disturbed, or normal Ss. Differences in methodology probably explain the disparate results. Spitz and Lipman employ three-dimensional models to demonstrate or "teach" Ss the response under investigation. Spivack and Levine do not do this and therefore may not use Ss with long latencies for report of reversal. Such Ss would contribute data yielding a negatively accelerated curve. Another procedural difference is that Spitz and Lipman do not afford their Ss prior experience with the Necker cube, and Spivack and Levine use the Necker cube during the initial exploration to discover if S can report reversals. Prior experience has been shown to increase reversal rate (Mark, 1955) and in the present instance might have elevated subsequent performance to an asymptote.

The studies to date indicate that both BI and NBI retardates do not re-

[3] Personal communication.

port the experience of reversal of perspective as easily or as spontaneously as do normals. BI retardates report fewer reversals over short periods of time than NBI retardates, a finding consistent with those reported with BI *S*s of somewhat higher intelligence (Spivack & Levine, 1959). To date an NBI-retarded group has not been compared with a normal group for reversal rate, although the findings of Spitz and Lipman with an unspecified retarded group suggest that retardation as well as BI reduces reversal rate. This notion is given some support by the .44 correlation between IQ and reversal rate reported by Spivack and Levine in the male BI group. A question remains about whether the slow rate of development and dissipation of reversal rate through time found by Miller and Spitz and Spitz and Lipman occurs as a consequence of BI or retardation, or whether it occurs only when both conditions exist.

Phi movement

Werner and Thuma (1942) compared the phi performance of 20 BI mild and borderline retarded *S*s with the performance of a matched group of NBI *S*s. Three stimulus figures were employed, two involving pairs of lines and one a pair of lines comprising the pendulum part of a clock figure. Apparently only descending trials were given (from alternation to movement to simultaneity). The *E*s do not describe the instructions given their *S*s. The results indicate there was no group difference in the report of movement with the clock figure, but significantly more NBI *S*s reported movement with the line figure than did BI *S*s. The two groups did not differ in movement thresholds for the clock figure, although the BI group had significantly higher simultaneity thresholds for the line figure.

In some respects the data of Werner and Thuma are puzzling. While making no note of the fact, they do not present data for the simultaneity thresholds for the clock figure. The omission is difficult to interpret in view of the fact that simultaneity thresholds for the line figures were significantly different for the two groups. Further, the movement threshold numbers given in the table of results indicate that movement was reported at exactly the same point (1,175 milliseconds) in 8 BI and 16 NBI *S*s. This fact, plus the fact that most of the remaining clock movement numbers are close to 1,175 milliseconds, suggests some procedural artifact or consistent response characteristic intruding upon performance. It is interesting to note that nearly all *S*s reported movement for the clock almost immediately after the descending trials began (1,250 milliseconds). The most striking finding is the total absence of reported movement to the line figures in the BI group. This is taken to mean that such *S*s are perceptually deficient. Alternative possibilities are not noted, such as differential response availability in the two groups (Garner et al., 1955) or intrusion of differential response characteristics (e.g., suggestibility) as a consequence of the ambiguity of the experimental situation.

Brenner (1956) states that she reproduced the results of Werner and Thuma when using their apparatus and procedure, the reports of the BI *S*s depending upon the meanings attributed to the stimuli. She adds that meaning affected the report of movement particularly when the apparatus gave cues encouraging "inferred movement." With what she feels is improved apparatus, Brenner then presents data inconsistent with that of Werner and Thuma and concludes that the findings of Werner and Thuma may have been due to "inadequate apparatus and procedure which precluded the perception of visible movement and emphasized dependence on stimulus meaning" (p. 204).

Keller (1958) states that in pilot work he was unable to get meaningful results using the procedure of Werner and Thuma. He then presents data from a factor analysis which included a measure of phi movement, a rating of presence or absence of BI, and verbal and performance IQs. The phi movement stimuli were two lines, and the method of discrete settings was employed. The score was the number of times S reported movement at various interval settings. Most of the Ss were mild and borderline retardates. The results indicate a slight loading (.26) of phi movement mean thresholds on an intelligence factor, indicating that the more intelligent Ss tended to report movement at faster intervals. The total number of phi movement responses loaded .80 on a factor labeled "suggestibility." No reliable BI factor emerged, although BI ratings loaded .31 on a factor labeled "poor comprehension of the apparent movement task."

Mark and Pasamanick (1958) and Spivack and Levine (1961) have compared the phi movement responses of BI and normal Ss, concluding that BI affects performance. Mark and Pasamanick did not find a relationship between simultaneity thresholds and IQ within the IQ range of 64 to 121. Spivack and Levine found both simultaneity and alternation thresholds unrelated to a verbal measure of intelligence.

The evidence to date suggests that mental retardation is not related to phi movement thresholds. BI groups perform differently from NBI groups across a broad IQ range.

Critical flicker frequency

Werner and Thuma (1942) compared the CFF thresholds of 20 BI and 20 matched NBI Ss, most of whom were mild or borderline retardates. The method of limits was employed and three brightness levels were utilized. At all three brightness levels the BI group had significantly lower thresholds.

Mark, Meier, and Pasamanick (1958) have demonstrated significantly lower CFF thresholds in BI Ss but found no relationship between CFF and intelligence. Keller (1959) reports that variability in CFF threshold loaded —.44 on his intelligence factor, although the mean CFF threshold measure did not.

Present evidence indicates that the CFF threshold is affected by BI but is not related to IQ.

SUMMARY OF FINDINGS

The results to date suggest that retarded Ss as a group are less efficient than those with normal intelligence in the ability to make fine discriminations between different points along a single stimulus dimension and less able to recognize or identify complex stimuli when exposed for brief intervals.

There are no data available regarding whether or not poor discrimination or recognition ability is a characteristic or "trait" of a retarded individual, such that poor performance in one modality is accompanied by poor performance in other modalities. Also, there are no data bearing on the relationship between discrimination efficiency and ability to recognize or identify complex stimuli.

Retardates are less efficient than normals in the ability to locate single cutaneous stimuli, when these stimuli are appled to certain body surface areas. They are as efficient as normals in locating cutaneous stimuli applied to other body surface areas. When double simultaneous cutaneous stimuli are employed, intelligence is a factor depending upon MA level and the conditions of stimulation. It is not known whether the deficiencies that retardates exhibit in locating or identifying cutaneous stimuli bear any relationship to the deficiencies they exhibit in the discrimination and recognition tasks that have been studied.

Available data indicate that retardates exhibit less VFA than normals and that the buildup and dissipation of VFA is less rapid in retardates than in individuals of normal intelligence. Retardates do not report reversals of perspective as easily or as spontaneously as those with normal IQ and are less able than normals to ignore distal cues and/or to be guided by proximal cues in a constancy situation. These findings suggest that certain experimental techniques and instructional acts that bring about shifts or modification in perceptual performance in normals are less operative in retardates. Perhaps this reflects an intraindividual characteristic in retardates, although attempts to date to demonstrate correlations between aftereffect and reversible figure performance among BI and NBI retardates have been in the main unsuccessful (Spitz & Blackman, 1959; Spivack & Levine, 1957, 1959).

Data regarding SVA, KFA, reversible figure reversal rate, and buildup and dissipation of reversal rate through time are questionable due to the possible presence of BI Ss within the retarded groups studied.

There is evidence indicating that retardation does not affect figure-background, constancy, phi movement threshold, and critical flicker frequency threshold responses, nor does it affect response to the Muller-Lyer, Ponzo, and size-weight illusions. It is worth noting that, with the exception of the Ponzo illusion stimuli, there is evidence that retardates *with* BI perform differently from NBI Ss when confronted with these perceptual tasks.

METHODOLOGICAL CONSIDERATIONS

In considering the studies completed to date, certain issues are worth noting. Most of the data have been obtained from adolescent and slightly older Ss. Whether or not the results apply to younger or older retarded Ss remains an open question. No developmental studies of perceptual processes in retardates are reported in the literature. The perceptual constancy performance of an adolescent retardate may not differ from that of a normal adolescent, but it is possible that constancy developed at a different rate or had a different curve of development during childhood or latency years. That developmental research might prove fruitful finds support in the work of Teuber and Rudel (in press), who found differences between the perceptual performance of normal and BI Ss depending upon CA and the perceptual task employed. On one task, BI and normal groups differed significantly at CA of 5, but the difference diminished with increase in CA, and at CA of 13 the BI and normal groups did not differ. On another perceptual task, the BI and normal groups did not differ at CA of 6, but performance diverged with increase in CA until at CA of 11 significant group differences in performance were found.

Many studies employing retarded Ss have focused upon the issue of BI rather than retardation per se. Although there may be both practical and theoretical problems in the "exogenous-endogenous" conception, the data suggest that BI and NBI Ss differ in performance on certain perceptual tasks irrespective of IQ, while on other perceptual tasks they do not differ in performance or differ only at certain IQ levels. It is often difficult therefore to interpret those findings based on mixed or undefined retarded groups. Inferior performance by retarded groups, relative to normals, may reflect only a substantial deficiency in a BI subgroup, and unwarranted conclusions may be drawn about retardation that are pertinent only to BI. Probably no one is entirely satisfied with the diagnostic vehicles employed in diagnosing BI, but the fact remains that these vehicles define subgroups of retarded (and nonretarded) Ss that perform differently on certain perceptual tasks. As Sarason and Gladwin (1958) suggest: "Neither the mentally deficient [with organic pathology] nor the retarded [with no organic pathology] are homogeneous with respect to etiology . . . among themselves, but if we do not at least make a separation in our research on the basis of the one obvious factor we know to be operative—presence or absence of organic pathology—our task will be hopelessly confounded" (p. 9).

A point of interest, as well as significance in interpretation of results, is the fact that most of the retarded Ss that have been studied reside in institutions. Certainly institutions differ from one another in the type of child under their care; it is also quite possible that institutionalized children differ in background and behavior from noninstitutionalized children of equivalent IQ living at home and attending special classes or day schools, or who have found a vocational or social niche in the community. Such differences may initially motivate institutional placement or evolve as a result of such placement. What is important is that the symptom picture, the attitude and receptivity to being "tested," the significance of incentives if used, and the relationship between S and E may vary as a function of this factor. It is not safe to make any one generalization about the operation of this factor, and caution may be warranted when generalizing from the data at hand to noninstitutionalized retardates.

It is surprising that in perceptual research with retardates incentives are rarely employed as a vehicle in the maintenance of effort in the task. It has been noted, in jest, that in an experimental situation one can get the college sophomore to do almost anything and tolerate the intolerable (i.e., electric shock, repeated experimental failures, threats to self-esteem, boredom, etc.). Normals assume the role of the guinea pig, and "go along" with the experimenter. This is probably less true of many retarded children. They are generally indifferent to the prospect of contributing to "science," and make little if any attempt to identify with the enterprise at hand. Many quickly lose interest, anticipate failure, or become fidgety. Some will openly indicate aversive feelings. Even when no obvious feelings are manifest, the investigator may have cause for concern when he notes the casual way a response is "thrown off," the speed with which judgments are being made, or frequent questions, such as "How many more do I have to do?" In some studies it is clear that the investigators were not only aware of this factor, but informally attended to it in some fashion. Perhaps it would be well to consider this factor more formally in research design.

Another variable seldom noted is whether or not drugs were being taken by retarded *S*s at the time of the study. Solomons (1957) noted that all of her BI *S*s were on one drug or another, adding that in all probability their tactual perception performance was better than might have been the case without medication. While analyzing discrimination data, Spivack and Levine (1961) noted in the medical records that certain *S*s had been taking antihistamine preparations. Of the two *S*s in the BI group, one obtained the poorest score and the other the fourth lowest out of 10 *S*s. Both *S*s in the emotionally disturbed group receiving antihistamines were poorer than the other eight *S*s in their group! Too few *S*s were involved to come to any conclusions, but it points up the necessity of recording this type of data in perceptual work and perhaps the advisability of controlling for drug effects if at all feasible.

An unnoted problem that may contaminate the results of many perceptual studies with retarded (and BI) *S*s is that of response biases. The question is how and to what extent a particular response once given may affect a subsequent response, irrespective of change in stimulus circumstances. Psychophysical studies have in the past assumed that in a sequence of judgments, each perceptual judgment made is independent of every other judgment. Recent studies (Neisser, 1957; Verplanck, Collier, & Cotton, 1952) raise serious doubts about this assumption. This raises the possibility that retarded children may exhibit characteristic biases which affect their performance and lead to statements about their perceptual behavior which in fact are irrelevant to perception per se. Spivack and Levine (1961) investigated such biases in their study of visual discrimination. Of interest is the fact that not only were there such biases, but their appearance depended upon the experimental method employed. In two other studies, one dealing with NBI-retarded and the other BI-retarded *S*s, a type of response-response bias was noted. Dixon (1958) discovered that what at first appeared as a distinctive performance in a retarded group later turned out to be, under changed methodology, a response set carried over from his training procedure. Jenkin and West (1958), in studying the size-weight illusion, discovered that a response tendency developed to one standard stimulus carried over into the responses to the second standard stimulus.

Beyond the general considerations discussed up to this point, certain specific methodological issues warrant attention for two reasons. First, one likes to feel reasonably assured in dealing with individual differences that any differences obtained are not a function of irrelevant issues. A great problem when considering and comparing different studies stems from differences in methodology, differences which may be more crucial when studying retarded than normal individuals. Second, it is hoped that mention of certain specific methodological issues may help others avoid certain pitfalls in their research designs, pitfalls that are expensive both in terms of research time and, in the long run, in terms of the researcher's "psychic" well-being.

One such issue is the use of a motor indicator, particularly in the study of BI-retarded *S*s. A striking example is found in the study of Solomons (1957). In studying tactual discrimination, Solomons included a handicapped group, along with a nonhandicapped and a normal group. Problems arose, in that many handicapped *S*s needed help in grasping and releasing the stimuli, or they could not reach into a bag to search for a block that would match a standard. This required that a verbal description be substituted with these *S*s, while the other groups worked under the quite different searching procedure. It also required that liberal praise be given to allay anxiety about failure.

The frequent comment in research studies that none of the *S*s employed "had gross motor deficiencies" indicates awareness of this issue. The question is whether the control of gross motor problems is always sufficient. Spivack and Levine (1961) did not work with *S*s suffering any obvious or apparent motor deficiencies. Yet, they noted a significant correlation between failure on tasks in a neurological examination requiring finer and more stringent motor performance and reliability of discrimination when *S*s adjusted a comparison bar by a technique requiring them to *turn* a knob *by hand*. It is interesting to note that Cruickshank, Bice, and Wallen (1957), fully aware of the need to be certain that their cerebral-palsy children would have no motoric reproduction problem, discovered that both their CP groups compressed their design drawings significantly more than the controls. They conclude: "Due to known motor involvement . . . it is difficult to evaluate the psychological importance of this finding" (p. 99). It would seem judicious to carefully assess any motor indicator for possible contaminating effects and to consider, when there is serious question, the concurrent use or substitution of a verbal indicator.

The issue of verbal indicators, however, is not without problems demanding consideration and discrimination on the part of the investigator. It is important to feel assured that *S* has a sufficiently available and articulated set of verbal labels appropriate to the task demand. For instance, an investigator plans to present a series of cards each with two lines of different length, side by side, and *S* is to tell *E* whether the line on the right or left is longer. Being aware of a potential problem, *E* first asks each *S* to raise his right hand to check whether *S* knows the difference between right and left. *E* proceeds, unaware of the fact that certain *S*s still get confused periodically, calling "left" "right," and vice versa. The thought strikes him when one *S* happens to point to the left line on one trial, commenting, "This right one is longer." Subsequently, *E* alters his method, asking each *S* to *point* to the longer line.

Response inhibition also must be considered. This relates to the instance wherein *S* has the verbal label, but hesitates using it for one or another reason. The reviewer has noted this particular problem in studying Necker cube reversals. In certain *S*s, facial change suggested that they saw something "strange" when first given the card. Asked to report what they saw and if "anything happened as they looked at the card," such *S*s would reply that nothing happened, and with a suspicious look immediately attempt to give back the card. In some instances, seeing a two-dimensional drawing "move" caused fear, or the suspicion that the investigators were playing tricks on them.

A general problem with verbal labels is uncertainty about whether the label has the same referent for both *E* and *S*. A prime example of this problem arises in the instance of "inferred" movement with the phi phenomenon. *S* reports movement, but when questioned says that the line must have moved because it was on one side and then the other. Questioned further, he admits that he did not really see it move, but concluded it must have. The problem of *S*'s imparting meaning to a stimulus has been noted by Halpin (1955). She mentions how some retarded *S*s would impart a particular meaning to a Bender-gestalt figure and then set out to draw a form to match the meaning rather than the stimulus on the card.

The importance of the verbal label employed in determining performance has been demonstrated by Miller and Spitz (1955, 1960). A group of 36 retarded *S*s were tested for Necker reversal rate and 6 to 8 weeks later split into three groups and tested with the Rubin vase figure. With the Rubin vase, one group was told merely to say "now" every time they saw a reversal. A second group was asked to report reversals by saying "black" and "white," referring to the two perspectives of the total figure. A third group was asked to assign their own labels to the two aspects, and then asked to use their own labels in reporting reversals. The performances of the first two groups were significantly correlated with the earlier Necker performance, .61 and .65, respectively. The performance of the group employing their own labels was not related to the earlier Necker performance, the correlation being —.37.

Another issue worth noting is the use of the reproduction method of response as the operation from which to assess perceptual performance. It has been noted earlier that one order of problem is potential contamination of the response by motor characteristics. A further issue having perhaps broader implications arises. There is evidence suggesting that in reproducing a stimulus the typical *S* satisfies himself in achieving "sameness" with a broader and looser standard than he demands or is capable of employing when given comparison stimuli with which to match or compare. Cassel (1949) noted better performance in both his BI and NBI groups when asked to find a stimulus within a matrix of stimuli, as compared with the success they had in reproducing the stimulus. That a different standard is used by adults is clearly indicated by the results of Bortner and Birch (1960) and Ross (1954), both studies indicating that a multiple-choice procedure dramatically altered performance in comparison with reproduction data, showing significantly better perceptual ability than would have been suspected from the reproduction data alone.

Garner, Hake, and Eriksen (1956), in discussing how response processes can affect the nature of response rather than the perceptual system, note the importance of the set of responses E provides S. In one example, they note how the number of response alternatives afforded S may affect the amount of error in discrimination. That such an issue has direct relevance to research with retardates can be noted in the study of Ohwaki (1953). Ohwaki was interested in examining how retarded Ss discriminate weight when size of the stimuli is held constant. He first had them compare 3-, 15-, and 30-gram boxes. He noted that all of his Ss could successfully discriminate between the 3- and 30-gram boxes. He then required them to arrange, in order of weight, three, four, and five such boxes, all differing in weight by 30 grams, a difference all were capable of discriminating when only two boxes were involved. No S with an MA under 4 could perform any of these tasks. With the higher-MA Ss, the task was harder the more boxes involved, and the higher the MA, the better the performance with any one set of boxes. Even in his highest-MA group (6.0 to 11.0) 2 out of 12 failed with three boxes, 3 out of 12 with four boxes, and 7 out of 12 with five boxes. It is clear that these failures did not reflect the inability to discriminate a difference of 30 grams, but rather other response characteristics which were elicited by the way the task was constructed.

The issue that probably demands the greatest vigilance, offers the most subtle confounding potential, and yet is the most difficult to control and manipulate is that of S's set to the experiment as a whole and the tasks given in particular. If a crucial element in perceptual research is the contingent relationship between stimulus and response, it behooves E to maximize the probability that S understands what he is to do and is attending and responding to the stimulus as defined by E. S enters with certain expectations regarding success and failure, he establishes a relationship with E, and he wonders how he is doing and what will happen to him as a consequence of what he does. Initial work has suggested that retarded Ss do have different expectancies regarding success and failure and that this affects their response to success and failure in the experimental situation (Cromwell, 1959). The findings of Stevenson and Zigler (1957) and Keller (1958) indicate that both BI and NBI retarded Ss are sensitive to the investigator as a stimulus to which they respond and from whom they extract cues as to how they "should" perform. In all likelihood, it is the rare study that includes in its printed form the various exceptions to the formal instructions necessary in actually preparing S. Perhaps we all owe it to our colleagues to draw as complete a picture as possible of what was actually said to S, and of those difficulties encountered in working with him.

CONCLUSIONS

The studies completed to date reveal a number of varied and interesting findings and raise even more challenging questions. However, the paucity of research data on perceptual processes in retardates is striking and the results too fragmentary to permit meaningful integration. It seems clear that much more concentrated work is needed before interpretive generalizations can be made with confidence. A hopeful sign is the increase in research interest in perceptual processes in general, reflected in the fact that a large proportion of the studies completed with retardates has been within the last decade, with a heavy concentration within the last few years.

The reviewer has emphasized methodology since research with retardates requires not only knowledge of research design and statistics but awareness of a number of unique problems encountered when working with individuals with limited intellectual ability. In all likelihood, awareness of these unique problems, as well as generation of new and interesting research hypotheses, would be abetted by firsthand day-to-day experience with retardates. Heber states: "In my opinion, the failure to obtain conclusive findings in many studies can be attributed to the blind application of methodologies and techniques, which may have been highly successful in animal and other areas of experimentation, to research problems in mental retardation" (1961, p. 5).

It is clear that only a limited number of areas in perceptual research have been studied in retardates. What should be studied to offer the maximal "yield" must be left to the ingenuity and creativity of the individual researcher. It is likely however that the most productive research will result when the researcher follows up his own leads and pursues a question through a series of studies. Too often the "single-shot" study raises more questions than are answered and is rarely followed up by others. The result, as in the present instance, is an aggregate of discrete findings that are impossible to integrate.

In studying perceptual processes in retardates, the greatest challenge is the absence of clearly defined paths to follow. There being little to build upon, the field offers infinite possibilities for the careful pursuit of the new idea.

REFERENCES

BARNETT, C. D., & PRYER, MARGARET W. Note on depth perception in defectives. *Percept. mot. Skills,* 1958, 8, 130.

BARTLEY, S. H. *Principles of perception.* New York: Harper, 1958.

BELMONT, LILLIAN, & BIRCH, H. G. The relation of time of life to behavioral consequence of brain damage. I. The performance of brain-injured adults on the marble board test. *J. nerv. ment. Dis.,* 1960, 130, 91–97.

BIRCH, H. G., & BELMONT, LILLIAN. The relation of time of life to behavioral consequences in brain damage. II. The organization of tactual form experience in brain injured adults. *J. nerv. ment. Dis.,* 1960, 131, 489–494.

BLAU, T. H., & SCHAFFER, R. E. The spiral aftereffect test as a predictor of normal and abnormal electroencephalographic records in children. *J. consult. Psychol.,* 1960, 24, 35–42.

BORTNER, M., & BIRCH, H. G. Perceptual and perceptual-motor dissociation in brain-damaged patients. *J. nerv. ment. Dis.,* 1960, 130, 49–53.

BRENNER, M. W. The effects of brain damage on the perception of apparent movement. *J. Pers.*, 1956, 25, 202–212.

CANTOR, G. N., & GIRARDEAU, E. L. Rhythmic discrimination ability in mongoloid and normal children. *Amer. J. ment. Defic.*, 1959–60, 64, 621–625.

CASSEL, R. H. Relation of design reproduction to the etiology of mental deficiency. *J. consult. Psychol.*, 1949, 13, 421–428.

COLEMAN, T. W. A comparison of young brain-injured and mongolian mentally defective children on perception, thinking and behavior. Unpublished doctoral dissertation, Univer. of Michigan, 1960.

CROMWELL, R. L. A methodological approach to personality research in mental retardation. *Amer. J. ment. Defic.*, 1959–60, 64, 341–45.

CRUICKSHANK, W. M., BICE, H. V., & WALLEN, N. E. *Perception and cerebral palsy.* Syracuse Univer. Press, 1957.

DAVIDS, A., GOLDENBERG, L., & LAUFER, M. W. The relation of the Archimedes spiral aftereffect and trail making test to brain damage in children. *J. consult. Psychol.*, 1957, 21, 429–433.

DIXON, J. C. Reactions of superior and feebleminded children to an illusion. *J. genet. Psychol.*, 1958, 93, 79–85.

DOLL, E. A. The DeMoor size-weight illusion. *Train. Sch. Bull.*, 1913, 9, 145–149.

DOLPHIN, J. E., & CRUICKSHANK, W. N. The figure background relationship in children with cerebral palsy. *J. clin. Psychol.*, 1951, 7, 228–231.

FERNBERGER, S. W. Instructions and the psychophysical limen. *Amer. J. Psychol.*, 1931, 43, 361–376.

FINK, M., GREEN, M. A., & BENDER, M. Perception of simultaneous tactile stimuli by mentally defective subjects. *J. nerv. ment. Dis.*, 1953, 117, 43–49.

GARDNER, R. W. Individual differences in aftereffects and response to reversible figures. *Brit. J. Psychol.*, 1961, 52, 269–272.

GARNER, W. R., HAKE, H. W., & ERIKSEN, C. W. Operationism and the concept of perception. *Psych. Rev.*, 1956, 63, 149–159.

GIBSON, J. J. The concept of the stimulus in psychology. *Amer. Psychol.*, 1960, 15, 694–703.

GORDON, A. M. Some aspects of sensory discrimination in mongolism. *Amer. J. ment. Defic.*, 1944–45, 49, 55–63.

GRIFFITH, ANN H. The effects of retention interval, exposure time, and IQ on recognition in a mentally retarded group. *Amer. J. ment. Defic.*, 1959–60, 64, 1000–1003.

HALPIN, VIRGINIA C. Rotation errors made by brain-injured and familial children on two visual-motor tests. *Amer. J. ment. Defic.*, 1954–55, 59, 485–489.

HARROWER, MOLLY R. Changes in figure-ground perception in patients with cortical lesions. *Brit. J. Psychol.*, 1939, 30, 47–51.

HEBB, D. O. The effect of early and late brain injury on test scores, and the nature of normal adult intelligence. *Proc. Amer. Phil. Soc.*, 1942, 85, 275–292.

HEBER, R. A manual on terminology and classification in mental retardation. *Amer. J. ment. Defic.*, 1959, 64, Monogr. suppl.

HEBER, R. A decade of research in the behavioral sciences. Proc.: Conf. on res. opportunities in ment. retardation in Pa., Pa. Dept. Public Welfare, March 13–15, 1961.

HOCHBERG, J. Perception: toward the recovery of a definition. *Psychol. Rev.*, 1956, 63, 400–405.

JENKIN, N. Developmental and intellectual processes in size-distance judgment. *Amer. J. Psychol.*, 1960, 73, 268–273.

JENKIN, N., & MORSE, SALLY. Size-distance judgment in organic mental defectives. *J. consult. Psychol.,* 1960, 24, 139–143.

JENKIN, N., & WEST, N. I. Perception in organic mental defectives: an exploratory study. I. The size-weight illusion. *Train. Sch. Bull.,* 1958, 55, 5–10.

JENKIN, N., & WEST, N. I. Perception in organic mental defectives: an exploratory study. II. The Muller-Lyer illusion. *Train. Sch. Bull.,* 1959, 55, 67–70.

KELLER, J. E. The investigation of a specific cognitive deficiency. *Am. J. ment. Defic.,* 1953–54, 58, 560–565.

KELLER, J. E. Interrelationships between several measures of visual perception in mentally retarded children. Unpublished doctoral dissertation, Univer. of Michigan, 1958.

LEIBOWITZ, H. Apparent visual size as a function of distance for mentally deficient subjects. *Amer. J. Psychol.,* 1961, 74, 98–100.

LEIBOWITZ, H., & HEISEL, M. A. L'évolution de l'illusion de Ponzo en fonction de l'âge. *Arch. de Psychologie,* 1958, 36, 328–331.

LEIBOWITZ, H., WASKOW, I., LOEFFLER, N., & GLASER, F. Intelligence level as a variable in the perception of shape. *Quart. J. exp. Psychol.,* 1959, 11, 108–112.

MCMURRAY, J. G. Visual perception in exogenous and endogenous mentally retarded children. *Amer. J. ment. Defic.,* 1953–54, 58, 659–663.

MARK, H. J. Studies in perception in brain-injured children. Unpublished doctoral dissertation, Johns Hopkins Univer., Sch. Hyg. Publ. Hlth, 1955.

MARK, H. J., MEIER, P., & PASAMANICK, B. Variability of critical flicker fusion thresholds in brain-injured children. *A.M.A. Arch. Neurol. Psychiat.,* 1958, 80, 682–688.

MARK, H. J., & PASAMANICK, B. Asynchronism and apparent movement thresholds in brain-injured children. *J. consult. Psychol.,* 1958, 22, 173–177.

MERACHNIK, D. A. A study of color discrimination in adolescent groups of differing mental capacities. Unpublished doctoral dissertation, New York Univer., 1960.

MILLER, M. B., & SPITZ, H. H. Differences in reversal rate of ambiguous figures as a function of stimulus "meaningfulness" in a retarded group: an exploratory study. *Abstr. Peabody Stud. ment. Retarded,* 1955–60, 1, No. 63.

NEISSER, U. Response sequences and the hypothesis of the neural quantum. *Amer. J. Psychol.,* 1957, 70, 512–527.

OHWAKI, S. A developmental study of weight perception, especially on Charpentier's illusion. *Tohoku Psychol. Folia,* 1953, 13, 120–142.

PINTNER, R., & ANDERSON, MARGARET, M. The Muller-Lyer illusion with children and adults. *J. exp. Psychol.,* 1916, 1, 200–210.

POLLACK, M., & GORDON, E. The face-hand test in retarded and non-retarded emotionally disturbed children. *Amer. J. ment. Defic.,* 1960–61, 65, 758–760.

PRICE, A. C., & DEABLER, H. L. Diagnosis of organicity by means of the spiral aftereffect. *J. consult. Psychol.,* 1955, 19, 299–302.

REY, A. Contribution a l'étude de poids chex les anormaux. *Arch. Psychol., Geneve.* 1930, 22, 285–297.

ROSENBERG, S. Searching behavior in the retarded as a function of stimulus exposure conditions and IQ. *Amer. J. ment. Defic.,* 1961, 65, 749–752.

ROSS, A. O. Tactual perception of form by the brain injured. *J. abnorm. soc. Psychol.,* 1954, 49, 566–572.

RUDEL, RITA G., TEUBER, H., LIEBERT, R. S., & HALPERN, S. Localization of auditory midline and reactions to body tilt in brain-injured children. *J. nerv. ment. Dis.,* 1960, 131, 302–309.

SARASON, S. B., & GLADWIN, T. Psychological and cultural problems in mental subnormality: a review of research. *Genet. Psychol. Monogr.,* 1958, 57, 3–290.

SATTER, G., & CASSEL, R. H. Tactual-kinesthetic localization in the mentally retarded. *Amer. J. ment. Defic.,* 1954–55, 59, 652–657.

SCHLANGER, B. B. Results of varying presentation to brain-damaged children of an auditory word discrimination test. *Amer. J. ment. Defic.,* 1958–59, 63, 464–468.

SHAPIRO, M. B. An experimental investigation of the block design rotation effect. An analysis of a psychological effect of brain damage. *Brit. J. Med. Psychol.,* 1954, 27, 84–88.

SINGER, J. Personal and environmental determinants of perception in a size constancy experiment. Unpublished doctoral dissertation, Univer. of Pennsylvania, 1950.

SOLLEY, C. M., & MURPHY, G. *Development of the perceptual world.* New York: Basic Books, 1960.

SOLOMONS, HOPE C. A developmental study of tactual perception in normal and brain injured children. Unpublished doctoral dissertation, Boston Univer. Sch. Educ., 1957.

SPITZ, H. H. Neural satiation in the spiral aftereffect and similar movement aftereffects. *Percept. mot. Skills,* 1958, 8, 207–213.

SPITZ, H. H., & BLACKMAN, L. The Muller-Lyer illusion in retardates and normals. *Percept. mot. Skills,* 1958, 8, 219–225.

SPITZ, H. H., & BLACKMAN, L. A comparison of mental retardates and normals on visual figural aftereffects and reversible figures. *J. abnorm. soc. Psychol.,* 1959, 58, 105–110.

SPITZ, H. H., & LIPMAN, R. Some parameters in the perception of the spiral aftereffect. *Percept. mot. Skills,* 1959, 9, 81.

SPITZ, H. H., & LIPMAN, R. Reliability and intercorrelations of individual differences on visual and kinesthetic aftereffects. *Percept. mot. Skills,* 1960, 10, 159–166.

SPITZ, H. H., & LIPMAN, R. Some effects of spacing, massing and rest on the rate of Necker cube reversals. Paper read at East. Psychol. Ass., New York, 1960.

SPITZ, H. H., & LIPMAN, R. Kinesthetic figural aftereffects in mental retardates and normals. *J. abnorm. soc. Psychol.,* 1961, 62, 686–687.

SPIVACK, G. Perceptual attitude, motivation and their interaction in a size constancy situation. Unpublished doctoral dissertation, Univer. of Pennsylvania, 1954.

SPIVACK, G., & LEVINE, M. The spiral aftereffect and reversible figures as measures of brain damage and memory. *J. Pers.,* 1957, 25, 767–778.

SPIVACK, G., & LEVINE, M. Spiral aftereffects and measures of satiation in brain-injured and normal subjects. *J. Pers.,* 1959, 27, 211–227.

SPIVACK, G., & LEVINE, M. Illusions, aftereffects and perceptual judgments in brain damage. *Rep. nat. Inst. Hlth,* M-2724, 1961.

STEVENSON, H. W., & ZIGLER, E. F. Discrimination learning and rigidity in normal and feebleminded individuals. *J. Pers.,* 1957, 25, 699–711.

SWANSON, R. Perception of simultaneous tactual stimulation in defective and normal children. *Amer. J. ment. Defic.,* 1956–57, 61, 743–754.

TEUBER, H. L., & RUDEL, RITA G. Behavior after cerebral lesions in children and adults. *Cerebral Palsy Bull.,* in press.

TRUSS, C. V., & ALLEN, R. M. Duration of the spiral aftereffect in cerebral palsy: an exploratory study. *Percept. mot. Skills,* 1959, 9, 216–218.

VERPLANCK, S., COLLIER, G. H., & COTTON, J. W. Non-independence of successive responses in measurements of the visual threshold. *J. exp. Psychol.*, 1952, 44, 273–282.

WERNER, H., & STRAUSS, A. A.   Causal factors in low performance. *Amer. J. ment. Defic.*, 1940–41, 45, 213–218.

WERNER, H., & STRAUSS, A. A.   Pathology of figure-background relation in the child. *J. abnorm. soc. Psychol.*, 1941, 36, 236–248.

WERNER, H., & THUMA, B. D.   Critical flicker-frequency in children with brain injury. *Amer. J. Psychol.*, 1942, 55, 394–399.

WERNER, H., & THUMA, B. D.   A deficiency in the perception of apparent motion in children with brain injury. *Amer. J. Psychol.*, 1942, 55, 58–67.

WHITE, R. P.   Face-hand test responses of psychotic and mentally defective patients: the relation of age to sensory errors in chronic patients. *A.M.A. Arch. Neurol. Psychiat.*, 1957, 77, 120–125.

16

LANGUAGE AND COMMUNICATION OF MENTAL DEFECTIVES

Joseph E. Spradlin[1]

INTRODUCTION

The term "language," as commonly used, refers to a conglomeration of events ranging from gestures to hieroglyphics. However, within the present context language will refer to the speech and gestures of a speaker and to the responses to speech and gestures made by a listener. The term "speaker" refers to a person who makes either a speech or a gestural response. The term "listener" refers to the person who responds to either a speech or a gestural response.

Communication simply refers to language which is interpersonal. Ordinarily communication involves verbal exchange; however, it need not. Communication can be one way, as in the case of commands. The response of the listener need not be immediate for communication to occur. For example, a speaker may tell his listener, "When you go to the grocery store, bring me a pack of cigarettes." Usually the listener will make a verbal response to such a request, but he might not. However, if at a later time the listener brought the speaker the package of cigarettes, then communication would have occurred.

In view of the above statement the reader might expect a discussion of speech, gestures, the listener's reaction to speech and gestures (language comprehension), and the various interactions of speaker-listener behavior. Actually, the state of language research in the area of mental deficiency

[1] The author is field director for the Parsons Research Project, which is jointly sponsored by the Bureau of Child Research at the University of Kansas and the Parsons State Hospital and Training Center. The Parsons Research Project is supported in part by NIMH grant MH111. The author is very much indebted to members of the Project staff for every phase of development of the chapter and especially to Mrs. Ruth Staten for typing the manuscript.

allows for no such discussion. Research into language and communication has been confined primarily to the study of speech. Systematic studies of the gestures or of the language comprehension of mental defectives are, in the main, absent. For this reason a disproportionate amount of space is given to speech of mental defectives while references to other language events are sparse. An area obviously related to language is hearing. However, since a complete chapter is devoted to sensory disorders, hearing will not be discussed in this chapter.

Measurement considerations

Quantification of language can be considered as a process in which language responses are sampled, classified, and counted. While language might be sampled in many different situations, the language responses of mental defectives have most frequently been sampled in a dyadic situation with an adult examiner. This fact presents no particular problem if these langauge responses are representative of those about which one generalizes. However, if samples of language responses obtained in such dyadic test situations are not representative, what appears to be a body of knowledge about the characteristics of the language of mental defectives may be valid only for mental defectives in test situations. In other words, the body of knowledge may have limited applicability. This is a problem which those who study language should consider seriously.

Regardless of how language responses are sampled, the problem of classification arises. Certain classifications such as gesture versus vocal responses can be made on the basis of the physical characteristics of the responses alone. Other classifications involve some type of evaluation of the response. Evaluative classifications always involve a comparison between the language response to be classified and other language responses.

One system of evaluation is based on the comparison of the subject's response with the responses of a normative population to a similar situation. If the subject's response is commonly given by individuals of a normative group, it is classified as "correct" or "appropriate." If the subject's response occurs quite infrequently, it may be classified as incorrect or inappropriate. When the basis for classification resides in the frequency with which the response is encountered in a normative group, the criteria for correctness or appropriateness are entirely independent of the subject. It makes no difference how consistently the subject emits a given response in a situation; what is critical is how frequently the norm group responds in that manner. Thus, the fact that a subject consistently substitutes the sound "g" for "d" in the word "doll" does not make the response "goll" any more correct if such a substitution occurs infrequently in the norm group.

In other systems of evaluation the consistency with which a subject makes a given response in a situation is an important classification determinant. This is true with reference to the concept of intelligibility. Intelligibility can be specified in terms of a two-person situation in which a listener is required to perform some task on the basis of the language behavior of the speaker whose intelligibility is to be assessed. The more accurately the listener performs the task (such as repeating or carrying out instructions), the more intelligible is the language behavior of the speaker. Initially the similarity or dissimilarity of the language responses of the speaker and persons with whom the listener ordinarily interacts (normative group) is a critical determiner of the listener's behavior. However, if the listener experiences the speaker's language behavior in many contexts repeatedly, the consistency with which the speaker uses particular language responses becomes critical. That is, even though a given language response such as "goll" may be extremely rare or nonexistent in a norm group, if the subject consistently makes this response when confronted with a picture of a doll and never uses it in response to other pictures, the word "goll" will become completely intelligible to the listener. In short, the frequency with which a speaker emits a response in a specific range of situations relative to the frequency with which he emits the response in other situations, in part, determines the intelligibility of the response for a listener.

Probably such classifications as adequate-inadequate and meaningful-non-meaningful can also be analyzed according to frequency principles.

Some language measures such as sentence length and type-token ratio appear at first glance to be based primarily on the physical dimensions of the responses. However, when one looks more closely he sees that sentence length and type-token ratio are based on how closely certain sounds (words) and certain larger speech units (sentences) approximate the sounds and speech units of the community at large (norm group). Verb-adjective ratio and other ratios of one component of speech to another have the same basis.

Once language responses have been classified, obtaining the various language measures becomes a problem of counting and statistical manipulation. Some scores are simply the sum of all of a certain type of response. For example, an articulation score is the sum of either all of the correct or incorrect responses to the items of the test situation. The type-token ratio is simply the ratio of different response words to the total number of words in a fixed number of responses.

It is evident from the previous discussion that the study of language has involved intensive use of human instruments. When such human instruments are used to quantify language in an experimental or survey study, several serious problems arise. First, there is a possibility of differences between individuals in the way they score or rate subjects on many language measures. Differences may show up in low reliability between examiners; i.e., they may tend to rank subjects differently. On the other hand, differences may not show up on reliability, but may show up as an individual constant—examiners may score subjects so that they maintain the same ranks, but one examiner may systematically score subjects higher or lower than other examiners. For example, Siegel (1962) compared the results of four articulation examiners (two experienced and two inexperienced) for articulation scores on the Templin-Darley 50 Item Articulation Test. All examiners administered the test to the same sample of mentally defective children. Reliability between examiners for number of correct items was high (.80 to .99). However, 16 out of 18 comparisons between examiners yielded significant differences for the mean number of correct responses. The problem of examiners' differences is not serious if the researcher incorporates procedures in his research for maintaining high examiner reliability and does not confound examiner effects with the variables to be investigated.

Second, if reliability and equivalence data are to be useful in evaluating human instruments, then precautions must be taken to assure independence of observation. If two persons are rating in a situation and one person can respond not only to the situation being rated but also to the other observer's behavior, there is a high probability that reliability and equivalence data will show much greater similarily of ratings than if ratings are made independently.

Third, the hypotheses and beliefs of the human instrument may affect the results obtained. Studies by Azrin, Holz, Ulrich, and Goldiamond (1960) and Rosenthal, Fode, Friedman, and Vikan (1960) have shown that the results obtained by student experimenters are in part a function of what they are told will happen in the experiment. One may question whether or not generalization from students to experimenters is justifiable. However, Wilson may be quite correct when he says, "No human being is even approximately free from these subjective influences; the honest and enlightened investigator devises the experiment so that his own prejudices cannot influence the result, only the naive or dishonest claim that their own objectivity to a sufficient safeguard" (Wilson, 1952, p. 44). In some experimental studies this problem can be overcome by keeping the person making ratings or measurements ignorant of the identity of subjects in the various treatment and control groups. In other experiments it is impossible to keep these identities from the person making the ratings or measurements. In such cases experimenter bias may be minimized by keeping the person or persons making the measurements ignorant of the experimental hypothesis.

Fourth, the same human instrument may record or rate the same behavior differently over time. For example, if a person is to count the intelligible and unintelligible responses of a mentally defective child, the first time the child says something like "Gi e ga" he will probably record it as unintelligible. However, if he consistently hears the child make this response while reaching for a doll in another person's hands, he will very likely record the response as intelligible. This could lead to very misleading conclusions if the experimental hypothesis involved changes in the intelligibility of children's speech over time or trials. Once again, the problem presented is far from insurmountable. The language of the subject can be filmed or tape-recorded. These films or recordings can be broken into time segments, and these segments can be randomly presented to the person who rates, counts, or records them. Thus, systematic biases as a function of changes in the human instrument can be avoided.

Fifth, if the human instrument is to record or transcribe the language of the subject, systematic distortions may be included in the record. In a transcription it is assumed that there is a point-to-point relationship between the language of the subject and the transcription system of the recorder. When one is dealing with the language of severely defective persons, this is very unlikely. When there is not a point-to-point relationship between subjects' language and the transcription system, parts of the subjects' language must be omitted or distorted so that it fits the transcription system. Most of the transcription systems currently used were developed to transcribe conventional language; so transcriptions of subjects' language responses are probably more often distorted in the direction of conventionality. Thus, "Gi e ga" becomes "Gi me gol" or "Give me the doll." The writer knows of no way to avoid this problem. However, the use of the International Phonetics Alphabet should greatly decrease this source of distortion since the International Phonetics Alphabet codes isolated speech sounds rather than meaningful words, phrases, and sentences.

Finally, when human instruments are used to record, classify, or count language responses within a therapy or experimental session, different treatments may introduce systematic bias into the measurement even if the person doing the recording is unaware of the experimental hypothesis. For example, Ezell (1960) did a language training study with mentally defective children with extremely limited speech. There were three treatment methods. One involved telling the therapists to use whatever techniques they liked to get the children to talk. Therapists of a second treatment method were told to stimulate the children by naming objects and to reward each child's response by praising the child or imitating the response. The therapists of a third group were told to respond to each vocal response by praising the child or repeating the child's response. They were to initiate no activity. Analyses of tape recordings showed that therapists of the first two groups seldom repeated the child's response, while most of the responses of the therapists of the third group were repetitions. Ezell had observers count three classes of responses for each child—noise, one word, and sentences. Had the observers recorded more one-word and sentence responses for group three than for the other two groups, the results would have been difficult to interpret. One would have had to ask whether the differences were a function of children's responses or of additional cues provided by the imitative responses of the therapist.

While there are other important methodological problems, such as the selection of a representative sample of subjects and the use of adequate control, these are common to all behavioral research and will not be given special discussion here. Nevertheless, in the evaluation of language research these factors will be taken into account.

LANGUAGE RESEARCH WITH MENTAL DEFECTIVES

The review of language research with mental defectives will cover (1) the development of language measurements, (2) the prevalence of language deficiency among mentally defective populations, (3) the relationship of language and nonlanguage variables, (4) the effect of environmental manipulation on languages, and (5) the effect of manipulation of language behavior on nonlanguage behavior.

Development of language measures

It seems quite likely that the science of language will proceed no more rapidly than the development of language measures. The development of language measures to be used with mentally defective persons has been characterized by an increase in the objectivity and precision of traditional speech measures and the development of new language measures based on behavior theory and psychological concepts of language. Mecham (1955) provided techniques for standardized presentation of stimuli for the measurement of articulation, auditory discrimination, and auditory memory. His procedure for measuring articulation consisted of 10 consonants, diphthongs, and vowels which were tested in 10 syllables constructed according to procedures used in the Bell Telephone Laboratories for developing articulation items. The syllables were recorded on magnetic tape and played back to the subject through earphones. Subjects' responses were tape-recorded and presented to a panel of judges for transcription. The test-retest reliability for ten 9- to 15-year-old institutionalized mental defectives with IQs between 55 and 85 was .92.

The stimulus materials for Mecham's sound discrimination measure consisted of 86 cards. Three pictures were mounted on each card. While viewing the pictures, the subject was presented three tape-recorded words through earphones. One of the words was the name of one picture. The other two words were acoustically similar to the names of the other two pictures. For example, the words "feet, fun, money" might be presented while the subject viewed pictures of a seat, sun, and money. Pointing to the picture of money constituted a correct response. The odd-even reliability was .95 for thirty-one 9- to 18-year-old institutionalized mental defectives with IQs between 41 and 81.

The auditory digit memory span test consisted of 16 items. There were four items at each of four levels of difficulty—2-, 3-, 4-, and 5-digit items. Only single syllable digits were selected for item construction. These were randomly drawn with two exceptions. No digit could appear twice in the same item, and no digit could follow a digit which preceded it in the Arabic numerical system. The items were randomly presented to the subject through earphones from a tape recording. The digits within an item were separated by a 1-second pause, and items were separated by a 10-second pause. The odd-even reliability for 31 mentally defective children was .95.

In addition to his work on standard presentation of items for the three measures, Mecham used the cards of the Children's Apperception Test to obtain samples of speech from which such measures as type-token ratio and mean sentence length could be obtained. The subjects' speech responses were tape-recorded and transcribed. The test-retest reliability for type-token ratio and mean sentence length was .14 and .46, respectively, for the ten 9- to 15-year-old mentally defective children with IQs between 55 and 85.

The correlation between the auditory discrimination and auditory memory span tests was .50 for twenty-nine 9- to 18-year-old mentally defective children. None of the other correlations among the five language variables were significant.

Lassers and Low (1960) developed measures of speech and language which were based on a conception of languages as a social process. The measures of the scale, the San Francisco Inventory of Communicative Effectiveness (SFICE), were derived from tape recordings of a child's performance in a standardized interview situation. Judges rated the tape recording of the child's response to the interview on immediacy, frequency, enthusiasm, involvement, ease in social situations, understandability, articulation, average length of response, appropriateness, complexity of ideation, and overall communicativeness.

The examiners who administered the SFICE had participated in the development of the test, had used the test with 25 or more mentally retarded· children, and had administered the final form to several children to establish uniformity of procedures. The judges were given a series of intensive training sessions in which the criteria for evaluation were studied and discussed. The scale was then used in judging a series of pilot tapes. When agreement "appeared to be high," judges rated 180 pre- and postrecorded samples from 90 noninstitutionalized mentally retarded children (CA 7 to 15 years; IQ 40 to 79). Judges rated the first 25 samples and submitted these for statistical recording. Then they compared samples and analyzed and discussed their disagreements. This type of review was also made after 75 and 125 samples had been obtained. Ratings of samples obtained from 37 subjects were analyzed to determine interjudge reliability. The median reliability between judges ranged from .61 on appropriateness to .89 on overall communicativeness.

Measures of sentence complexity, grammatical complexity, and length of response were taken from transcriptions of the subject's responses to nine standard situations or questions. Experts in the field of English usage obtained these measures from the transcripts.

Dunn (1958) published the results of his work with the Peabody Picture Vocabulary Test (PPVT). The PPVT can be considered an auditory word comprehension test consisting of 150 plates with four pictures to each plate. For each plate the examiner says a word and the child is to indicate to which picture the word refers. The test has been administered to 4,012 children between the ages 2 years, 6 months and 18 years. Prior to age 5, norms are provided for each 6-month age group. After age 5, norms are provided for each year. Both age equivalent scores (vocabulary age) and standard scores (vocabulary quotients) are provided. Alternative form reliabilities of the PPVT range from .67 at the 6-year level to .84 at the 17- and 18-year levels. Since the procedures used for calculating reliability partials out most of the variance associated with age, such correlations are impressive. The alternative form reliability was .76 for 130 noninstitutionalized 7- to 15-year-old mentally retarded children whose IQs on the Revised Stanford-Binet Form L (RSB-L) ranged from 50 to 80. Alternative form reliability of the PPVT was .87 for 364 noninstitutionalized 6- to 16-year-old mental defectives with IQs between 30 and 50.

Dorothea McCarthy (1959) developed language evaluation procedures as a part of a more complete psychological evaluation battery. The langauge section of the battery includes five subscores: (1) pointing to pictured objects, (2) picture naming, (3) vocabulary, (4) oral language usage, and (5) intelligibility. The first three scores are obtained from tests. The last two are based on examiner ratings of the child's speech heard during the test situation. In addition to the measures classified as language measures by McCarthy, there are also three *conceptual measures* which the present writer would classify as language measures. These are controlled verbal association (how many "things to ride on" a subject can name in 20 seconds), verbal absurdities, and opposite analogies. The test has been given to 96 institutionalized mentally defective children (10 at age 6, 20 at age 8, 21 at age 10, 21 at age 12, and 24 at age 14). Testing was done by two experienced clinicians.

An overall correlation of .82 was found between the weighted language and conceptual sections. Individual subscores in both the language and conceptual sections show an increase with CA and a relationship with the institutional categories of nontrainable, trainable, and educable. McCarthy did not present data concerning the correlation between the subscores of either the language or conceptual sections.

The development of measures by Lassers and Low, Mecham, and McCarthy was nontheoretical. In contrast to the nontheoretical approaches of these test constructors, Sievers (1955), Kirk and McCarthy (1958, 1961), and Spradlin (1960) have attempted to derive language evaluation procedures from learning models.

Sievers (1955) reported on her work with the Differential Language Facility Test (DLFT). Kirk and McCarthy (1958, 1961) used Sievers' work as a springboard for developing the Illinois Test of Psycholinguistic Abilities (ITPA). As was the case with Sievers' work, Kirk and McCarthy's rationale has been drawn primarily from the work of Osgood (1953, 1957). According to the rationale used in developing the ITPA there are two basic modes of input (visual and auditory) and two basic modes of output (vocal and gestural). There are two levels of organization—the automatic sequential and the representational; and there are three psycholinguistic processes—decoding, association, and encoding.

According to Kirk and McCarthy, at the automatic-sequential level of organization language is primarily imitative and sequential. At the representational level language is *meaningful*. For example, the child learns to say, "da da" in the presence of the appropriate stimulus.

Decoding, the authors state, refers to the ability to obtain *meaning* from visual and auditory stimuli. Association is the ability to manipulate linguistic symbols internally. It is a central process which is elicited by decoding and which in turn elicits expressive processes. Encoding is the sum of those abilities required to express ideas.

The current version of the ITPA consists of nine subtests designed to differentiate defects in (1) the three processes of communication, (2) the levels of language organization, and/or (3) the channels of language input or output:

Test 1. *Auditory Decoding* consists of a series of questions which can be answered by either a "yes" or "no" vocal or gestural response. For example, "Do airplanes fly?"

Test 2. *Visual Decoding* consists of a series of items presenting the child with a stimulus picture which is then removed. After the stimulus picture is removed the child is asked to point to the correct picture among a set of four pictures. The stimulus picture and the correct picture are semantically identified but physically different, i.e., a table knife and a jack knife.

Test 3. *Auditory Vocal Association* consists of a series of analogies such as, "Father is big, baby is _____."

Test 4. *Visual-Motor Association.* On each item the child is presented a single picture stimulus and a set of four other pictures, one of which is associated with the stimulus picture. He is asked to choose the picture which is similar to the stimulus picture.

Test 5. *Vocal Encoding.* The child is shown a series of objects and is asked to "Tell me all about this." The score consisted of the number of "discrete concepts enumerated."

Test 6. *Motor Encoding.* Objects or pictures are shown to the subject and for each object or picture he is asked to "Show me what we should do with this." The subject is to make the appropriate motion.

Test 7. *Auditory-Vocal Automatic Ability.* This is primarily a grammar test. For example, the child is shown a picture of a ball and a picture of two bats and the examiner says, "Here is a ball. Here are two _____." The child should complete the sentence with the plural form of the noun. The test increases in difficulty by requiring use of increasingly less frequent English inflections.

Test 8. *Auditory Vocal Sequential Ability* is assessed by a digit repetition test. Digits are repeated at the rate of one every 2 seconds, and the child is allowed two trials.

Test 9. *Visual Motor Sequential Ability.* This task requires the subject to duplicate a sequence of pictures or designs which have been presented by the examiner and then removed.

Kirk and McCarthy report that the latest revision of the ITPA has been standardized on 700 children between the ages of $2\frac{1}{2}$ and 9 years. However, to date these data have not been published.

Spradlin (1960) developed procedures for sampling language (Parsons Language Sample PLS) based primarily on the system provided by Skinner (1957). The PLS has two subsections, vocal and nonvocal. The vocal subsection consists of (1) the tact subtest, which samples picture and object naming; (2) the echoic subtest, which is a series of items requesting the subject to repeat sentences and numbers of varying degrees of complexity; and (3) the intraverbal subtest, which consists of items ranging from simple questions, such as, "What do we do when we are hungry?" to

"In what way are an egg and a seed alike?" The nonvocal section consists of (1) the echoic gesture subtest, which is composed of items which evaluate the child's ability to imitate a motor act; (2) the comprehension subtest, which consists of items in which the examiner directs the child to complete motor tasks by both vocal and gestural instructions; and (3) the intraverbal gesture subtest, which consists of questions which can be answered by either a vocal or gestural response. Some of the questions of the intraverbal gesture subtest, such as "Where is your ear?" have a high probability of eliciting gestures. Others, such as, "What do you do with a handkerchief?" are much less apt to elicit a gestural response—only gestures are scored.

The PLS has been administered to 275 institutionalized 8- to 15-year-old mental defectives. Of these 275 subjects 188 scored on the vocal section and 223 scored on the nonvocal section. Four examiners, without previous psychometric training, administered from 58 to 83 tests each. Statistical analyses indicated no differences between the score distributions of the four examiners beyond chance expectation. Odd-even reliability for the subtests ranged from .85 on the intraverbal gesture subtest to .96 on the intraverbal subtest. Correlations between the tact, echoic, intraverbal, comprehension, and echoic gasture ranged from .62 to .82. Correlations between the intraverbal gesture and the other five subtests ranged from —.02 to .32. Such correlations would indicate that the five subtests of the PLS are sampling highly related behavior while the intraverbal gesture subtest is sampling behavior which is quite unrelated to them. The correlation between the vocal and nonvocal sections was .64.

Test-retest correlations on 15 subjects tested by the same examiner after 2 to 5 months and 15 subjects tested by different examiners after 2 to 5 months ranged from .64 on the echoic gesture to .99 on the intraverbal. There appeared to be no difference in the correlations as a function of whether the same examiner or a different examiner administered the test and retest.

Several types of validity have been obtained on the PLS. There have been clear-cut differences on such measures as number of responses, type-token ratio, and total number of words spoken in an experimental session when children have been classified into high and low groups on the basis of the test's vocal section (Rosenberg, Spradlin, & Mabel, 1961; Siegel, 1963; Harkins, 1961; Spradlin & Rosenberg, 1959).

Second, five cottage aides were asked to rank the children of their respective cottages on speech and nonspeech communication. The five correlations between the aides' inverted speech ranks and the PLS vocal section score ranged from .33 to .86 with a median correlation of .62. The five correlations between inverted aide ranks for nonspeech communication and the PLS nonvocal section ranged from .18 to .80 with a median correlation of .40.

Finally, the vocal subsection has been correlated with the percentage of intelligible speech emitted by 9- to 12-year-old severely retarded children in a small group setting (three children and one adult). Instances of both intelligible and unintelligible speech during a 15-minute session for each child were recorded three times during a 6-week period by each of two examiners. The percentage of total intelligible instances of speech to total vocalization emitted correlated .51 with scores on the vocal section of the PLS.

The ITPA and the PLS are both based on learning models; however, there are considerable differences between the rationales for the two tests. The rationale for the ITPA assumes that the test items are measuring implicit processes within the person and that the language responses are merely effects of these processes. Since the implicit processes are not observable independently of the language responses, the rationale involves problems of dualism and circularity. The authors often slip outside of their "theoretical" system as when they say, "Encoding is the sum of those abilities required to express *ideas* in words or gestures." In this statement the term "idea" is extraneous to the system. Moreover, while the authors claim to be operational in their definitions of constructs, such constructs as "representational level" and "association" cannot be reduced to operations. In contrast, the PLS is based on a descriptive model which assumes only that observable language responses are being sampled and evaluated in various situations. Its importance as a measure does not rest on an inference concerning implied internal processes but on an empirical relationship between scores based on language sampled in a test situation and language external to the test situation.

The development of measures of language represents a step forward in language research with mental defectives. Yet the language measures just described leave much to be desired. In most cases the use of an instrument has been limited to defectives of a single institution or geographical location. Thus, scores are not too meaningful outside the contexts in which the measures were initially developed. Age equivalent norms based on groups of normal children, as have been provided by Dunn for the PPVT, would increase the utility of these measures.

Language has been sampled and evaluated in only a very limited number of social situations. This situation in which the language of mentally defective children has been measured has almost inevitably involved an adult in a highly contrived or controlled situation. The child's behavior in this situation may or may not be representative or predictive of behavior in other situations.

All the measures discussed previously are cross sectional. That is, while they sample learned behavior they do not allow for any estimate of current speed of learning or acquisition. Measures of speed of acquisition of language and language comprehension might be quite useful in predicting improvement in therapy or training.

Most of the investigators have been quite concerned with the standard presentation of stimulus materials or test items. Mecham (1955) provided a procedure for presenting stimuli which eliminates inconsistency by excluding the examiner. This procedure is ideal insofar as it is completely replicable. However, it is an empirical question whether language responses obtained by the nonsocial presentation of stimuli will be predictive of the individual's language responses in a social setting. In contrast to Mecham's procedure, most investigators have attempted to assure standardized presentation of items by the selection and extensive training of examiners.

All the measures except those developed by Mecham (1955) and Lassers and Low (1960) rest on the evaluation or judgment made by the test examiner. In both studies tape recordings were made of the children's speech and were rated by judges. This procedure reduces experimental design problems in an experimental therapy or treatment study since pre- and posttherapy tapes from experimental and control groups can be randomized and presented to judges who are unaware of the identity of subjects, thus completely eliminating the effects of such variables as changes in examiner judgments and examiner bias. The procedures used for scoring non-tape-recorded measures do not allow for such purity in scoring pre- and post-responses. Moreover, test constructors have not been sufficiently concerned with examiner constants or biases. In most cases, after the examiners have been selected and trained, examiner equivalence has been assumed rather than evaluated. It is certainly an important consideration if comparisons are to be made on groups tested by different examiners.

Prevalence of language disorders among mental defectives

There have been no comprehensive studies of the total range of language deficits in mentally defective populations. Most investigators have focused primarily on speech deficits. As early as 1915 Wallin surveyed the children in special classes for mental defectives of St. Louis to determine the percentage of children with speech problems (Wallin, 1949). He found that 26 per cent of the special-class children had speech defects as compared with only about 3 per cent of the regular school children. Since Wallin's early study numerous surveys have been carried out to determine the prevalence of speech defects among institutionalized mental defectives (Kennedy, 1930; Lewald, 1932; Sirkin & Lyons, 1941; Sachs, 1951; Schlanger, 1953; Gens, 1951; Schlanger & Gottsleben, 1957). The prevalence of speech defects found among a wide range of undifferentiated institutionalized mental defectives ranged from 57 per cent found by Sachs to 79 per cent found by Schlanger and Gottsleben.

Lubman (1955) and Schneider and Vallon (1954) surveyed speech problems among severely retarded children in parent-sponsored day schools. Lubman found that 82 per cent of her sample had speech defects as did 72 per cent of the Schneider and Vallon sample.

Donovan (1957) surveyed the children of the classes for Children with Retarded Mental Development in New York and found that only 8 per cent of the children with IQs between 50 and 75 manifested speech defects.

Certain investigators (Sirkin & Lyons, 1941; Bangs, 1942; Irwin, 1942; Sachs, 1951; Karlin & Strazzula, 1952; Schlanger & Gottsleben, 1957) have attempted to describe the type of speech manifested among mentally defective persons. The results of these studies are very difficult to interpret since the various investigators used different systems for classifying speech defects or speech characteristics and since criteria for such classifications are, in the main, unspecified. For example, Sirkin and Lyons used such classifications as (1) no speech, (2) defective phonation or sound substitution, (3) monophasia, (4) lalling, (5) lisping, and (6) organic speech disorders. On the other hand, Irwin merely classified sounds emitted by the child as labial, postdental, and glottal and compared the relative frequency of occurrence of each of these sounds with that occurring in normal adult speech. Schlanger and Gottsleben's study of 516 institutionalized children is perhaps the most nearly adequate study of the percentage of various types of speech defects among the total undifferentiated population as well as the percentage of the various types of speech defects among diagnostic groups. Their results are shown in Table 16-1 below, which was taken from their article in the *Journal of Speech and Hearing Disorders*.

The studies of speech defects among mentally defective persons leave much to be desired in terms of measurement considerations and precise descriptions of experimental populations. Nevertheless, the following conclusions seem justified:

1. An extremely high percentage (57 to 72) of institutionalized mental defectives have speech defects.

2. An equal or higher percentage (72 to 82) of severely retarded children in parent-sponsored day schools have speech defects.

3. Far fewer (8 to 26 per cent) of the children in special classes of the public schools have speech defects.

4. Articulation and voice problems constitute the largest percentage of speech difficulties among both mentally defective and nonmentally defective children.

Relationship between language measures and other variables

The research on language of mentally defective persons has been characterized by attempts to relate language measures to other variables. Numerous studies have investigated the relationship between language measures and sex, age, intelligence, environment, and diagnostic classification.

Sex and language. Studies with normal children have shown a slight but rather consistent superiority of girls over boys in such language measures

TABLE 16-1

Speech defects in clinical types of mental retardates

Etiological classification	N	Articulation	%	Voice	%	Stutter	%	No speech
0 Undifferentiated	137	110	80	63	45	18	13	
1 Familial	64	42	66	14	22	6	10	
2 Mongolism	44	42	95	32	72	20	45	1
3–12 Organic	189	159	84	106	56	35	18	4
13 Mixed (F-O)	18	17	94	6	33	2	11	
14 Other forms	20	16	80	9	45	3	15	
15 Not mentally retarded	26	11	42	10	38	3	12	
No etiology	18	3	17	1	6	2	11	
Total	516	400	78	240	47	89	17	

as frequency of vocalization, onset of words, length of response, and vocabulary (McCarthy, 1954). This same trend occurs but is less consistent in the few studies among mentally defective populations. Sirkin and Lyons (1941) studied 1,427 female and 1,095 male defectives. Twenty per cent of the males had no speech as compared with fourteen per cent of the females. Of the persons who had speech 74 per cent of the males had defective speech. Only 51 per cent of the females had defective speech. Finally, 43 per cent of the females had normal speech as contrasted with 21 per cent for the males.

Goda and Griffith (1962) studied mean sentence length, percentage of complete sentences, percentage of complex sentences, structure variety, tense variety, and articulation in 35 female and 61 male high-grade mentally defective children between 13 and 21 years of age. A sample of vocal language behavior was elicited by presenting each subject with 25 pictures. Twelve pictures were presented individually; two sets of four and one set of five pictures were presented according to a narrative sequence. Articulation was measured with the Henja Developmental Articulation Reference Schedule. A significant correlation of .40 was found between tense variety and sex. All other correlations between sex and language measures were nonsignificant.

Spradlin (1960) reported data which allowed for comparison of 93 boys and 94 girls on the nine measures of the PLS. The nature of the population has been discussed previously in the section on the development of new test instruments. Girls were superior in their performance on the echoic measure (digit and sentence repetition). Boys were superior in their performance on the intraverbal gesture measure. There were no significant differences between boys and girls on the other seven measures of the PLS.

Studies comparing institutionalized male and female subjects on variables such as speech and language are subject to a severe limitation. If differences between the sexes are found, they could be due to any one of several variables such as genetic factors, boys' greater weight and greater proneness to injury at birth, differences between parental reactions to boys and girls, and differences in factors determining institutionalization for the two sexes.

Age and language. There would seem to be little doubt that in the normal population chronological age (CA) and language are related in a nonlinear fashion. That is, prior to age 6 there would be a high relation between language measures and CA. However, depending on the language measure, the correlation between CA and language after age 10 would probably decrease rapidly to almost zero. Since most of the correlations between language measures and CA have been on mental defectives over age 8 it is not surprising that the correlations found are small. Schlanger (1953) correlated CA with articulation, auditory memory, and auditory sound discrimination for 74 institutionalized children between 8 and 16 years of age with RSB-L IQs above 40. The correlations between CA and articulation, CA and auditory memory, and CA and sound discrimination were .30, .07, and .38, respectively.

Badt (1958) studied the relationship between the abstraction level of definitions given by institutionalized mental defectives and their CA. The abstraction level was determined by administering the vocabulary test of the RSB-L and then scoring the test according to the system illustrated below.

Word	Level	Example	Score
Orange	Abstract	"A fruit"; "a color"	5
Orange	Use	"To eat"	3
Orange	Description	"It's round and yellow"	1

The correlation between CA and abstraction level was .34, which is statistically significant but accounts for only a minor part of the variance.

Goda and Griffith (1962) correlated CA with mean sentence length, percentage of complete sentences, percentage of complex sentences, structural variety, tense variety, and articulation score. They found that CA correlated —.32 with tense variety and .32 with articulation. CA did not correlate significantly with any of the four other measures.

Spradlin (1960) found that for 187 mental defectives age 8 to 16, correlations between CA and the nine language measures of the PLS ranged from .00 on the intraverbal gestures measure to .32 on the intraverbal measure. Once again, the correlations indicate that CA and language measures have only a very small percentage of variance in common for the institutional population studied.

Intelligence and language. Numerous investigators have studied the relationship between language measures and intelligence measures among normal children (McCarthy, 1954; Winitz, in press). Much effort has also been given to determining the relationship between intelligence measures and language measures among mentally defective populations.

Town (1912) was one of the first investigators to become interested in the relationship between language and intelligence. The data she presents indicate a rather clear relationship between levels of mental deficiency based on the Binet scales and the development of such language responses as understanding gestures, imitating gestures, use of gestures, understanding of words, repetition of words, use of words, and use of sentences. She also found a regular progression of both vocabulary usage and understanding from mental ages 3 through 6.

Sirkin and Lyons (1941) reported a rather clear-cut relationship between percentage of subjects with speech defects and categories of mental deficiency based on IQ. Thirty-one per cent of 90 institutionalized subjects with IQs above 69 had defects. Forty-seven per cent of 550 "morons" had defects. Seventy-four per cent of 592 "imbeciles" had defective speech. Finally, all subjects classified as idiots had defective speech. The intelligence measure on which the subjects were classified was not given.

Karlin and Strazzula (1952) related IQ to age at onset of babbling, words, and sentences for 50 mentally defective patients of children's outpatient clinics. The mean age of onset for all three measures differed between the three IQ groups—15 to 25, 26 to 50, and 51 to 70. However, since measures of variance are not provided, it is impossible to tell whether these differences are significant.

Several investigators (Bangs, 1942; Schlanger, 1953; Mecham, 1955; Goda & Griffith, 1962; Riello, 1958; Lassers & Low, 1960) have studied the relationship between articulation and intelligence measures. As can be seen in Table 16-2 the four studies which correlated articulation measures and intelligence measures for institutional populations show correlations ranging from .41 to .58 between articulation and IQ and correlations ranging from .33 to .52 between articulation and MA. Riello obtained a .16 correlation between articulation and IQ and a .31 correlation between articulation and MA for 100 public school children with IQs between 45 and 81.

Mecham reported a correlation of .11 between auditory discrimination and IQ. However, Schlanger reports only a .71 correlation between auditory discrimination and MA. The data reported by Schlanger and Mecham indicate a relatively small relationship between auditory memory and IQ (.29) and between auditory memory and MA (.25) for institutionalized children between 8 and 16 years of age.

Horowitz correlated the PLS vocal, nonvocal, and total scores with the Wechsler Intelligence Scale for Children (WISC) Verbal, Performance, and Full Scale IQs. The results of this study indicated that the vocal section of the PLS was highly related to the WISC Verbal ($r = .75$). The PLS nonvocal section is apparently measuring something quite different from the WISC performance scale since the correlation was —.10. The PLS total score correlated .58 with the WISC full scale IQ.

Both the conceptual scale and the language scale of Dorothea McCarthy's test battery correlated .91 with IQ.

Nowhere is it more apparent than in the area of intelligence and language that a mass of data can lead to confusion rather than conceptual clarity. Few investigators have given serious consideration to the nature of the measures they were using. As an extreme example, in some cases the intelligence test is not even designated. Moreover, the studies have been conducted on very different populations with regard to CA and IQ. These differences in populations are important when one variable is being correlated with another.

Several types of intelligence measures have been used in the different studies. In the earliest study relating intelligence to language skill, Town used an early form of the Binet to classify groups. Sirkin and Lyons, Bangs, and Mecham did not indicate the intelligence tests used. Horowitz and Goda and Griffith correlated language measures with scores derived from Wechsler Intelligence scales. Karlin and Strazzula, Schlanger, and Riello used the RSB-L. In spite of the fact that many intelligence tests correlate highly with each other, the results would be more easily interpreted if the studies had used a single intelligence measure.

The interpretation of the various studies is made more difficult by the fact that two measures, IQ and MA, are yielded by the same test. If the CA range is very narrow or only persons older than 15 years of age are included, IQ and MA will yield similar correlations with a third variable since IQ is determined on the basis of a relationship between MA and CA. For example, if the intelligence test used is the RSB and the population is below 15 years

TABLE 16-2

Correlations between intelligence and language measures

Language measure	Investigator	Population	Intelligence test	IQ range	CA range, yr	Correlations IQ	Correlations MA
Articulation	Bangs, 1942	Institutionalized defectives	Not designated	Not designated	Not designated	.41	.33
	Schlanger, 1953	Institutionalized defectives	Revised Stanford-Binet	Above 40	8–16	.....	.37
	Mecham, 1955	Institutionalized defectives	Revised Stanford-Binet	45–81	9–18	.48	
	Goda & Griffith, 1962	Institutionalized defectives	Wechsler scales	45–85	13–21	.58	.52
	Riello, 1958	Public school children	Revised Stanford-Binet	45–80	8–15	.16	.31
Mean sentence length	Mecham, 1955	Institutionalized defectives	Not designated	45–81	9–18	.42	
Type-token ratio	Mecham, 1955	Institutionalized defectives	Not designated	45–81	9–18	−.04	
Structural variety	Goda & Griffith, 1962	Institutionalized defectives	Wechsler scales	45–85	13–21	.05	−.15
Tense variety	Goda & Griffith, 1962	Institutionalized defectives	Wechsler scales	45–85	13–21	.21	.12
Percentage complete sentences	Goda & Griffith, 1962	Institutionalized defectives	Wechsler scales	45–85	13–21	.23	.17
Percentage complicated sentences	Goda & Griffith, 1962	Institutionalized defectives	Wechsler scales	45–85	13–21	.08	−.02
Auditory discrimination	Schlanger, 1953	Institutionalized defectives	Revised Stanford-Binet	Above 40	8–16	.....	.71
	Mecham, 1955	Institutionalized defectives	Not designated	45–81	9–18	.11	
Auditory memory	Schlanger, 1953	Institutionalized defectives	Revised Stanford-Binet	Above 40	8–16	.....	.25
	Mecham, 1955	Institutionalized defectives	Not designated	45–81	9–18	.29	
PLS vocal	Horowitz	Institutionalized defectives	WISC verbal		8–16	.75	
PLS nonvocal	Horowitz	Institutionalized defectives	WISC performance		8–16	−.10	
PLS total	Horowitz	Institutionalized defectives	WISC performance		8–16	.58	
Language section	McCarthy, 1959	Institutionalized defectives	Mostly RSB	15–72	6–14	.....	.91
Conceptual section	McCarthy, 1959	Institutionalized defectives	Mostly RSB	15–72	6–14	.....	.91

of age, IQ = MA/CA. If CA is held constant, MA and IQ are perfectly correlated and will correlate equally with a third variable. However, if CA in a population below age 15 is allowed to vary, IQ and MA do not bear this perfect relationship and will yield different correlations with a third variable. Thus, the need for considering the means and variances for CA in the populations is of extreme importance. It is also important to know the ranges of MA or IQ as well as the ranges of language measures if correlations are to be interpreted since a restriction in the range of either the intelligence scores or the language scores will generally result in lower correlations than would be obtained if the ranges of both measures were unrestricted.

The language measures used range all the way from age of onset of babbling to variety in grammatical structure. Even when investigators theoretically were correlating the same language measure (articulation) with intelligence, they have used different tests of articulation and there is little information concerning the relationship between the articulation tests used.

The studies involving the relationship between intelligence and language have also involved serious conceptual problems. Both language and intelligence have been considered nonobservable hypothetical constructs. For example, Karlin and Strazzula (1952) defined language as follows: "Language is a psychic process centered in the cortex and in its broadest sense signifies the expression of thoughts and ideas" (p. 286). In writing of the intelligence test Terman and Merrill (1937) state, "It is a method which, to paraphrase an oft-quoted statement by Galton, attempts to obtain a general knowledge of the capacities of a subject by the sinking of shafts at critical points" (p. 461). This type of approach has led investigators into viewing their work as studies of nonobservable processes rather than as studies of the relationship between two sets of behaviors sampled in similar or different stimulus situations. If, instead of attempting to measure nonobservable implicit processes, investigators had given serious consideration to the operations involved in sampling language behavior and intelligence behavior, fewer and more meaningful studies might have been executed.

The investigator who looks at his measures from an operational point of view may be quite surprised to find that his test of intelligence and a test of language present the same kinds of stimuli, evaluate the same kinds of behavior, and classify the behavior on the same bases. If this is the case, he should not be surprised when the measures are highly correlated.

This same kind of analysis of two language measures might show them to be providing different kinds of stimuli, evaluating different responses, and classifying the responses on a different basis. In this case it might prove useful to evolve two separate constructs and to study the relation between these, while in the former it might prove profitable to collapse "intelligence" and "language" into a single construct.

It is, no doubt, apparent that only additional data can determine where constructs can be collapsed and where separate constructs need to be derived. However, the writer is suggesting that persons working in the area of language may find it more fruitful to develop measurement constructs on the basis of similarity and differences of stimuli presented, responses evaluated, and bases of evaluation rather than on the bases of conceptual systems relying heavily on inferred nonobservable processes or hypothetical constructs.

Anxiety and language. Goda and Griffith (1962) correlated scores on a modified form of the Children's Manifest Anxiety Scale (CMAS) with measures of articulation, sentence length, structural variety, tense variety, percentage of complete sentences, and percentage of complicated sentences. They report that they set the direction of all variables so that high scores indicate higher levels of development. Although unstated by the authors, the context of their article indicates that when this was done for the CMAS, scores that would have been high if the test had been scored in the customary manner were now low and vice versa. Thus correlations between Goda and Griffith's anxiety scores and other variables are in a reverse direction from the correlations which would have been obtained if the CMAS had been scored in the customary manner. All the correlations between anxiety and language measures were negative with the exception of the relationship between anxiety and articulation. However, only the correlation of $-.33$ between percentage of complete sentences and anxiety was significant. The authors construe the CMAS as a measure of the construct, drive. Goda and Griffith hypothesize that drive facilitates learning; thus language ability and the CMAS scores should be negatively correlated. As was previously stated, with the exception of the correlation between anxiety and articulation, the correlations were in the direction indicated by the hypothesis. However, the correlations were quite small and could have easily arisen by chance.

Organic condition and language. The organic-familial dichotomy of mental defectives has had its influence on the study of language behavior. One of the first studies to investigate differences in the language behavior of familial and organic defectives was conducted by Bijou and Werner (1945). They compared the vocabulary responses of 19 brain-injured mentally defective children with those obtained from 19 familial children matched on CA and IQ. The mean CA of the brain-injured group was 14 years, 5 months and 14 years for the familial group. The mean IQs were 68 for the brain-injured and 69 for the familials. The criteria for brain injury were (1) evidence in the developmental history of prenatal, natal, or postnatal injury to the brain; (2) absence of feeblemindedness in the immediate family; and (3) presence of neurological signs. The criteria for familial were (1) no indication of injury to the brain in the developmental history, (2) feeblemindedness in the immediate family, and (3) absence of neurological signs.

The experimental task involved administration of a vocabulary list of 57 words. The results indicated that brain-injured children defined more words correctly and gave superior definitions.

Gallagher (1957) administered Sievers' DLFT to 24 brain-injured and 24 familial children (classified on the basis of the Riggs & Rain system) who were matched on the basis of CA and Binet IQ. The mean CA was 11 years, 3 months for the brain-injured group and 10 years, 11 months for the familial group. The mean IQ was 49.9 for the former group and 52.4 for the latter. There were no significant differences between the two groups on total language performance. However, the familial group was significantly better on an object association test, visual form tracing, and on a vocal "close" test which required the child to fill in a verbal blank such as, "Daddy, _____ to work." The brain-injured group was superior on a picture series description test, nonsense grammatical mimicry subtest, speech sound mimicry, and object labeling.

Weatherwax and Benoit (1957) compared 25 organic children with visible neurological signs with 25 nonorganic children without visible neurological signs on word recall abstraction tasks. The organic group was between 9 years, 3 months and 15 years, 2 months (mean, 12 years, 4 months). The nonorganic group ranged from 7 years, 2 months to 14 years, 7 months (mean, 11 years, 11 months). The IQs of the organic group ranged from 37 to 73 (mean, 50), and the IQs of the nonorganic group ranged from 37 to 73 (mean, 52). The task involved showing the subject a series of 12 pictures in a modified random order and then having him recall as many of the pictures as possible. The 12 pictures were presented six times. The pictures could be placed into four distinct categories—objects used in bathing (soap, towel), objects used in smoking, domestic animals, and food objects. Abstraction was measured according to the tendency of a word to follow a word in the same class in the recall test. Both the organic and familial group showed a greater tendency for a word in the same class to follow each other than would be expected on the basis of chance. However, the two groups did not differ from each other. When 13 of the organic group were given an unspecified type of training, their abstraction scores were higher than 12 controls who received no such training.

Sievers and Rosenberg (1960) related test patterns on Sievers' DLFT to EEG patterns in a population of mentally defective children. All the children were diagnosed as having brain damage resulting from infections, birth injury, toxins, destruction of brain tissue due to hydrocephaly, postnatal trauma, and epilepsy. Children were classified into four groups on the basis of EEG patterns which were (1) grand mal, pure; (2) grand and petit mal, mixed; (3) hypothalamic, and (4) slowing. There were significant differences among the four groups for only 2 of 12 language measures— nonsense grammatical mimicry and vocal close grammar. In both cases the grand mal mixed group showed the largest deficit with the slowing group showing the least language deficit.

The research based on the brain-injured–non-brain-injured classification results in findings which are, at best, only suggestive. In most of the studies social variables were confounded with physiological variables in the delineation of the groups. For example, by definition no familial defective is subjected to the cultural influence of a father who is a bank president, a mother who is a college art instructor, and two siblings who lead their respective classes in academics, drama, music, and athletics. In view of such confounding, it is entirely possible that any differences between organic and nonorganic defectives are as much a function of different linguistic environments as of differences in central nervous tissue.

The study by Sievers and Rosenberg is less vulnerable to the above criticism since there is little likelihood that social variables are confounded with EEG patterns in a sample of brain-injured children.

Environment and language. The relationship between environmental variables and language has been subject to much speculation and some research. Skeels, Updegraff, Wellman, and Williams (1938) studied the language development of preschool-age children in an orphanage. They report that language quotients of children decreased over an 18-month period. Moreover, institutionalized children were inferior to noninstitutionalized children on vocabulary. Children who were placed in a preschool nursery program made higher scores on the vocabulary test than did children of a control group. However, the nursery program group did not show a statistically significant superiority over the control group on a general language measure. Spitz (1945–1946) reported that infants who were raised in a hospital environment in which they had little contact with adults were inferior in language development to infants raised in an institution where mothers or foster mothers were allowed to care for them. Goldfarb (1943, 1944, 1945–1946) reported similar effects of maternal deprivation in an institution for orphans. McCarthy (1954) reported that children of upper-middle-class families were more advanced in their verbal development than children from working-class families and that the amount of time spent in close contact with adults was related to children's vocabulary scores. Schlanger (1954), Badt (1958), and Lyle (1959) have all related environmental variables to language in mental defectives. Schlanger found that a group of 21 institutionalized mentally defective children were inferior in mean sentence length and number of words per minute when they were compared with a group of 21 special-class children with whom they had been individually matched on the bases of CA, IQ, MA, and articulation performance.

Schlanger gave the following possible explanations of the inferiority of institutionalized defectives:

1. Severance of family ties and emotional reactions to interpersonal relations
2. Lack of continued imitation of family models
3. Use of overt action as a substitute for speech
4. Association with subnormal peers which may do away with the need for communication
5. Lack of privacy and overstimulation
6. Lack of speech motivation due to too few challenges in the environment

Badt (1958) correlated abstraction level of the responses to the vocabulary of the SB-L with length of institutionalization for 60 institutionalized children between 7 and 15 years of age. The correlation was —.61. When MA was partialed out, the correlation between length of institutionalization and abstraction score was —.71. These data were interpreted as showing that early institutionalization and maternal deprivation affect the level at which children define words and "manipulate concepts."

Lyle (1959) compared the verbal scores on the Minnesota Preschool Scale of a group of 77 institutionalized children with 117 children in day schools. All children had IQs between 20 and 50 on the nonverbal portion of the Minnesota Preschool Scale. The CAs of the total group of children ranged from 6 years, 6 month$ to 13 years, 6 months. The institutional sample consisted of 34 mongoloid and 43 nonmongoloid children. The day-school sample consisted of 76 mongoloid and 41 nonmongoloid children.

Lyle's statistical analyses indicated that day-school children made higher verbal scores than did institutionalized children and that nonmongoloid children made higher verbal scores than mongoloid children. Lyle interprets his former finding as follows: "It appears, therefore, that the differences in verbal intelligence between imbeciles in the institution and those at day schools is [sic] almost certainly due to the effects of the different environments in which they live" (Lyle, 1959, p. 127).

The work of Schlanger, Badt, and Lyle, as well as the work of earlier environmentalists, is provocative but not conclusive. The studies by Skeels et al., Goldfarb, and Spitz have been discussed earlier and so will not be critically examined here. Schlanger, Badt, and Lyle have all concluded on the bases of their findings that an institutional environment is detrimental to language development. Yet the designs of all three studies allow for other interpretations.

Schlanger and Lyle both compared institutionalized defectives with defectives living at home. Such comparison studies involve serious methodological problems. The differences found between the language scores of institutional and noninstitutional samples could be a function of (1) differential early experiences (previous to the age when the institutional children were admitted), (2) selection factors, and (3) examiner bias. It seems quite likely that parents who have institutionalized a child at an early age provided a different environment for the child when he was in the home from that provided by parents who took other measures. For example, there may have been long periods of family turmoil or avoidance of the child prior to institutionalization.

It is possible that either language or some variable which is closely related to language development, such as response to adults, determines whether or not a child is institutionalized. If this is true, such differences might be expected, but not as an effect of length of institutionalization.

It is also very likely that an examiner may respond differently when testing children in an institutional setting and when testing children in a noninstitutional setting. This especially is true if the examiner is aware of the hypothesis being tested.

Selection factors could have also played a part in Badt's study. Suppose that "concrete" behavior invites the early labeling of a child as mentally defective. This could lead to earlier institutionalization of children with more concrete behavior, and, ultimately, a negative correlation between length of institutionalization and abstraction score. This possibility is not unlikely. The child who enters the first grade and responds to the isolated physical characteristics of objects may fail much more rapidly in school than the child who responds to the functions of objects or more abstract class properties. For example, the child who places a checker with a silver dollar because "both are round" and places a dollar bill with a checker board because "both are flat and made out of paper" will more likely be labeled as retarded than the child who places the silver dollar with the paper dollar because "both are money," or because "you can buy bubble gum with both." It is also likely that concrete behavior is related to other behavioral characteristics such as inadequate academic skills (arithmetic and reading), limited "understanding," reduction of perseverance on tasks requiring time, or other behavior which may be annoying to such adults as parents or teachers. If this is the case, one might expect a correlation between length of institutionalization and abstract definitions in an institutional group with a limited CA range.

The previous discussion should not be taken as an indication that the writer does not consider environmental variables important in language development. Rather, he simply wishes to point out that the design of some studies allows for interpretations other than the ones given.

The manipulation of language

The studies which have been discussed in the previous pages have involved a rather elementary type of research paradigm in which the investigator merely selected a sample of subjects and then determined what percentage of the sample manifested a certain characteristic or asked whether two variables were related. While this type of research results in information relevant to the extent of language problems among mental defectives as well as the relationship between language and other dependent variables, it offers little information concerning the variables which control language behavior. On the other hand, the following studies of the effects of therapy, training, and experimental treatments are attempts to evaluate methods for modifying or controlling language.

Language therapy and training studies. Strazzula (1953) compared a group of 17 mongoloid children who were given speech therapy once each week with a group of 15 who did not receive therapy. Only children above 6 years of age were included in the study. The 15 children of the control group were mongoloid children who were waiting for speech therapy or who could not avail themselves of the program. Results are reported in general terms. The parents of the children in therapy reported that their children were more alert and were functioning at a higher level. The therapist rated the improvement of the children in both the therapy and the control groups. Of the 17 children in the speech therapy group, two made excellent progress, ten made good progress, four made fair progress, and one made no progress. Of the 15 children in the control group, none made excellent progress, two made good progress, six made fair progress, and seven made no progress.

As a part of this same program 17 children were given thyroxin. A group of 23 children did not receive thyroxin. When these groups were compared, 5 of the 17 children who received thyroxin had voices which approached the norm for age and sex. None of the 23 who had not taken thyroxin had voices approaching the norm. The author does not state whether the 17 subjects who received thyroxin were the same subjects who received therapy.

Schlanger (1953) attempted to evaluate the effects of speech therapy on 62 mentally defective special class students with IQs ranging from 39 to 77. The mean MA and CA was 7 years, 2 months and 11 years, 11 months, respectively. Speech defects included articulation defects, voice defects, and stuttering. A variety of activities including oral speaking, creative drama, interview situations, games, and phonics drill were administered in a group setting two to three times per week throughout the school year. The criteria measures consisted of pre- and posttests of articulation, mean sentence length, percentage of complete sentences, number of words per minute, and the score on the Templin Sound Discrimination Test. The pre- and post-tests indicated a significant increase in articulation scores, mean sentence length, and percentage of complete sentences; however, the increases in words per minute and sound discrimination scores were not significant.

Schneider and Vallon (1955) reported the results of a therapy program with 28 severely defective children in a private day school project. The CAs of the children ranged from 4 years, 10 months to 16 years. The IQs ranged from 23 to 57 and the MAs from 1 year, 9 months to 5 years, 9 months. They reported improvement in language development, sentence production, and articulation. The journal article provides only minimal information concerning the specific nature of the therapy and the measures used to evaluate speech and language. No control group was included.

Mecham (1955) studied the effects of speech therapy with a group of 21 institutionalized retarded children. The changes in test-retest scores for this group were compared with those of a group of 10 children who were randomly selected from the same classes as the speech therapy group. The range of ages was from 9 to 18 years. The IQ range for the two groups was 41 to 85. The mean CA for the speech therapy group was 13 years, 4 months and 11 years, 6 months for the control. The mean IQ for the experimental group was 58.5 and for the control, 67.9. Two therapists administered both individual and group therapy over an 8-week period. The therapist attempted to improve articulation, auditory discrimination, and auditory memory span as well as further oral language development. Specific procedures were left to the therapist's discretion. Pre- and post-therapy data were acquired for articulation, discrimination, memory span, and average length of sentence. The experimental group improved significantly on all measures, whereas the control group improved significantly on memory span only. No direct comparisons were made between the two groups.

The results are not conclusive since the control group was superior to the experimental on articulation performance prior to therapy, indicating that the speech therapy group had more severe speech problems than the control.

Lubman (1955) reported on the effects of speech therapy with 93 severely retarded children (IQ 19 to 50) between ages 6 and 21. Individual therapy was given to 75 children once each week; the remaining children were seen in groups of two to four. The therapist also discussed the speech program with the teacher so that there would be maximum carry-over. Eighty-five of the ninety-three children were retested. Parents and classroom teachers were consulted to determine the degree of achievement in each child. It was agreed by "the three observers" (presumably teacher, parent, and therapist), and supported by test results, that 62 children had improved. According to these criteria 10 of 12 stutterers improved, older children (17 to 21) improved less than younger, and mongoloid children showed more rapid and permanent improvement than did those classed as brain-damaged.

Kolstoe (1958) compared a group of 15 institutionalized mongoloid children who received individual speech therapy with an individually matched group of 15 mongoloid children who received no speech therapy. The age range of the two groups was from 5 years, 6 months to 14 years, 6 months. The mean Kuhlmann MA was 2 years, 2 months in both groups; the mean IQ was 23.07 for the control group and 24.54 for the experimental group. The general approach used in speech therapy was derived from reinforcement theory. Most of the reinforcements were social or verbal. Three teachers were each randomly assigned five of the experimental children. All the teachers either had background in psychology and learning theory or had had previous teaching experience. Experimental subjects were given 45-minute teaching sessions 5 days each week for a period of 5½ months. Each child was seen on approximately 90 occasions. Materials consisted of cards with pictures, various kinds of dolls and doll furniture, farm animal miniatures, mechanical toys, silent movies, field trips, and phonograph records. The Kuhlmann Test of Mental Development, observational measures on language development, and a composite test made up of verbal items from the Kuhlmann and Stanford-Binet Form L tests were used for pre- and posttesting. Final testing was done by three persons who did not know which children were experimental and which were control. The results indicated that (1) while both groups lost on Kuhlmann scores, the experimental group lost less than did the control, (2) there were no differences on the observational ratings between the two groups, (3) experimental children made higher scores on a post DLFT than the control children, (4) there were no significant differences on the composite scale, and (5) children with high IQs profited more than did children with low IQs.

Rigrodski (1958) compared the effects of speech therapy based on Mowrer's autistic theory of language development with the effects of traditional stimulation therapy on two control groups. Mowrer's autistic theory of language development holds that if a person is stimulated with sounds while being provided with rewarding or pleasant experiences, the sounds themselves will acquire reward or reinforcement properties through the secondary reinforcement process. Moreover, when the person then accidentally makes sounds similar to the ones he was stimulated with in the "pleasant" situation, these sounds will tend to be self-reinforcing. This results in a sort of "self-practice." Effects of therapy on the sounds /θ/ and /v/ were tested. Each subject of two experimental groups and the teacher control were seen individually for forty 15-minute sessions.

The subjects who received therapy derived from the Mowrer hypothesis were placed in a situation in which the therapist tried to maintain a pleasant atmosphere. The sound to be learned was introduced 10 times during each 15-minute session. If the subject attempted to repeat the sound, he was praised.

The subjects who were given stimulation therapy received 5 days of ear training, 3 days of stimulation and production of a sound in isolation and in nonsense syllables, 6 days in transferring sounds to words, and 3 days using the sounds in words. This procedure was repeated for the two criterion sounds. Subjects were 72 mental defectives. Half the group had IQs between 45 and 72, and the remaining half had IQs between 12 and 44. The age range was from 6 to 16 years, 11 months. There were two therapists who each administered both experimental treatments to a group of six high children and a group of six low children. There were six high children and six low children in each of the two control treatments. Criterion measures were four articulation tests for the /θ/, /v/, /ɚ/, and /S/ sounds. These tests were an object test, picture test, auditory stimulus test, and a spontaneous speech test. Each measure was based on the rating of five judges who made their judgment on the basis of a tape recording. Judges were unaware of which children were in each group, and the sequence of tapes was randomized. Average reliability indices between judges ranged from .63 to .90 on the four measures. The results indicated that high defectives make fewer articulation mistakes than low defectives. There was a significant treatment by therapy interaction on the picture articulation test. There were no significant differences between the therapy and control groups.

Hartman (1958) attempted to determine the effect of the use of hearing aids on the speech of six mentally defective persons with auditory disorders. The IQs of the auditory impaired subjects ranged from 41 to 75. Their CAs ranged from 16 to 27. Subjects were given 4 weeks of training in use and care of the hearing aid. They were also given 15 minutes of auditory training with musical stimulation, speech, and simple conversational stimulation. The total daily sessions lasted from 1 to 1½ hours per day. At the end of 4 weeks the subjects were given their hearing aids. The program lasted 24 weeks. Subjects were reported to improve in functional speech during the period. No control group was included in the study, and measurements were based on observational reports.

Johnson, Capobianco, and Miller (1960) compared a group of 24 trainable mentally defective children who received speech therapy with a group of 24 controls who received no such training. Subjects of the two groups were individually matched on MA and IQ. One therapist administered individual speech therapy to each child. The two groups were compared on the basis of scores on the DLFT and on an articulation test which tested the "s," "z." "th," "r," "l," "ch," "h," "g," "j," and "v" sounds in three positions. The results indicated that the experimental group did not improve significantly more than the control group. The type of school program in which the control group was enrolled was not described.

Lassers and Low (1960) hypothesized (1) that speech of retarded children could be improved through speech therapy and (2) speech proficiency could be more effectively improved with a procedure which duplicated life experiences than with a drill type of therapy. The subjects used in their study were mentally retarded Caucasian children in special classes in California. Their IQs ranged from 40 to 79 and their CAs from 7 to 15 years. The subjects included in the study were not mute, had significant articulation defects, did not stutter, had normal hearing, had no demonstrable neurological pathology, were from unilingual backgrounds, and were emotionally stable enough to fit into the therapy group. One experimental group provided traditional speech therapy training in which subjects were given practice on sound discrimination and sound production, while a second experimental group was characterized by providing situations which replicated real-life experiences. In the second experimental group there was an attempt to assess the "needs" of the group, to unify the group, and to arrange activities which would stimulate both verbal and nonverbal activities. The therapist tried to arrange conditions so that acceptable behavior would occur and then encouraged the child once such behavior had occurred; however, if the child responded in an unacceptable manner such behavior was not punished. The San Francisco Inventory of Communicative Effectiveness (SFICE), the Articulation Profile, and a sound discrimination test were given to the two experimental groups as well as to a control group prior to and after the 15-week therapy period to evaluate the effects of therapy.

The articulation test and the sound discrimination test were scored in the test situation by the examiner. The tapes from which the SFICE scores were derived were presented in a random order and scored by judges. Care was taken to keep judges from knowing which treatment a subject had been administered and to eliminate confounding of factors with either treatment or pre- or posttest.

Only the articulation profile yielded significant differences among the communicative therapy group, the traditional therapy group, and the control group. The two examiners who had served as therapists in the communicative therapy procedure gave the articulation test to children of the traditional therapy group. One of the therapists from the traditional therapy treatment group tested the articulation of children of the communicative therapy group. All three therapists tested the children of the control group.

Ezell (1960) investigated three different methods of increasing the amount and complexity of the verbal behavior of institutionalized severely defective children between 9 and 12 years of age. The 36 subjects of the study scored below the 40th percentile of the institutional population at Parsons State Hospital on the verbal part of the PLS. Children were seen in groups of three by hospital aides, who functioned as the language therapists. Two aides were randomly assigned to each of three experimental treatments—(1) reinforcement, (2) bombardment, and (3) control. In the reinforcement treatment aides were instructed to respond to each vocal response of the child by imitating the child's vocal response or by praising the child. The aides in the bombardment group were instructed to stimulate the children by talking to them in short sentences and to imitate or praise the child whenever he made a vocal response. Theoretically, this treatment is characterized by setting the conditions for the child's response and then reinforcing the response once it occurs. The aides of the control group were instructed to "get the kids to talk" in whatever way feasible. The aides saw two groups of three children for a 15-minute session 5 times each week for 18 weeks. Two listeners tallied the number of sentences, one-word responses, instances of praise, instances of reprimand, and repetition of the children's responses from tape recordings of the aides' speeches which were made during one session each week. Analysis of the data for the first 6 weeks of the experiment indicated that the aides of the reinforcement group, in keeping with their instructions, made more imitation responses and less question and statement responses than the other two groups, which did not differ from each other. There was virtually no praise or reprimand in any of the three groups.

Changes in amount and complexity of the childern's verbal responses were evaluated by the observer ratings of noise, one-word, and sentence responses during the first 6 weeks of the experiment, and by test-retest scores on the PLS. There were no significant differences between the groups on any of the measures of child behavior. In all cases measures were obtained by persons who were unaware of the hypothesis being tested or the purpose of the experiment.

Bowman (1960) studied the effects of two different methods of teaching word comprehension to 24 institutionalized children, aged 6 years, 11 months to 13 years, 8 months. The Leiter International Performance Scale MAs of the subjects ranged from 1 year, 9 months to 6 years, 9 months. The 24 subjects were given a word comprehension test developed by Bowman. The test consisted of 19 pairs of word opposites in the 500 most commonly used words as listed by Thorndike and Lorge (1944). With the exception of one word, "least," the words included in the tests also appeared in "A Developmental Vocabulary Check-list for the Mentally Retarded," which was published by the State Department of Education at Madison, Wisconsin. The 24 subjects were pretested with 38 items (19 pairs of opposites) which required the subjects to indicate a correct response; e.g., "Which is the *back* of the dress?" Items on the test could be answered merely by pointing. Four teachers were used to train the children in language comprehension, and each teacher was randomly assigned two groups of three children. The children of one group were administered one treatment; the children of the second group were administered another treatment. Subjects were seen for 15-minute sessions daily for 3 weeks. Prior to the study, teachers were provided with a complete set of instructions for each treatment procedure. From the initial set of 19 pairs of words the 12 most difficult were selected for use in the study. Six of the 12 pairs were selected randomly and taught to the children. The other six sets functioned as control words.

One treatment method was characterized by the teacher's asking the child to point to the activity which was represented by one of the words and then telling him whether he was right or wrong. The other method involved telling the child what he had done. For example, if the teacher asked the child to point to the back of the doll and the child pointed to the back of the doll, the teacher would say, "You pointed to the back of the doll." If the child pointed to the front of the doll the teacher would name that activity also. The results of the study indicated that there was no difference between the two methods, nor was there a difference between the experimental and control words. There was a pre- and posttest difference which is, however, difficult to interpret. It could have been due to a general change in the child brought about by one of many factors: increased interaction with the teacher and children or a change in the hospital or in the administration and scoring of the test by the examiner.

Designing a study to determine the effects of therapy or training is far from easy. The very best studies in this area are open to serious questions concerning methodology. For this reason few if any conclusions can be derived from the results of these studies. Of 12 studies reported in this section, 7 find that therapy or training resulted in improvement in speech or language skill. An eighth study (Kolstoe) indicated that there was a decrease in scores on some language measures but that it was less for the therapy group than for the nontherapy control group. Four studies (Bowman, 1960; Ezell, 1960; Rigrodski, 1958; Johnson, Capobianco, & Miller, 1960) report that therapy resulted in no improvement in language skills. Interestingly, all the studies which reported no therapeutic effects included some type of experimental control in the design. This was true of only four of the studies reporting effects (Kolstoe, 1958; Strazzula, 1953; Mecham, 1955; Lassers & Low, 1960). None of the controls used in the four studies which employed controls could be classed as adequate. Strazzula's control group consisted of mongoloid children who were on a waiting list or could not avail themselves of speech therapy. It seems quite likely that a selection factor could have resulted in the differences in speech improvement reported between the therapy group and the nontherapy group. One could speculate that the parents who were most interested in their child's progress are the parents who would see that the child was available for therapy. Mecham's study employed a control group drawn randomly from the school classes of the subjects receiving therapy. The control group, as one might suspect, had less severe speech problems than the children who had been referred for speech therapy. It seems likely that there was less room for improvement in the control group than in the therapy group. Moreover, no direct comparison of improvement between the two groups was made. Rather, the conclusions were based on the finding that the therapy group showed significant gains on posttests while the control group did not. The conclusion that there were differences in the progress of the two groups is dubious since no direct comparison of change scores between the groups was made.

Lassers and Low (1960) used a variety of measures in evaluating the effects of their two therapy procedures. One set of measures was based on judges' ratings of tape recordings of children's responses. The recordings were randomized, and judges did not know to which of the three groups each subject belonged. On this set of measures there is a general lack of difference among the three groups. There was a significant difference in articulation scores between the two experimental groups in favor of the hypothesis on posttherapy testing. However, there was a confounding of examiners and treatments for the articulation evaluation. In the light of

Siegel's study, in which individual differences among articulation examiners were found, it seems quite likely that the differences obtained may have resulted from examiner bias.

Of the studies reporting language training or therapy effects, only Kolstoe's will withstand scrutiny of the design. Even the outcome of this study, however, could be the result of giving children increased adult attention in an individual setting in contrast to the effects of the specific type of therapy administered. If one is to evaluate the effects of a specific therapy, a control group in which children received an equal amount of adult and/or child-peer contact should be included.

In the studies in which no control group was used, it seems likely that such factors as (1) increase in rapport between the judges or examiners and the children, (2) changes in judges or examiners over time, (3) experimenter bias, and (4) factors similar to the Hawthorne effect may have influenced the results.

A factor that becomes obvious in the review of these studies is the lack of standardized measures. The most common type of language measure used was the articulation measure. However, several tests were used to analyze this same function. Some of the studies base evaluation of speech improvement on mere judgment of someone closely associated with the children, such as teachers, therapists, or parents. Most of the other studies used measures which are not commonly known. In some cases it seems likely that the measurements were not closely related to rationale for training or therapy; thus there was no reason to expect change. In most studies there was at least a partial confounding of the individual therapist with the experimental treatment or treatments. In some studies only one therapist administered the treatment. It is easy to see that in such a situation the interaction of a particular person with the child might be just as important as the specific experimental treatment. Exceptions to this procedure were the studies by Ezell and Bowman. These two studies represent two different methods of handling the therapist problem. In the Ezell study, two therapists were randomly assigned to each experimental treatment. Each therapist administered only one treatment. The procedure allows for evaluation of individual therapist effect. However, if there are therapist effects, the procedure does not provide as much precision for evaluating the treatment as does the Bowman design. In Bowman's study each teacher administered both treatments. The type of design used by Bowman is not feasible, however, if the teacher or therapist is unable to maintain the two different roles required to administer the two treatments.

Up to this point most of the discussion has been geared toward defining factors which lead to the conclusion that effects occur when, in fact, no treatment effects exist. The possibility of one's design failing to demonstrate treatment effects probably occurs equally often. Such factors as the use of unreliable or irrelevant measures, randomization rather than control of important variables, failure to see that adequate therapy procedures were used throughout the therapy program, and short duration of treatment could all lead to negative findings.

In view of the factors discussed previously, it seems that the value of speech therapy is still open to question. There are many methodological errors in those studies in which improvement due to therapy is reported. And, the studies which report no differences are hardly of sufficient precision that one could say that therapy has no effect.

Reinforcement and language behavior. If, as this writer believes, language is subject to the same principles as other behavior, one might expect that reinforcement theory would lead to fruitful predictions concerning the modification of language. This should be true of both speech and gestures. Several investigators have studied the effect of reinforcement upon speech (Greenspoon, 1955; Krasner, 1958; Salziner, 1959). However, to date the writer knows of no one who has studied the effect of reinforcement on gestural behavior.

Barnett, Pryer, and Ellis (1959) studied the effect of verbal reinforcement on the verbal behavior of mental defectives. Their experimental procedure was similar to that used by Greenspoon (1955). The materials consisted of 80 index cards on which 80 common verbs were printed. Six pronouns (I, we, she, he, you, and they) were placed below each verb. The subject was told to make a sentence using one of the pronouns. The experimenter prompted the subject on all verbs that he did not know. The experimenter reinforced any sentence beginning with an "I" or "we" for the 20 experimental subjects with the word "good." The 20 subjects of the control group were given no reinforcement. The subjects were institutionalized mental defectives between 12 years, 6 months and 35 years, 1 month. The MAs ranged from 7 years, 0 months to 12 years, 0 months. Criterion measurements were the number of sentences starting with I or we in each block of 20 responses. The data indicated that the experimental group started more sentences with I or we than the control group and that the number of I and we responses increased over the four-trial blocks in the experimental group but remained stable or decreased in the control group.

Spradlin and Dickerson[2] studied the effect of reinforcement upon the vocal responses of severely defective institutionalized 9- and 10-year-old children in a free operant conditioning situation. Eight children who were "untestable" on tests such as the RSB-L, Leiter, and WISC, and who made no vocal responses to the items of the PLS, were selected. These subjects were all given pretraining in the following manner. First, the operant conditioning equipment was set to deliver a reinforcement (M & M candies or Sugar Pops) every 20 seconds. One of the experimenters then took the child into the room and trained him to take candy from the goal box and to eat it. This procedure usually involved placing the reinforcement on the child's tongue, having him reach for the candy, and then having the child take the candy from the goal box. Each session lasted 15 minutes. The experimenter left the experimental room after 10 minutes of the second session. The third 15-minute session ended the pretraining. After pretraining, five more 15-minute sessions were given in which the reinforcement mechanism was activated each 30 seconds with the exception of a

[2] Donald Dickerson was formerly a research assistant with the Parsons Research Project and is currently a Mental Deficiency Fellow at George Peabody College.

2-minute period between the tenth and twelfth minute. During this time the child's vocalization was tape-recorded for subsequent counting. At the end of the five sessions, children were ranked according to the number of vocal responses made during the five 2-minute measurement periods during the first phase of experimentation. At this point one of the highest two was randomly assigned to the experimental group, the other to the control group. Then the subjects of the next highest pair were randomly assigned to the two groups and so on until all eight subjects were assigned.

Subjects of the experimental group were given five sessions in which each vocal response was reinforced with the exception of the 2 minutes between the tenth and the twelfth minute in each 15-minute period.

Subjects of the control group were given reinforcement every 30 seconds with the exception of the 2-minute measurement period.

During the third block of five sessions, subjects of both the control and experimental groups were maintained on the same schedule as during the second block except that potatoes, dessert, butter, and bread were withheld from the children at lunch. Tapes of the fifteen 2-minute periods were randomized, and vocalizations were counted by a listener who had no knowledge concerning the experiment. In every case for the experimental group the amount of noise increased. In all four cases there was a decrease in vocalization for the control group. These differences approached but did not reach significance at the .05 level in a analysis of variance.[3]

Copeland (1960) hypothesized that certain modification of the auditory stimuli produced by the child's own vocal response would serve as a reinforcer (i.e., increase the frequency of vocal responses) for mentally defective children. His subjects were 7 years, 5 months to 16 years, 7 months of age and ranged from untestable to an IQ of 80 on the WISC. He divided subjects into high verbal subjects and low verbal subjects on the basis of the PLS. High subjects scored above the 63rd percentile of the institutional population, while low subjects scored below the 27th percentile. The children were placed individually in a sound-treated room for 5 minutes with no manipulation of their voices during one portion of the experiment. In a second part of the experiment vocalizations were amplified and played back to the subject after a 1-second delay. Delay and nondelay conditions were counterbalanced. The results of the study indicated that lows vocalized more than highs regardless of experimental condition. Both high and low groups increased vocalization during delayed feedback.

The studies in this section, as in previous sections, have certain limitations. The study by Barnett et al. does not give any information concerning the experimenters, and it is assumed that one or at most two administered the treatment. If two experimenters were used, no doubt they were aware of the experimental hypothesis. Although the experimenter may

---

[3] A modified replication of this study, which was completed after the final draft of this chapter had been submitted, yielded no increase in vocalizations for the reinforcement group in the second and third blocks of trials. The modifications of the initial study involved a different experimenter, a different room, and no food restriction during the third block of five trials. In view of the failure to obtain an increase in vocalizations for the reinforcement group in the replication, the results of the initial study should not be generalized at this time.

consider his behavior unaffected by that of the subject, one can never be sure. It is quite likely that the most powerful reinforcing events in the experimental situation are operating on him. These are, of course, the events which tend to confirm his hypothesis.

The study by Spradlin and Dickerson is subject to some of the same criticisms since one experimenter delivered all reinforcement. However, since he was not in a face-to-face situation with the subject, as was the case with the Barnett et al. study, effects on the experimenter seem less likely. Finally, the criterion measure was made by a person who was unaware of the experimental hypothesis.

The study by Copeland was done almost entirely by instrumentation, and it seems quite unlikely that experimenter bias could have entered into it in any way.

One may question the inclusion of the studies by Spradlin and Dickerson and Copeland since they involve nonlanguage behavior. However, it is quite likely that these vocalizations are highly related to the development of speech. With some qualifications the studies suggest that the vocal behavior of mental defectives, like the nonvocal behavior of retardates and other organisms, can be brought under the control of reinforcement.

Background noise and auditory discrimination. Since the publication of Strauss and Lehtinen's book (1947) there have been many pages written concerning the detrimental effects of background stimuli on the performance of brain-injured mentally defective children. Schlanger studied the effects of background noise and music on the auditory discrimination of a group of 24 children diagnosed as "mentally retarded due to a brain defect." The means for MA, CA, and IQ were 4 years, 0 months, 10 years, 1 month, and 40, respectively. The experimental task consisted of an auditory word discrimination test containing 58 pairs of very similar words such as "pin—pen," "back—black," or "peach—peas." The subject was presented the words and then asked to select the picture of the correct word from a pair of pictures presented to him. Each subject performed the task under six conditions. The discrimination task was presented with *normal* background noises; with *tape-recorded* clocks ticking, chimes ringing, cups rattling, paper crumpling, etc.; and with Brahm's *Clarinet Quintet in E Minor*. The test was administered both live by an examiner and by a tape recording. The live presentation was always given first. The background effects were rotated for each individual. There were no differences as a function of background conditions. Subjects performed better on the live than on the taped presentation. It must be remembered that live versus taped condition and sequence were confounded in the experimental design.

Drugs and speech errors in mental defectives. There have been numerous attempts to relate behavioral functioning among mental defectives to the administration of pharmacological agents in recent years (Benson, 1960). Mecham, Courtney, and Soderberg (1955) studied the effects of administering Tolserol on the errors in speech production made by 22 mental defectives. Each subject of the study served as his own control. During the first week the subject received no treatment. The second week he was given a placebo (two tablets), and the third week he was given two tablets of Tolserol. The criterion task involved having the subject repeat phrases presented to him through earphones. Prior to the experiment all subjects were given experience with the phrases, which were repeated three times each week. Three repetitions of six different phrases were used as criterion measures for each week. The phrases from all three treatment periods were presented to judges in a random order and scored for errors. There were no differences between the therapy and placebo treatment. However, significantly fewer errors were made during the placebo treatment than when the subjects were receiving no treatment.

The results of the study are generally nonsignificant, and the use of a treatment by subject's design presents problems concerning independence of treatments. Nevertheless, the study presents a type of experimental manipulation which could eventually provide information concerning speech modification. Only extensive manipulative research will provide information concerning if and how the administration of various pharmacological agents affects speech.

Language in a two-person setting. Nearly all the research presented thus far has dealt with language in an individual-type experimental setting. It is important to focus on the language of the individual mentally defective person. However, it may be equally important to study the language reactions of persons who interact with a mentally defective person. It is possible that the behavior of mentally defective persons sets up specific kinds of reactions in other persons assembled with them. If these specific kinds of reactions do occur, they may either facilitate or retard the subsequent language behavior of the mentally defective person. For example, when a normal adult is confronted with another person who speaks indistinctly or not at all, he may raise his voice, repeat what he has said, accompany his speech with gestures, simplify his speech patterns, or perhaps withdraw from the social situation. Two questions occur. First, to what extent do such behaviors occur in the listener, and second, what effects do they have on the behavior of the defective person?

Several studies have been done recently which bear, at least indirectly, on these questions. A series of studies have been done by Spradlin and Rosenberg (1959), Siegel (1963), and Harkins (1961) to determine some of the effects of children with different levels of linguistic deficiency on the speech behavior of normal adults who are assembled with them in a dyadic situation.

Spradlin and Rosenberg (1959) hypothesized on the basis of a reinforcement rationale that adults would emit different percentages of binary and multiple[4] questions in an interview situation according to whether they were assembled with mentally defective children with high or low linguistic ability. Junior college students were assembled with children who had been dichotomized into those above the median and those below

[4] A binary question is one which can be answered by one of two responses. For example, "Is your hair black or brown?" or "Can a dog run?" are questions which can be answered by one of two possible responses. A multiple question allows multiple possibilities for an answer. For example, "Where do you live?" and "How old are you?" are both multiple questions.

546 Handbook of Mental Deficiency

the median on the PLS tact and intraverbal subtests. Each of 24 adults saw six children for a 20-minute interview. Six adults saw six high children. Six adults saw six low children. Six adults saw three high children followed by three low children. Six adults saw three low children followed by three high children. All interviews were tape-recorded. Tapes were then randomized, and judges who were unfamiliar with the study counted binary and multiple questions. There were no differences between adult groups for percentage of binary and multiple questions as a function of high and low assemblages. However, a *post hoc* analysis indicated that adults assembled with low children emitted more questions than did those assembled with highs.

Siegel (1963) assembled 10 female junior college students with high and low mentally defective girls. The high and low dichotomy was based on the PLS vocal section scores and an articulation test. Adult subjects were divided into two groups. Adults of one group were instructed not to ask questions, to make their responses relative to what the child said, to initiate verbalization without forcing the child to participate, and to use silence to elicit verbal responses. Adults of the other group were instructed to obtain certain kinds of information from the child. Each adult was assembled with two high and two low children for 15 minutes each. All sessions were tape-recorded. Tapes were randomized and transcribed by a typist. Persons unfamiliar with the hypothesis made counts and obtained the measures used to evaluate both adult and child behavior. The results indicated that the number of adult words and mean length of adult responses did not vary according to the level of child with whom they were assembled. However, the adults' type-token ratio was higher when assembled with children with high verbal facilities.

High and low children differed on number of words used. However, the instructions which the adults were given had no measured effects on the children's responses.

Harkins (1961) assembled 21 male junior college students with 8- to 14-year-old mentally defective boys with high and low linguistic levels. Each adult was assembled with one high and one low child. High children scored in the upper 25 per cent of the institutional population on the PLS vocal section. Lows scored between the 25th and 50th percentiles. High subjects were also screened on the basis of articulation. Measures were taken in two situational contexts. First, measures were taken when adults were merely taking care of the child in a "free" experimental situation. Then measures were taken in a situation in which the adult was attempting to train the child to perform on a form board. Once again, all sessions were tape-recorded.

There were no differences between high and low treatments on the number of words emitted by the adult. The number of questions emitted by the adults was greater but not significant. The type-token ratio and the mean number of words per response were greater for adults when assembled with high children than when assembled with low. When adults were engaged in the training task, they made more responses and asked fewer questions than when in the free situation. There were, once again, differences in the number of words emitted by children in the high and low groups. Moreover, children of both groups made fewer responses in the training situation.

Rosenberg, Spradlin, and Mabel (1961) studied the effect of similarity or discrepancy of language levels of mentally defective children on interaction in a dyadic situation. Twenty male and female mentally defective children between 12 years, 11 months and 15 years were subjects. Subjects were classified as either high or low on the basis of the tact and intraverbal subtests of the PLS. The 20 children were divided into five subgroups of four children each. All four children in a subgroup were of the same sex. There were two highs and two lows in each subgroup. Thus, by varying the assembly of dyads there could be high-high, low-low, and high-low assemblies. Dyads were assembled on 13 occasions. However, observations and measurements were analyzed for only the last four sessions. Observers watching through a one-way-vision mirror recorded gestures, vocalizations, and the number of times each child initiated contact. The analysis indicated that when two children of the same language level were assembled, there were many gestures and vocalizations. However, when the children were of different levels, gestures and vocalizations dropped to near zero. The greatest amount of physical contact occurred when two low children were assembled.

The dyadic interaction studies are rather novel in the field of mental deficiency research. Moreover, the rationale on which they are based is slightly different from that on which most studies in the field are based. The studies are based on the hypothesis that the behavior of either of two participants is, in part, under the control of the second participant. This is as true for the normal adult interacting with the mentally defective child as it is for the child. The notion that there may be interpersonal processes which perpetuate language retardation is still to be tested. Nevertheless, the initial studies are promising. Such studies are not without problems. Measurement problems are increased since the responses of two persons, rather than one, must be recorded. Statements of response contingency are open to question since the experimenter has no direct control of the responses of either of two subjects. Even though one can show that an adult has a greater type-token ratio and mean response length when with a child who has a high language level than when with a child who has a low language level, such a difference may still have no effect on the child.

Language training on nonlanguage performance. There is ample evidence that language and nonlanguage behavior are correlated. In addition, writers in several areas have indicated that the acquisition of language responses may affect nonlanguage behavior (Whorf, 1958; Sarason, 1953; Liublinskaya, 1957; Miller, 1948). This particular approach to the relationship between language and nonlanguage behavior may shed light on some old and perplexing problems concerning human behavior. While it has been customary to speak of both language and nonlanguage behavior as products of some third nonobservable variable, such as intelligence, it may be more fruitful to investigate the effect that certain types of linguistic training have on nonlanguage behavior. Acquisition of linguistic behavior may enable persons to perform a nonlanguage task more adequately. For example, there seems to be little doubt that counting (a language system) aids in the solution of certain nonlanguage tasks. Numerous experiments have been conducted with normal children and adults which have studied the effect of modification of language behavior on nonlanguage performance (Dietz, 1955; Cantor, 1955; Maltzman, Brooks, Bogartz, & Summers, 1958; Stevenson & Weir, 1959). Recently Barnett, Ellis, and Pryer (1959) and Smith and Means (1961) studied the effects of verbal pretraining on delayed reaction time and discrimination in mentally defective persons.

Barnett et al. investigated the effects of teaching verbal labels for stimuli on the response to a Hunter-type delay task. Subjects were 80 institutionalized mental defectives. The 80 subjects were divided into two groups. The MAs of one group (*low*) ranged from 5 years, 7 months to 6 years, 10 months. The MAs of a second group (*high*) ranged from 7 years to 9 years. Half of the subjects in each group were taught to name the two stimuli. The other half of the subjects were taught merely to discriminate between the two stimuli but given no names for them. Each group of subjects were then tested on the delay task with four different periods of delay—10 seconds, 30 seconds, 1 minute, and 5 minutes. The results indicated that teaching the child to name the stimuli does facilitate performance on a delay task. The results also indicated that accuracy decreased with increased delay periods. There were no differences between the two MA levels.

Smith and Means (1961) studied the effects of five different types of stimulus pretraining on subsequent discrimination between two stimuli. Eighty-five institutionalized mental defectives between 13 and 45 years of age and between IQ 35 and 85 were used as subjects. Subjects were *relatively free* of speech defects and had no physical defects which might interfere with their performance on the task. The 85 subjects were divided into five groups. One group learned irrelevant nonsense syllables. A second group was given training in matching the stimuli used in the discrimination task (matching group). A third group was taught nonsense names for the stimuli (nonsense relevant). A fourth group was taught a motor name or gesture for each stimulus (motor name), and a fifth group was taught names for the stimuli which would already be associated with them (meaningful-name group). The results indicated that both the motor-name group and the meaningful-name group performed significantly better than did the other three groups, which were not significantly different from each other.

There are certain criticisms which could be leveled at the two studies reported in this section. First, the samples of subjects are inadequately described. Second, possible experimenter signaling was not adequately controlled or described. Nevertheless, the studies and their results are intriguing. If subsequent studies obtain the same type of results, a great deal of enlightenment concerning the relation between nonlanguage behavior and language behavior will follow.

AN EMPIRICAL APPROACH TO LANGUAGE
AND MENTAL DEFICIENCY

Many of the problems occurring in language research in the area of mental deficiency result from the way in which the terms "language" and "mental deficiency" are construed. Language has been construed in at least three different ways. First, it has been viewed as a set of responses subject to the control of nonobservable processes within the organism. Second, language has been treated as a nonobservable process which gives rise to speech, gestures, and writing. Third, language has been construed as a set of responses subject to manipulative control.

Mental deficiency has also been construed in a number of different ways. First, it has been viewed as an implicit process producing general behavioral limitations. Secondly, it has been considered a complex set of behavioral limitations due to nonobservable implicit processes such as lack of ideation. Finally, mental deficiency has been considered as a set of behavioral limitations due to genetic and environmental factors.

The way the terms "language" and "mental deficiency" are construed would make no difference if it were not for the fact that these constructions determine the type of questions which will be asked and consequently the type of research which will be done. When language is viewed as a set of responses subject to the control of nonobservable processes, several unanswerable questions usually become the focal point of discussion. The first question is often, "How can we measure the nonobservable processes?" For example, "How can we measure anxiety, intelligence, or self-concept?" A second question is, "What is the relative importance of each of these hypothetical processes in determining language behavior?" For example, "What are the relative importances of intelligence and anxiety in determining language ability?" These types of questions, though themselves unanswerable and not directly related to any empirical data, lead to certain types of studies. These studies usually involve either simple classification of groups and counting or correlation. The results allow only for prediction and not modification of behavior. While the explanation of language behavior by appealing to nonobservable processes may be reinforcing to some persons, it is rather upsetting to those who realize that if one accepts this formulation he is faced with the even more troublesome problem of understanding the determinants of the nonobservable processes.

When language is construed as a nonobservable process exactly the same problems are faced but different words have been substituted. The term language in this case, like the terms intelligence, anxiety, and self-concept in the previous case, adds nothing to the functional analysis of behavior. It is merely an extra term in a behavioral equation which tends to increase the occurrence of questions which cannot be answered empirically.

Mental deficiency has also been subject to these same kinds of theorizing. The writer has made no check, but he would not be surprised to find that more pages have been written in the *American Journal of Mental Deficiency* on pseudo questions (i.e., "can mental deficiency really be cured?" or "does environment affect true intelligence?" or "what proportion of institution-alized persons are pseudo mental defectives?") than have been devoted to the reporting of research investigations.

The third construction for both language and mental deficiency leads to a different set of questions. With regard to language the first question might be, "To what behaviors shall the term language refer?" This question is to be answered arbitrarily; nevertheless, the individual examiner can answer it for the purposes of his own research. The second question might be, "In what way are the classes of behaviors included under the label 'language' related to each other?" Finally, "What are the variables which control the various classes of language behavior?" Specific research questions based on the above formulation would lead directly to a body of knowledge concerning the prediction and control of language behavior based on a systematic program of manipulation of the relevant variables.

If mental deficiency were similarly construed, a similar body of knowledge concerning prediction and control would be obtained.

The approach just presented is not new. Skinner (1957), Kantor (1952), and Turner (1961) have all made statements similar to those made by the present author. This fact, of course, does not indicate endorsement by Skinner, Kantor, and Turner of statements made in this chapter.

SUMMARY AND OVERVIEW

Within this chapter language referred to speech and gestures and to the reactions of another person to speech and gestures. A review of research on speech and gestures, the listener's understanding of speech and gestures, and the interaction of speaker and listener followed from this conception of language.

A review of new language evaluation procedures revealed that most of the procedures included provisions for sampling both speech and speech comprehension. In addition, two tests (the PLS and the ITPA) yielded provisions for sampling either gestures or the comprehension of gestures. The PLS and ITPA are both based on learning models and hold promise not only for sampling language in a better organized fashion but also for bringing the study of language in line with broader general behavior systems. The tests present two possible limitations. First, although both tests are based on learning models, neither provides any measure of current rate of acquisition. Second, both obtain their samples of language in a formal situation with an adult examiner. These samples may or may not be representative of language samples obtained in other situations.

There have been numerous studies of the prevalence of speech defects among mentally defective populations. In spite of the use of differing populations of defectives and differing criteria for speech deficits, the results indicate that from 57 to 72 per cent of institutionalized mental defectives have speech defects. The most frequently occurring ones appear to involve articulation and voice. There appears to be no evidence to suggest that mentally defective persons are subject to speech defects to which non-mentally defective persons are immune.

The studies which have correlated language measures with such variables as sex, age, anxiety, intelligence, and gross diagnostic categories have been very unenlightening. The relationships between language measures and sex, age, anxiety, and gross diagnostic categories have been quite limited. On the other hand, relationships between language measures and intelligence measures vary from —.10 to .92. The writer has suggested that an analysis of the similarities between stimuli presented, responses sampled, and the manner in which the responses are classified might lead to a better understanding of the relationships between the various language and intelligence measures.

Two investigators have found differences in language skills between institutionalized and noninstitutionalized children matched on the basis of intelligence measures. A third investigator has found a relationship between length of institutionalization and abstraction score on a vocabulary test. The investigators suggest that these differences are the result of the institutional environment. The possibility is provocative; however, the studies are only suggestive since numerous other factors were confounded with the environmental variables under investigation.

There have been numerous attempts to evaluate the effects of therapy and training procedures on the speech of mentally defective children. The results of these studies are far from conclusive. The investigations which have reported experimental treatment effects have frequently suffered from the lack of an adequate control group and the confounding of nonexperimental variables with the variables under investigation. On the other hand, the studies which have found no significant treatment effect have not been of sufficient precision to allow for a definitive negative statement.

Studies of the effect of reinforcement on speech and vocal behavior, though far from conclusive, indicate that vocal language behavior may be subject to the same reinforcement principles as nonlanguage behavior. If this is true, then great strides might be made through the application of these principles to increase the frequency of language responses, to shape these responses, and to bring these responses under stimulus control.

The study of the language of mentally defective and nonmentally defective persons in a variety of interpersonal settings promises to provide valuable information concerning the language behavior of the mental defective and the effect of such behavior on normal persons. Moreover, such studies could point up processes which tend to limit or facilitate language development in mentally defective persons.

Perhaps the most exciting single area is the research on the effect of language training on the performance of other language and nonlanguage tasks. This kind of research could give us valuable and precise information about that important behavior which has often been discussed under the labels of thought, abstraction, and higher mental processes.

REFERENCES

AZRIN, N. H., HOLZ, W., ULRICH, R., & GOLDIAMOND, I. The control of content conversation through reinforcement. *J. exp. anal. Behav.*, 1960, 4, 25–30.

BADT, MARGIT. Levels of abstraction in vocabulary definitions of mentally retarded school children. *Amer. J. ment. Defic.*, 1958, 63, 241–246.

BANGS, J. L. A clinical analysis of the articulatory defects of the feeble-minded. *J. speech Disord.*, 1942, 8, 343–356.

BARNETT, C. D., ELLIS, N. R., & PRYER, MARGARET. Stimulus pretraining and the delayed reaction in defectives. *Amer. J. ment. Defic.*, 1959, 63, 104–111.

BARNETT, C. D., PRYER, MARGARET, & ELLIS, N. R. Experimental manipulation of verbal behavior in defectives. *Psychol. Rep.*, 1959, 5, 393–396.

BENSON, W. M. Pharmacological approach. *Amer. J. ment. Defic.*, 1960, 65, 172–181.

BIJOU, S. W., & WERNER, H. Language analyses in brain-injured and non-brain-injured mentally deficient children. *J. genet. Psychol.*, 1945, 66, 239–254.

BOWMAN, V. J. A study of the effects of two different methods of teaching word comprehension. Parsons Research Project Working Paper No. 24a, 1960.

CANTOR, G. N. Effects of three types of pretraining on discrimination learning in preschool children. *J. exp. Psychol.*, 1955, 49, 339–342.

COPELAND, R. H. The effects of free-field feedback modification on verbal behavior. Paper presented at Amer. Speech Hear. Ass., Los Angeles, November, 1960.

DIETZE, DORIS. The facilitating effect of words on discrimination and generalization. *J. exp. Psychol.*, 1955, 50, 255–260.

DONOVAN, HELEN. Organization and development of a speech program for the mentally retarded children in the New York City public schools. *Amer. J. ment. Defic.*, 1957, 62, 455–459.

DUNN, L. M. *Peabody picture vocabulary test manual* (tentative edition). Nashville, Tennessee: George Peabody Coll. for Teachers, 1958.

EZELL, DOROLYN. The effects of verbal reinforcement on the language behavior of mentally retarded children. Paper presented at Amer. Speech Hear. Ass., Los Angeles, November, 1960.

GALLAGHER, J. A comparison of brain-injured and non-brain-injured mentally retarded children on several psychological variables. *Child Develpm. Monogr.*, 1957, 22, No. 65.

GENS, G. W. The speech pathologist looks at the mentally deficient child. *Train. Sch. Bull.*, 1951, 48, 19–27.

GODA, S., & GRIFFITH, B. C. The spoken language of adolescent retardates and its relation to intelligence, age, and anxiety. *Child. Developm.*, 1962, 33, 489–498.

GOLDFARB, W. Infant rearing and problem behavior. *Amer. J. Orthopsychiat.*, 1943, 13, 249–265.

GOLDFARB, W. Infant rearing as a factor in foster home placement. *Amer. J. Orthopsychiat.*, 1944, 14, 162–170.

GOLDFARB, W. Effects of psychological deprivation in infancy and subsequent stimulation. *Amer. J. Psychiat.*, 1945–46, 102, 18–33.

GREENSPOON, J. The reinforcing effect of two spoken sounds on the frequency of two responses. *Amer. J. Psychol.*, 1955, 68, 409–416.

HARKINS, J. P. A study of the verbal behavior of adults assembled in two conditions with institutionalized mentally deficient children of two verbal levels. Unpublished master's thesis, Univer. of Kansas, 1961.

HARTMAN, B. T. Study of therapeutic and functional values of hearing aids for the mentally handicapped. *Amer. J. ment. Defic.*, 1958, 62, 803–809.

HOROWITZ, FRANCES D. The relationship between the Parsons language sample scores and Wechsler intelligence quotients of mentally retarded subjects. Unpublished manuscript.

IRWIN, O. E. The developmental status of speech sounds of ten feeble minded children. *Child Developm.,* 1942, 13, 29–39.

JOHNSON, G. O., CAPOBIANCO, R. J., & MILLER, P. Y. Speech and language development of a group of mentally deficient children enrolled in a training program. *Except. Child.,* 1960, 27, 72–77.

KANTOR, J. R. *An objective psychology of grammar.* Bloomington, Indiana: The Principia Press, 1952.

KARLIN, I. W., & STRAZZULA, MILICENT. Speech and language problems of mentally deficient children. *J. speech hear. Disord.,* 1952, 17, 286–294.

KENNEDY, LOIS. Studies in the speech of the feeble-minded. Unpublished doctoral dissertation, Univer. of Wisconsin, 1930.

KIRK, S. A., & MCCARTHY, J. J. A study of the language progress of pre-school cerebral palsied children. (A progress report on United Cerebral Palsy Grant for the period of September, 1954, to February, 1958.)

KIRK, S. A., & MCCARTHY, J. J. The Illinois test of psycholinguistic abilities—an approach to differential diagnosis. *Amer. J. ment. Defic.,* 1961, 66, 399–412.

KOLSTOE, O. P. Language training of low-grade mongoloid children. *Amer. J. ment. Defic.,* 1958, 63, 17–30.

KRASNER, L. Studies of the conditioning of verbal behavior. *Psychol. Bull.,* 1958, 55, 148–170.

LASSERS, L., & LOW, G. A study of the relative effectiveness of different approaches of speech therapy for mentally retarded children. Report to Office of Education on Contract No. 6904. (1960)

LEWALD, J. Speech defects as found in a group of 500 mental defectives. *Proc. and addresses for Amer. Ass. for Study of Feeblemindedness,* 1932, 37, 291–301.

LIUBLINSKAYA, A. A. The development of children's speech and thought. In B. Simon (Ed.), *Psychology in the Soviet Union.* Stanford, California: Stanford, 1957, 197–204.

LUBMAN, CHARLOTTE. Speech program for severely retarded children. *Amer. J. ment. Defic.,* 1955, 60, 297–300.

LYLE, J. G. The effect of an institution environment upon verbal development of imbecile children. *J. ment. Def. Res. (London),* 1959, 3, 122–128.

MCCARTHY, DOROTHEA. Language development in children. In L. Carmichael (Ed.), *Manual of child psychology.* New York: Wiley, 1954, 492–630.

MCCARTHY, DOROTHEA. A preliminary report on the verbal items of a new psychological appraisal test with institutionalized mentally retarded children. Paper read at the Council for Except. Child., Northeast. Ass., Atlantic City, April, 1959.

MALTZMAN, I., BROOKS, L. O., BOGARTZ, W., & SUMMERS, S. S. The facilitation of problem solving by prior exposure to uncommon responses. *J. exp. Psychol.,* 1958, 56, 399–406.

MECHAM, M. J. The development and application of procedures for measuring speech improvement in mentally defective children. *Amer. J. ment. Defic.,* 1955, 60, 301–306.

MECHAM, M. J., COURTNEY, S., & SODERBERG, G. Effects of Tolserol on the speech errors of mentally defective children. *Amer. J. Phys. Med.,* 1955, 34, 535–536.

MILLER, N. E. Theory and experiment relating psychoanalytic displacement to stimulus-response generalization. *J. abnorm. soc. Psychol.,* 1948, 43, 155–178.

OSGOOD, C. E. *Method and theory in experimental psychology.* New York: Oxford Univer. Press, 1953.

OSGOOD, C. E. *A behavioristic analysis of perception and language as cognitive phenomena.* Cambridge, Mass.: Harvard, 1957, 75–118.

RIELLO, A. Articulatory proficiency of the mentally retarded child: an investigation to determine the relationship between articulatory proficiency and the IQ of the educable public school children of retarded mental development. Unpublished doctoral dissertation, New York Univer., 1958.

RIGRODSKI, S. Application of Mowrer's autistic theory to the speech habilitation of mentally retarded pupils. Unpublished doctoral dissertation, Purdue Univer., 1958.

ROSENBERG, S., SPRADLIN, J. E., & MABEL, S. Interaction among retarded children as a function of their relative language skills. *J. Abnorm. soc. Psychol.*, 1961, 63, 402–410.

ROSENTHAL, R., FODE, K. L., FRIEDMAN, C. J., & VIKAN, L. L. Subjects' perception of their experimenter under conditions of experimenter bias. *Percept. mot. Skills,* 1960, 11, 325–331.

SACHS, M. H. A survey and evaluation of the existing interrelationship between speech and mental deficiencies. Unpublished master's thesis, Univer. of Virginia, 1951 (abstr. *Speech Monogr.*, 1952, 19, 197–198).

SALZINGER, K. Experimental manipulation of verbal behavior: a review. *J. gen. Psychol.*, 1959, 61, 65–94.

SARASON, S. B. *Psychological problems in mental deficiency* (2nd ed.) New York: Harper, 1953.

SCHLANGER, B. B. Speech examination of a group of institutionalized mentally handicapped children. *J. speech hear. Disord.*, 1953, 18, 339–349.

SCHLANGER, B. B. Speech therapy results with mentally retarded children in special classes. *Train. Sch. Bull.*, 1953, 50, 179–186.

SCHLANGER, B. B. Environmental influences on the verbal output of mentally retarded children. *J. speech hear. Disord.*, 1954, 19, 339–345.

SCHLANGER, B. B., & GOTTSLEBEN, R. H. Analysis of speech defects among the institutionalized mentally retarded. *J. speech hear. Disord.*, 1957, 22, 98–108.

SCHNEIDER, B. D., & VALLON, J. A speech therapy program for mentally retarded children. *Amer. J. ment. Defic.*, 1954, 633–639.

SCHNEIDER, B., & VALLON, J. The results of a therapy program for mentally retarded children. *Amer. J. ment. Defic.*, 1955, 59, 417–424.

SIEGEL, G. M. Experienced and inexperienced articulation examiners. *J. speech hear. Disord.*, 1962, 27, 28–35.

SIEGEL, G. M. Language behavior of adults and retarded children in interpersonal assemblies. *J. speech hear. Disord., Monogr. Suppl.*, 10, 1963, 32–53.

SIEVERS, DOROTHY J. Development and standardization of a test of psycholinguistic growth in preschool children. Unpublished doctoral dissertation, Univer. of Illinois, 1955.

SIEVERS, DOROTHY J., & ROSENBERG, C. M. The differential language facility test and electroencephalograms of brain-injured mentally retarded children. *Amer. J. ment. Defic.*, 1960, 65, 46-50.

SIRKIN, J. E., & LYONS, W. F. A study of speech defects in mental deficiency. *Amer. J. ment. Defic.*, 1941, 46, 74–80.

SKEELS, H. M., UPDEGRAFF, RUTH, WELLMAN, BETH, & WILLIAMS, H. M. A study of environmental stimulation: an orphanage preschool project. *Iowa Stud. Child Welf.* 1938, 15, No. 4.

SKINNER, B. F. *Verbal behavior.* New York: Appleton-Century-Crofts, 1957.

SMITH, M. P., & MEANS, J. R. Effects of type of stimulus pretraining on discrimination learning in mentally retarded. *Amer. J. ment. Defic.*, 1961, 66, 259–265.

SPITZ, R. A. Hospitalism: a follow-up report on investigation described in Vol. I, 1945. *The psychoanalytic study of the child*, 1946, 2, 113–117.

SPRADLIN, J. E. Assessment of language skills among mentally retarded children. Parsons Research Project Working Paper 29, 1960.

SPRADLIN, J. E., & ROSENBERG, S. Complexity of adult verbal behavior in a dyadic situation with retarded children. Parsons Research Project Working Paper 18, 1959.

STEVENSON, H. W., & WEIR, M. W. The effect of verbalization in the children's learning as a function of chronological age. *Child Develpm.*, 1959, 30, 143–149.

STRAUSS, A. A., & LEHTINEN, L. E. *Psychopathology and education of the brain-injured child.* New York: Grune & Stratton, 1947.

STRAZZULA, MILLICENT. Speech problems of the mongoloid child. *Pediatrics*, 1953, 8, 268–273.

TEMPLIN, MILDRED, & DARLEY, F. *The Templin-Darley tests of articulation.* Iowa City, Iowa: State Univer. of Iowa, 1960.

TERMAN, L. M., & MERRILL, MAUD A. *Measuring intelligence.* Cambridge, Mass.: Riverside Press, 1937.

THORNDIKE, E. L., & LORGE, I. *The teacher's word book of 30,000 words.* New York: Teachers Coll., Columbia Univer., 1944.

TOWN, CLARA H. Language development in 285 idiots and imbeciles. *Psychol. Clin.*, 1912–13, 6, 229–235.

TURNER, W. S. A re-examination of the two kinds of scientific conjectures. *Psychol. Rec.*, 1961, 11, 279–298.

WALLIN, J. E. W. *Children with mental and physical handicaps.* Englewood Cliffs, N.J.: Prentice-Hall, 1949.

WEATHERWAX, J., & BENOIT, E. P. Concrete and abstract thinking in organic and non-organic mentally retarded children. *Amer. J. ment. Defic.*, 1957, 62, 548–553.

WHORF, B. L. Language and stereotypes. (3rd ed.) In Eleanor Maccoby, T. M. Newcomb, & E. L. Hartley (Eds.), *Readings in social psychology.* New York: Holt, 1958. Pp. 1–9.

WILSON, E. B., JR. *An introduction to scientific research.* New York: McGraw-Hill, 1952.

WINITZ, H. Research in articulation and intelligence. *Child Developm.* (in press).

17

PSYCHOPHYSIOLOGICAL STUDIES IN MENTAL DEFICIENCY

Gershon Berkson[1]

Defects in school and social adjustment, together with low scores on formal psychological tests, constitute the most commonly agreed upon characteristics of mental deficiency and have been the subject of most of the psychological research in this field. Such an emphasis on inadequacies in complex behavioral adjustments is entirely appropriate for workers concerned primarily with the social and educational aspects of mental deficiency. It encourages research on learning, language, and social processes, which should ultimately result in the improvement of the status of the mentally deficient as well as contribute to the understanding of these complex behaviors.

There are other characteristics which, though not as obviously related to educational and social adjustment, may also contribute to an understanding of mental deficiency. Among these characteristics is the generally lower biological status of defectives reflected in the existence of multiple handicaps and in the evidence of brain abnormality, especially in institutionalized patients. These abnormalities have been of major concern to medical research workers studying etiology and somatic therapy, while psychologists have taken the lead in studying the relationship of these defects to behavior. Medical researchers in mental deficiency usually have not been interested in behavior. When they have been, their approach has characteristically focused on the IQ as a major dependent variable. Psychologists have used more refined behavioral measures but have been limited in other ways. Their conceptions of brain injury, for instance, have been very gross.

[1] This chapter was written while the author was a National Institute of Mental Health Postdoctoral Fellow.

This is manifest in the crude techniques used to form groups in comparisons of patients with and without evidence of *organicity*.

It is only when medical and psychological workers become more sophisticated about each other's concerns and when cooperative research projects involving the best of both areas are initiated that important progress can be expected in the understanding of the relationship between behavioral and bodily defects in mental deficiency.

Such a *rapprochement* would parallel a similar union of general psychology and biology. Recent developments in the biological sciences have demonstrated the usefulness of refined behavioral study in the analysis of such widely divergent fields as taxonomy, genetics, pharmacology, and neurophysiology. The last decade has also found psychology going "under the skin" and losing its reluctance to explore the intricacies of biological phenomena and the relationship of these phenomena to more gross behaviors.

Therefore, it is worthwhile for research workers in mental deficiency to take advantage of the current resurgence of interest in the relationship between physiology and behavior and to ask what contribution the field of physiological psychology can make to the understanding of mental defects.

There are two broad areas of physiological psychology which have been especially relevant to problems in mental deficiency. The first of these is the study of the behavioral effects of brain abnormality in humans. This area is perhaps the most obviously relevant because of the fairly high proportion of institutionalized defectives with demonstrable brain maldevelopment or injury. It seems likely that theories of human brain injury and the techniques that have been developed for its study might be useful in a consideration of the fundamental disorganization of behavior in the mentally deficient.

A second area within physiological psychology concerns the study of *primitive responses* to the environment, including eye movements, brain activity, heart rate, respiration changes, and electrodermal activity. Experiments dealing with these responses have been done with mentally deficient subjects and have usually involved an assessment of the relationship between them and intelligence level. Most studies have shown that the mentally deficient as a group respond less to short duration stimuli than do normals. However, it is clear from the few existing experiments that the question of the responsiveness of the mentally deficient person to his environment is exceedingly complex and that a good deal more work is required to yield generalizations about individual differences and their relationship to general intelligence.

These fields of physiological psychology, then, would appear to be promising approaches to the study of mental deficiency. The choice of considering them involves the conception that mental deficiency is an area which can be viewed from a biological as well as from a social perspective. It therefore seems worthwhile to consider mental defectives as organisms with abnormal brains who have defects in primitive behaviors as well as in more complex adjustments.

BRAIN ABNORMALITY IN HUMANS

A number of writers have summarized evidence (e.g., Tredgold & Soddy, 1956) showing that the neuropathology among institutionalized defectives tends to be diffuse rather than of restricted locus, although in certain cases pathology may be concentrated more heavily in some areas of the brain than in others. Thus, it seems likely that while a most promising area of study in mental deficiency is that of the general behavioral effects of diffuse damage, a consideration of the effects of abnormalities of restricted locus may also be useful.

One approach to the study of localization of brain function in humans is the psychological examination of patients with localized brain lesions. Milner (1954) has done this type of study with patients who have had operations for abnormalities in the temporal lobe, and Teuber and his associates (e.g., Teuber, Battersby, & Bender, 1960) have analyzed sensory effects of injuries received from penetrating gunshot wounds.

A study of localization of brain function by behavioral testing of patients with brain lesions requires that the lesions be localized and that the locus be known. The experimenter can be fairly certain that these conditions are fulfilled if the lesions have been made by neurosurgery or by a restricted gunshot wound. In the mentally deficient these conditions do not usually obtain. More typically, damage is diffuse, and a localization of the damage is difficult until autopsy. Nevertheless, it may be that localization studies could be done with the mentally deficient. In some cases electroencephalographic (EEG) abnormalities may be focused in one part of the head rather than another, and patients with foci of abnormal activity in different areas could be compared on behavioral measures.

In the main though, psychologists in mental deficiency have been concerned with the grosser effects of brain damage. This concern has been reflected in their comparisons of patients who have evidence of organicity with those who are not apparently brain-injured. Usually, when differences are found, it is assumed that such differences reflect a general effect of brain abnormality. Similar studies have been done with brain-injured patients who are not necessarily mentally deficient. Klebanoff, Singer, and Wilensky (1954) have reviewed many of these studies, and their article shows how widespread the behavioral defects are in patients with brain injury. Much early work involved the study of impairment in the more complex psychological processes such as thinking and learning. More recently there has been an increase of interest in functions such as perception and sensorimotor skills.

It appears that brain abnormality can have an effect at all levels of behavioral functioning. To the extent that the mentally deficient can be assumed to have diffuse brain abnormality, the principle can be expected to hold. Mental defectives do have deficiencies in primitive as well as complex functions. Evidence for this position will be reviewed later.

Theories of the effects of brain injury have also emphasized its effect on different levels. Hughlings Jackson (1932) suggested that in evolution, neurological functions develop from centers controlling simple, automatic, well-organized behaviors to those involving the direction of complex, voluntary, less firmly organized functions. Jackson regarded *dissolution* of function in brain pathology as following a course, in general, opposite to evolution. That is, in brain abnormality, he believed the higher functions to be most readily affected. Goldstein (1942) took a similar position in regarding brain-injured people as having an "impairment of the attitude toward the abstract." He differentiated between two "attitudes" toward the world. The abstract attitude is the higher function in which responses are independent of immediate environmental stimuli but are based largely on concepts abstracted from previous experience. The concrete attitude, on the other hand, involves responding primarily to the stimuli present in the environment. According to Goldstein, the loss of the abstract attitude in brain-injured patients results in their falling prey to the influence of immediate stimuli. The brain-injured person fails to differentiate figure from background in the environment, and the world appears chaotic. He may appear indifferent to a particular stimulus because his attention "flits" from one aspect of his environment to another; or he may respond inappropriately to a stimulus again and again. Such perseveration occurs particularly when the patient is confronted with a difficult problem.

The functions which Goldstein emphasized were primarily the higher mental functions such as perception, thought, and speech. However, he also suggested the hypothesis that damage causes a rise in the threshold of a neurological function. This conception is rather similar to Head's idea of *vigilance* (1926), which is described as the readiness of an area of the nervous system to respond; this readiness can be lowered by injury, among other agents.

Both Goldstein's hypothesis and Head's theory of vigilance were applied to functions subserved by local areas of the brain. Thus, a local lesion in the occipital lobe might raise the threshold of visual functions but leave other functions relatively intact. These theories might lead to a prediction that *if the damage is diffuse and widespread the threshold of all functions, sensory, central, and motor, would be raised.*

Perhaps in primitive as well as in more complex behavior patients with diffuse injury would, in reacting to the same stimuli, respond with less vigor than would normals. Jackson's principle of dissolution suggests that in cases of diffuse damage the effects would be more severe for complex than for primitive processes.

PSYCHOPHYSIOLOGICAL CONCEPTS AND MENTAL DEFICIENCY

Since many mental defectives have diffuse brain abnormalities, they represent an appropriate population for the study of predictions deriving from the theories of Goldstein, Head, and Jackson. The study of primitive responses has up to now shown some support for the concept that the mentally deficient are less responsive to stimuli than are normals. However, this conclusion must be qualified, and some evidence opposes it.

Most experiments which have used mentally deficient subjects in the study of primitive responses have been methodologically simple and have lacked theoretical foundation. This is to be expected in any new field, but as a previous review has indicated (Berkson, 1961), there is enough evidence now to indicate that experiments in this area are feasible and that they have produced repeatable results. Such studies have been scattered, and a great deal more work will have to be accomplished in order to answer some of the questions raised by the previous research. Although studies of primitive responses of mental defectives have lacked a theoretical foundation, there are a number of general concepts in the field of physiological psychology which might help in organizing the results of such investigations.

Activation. The first of these concepts is activation. A number of writers have expressed the belief that behavior can be scaled along an intensive (as opposed to a directional) dimension of behavior. This intensive dimension has been variously referred to as activation, arousal, energy level, motivation, and general drive. One way of conceiving of this dimension is as a continuum from death and coma through sleep and wakefulness to strong emotion. Lindsley (1960) has described arousal in this way and has hypothesized a relationship between states of "awareness" and characteristics of a person's EEG at different points on the arousal continuum. There is fairly general agreement that there is a predictable relationship between activation and behavioral efficiency (Duffy, 1957; Hebb, 1955; Schlosberg, 1954). This relationship is usually termed the inverted U function. With increasing activation, behavioral efficiency is said to increase to an optimum and then to decrease (Stennett, 1957).

The intensity dimension of activation has been most fully developed in physiological research. The *direction* of activation has also been considered, especially in the older literature on attention (Woodworth & Schlosberg, 1954). Recent developments in this area have included studies of curiosity (Berlyne, 1960) and the neurophysiological substrate of attentional responses (Lindsley, 1960).

The Pavlovian concept of the orienting reflex developed by Russian scientists has recently attracted a good deal of interest outside of Russia. Theories of the orienting reflex contain both intensive and directional aspects, and much recent work has concerned the primitive orienting responses to stimuli (Razran, 1961; Sokolov, 1960).

The significance of the activation concept in mental deficiency has been considered only recently. Duffy (1957), although not mentioning intelligence, has expressed the belief that individual differences in responsiveness are reliable. Lindsley (1957) has suggested that the mentally deficient may have a defect in the functioning of the ascending reticular activating system of the midbrain. Elsewhere in this volume, Ellis suggests that the effect of stimuli may be less pronounced for mental defectives than for normals. Berkson (1961) has summarized evidence suggesting that mental defectives respond less vigorously to certain stimuli than do normals.

There are two general methods used in gauging responsiveness. The first concerns the amount of activity in a response measure when the environment is relatively unchanging. In such a situation the measure tends to remain relatively stable and is called the *basal* or *resting* level. Another measure of responsiveness is made when the experimenter presents a stimulus of relatively short duration and there is a resulting change in the measure. These responses to short-duration stimuli usually begin within approximately a second after the stimulus.

Occasionally, responses are measured while the subject performs a complex activity. Such a study is that of Carrier, Malpass, and Orton (1961), who compared bright, normal, and retarded children on measures of physiological and gross motor activity during learning tasks. They found that, while there were clear group differences in learning, physiological indices discriminated between the groups in only two comparisons. These findings may point to a difficulty in working with certain physiological measures during the performance of more gross activities but are also consistent with the principle that primitive responses are less obviously affected in the mentally deficient than are more complex processes.

Law of initial values. A second psychophysiological concept deals with the relationship of amplitude of a response to the level the subject manifests prior to stimulation. This law of initial value (Lacey, 1956; Wilder, 1958) is said to reflect a homeostatic mechanism which introduces an inhibition of response to the extent that a response system is already reacting.

One approach has used the relationship between level and response as a measure of individual differences (Lacey, 1956). Bridger and Reiser (1959) have studied the relationship between prestimulus heart rate and the change in rate following a stimulus. They find that within an individual there is a negative relationship between change and initial level. But they also show a "paradoxical effect" (see Lacey, 1956) which amounts to a change in direction of response following very high initial levels. Thus, while there is an increase in heart rate to stimulation when initial rate is low or moderate, the stimulus produces a decrease in heart rate when initial level is very high. There is also an intermediate point when stimulation produces no change at all. Bridger and Reiser suggest that this crossover point and the regression between level and response may be valid measures of individual responsiveness.

Most experiments using mental defectives as subjects have been concerned with group comparisons on either the basal level or the amplitude of response. None has involved the study of the relationship between prestimulus level and a dependent response. The more nearly analytic study of relationships within individuals and the use of these relationships as an expression of individual differences is a promising approach to the study of response mechanisms in mental deficiency.

Response pattern specificity. Still another approach involves the principle of response pattern specificity. This principle depends on the fact that in many experiments multiple measures are made simultaneously on the same individual. Thus heart rate, respiration, skin resistance, and other measures may be obtained at the same time. From activation theory one might suppose that an increase in one measure may be accompanied by increases in the others if arousal is a general phenomenon. It is true that under conditions meant to be arousing, all measures tend to rise (Schnore, 1959; Lacey, Bateman, & Van Lehn, 1953). However, not all measures increase equally. Rather a person responds with an individual *pattern* of responses, more intensely in some measures than in others. Although there appear to be individual patterns of responding which are trans-situational, there is also some evidence that the nature of stimuli can affect response patterns (Davis & Buchwald. 1957; Davis, Buchwald, & Frankmann, 1955).

A recent study by Vogel (1961) was concerned with the effects of stimulus variables as well as IQ and age on patterns of response. He compared the reactions of mentally retarded, normal, and gifted children of two different ages to a loud tone and the cold pressor test. The measures he obtained were skin resistance, pulse rate, finger volume, breathing rate, and three measures of blood pressure. Normal subjects were more reactive than the defectives in pulse rate but were less reactive than the defectives in respiration rate. In addition, a composite score of recovery from stimuli on all measures showed that the defectives recovered more quickly than did either the normals or the gifted and that there was a tendency for the younger children to recover more quickly than the older ones. Finally, Vogel investigated the relationship between IQ and differential effects of stimuli on response patterns. He found that with an increase in IQ there was a decreasing tendency for different stimuli to produce different response patterns. This relationship with IQ was also apparent in the comparison of the gifted with the normal children.

In summary, response pattern specificity, a theory of general activation, and the law of initial value appear to be important for research on responsiveness of defectives. There is good evidence for a conception of an intensive dimension along which all behaviors can be scaled, and the relationship between prestimulus level and response intensity may help to clarify the significance of arousal for the study of individual differences. The use of more than one response measure demonstrates that there is a general increase in all measures in situations that are intended to be arousing. However, there is a tendency for this increase to be unequal in the different measures; i.e., there are patterns of responsiveness. These patterns reflect reliable individual differences and vary with different stimuli.

PRIMITIVE RESPONSES OF THE MENTALLY DEFICIENT

Studies of primitive responses of defectives have usually involved comparisons with normals or correlations of single response measures with IQ in the defective range. Other studies have included comparisons of clinical groups among the defective population, while few have dealt with the effects of specific stimuli or situational changes on reactions.

A fairly wide variety of responses has been examined by researchers in mental deficiency. However, there are few studies dealing with particular measures, and experiments have been exploratory rather than definitive.

Muscle activity. The only experiments that have studied myographic phenomena in defectives have dealt with tendon reflexes. Travis and Dorsey (1930) found no differences in the speed of the patellar tendon reflex in superior and defective children; and Whitehorn, Lundholm, and Gardner (1930) showed a negligible correlation of patellar reflex time with mental age. An earlier study by Chaney (1924) showed that tendon reflexes in cases of myxedema are slow and require greater stimulation than normal for their elicitation. However, Chaney concluded that when a patient with myxedema is treated with thyroid extract, his tendon reflexes seem to function normally.

These three studies are all quite old and bear repeating with modern techniques. Chaney's observations suggest that spinal reflex speed is related to a functionally normal thyroid gland. In patients having defects in thyroid function, a deviation from normal reflex speed might be found. Whether such a defect may also be reflected in the speed of other reflexes could be investigated and the significance of slow reflexes to neural or synaptic conduction time might be considered. Although, on the basis of these studies, defectives do not generally appear to have slower tendon reflexes than do normals, it may be that some do, and that for these selected patients, a general slowing of physiological responsiveness has been an important factor in their mental defect.

Further experimentation on tendon reflexes might concern itself with the amplitude as well as the speed of these reflexes. Since there is some evidence to indicate that defectives do not respond to short-duration stimuli as vigorously as do normals, it would be interesting to know if this applies to tendon reflexes. It might also be illuminating to investigate the difference in responsiveness between normals and defectives as a function of the complexity of the reflexes studied (tendon reflexes are relatively simple stimulus-response events).

Electromyographic (EMG) techniques could be used in many measurements besides tendon reflexes. Measures of general body tension could be made by a study of the levels of response in a number of muscle groups. Such studies might help to clarify whether defectives are any more or less "arousable" than normals under different conditions.

Such a study might be conducted in relation to other measures. The characteristics of specific muscle movements could also be investigated. One such problem would be a refinement of reaction time (RT) experiments. It has been shown consistently that normals are faster than the retarded in RT and that speed is positively related to intelligence within the defective range (Berkson, 1960a). Berkson (1960c) has suggested that this slowness may be related to difficulty in the initiation or performance of a response rather than to any slowness of sensory or central functions. Perhaps the measurement of muscle potential during the performance of an RT task would shed light on this issue.

Blood circulation. Typically, three measures of blood circulatory activity are studied. The first is heart or pulse rate, which is a measure of the number of heart beats per minute. Vogel (1961) found that normal children were more reactive to stimuli in terms of pulse rate than were defectives. Berkson, Hermelin, and O'Connor (1961) found that the resting level of heart rate did not significantly differentiate between normals and various groups of defectives, but that there was a tendency for heart rate to increase with a decrease in intelligence. No comparison of blood pressure levels or responses has been reported for defectives in experimental situations. Vogel (1961) did make comparisons between his normal and gifted subjects with respect to blood pressure responses and reported differences between these two groups. He was unable to obtain blood pressure recordings from the defective group.

Blood volume, in addition to heart rate and blood pressure, is a third measure of circulatory change. Vogel (1961) reported no differences in finger volume change between normals and defectives in response to stimuli. However, Vinogradova (as quoted by Razran, 1961) showed that normals gave more vascular responses than did defectives to a variety of stimuli.

The experiments on circulatory changes have provided evidence that defectives tend to be less responsive than normals to stimuli of short duration. There is only suggestive evidence that they are different from normals in resting levels. A finding that circulatory responses are inadequate in the defective may be significant because of the role blood plays in the support of gross behavioral responses. A poor supply of blood to muscles or the nervous system might be reflected in a lower efficiency of these systems with a resulting inefficiency of behavior in general.

Brain activity.   Although recordings of brain activity have been made with electrodes in the brain or on the cerebral cortex, all studies using EEG techniques in mental deficiency have used electrodes on the scalp. The most commonly studied brain rhythm, called the *alpha* rhythm, has a frequency of 8 to 12 per second and usually has its major amplitude at the back of the head. It occurs most often when the subject is resting quietly and disappears when the person is attentive or when he goes to sleep. Five parameters of the alpha rhythm have been studied, and there is information regarding all of these from studies of mental defectives. The most commonly measured parameter is the frequency of the rhythm which in normals averages about 10 per second. Berkson et al. (1961) found no differences between normal and defective adults in alpha frequency. Gibbs, Rich, Fois, and Gibbs (1960) showed no differences in average frequency but did find that there were slightly more subjects in the mentally deficient group with either slow or fast rhythms. Kreezer (1939) found no relationship between MA and alpha frequency in mongoloid subjects. Kreezer and Smith (1950) also failed to find a correlation between MA and alpha frequency in an undifferentiated familial group. On the other hand, Knott, Friedman, and Bardsley (1942) found a significant correlation between IQ and alpha frequency in 8-year-old normal and retarded children.

Two other aspects of the alpha rhythm are its average amplitude and the proportion of time it is seen in the record when the subject is resting quietly. Kreezer (1939) found a significant correlation of both these measures with mental age in a mongoloid group, but Kreezer and Smith (1950) found no such relationship in a familial group. Neither Knott et al. (1942) nor Berkson et al. (1961) found a relationship between IQ and per cent time alpha.

Two other parameters of the alpha rhythm are measures of responses to short-duration stimuli. When a person rests quietly in a darkened room, the alpha rhythm tends to be most distinguishable. But if a stimulus such as a flash of light is presented, the alpha rhythm is reduced for a short period of time and then returns often at an increased amplitude. This disappearance of the alpha rhythm is called *blocking,* and the length of time it remains blocked has been named *perseveration time* (Travis & Knott, 1937). No published study has investigated the relationship between IQ and speed of alpha blocking. However, in an unpublished experiment, Lindsley and Berkson found no difference in this measure between superior and defective subjects. With regard to the length of time that the alpha remains blocked, Berkson et al. (1961) and Lindsley and Berkson showed that the perseveration time of normals is on the average longer than that of the defectives.

Besides alpha blocking there are other measures of brain responsiveness as measured by the EEG. These are typically used in clinical electroencephalography but have been employed for experimental purposes. The first of these involves the evocation of abnormal brain activity from patients who may have normal resting records but who are suspected of having brain abnormalities. The evoking of high-frequency spikes or of slow waves may be accomplished by having the subject breathe deeply for some minutes (hyperventilation) or by directing a high-intensity, flickering light into his eyes. The use of the flickering light also provides a second method of assessing a type of brain responsiveness. This response involves the measurement of the extent to which rhythms in the occipital region of the head can be "driven" at the same frequency as that of the flickering light. In two studies using these techniques, Walter, Yeager, and Rubin (1955, 1956) compared mongoloid subjects with groups of undifferentiated defectives with and without histories of epilepsy. They showed that the mongoloid subjects had fewer abnormal EEGs than did the undifferentiated subjects. They also found that undifferentiated defectives who had a history of seizures were more responsive to the flickering light than were undifferentiated subjects without such a history and that both undifferentiated groups were more responsive than mongoloid subjects. When Metrazol was injected along with the administration of the flickering light, these differences were enhanced.

The experiments which have been done in mental deficiency indicate that EEG parameters may be related to IQ. However, these studies are few, and the findings usually reflect low correlations. Thus, all these experiments bear repeating.

Electrodermal responses.   Experiments employing electrodermal measures in defectives have concentrated mainly on basal level and GSR as related to IQ. The pattern of results obtained is fairly complex and apparently depends on the group being studied.

O'Connor and Venables (1956), Ellis and Sloan (1958), and Berkson et al. (1961) have all shown that institutionalized adult defectives have higher basal conductance (*lower* resistance) than normals. O'Connor and Venables (1956) demonstrated a negative correlation between IQ and conductance among institutionalized defectives. Pryer and Ellis (1959) found that high-level Caucasian female defectives have higher conductance than low-level female defectives or high-level males and Negro females.

The results of research on basal level with defective school children seem to reflect a different pattern. Collmann has shown (1931, 1959) that the retarded have *higher* basal resistances than normals of the same age.

On the other hand, studies of the GSR to stimuli appear to present a more consistent picture. Collmann (1931, 1959), using a resistance measure with school children, and Berkson et al. (1961), measuring skin potential with institutionalized adults, showed that defectives had smaller responses to stimuli than did normals. Paramonova (as quoted by Razran, 1961), using only a defective group, also showed that they had fewer responses than would have been expected from data on normals.

Special mention should be made of the results obtained with mongoloids. Clark, working in O'Connor's laboratory at the Fountain Hospital, London, has recently shown that basal conductances of mongoloids are lower than those of other imbeciles of the same IQ. Berkson et al. (1961) also obtained this result, and in their experiment the basal conductances of mongoloids were not different from those of normals. This was true even though the GSR of the mongoloid subjects was smaller than that of either normals or other defective groups.

The studies of electrodermal activity seem to indicate that response amplitude in defectives is less than that in normals. The studies of basal level give different results apparently depending upon whether the subjects are school children, adult patients, or mongoloid.

Eyeblink. There have been three studies of the eyeblink reflex of defectives. Two of these have dealt with the conditioning of the response and one with its inhibition.

Berger (1954) performed a study on the inhibition of the eyeblink reflex in three groups of mentally retarded boys and in one group of normals. He predicted that a brain-damaged group would have more difficulty inhibiting the blink reflex if the ability to inhibit depended upon the integrity of the nervous system. Employing a technique in which a hammer struck a plate of glass near the subject's eye, he found that the organic, familial, and psychogenic defective groups all inhibited less than did the normals. Differences among the defective groups were, in general, not significant. In an eyelid-conditioning experiment, Franks and Franks (1960) showed that organics gave fewer responses from the very beginning of the experiment than did either familial or normal comparison groups. There were no differences between familials and normals. This pattern of results suggested to Franks and Franks that it was *organicity* rather than IQ itself which interfered with classical conditioning. Cromwell, Palk, and Foshee (1961) have shown a low but statistically significant relationship between MA and eyelid conditioning among a group of defectives. There was no relationship between conditioning and IQ. There was some indication that fewer voluntary eyeblinks occurred in subjects with lower IQs.

Besides confirming a tendency for lowered responsiveness in defectives, the eyeblink-reflex studies have suggested a lead in the analysis of the relationship between learning and differences in responsiveness. A separation of initial differences in responsiveness from a consideration of rate of change in response level over learning trials permits a more refined analysis of comparative learning abilities than has hitherto been employed with the mentally deficient.

A further conclusion from one of the eyeblink experiments is that lowered responsiveness in the mentally deficient may be related to demonstrable brain abnormality rather than tested intelligence. Such a conclusion might imply that brain-injured patients with normal IQs would be less responsive than non-brain-injured normals. Electroencephalographic studies by Blum (1957) appear to support this implication, but further research is needed to confirm it.

Phosphenes. A low-intensity a-c current passed between electrodes on the forehead and the temple produces visual sensations called phosphenes whose character is dependent on the nature of the stimulation. Clausen and Karrer (1961) compared the threshold for evocation of these sensations in normal and retarded subjects and found that the retarded as a group had a higher-than-normal threshold. They also found that within the mentally deficient group there was no relationship of phosphene threshold with etiology, gross neurological signs, clinical EEG, or certain behavioral tests. These workers did, however, demonstrate a significant relationship between phosphene threshold and the per cent time alpha of the EEG. They suggested that retarded subjects may have faster accommodation of nerve response to stimuli or a reduced excitability of the nervous system.

Eye movements. All the measures discussed so far give information regarding the intensity of responses either to a short-duration stimulus or in a situation where stimuli are fairly constant. There are a number of problems in which it would be useful to monitor shifts in the direction of behavior. Through these measures of direction, physiological activities might be related to grosser types of responses such as scanning the visual field, tracking, and perhaps even learning and problem solving.

Although it is not always so, it is commonly the case that when visual stimuli are used, a good measure of the direction of behavior is the orientation of the subject's eyes. When a person is stimulated, he often turns his eyes toward the source of stimulation; and when he explores a visual field, the progress of his exploration can be followed by watching the successive fixations of the eyes.

The only experimental study of eye movements in the mentally deficient was done by O'Connor and Berkson (unpublished), and it compared normals, mongoloids, and nonmongoloid imbeciles. Each subject was tested in a dark room and presented with a varying number of small lights. In all three groups, there was an increase in number of eye movements associated with an increase in the number of lights displayed. The mongoloid subjects showed more eye movements than did the imbeciles or normals. There was a weak suggestion, observed only under the most complex experimental condition, that the eyes of the imbeciles moved more than did those of the normals. It is not known why the mongoloid subjects moved their eyes so much, although apprehensiveness in the experimental situation is a possible explanation.

Studies of eye movements in defectives might help to clarify a number of interesting relationships that have previously been described. In Rosenberg's experiment on searching behavior (1961) severely defective patients took longer to detect and choose a nonsense shape from a matrix of shapes than did more mildly retarded patients. An analysis of eye movements during such a task might help to determine the mechanism that differentiated the groups during the search-choice process. It would also be interesting to know whether the speed of orientation to a novel stimulus is as rapid in defectives as in normals or whether, as in other studies of reaction time, (Berkson, 1960a), defectives are slower in eye-movement orientation.

Startle reflex.   The final experiment with defectives to be reviewed is that included in the study of the startle reflex by Landis and Hunt (1939). This reflex is a complex pattern of activities including blinking and a characteristic facial expression and body response. It occurs in a number of mammalian species in response to a sudden loud sound. Landis and Hunt evoked the reflex with a gun fired closely behind the subject and measured the response with high-speed photography. They found that defective patients manifested a more intense response than did normals. This was in contrast to an epileptic group who showed an attenuated response relative to normals.

Aside from Vogel's results with change of respiration rate, the finding that the mentally deficient show a greater startle reflex is the only evidence to indicate that defectives are more responsive to short-duration stimuli than are normals. These findings suggest that degree of responsiveness as related to IQ may depend on the response chosen. Another possibility is that intensity or some other characteristic of stimulation may have had an effect, since in the studies of respiration and startle rather intense stimuli were used. For instance, there may be an interaction such that defectives are less responsive than normals to stimuli of low intensity, equally responsive to moderate stimulation, and overresponsive to loud sounds or bright lights.

Summary.   Studies dealing with the physiological responsiveness of defectives show no evidence, except in patients with cretinism, that the speed of reflexes is slower in defectives than in normals. Any hypothesis that the slower reaction time of voluntary responses in defectives has a basis in slower conduction of nerve impulses thus enjoys no empirical foundation from reflex studies. A final conclusion regarding this hypothesis awaits experiments using more refined techniques than have hitherto been employed. At this time the application of a hypothesis involving speed of neural conduction as differentiating defectives from normals is not attractive.

On the other hand, by reason of a lower number of functional neurons or because of defects in neural functioning, the mentally deficient may have abnormalities in temporal or spatial summation at synapses throughout the nervous system. This defect in summation could produce higher thresholds in individual neurons of the person with diffuse damage, and if the damage is widespread, could account for a generally lower responsiveness to stimuli.

Conceptions emphasizing individual differences in basal activation and responsiveness can be important. There is some evidence from experiments on skin conductance that basal level of activation is inversely related to IQ, at least within the lower half of the IQ continuum. This conclusion should be limited to institutionalized patients, since the results with defective school children have been in the opposite direction. It may be that the higher activation level in defectives is related to anxiety in an unfamiliar situation, but this seems unlikely since, even after adaptation to the experimental situation, normals and defectives seem as far apart in skin conductance as they were initially (Ellis & Sloan, 1958; Berkson et al., 1961), although conductance of both groups has decreased. The primary evidence for greater resting activation in institutionalized defectives comes from studies of skin conductance; however, there is also some support for this from experiments on eye movements and heart rate. There is nevertheless a need to broaden the basis for this conclusion by testing it with other measures and to ascertain whether it results from level of nervous system activity or from some peripheral mechanism.

Although the evidence from studies of basal level is rather limited results regarding responsiveness to short-duration stimulation have been found with a larger group of measures. In general, defectives are less responsive to stimuli than are normals. This conclusion is based on measures of GSR, EEG, phosphene thresholds, change of pulse rate, and vascular response. Although defectives appear less responsive to stimuli, there is contradictory evidence from a measure of respiration rate and from a study of the startle response. Moreover, when differences in basal level or response amplitude do exist between defectives and normals, the differences are very small and there is a marked degree of overlap between the groups. Thus responsiveness is hardly diagnostic of mental deficiency.

CONCLUSIONS

There is some evidence to support the notion that mental defectives are less responsive to stimuli of short duration than are normals, and there is reason to believe that such a defect in responsiveness is related to the diffuse brain abnormality found in this group. Whether lowered responsiveness is a function of abnormality in the reticular formation of the midbrain or whether it is a reflection of more extensive neuropathology may be a question that can only be answered by subjecting infrahuman animals to localized experimental lesions.

Should a concept of lowered responsiveness in the mentally deficient be established more firmly, it could have implications for analyses of defects in more complex behavioral functions. It may be, for instance, that the slower reaction time of the mentally deficient is related to a generally low responsiveness to short-duration stimuli. In learning experiments, certain of the mentally deficient may differ from normals, not so much in the rate at which they learn, but in their initial and final level of response to the learning material (Berkson, 1960b; Franks & Franks, 1960).

However, it is clear from the experiments that have been done that defectives are not always less responsive to short-duration stimuli than are normals. In some instances, they have been shown to give greater responses. Future studies would do well to clarify the conditions under which a concept of "lower responsiveness" of defectives holds and when it must be qualified.

Another issue concerns the response level of defectives when presented with a relatively unchanging environment. In this instance, the results of experiments appear to vary with the group of defectives studied. It is possible that results with resting measures depend on the nature of the environment as well as the group.

A study of the relationship between basal or prestimulus levels to the amplitude of responses to short-duration stimuli may clarify the underlying mechanisms of abnormal responsiveness. The law of initial value might lead one to expect that the lowered responsiveness of defectives is related to their deviant basal levels. Berkson et al. (1961) found no correlation between basal skin resistance and skin potential change. However, their method was quite crude, and the question of whether lowered responsiveness is related to deviant basal level is far from settled.

Another approach might emphasize a possible relationship between responsiveness to short-duration stimuli and attention to situational stimuli. An individual might manifest a less vigorous response to short-duration stimuli as a reflection of a generally lower responsiveness to all stimulation. On the other hand, the defective might not respond to short-duration stimuli because he is responding preferentially to other aspects of the environment. It might be productive to vary the characteristics of various types of short-duration stimuli and of situational stimuli independently and to observe the effects on response and basal levels. Attention to the environment should be reflected in changes when the surroundings are varied, and likewise the relative effect of short-duration stimulation could be assessed by changes in amount of responsiveness as short-duration stimuli are varied. Eye fixation and movement measurements might be useful in such experiments.

The use of multiple response measures has been shown by Vogel (1961) to give special information about response patterns in the mentally deficient. His finding that different stimuli have a greater differential effect on physiological responses in children with lower IQs suggest that the mentally deficient may be a useful group for the study of stimulus effects on primitive responses. The theoretical implications of his findings are not yet clear but could be important in a consideration of the biological bases of intelligence.

Animal experiments, too, may be important in the study of responsiveness of organisms with widespread neuropathology. Animals exposed to anoxia during development are a useful experimental preparation for showing the effects of diffuse brain abnormality. Two experiments (Meier, Bunch, Nolan, & Scheidler, 1961; Saxon, 1961) have indicated that such preparations seem less responsive to their environment than are normal animals. Thus it appears that animals with diffuse damage may be less responsive than normal animals. Other potentially useful preparations are animals raised on high phenylalinine diets (Waisman, Palmer, & Harlow, 1960). The use of animals for experiments in which control of historical and experimental variables simulating those probably operative in mental deficiency has occurred rarely. However, some animal studies have been done by others who have shown the large number of agents that can produce developmental defects. These studies also demonstrate that many of the problems which concern research workers in mental deficiency can be fruitfully studied with animals as well as with human subjects. Finally, studies of developmental defects in animals emphasize the biosocial character of the development of behavior and suggest that it is worthwhile to consider developmental defects in terms of the interplay between biological and social influences.

By far the most prevalent biological approach to the study of mental deficiency has been etiological research. In contrast with this approach, psychologists have been less concerned with questions of etiological mechanisms, but rather have studied the implications of defects for behavioral adaptation. Their research has ordinarily involved experiments with relatively complex behavioral functions such as perception and learning. The study of primitive response systems represents a union of psychological and biological approaches. The psychobiological approach emphasizes the constant involvement of the organism in his surroundings and the interplay of defects with the demands of a physical and a social environment.

REFERENCES

BERGER, A.   Inhibition of the eyelid reflex in three etiologic groups of mentally retarded boys as compared with normals. *Train. Sch. Bull.,* 1954, 51, 146–152.

BERKSON, G.   An analysis of reaction time in normal and mentally deficient young men. I. Duration threshold experiment. *J. ment. Defic. Res.,* 1960, 4, Pt. 1, 51–58. (a)

BERKSON, G.   An analysis of reaction time in normal and mentally deficient young men. II. Variation of complexity in reaction time tasks. *J. ment. Defic. Res.,* 1960, 4, Pt. 1, 59–67. (b)

BERKSON, G.   An analysis of reaction time in normal and mentally deficient young men. III. Variation of stimulus and of response complexity. *J. ment. Defic. Res.,* 1960, 4, Pt. 2, 69–77. (c)

BERKSON, G.   Responsiveness of the mentally deficient. *Amer. J. ment. Defic.,* 1961, 66, 277–286.

BERKSON, G., HERMELIN, B., & O'CONNOR, N.   Physiological responses of normals and institutionalized mental defectives to repeated stimuli. *J. ment. Defic. Res.,* 1961, 5, Pt. 1, 30–39.

BERLYNE, D. E.   *Conflict, arousal, and curiosity.* New York: McGraw-Hill, 1960.

BLUM, R. H.   Alpha-rhythm responsiveness in normal, schizophrenic, and brain-damaged persons. *Science,* 1957, 126, 749–750.

BRIDGER, W. H., & REISER, M. F.   Psychophysiologic studies of the neonate: an approach toward methodological and theoretical problems involved. *Psychosom. Med.,* 1959, 21, 265–276.

CARRIER, N. A., MALPASS, L. F., & ORTON, K. D.   *Responses of bright, normal, and retarded children to learning tasks.* Carbondale: Sth. Illinois Univer., 1961.

CHANEY, W. C.   Tendon reflexes in myxedema. *J. Amer. Med. Ass.,* 1924, 82, 2013–2016.

CLAUSEN, J., & KARRER, R.   Electrical sensitivity of the eye in the mentally retarded. *Train. Sch. Bull.,* 1961, 58, 3–13.

COLLMANN, R. D.   The psychogalvanic reactions of exceptional and normal school children. *Teach. Coll. Contr. Educ.,* 1931, No. 469.

COLLMANN, R. D.   The galvanic skin responses of mentally retarded and other children in England. *Amer. J. ment. Defic.,* 1959, 63, 626–632.

CROMWELL, R. L., PALK, B. E., & FOSHEE, J. G.   Studies in activity level. V. The relationships among eyelid conditioning, intelligence, activity level, and age. *Amer. J. ment. Defic.,* 1961, 65, 744–748.

DAVIS, R. C., & BUCHWALD, A. M.   An exploration of somatic response patterns: stimulus and sex differences. *J. comp. physiol. Psychol.,* 1957, 50, 44–52.

DAVIS, R. C., BUCHWALD, A. M., & FRANKMANN, R. W.   Autonomic and muscular responses and their relation to simple stimuli. *Psychol. Monogr.,* 1955, 69, No. 20 (Whole No. 405).

DUFFY, E. The psychological significance of the concept of "arousal" or "activation." *Psychol. Rev.*, 1957, 64, 265–275.

ELLIS, N. R., & SLOAN, W. The relationship between intelligence and skin conductance. *Amer. J. ment. Defic.*, 1958, 63, 304–306.

FRANKS, V., & FRANKS, C. M. Conditioning in defectives and in normals as related to intelligence and organic deficit. Paper read at London Conf. on the scientific Stud. of ment. Def., 1960.

GIBBS, E. L., RICH, C. L., FO:S, A., & GIBBS, F. A. Electroencephalographic study of mentally retarded persons. *Amer. J. ment. Defic.*, 1960, 65, 236–247.

GOLDSTEIN, K. *Aftereffects of brain injuries in war.* New York: Grune & Stratton, 1942.

HEAD, H. *Aphasia and kindred disorders of speech.* Vol. 1. New York: Macmillan, 1926.

HEBB, D. O. Drives and the C.N.S. (Conceptual nervous system). *Psychol. Rev.*, 1955, 62, 243–254.

JACKSON, J. H. *Selected writings of John Hughlings Jackson.* Vol. 2. London: Hodder, 1932.

KLEBANOFF, S. G., SINGER, J. L., & WILENSKY, H. Psychological consequences of brain lesions and ablations. *Psychol. Bull.,* 1954, 51, 1–41.

KNOTT, J. R., FRIEDMAN, H., & BARDSLEY, R. Some electroencephalographic correlates of intelligence in eight year and twelve year old children. *J. exp. Psychol.*, 1942, 30, 380–391.

KREEZER, G. Intelligence level and occipital alpha rhythm in the mongolian type of mental deficiency. *Amer. J. Psychol.*, 1939, 52, 503–532.

KREEZER, G., & SMITH, F. W. The relation of the alpha rhythm of the electroencephalogram and intelligence level in the nondifferentiated familial type of mental deficiency. *J. Psychol.*, 1950, 29, 47–51.

LACEY, J. I. The evaluation of autonomic responses: toward a general solution. *Ann. N.Y. Acad. Sci.*, 1956, 67, 123–164.

LACEY, J. I., BATEMAN, D. E., & VAN LEHN, R. Autonomic response specificity. *Psychosom. Med.*, 1953, 15, 8–21.

LANDIS, C., & HUNT, W. A. *The startle pattern.* New York: Holt, 1939.

LINDSLEY, D. B. Psychophysiology and motivation. In M. R. Jones (Ed.), *Nebraska symposium on motivation.* Lincoln: Nebraska Univer. Press, 1957.

LINDSLEY, D. B. Attention, consciousness, sleep, and wakefulness. In J. Field, H. W. Magoun, & V. E. Hall (Eds.), *Handbook of physiology.* Sec. 1, Vol. 3. Washington: American Physiological Society, 1960.

MEIER, G. W., BUNCH, M. E., NOLAN, C. Y., & SCHEIDLER, C. H. Anoxia, behavioral development and learning ability: comparative-experimental approach. *Psychol. Monogr.*, 1960, No. 74 (Whole No. 488).

MILNER, B. Intellectual function of the temporal lobes. *Psychol. Bull.*, 1954, 51, 42–62.

O'CONNOR, N., & VENABLES, P. H. A note on the basal level of skin conductance and Binet IQ. *Brit. J. Psychol.*, 1956, 47, 148–149.

PRYER, R. S., & ELLIS, N. R. Skin conductance and autonomic lability as a function of intelligence in mental defectives. *Amer. J. ment. Defic.*, 1959, 63, 835–838.

RAZRAN, G. The observable unconscious and the inferable conscious in current Soviet psychophysiology: interoceptive conditioning, semantic conditioning and the orienting reflex. *Psychol. Rev.*, 1961, 68, 81–147.

ROSENBERG, S. Searching behavior in the retarded as a function of stimulus exposure conditions and IQ. *Amer. J. ment. Defic.*, 1961, 65, 749–752.

SAXON, S. V. Differences in reactivity between asphyxial and normal rhesus monkeys. *J. genet. Psychol.*, 1961, 99, 283–287.

SCHLOSBERG, H. Three dimensions of emotion. *Psychol. Rev.*, 1954, 61, 81–88.

SCHNORE, M. M. Individual patterns of physiological activity as a function of task differences and degree of arousal. *J. exp. Psychol.*, 1959, 58, 117–128.

SOKOLOV, E. N. Neuronal models and the orienting reflex. In M. A. B. Brazier (Ed.), *The central nervous system and behavior*. New York: Josiah Macy, Jr., Foundation, 1960.

STENNETT, R. G. The relationship of performance level to level of arousal. *J. exp. Psychol.*, 1957, 54, 54–61.

TEUBER, H., BATTERSBY, W. S., & BENDER, M. B. *Visual field defects after penetrating missile wounds of the brain*. Cambridge, Mass.: Harvard, 1960.

TRAVIS, L. E., & DORSEY, J. M. The relationship of "intelligence" and reflex conduction rate as found in hypophrenic children. *J. exp. Psychol.*, 1930, 13, 370–372.

TRAVIS, L. E., & KNOTT, J. R. Brain potential studies of perseveration. II. Perseveration time to visually presented words. *J. exp. Psychol.*, 1937, 21, 353–358.

TREDGOLD, R. F., & SODDY, K. *A text-book of mental deficiency*. London: Baillière, 1956.

VOGEL, W. The relationship of age and intelligence to autonomic functioning. *J. comp. physiol. Psychol.*, 1961, 54, 133–138.

WAISMAN, H. A., PALMER, G., & HARLOW, H. F. Phenylketonuria in infant monkeys. Paper read at London Conf. on the scientific Stud. of ment. Defic., 1960.

WALTER, R. D., YEAGER, C. L., & RUBIN, H. K. Mongolism and convulsive seizures. *Arch. Neurol. Psychiat.*, 1955, 74, 559–563.

WALTER, R. D., YEAGER, C. L., & RUBIN, H. K. An electroencephalographic survey with activation techniques of "undifferentiated" mental deficiency. *Amer. J. ment. Defic.*, 1956, 60, 785–791.

WHITEHORN, J. C., LUNDHOLM, H., & GARDNER, G. E. Concerning the alleged correlation of intelligence with knee jerk reflex time. *J. exp. Psychol.*, 1930, 13, 293–295.

WILDER, J. Modern psychophysiology and the law of initial value. *Amer. J. Psychother.*, 1958, 12, 199–221.

WOODWORTH, R. S., & SCHLOSBERG, H. *Experimental Psychology*. New York: Holt, 1954.

18

ABNORMAL BEHAVIOR AND MENTAL DEFICIENCY

Sol L. Garfield

INTRODUCTION

The task of discussing abnormal behavior in the mentally retarded is beset with certain difficulties. One of the difficulties pertains to the variations in the definition of mental retardation and the types of disturbed adjustment to be included within this category (Benda, Farrell, & Chipman, 1951; Clarke & Clarke, 1958; Garfield & Wittson, 1960a; Neham, 1951). Although such terms as mental retardation and psychosis are used to refer to different types of behavior, the distinction is not always easy to make. This problem is particularly evident in the appraisal of disturbed behavior in children. Varying interpretations are possible for many reasons: the child's development is incomplete, similar or overlapping symptoms may be noted in different disorders, communication on the part of the child is frequently limited, and diagnostic techniques are far from adequate. As a result, one encounters variations in the diagnostic and theoretical views pertaining to disturbed behavior in children. An example of this is the psychotic child who functions intellectually at what appears to be a retarded level. One person may view this pattern as reflecting a condition of mental retardation, whereas another may interpret it as a temporary impairment of intellectual functioning, secondary to psychosis. In one instance the child is considered retarded and in the other he is diagnosed as psychotic.

Another aspect of this problem is reflected in the term pseudofeeble-mindedness, which has been used in the past to denote individuals who appeared to be retarded or were diagnosed as retarded, but who were found on later examinations not to be retarded (Arthur, 1947; Cutts,

1957; Garfield & Affleck, 1960; Sloan, 1947). While emotional problems have been mentioned in this regard as a factor influencing intellectual performance, other factors such as delayed speech and sensory handicaps may also be important (Arthur, 1950; Garfield, 1959). Studies of this type illustrate how performance may be influenced by personality and related variables with resulting variation in diagnostic conclusions. The latter, in turn, affect the data available for research appraisal.

There is also the related problem of the accuracy and comparability of diagnosis, since different centers and investigators may vary considerably in their diagnostic procedures and criteria. In this connection it is pertinent to point out that diagnoses of childhood schizophrenia and related disorders were comparatively rare 30 years ago but apparently are more frequent in recent years (Benda, 1954; Bender, 1960; Bradley, 1941; Sarason & Gladwin, 1958). Changes and modifications in definitions of mental deficiency also bear on this problem (Garfield & Wittson, 1960a, 1960b; Heber, 1959b). While little more will be said about this matter here, it can be pointed out that the Report of the Royal Commission on the law relating to mental illness and mental deficiency (1954–1957) differentiates the lower-grade defectives from the higher-grade defectives (feebleminded) and groups the latter together with individuals judged to be psychopaths (Clarke & Clarke, 1958). Such a change undoubtedly will have some influence on who is considered retarded or psychopathic and the types of behaviors included in these groups.

Another problem pertains to the incidence of certain types of behavioral disturbance among the mentally retarded. It is exceedingly difficult to secure adequate data of this type. For one thing, most institutions for the retarded do not keep systematic records of the diverse behavioral patterns of the individuals in their institutions. Furthermore, since the institutionally retarded represent only a portion of all the mentally retarded, and undoubtedly constitute a nonrepresentative sample, observations on such groups would not give us a true picture of the problem. While there are many variables which influence institutionalization, those individuals of subaverage ability who get into difficulties because of aberrant or socially unapproved behavior are more likely to be placed in institutions (Heiser, 1957; Penrose, 1954; Saenger, 1960).

The above-mentioned difficulties concerning diagnostic clarity and variability, as well as the scarcity of data on the behavioral patterns of the institutionalized and noninstitutionalized retarded alike, obviously limit the generality of our findings. Nevertheless, one can attempt to review and evaluate what data are available. The plan of the chapter is to discuss first some of the severe personality and behavioral disorders in children which frequently present problems of diagnosis with reference to mental retardation. This will be followed by a review of the problem of psychosis and mental deficiency. Afterward, some of the studies of disturbed behavior in the mentally retarded will be discussed and evaluated. This in turn will be followed by a section on psychosis in the severely retarded, a brief section on sociopathic behavior, and a section on psychological studies. Finally, an attempt will be made at the end of the chapter to summarize the major trends and problems discussed with particular reference to research needs.

EMOTIONAL DISORDERS AND PROBLEMS OF DIAGNOSIS

Before an attempt is made to survey abnormal behavior in those considered mentally retarded, it is important to mention some severe disorders which occur in children and which result in impaired intellectual functioning. As we shall see, several clinical syndromes have been reported which are sometimes difficult to differentiate from each other and from cases of mental deficiency. Furthermore, since intellectually retarded children may also show various types of disturbed behavior, the problems of diagnosis and research become difficult.

Schizophrenia in children

Childhood schizophrenia is one of the major diagnostic categories of severe disturbance in children. Apart from possible problems of differential diagnosis between this category and mental deficiency, there exists a wide range of views concerning what childhood schizophrenia is and how it differs from other syndromes. Whether childhood schizophrenia is a unitary syndrome or disease and whether it is genetically transmitted, organically determined, or a result of severe psychological deprivation are not items of primary concern here. The same can be said concerning controversies over whether it is a psychosis or not (Benda, 1960; Bender, 1960). Of some significance, however, is the fact that the disorder is a severe one and, among other things, may result in severely retarded intellectual functioning. As a consequence, schizophrenic individuals with presumably normal intellectual potential may be diagnosed as mentally retarded (Benda, 1954; Bradley, 1941; Garfield & Wittson, 1960a; Sarason, 1953; Sarason & Gladwin, 1958). Conversely, mentally deficient individuals also may develop or display schizophrenic symptoms and behavior. There thus may be considerable similarity and overlap of behavior between these groups.

Bradley (1941) has summarized some of the main symptoms reported for childhood schizophrenia. In condensed form these can be listed as follows:

1. Diminished interest in the environment
2. Emotional disturbances—anxiety, negativism, instability, diminution of affect
3. Symptoms of regression—return to more primitive forms of behavior
4. Alterations of motor behavior—increased activity, immobility, bizarre or stereotyped behavior
5. Speech disturbances—incoherence, disturbed communication, autism
6. Disturbances of thinking—bizarre and dereistic thought
7. Overt behavior—seclusiveness, daydreaming, bizarre behavior
8. Hallucinations and delusions—(Bradley, 1941, pp. 25–37)

While other symptoms are also mentioned, those which have been listed above appear to be most frequent.

Not only will individuals diagnosed as mentally deficient show some of the symptoms mentioned above, but there exists such a number of diverse views concerning childhood schizophrenia and related conditions as well as the relationship between these conditions and mental deficiency that some confusion is inevitable (Benda, 1954; Bender, 1956, 1960; Bradley, 1941; Ekstein, Bryant, & Friedman, 1958; Kanner, 1957). Some clearly distinguish between psychosis and mental defect, whereas others are somewhat more ambiguous in their discussions. For example, Bender (1960) refers to "mentally defective or retarded schizophrenic children" and believes that many of them can be treated in an institution for the retarded. Bender also refers to the pseudodefective or autistic type of schizophrenic child. Kugelmass (1954) makes mention of an "emotional pseudo amentia" and Tredgold (1952) refers to "schizophrenic amentia." The term "propf schizophrenia" has also been offered as a type of schizophrenia which develops in congenitally defective individuals and "controversy over whether patients so classified are essentially feebleminded or essentially schizophrenic has waged intermittently for the past forty years" (Bradley, 1941, p. 54). The issue is further complicated by the view held by some that a number of schizophrenic children never show normal development and thus the history of the individual would not offer a positive basis for differential diagnosis (Ekstein, Bryant, & Friedman, 1958).

Recently, Pollack (1958) has discussed the overlap in levels of intellectual functioning between children diagnosed as schizophrenic and those diagnosed as mentally deficient. He believes that when both severe behavioral disturbance and intellectual defect are found in children, the specific defect stressed—retardation or behavior disorder—is related to the observer's orientation rather than the behavior of the child. According to him, the diagnostic emphasis could be placed on those aspects of the case which appear to be most prominent, i.e., either the behavioral disturbance or the mental retardation. How well this would work in practice is, of course, unanswered at present. In any event, children with schizophrenic symptomatology frequently present problems of diagnosis since many of them appear retarded in mental functioning, exhibit difficulties in attention and communication, and are difficult to examine. Mentally deficient children may also display various symptoms of emotional disturbance. In the young child, in particular, the diagnostic problem may be a difficult one (Garfield, Wilcott, & Milgram, 1961).

Early infantile autism

Another severe disorder has been called *early infantile autism* by Kanner (1943, 1944). This condition is noted usually within the first few years of life. The outstanding features are a detachment from people, isolated aloneness, and an obsessive type of repetitious behavior and ritualism. According to Kanner: "The two principal *diagnostic criteria,* presenting themselves as extreme self-isolation and the obsessive insistence on sameness, could be recognized as the source from which the other clinical manifestations derived" (Kanner & Eisenberg, 1955, p. 227). It is believed by Kanner and others that this disorder is sufficiently distinctive to be

considered as a separate category. Kanner also feels the condition is a
psychotic one which probably should be included within the general
category of schizophrenia.

Whether infantile autism is a separate category of disturbance or whether
it is a variant of childhood schizophrenia is not of crucial importance in
our present discussion (Benda, 1960). It is important, however, to point
out that a problem of differential diagnosis may exist between such a
syndrome and mental retardation. As Kanner mentions: "Many of these
children were brought to us primarily with the assumption that they were
severely feebleminded or with the question of auditory impairment" (1944,
p. 211). Although these children performed poorly on psychometric tests,
careful evaluation indicated that "the children's cognitive potentialities were
only masked by the basic affective disorder" (Kanner, 1944, p. 211). In
some instances, the children had shown remarkable feats of rote memory,
and in all instances it was demonstrated that hearing was not defective.
These children relate well to objects but not to people. Another common
feature mentioned by Kanner (1957) is that all these patients have highly
intelligent parents.

In the autistic children studied by Kanner, a significant impairment or
lack of development of speech was noted in a large minority. In a follow-up
study of 42 cases, 19 appeared to have renounced the use of speech: "they
either were mute throughout, or began to avail themselves sparingly of
the linguistic tool only after five or more years of age, or—having said a few
words—abandoned articulate language altogether" (Kanner & Eisenberg,
1955, p. 232). The absence of speech also appeared to be a negative
prognostic sign in this group of children. Delusions and hallucinations were
not noted.

It is apparent that autistic children lacking in speech may sometimes
be diagnosed as mentally retarded. Since they tend to be unresponsive,
they may be difficult to evaluate by means of standard tests. This particular
problem is commented upon by Sarason and Gladwin (1958) in the
following way:

> As a result of work in the last 20 years on childhood schizophrenia,
> there is little doubt that many children who were committed to an institu-
> tion for the mentally defective were in fact misdiagnosed and misplaced.
> Kanner's now classic descriptions of the autistic child provided further
> evidence that our institutions contained cases in which personality or
> affective rather than intellectual maldevelopment was the primary factor.
> While one would like to believe that our institutions are admitting far
> fewer of these cases, there is no evidence that this is the case (p. 179).

According to Benda (1960), this type of child will be referred most
frequently at an age between 2 and 4, when the problem or type of mental
deficiency is usually different from that occurring in later years. At this
age mental deficiency represents mainly the organic forms of mental
retardation. Although there may be diagnostic difficulties in a specific case,
he believes that the physical and neurological defects in the mentally

defective group at this age are quite evident. In contrast to the defective child, Benda (1960) states:

> The autistic child is usually well developed and often handsome, moving rapidly and gracefully at the time of examination and revealing an amazing grasp of the situation even if he seems completely without contact and withdrawn. The observer is always surprised at how these children are able to run away, climb, handle mechanical problems, avoid being hurt, and achieve their own purposes though these may be very different from the demands made on them by their environment. One characteristic alone is common to all: the lack of speech and verbal communication (p. 472).

While the autistic child may be diagnosed by means of a careful clinical evaluation and adequate history, problems in differential diagnosis do occur. Some retarded individuals display a relative lack of speech and verbal communication and may also appear withdrawn in social behavior. In fact, since most types of behavior have been noted in mentally retarded individuals, there is probably no disorder which seemingly is not found in the retarded or mirrored in their behavior. Nevertheless, Kanner and Eisenberg (1955), as well as others, believe it is important to differentiate these two conditions. They state that "the observed fundamental differences between autistic and oligophrenic children cannot be simply dismissed as differently structured variants of essential feeblemindedness" (p. 229).

In spite of Kanner's careful clinical delineation of the autistic child and its acceptance by other workers in the field of child psychiatry, Bender (1959) takes issue with Kanner's formulation. She states that "as many autistic children come from a background of defective or mediocre intellectual attainment, with all kinds of social, family and personality constellations, as come from families of cold and over-controlled intellectuals described by Kanner" (p. 82). Furthermore, she appears to question Kanner's statement that the autistic child has greater intellectual potential than retarded children. In discussing the follow-up investigation of Kanner's cases she concludes: "Thus it would appear that the non-speaking autistic child under the age of 5 years, of Kanner's classification, cannot be differentiated from other mentally retarded or defective children as far as their ability to function intellectually or socially, or as far as their future outcome is concerned" (1959, p. 82).

Essentially, Bender, unlike others such as Benda (1960) or Mahler (1952), does not view early infantile autism as a specific clinical or etiological entity. She also does not consider it to be synonymous with psychosis. Rather, she believes autism is a primitive form of behavior which may be utilized as a defense by children with a variety of organic or social pathologies.

While no resolution of these differences in point of view will be attempted here, a few comments can be offered. There appears to be little question that some children display the type of behavior described by Kanner and that some of them have been viewed as mentally defective. It is also apparent that a number of these children have responded to different therapeutic attempts and have given clear indication of not being mentally retarded. (Kanner & Eisenberg, 1955; Kanner, 1957). It is also possible, or likely, that the patterns of behavior described by Kanner can be noted in other groups of children as stated by Bender. In the absence of an adequate history of early development, it is frequently a difficult task to make a precise diagnosis of disturbed behavior in children.

Heller's disease

Another severe disturbance of childhood is that termed *Heller's disease* or *dementia infantilis*. This refers to an apparent deteriorating pattern of disturbance which occurs at around 3 or 4 years of age. It is considered to be a degenerative metabolic disorder in which there is degeneration of the nerve cells and atrophy of the brain (Benda, 1960), although there is still some controversy over whether it is a syndrome produced by several etiological factors (Yakolev, Weinberger, & Chipman, 1948). Heller's description of these cases is translated by Benda (1960) as follows:

> Without previous illness, a change in character could be noticed which was especially evidenced by a change of mood. Formerly quiet and vivid, they become irritable, negativistic, disobedient. They had un-provoked outbursts of temper, cried and destroyed toys. . . . Many showed anxiety, sometimes of a hallucinatory character; and with the occasionally insidious increase of violent manifestations, a mental regression took place which led to a complete loss of speech and complete deterioration within a few months. Language became poor with gradual transposition of words, the child was unable to repeat sentences and finally stopped speaking. Perception of speech was also lost except for a few primitive remnants. A change in motor behavior became manifest during this process of deterioration. The children developed automatic movements, tics, or grimacing, and manifested certain odd positions which would remind one of the erethism of some idiots (p. 485).

According to the parents of these children, the latter had shown normal intellectual development prior to the onset of the disease. Usually the loss of intellectual functions took place within a period of 9 months with the children reaching a state of complete mental deterioration. Motor over-activity, stereotyped behavior, mannerisms, and tics were prominent. Apparently there was no improvement in these cases, and the children displayed rather profound deterioration. The incidence of this disorder appears to be quite infrequent, although exact rates of occurrence are not available.

The syndromes reviewed here by no means exhaust those mentioned and described with reference to severe psychopathology in children (Benda, 1952; Bradley, 1941; Ekstein, Bryant, & Friedman, 1958; Goldfarb & Dorsen, 1956; Kanner, 1957). There are many others including the "symbiotic infantile psychosis" of Mahler (1952). However the syndromes discussed have most frequently been mentioned with reference to problems of differential diagnosis pertaining to mental deficiency and will serve to illustrate this type of problem.

ABNORMAL BEHAVIOR IN THE
MENTALLY RETARDED

When one turns to some of the standard textbooks on mental deficiency for comprehensive data and descriptions of disturbed or abnormal behavior, one finds surprisingly little information presented. In some instances the results of a survey in a particular institution are reported, although it is impossible to tell how representative these findings are. In other instances, there may be a chapter or less devoted to "mental disorder" in the retarded. These essentially state that all types of psychopathology are found within the group of individuals diagnosed as retarded, but reliable data on incidence is lacking as well as the significance of such pathology for the entire group. More typically, descriptions of the varied behaviors encountered with various types and subgroups of the retarded are given in a discursive fashion. Not infrequently one may find conflicting personality and behavioral descriptions given for the same groups. For example, individuals with phenylketonuria are described by Penrose (1954) as generally pleasant and "good-tempered," but are characterized by Benda (1952) as frequently being aggressive and rather "wild" in behavior. Studies of specific patterns of behavior in well-defined samples of the retarded are a rarity.

Psychotic behavior in the mentally retarded

Various types of psychotic behavior have been reported for mentally retarded individuals, although precise incidence figures to indicate the frequency of such behavior are infrequent. Psychosis occurs at all levels of subnormal intellectual functioning, may be of a short or long duration, and does not follow any particular course. In their review of this problem, Sarason and Gladwin (1958) state:

> Practically every major psychotic symptom which has been described in the nondefective patient has also been noted in many of the defective cases. There appears to be little justification for the generalization that when psychosis occurs in a mentally defective individual it is necessarily less "complex" than when found in the nondefective individual. There is also little support for the equally sweeping generalization that psychosis or psychotic-like behavior in the defective individual tends to be of short duration (p. 179).

The incidence of psychotic disturbance among the total group of mentally retarded is thought by some workers to be higher than that which occurs in the general population. However, such judgments are based on varying definitions and criteria for mental deficiency. Sarason and Gladwin (1958), for example, state that psychosis occurs more frequently among the mentally deficient than in the population at large. However, their definition of mental deficiency refers only to those with some organic brain pathology.

Tredgold (1952) believes that there is a close relationship between mental deficiency and mental abnormality. "There is, in fact, reason to think that in many instances these various conditions may be merely different clinical manifestations of one and the same germ abnormality" (p. 380). He also states that the clinical resemblances between these various conditions are sometimes so great that differential diagnosis is a difficult problem. In addition, he believes that "a considerable proportion of individuals who are definitely mentally defective acquire psychoneuroses, psychoses, or pass into a state of dementia" (p. 380). The defective individual is thus considered to be much more prone to mental disturbance than is the nondefective (Pollock, 1945; Tredgold, 1952).

Penrose (1954), another leading British writer on mental deficiency, takes a somewhat different view from that of Tredgold concerning psychoses and mental deficiency. He believes that mental disorder and mental defect should be distinguished and considered as two dimensions of variation.

> Thus, theoretically, a person of any level of intellectual capacity can suffer from any degree of mental illness. The susceptibility to disorder may indeed be correlated with intelligence level, in that certain kinds of defect may predispose to epilepsy or psychosis. In epiloia, for instance, mental disorder is part of the symptom complex. Conversely, mental illness, as the primary condition, may contribute to a lowering of intellectual capacity . . . (p. 198).

As has been indicated, varying views have been expressed concerning the relationship between psychosis and mental deficiency. While some have expressed the view that a true psychosis is rare among mental defectives (Annotations, 1952), others such as Tredgold have maintained a greater susceptibility to psychosis on the part of the retarded. Kallmann, Barrera, Hoch, and Kelley (1941) have reviewed this literature and appraised it in terms of their studies of schizophrenia in 365 twin pairs. In general they find no support for the view that mental deficiency is biologically related to schizophrenia. One of their conclusions is as follows:

> A survey of the taint conditions in the kinships and twin partners of schizophrenic and mentally defective cases has produced no evidence either of an increased incidence of schizophrenic psychoses in the consanguinity of mental defectives or of an increased tendency for the blood-relatives of schizophrenics to be feebleminded. It seems to us unwarranted, therefore, to maintain the theory that the presence of a genetic factor for mental deficiency might, under certain circumstances, be sufficient to produce a genuine schizophrenic psychosis or that the possession of a schizophrenic genotype might contribute significantly to the incidence of true (idiopathic) feeblemindedness in the given type of tainted individual (p. 537).

Another view held by many is that the mental disturbances which occur in the mentally retarded are of a mild and transitory nature (Henderson & Gillespie, 1956). Generally, such statements are not accompanied by any supporting data. Tredgold (1952), however, does add that mental defectives may have more severe and prolonged disturbances and may require hospitalization.

Tredgold also believes that psychotic attacks of maniacal excitement are the commonest forms of psychosis among the mentally retarded. Again, no precise data pertaining to incidence are given by him. Penrose (1954), on the other hand, states that only a few patients with affective psychoses are found among institutionalized defectives. While mentioning that it is sometimes difficult to differentiate a mild manic attack in defectives from a hysterical manifestation, he believes that manic and depressive states in defectives tend to be milder than in individuals with average ability.

Most investigators have tended to report that psychosis of a schizophrenic nature appears to be the most common among the institutionalized mentally deficient (Penrose, 1954). The simple type of schizophrenia in particular may be indistinguishable from a state of profound defect. Some of the symptoms of schizophrenia are also noted among varied categories of the retarded including mongolism and phenylketonuria: "Catatonia with waxy flexibility, stuporous states, outbursts of violence, stereotopy, negativism and mannerisms occur in low-grade defectives, and their psychiatric significance is difficult to determine" (Penrose, 1954, p. 214).

It is difficult to compare the various statements in this regard, since in addition to possible variations in diagnostic criteria, some writers interpret particular patterns of disorder in somewhat unique ways. Tredgold, for example, discusses "schizophrenic amentia" and appears to refer to a schizophrenic type of disturbance which leads to deterioration. While he states that the incidence of such disturbances is probably about 1 per cent among all defectives, one may question whether, on the basis of his own descriptions, these cases would be seen by all workers as mentally deficient. For example, Tredgold makes reference to the fact that the individual's mental development had proceeded normally prior to the onset of the psychosis.

The preceding statements illustrate the variations in viewpoint and the lack of adequate data existing in this area. Because of this it is both difficult and precarious to attempt some synthesis and conclusion concerning psychotic behavior in the mentally retarded. Consequently, we shall postpone such an attempt until additional material related to this problem has been reviewed in succeeding sections of the chapter.

Studies of disturbed behavior in the mentally retarded

The previous discussion reflects the type of statements frequently made in "authoritative" textbooks concerning severe personality disturbance in mentally deficient individuals. References to carefully carried out research surveys are relatively rare. However, some attempts have been made to secure data on this problem. One survey of institutionalized retardates is reported by Penrose (1954), and the results are given in Table 18-1.

In this survey approximately one-third of the patients examined were considered to have some type of mental disorder, and if we exclude epilepsy, almost 16 per cent showed some type of neurotic or psychotic pattern. From what has been said before, it should be apparent that one cannot generalize from the findings of this survey to the entire group of mentally retarded individuals. It is most likely that individuals who display some type of behavioral or adjustment difficulty are the ones who may be more readily institutionalized. The findings, however, are of interest in demonstrating that various types of abnormal behavior do occur at all levels of mental deficiency and that psychotic behavior at any given time occurs in a relatively small percentage of institutionalized defectives—in this instance less than 10 per cent of the cases.

Neuer (1947) reports a study of 300 admissions to the Lincoln State School and Colony. Of these, 39 per cent had signs of organic disorder, and 28 per cent were considered to be a *neuropsychotic* group with a history of major or minor psychosis. Of this latter group 45 per cent were judged to be neurotic, 39 per cent were considered to have had a psychosis of some type, and in the remaining cases no differential diagnosis was possible. These findings appear to be somewhat higher than those reported by Penrose, but it is impossible to determine how comparable the diagnostic criteria were. Neuer also states that he believes that mental deficiency in neurotic and psychotic children is the result and not the underlying cause of such disturbance in childhood.

In another study, Angus (1948) reported that in a review of 150 recent admissions to the Devereaux Schools, 43 individuals or 28 per cent of the group could be diagnosed as schizophrenic. The latter ranged from clear-cut to borderline cases. The sample, however, cannot be considered representative of all retardates.

Another estimate of behavioral disturbance is available in a report of the Rhode Island mental deficiency register (Wunsch, 1951). Although this is not a complete register of all cases in the state, it is based on over 6,000 cases obtained from various sources since 1941. Since the data come from

TABLE 18-1

Distribution of cases whose main symptoms were those of mental disorder (Colchester survey, 1938)

Diagnosis of mental disorder	Mental grade				
	Dull	Feeble-minded	Imbe-cile	Idiot	Total
Idiopathic epilepsy	30	57	81	42	210
Psychoneurosis and perversion	56	53	20	3	132
Affective psychosis	4	17	3	0	24
Schizophrenia	8	11	16	13	48
Total mentally disordered	98	138	120	58	414
Total population of patients examined	179	448	433	220	1,280

Source: Penrose, 1954, p. 203.

diverse sources with varying types of evaluative criteria, they are difficult to appraise. Of the total group, 25 per cent are classified as having poor social adjustment. However, this admittedly is not an objective classification and apparently such ratings did not include the 20 per cent who were institutionalized. Of 523 listed as having neuropsychiatric handicaps, 77 were classified as psychotic. This is just over 1 per cent of all those on the register, but the real significance of this figure is difficult to evaluate.

On the whole, one does not gain any clear picture of the extent of extreme personality and behavioral disturbance among the mentally retarded from such surveys. Apart from the variability in the figures reported, one has no way of knowing if such diagnostic terms as neurosis and psychosis are utilized in the same way by different individuals in diverse settings. Furthermore, such terms as neurosis are particularly difficult to define and can be used to denote varying symptoms or degrees of psychopathology.

Another source of information pertaining to frequency of severe personality disturbance among individuals considered to be mentally retarded is studies of mental hospitals. One such survey which has been widely quoted in the literature is a study by Pollock (1945) of first admissions to state hospitals in New York. The annual admission rate for individuals diagnosed as mentally defective over a 3-year period was found to be "several times as high as among nondefectives." In the hospitalized group of individuals judged to be defective, the most frequent diagnosis was psychosis with mental deficiency, which accounted for almost 40 per cent of the cases; 18 per cent were diagnosed as dementia praecox. Pollock does not state how the diagnoses of mental deficiency were arrived at. However, his conclusion is very positive: "We are now in a position to state positively that the general rate of incidence of mental illness is higher among subnormal persons than among the general population and our data indicate that the rate of mental disease declines as the degree of intelligence advances" (p. 478).

Mention can be made of another similar study (Duncan, Penrose, & Turnbull, 1936). This was a survey of over 2,000 patients in a large English mental hospital. In this study, 17.8 per cent of the patients were judged to be mentally defective. The judgments were based on a few standardized test questions and the past history of the patient including his school record. Taken at face value, this study and that of Pollock's indicate an apparently higher frequency of psychosis among retarded individuals.

As the preceding pages indicate, most of what we know about the behavior of retarded individuals comes from studies of those who have been institutionalized. This sample is biased in at least two important ways. It is overweighted with the severely retarded, and in the cases of the higher grades of defectives, a disproportionate sample of those who get into difficulties are institutionalized (Saenger, 1960).

Studies of emotional disturbance among retardates who are at large in society are extremely sparse. In one such study of individuals in the Canadian Army by Dewan (1948), it is reported that almost 48 per cent of individuals judged to be mentally retarded were also considered to be emotionally unstable. This is an exceedingly high figure, and one can question what is meant by a finding of emotional instability. As mentioned in the article, "any recruit whose history, complaints and objective findings indicated psychoneurosis, psychopathic personality, psychosis, etc. was downgraded as unfit for . . . service" (p. 549) and included in the emotionally unstable category. The diagnosis of mental deficiency was based on clinical evaluation and scores on the Canadian Army M test. Generally it was used for those who were considered unable to master basic infantry training. While there was a marked relationship between the test scores and diagnoses of instability, the incidence of instability for the nonretarded individual was also quite high, namely, 19.7 per cent. One wonders if there was a tendency on the part of the 40 psychiatrists who made these assessments to diagnose more readily some type of instability in individuals who were obviously retarded, or whether these two judgments were independent.

A somewhat related study is reported by Weaver (1946) concerning the adjustment of 8,000 defectives in the United States Army. The data were gathered from a variety of sources, and it is stated that a majority of these cases had an IQ below 75. The group studied was a somewhat selected group in that they were accepted into the army and went on to basic or speciality training. Of the total group, 56 per cent of the males and 62 per cent of the females made a satisfactory adjustment to the military situation. The remainder became psychiatric or psychosomatic problems or "committed repeated acts of misconduct." Although those who were unable to adjust were subdivided into those with psychopathy, severe anti-social behavior, and psychiatric or psychosomatic problems, the percentages given are unclear. Apparently 13 per cent of the white subjects and 6.5 per cent of the colored were given medical discharges "because of severe psychiatric and physical conditions." The median IQ of the successful group was 72 as contrasted with a median IQ of 68 in the unsuccessful group. Weaver concluded that "personality factors far overshadowed the factor of intelligence" (p. 243) in the adjustment of these individuals to military service.

It is obviously difficult to compare the findings of Weaver with those of Dewan since very different criteria were used in selecting the groups for study and in judging maladjustment. However, O'Connor (1951) in a study of emotional instability in 104 high-grade male defectives secured findings which were somewhat similar to those reported by Dewan. In terms of ratings of stability, 44 per cent were judged to be unstable. Since these results approximated those of Dewan's but differed from Penrose's report of 9.6 per cent neurosis in the Colchester survey, O'Connor attempted to differentiate neurosis from instability. Utilizing a battery of psychological tests and other data, he concluded that about 12 per cent of his subjects could be designated as neurotic and 32 per cent as emotionally unstable. He believed that the term neurotic should be used in a more specific manner, and in this way the discrepancy in findings could be resolved.

A brief reference can also be made to a recent study by Craft (1960) of 9,434 patients referred to the out-patient department of the Maudsley Hospital in London. Of these patients, 119 were diagnosed as mentally deficient. Craft does point out that one cannot assume that this group represents all defectives or that all the diagnoses were correct—e.g., four patients had IQs of 90 or better, and in 10 other cases the diagnoses were considered as doubtful. Craft lists the percentages of occurrence of the various disorders in the group and compares these with the rates for the entire group of patients. Although he states that depressions are rare in defectives and that personality disorders are twice as frequent in defectives as in the total group of patients, no statistical tests of significance are reported. Thus, one may not necessarily agree with his conclusion that defectives "suffer the same type of illness as the general population, although in different degree" (p. 723).

Undoubtedly, the various estimates and findings reviewed reflect differences in the samples and criteria used. O'Connor and Tizard (1956) in discussing some of this literature come to the following conclusion:

> It may be expected, therefore, that a higher figure for instability and emotional disturbance will be found in any defective population than for a normal population, and that the figure is likely to be unusually high in hospitals where patients are often sent because disturbed or "psychopathic," rather than because they are cognitively defective (p. 66).

While most workers in the area of retardation appear to agree that the rate of emotional disturbance or mental illness is higher among defectives than among normals, there is, as we have noted, some variability in the points of view held and in the estimates given. In the survey by Penrose (1954) mentioned previously, the incidence of neurosis among 1,280 institutionalized defectives was approximately 10 per cent. This does not appear unusually high for an institutionalized group nor does this figure diverge greatly from the estimate for neurosis in the normal population given by O'Connor and Tizard. For obvious reasons, however, one cannot make a direct comparison between these two estimates.

Before proceeding to the next section it may be worthwhile to discuss briefly the results and opinions reviewed in the preceding pages. The bulk of the material would appear to indicate a higher incidence of severe personality disturbance among the mentally retarded than is true of the nonretarded. However, several possible factors should be considered in evaluating these data. First, there is no consistent incidence rate reported in the various surveys, and these vary rather widely. Second, there is no uniform set of criteria upon which the diagnoses are based. Third, none of the samples studied can be said to be truly representative of all the mentally retarded. Fourth, with regard to individuals in mental hospitals it can be pointed out that many psychotic patients who are not retarded will do poorly on intellectual tests and impress examiners as being retarded (Chapman & Pathman, 1959; Raub, Mercer, & Hecker, 1952). Fifth, if emotional disturbance is in fact more frequent among retarded persons, this may be due to factors other than retardation per se. In this connection it is possible to hypothesize that the retarded child is more frequently rejected than the normal child or more frequently encounters frustration, failure, and ridicule (Robinson & Paseward, 1951). Such experiences may play a more significant role in the individual's personality formation than his limited intellectual ability. Sixth, since there appears to be some association between social class variables and types of personality disorders (Hollingshead & Redlich, 1958), such variables may also play a role in the findings obtained. For example, the association between hospitalization rates and intellectual level discussed by Pollock (1945) also reflects the relationship of these two factors to social class variables. As a result of such considerations, it should be apparent that the problem is not a simple one and that one cannot draw firm conclusions at this time.

Thus, while the individual who attempts to survey some of the literature in this field may be impressed with the prevailing opinion that emotional disturbance is relatively more frequent among defectives than among normals, there are other related conclusions which should also be considered. The incidence of disturbance among retarded individuals is not so high that one should associate one with the other. Most mental retardates do not give evidence of serious emotional disturbance, nor do they manifest a particular stereotyped personality. "However the question of psychopathy is decided, it is obvious that defectives differ greatly among themselves in their personalities. In this respect they resemble normal people" (O'Connor & Tizard, 1956, p. 61). In this connection it is pertinent to again point out that individuals with defective intelligence also are influenced by the types of experiences and interpersonal relationships they have. Understanding, support, rejection, ridicule, failure, and similar types of experience will have their differential effects on the retarded individual.

In terms of the preceding discussion, it is worth making some reference to a study by Marcotte (1947). After pointing out that in the past mental deficiency frequently was used as an explanation for a variety of behavioral and social pathologies, he attempted to appraise the significance of other factors in accounting for behavior problems in 20 mental defectives. Ratings were made on four factors—level of mentality, physical factors, family influences, and school influences. Although the study has certain flaws, the findings are of some interest. Mentality was judged to play a role in 45 per cent of the behavior problems, family influences in 41 per cent, school influences in 32 per cent, and physical factors in 16 per cent. Although mentality slightly exceeded home influences as a factor of importance, the rating system used and the fact that all of the cases were retarded would appear to bias the results in this direction. Regardless of this, family influences were seen as important in over 40 per cent of the cases. The data thus suggest that while limited intellectual ability is a factor of importance in the individual's adjustment, the type of family and home situation in which the individual lives and develops is also of great significance. A similar interpretation was made by Woodward (1960), who studied the social responses of 90 severely retarded mentally defective children, 3 to 10 years of age. The median IQ was below 30. Over one-third of these children showed distress or avoidance when confronted with a strange person in a new setting, and it was concluded that the "disturbed social response was the outcome of adverse early experience" (p. 131).

Psychosis in the severely retarded

The study of psychotic behavior in the severely mentally deficient has been a special area of interest for a number of individuals. Greene (1930) described regular periods of psychotic excitement and depression in one patient with an IQ of 16 and the bizarre behavior associated with schizophrenia in another. In both of these patients, apparent deterioration and personality change occurred. Earl (1934) has described in some detail psychoses in 38 defective individuals classified as idiots. He refers to the psychosis in these individuals as the "primitive catatonic psychosis of idiocy." These patients exhibited definite signs of deterioration, catatonic features such as catalepsy, muscular catatonia, autism, mutism, and a wide range of emotional behavior including excitement, depression, rage, crying, and unusual mannerisms and postures. Earl also stated it was difficult to assess the depth of psychosis in these patients since the overall picture was confused by the severe degree of intellectual deficiency. The cases included a variety of types of mental deficiency.

It is unfortunate that the data about these patients are somewhat inadequate. Although it is stated that the psychosis was clearly established in most instances before the age of 10, adequate data for the early developmental years are crucial for a comprehensive understanding of possible contributing factors. Since Earl states that congenital profound idiocy did not occur in any of these cases, one may surmise that the original level was above that of idiocy (Sarason & Gladwin, 1958). It is thus difficult to know what the actual level of intellect was prior to psychosis and to what extent deterioration in intellectual performance occurred.

More recently O'Gorman (1954) has referred to Earl's work and raised the question of whether mental deficiency in some cases may be caused by psychosis. Instead of a specific catatonic psychosis occurring in idiots, O'Gorman asked if "in some patients of this type, idiocy is caused by a psychotic process which also subsequently causes catatonia?" (p. 394). In other words, was the severe mental deficiency in Earl's patients a result of deterioration due to psychosis? O'Gorman studied two small hospitals for defectives and found 29 per cent of the patients in one hospital to be psychotic. These patients were classified as imbeciles and apparently showed mainly hebephrenic symptomatology. In terms of his findings, O'Gorman raised the possibility that the type of psychosis and degree of deficiency are related to the extent of deterioration, with the most profound catatonia being found in idiots. He suggested that schizophrenia be considered a possible etiological factor in mental deficiency and that as a consequence, early diagnosis and detection were important.

A somewhat different view is presented by le Vann (1950), who has noted a "wide range of schizophrenic symptomatology" among lower-grade defectives. Some appear to be typical demented schizophrenics who are at times oblivious to their environment and at other times display what appears to be catatonic excitement. The symptoms are apparent at 4 to 5 years of age and many of the patients are nonverbal. "As they reach adult age, their appearance is so similar to the chronic institutionalized schizophrenic as to make them indistinguishable" (p. 470). Le Vann does not believe that the schizophrenic pattern is a manifestation of regressive behavior. Instead he feels it can be seen as congenital schizophrenia.

Another interesting study of defective children with IQs below 50 is reported by Bourne (1955). Out of 154 successive admissions to the Fountain Hospital, London, there was a group of 16 children who apparently had no findings of an organic nature. The social histories of these children were compared with the 138 who had an evident organic cause. The two groups differed most in terms of the home environment from which they came and the kind of parental relationships experienced. The presence of severe abnormal behavior in the mother as well as the absence of the mother were significantly more frequent in the nonorganic group of 16 cases. The latter thus came from emotionally unfavorable environments, which are usually considered to have an adverse effect on the intellectual and personality development of the child. These children are described by Bourne in the following manner:

> The young child, though physically healthy, will present severe backwardness evident from about the second year, with curious behavior disorder and a history of perverted mothering in infancy. In his first two years he will either have been reared by an extremely disordered person, commonly a psychopath, or else deprived for long and repeated periods of the mother or her substitute; usually he will have suffered both misfortunes.

> Clinically these children's backwardness is uneven; despite an IQ about 40, their early milestones are not much delayed, and they lack the clumsiness and impoverished expression of other imbeciles—some, indeed, are very graceful and attractive. At times they appear extraordinarily remote and even deaf, tending to monotonous mannerisms, banging their head, and tearing out their hair . . . (p. 1162).

Bourne states that about 10 per cent of the severely retarded in his hospital were in this category. He also hypothesizes that slightly less negative environments may be a contributing factor in less severely retarded cases. While these children may be deemed to show some resemblance to schizophrenics, Bourne feels this is only superficial. He believes the condition involves "an aborted organization of the personality" rather than the disorganization implied in psychosis and names it protophrenia. Basically, he views it as a failure of ego formation. In any event, his findings are provocative and would appear to justify attempts on the part of other investigators to make similar investigations.

Since many types of clinical syndromes have been reported which have some apparent similarity, it is difficult to know if really dissimilar conditions are being described. One can only speculate concerning the etiological and temporal significance of the various facets of personality and behavior in these varied cases. Do some of these cases have limited intellectual potential at birth, or is the mental retardation part of the symptom complex resulting from adverse experience in the early years of life? Furthermore, in the case of intellectually deficient children, what types of experiences appear to influence significantly their behavior and personality adjustment? These are important questions which deserve research investigations of a systematic sort. If Bourne and others are correct in hypothesizing that some cases of severe mental deficiency are the result of psychological influences, early detection conceivably may lead to prevention or reclamation of such cases.

Antisocial and delinquent behavior

No attempt will be made here to review even a limited segment of all the reports and pronouncements that have been published concerning the relationship of antisocial behavior and mental deficiency. Wallin (1956) has provided us with a comprehensive and critical review of past work in this area and other reviews are also available (Lowrey, 1944; Woodward, 1955). It is worthwhile, however, to make a brief reference to this problem in order to illustrate the rather marked change in findings and point of view in the past 50 years. As is true of other areas in the field of mental retardation, as better diagnostic and research procedures are utilized, there are fewer sweeping generalizations forthcoming concerning the inadequacies of the mentally retarded and an increasing awareness of the complexity of the problem under consideration.

As is pointed out by Wallin (1956), there has been a definite change in the views held with regard to mental deficiency and sociopathic behavior— "From an exaggerated emphasis during the early part of the century on the relation of defective intelligence to various sociopathic states, the pendulum now seems to have swung to the opposite extreme . . . " (p. 48). In a summary of studies reported prior to 1930, the percentage of mental defectives among individuals in prisons or courts ranges from 22 per cent to 90 per cent (Wallin, 1956). The earlier point of view is reflected in an address by Walter E. Fernald, then medical superintendent of the Massachusetts School for the Feebleminded, before the Massachusetts Medical Society in 1912:

> Every feeble-minded person, especially the high grade imbecile, is a potential criminal needing only the proper environment and opportunity for the development and expression of his criminal tendencies. . . . Feeble-minded women are almost invariably immoral. . . . It has been truly said that feeble-mindedness is the mother of crime, pauperism, and degeneracy" (quoted by Wallin, 1956, pp. 78–79).

There is no need to repeat similar statements made by other authorities of the time.

It is readily apparent that sweeping statements of the type quoted reflect a tendency to generalize from inadequate data. Somewhat similar statements have been made about the relationship between mental deficiency and psychopathy (Wallin, 1949). One of the obvious limitations of many of the studies is the matter of accuracy of diagnosis. A second important limitation has been the tendency to overlook the significance of social and environmental variables and to control for them in such studies (Wallin, 1956; Woodward, 1955).

Before leaving this topic it may be worthwhile to refer to the studies by Bromberg and Thompson (1937) and Tulchin (1939). The former studied almost 10,000 prisoners who came to the psychiatric clinic of the Court of General Sessions in New York City. The sample was comprised of all prisoners indicted for felonies in New York County and who were judged guilty by the court. All individuals considered to be mentally defective were examined by a psychiatrist and given a battery of two or more psychological tests. A mental age of 10 years, 6 months and an IQ of 66 were used as the upper border for mental deficiency. In this investigation, only 2.4 per cent of the cases were found to be mentally defective. The distribution of intelligence for the entire group of prisoners was not too dissimilar to that of the white draft in World War I. The authors concluded that mental deficiency plays a relatively minor role in the causation of crime. Somewhat comparable findings are also reported by Tulchin (1939), who studied over 10,000 inmates in penal and correctional institutions in Illinois. This group of prisoners secured intelligence test results which closely approximated those for the Illinois Army draft during World War I.

More recent studies thus show markedly different results concerning the relationship of mental deficiency to sociopathic behavior from those reported in earlier studies. The change in findings appears to be due to better diagnostic criteria and an awareness of the significance of socioeconomic variables for this problem.

Psychological studies

Most of the chapter has dealt with severe personality disorders among mentally retarded individuals and related disorders of childhood. The majority of the studies have been clinical in nature, have tended to be medically or psychiatrically oriented, and have been concerned with the extent of personality disturbance among the retarded. Until fairly recent years, psychologists have not shown as much interest in research on such problems as they have in other areas. As a rule, they have tended to be more concerned with studies of general personality variables than specifically with the area of abnormal behavior, although, of course, these areas overlap.

As a consequence, psychologists have contributed relatively little to the study and understanding of abnormal behavior in the mentally retarded. There have been studies of particular personality traits and characteristics (O'Connor & Tizard, 1956; Wallin, 1949) which help to dispel certain stereotypes of the mentally defective as being either docile or impulsive and emphasize the variability in patterns of response. There have also been studies utilizing projective and related techniques. Some studies of this type have indicated that personality disturbance is found frequently among individuals considered to be retarded and have also raised the question of whether the retardation is a symptom of the personality disturbance (Jolles, 1947; Sloan, 1947). As has been pointed out by Sarason (1953) and Wallin (1949), however, these and related studies utilizing the Rorschach test have several shortcomings. Frequently, personality disturbance is inferred solely on the basis of the test findings with little or no corroborating data from other sources, particularly evaluations of actual behavior. Other limitations pertain to the estimation of intellectual level on the basis of the Rorschach and the rather inadequate normative data available for diagnosing mental retardation. It is not uncommon, also, for clinical examiners to overemphasize pathology on the basis of test findings (Little & Shneidman, 1959). Nevertheless, while the results of studies utilizing the Rorschach should not be accepted uncritically, such studies and others reviewed by Sarason (1953) have tended to focus more attention on the personality characteristics of retarded individuals and have shown that "the defective individual, like the normal one, has fears, anxieties, wishes and needs which may affect his intellectual functioning in varying degrees" (Sarason, 1953, p. 261). Studies by Abel (1945) and Sarason (1943), for example, utilizing the Thematic Apperception Test have indicated the concern of defective individuals with aggression, affection, loneliness, and family conflicts.

Research utilizing projective as well as other types of tests would be of greater value if diagnostic indices and prognostic statements based on test data were evaluated in relation to actual behavior. Studies by Sloan (1948) in predicting the extramural adjustment of mental defectives by means of the Rorschach test and by Lipman (1959) in relating the Rosenzweig Picture Frustration Study and the Childrens Manifest Anxiety Scale to overt aggressive behavior generally produced disappointing results.

Reference has already been made to the study by O'Connor (1951) of emotional instability in high-grade defectives and the study by Woodward (1960) of the social response of severely retarded individuals. The former used tests of suggestibility, locomotor coordination, and persistence which correlated positively with clinical ratings. Woodward utilized a standard test situation and related the response of the child to his early life experience.

Gallagher (1957) compared 24 brain-injured defectives with 24 subjects having familial etiology on a number of psychological variables, including personality and behavioral variables. The latter were evaluated by means of a specially constructed rating scale. Specific predictions concerning personality differences between these two groups of subjects were made and in general were confirmed. Some of the findings were that the brain-injured group was more hyperactive, less free from anxiety, less able to postpone gratification, and more in need of affection. The study is noteworthy in terms of its careful design, the drawing upon theoretical concepts in psychology, the setting up of specific predictions to be tested, and the explicit mention by the investigator of possible limitations of the study.

More recently an attempt was made by Wiener, Crawford, and Snyder (1960) to study the relation of test anxiety, general anxiety, and performance on the Bender gestalt test to scholastic achievement in 52 institutionalized male defectives. The subjects had a mean IQ of 65 and no evidence of organic pathology. The tests of anxiety and an 11-item "lie" scale were adapted for use with these subjects. It was found that the low achievers erred significantly more on the Bender gestalt test when achievement was considered independently of IQ and age. Although the other two measures of anxiety were not related to achievement, the lie scale showed a significant negative correlation with both of these anxiety measures. When the lie scores were added to the anxiety-test scores, high test anxiety was significantly related to poor achievement. It was hypothesized that lie scores were a manifestation of attempts to conceal anxiety and that failure to achieve may be a reflection of anxiety. The study is of interest in that it applies concepts and techniques to the study of retarded individuals, which for the most part had not been applied or seen as relevant for this group.

O'Connor and Tizard (1954) have reported on the incidence of certain habit disorders in their survey of 12 mental deficiency hospitals in England. Thirteen per cent of the patients were reported to be doubly incontinent, and an additional 5 per cent were enuretic. The majority of such cases were children or idiots. It is pointed out by Tizard (1958) that he does not know of any surveys of other habit disorders such as thumb sucking, rocking, head rolling, etc., although these and other behaviors are supposedly common in institutional defectives. Systematic observations of the behavior of retarded children in school, ward, and dormitory situations would be of value. While it is likely that some of the behavioral patterns manifested may be related to the type of environment in which the individual lives, it would be important to secure data on such relationships.

Although some of the studies mentioned have relevance for the area of abnormal behavior, one can still state that research studies by psychologists of abnormal behavior in the mentally retarded have been few. In this connection it is interesting to point out that in a Symposium on Research Design and Methodology in Mental Retardation (1959), there was no specific discussion of research on abnormal behavior. Two of the presentations dealt with the related areas of personality development and personality research. Gallagher (1959) commented on the relative lack of work pertaining to the measurement of personality development in the retarded. According to him, the lack of adequate instruments for research probably accounted for this situation. Objective self-report instruments are limited because they demand reading ability and accurate self-perception on the part of the subject. Projective tests were seen as limited by the inadequate verbal production of retarded children and by the latter's being unduly influenced by recent events. Observational methods were also criticized in terms of the variability of behavior in the retarded and the use of untrained observers. He suggested that observation and description of actual behavior which could be cataloged to fit a specific theoretical system and which might reveal typical reactions to stress could perhaps be of value.

The second paper referred to above by Cromwell (1959) was largely concerned with a methodological approach to personality research. Several researches utilizing the concept of expectancy as applied to studies of retarded children were described. The approach utilized with reference to the expectancy of failure on the part of the retarded would appear to have potential value in studying severely disturbed behavior, providing adequate cooperation from subjects can be secured.

Finally, it can be noted that psychologists have participated actively in clinical and investigative work pertaining to psychotherapy (Cotzin, 1948; Gunzburg, 1958; O'Connor & Tizard, 1956; Sarason, 1953; Thorne, 1948). While a discussion of this area is beyond the scope of the present chapter, it is mentioned to highlight the attitude of many workers that changes in the personality and behavior of mental defectives are possible (Harris & Sievers, 1959; Neham, 1951). Research in this area could also contribute to a deeper understanding of the personality and behavior of the retarded.

SUMMARY AND CONCLUSIONS

In the preceding pages some of the literature pertaining to abnormal behavior and mental retardation has been reviewed. No attempt was made to review the various clinical types of mental deficiency or the behavioral syndromes related to organic brain damage. Rather, the emphasis was placed on the broader problem of general findings and conclusions pertaining to the association of abnormal behavior and mental retardation. Although it is readily apparent that the terms mental retardation and mental deficiency encompass a wide variety of syndromes and patterns of behavior, the terms frequently are used as if they denoted some restricted or uniform type of behavior. As a result, one finds many generalizations pertaining to the behavior of the retarded as a group. It was the purpose of this chapter to review the views and pronouncements made in the area of abnormal behavior, to evaluate the findings reported in support of such statements, and to attempt to draw some conclusions and recommendations.

From our review it appears as if there has been a tendency to overgeneralize about the personality and behavior of the mentally retarded. In a similar fashion, there has been a tendency frequently to stereotype the personality of some of the more specific subgroups of retarded such as mongols or phenylketonurics. Many of these generalizations, furthermore, have been based on the clinical impressions of various individuals rather than on systematic investigations. The evidence of more recent studies and the accompanying change in point of view suggest considerable variability in the personality and behavior of individuals considered to be retarded.

With regard to abnormal behavior, specifically, there have been a number of diverse views presented. These have ranged from the statement that psychoses do not develop fully in the mentally retarded to the view that the latter are particularly susceptible to psychoses. In a related fashion some observers have stated that mental deficiency may result from psychosis, while others have hypothesized that mental deficiency is likely to lead to specific types of psychoses. Surveys of psychotic and neurotic behavior, emotional instability, and sociopathic behavior in diverse samples of individuals diagnosed as mentally retarded have also resulted in findings which show considerable variation. Similar variability is manifested in statements relative to the treatment of emotional disturbance in the mentally retarded. Some therapists believe the prognosis is poor while others hypothesize that the greater inability of the retarded to retreat into a world of fantasy may make those with schizophrenic symptoms easier to treat (Wolfensberger, 1960).

When one finds such discrepant findings in the literature, one is usually safe in inferring that some of the differences in findings are due to inadequate diagnostic criteria, unreliable or faulty evaluative techniques, poorly defined or inadequate samples of subjects, and poor research designs. One or more of these deficiencies would seem to be present in a number of the studies reported. In the area of abnormal behavior, particularly, we are likely to encounter a large number of poorly defined diagnostic entities which may be interpreted and diagnosed in different ways by different examiners. In the case of the mentally retarded, the problem of evaluating and understanding aberrant behavior may be even more difficult since many of these individuals have difficulty in communicating their feelings and, conceivably, in explaining their behavior. Furthermore, the diagnosis of mental deficiency has also been made in terms of varying criteria. Thus, although most types of behavioral disorders have been noted in patients diagnosed as mentally deficient, adequate appraisals of this problem are lacking. Some of the questions which still are not answered adequately and appear to merit further research are:

1. How important is limited intelligence in the eventual development of behavioral or emotional disturbance? A few studies have shown a modest negative relationship between intelligence and certain types of instability; yet, even if we accept these findings, intelligence would still be seen as a relatively minor contributing factor as far as the bulk of such disorders are concerned.

2. Are individuals with limited intellectual ability more prone to certain types of behavioral disturbance or adjustive defenses than other types, or do they show relatively the same variation as nonretarded individuals? Are there differences between different levels of deficiency and the different clinical types in this regard?

3. If differences in patterns of disturbed behavior are obtained between retarded and nonretarded individuals, what are the significant variables which seem to be related to the disturbed behavior? Is the behavior a result of early parent-child relationships, rejection, hostility, etc.? Does subnormal cognitive ability limit the ability of the individual to adapt to the normal frustrations and adjustments of everyday life? Is failure more frequent in the life of the retarded and a possible factor in disturbed adjustment? How important is awareness of intellectual inferiority in the development of anxiety and feelings of insecurity? (Feldman, 1946).

4. Another problem suggested by several studies is in the general area of the relationship of severe personality disturbance in children to mental retardation or apparent retardation. What are the differences between an autistic or schizophrenic child functioning at a retarded level and a mentally retarded child who functions at a comparable level? Is it important to attempt to differentiate between these different categories, or should we treat children who behave in the same fashion in a similar manner? Is this merely a semantic problem, or does it reflect a problem of possibly different etiologies about which we have much to learn? Conceivably, psychologists with different theoretical orientations will view the problem in different ways. Those with behavioristic leanings may tend to emphasize the similarities in behavior, while clinically or dynamically oriented psychologists

will be more concerned with the differential factors in the past development of these cases.

5. It would appear exceedingly important to study intensively the very early development of retarded or potentially retarded children. There is a large group of mentally retarded children about whom we know very little concerning the possible causes of their retardation. On the basis of existing studies concerning the adverse influence of early separation from the mother, indequate mother-child relations, sensory deprivation, and similar areas, it has been postulated that such experiences may have a significant impact on the intellectual and emotional development of the child. We need more definitive knowledge concerning the impact of such experiences on the development of mental retardation, disturbed behavior, and the interrelationship of cognitive and emotional factors in children who have undergone such experiences. There has been a tendency to treat intellectual development and emotional or personality development as separate phenomena, when it is clear that they are conceptualized aspects of a total functioning organism.

6. From what has already been said it is evident that psychologists should be able to contribute to an understanding of disturbed behavior in individuals who show limited intellectual ability. Apart from the knowledge of more rigorous research design which the psychologist may bring to this field, psychologists can utilize and apply many of their current theories pertaining to frustration, level of aspiration, expectancy, the self-concept, personality development, and the like. There is a great need for the accumulation of reliable data in this area, and theoretically guided research and the application to the retarded of research techniques utilized with normals may be fruitful. Comparatively little is known "of both the behavioral and situational variables critically related to the ultimate adjustment of retarded persons" (Heber, 1959a, p. 1019). In this connection, however, it is important to keep in mind that much of the research has been and undoubtedly will continue to be done with institutionalized individuals. The quality of the institutional environment, therefore, can be expected to be a variable of some importance. In addition, some of the findings obtained may not be applicable to retarded children outside of an institution.

7. Finally, the writer would like to emphasize the importance of viewing the retarded individual as a person with some uniqueness and individuality who requires as much study and understanding as other persons. In the past there has been a definite tendency to explain the defective's behavior on the basis of limited intelligence. While level of mental ability is certainly important, one may seriously question its use as the main explanation for a variety of abnormal patterns of behavior. While psychologists and workers in related disciplines tend to emphasize the importance of early experience and parental influences for the subsequent behavior of the nonretarded child, a comparable emphasis seems to be lacking in the case of the retarded; yet one might expect the same types of principles to apply. As Sarason and Gladwin (1958) have emphasized, the mental defective has rarely been studied in this way. His experiences, feelings, and attitudes have not been explored as thoroughly as those of nonretarded individuals. There

certainly exists a need for adequate data in this area. Why do some retarded individuals show disturbed or psychotic patterns of behavior while supposedly similar types of retarded individuals do not? If, in fact, the mental deficiency is a presumed cause of disturbed behavior in some cases, why does it not lead to aberrant behavior in others with mental deficiency?

When we devote as much clinical and research efforts to understanding the retarded as we have to other groups, we can expect that our knowledge of this complex group will increase and that this knowledge will also contribute to our understanding of related problems.

REFERENCES

ABEL, THEORORA M. Responses of negro and white morons to the Thematic Apperception Test. *Amer. J. ment. Defic.*, 1945, 50, 251–256.

ANGUS, L. R. Schizophrenia and schizoid conditions in students in a special school. *Amer. J. ment. Defic.*, 1948, 53, 227–238.

ARTHUR, GRACE. Pseudo Feeblemindedness. *Amer. J. ment. Defic.*, 1947, 52, 137–142.

ARTHUR, GRACE. Some factors contributing to errors in the diagnosis of feeblemindedness. *Amer. J. ment. Defic.*, 1950, 54, 495–501.

BENDA, C. E. *Developmental disorders of mentation and cerebral palsies.* New York: Grune & Stratton, 1952.

BENDA, C. E. Psychopathology of childhood. In L. Carmichael (Ed.), *Manual of child psychology* (2nd ed.) New York: Wiley, 1954. Pp. 1115–1161.

BENDA, C. E. Childhood schizophrenia, autism and Heller's disease. In P. W. Bowman & H. V. Mautner (Eds.), *Mental retardation. Proc. first int. med. Conf.* New York: Grune & Stratton, 1960. Pp. 469–492.

BENDA, C. E., FARRELL, M. J., & CHIPMAN, CATHERINE E. The inadequacy of present day concepts of mental deficiency and mental illness in child psychiatry. *Amer. J. Psychiat.*, 1951, 107, 721–729.

BENDER, LAURETTA. Medical factors in diagnosis contributing to management and treatment programs. In M. E. Wright & H. T. Croley (Eds.), *Research in the management of the mentally retarded child.* Winfield, Kansas: Winfield State Training School, 1956. Pp. 25–35.

BENDER, LAURETTA. Autism in children with mental deficiency. *Amer. J. ment. Defic.*, 1959, 64, 81–86.

BENDER, LAURETTA. Diagnostic and therapeutic aspects of childhood schizophrenia. In P. W. Bowman & H. V. Mautner (Eds.), *Mental retardation. Proc. first int. med. Conf.* New York: Grune & Stratton, 1960. Pp. 453–468.

BOURNE, H. Protophrenia. A study of perverted rearing and mental dwarfism. *Lancet*, 1955, 1156–1163, Part II.

BRADLEY, C. *Schizophrenia in childhood.* New York: Macmillan, 1941.

BROMBERG, W., & THOMPSON, C. B. The relation of psychosis, mental defect and personality types to crime. *J. Crim. Law Criminol.*, 1937, 28, 70–89.

CHAPMAN, L. J., & PATHMAN, J. H. Errors in the diagnosis of mental deficiency in schizophrenia. *J. consult. psychol.*, 1959, 23, 432–434.

CLARKE, ANN M., & CLARKE, A. D. B. (EDS.). *Mental deficiency. The changing outlook.* New York: Free Press, 1958.

COTZIN, M. Group psychotherapy with mentally defective problem boys. *Amer. J. ment. Defic.*, 1948, 53, 268–283.

CRAFT, M. Mental disorder in a series of English outpatient defectives. *Amer. J. ment. Defic.*, 1960, 64, 718–724.

CROMWELL, R. L.   A methodological approach to personality research in mental retardation. *Amer. J. ment. Defic.*, 1959, 64, 333–340.

CUTTS, R. A.   Differentiation between pseudo-mental defectives with emotional disorders and mental defectives with emotional disturbances. *Amer. J. ment. Defic.*, 1957, 61, 761–772.

DEWAN, J. G.   Intelligence and emotional stability. *Amer. J. Psychiat.*, 1948, 104, 548–554.

DUNCAN, A. G., PENROSE, L. S., & TURNBULL, R. C.   A survey of the patients in a large mental hospital. *J. Neurol. Psychopathol.*, 1936, 16, 225–238.

EARL, C. J. C.   The primitive catatonic psychosis of idiocy. *Brit. J. Med. Psychol.*, 1934, 14, 230–253.

EKSTEIN, R., BRYANT, K., & FRIEDMAN, S. W.   Childhood schizophrenia and allied conditions. In L. Bellak (Ed.), *Schizophrenia, a review of the syndrome.* New York: Logos Press, 1958. Pp. 555–693.

FELDMAN, F.   Psychoneuroses in the mentally retarded. *Amer. J. ment. Defic.*, 1946, 51, 247–254.

GALLAGHER, J. J.   A comparison of brain-injured and non-brain-injured mentally retarded children on several psychological variables. *Monogr. soc. Res. Child Developm.*, 1957, 22, No. 2, 3–79.

GARFIELD, S. L.   Problems in the psychological evaluation of the subnormal individual. *Amer. J. ment. Defic.*, 1959, 64, 467–471.

GARFIELD, S. L., & AFFLECK, D. C.   A study of individuals committed to a state home for the retarded who were later released as not mentally retarded. *Amer. J. ment. Defic.*, 1960, 64, 907–915.

GARFIELD, S. L., WILCOTT, JOHANNA B., & MILGRAM, N.   Emotional disturbance and suspected mental deficiency. *Amer. J. ment. Defic.*, 1961, 66, 23–29.

GARFIELD, S. L., & WITTSON, C. L.   Some reactions to the revised "Manual on terminology and classification in mental retardation." *Amer. J. ment. Defic.*, 1960, 64, 951–953. (a)

GARFIELD, S. L., & WITTSON, C. L.   Comments on Dr. Cantor's remarks. *Amer. J. ment. Defic.*, 1960, 64, 957–959. (b)

GOLDFARB, W., & DORSEN, MARILYN M.   *Annotated bibliography of childhood schizophrenia.* New York: Basic Books, 1956.

GREENE, R. A.   Psychoses and mental deficiencies, comparisons and relationship. *Proc. and addresses Amer. Ass. Stud. of Feebleminded.* 1930, 35, 128–147.

GUNZBURG, H. C.   Psychotherapy with the feebleminded. In Ann M. Clarke & A. D. B. Clarke (Eds.), *Mental deficiency: the changing outlook.* New York: Free Press, 1958. Pp. 365–392.

HARRIS, LUCY M., & SIEVERS, DOROTHY J.   A study to measure changes in behavior of aggressive mentally retarded adolescent girls in a permissive classroom. *Amer. J. ment. Defic.*, 1959, 63, 975–980.

HEBER, R.   Promising areas for psychological research in mental retardation. *Amer. J. ment. Defic.*, 1959, 63, 1014–1019. (a)

HEBER, R.   A manual on terminology and classification in mental retardation. *Amer. J. ment. Defic., Monogr. Suppl.*, 1959, 64, No. 2, 3–11. (b)

HEISER, K. F.   Mental deficiency in the urban community. *Amer. J. Orthopsychiat.*, 1957, 27, 484–489.

HENDERSON, D., & GILLESPIE, R. D.   *A texbook of psychiatry.* (8th ed.) London: Oxford Univer. Press, 1956.

HOLLINGSHEAD, A. B., & REDLICH, F. C.   *Social class and mental illness.* New York: Wiley, 1958.

JOLLES, I. A study of mental deficiency by the Rorschach technique. *Amer. J. ment. Defic.*, 1947, 52, 37–42.

KALLMANN, F. J., BARRERA, S. E., HOCH, P. H., & KELLEY, D. M. The role of mental deficiency in the incidence of schizophrenia. *Amer. J. ment. Defic.*, 1941, 45, 514–539.

KANNER, L. Autistic disturbances of affective contact. *Nerv. Child.*, 1943, 2, 217–250.

KANNER, L. Early infantile autism. *J. Pediatr.*, 1944, 23, 211–217.

KANNER, L. Child psychiatry. (3rd ed.) Springfield, Ill.: Charles C Thomas, 1957.

KANNER, L., & EISENBERG, L. Notes on the follow-up studies of autistic children. In P. H. Hoch & J. Zubin (Eds.), *Psychopathology of childhood.* New York: Grune & Stratton, 1955. Pp. 227–239.

KUGELMASS, I. N. *The management of mental deficiency in children.* New York, London: Grune & Stratton, 1954.

leVANN, L. J. A concept of schizophrenia in the lower grade mental defective. *Amer. J. ment. Defic.*, 1950, 54, 469–472.

LIPMAN, R. S. Some test correlates of behavioral aggression in institutionalized retardates with particular reference to the Rosenzweig Picture Frustration Study. *Amer. J. ment. Defic.*, 1959, 63, 1038–1045.

LITTLE, K. B., & SHNEIDMAN, E. S. Congruencies among interpretations of psychological test and anamnestic data. *Psychol. Monogr.*, 1959, 73, No. 6 (Whole No. 476).

LOWREY, L. G. Delinquent and criminal personalities. In J. McV. Hunt. (Ed.), *Personality and the behavior disorders.* Vol. 2. New York: Ronald, 1944. Pp. 794–821.

MAHLER, MARGARET S. On child psychosis and schizophrenia. Autistic and symbiotic infantile psychoses. In *Psychoanalytic study of the child.* Vol. 7. New York: Int. Univer. Press, 1952. Pp. 286–305.

MARCOTTE, J. E. A. Mental deficiency in behavior problems. *Amer. J. ment. Defic.*, 1947, 51, 407–419.

NEHAM, SARA. Psychotherapy in relation to mental deficiency. *Amer. J. ment. Defic.*, 1951, 55, 557–572.

NEUER, H. The relationship between behavior disorders in children and the syndrome of mental deficiency. *Amer. J. ment. Defic.*, 1947, 52, 143–147.

O'CONNOR, N. Neuroticism and emotional instability in high-grade male defectives. *J. Neurol. Neurosurg. Psychiat.*, 1951, 14, 226–230.

O'CONNOR, N., & TIZARD, J. *The social problem of mental deficiency.* New York: Pergamon Press, 1956.

O'GORMAN, G. Psychosis as a cause of mental defect. *J. ment. Sci.*, 1954, 100, 934–943.

PENROSE, L. S. *The biology of mental defect.* (Rev. ed.) London: Sidgwick & Jackson, 1954.

POLLACK, M. Brain damage, mental retardation and childhood schizophrenia. *Amer. J. Psychiat.*, 1958, 115, 422–428.

POLLOCK, H. M. Mental disease among mental defectives. *Amer. J. ment. Defic.*, 1945, 49, 477–480.

RAUB, E. S., MERCER, MARGARET, & HECKER, A. O. A study of psychotic patients assumed to be mentally deficient on the basis of school progress and social adjustment. *Amer. J. ment. Defic.*, 1952, 57, 82–88.

ROBINSON, R. C., & PASEWARD, R. Behavior in intellectual deficit; a critical review of the literature. *Amer. J. ment. Defic.*, 1951, 55, 598–607.

SAENGER, G. *Factors influencing the institutionalization of mentally retarded individuals in New York City.* Albany, N.Y.: Interdepartmental Health Resources Board, 1960.

SARASON, S. B. The use of the Thematic Apperception Test with mentally deficient children. I. A study of high grade girls. *Amer. J. ment. Defic.*, 1943, 47, 414–421.

SARASON, S. B. *Psychological problems in mental deficiency.* (2nd ed.) New York: Harper, 1953.

SARASON, S. B., & GLADWIN, T. Psychological and cultural problems in mental subnormality: a review of research. *Genet. Psychol. Monogr.*, 1958, 57, 3–289.

SLOAN, W. Mental deficiency as a symptom of personality disturbance. *Amer. J. ment. Defic.*, 1947, 52, 31–36.

SLOAN, W. Prediction of extramural adjustment of mental defectives by use of the Rorschach test. *J. consult. Psychol.*, 1948, 12, 303–309.

Symp. res. design and methodology in ment. retardation. *Amer. J. ment. Defic.*, 1959, 64, 227–430.

THORNE, F. C. Counseling and psychotherapy with mental defectives. *Amer. J. ment. Defic.*, 1948, 52, 263–271.

TIZARD, J. Individual differences in the mentally deficient. In Ann M. Clarke & A. D. B. Clarke (Eds.), *Mental deficiency. The changing outlook.* New York: Free Press, 1958. Pp. 154–174.

TREDGOLD, A. F. *A textbook of mental deficiency.* (8th ed.) Baltimore: Williams & Wilkins, 1952.

TULCHIN, S. H. *Intelligence and crime.* Chicago: Univer. of Chicago Press, 1939.

WALLIN, J. E. W. *Children with mental and physical handicaps.* Englewood Cliffs, N.J.: Prentice-Hall, 1949.

WALLIN, J. E. W. Mental deficiency; in relation to problems of genesis, social and occupational consequences, utilization, control, and prevention. Brandon, Vt.: *J. clin. Psychol.*, 1956.

WEAVER, T. R. The incident of maladjustment among mental defectives in military environment. *Amer. J. ment. Defic.*, 1946, 51, 238–246.

WIENER, G., CRAWFORD, E. E., & SNYDER, R. T. Some correlates of overt anxiety in mildly retarded patients. *Amer. J. ment. Defic.*, 1960, 64, 735–739.

WOLFENSBERGER, W. Schizophrenia in mental retardates: Three hypotheses. *Amer. J. ment. Defic.*, 1960, 64, 704–706.

WOODWARD, MARY. The role of low intelligence in delinquence. *Brit. J. Delinq.*, 1955, 5, 281–303.

WOODWARD, MARY. Early experiences and later social responses of severely subnormal children. *Brit. J. Med. Psychol.*, 1960, 33, 123–132.

WUNSCH, W. L. The first complete tabulation of the Rhode Island mental deficiency register. *Amer. J. ment. Defic.*, 1951, 55, 293–312.

YAKOLEV, P. I., WEINBERGER, M., & CHIPMAN, CATHERINE C. Heller's syndrome as a pattern of schizophrenic behavior disturbance in early childhood. *Amer. J. ment. Defic.*, 1948, 53, 318–337.

19

MOTOR SKILLS IN
MENTAL DEFICIENCY[1]

Leslie F. Malpass

There are very few forms of human behavior which do not involve some type of movement. Indeed, motility is one biological criterion for life itself. The study of motility and motor characteristics has important social, educational, and vocational implications beyond those relating to theoretical or scientific interest. Coordination, speed, accuracy, gracefulness of movement in walking, dancing, and handling utensils, for example, can be expected to have some effect on responses of others to the individual. Every kind of occupational enterprise involves not only ability to distinguish what is required but also the capability to make appropriate motor responses at the proper time. In a very real sense, if a person is unable to perform required motor skills he cannot participate in educational enterprises or be self-dependent.

Lorenz (1950) has suggested that behavior patterns (i.e., complex series of movements) are as useful as anatomical-physiological characteristics for distinguishing between and among species. Another writer (Tuke, as quoted by Wallin, 1949, pp. 124–125) has suggested classifying mental defectives[2] according to motor abilities. The broad classifications of mental defectives according to this system would be (1) those capable of reflex movements

[1] Drs. William Sloan and Margaret Fisher read the original draft of this chapter and made valuable suggestions. Their help is gratefully acknowledged.
[2] For this chapter, *mental defectives* and *retardates* refer to individuals judged to be subnormal in psychometric intellectual status. As general terms they refer to a group of Ss or an individual with IQ(s) below 80. *Low-grade defective* refers generally to the IQ range 0–50; *moderately retarded* or *educable mentally handicapped* refers to those in the IQ 50–80 range.

only, (2) those capable of idiomotor and emotional responses, and (3) those capable of volitional acts.

The lack of precision in this classification prevents it from being feasible for practical investigation. The categories are too broad and the number of subjects that would be included in the first two is so small compared with the number in the third that little effective use could be made of this system. Tuke's classification system points up a common problem—authorities typically have used broadly descriptive terms to denote motor characteristics of the mentally retarded. Standard measurements of motor skills of defectives are of relatively recent origin. There is hope that a more appropriate classification of these skills will become available.

It is the purpose of this chapter to discuss some of the major factors underlying motor ability, to present and evaluate methods used to assess motor skills, and to indicate briefly some implications of motor proficiency for vocational success. Distinctions between types of motor characteristics deserve to be made because of confusion and contradictions that attend their use.

Motor ability, motor proficiency, and motor skill

Various terms are often used ambiguously to designate types and aspects of motor characteristics. For the purposes of this chapter *motor ability, motor proficiency,* and *motor skill* will all refer in general to types or sequences of motor response. Proficiency, ability, and skill all connote the attainment of a designated level of performance. Studies of such characteristics indicate that motor skill is not a unitary factor and that correlations between tests of motor ability are usually lower than between parts of IQ tests (Sloan, 1955). Motor-response mechanisms are controlled essentially by kinesthetic (internal) and various kinds of external stimuli: they are mediated by the neuromusculature, more specifically, synapses, motor nerves, and the muscles. Knowledge of motor abilities can be used to predict the rate at which specific sequences of responses (i.e., motor skills) can be learned or the level of proficiency that can be expected. Driving an automobile or operating a sewing machine involves many specific kinds of abilities—spatial orientation, coordination of hand-arm-leg movements in proper time sequences, appropriate strength or pressure for different operations, and the like. Such activities cannot be expected from persons who cannot demonstrate the particular requisites of the general skill. Proficiency depends not only on biological determiners of task performance but also on how well the person can utilize experience with the task itself.

Force, speed, and precision as components of motor ability. The major components of motor ability include force, speed, and precision. The *force* required to perform a given task becomes an index of the strength of the subject and the direction and persistence of movements involved. It is primarily a function of the muscle groups used. Strength of grip, as measured by a dynamometer, is an example of this characteristic. Typically, strength rather than force is reported as the variable of concern in experiments with mental defectives but force exerted would, perhaps, be a more accurate denotation. An excellent description of measures of strength, both dynamic (lifting or propulsion of body weight) and static dynamometric strength (spring dynamometers used to evaluate squeezing, pulling, lifting, and pushing) has been provided by H. E. Jones (1949). His study indicated incremental changes in strength with age through adolescence and suggested that static dynamometric strength is strongly related to biological growth and constitutional factors. The increase in boys' strength with age is more marked than that for girls.

Speed of motor performance is a function of the intensity of the stimulus, the sense organ being stimulated, and the complexity of response required. Reaction time is one of the most widely reported variables in experimental psychology. Studies comparing reaction times of mental defectives and normals indicate that, in general, the lower the IQ the poorer the performance of defectives as compared with normals (Scott, 1940; Pascal, 1953; Ellis & Sloan, 1957; Berkson, 1960a, 1960b, 1960c). One of the studies (Ellis & Sloan, 1957) indicated greater variability among defectives than normals with respect to reaction time. Bensberg and Cantor (1957) reported that clinical etiology is related to reaction time for both simple and complex learning tasks. Defectives diagnosed as familial performed significantly faster than the organics. The Berkson studies demonstrated that when the stimulus is held constant and complexity of the required response is varied, a resulting significant interaction between IQ and motor tasks can be expected. None of these studies indicates that IQ is related to speed of information reception (for Ss with no observable central nervous system lesions) or to cortical processes involved in making the movement. Rather, they suggest that the slower reaction time of defectives is primarily a response function.

The third major component of motor ability is *precision*, or accuracy of movements. In general, low-grade defectives, when compared with normals, demonstrate greater difficulty in placing, turning, and positioning movements, in control of continuous movement, and in muscular steadiness. These characteristics, too, vary as a function of the complexity of the task required (Heath, 1942).

Motor development

As commonly used, this term refers to incremental changes in observed motor performance with increasing age. Infants and young children show greater variety of motor performance and greater proficiency in particular movements with practice. Espenschade (1940) reports that "motor performance is related to age, sex, physical growth, weight and height during the elementary and high school years" (p. 9). This is true for both sexes and evidently is related to physiological maturity. However, the nature and extent of this influence have not been established.

Many of the measures that have been used to evaluate motor performance of different age groups were not standardized for this purpose and should not be considered as motor development scales. However, there are some tests which have been devised specifically for this purpose, e.g., the Oseretsky Motor Development Scale and its revisions. Findings of studies utilizing such measures will be given in the section dealing with motor development measures.

Motor educability

Motor learning per se has been discussed in other chapters. Most of the psychological literature deals with learning specific kinds of motor skills. When used in this chapter the term will refer to incremental changes in motor responses as a function of experience or practice. Motor educability is a less-used term and refers essentially to the effects of training on the performance of complex motor tasks such as physical education stunts and/or body exercises. Several measures of motor educability will be described in a later section. The relatively few studies concerning the motor educability of mental defectives will be discussed, also.

Motor disability

Typically, motor disability refers to any neurophysiological handicap which is responsible for substandard motor performance. The term is used rather loosely. Since mental defectives tend to demonstrate more defects than normals in the sensorium, in neuromusculature, and in other organic structures and functions, it is not surprising that they tend to demonstrate more motor disabilities (Tredgold, 1950; Malpass, 1959). Consideration of some of the etiological variables underlying motor performance in general points up many of the more specific reasons why motor disability and mental status, at least for low-grade defectives as contrasted with normals, are related.

ETIOLOGICAL CONSIDERATIONS IN MOTOR DISABILITY

A variety of factors are related to motor performance. Biological, psychological, and cultural considerations contribute to response tendencies of all types. There is evidence to suggest that genetic factors, damage to the central nervous system, sensory-motor dysfunction, delayed maturation, and lack of appropriate stimulation may all interfere with the acquisition and maintenance of motor skills.

Heredity

Individual variations in motor skills are easily observable. That heredity contributes to such variations, either primarily or secondarily, seems irrefutable, although the extent and nature of the contribution are speculative. Responses of monozygotic twins to motor tests are less divergent than those of dyzygotic twins. As might be expected, both types of twins show fewer differences than do pairs of unrelated subjects matched for age and sex (McNemar, 1933; Brody, 1937). Further, there is no consistent effect of practice on the degree of difference in motor performance between the types of twins.

Investigations of mental defectives relating genetic factors and motor skills have been reported, but genetic factors per se have not been investigated. Strauss and Lehtinen (1951) provide criteria for distinguishing exogenous and endogenous brain-injured children, and several studies have differentiated between familial and organic defective groups. A fundamental question in these studies concerns the basis for classification. It is possible that many defects once considered to be determined by developmental anomalies or attributed to "unknown causes" may turn out to be genetically determined. This has already been demonstrated for mongolism and phenyl-pyruvic oligophrenia, for example. Moller (1961) has reported that between 1958 and 1961 some twenty such defects have been related to chromosomal imbalances due to mutations or other hereditary faults.

In the broad sense, then, heredity undoubtedly plays some part in determining motor proficiency of mental defectives and has been related to specific types of motor disability. For most motor characteristics, however, it is probably the interaction between genetic, developmental, and stimulus-reinforcement conditions which determines the level of proficiency that is demonstrated.

The central nervous system

That lesions of the brain (particularly in the central sulcus), the spinal cord, or motor nerves are sources of motor disability has long been recognized. One of the major problems in relating such variables is the lack of adequate diagnostic criteria, for both motor proficiency and biological faults. Gallagher (1957) has pointed out the general inadequacies of most motor-ability tests used to discriminate brain damage, e.g., the Strauss-Lehtinen tests. A promising breakthrough in the area of predicting not only presence or absence of brain injury but also the localization, extent, and even etiological aspects of damage has been provided by Halstead (1947) and Reitan (1959). A tacit assumption frequently made when examining brain-behavior relationships in neurologically impaired defectives is to view brain injury as a unitary variable with certain inevitable behavioral consequences (McFie, 1960).

Reitan has demonstrated that differential patterns and degrees of adaptive ability can be associated with specific CNS disease processes and sites of involvement. Matthews (1961) used the Halstead-Reitan battery with mental defectives. His study suggests that motor performance of retardates is comparable with that of recently brain-injured subjects testing at the same Wechsler IQ level (but whose pretrauma IQs were normal) on a tactual-motor task.

It is expected that considerable advances will be made in relating motor proficiency and central nervous system functions with improvement of diagnostic criteria in both areas.

Sensory-motor functions

Analysis of responses to sensory stimulation constitutes a major concern of experimental psychology and physiology. The anatomical and physiolog-ical aspects of vision, hearing, olfaction, gustation, and tactile and kinesthetic behavior are fairly well known. However, the methodologies employed to study sensory-motor functions in mental defectives have been questionable, for the most part, and few conclusive generalizations are possible.

Problems in evaluating sensory-motor characteristics of defectives arise from several sources. These include the use of different criteria by different investigators; inadequate control of presentation conditions (Foale & Patterson, 1954); administration problems in getting defectives to respond to a signal (Atkinson, 1959); and a confounding of perceptual with response activities (Goldiamond, 1959). It seems likely that it is in terms of response factors, rather than perceptual factors, that retardates suffer in comparisons with normals.

Seven studies of audiometric testing indicate as many different estimates of hearing loss (Kodman, 1957). Atkinson (1959) has contributed the most comprehensive survey of hearing of mental defectives. Using four hearing tests introduced to subjects with operant rather than respondent conditioning procedures, he found "no difference among mentally retarded and normal children tested in terms of hearing loss to the extent that it would impair educational or social processes" (p. 42). Incidence of hearing loss among both institutionalized and noninstitutionalized defectives has been reported to be about 15 to 50 per cent in several studies; Atkinson claims it is no higher than the 1 to 2 per cent reported for the population at large.

Regarding vision, Goldiamond's (1959) elegant work with retardates represents some of the best research done in the area. He found that the voltage required for forced location of visual signals was independent of IQ but varied inversely with age. However, in terms of responses to the visual stimuli, he says:

> Children with lower IQs gave consistently more overestimative responses in signal detection, needed more definite responses, gave more false alarms, and reported more signal detection at intensities too low for accurate location, than did normal children, for whom such responses tended to diminish with age. Retarded children also required more time to complete tasks and there was considerable response attenuation in the absence of training and prompts (p. iv).

These data indicate strongly that auditory and visual instatement in mental retardates is little different from that in normals. It is responses associated with such stimulation that differentiate defectives from normals. Since motor behavior is typically dependent on sensory stimulation, considerably more work in basic psychophysics akin to that of Atkinson, Goldiamond, and Berkson is required in the area of mental retardation. A great deal has been written about perceptual-motor abilities. Until better means of separating these functions is available, it seems only confusing to discuss them together. Therefore, only observable motor performance is considered in this chapter.

Skeletal-muscular coordination

Most of the research and clinical reports about the motor skills of mental defectives pay little attention to skeletal and muscular components of the behavior. Low-grade defectives are known to have a higher incidence of skeletal deformities and a lower level of general coordination than normals. Tredgold (1956) epitomizes the views of most clinical investigators in his general description of muscular coordination in institutionalized defectives:

> In persons with even the mildest degree of amentia, coordination is often acquired with difficulty and remains imperfect; and although many of them may learn to use their hands with a considerable amount of dexterity, the balance and movement of the body often continues clumsy and ungainly. . . . Even the best of them (with a few remarkable exceptions) rarely attain to the precision and neatness of movement of which an ordinary well-trained child is capable" (p. 127).

This observation seems at variance with those of Sherman (1945) and others, who claim that moderately retarded children can learn simple sensory-motor activities as quickly and efficiently as normal children. Tredgold's sweeping statement is probably based principally on clinical observation of defectives. Studies in the United States of noninstitutionalized as well as institutionalized subjects suggest caution in accepting his conclusion. Kreezer (1935), for example, found no difference between retardates and normals in motor chronaxy in the biceps, although mental defectives fell below normals in 90 per cent of joint movements (Glanville & Kreezer, 1937). Many moderately retarded individuals do not demonstrate observable motor defect to the degree suggested by Tredgold.

An important consideration in evaluating motor proficiency is the complexity of muscular performance required in a task, in conjunction with the coordination of one or several sensory fields. Although most measures of motor ability are based on such considerations, few investigators have been concerned with analyses of the specific factors involved.

Maturation and motor skills

It is reasonable to assume covariation between increases in general body growth, general motor proficiency, and increases in age through childhood. Several studies have demonstrated this in a variety of ways. Thompson (1954) provides an excellent review of research in this area. It would be superfluous to repeat all her findings here. Gross motor skills tend to increase with chronological age (CA) until about age 16. A plateau occurs in the curve until about age 20, and then there is a decrease. This is true for global motor skills but not for particular skills. While the shapes of developmental curves for retardates approximate those for normals, there is, in general, a delay in demonstration of motor skills dependent on the age and IQ group considered and the types of motor performance evaluated. There is general agreement that infant development schedules (sometimes erroneously referred to as infant intelligence scales) cannot be used to predict mental status in later life (Bayley, 1933; Jones, 1954). On the other hand, there is some striking evidence that children designated as retarded in adolescence demonstrated developmental retardation in infancy. For example, Malpass (1959) reported that more than 45 per cent of his retarded adolescents were not walking by the sixteenth *postpartum* month and 20 per cent did not walk until after 26 months of age. Fifty-two per cent of retardates had not achieved bowel control, and fifty-five per cent had not achieved urinary control by 2 years of age, an age at which 80 to 90 per cent of normals achieve such control.

As age increases through adolescence, differences between normals and retardates in gross motor skills tend to increase. Between the ages of 8 and 14 moderately retarded children demonstrate a delay of 2 to 4 years in complex motor performance (Francis & Rarick, 1960). The motor retardation of this group is possibly greater than might be supposed from casual observation of such children in special education classes or in neighborhood play.

The fact that the curves for motor maturation of educable retardates are similar to those of normals suggests that defectives may be able to profit from the same kinds of experiences with which normals are provided, but that more patience is necessary in setting expectations for their performance. Reports from many institutions indicate that even severely retarded adolescents and adults can learn to perform fairly complex motor skills although, as suggested previously, the level of performance complexity is a function of age and the mental status level for this group (Sherman, 1945; Tizard & O'Connor, 1950).

Opportunities for learning motor skills

It is very likely that mental defectives are not stimulated to practice motor skills as much as, or as appropriately as, normals. This does not mean that many retarded children are not given sufficient opportunities to demonstrate developmental proficiencies. Undoubtedly, many individual retardates receive a good deal more attention from adults when they indicate delay. But in such cases the attention they receive, in the form of discriminative stimuli and social reinforcements supplied by the parents, is all too often inappropriate for the motor-maturational-intellectual development of the child.

Interviews by the writer with many parents of defective children revealed that they have considerable concern about their children's motor development and also considerable difficulty in utilizing procedures for helping their children learn motor skills appropriate to their mental status. It is not surprising that biological faults which may contribute to substandard motor development are often compounded by ineffective opportunities for learning. Procedures such as those suggested by Rosenzweig and Long (1960) and Kirk and Johnson (1951) for helping both severely and moderately retarded children learn motor activities, such as manipulating eating utensils, marching, clapping in rhythm, and simple games, can be of immense practical help to parents and teachers of such children.

METHODS OF ASSESSING MOTOR SKILLS

Interest in systematic measurement of motor performance has received impetus from several sources: (1) analysis of measures of individual's intellectual status or development (viz., the Gesell and Cattell scales for infants, the Binet and Wechsler IQ scales), which indicates that success on many subtests varies directly with sensory-motor activity; (2) evaluation of complex motor skills for purposes of research in and application to educational procedures (e.g., for classifying students in homogeneous groups in physical education classes); (3) the development in Europe of the Oseretsky tests of motor proficiency and the subsequent translation and revision of these scales in America; (4) utilizing motor skills for predictive success in educational-vocational pursuits. (In this connection, the military services in many countries have underwritten much research dealing with basic psychophysiological as well as applied aspects of motor performance.)

From these sources have come a variety of procedures for assessing motor skills. Many of them have been used to study mental defectives. Some are concerned with discrete types of motor performance, others with complex motor skills. The Oseretsky Motor Development Scale and its revisions have been used to compare the motor development of different categories of defectives and for comparing defectives with normals. Several scales, originally devised for normals, have been used to evaluate the motor educability of defectives.

So many motor tasks have been used to evaluate particular motor behaviors that it is not possible to discuss all of them. Only some of the procedures which have been used already, or which have potential value for evaluating motor abilities of retardates, will be described in the following sections.

MEASURES OF PARTICULAR SKILLS

Measures of particular motor skills can be categorized in terms of essential limb functions involved. Tests of balance and locomotion involve principally the feet, legs, and trunk; tests of manual dexterity involve principally finger-hand-arm movements. There is some evidence that balance-locomotion tasks may require involvement of a greater number of sensory modalities than manual tasks (Heath, 1953). On the supposition that defectives have greater difficulty than normals in coordinating several biological demands, one might expect a greater covariance between manual-mental skills than between locomotor-mental abilities. There is little but conjecture regarding this point, however.

Balance and locomotion measures

The Vineland Railwalking Test (Heath, 1942) and the Springfield Beam-walking Test (Seashore, 1947) have been devised as measures of locomotor coordination and general skeletal-muscular control. The railwalking test consists of three wooden rails 6- and 9-feet long and varying in width from 1 to 4 inches. The subject traverses the rails in a heel-to-toe fashion without support. Heath (1953) reports correlations of .57 to .62 between railwalking and MA for familial defectives but low *rs* (.15 to .23) between these variables for brain-injured subjects. Results do not suggest that the test is appropriate for differentiating between mental defective classification types, although differences were reported between the groups mentioned.

After 7 years of age, sex differences in favor of boys appear in railwalking performances (Heath, 1942; DiStefano, Ellis, & Sloan, 1958). There is a tendency for railwalking to vary with age up through the middle adolescent years (Fisher, 1946). This may be a function of general maturation. Rail-walking has been used without success to differentiate potential employable and nonemployable defectives in a sheltered workshop. It is probable that age and maturation factors contributed to the observed lack of differences (MacDonald Training Center Report, 1959).

The beam-walking test was originally devised to measure balance in normal children. The beams used are similar to those used by Heath, except that all are 10 feet long and some are as narrow as $\frac{1}{4}$ inch. Subjects are required to take 10 steps heel-to-toe with hands on hips. Three trials are given and subjects receive scores for various body movements used to maintain balance. The test was standardized on public school children in all age groups. Test scores bear no relationship to measures of mental ability. In view of the standardization data, the ease of obtaining materials and administering the test, and previous work with similar tests, it is somewhat surprising that Seashore's scale has not been used more to evaluate locomotor abilities of retarded children.

Manual dexterity

Motor skills, such as placing, turning, and positioning, which require accuracy, steadiness, and/or speed, have been measured by use of the Purdue Pegboards, the Minnesota Rate of Manipulation Test, and similar assembly tasks. Dynamometers have been used to measure grip strength. One battery of tests has been standardized for children in the age range where changes in manual skills typically occur. The Van der Lugt battery (Buros, 1953) consists of 10 dexterity tasks which have acceptable reliability coefficients. However, no validity estimates are given for the claim that the tasks reflect changes with age, and the equipment is somewhat difficult to obtain and administer. This may account for the fact that it has been used very little to study the motor performance of retarded children.

Covariations between manual dexterity and age, sex, and IQ have been reported. In general, "one can expect to find marked inability to perform tasks involving manual dexterity in those whose IQs are roughly, below 60" (Cantor & Stacey, 1951, p. 409). It is probable that most moderately retarded individuals do not demonstrate as high an ability in manual tasks as normals (Holman, 1933). On the other hand, there is a good deal of overlap in adult groups so far as these abilities are concerned, and many individual adult retardates can perform particular tasks requiring eye-hand coordination as competently as the majority of normals.

No differences between institutionalized Negro and Caucasian males have been observed, but males demonstrate slightly better turning and placement skills, hand steadiness, and grip strength than females in the age range 9 to 29 years (DiStefano, Ellis, & Sloan, 1958).

MEASURES OF MULTIPLE COMPLEX MOTOR SKILLS

Many measures of general motor skills have been devised for the purposes of judging physical growth and maturity, evaluating motor development, and classifying pupils in physical education programs.

General motor skills

In 1932 Johnson reported that over 60 tests of motor performance involving gross muscle skills and coordination were available. Since then several others have been reported. Some of these scales deserve description.

The Johnson Skill Test (Johnson, 1932) was devised for the age range 11 years to adulthood. It provides a rather crude screening of several basic physical education activities (front roll, jumping full turns, straddle jump, and the like). Scores correlate between .13 and .49 with measures of mental ability for normal junior high school and college students.

The Brace Scale of Motor Ability (Brace, 1927) has been used widely in physical education research. It is composed of twenty physical education "stunts" in which strength and size are minimized and agility, balance, control, and flexibility are emphasized. The original scale was revised and shortened by McCloy in 1937. The scales correlate about .78 with each other (Gire & Espenschade, 1942). These tests have been used to classify students for individual activities in physical education classes. Espenschade (1940) used several indices, including the Brace scale and the Iowa-Brace scale, to study motor development in children. She reported low but positive relationships between them and chronological and physiological maturity for adolescent boys but not for girls.

These scales cannot properly be called developmental scales because they were not standardized to show incremental age changes in motor performance. They do offer some promise as evaluations of gross motor skills of retardates, particularly in terms of common physical education requirements.

Figure 19-1. Mean strength of right grip for normal and mentally retarded boys and girls. [*Data on normal boys and girls adapted from Meredith* (1935), *Metheny* (1941), *and Jones* (1949) *by Francis & Rarick* (1960). *Data for retarded boys and girls from Francis & Rarick* (1960).]

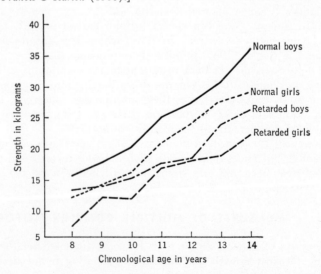

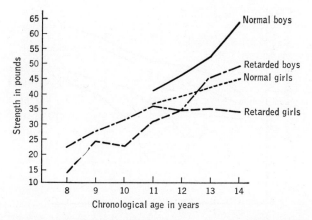

Figure 19-2. Mean shoulder girdle strength of normal and mentally retarded boys and girls: Pull. [*Data on normal boys and girls adapted from Meredith* (1935), *Metheny* (1941), *and Jones* (1949) *by Francis & Rarick* (1960). *Data for retarded boys and girls from Francis & Rarick* (1960).]

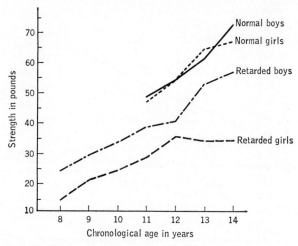

Figure 19-3. Mean shoulder girdle strength of normal and mentally retarded boys and girls: Thrust. [*Data on normal boys and girls adapted from Jones* (1949), *Neilson & Cozens* (1934), *and Espenschade* (1940) *by Francis & Rarick* (1960). *Data for retarded boys and girls from Francis & Rarick* (1960).]

Several of the individual tests were used by Francis and Rarick (1960) in comparing large groups of educable mentally retarded boys and girls with data on normal children. Static strength (hand grip), running speed, power strength (jumping and throwing for distance), balance (beam walking), and agility (body squat thrusts) were the skills measured. Figures 19-1 through 19-8 give their findings. The results suggest that age trends for retarded children are comparable to those of normal children for most of the tasks. Age and sex differences for retardates are also comparable to those

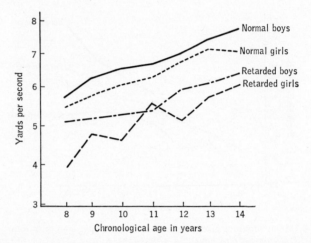

Figure 19-4. Speed-of-running data for normal and mentally retarded children, by chronological age. [*Data on normal boys and girls adapted from Jones (1949), Neilson & Cozens (1934), and Espenschade (1940) by Francis & Rarick (1960). Data for retarded boys and girls from Francis & Rarick (1960).*]

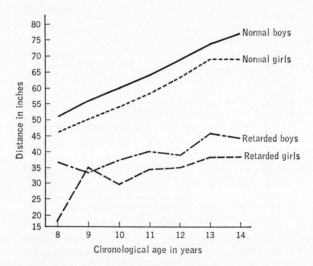

Figure 19-5. Comparison of mean performance scores in the standing broad jump for normal and mentally retarded children, by chronological age. [*Data on normal boys and girls adapted from McCloy (1954) and Neilson & Cozens (1934) by Francis & Rarick (1960). Data for retarded boys and girls from Francis & Rarick (1960).*]

observed in normals. With increasing age, the discrepancy between the retarded and normal groups tends to increase on most tasks. This tendency is most marked for the most complex skills (e.g., standing broad jump, the distance throw, and the body squat thrust measures).

In the late 1950s and early 1960s several novel approaches were introduced for evaluating motor activities of mental defectives. Of particular

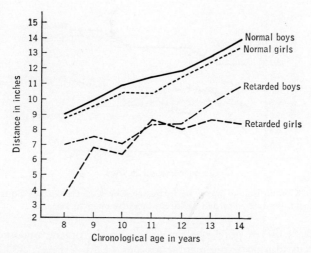

Figure 19-6. Comparison of mean performance scores in the vertical broad jump for normal and mentally retarded children, by chronological age.

Figure 19-7. Comparison of mean performance scores of the softball throw for distance for normal and mentally retarded children, by chronological age.

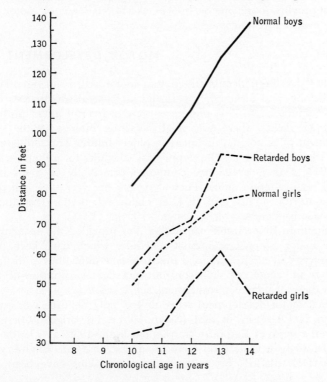

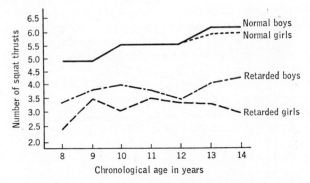

Figure 19-8. Comparison of mean performance scores on the Burpee Squat-thrust test for normal and mentally retarded children, by chronological age.

note is Ellis's use of photoelectric circuits to get precise measures of gross body activity during experimental sessions (Ellis & Pryer, 1959). Carrier et al. (1961) utilized a rather complex set of measures (GSR, plethysmograph, and pneumograph, and one-way-screen observations of body movements recorded on a grid) to evaluate changes during learning. Fleishman (1958) has described an apparatus designed for the Air Force which provides a multidimensional analysis of synchronous voluntary movements. His techniques are adaptable to the study of mental defectives. These types of measures provide more precise indices of various kinds of motor activities than the cruder instruments already described.

MOTOR–DEVELOPMENT SCALES

Although it has been demonstrated that motor skill is an essential part of most behavior, and although practically all general ability tests of an individual-administration type require varying degrees of motor proficiency at different age levels, there was relatively little interest in the systematic measurement of motor development in older children and adults until after 1930 in the United States. Developmental schedules for infants (e.g., Gesell, 1928, 1947; Cattel, 1940) are composed principally of items measuring observed sensory-motor skills. These tests are not very useful in predicting scores on mental ability tests in later childhood, perhaps because of their almost exclusive reliance on such items (Bayley, 1933).

The Stanford-Binet Intelligence Scale has provided the structural prototype for many motor-development schedules which have been published. Parenthetically, it might be added that the same difficulties in distinguishing "native" from "acquired" skills confront investigators of motor-development scales as those of mental measurement age scales.

The first motor-development schedule for older children was reported by a Russian, N. Oseretsky, in 1931 (Sloan, 1951). The original Oseretsky scale underwent a series of European translations in the 1930s and 1940s (Lassner, 1948). In 1946, a translation from the Portuguese into English was sponsored by Doll (1946). Since then several revisions have been made by

American investigators. The original Oseretsky scale was composed of 85 items contained in six subtests at each age level from 4 to 16 years. Oseretsky claimed that his items measured general static coordination, dynamic manual coordination, general dynamic coordination, motor speed, simultaneous voluntary movements, and asynkinesia (i.e., lack of movement, lack of precision in movement, or surplus movement). The test was widely used in Europe before its translation into English, but assumptions about the categorical placement of test items into the six types of motor behavior, and the age placement of several items, are questionable (Sloan, 1955).

In 1948, Sloan devised his first adaptation of the Oseretsky scale, using all the original items. This adaptation was not made available for general public use but was circulated privately. Between 1950 and 1955, Sloan made a thorough revision of the 1948 scale, eliminating many of the original items and standardizing his 36-item scale on 749 children from 6 to 14 years of age. He obtained acceptable split-half reliability coefficients (practically all between .82 and .94) and reported validity measures in terms of age performance changes and estimates of test content (Sloan, 1955). This revision, commonly known as the Lincoln-Oseretsky scale, provides separate norms for boys and girls. The norms were arrived at independently, so they are not comparable. Scores for the girls' items were based on a different standard from that for the boys' items. For each group, separately, scores were assigned to certain tasks so that a distribution of scores was obtained

Figure 19-9. Age norms for the Lincoln-Oseretsky Motor Development scale. Norms for males.

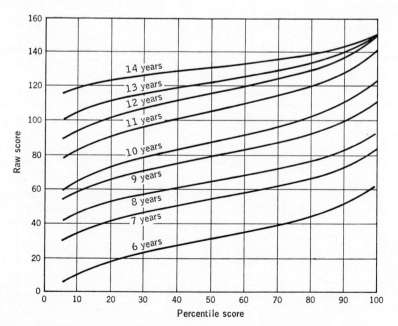

which represent an age-grade progression. Girls and boys were never compared directly. The Lincoln-Oseretsky has been widely used as an index for evaluating motor performance of both normal and retarded children. The age norms for the standardization groups are given in Figures 19-9, 19-10, and 19-11.

Thams (1954) made a factor analysis of the Lincoln-Oseretsky Scale and reported that it discriminates between normal children at different age and grade levels. Obtained scores did not correlate with measures of physique. The study indicates that height and weight are independent variables in motor proficiency as measured by this scale. In spite of some methodological shortcomings (e.g., lack of cross validation, lack of precise definition of exactly what it is that test items measure, and lack of scoring equivalence for some items), the Lincoln-Oseretsky is the best standardized motor-development scale available. Reports of its use in comparing motor proficiency and mental ability will be presented in a separate succeeding section.

Other revisions of the original Oseretsky scale include the Vineland revision (Cassel, 1949) and the Berk-Oseretsky (Berk, 1957). Reliable differences between familial and brain-injured groups of mental defectives were found with the Vineland-Oseretsky (Cassel, 1959), suggesting some clinical utility for this revision. Difficulties in validating the classification types themselves limit generalizations from this measure, however. Neither the Vineland nor the Berk revision has been used very widely in research with mental defectives.

Figure 19-10. Age norms for the Lincoln-Oseretsky Motor Development Scale. Norms for females.

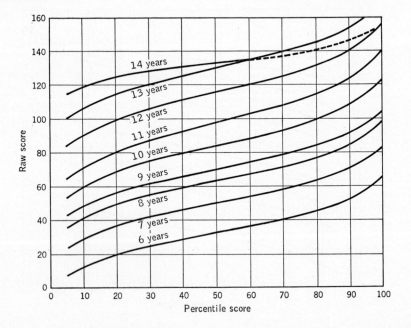

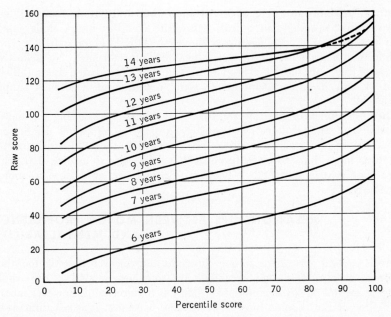

Figure 19-11. Age norms for the Lincoln-Oseretsky Motor Development Scale. Norms for males and females combined.

MEASURES OF MOTOR EDUCABILITY

As commonly used, motor educability refers to helping individuals learn complex motor skills by means of standard training procedures. Attainment of the skill in itself constitutes the criterion of successful training. Few investigators of motor skills in mental defectives have utilized tests of motor educability devised by physical educators (Brace, Johnson, Espenschade, et al.), although the Francis and Rarick study is a notable exception. Such tests apparently are deemed not precise enough to evaluate changes in motor performance due to training.

Holman (1933) and others have reported studies suggesting that initial discrepancy scores between retardates and normals on motor and mechanical performance tasks tend to decrease with training. Essentially the difference decrease seems to be a function of greater increase in the defectives' scores with practice. A study of low-grade defectives in England suggests that a greater proportional increase in speed of performance can be expected with training when such subjects are compared to normals, even though the completion trials showed significant performance differences favoring the normals (Gordon, O'Connor, & Tizard, 1954). Carrier, Malpass, and Orton (1961) also reported significant improvement in multiple-trial motor-learning tasks with moderately retarded adolescents, although this group did not learn as efficiently as either normal or bright children of comparable ages and sex.

One of the significant areas of research still to be examined is the retentive capabilities of defectives. An interesting study by Ammons (1958) indicates that normals can quickly reinstitute complex motor skills which have not been practiced for up to 2 years. This kind of capability has obvious significance for the motor educability of retardates. No definitive studies of the variable have been published, but Tizard and Loos (1954) reported that imbeciles demonstrate some retention of a learned simple motor skill.

The importance of utilizing multiple-trial criteria in assessing the motor educability of mental defectives seems obvious. Novel situations demanding unique motor performance in single-trial learning sessions may affect mental defectives more than normals. In general, it seems safe to assume that principles that govern most other types of learning are applicable to motor educability.

RELATIONSHIPS BETWEEN MOTOR PROFICIENCY AND MENTAL ABILITY

There is general agreement among clinicians and research investigators that motor proficiency and mental ability are somehow related if the whole range of mental ability is considered. There is disagreement, however, about the degree of the relationships between these variables. It is not difficult to understand why there is some confusion about the question. Measures of motor proficiency do not correlate well with each other, complexity of motor demands varies with different measures, there is an apparent absence of any general factor of motor ability, and different investigators have used different criteria to assess both motor and mental abilities.

As anyone who has observed low-grade mental defectives compared with normals can testify, the former do not perform as well as normals in motor skills. Individuals in the lower-IQ ranges do not demonstrate as much co-ordination, precision, and speed of reaction as normals. This is true in such everyday activities as walking and running, articulation of movements in dressing and eating, or manipulation of work implements. It is also true for more precise tasks such as disc assembly and the like (Carrier, et al., 1961). On the other hand, studies of high-grade defectives and normals are not so equivocal in their results, and many visitors to classes for educable mentally handicapped children or sheltered workshops for potentially employable retardates are surprised at the motor efficiency of many of these people.

In view of the confusion which exists because of differences in results of several individual studies, it seems advisable to examine studies of the motor proficiency of normal, severely retarded, and moderately retarded groups. This will permit some general conclusions about relationships which exist within these groups, as well as between them.

Subjects with normal mental ability

This group is psychometrically defined as between IQ 90 and 110 on most intelligence tests. In practice, however, many studies include children with IQ above 110. Most investigators have reported studies involving complex motor functions. Results indicate that there are insignificant or low positive relationships between motor and mental ability variables (Perrin, 1921; Muscio, 1923; Keller, 1938; Ray, 1940; Johnson, 1942; & Malpass, 1960). As mentioned previously, motor abilities are relatively specific, and no general motor factor or ability has been designated (Seashore, 1951). Even fine and gross motor abilities are not related to each other. So it is not surprising that measures of motility which involve different muscle groups do not show high correspondence in studies of normal subjects. As a general conclusion, there is little correlation between mental and motor abilities, as typically measured for persons in the normal IQ range.

Motor proficiency has been related on most measures to age through the age range 14 to 16 years. A sex difference on measures depending on strength, speed, and agility is observed through this age span (Francis & Rarick, 1960). Rabin (1957) also reported sex differences in motor proficiency of retardates on the Lincoln-Oseretsky scale. His findings are open to some question, however, because of the separate sex norms used in standardizing the scale. Undoubtedly, specific training and general social reinforcement for particular kinds of motor skills may produce both age and sex differences.

Mentally retarded subjects

It is not accidental that most research dealing with motor proficiency in mental defectives has been conducted with children between the ages of 6 and 16. Maturation of most motor skills is completed by age 16, and no significant changes in motor proficiency have been reported after this age. Moreover, 16 years is the upper age limit for inclusion of retarded children in most public schools. Another contributing factor is lack of availability of standardized measures of motor proficiency for defectives beyond 16 years of age. The Oseretsky scale and its revisions have ceilings between 14 and 16 years.

A survey of seven recent studies of mental defectives (Heath, 1942, 1953; Sloan, 1950; Rabin, 1957; Distefano, Ellis, & Sloan, 1958; Malpass, 1960; Francis & Rarick, 1960) reveals that the majority of these investigations report moderate covariation between motor proficiency and mental status. The results are summarized in Table 19-1. The institutional groups include more older subjects and wider IQ range than do public school groups. Differential reporting of mental age and IQ scores confuses the picture somewhat, but the consistency of results suggests that motor ability and mental deficiency are related within the age ranges reported. For convenience, discussion of these studies has been arranged in terms of the measures used to determine motor proficiency.

Particular motor skill tests and mental ability. Heath's studies with the Railwalking Test have already been noted. In both the 1942 and 1953 studies, he investigated relationships between railwalking performance and mental ability (1916 Stanford-Binet Scale), using comparable groups of institutionalized familial and nonfamilial defectives. The reported rs between railwalking and mental test performances were much lower for familial than for nonfamilial subjects (.23 and .15 for familials, .60 and .57 for non-

TABLE 19-1

Summary of studies relating motor proficiency to mental deficiency

Investigators	Measures used	Population studied N	Source	Classification	Chronological age, yr	Mental status	Relationships reported (motor & mental ability scores)
Heath (1942)	Vineland Railwalking Test Vineland Railwalking Test	53 40	Institutional Institutional	Familial Nonfamilial	Mean 18.0 Mean 21.3	Mean MA 8.5 yr Mean MA 8.5 yr (1916 Stanford–Binet)	(Correlation) $r = .62$ $r = .23$
Heath (1953)	Vineland Railwalking Test Vineland Railwalking Test	80 52	Institutional Institutional	Familial Nonfamilial	Mean 17.9 Mean 21.5	Mean MA 8.1 yr Mean MA 8.1 yr (1916 Stanford–Binet)	(Correlation) $r = .57$ $r = .15$
Sloan (1950)	1948 Lincoln-Oseretsky	20	Institutional	Nonorganic	Mean 10	Mean IQ—54 (male) 56 (female) (1937 Stanford–Binet)	(Analysis of variance) Mean square 546.575 F-ratio 5.30 $P = .01$
Rabin (1957)	1955 Lincoln-Oseretsky	60	Institutional	Familial	Range 10–14	IQ range 40–60 (1937 Stanford-Binet)	(Analysis of variance) Mean square 3.15 P not significant
Distefano, Ellis, & Sloan (1958)	1955 Lincoln-Oseretsky Vineland Railwalking Minn. Rate of Manipulation a. Turning b. Placement Hand steadiness Strength of grip	40 36	Institutional males Institutional females	Mixed Mixed	Mean 19 (Range 9–29) Mean 22 (Range 11–32)	MA range 5.3–11.5 yr (Mean 9.9) MA ranges 5.5–10.8 yr (Mean 9.1) (1937 Stanford–Binet)	(Correlations) Males Females $r = .40$ .58 $r = .04$ .32 $r = .41$ .45 $r = .38$ .37 $r = .16$ .05 $r = .03$ .26
Malpass (1960)	1955 Lincoln-Oseretsky	47 56	Public School Institutional	Educable mentally handicapped Educable mentally handicapped	Mean 11.8 (Range 8–14) Mean 11.7 (Range 8–14)	Mean IQ 67.8 IQ range 56–80 (WISC) Mean IQ 62.8 IQ range 52–78	(Correlation) $r = .440$ (boys .339 girls .755) (WISC) $r = -.447$ (boys .515 girls .266)
Francis & Rarick (1960)	Static strength, dynamic strength, balance, and agility	256	Public School	Educable mentally handicapped	Range 8–14	Mean IQ range Boys 68–70 Girls 64–70 (1937 Stanford-Binet)	Boys: 81 of 84 correlation coefficients "low but positive" Girls: "many coefficients negative or close to zero"

familial *S*s). DiStefano et al. (1958) examined sex differences in an institutional population with mixed etiologies and of approximately the same mean CA as Heath's groups. The mean MAs for this group were slightly higher than for Heath's (9.9 years and 9.1 years for males and females, respectively, in contrast to Heath's groups' mean MAs of 8.5 and 8.1 years, respectively. Heath's groups were not broken down according to sex). The DiStefano study reported *r*s of .04 and .32 for males and females, respectively. This suggests that sex differences might be at least as important as etiological differences in determining correspondence of railwalking performance and mental test scores.

Other measures of particular motor skills have been related to mental test performance of defectives. The DiStefano study included use of the Minnesota Rate of Manipulation Test (turning and placement subtests) and a hand-steadiness test. Correlation coefficients ranging from .37 to .45 were reported for their institutionalized groups between the subtests and 1937 Stanford-Binet Scale scores. Very low *r*s were noted between hand-steadiness and mental test scores (.16 for boys, .05 for girls).

Francis and Rarick (1960) reported that 81 of 84 correlation coefficients between their six measures of motor performance (described earlier) and the 1937 Stanford-Binet Scale scores were "very low but positive" for boys. For girls, most of the *r*s were close to zero, with several being slightly negative.

These results suggest that correlations between measures of unitary motor skills and intelligence test scores can be expected to vary. None of the investigations demonstrates true predictive significance of mental ability from a knowledge of the motor skill, or vice versa. Perhaps the best that can be stated is that scores from some of these measures of particular skills (e.g., the Railwalking Test and Minnesota Rate of Manipulation Test) correspond somewhat with Stanford-Binet Scale scores for institutionalized mental defectives.

The Lincoln-Oseretsky Scale and mental ability. Sloan (1950) reported a significant relationship between scores of institutionalized defectives on his 1948 adaptation of the Oseretsky scale and the 1937 Stanford-Binet. His group was small ($N = 20$) and consisted of patients diagnosed as "nonorganic." The Lincoln-Oseretsky scale (Sloan, 1955) has been used by several investigators interested in relating motor and mental performance.

Rabin (1957) studied 60 institutionalized familial defectives; Distefano et al. (1958) use 76 institutionalized defectives of mixed etiology; Malpass (1960) reported on 56 institutionalized and 47 noninstitutionalized retarded children of comparable mental ability. The groups from these studies seem to have been roughly comparable in mental age, although DiStefano's population was approximately 7 years older than the samples in the other two studies.

Rabin, using analysis of variance for statistical comparisons, found no significant relationship between scores on the Lincoln-Oseretsky and Stanford-Binet scales. He attributed the lack of relationship to an uncontrolled "examiner-institutional" variable and suggested that, if this variable had been controlled, significant relationships between test scores might have been obtained. Both of the other studies reported significant product-moment correlations (*r*s) between motor and mental test scores. DiStefano et al. reported *r*s of .40 and .58 for institutionalized boys and girls, respectively; Malpass reported *r*s of .48 and .27 for institutionalized boys and girls. In addition, the latter study found *r*s of .34 and .75 for noninstitutionalized boys and girls, respectively. (There were only 23 girls in the noninstitutional group, however, so the high *r*, not being statistically significant, was presumed to be due to chance sampling factors.) Correlation coefficients for combined groups of institutionalized and noninstitutionalized retardates in the Malpass study were .44 and .47, respectively.

The weight of evidence from these studies suggests that the motor proficiency measured by the Lincoln-Oseretsky is moderately related to mental ability as measured by the Stanford-Binet test and the Wechsler Intelligence Scale for Children.

The measurement of motor ability in *severely retarded* persons is hampered by their lack of responsiveness to directions. There are very few reliable objective studies of the motor performance of such groups. Many clinical observations have been made about their general motor capabilities and, as has been already noted, there is agreement that those people with IQs roughly below 50 demonstrate considerably less motor proficiency than those in the moderately retarded and normal classifications. Clinical etiology of mental deficiency is of some importance. Several authorities suggest that individuals diagnosed as *exogenous*, or brain-damaged, tend to demonstrate quantitatively more, and qualitatively more severe, motor defects than those diagnosed as *endogenous*, or familial.[3] Strauss and Lehtinen (1947) distinguish between the kinds of tasks which differentiate these groups, and Strauss and Kephart (1955) have made many valuable suggestions about training brain-injured children in terms of motor activities.

There has been a commendable increase in the number of public school programs for trainable retarded children (IQs roughly between 40 and 60). These programs emphasize helping severely retarded children learn very rudimentary motor and educational activities. Hopefully, they lead to a reduction in the amount of supervision that most of them probably will always require.

In summary, although few studies of the severely retarded are available, direct observation of their motor performance indicates a considerable reduction in their motor proficiency and in their achievement of motor skills required for self-maintenance in adulthood.

Most communities in the United States now support special classes for children in the *moderately retarded* range. The majority of the institutions for mental defectives also have educational programs for such individuals. Retarded children from public school classes tend to score higher on motor proficiency measures than those of similar age, sex, and IQ range in institutions. Malpass (1960) reported means of 77.8 and 68.5 on the 1955 Lincoln-Oseretsky scale for public school and institutionalized children, respectively. These score differences may indicate that public school retarded children who have greater motor proficiency are less likely to be institu-

[3] The reader is referred to Sarason (1949, pp. 39–42) for a discussion of these types. There is some disagreement about the definition of endogenous mental deficiency.

tionalized than those who demonstrate lower motor skills. They may also reflect the possibility that noninstitutionalized retarded children receive more stimulation and social reinforcement for motor activities than do their institutionalized counterparts. (It is also possible, of course, that noninstitutionalized children respond more favorably to testing conditions than do children in institutions and that observed score differences are due to this consideration rather than to differential proficiency. The writer's experience with both groups of defectives does not support this possibility, however.)

There is considerable backing for the contention that moderately retarded children do not show as high a level of motor proficiency as do normals (Sloan, 1950; Francis & Rarick, 1960; Malpass, 1960). Results of these studies do not demonstrate that these individuals cannot learn to perform as well as normals. As has been already pointed out, many do. The clear implication is that the moderately retarded may be able to improve their comparatively lower motor skills, but more stimulation and better training methods, probably over a longer period of time, are required.

VOCATIONAL IMPLICATIONS OF MOTOR PROFICIENCY

There is a good reason to believe that many moderately retarded persons can become vocationally self-dependent (Tizard, 1950; Tizard & O'Connor, 1954). Public and private institutions in the United States and Europe have emphasized educational programs designed for this purpose. The U.S. Office of Vocational Rehabilitation, the U.S. Department of Health, Education, and Welfare, the National Association for Retarded Children, and many universities and private agencies supply funds and facilities to find ways to help with the vocational training and placement of mental retardates. These programs are more or less concerned with either research about motor skills necessary for job performance or applications of research for employment potentialities.

Job possibilities for moderately retarded are varied. Retardates can be trained not only for menial tasks, such as manual labor or simple craft and domestic work, but also for routine industrial tasks, such as assembly and production-line operations, and even for agricultural work demanding fairly complex motor skills.

No specific criteria have been presented which provide accurate estimates of how well defectives will perform on jobs requiring different motor skills (Laing, 1959). Tentative criteria have been suggested for selecting institutionalized defectives for work possibilities (Shafter, 1957) but many difficulties have prevented exact specification of predictive criteria for job selection and placement. One sheltered workshop study (MacDonald Training Center Report, 1959) determined that, of several measures used, the best combined predictors of employability of retardates were the WAIS Performance Scale and a disc assembly task. Tizard (1953) reported a study which indicates that either a strict or a friendly supervisor can maintain reasonable work efficiency in retardates. "Laissez-faire" supervision apparently is not effective with such persons. There is reason to believe that more and better research will be conducted in this area.

Annett (1957) and others have suggested that vocational training centers for the retarded can improve training procedures and job selection possibilities by making time-and-motion studies of various jobs. These would include analyses of specific psychomotor functions involved. A more precise definition of these functions should lead to more accurate appraisal of the motor performance required. Gross and fine movements involving coordination, precision, force, and speed could then be translated into more effective training procedures. In turn, these should lead to a higher level of employability of people with retarded mental ability.

SUMMARY

Clinical observations and research studies indicate that the mentally retarded tend to demonstrate less motor competence and skill than do normals of the same sex and same age. This is true for tasks requiring precise movements and reactions as well as for those requiring complex skills and gross motor coordination. There is correspondence between general ranges of mental ability and motor performance; the severely retarded are not as capable as the moderately retarded, and the moderately retarded as a group are not as proficient as people in the normal range of intelligence.

While there is little doubt that lesions in the central nervous system contribute significantly to both motor and mental retardation, little has been reported about specific relationships between these variables. It is possible that delayed maturation of motor functions, as a correlate of delay in general body maturation, plays some part in the differences observed between retarded and normal subjects. It is also reasonable to assume that less stimulation and fewer or less appropriate reinforcements for learning motor skills may play a considerable part in the lowered motor-response rate and general motor proficiency of mental defectives.

Several motor-proficiency tests are available for use with different age groups. Primary emphasis has been placed on evaluating the motor skills of children and adolescents. The best of the measures of gross motor ability (the 1955 revision of the Lincoln-Oseretsky Motor Development Scale) is in need of some refinement. Other measures lack either standardization or comprehensiveness in order to provide either precise measurement or wide-range generalizations. No general "motor factor" has been elucidated.

Motor proficiency has implications for educational, vocational, social, and recreational activities of mental defectives. More thorough analyses of the components of motility that contribute to such activities are required before conclusive generalizations can be drawn about the relationship of motor and mental abilities. Vocational implications of motor proficiency suggest the need for more refined job appraisal and training procedures for the mentally retarded.

REFERENCES

AMMONS, R. B., et al. Long term retention of perceptual motor skills. *J. exp. Psychol.*, 1958, 55, 318–328.

ANNETT, J. The information capacity of young mental defectives in an assembly task. *J. ment. Sci.*, 1957, 103, 621–631.

ASMUSSEN, E., & HEEBOLL-NEILSEN, K. Physical performance and growth in children. Influence of sex, age and intelligence. *J. appl. Physiol.*, 1956, 8, 371–380.

ATKINSON, C. Perceptual and response abilities of mentally retarded children as measured by several auditory thresholds. Sect. II. *Perceptual and response abilities of retarded children*, Carbondale, Ill.: Sth. Illinois Univer. Press, 1959. (Sponsored by the U.S. Office of Education Cooperative Research Program.)

BAYLEY, N. Mental growth during the first three years. *Genet. Psychol. Monogr.* 1933, 14, 1–93.

BENSBERG, G. J., & CANTOR, G. N. Reaction time in mental defectives with organic and familial etiology. *Amer. J. ment. Defic.*, 1957, 62, 534–537.

BERK, R. L. A comparison of subnormal, normal and gifted children on the Oseretsky tests of motor proficiency. Unpublished doctor's dissertation, Boston Univer., 1957.

BERKSON, G. An analysis of reaction time in normal and deficient young men, Part I. Duration threshold experiment. *J. ment. Def. Res.*, 1960, 4, 51–58.

BERKSON, G. Part II. Variation of complexity in reaction time tasks. *J. ment. Def. Res.*, 1960, 4, 59–67.

BERKSON, G. Part III. Variation of stimulus and of response complexity. *J. ment. Def. Res.*, 1960, 4, 69–77.

BIRCH, J. W., & MATTHEWS, J. The hearing of mental defectives; its measurement and characteristics. *Amer. J. ment. Defic.*, 1951, 55, 384–393.

BRACE, D. K. *Measuring motor ability*. New York: Barnes, 1927.

BRODY, D. Twin resemblances in mechanical ability, with reference to the effects of practise on performance. *Child Develpm.*, 1937, 8, 207–216.

BROWN, H. S. A comparative study of motor fitness tests. *Res. Quart.*, 1954, 25, 8–19.

BUROS, O. K. (ED.). *The Fourth Mental Measurements Yearbook*. Highland Park, N.J.: Gryphon Press, 1953. Pp. 653–655.

CANTOR, G. N., & STACEY, C. M. Manipulative dexterity in mental defectives. *Amer. J. ment. Defic.*, 1951, 56, 401–410.

CAREY, R. A comparative study of the Lincoln Adaptation of the Oseretsky Tests of Motor Proficiency with other selected motor ability tests. Unpublished doctoral dissertation, Univer. of Indiana, 1954.

CARPENTER, A. The measurement of general motor capacity and general motor ability in the first three grades. *Res. Quart.*, 1942, 13, 444–465.

CARRIER, N., MALPASS, L., & ORTON, K. Responses to learning tasks of bright, normal and retarded children. Tech. Bull., U.S. Office of Education Cooperative Research Program, Washington, D.C., 1961.

CASSEL, R. H. The Vineland adaptation of the Oseretsky tests. *Train. Sch. Bull.* Suppl. to Vol. 46, 1949, 11–32.

CATTELL, P. *Measuring intelligence of infants and young children*. New York: Psychological Corp., 1940.

CHARLES, D. Adult adjustment of some deficient adults. *Amer. J. ment. Defic.*, 1958, 62, 300–304.

CLARIDGE, G. S., & O'CONNOR, N. The relationship between incentive, personality type, and improvement in performance of imbeciles. *J. ment. Def. Res.*, 1957, 1, 16–25.

CLARKE, A. B., & HERMELIN, B. F. Adult imbeciles, their abilities and trainability. *Lancet,* 1955, 2, 337–339.

CLARKE, A. M., & CLARKE, A. D. B. *Mental deficiency: the changing outlook.* New York: Free Press, 1958.

DISTEFANO, M. K., JR., ELLIS, N., & SLOAN, W. Motor proficiency in mental defectives. *Percept. mot. Skills.* 1958, 8, 231–234.

DOLL, E. A. The Oseretsky Scale. *Amer. J. ment. Defic.,* 1946, 50, 485–486.

DOLL, E. A. *The Oseretsky tests of mental proficiency: a translation from the Portuguese adaptation.* Minneapolis: Educational Test Bureau, 1946.

ELLIS, N., & DISTEFANO, M. K., JR. Effects of verbal urging and praise upon rotary pursuit performance in mental defectives. *Amer. J. ment. Defic.,* 1959, 67, 486–490.

ELLIS, N., & PRYER, R. S. Quantification of gross bodily activity in children with severe neuropathology. *Amer. J. ment. Defic.,* 1959, 63, 1034–1037.

ELLIS, N., & SLOAN, W. Relationships between intelligence and simple reaction time in mental defectives. *Percept. mot. Skills,* 1957, 7, 65–67.

ESPENSCHADE, A. Motor performance in adolescence. *Monogr. soc. Res. Child Develpm.,* 1940, 5, No. 1.

ESPENSCHADE, A. Practice effects of stunt-type tests. *Res. Quart.,* 1945, 17, 242–253.

FALLERS, J. An investigation of the motor ability of 30 high-grade mentally defective girls with the Oseretsky tests of motor proficiency. Unpublished master's thesis, MacMurray College, 1948.

FISHER, M. B. A note on subjects used in standardizing a railwalking test and the ataxiagraph. *J. exp. Psychol.,* 1946, 36. P. 93.

FLEISHMAN, E. Dimensional analysis of movement reactions. *J. exp. Psychol.,* 1958, 55, 438–453.

FOALE, M., & PATTERSON, J. W. The hearing of mental defectives. *Amer. J. ment. Defic.,* 1954, 59, 254–258.

FOSHEE, J. G. Studies in activity level. I. Simple-complex performances in defectives. *Amer. J. ment. Defic.,* 1958, 63, 882–886.

FRANCIS, R. J., & RARICK, G. L. Motor characteristics of the mentally retarded. *Amer. J. ment. Defic.,* 1959, 63, 292–311.

FRANCIS, R. J., & RARICK, G. L. *Motor characteristics of the mentally retarded.* Washington: U.S. Office of Education Cooperative Research Program, Monogr. No. 1, 1960.

FULLER, J., & THOMPSON, W. *Behavior genetics.* New York: Wiley, 1960.

GALLAGHER, J. J. A comparison of brain-injured and non-brain-injured mentally retarded children on several psychological variables. *Monogr. soc. Res. Child Develpm.* 1957, 22. Pp. 3–79.

GESELL, A. *Infancy and human growth.* New York: Macmillan, 1928.

GESELL, A., & AMATRUDA, C. S. *Developmental diagnosis: normal and abnormal children.* New York: Hoeber-Harper, 1947.

GIRE, E., & ESPENSCHADE, A. The relations between measures of motor educability and the learning of specific motor skills. *Res. Quart.,* 1942, 13, 43–56.

GLANVILLE, A. D., & KREEZER, G. Deficiencies in amplitude of joint movement associated with mental deficiency. *Child Develpm.,* 1937, 8, 129–138.

GOLDIAMOND, I. Visual signal detection, perception, and response variables as functions of development and mental retardation. Sec. III. *Perceptual and Response abilities of mentally retarded children,* Carbondale, Ill.: Sth. Illinois Univer. Press, 1959.

GORDON, S., O'CONNOR, N., & TIZARD, J. Some effects of incentives on the performance of imbeciles. *Brit. J. Psychol.,* 1954–55, 45, 277–287.

Habilitation of mentally retarded youth. Tampa: MacDonald Training Center, 1959. (Mimeo. Rep.)

HALSTEAD, W. *Brain and intelligence.* Chicago: Univer. of Chicago Press, 1947.

HEATH, S. R., JR. Railwalking performance as related to mental age and etiological types. *Amer. J. Psychol.,* 1942, 55, 240–247.

HEATH, S. R., JR. The relations of railwalking and other motor performances of mental defectives to mental age and etiological types. *Train. Schl. Bull.,* 1953, 50, 110–127.

HIRSCH, I. J. *The measurement of hearing.* New York: McGraw-Hill, 1952.

HOLMAN, P. The relationship between general mental development and manual dexterity. *Brit. J. Psychol.,* 1932, 23, 279–283.

HOWE, C. A comparison of motor skills of mentally retarded and normal children. *Except. Child.,* 1959, 23, 352–354.

HUBBEL, H. G. Intensive training of the higher-grade defective. *Amer. J. ment. Defic.,* 1943, 48, 385–391.

JOHNSON, B. Practice effects in a target test. A comparison of groups of varying intelligence. *Psychol. Rec.,* 1919, 26, 300–316.

JOHNSON, G. B. Physical skill tests for sectioning children into homogeneous units. *Res. Quart.,* 1932, 3, 128–136.

JOHNSON, G. B. A study of the relationship that exists between physical skill as measured and the general intelligence of college students. *Res. Quart.,* 1942, 13, 57–59.

JONES, H. E. Relationships in physical and mental measurement. *Rev. Educ. Res.,* 1939, 9, 91–102.

JONES, H. E. *Motor performance and growth.* Berkeley: Univer. of California Press, 1949.

KELLER, L. D. The effect of maturation on physical skill as measured by the Johnson Skill Test. *Res. Quart.,* 1938, 9, 54–58.

KIRK, S. A., & JOHNSON, G. O. *Educating the retarded child.* Boston: Houghton Mifflin, 1951.

KODMAN, F., JR. On incidence of hearing loss in mentally retarded children. *Amer. J. ment. Defic.,* 1958, 62, 675–678.

KREEZER, G. Motor studies of the mentally deficient: quantitative methods at various levels of integration. *Train. Schl. Bull.,* 1935, 32, 125–135.

KREEZER, G. Electrical potentials of the brain in certain types of mental deficiency. *Arch. Neurol. Psychiat.,* 1936, 36, 1206–1213.

KREEZER, G., & BRADWAY, K. The relation between Binet mental age and motor chronaxia. *Arch. Neurol. Psychiat.,* 1935, 34, 1149–1171.

LAING, J. K. Some aspects of placing defectives in work. *Ment. Hlth., London,* 1959, 18, 56–59.

LASSNER, H. Annotated bibliography of the Oseretsky tests of motor proficiency. *J. consult. Psychol.,* 1948, 12, 37–46.

LORENZ, K. The comparative method in studying innate behavior patterns. In *Physiological mechanisms in animal behavior.* New York: Academic, 1950. Pp. 221–268.

MALPASS, L. F. Responses of retarded and normal children to selected clinical measures. Sec. I. *Perceptual and Response Abilities of Retarded Children.* Carbondale, Ill.: Sth. Illinois Univer. Press, 1959.

MALPASS, L. F. Motor proficiency in institutionalized and non-institutionalized retarded children and normal children. *Amer. J. ment. Defic.,* 1960, 64, 1012–1015.

MATTHEWS, C. G. Quantitative and qualitative differences in retardates and neurologically impaired patients on psychomotor and abstraction ability tasks. (Paper read at Amer. Ass. ment. Def. Convention, May, 1961. Mimeo.)

MATTHEWS, D. K. *Measurement in physical education.* Philadelphia: Saunders, 1958.

MCCLOY, C. H., & YOUNG, N. D. *Tests and measurements in health and physical education.* (3rd ed.) New York: Appleton-Century-Crofts, 1954.

MCFIE, J. Psychological testing in clinical neurology. *J. Nerv. ment. Dis.,* 1960, 131, 383–393.

MCNEMAR, Q. Twin resemblances in motor skills and the effect of practice thereon. *J. genet. Psychol.,* 1933, 42, 70–97.

MEREDITH, H. V. The rhythm of physical growth. *Univer. Iowa Stud. Child Welf.,* 1935, 11, 3. P. 128.

METHENY, E. The present status of strength testing for children of elementary school age. *Res. Quart.,* 1941, 12, 115–130.

MOLLER, S. National Institute of Health, Washington, D.C.: Personal communication, 1961.

MUNN, N. Learning in Children. In L. Carmichael (Ed.), *Manual of child psychology.* (2nd ed.) New York: John Wiley, 1954.

MUSCIO, B. Motor capacity with special reference to vocational guidance. *Brit. J. Psychol.,* 1923, 13, 157.

NEILSON, N. P., & COZENS, F. W. *Achievement scales in physical education activities for boys and girls in elementary and junior high schools.* Sacramento, Calif.: Department of Education, 1934.

O'CONNOR, N. Defectives working in the community. *Amer. J. ment. Defic.,* 1954, 59, 173–180.

PASCAL, G. R. The effect of disturbing noise on the reaction time of mental defectives. *Amer. J. ment. Defic.,* 1953, 57, 691–699.

PENROSE, L. S. *Mental defect.* London: Sidgwick & Jackson, 1933.

PERRIN, F. A. C. An experimental study of motor ability. *J. exp. Psychol.,* 1921, 4, 24–56.

RABIN, H. M. The relationship of age, intelligence and sex to motor proficiency in mental defectives. *Amer. J. ment. Defic.,* 1957, 62, 507–516.

RAY, D. Motor ability and intelligence. *Res. Quart.,* 1940, 11, 129.

REITAN, R. Investigation of the validity of Halstead's measures of biological intelligence. *Arch. Neurol. Psychiat.,* 1955, 73, 28–35.

REITAN, R. The Effects of brain-damage on a psychomotor problem-solving task. *Percept. mot. Skills,* 1959, 211–215.

REITAN, R. *The effects of brain lesions on adaptive abilities in human beings.* Indianapolis: Univer. of Indiana Medical School, 1959.

ROSENZWEIG, L., & LONG, J. *Understanding and teaching the dependent retarded child.* Darien, Conn.: Educational Publishing Co., 1960.

SARASON, S. *Psychological problems in mental deficiency.* (2nd ed.) New York: Harper, 1953.

SCOTT, W. S. Reaction time in young intellectual deviates. *Arch. Psychol.,* 1940, 36, No. 256.

SEASHORE, H. G. Some relationships of fine and gross motor abilities. *Res. Quart.,* 1942, 13, 259–274.

SEASHORE, H. G. The development of a beam-walking test and its use in measuring development of balance in children. *Res. Quart.,* 1957, 18, 246–259.

SEASHORE, R. H. Individual differences in motor skills. *J. gen. Psychol.,* 1930, 3, 38–66.

SEASHORE, R. H. Work and motor performance. In S. S. Stevens (Ed.), *Handbook of experimental psychology.* New York: Wiley, 1951.

SHAFTER, A. J. Criteria for selecting institutionalized mental defectives for vocational placement. *Amer. J. ment. Defic.,* 1957, 61, 599–616.

SHERMAN, M. *Intelligence and its deviations.* New York: Ronald, 1945.

SLOAN, W. Motor proficiency and intelligence. *Amer. J. ment. Defic.*, 1951, 55, 394–406.

SLOAN, W. The Lincoln-Oseretsky motor development scale. *Genet. Psychol. Monogr.*, 1955, 51, 183–252.

STRAUSS, A., & KEPHART, N. *Psychopathology and education of the brain-injured child.* Vol. II. Progress in theory & clinic. New York: Grune & Stratton, 1955.

STRAUSS, A. A., & LEHTINEN, L. E. *Psychopathology and education of the brain-injured child.* 4th printing. New York: Grune & Stratton, 1951.

Technical recommendations for psychological tests and diagnostic techniques. Prepared by a joint committee of the APA, A. Ed. Res. Assn. and Nat. Council on Measurements Used in Education. *Psychol. Bull.*, 1954, 51, No. 2, Part 2 (suppl.).

THAMS, P. F. Factor analysis of the Lincoln-Oseretsky motor development scale. Unpublished doctoral dissertation, Univer. of Michigan, 1955.

THOMPSON, H. Physical Growth. In L. Carmichael (Ed.), *Manual of child psychology.* (2nd ed.) New York: Wiley, 1954.

TIZARD, J. The effects of different types of supervision on the behavior of mental defectives in a sheltered workshop. *Amer. J. ment. Defic.*, 1953, 58, 143–151.

TIZARD, J., & LOOS, F. M. The learning of a spatial relations test by adult imbeciles. *Amer. J. ment. Defic.*, 1954, 59, 85–90.

TIZARD, J., & O'CONNOR, N. The employability of high-grade mental defectives. *Amer. J. ment. Defic.*, 1950, 54, 563–576 and 55, 144–157.

TREDGOLD, A. F., TREDGOLD, R. F., & SODDY, K. *A textbook of mental deficiency.* (9th ed.) Baltimore: Williams & Wilkins, 1956.

WALLIN, J. E. W. *Children with mental and physical handicaps.* Engelwood Cliffs, N.J.: Prentice-Hall, 1949.

WERNER, H., & THURMA, B. D. A. A deficiency in the perception of apparent motion in children with brain injury. *Amer. J. Psychol.*, 1942, 55, 58–67.

YARMOLENKO, A. The motor sphere of school-age children. *J. genet. Psychol.*, 1933, 42, 298–316.

20

RESEARCH IN ACTIVITY LEVEL[1]

Rue L. Cromwell

Alfred Baumeister

William F. Hawkins

Recently in the field of mental retardation increased attention has been directed toward research in motor activity level. This has concerned primarily the hyperactive, presumably brain-damaged, retarded child. Previously, only limited attention had been paid to this topic. In both human and animal behavior the focus has usually been on the principles governing how the organism learns or modifies his behavior rather than on laws related to the amount of motor output. As a result, the knowledge about activity level is both scattered and disorganized.

The purpose of this chapter is to review some of the important aspects of methodology, empirical correlates, and theoretical interpretations of activity level. Inevitably, the review will draw attention to unsolved problems and questions. Hopefully, the findings which are described, and the research which they may suggest, will have implications not only for the general study of behavior but also for the management and training of superactive and subactive retarded children.

PROBLEMS IN DEFINITION

A precise definition of activity depends invariably on how it is measured. However, the problem of precise definition is not simple. For example, if

[1] Much of the research reported in this chapter was supported by NIMH grants M-2311 and MY-4391. Acknowledgment and appreciation are offered to Gerald Wolf and Howard Spicker, who gave valuable assistance. The material reviewed in this chapter emphasizes the period up to May, 1960. Only selected references are used subsequent to that time. Since not all the research on activity could possibly be

activity were defined in terms of change of position in space, the large or heavy subject and the small or light one would yield the same amount of activity in shifting from one point to another. On the other hand, if activity level were defined in terms of energy or work output, the large, heavy subject has displayed more activity in this unit shift of position. Moreover, if one defines activity level in terms of energy output, oxygen or caloric consumption, or electrical activity in efferent nerves, the shift of position in space may have only gross inferential value. Finally, if activity were to be defined in terms of achievement or end product, the measurement would exclude irrelevant motion.

Every response an organism is capable of making, whether operant or respondent, external or internal, goal-directed or random, could be defined as activity. Taken to this extreme, then, the entire subject matter of psychology could be viewed as the study of activity. Obviously, such a term, so loosely construed, by fault of its inclusiveness, loses the property of entering into useful and meaningful relationships with other constructs. This statement does not mean, of course, that a generic construct of activity is always devoid of meaning, but it does suggest that in view of the current status of research and theory concerning this construct some effort must be made toward studying the relationship among measures of activity. As Reed observed in his 1947 review, there exists a large body of data on activity, but what is needed is a clarification of the concept in terms of the methods of measuring it.

The question must be raised whether or not it is possible to develop a unified theory. We are led to the conclusion that activity is merely a generic term and that no integrated set of laws will be formulated that will usefully cover everything which has been included in activity. Perhaps we might more profitably devote our energies to the discovery of the parameters of a variety of subclasses of activity rather than trying to find explanatory constructs that will cover the wide array of behaviors which are included in this broadly defined category. This array of behaviors may have very little in common. More will be said about the theoretical constructs useful in describing activity phenomena in the theory section later in the chapter.

METHODOLOGIES

The methods of measuring activity are described here in four major categories. These categories are not to be viewed as mutually exclusive. Instead, they merely represent a basis for organizing and discussing the diverse methodologies.

Direct visual observation

Perhaps the simplest and most straightforward approach to measuring activity level is to observe the subject and rate certain behaviors on a specially devised scale. A number of studies have been done in which teachers or

covered here, a complete bibliography may be obtained from the authors. The reader is also referred to earlier reviews by Munn (1950), Pratt (1946), Reed (1947), and Shirley (1929).

parents made ratings on activity levels of children (e.g., Hurwitz, 1954). This procedure has been refined by observing a particular time sample under standard stimulus conditions, counting particular types of behavior, and clocking the total time during which motion is observed. Rheingold[2] has succeeded in getting reliable measures of foot kicking in infants. Hurder[3] has obtained reliable measures of irrelevant foot movement in adult subjects. Foshee (1958) had judges activate a cumulative stopwatch whenever they observed any activity in retarded human subjects and deactivitate it when the subject was quiet. This procedure, which yielded high interjudge agreement, was used to validate a mechanical, ballistographic device for measuring activity.

These approaches of direct observation have the advantage of simplicity and minimum equipment. Also, for gross purposes, they are usually sufficiently reliable for studying activity level in relation to other variables. However, there are some disadvantages in these techniques. The method depends upon at least one full-time, attentive observer. In addition, the possibility of observer error in such a monotonous task is maximum. The visual observation, moreover, does not afford an adequate basis for ordering or quantifying the magnitude of activity involved in different types of movement.

Another paramount problem is that activity level, owing to its lack of clarity in definition, can be confused with other variables. For example, the subject with a short attention span who shifts quickly from one goal-directed activity to another may appear to the observer to have a higher rate of activity than a subject fixated at one task but exerting the same amount of activity. The authors have noted that the superactivity of the so-called "hyperactive brain-damaged child" may be partly, or even completely, illusory because of the short attention span and frequent shifts of goal direction of such subjects. If the observer is in the same room with the subject, the demands or dependency which the subject places on the observer may tend to spuriously elevate activity ratings. Likewise, with the unsophisticated observer, activity which appears meaningless and atypical may be rated higher than activity which is meaningful, anticipated, and "taken for granted" by the observer.

Bindra and Blond (1958) have suggested a modified free observation technique which, although devised for use with animal subjects, could readily be adapted for measuring activity in humans. In this method certain behavioral categories, such as locomotion, grooming, etc., are employed so that activity can be qualitatively differentiated. Utilizing a time sample approach, they obtain continuous records of these behavioral categories during a fixed interval of time. Substantial reliabilities, ranging upward from .85, were reported.

Some of the disadvantages inherent in the direct observation approach have been partially alleviated by the use of movie photography. Sainsbury (1954), using a 16-mm movie camera, took five 45-second samples of the subject's movements. Two observers then counted a specific movement

[2] Personal communication.
[3] Personal communication.

during various 5-second showings of the film. Split-half reliability was reported as .93; validity coefficients obtained by correlating time sample scores with simultaneous direct observation and with electromyograph (EMG) scores were reported as .998 and .87, respectively. Sainsbury concludes that his method is preferred over direct observation because it is less fatiguing and more accurate, requires shorter observation periods, and leaves the experimenter free. Benoit[4] recorded the activity of children with a movie camera hidden in one wall of a playroom. Activity level was measured by applying a weighting system of the kind used in time-and-motion studies in industry. Thus various movements of the limbs, trunk, etc., were summated to obtain a total activity score.

A particularly ingenious technique for quantifying movement of neonates has been proposed by Kessen, Hendry, and Leutzendorff (1961). These authors wished to obtain a uniform movement index which would preserve a record of moment-to-moment changes in the behavior of the baby. The method consists in photographing the subject over five 30-second film strips for several days from an overhead camera. After the film is processed, six frames, each separated from the next by a constant number of frames, are identified for analysis. A film analyzer is then used to measure frame-to-frame displacement of the image. The displacement, or activity, scores are based on seven points of the body and thus refer to part rather than total movement. The authors report that stable individual differences are measured even with one 30-second film strip and that systematic increases occur over the first 5 days of life. One particular advantage of this technique is that it permits rather reliable measurement of variations in laterality.

Free space traversal approach

A number of methods for activity measurement have been developed in which subjects are allowed to move freely within a restricted space (Beach, 1941; Behney, 1936; Fredericson, 1946; Isaac & Ruch, 1956; Montgomery, 1953a, 1953b; Siegel, 1946). Foshee, Palk, and Cromwell[5] have marked off the floor of a small room into grids. Looking through a one-way-vision screen an observer counts the number of squares a child traverses in a given period of time. Ellis and Pryer (1959) have designed an 8-foot square activity room with photoelectric equipment embedded in the walls at 2-foot intervals, 1.5 feet from the floor. The activity of 29 neuropathologic children was recorded in the room for 20 minutes a day for 8 days, yielding an odd-even day reliability coefficient of .92. A similar technique has been proposed by Koch,[6] who covered the entire floor area of a room with pneumatic pads of the kind ordinarily used to open supermarket doors. A separate switch was attached to each pad so that, as the subject moved about the room, his activity was recorded cumulatively on a counter.

One of the major advantages of traversal activity measures is that the subject is fairly unrestricted and capable of free movement. Furthermore, he is usually unaware that his activity is being recorded. The visual and

[4] Personal communication.
[5] Personal communication.
[6] Personal communication.

auditory stimuli of the recording mechanism, which are often involved in other measures of activity, can be controlled by concealing the equipment or placing it in another room. Silent counters and recording equipment can be used if the subject is within auditory range. However, some of the shortcomings of activity measures in general are especially apparent with regard to the traversal approach. Certain types of activity can be lost and other types can be overemphasized by virtue of the position of the subject and the nature of the recording device. For example, a child may be vigorously pounding with a hammer, or a rat may be scratching himself, but neither may be traversing a grid or breaking a light beam which produces an activity score. On the other hand, a child may be swinging his arm in minimal activity while standing in a certain position and thus record an extremely high count by repeatedly breaking a photoelectric beam. Nevertheless, in spite of these occurrences it must be emphasized that these techniques are highly reliable.

Another disadvantage of these techniques is the necessity to standardize the stimuli in the situation (e.g., play materials). It should be pointed out, moreover, that standard stimulus conditions are desirable with respect to all measures of activity. In addition, since activity is always, in part, a function of the stimulus situation, the stimuli provided should be fairly homogeneous in nature. Otherwise, activity may vary widely according to whether the subject's attention is focused on one stimulus or another. For example, one toy may evoke minimal activity while another evokes a great deal.

The expense of equipment and observer time must usually be considered among the advantages and disadvantages. The grid-marked floor would generally involve more observer time and, in some cases, would also involve the cost of one-way-vision installation. The photoelectric cell or pneumatic-pad technique requires less observer time and only a modest investment in equipment.

The kinetometer approach

The activity of an organism has also been measured by attaching a device to his limbs or his trunk. The most common instrument used in this approach has been the pedometer, which, when attached to the leg of a subject, measures his activity in terms of distance moved or, more precisely, in terms of a number of leg movements which are sufficient to make a unit change in the recording instrument.

Foshee, Palk, and Cromwell[7] have used boy scout pedometers on mentally retarded subjects. Schulman and Reisman (1959) have described a method for changing a self-winding calendar wristwatch into a device called an *actometer* for measuring activity level. They report a test-retest reliability coefficient of .67 with educable mentally retarded boys with 1 to 3 weeks between testings (Schulman, Lipkin, Clarinda, & Mitchell, 1961).

The advantages of the kinetometer approach to activity measurement are (1) the subject can be measured in activity without necessarily being removed from his normal living situation, (2) the activity of the subject can be measured over long periods of time, and (3) as with other mechanical

[7] Unpublished research.

devices, no observer is necessary. A disadvantage is that the subject is inevitably aware of the fact that the instrument is attached to him. In some cases, the kinetometer may become uncomfortable over long periods of time. Thus, a considerable amount of activity could potentially be accounted for by the subject reacting to the measuring device.

The fidgetometer approach

Finally, techniques have been used which measure the degree to which the subject jars or vibrates the cage or platform on which he is placed. Later graphic recording devices made it possible to obtain information regarding the time of occurrence, the duration, and the amplitude of the subject's motions (see Reed, 1947). Other slight modifications of the original design of the apparatus have been made (Campbell, 1954; Castanera, Kimeldorf, & Jones, 1955; Griffin & Welch, 1937; Harned, Cunningham, & Gill, 1952). Other investigators (Campbell & McLean, 1948) attempted further to improve data collection through use of an electronic integrating unit. Castanera et al. (1955) reported inconsistent results with this approach, although highly reliable results have been obtained subsequently by Foshee (1958). The stabilimeter has also been adapted to the study of infant activity (e.g., Irwin, 1932, 1941; Pratt, 1946). In this technique activity is recorded from a specially constructed crib. Other adaptations of the stabilimeter for the purpose of measuring activity in infants have been used by Escalona and Leitch (1958); Marquis (1931); Pratt, Nelson, and Sun (1930); and Lipsitt and DeLucia (1960). The last two investigators have described a device which will permit measurement of generalized activity as well as specific movements.

In instances where high sensitivity is required in recording activity, Dawson (1959) has suggested the use of the piezoelectric crystal similar to that found in a phonograph cartridge. Those crystals may be used for recording movement of a cyclic nature with a periodicity range between .05 and 5×10^{-6} seconds. The distortion of the crystal element through its mechanical coupling produces an electric signal proportional to its displacement. Dawson has used the crystal as a transducer for the oscillographic recording of minute responses from heart beat to gross activity of the fetal animal.

Mitchell (1959) has constructed an apparatus which appears to be sensitive to subtle movement. The organism's movements displace a small iron plate which, in turn, induces an electric current in a coil with a bar magnet core. The current thus produced is amplified electronically and recorded as activity.

A recent development in the measurement of human activity level has been the ballistograph, which is patterned after principles of both the ballistocardiograph and the stabilimeter (Foshee, 1958). In the ballistograph, the subject is seated in a chair which is suspended by cables from a supporting superstructure. Hydraulic dampers limit the oscillation of the chair when the subject initiates movement. (In an earlier version the chair was attached to a platform which was mounted on four rubber stoppers, allowing the platform to jiggle with the movement of the subject. This device was discarded in favor of the cable-suspension technique, which more adequately controlled for the weight of the subject.) The subject's move-

ments set up corresponding opposing movements in the dampered suspended apparatus. Any activity is mechanically amplified by a pendulum
which is activated by the displacement of the platform. A magnet attached
to the end of the swinging pendulum passes through the field of an electric
coil and sets up a wave impulse. (The phonograph cartridge technique was
also investigated. This device proved too sensitive for the reliable measurement of gross human activity. As well as recording activity, it also recorded
vibrations about the building, whistling, and other noises within the room.)
The wave impulse, corresponding to the movement of the chair, is then
electronically amplified and introduced into an electronic integrator. This
integrator, described by Stevens (1942), combines the amplitude and
frequency of the wave into a series of electric pulses which are then
recorded by a silent Hunter counter. The ballistograph has yielded a test-
retest reliability coefficient of .95 for 15 subjects over 2 successive days.
A validity coefficient of .89 was obtained with judges' stopwatch measures
as a criterion. After 10½ months, the activity scores of the highest 25 and
the lowest 25 subjects out of a group of 101 mentally retarded patients
remained significantly disparate, with only two cases in each original group
overlapping later into the distribution of the other group.

The devices for recording activity in this approach have both their
advantages and disadvantages. A graphic waveform recording has the
advantage that it can be analyzed with respect to the temporal pattern and
the amplitude of individual bursts of activity. On the other hand, the
quantification of total activity over a given period of time is difficult. When
the electronic integrator is used to combine the amplitude and frequency
of the waveform, one can obtain a reliable measure of total activity over a
given time sample. However, there is no opportunity to examine the amplitude and temporal aspects of activity. Moreover, if the electrical pulses
delivered by the integrator are recorded on moving paper, the activity
can be examined with respect to temporal bursts, but gross, as opposed to
fine, movements cannot be examined. Other limitations occur when tambours
and pneumatic devices are used to record activity. The pneumatic volume,
length of the recording arm, and flexibility of the recording system have to
be considered. Small subjects may show less recorded activity than large
subjects simply because of their weight. Perseveration of the recording
device and kinesthetic feedback to the subject also influence the recording
of the activity.

In general, one advantage of some of the fidgetometer approaches (e.g.,
suspended cage technique) is that the subject's activity is measured in his
normal surroundings. However, in the case of the ballistograph, the subject
is placed in a novel or unfamiliar situation.

Other approaches

Eichorn and Griffin[8] have employed suspended crib toys for measuring
activity in infants. The crib toy, suspended by a cord across the baby's
crib, allows a recording every time it is touched or hit by the baby.

Research at Prudhoe Hospital, Northumberland, England, is being carried

[8] Personal communication by Donald J. Stedman.

out to develop an electronic device based on a television camera which can count the changes in light while movement of the subject is occurring.

Another measure, not usually thought of as a measure of activity, is an organism's level of operant responding. This can provide baseline information about the subject's activity level.

Finally, the wheel has probably been used more than any other technique in the measurement of animal activity. As Reed (1947) points out, there are almost as many variations in the wheel technique as there are experimenters studying activity level. Yet, to the knowledge of the authors, no investigator has employed this technique with human subjects.

Interrelations among activity measures

Only a limited amount of work has been done to investigate the interrelations among various measures of activity. The information available is sufficient to suggest that activity level should not be viewed as a single or homogeneous phenomenon. Many investigators (e.g., Morgan & Stellar, 1950; Reed, 1947) have suggested several dimensions of activity—locomotor versus diffuse, relevant versus irrelevant, and goal-directed versus non-goal-directed. Reed (1947) comments that "what data we have point to more than one type, or at least more than one aspect, of activity." Hunt and Schlosberg (1939) have made a similar statement.

Foshee, Palk, and Cromwell[9] found that human activity measured by the grid-marked floor has no correlation with ballistographic activity. Similar studies have compared and found differential effects on various techniques (Finger, 1958; Furchgott & Echols, 1958; Hayes, 1957; Hoskins, 1927; Stern, 1957; Strong, 1957; Tainter, 1943). However, Isaac and Ruch (1956) seem to have made the first major exploration in the comparison of different activity measures. In seeking a reliable and valid procedure for measuring lightly motivated behavior in monkeys, four methods were compared: (1) ratings by an observer, (2) Siegel's photoelectric technique, (3) the suspended floor with a work adder, and (4) the suspended floor with oscillation. One metal cage was equipped to use all four methods at once. Reliabilities ranging from .93 and .99 were computed on each measure by correlating odd and even minute scores. Intercorrelations between the methods ranged from .79 to .97. The authors did a factor analysis of those intercorrelations which suggested that these methods were measuring essentially the same phenomena. However, the oscillation method had some specific variance which was probably owing to the fact that it would record slight movements which would be missed by the other methods. Isaac and Ruch judged the photoelectric technique to be the most suitable measure because of its reliability, its relationship to the other measures, and the ease with which it provides automatic recordings.

Comment on reliability coefficients

Typically, reliability is thought of as the degree to which an instrument consistently measures the same phenomenon. This is possible only if one assumes, as in the case of intelligence and ability, that the organism is

[9] Unpublished research.

invariable in the trait being measured. Since reliability is a measure of fluctuations of actual activity in the organism confounded with error fluctuations in the instrument, this assumption cannot be entertained without qualification with respect to activity. The reliability coefficient, therefore, is lowered from 1.00 by (1) any time change or variability in the activity level of the subject, which is still classified as error variance, and (2) any variability of the observer and apparatus when recording that activity. Instances of such error might best be noted in those studies of reliability which employ the test-retest method. For example, in cyclic behavior, if measurement made at one point in time is repeated at another point, the correlation between the two measures over different animals would tend to be a lowered estimate. However, this is not the case with split-half reliabilities. Here one runs the risk of spuriously high coefficients because error factors are held constant over the two sets of scores. Therefore, the procedure of splitting by minutes (e.g., Isaac & Ruch, 1956) yields a reliability that is higher than, and of different meaning from, one which splits by some larger unit.

In this regard, it should be pointed out that the conditions which are set up for the reliability measurement of activity determine the meaning of the reliability. If one attempts to establish conditions where the organism is as stable as possible (e.g., after a long period of adaptation), one may be increasing the degree to which the coefficient reflects error in the instrument. If one obtains a reliability coefficient under conditions where normal variation in activity of the organism occurs, the coefficient will be relatively more descriptive of the organism's behavior and relatively less descriptive of the instrument. The concept of reliability, therefore, changes its meaning depending on the conditions of its measurement.

THE EMPIRICAL CORRELATES OF ACTIVITY

Now that the various methodologies and some of their implications have been discussed, the factors found to be related to activity level will be considered. These will be organized roughly into categories representing stimulus, organismic, and response variables. First, those stimulus factors which have been studied with respect to activity are presented. Then, perceptual variables are discussed. Physiological and organismic correlates and finally response variables related to activity are considered. As previously noted with respect to the classification of methodologies, this organization is likewise arbitrary and not mutually exclusive. As will be seen, the interaction among these variables as they relate to activity are coming to assume high priority in research.

Stimulus variables

The effects on activity of external stimulation, such as noise, light, temperature, etc., have enjoyed the sporadic interest of animal researchers for quite some time. More recently the suggestions by Strauss and his associates (1947, 1955) have emphasized the possible importance of a stimulation-free environment for brain-injured children.

According to their theoretical conception of the brain-injured child, an environment of overstimulation should exaggerate the symptoms of distractible behavior, short attention span, and superactivity. As an approach to treating this condition, Strauss and Lehtinen (1947) give many suggestions regarding a stimulus-free classroom environment. This would include such aspects as uniformly painted walls, no pictures, no windows, no stimulus materials other than those being worked on, and individual stalls facing the wall. It is with this type of environment, Strauss and his associates feel, that the greatest accomplishment can be made in overcoming the symptoms which accompany brain injury.

Some recent research has been oriented in this direction. Gallagher (1960) has observed that a group of retarded children diagnosed as organic are rated as more active than a group of retardates without such diagnosis. Gardner, Cromwell, and Foshee (1959) have investigated the effects of distal visual stimulation in superactive, subactive, organic, and familial retarded subjects. They found that regardless of subject classification a decrease in activity occurred with increased visual stimulation, superactives showing a greater decrease than subactives. These results are interpreted to mean that with increased distal stimulation, attention responses were most likely to occur, and as this stimulation was decreased the defectives displayed more motor responses to proximal stimuli (e.g., clothing and chair). Golden (1956) supports the notion that retarded subjects respond more to physically proximal than to physically distal extraneous stimulation. Richards (1936), using a modified stabilimeter (diffuse activity crib), studied the effects of varying light intensities on the activity of human infants. He noted that infants subjected to continuous bright-light stimulation were less active than infants under moderate-light stimulation. Although infants subjected to a dark environment were less active than the moderate-light group, this may have been due to a quiescence artifact induced by measuring dark activity only 4 minutes after bright-light stimulation had been presented.

The effect of visual stimulation on activity and task performance in retardates was studied by Cromwell and Foshee (1960) in an attempt to assess the validity of the hypothesis suggested by Strauss and his colleagues (1947, 1955) that reduction in stimulation will reduce superactivity and increase learning and performance. Cromwell and Foshee found no effects from the visual stimulation on either activity or task performance.

The effects of auditory stimulation on activity have also been subjected to recent study. Although changes in activity have been found as a function of decrease in visual stimulation, Spradlin, Cromwell, and Foshee (1959) did not find such a relationship between activity and noise stimulation. Alexander and Isaac (1961) found that white noise does not affect activity level in animals as measured over broad time samples. On the other hand, it is commonly observed that noise in a novel situation will cause "freezing" or a momentary decrease in activity followed by a flight reaction in many animals. Kuhnke (1952) demonstrated that fright reaction in animals consists in a brief motor inhibition followed by flight and other overt emotional responses. A similar motor inhibition is exhibited by human beings in response to unexpected noises. This response is probably an activity immobilization reflex due to fright.

Childers (1935), who felt that only a minority of superactive cases could be attributed to neurological diseases in older children, saw overstimulation, insecurity, and unstable homes as possible causative factors. He recommended that the child gain weight, add 1 hour of sleep per night, and have frequent rest periods. Also the child should be furnished guided activities and a sense of both security and freedom in the classroom. He felt it best to avoid sedation if possible.

Later treatment approaches have concentrated on barbituates, tranquilizers, amphetamines, and the stimulus-free environment.

Generally speaking, any strong stimulation will arouse an organism, particularly if the stimulation is noxious. However, there is evidence that novel stimulation may arouse curiosity and consequent exploratory behavior. Curiosity itself is viewed as a drive by many writers (Morgan, 1961).

Following the theoretical notion that superactivity may be due to a seeking of kinesthetic, tactual, and general stimulation because of partially blocked neural pathways, Foshee, Pait, and Cromwell[10] examined the activity levels of a group of superactive retarded children below 10 years of age who were living at home during a period when they were experimentally administered close tactual (lapsitting, bouncing, handling), visual, and other playroom-type stimulation in regular sessions by research assistants. A similar group was given no such treatment. Both groups declined significantly in measured activity level. Since the experimental group was not significantly different from the control group, no firm conclusions could be drawn from the results.

A number of observations from everyday life suggest that weather and barometric pressure affect activity level. In the calm just before a storm, cows have been observed to "bull" each other and cavort in the pasture. Farm children (but not adults necessarily) have recalled the urge to run across the fields during this period. Neuropsychiatric ward attendants have noticed that the time when fights are more likely to occur is just before a storm. Elementary school teachers have observed that when the class is unusually noisy, one can predict it is going to rain. The only research found in the literature which bears on these observations is by Watson, Dimasco, Kanter, Suter, and Greenblatt (1957). In 36 psychotherapeutic sessions, heart rate, finger skin temperature, rate of speaking, and "emotional involvement" were obtained in the patient. These were related to air temperature, relative humidity, and atmospheric pressure. Among other findings, it was reported that the patient's speaking rate correlated with atmospheric pressure —.47. These findings support the contention that air pressure, a rapid change in atmospheric pressure, or some other variable which changes with it facilitates a change in motor activity level.

Perceptual variables

Of interest are basic parameters of perception which may be correlated with motor-activity level. For example, in the theory of brain injury ad-

[10] Unpublished research.

vanced by Strauss and his coworkers (1947, 1955), the implication can be drawn that a disturbance in perceptual ability could be related to increased activity.

The Rorschach test has come under close scrutiny recently as a useful measure of normal perceptual variables. When asked to look at an ambiguous inkblot and tell what he sees, a person's verbal response is assumed to reveal something about how he perceives the stimulus properties of the inkblot. For those concerned with relating Rorschach variables to activity level, the movement response M represents a primary area of interest. As so often happens, the hypotheses go both ways. A high need for activity could be reflected in a high tendency to describe the inkblot percepts as being in motion; on the other hand, a tendency to inhibit one's motor output may be related to a high production of movement responses, since unsatisfied needs tend to make their way into one's percepts. The latter hypothesis is the one which has borne more fruit. Singer, Meltzoff, and Goldman (1952) pursued the hypothesis that motor inhibition correlates with a high production of movement responses. Less movement responses were expected in motor-active subjects. They found that enforced motor inhibition increased M responses, but enforced superactivity did not yield the differences expected. Meltzoff, Singer, and Korchin (1953) used enforced slow writing to induce motor inhibition. The inhibited subjects showed a trend in the direction of more M responses. Singer and Hermann (1954) divided schizophrenics into high- and low-M groups. The high-M subjects had longer motor-delay capacity and showed less spontaneous activity when alone in a waiting room. Singer and Spohn (1954) essentially confirmed these findings. In addition, they found that color responses tended to be greater with those having higher activity in the waiting room. When M responses were considered as active or passive, Singer and Spohn found that schizophrenic subjects with the active movement responses were more motor-inhibited than those with passive movement responses. Hurwitz (1954) had teachers, parents, and therapists rate activity level in children and found that subactive children not only had more human movement responses M in their Rorschach records but also had more form-dominated responses than the superactives.

Wolfensberger, Miller, Foshee, and Cromwell (1962), using the Foshee ballistograph, identified junior and senior high school students in the extreme quartiles in activity level and administered Rorschach tests to them. The initial hypothesis was that highly active subjects would have "Erlebnistypus" ratios with more movement than sum of color responses. This ratio, $M:\Sigma C$, measures the experience balance of introversive-extratensive tendencies. The introversive individual $(M > C)$ presumably responds more to thought-process stimuli and less to external stimuli; therefore, he would be less active. This prediction was not upheld. However, an unpredicted finding was that subactive subjects had a greater number and variety of determinants (movement, color, shading, etc.), as well as less form-controlled responses, than did the superactive subjects.

Although the findings regarding perceptual variables appear inconclusive, they suggest that more than one underlying factor may be operating. First, research on the Rorschach movement response suggests the existence of an activity need or drive which, when deprived or controlled, will affect perception in such a way that the individual will describe movement in the ambiguous stimuli which he views. Another look at the research evidence suggests that a major factor in subjects giving a high number of M responses is the ability of general self-inhibition and control. Besides having motor inhibition and less activity, high-M subjects have been found to take more time to respond to stimuli in the Rorschach testing situation (Bieri & Blacker, 1956). Also, high-M subjects appear more intelligent to observers even when mental test evidence does not support a difference in intelligence (Barron, 1955). This unusual finding makes one suspect that perhaps the high-M subject appears to observers to have a "thoughtful, controlled, sagelike" attitude. The possibility is suggested, therefore, that M responses reflect a conceptual or perceptual system with inhibitory, controlling functions which would limit impulsive, rapid acting-out responses in order that stimuli might first be carefully perceived and conceptualized. Thus, an indirect effect on overt activity level would be realized.

The study by Wolfensberger, Miller, Foshee, and Cromwell (1962) offers a further interpretation. The sheer number of determinants included in a verbal response to a stimulus, rather than M alone, may represent the degree of perceptual and conceptual organization of which the individual is capable. Thus, the person with high perceptual and conceptual capabilities is more relaxed in the novel situation. On the other hand, the individual whose responses are more limited in range of perceptual determinants is probably more fidgety, perhaps more distressed, and more in need of a familiar source of self-imposed proprioceptive stimulation in such situations. These findings must also be considered in the light of the fact that activity level has been found to have an inverse relationship to intelligence or mental age in certain populations (Cromwell, Palk, & Foshee, 1961; Foshee, 1958).

Pain responsivity represents another area of perception which has been investigated. Stengel, Oldham, and Ehrenberg (1958) report that subjects who are more sensitive to pain are rated as more active. This finding regarding pain sensitivity suggests still another underlying factor of general arousal or receptor sensitivity. This interpretation would be supported by the fact that subjects who show more activity while they are asleep show faster alpha-blocking latencies when tested with simple visual and auditory stimuli while awake. Such subjects also show faster reaction times.[11]

There is evidence that persons under sensory deprivation seek motor activity (Heron, Doane, & Scott, 1956). Dogs under similar conditions display "running fits" when released (Thompson, Melzack, & Scott, 1956). Some of these observations are similar to reports of superactivity in brain-injured children who, although having sensory and afferent apparatus intact, seem to act in a "sensory-deprived" way. Berkson (1961) has observed the similarity between the stereotyped, repetitive activities of retardates and of chimpanzees who were raised in restrictive captivity.

The relation of pathological breakdown in perceptual-motor response

[11] R. Cromwell, G. Wolf, and B. E. Palk, unpublished research.

and activity level has recently been examined by Duncan and Cromwell.[12] Retarded subjects, measured on activity level, were given the Bender Gestalt test and Graham-Kendall designs, reproduced under both immediate and 10-second delay conditions. The Strauss marble board was administered. From this a progression score (amount of skipping around or deviation from an orderly progression) and an error score (number of marbles misplaced in the final design) were devised. The relationship between the paper-and-pencil tasks (Bender Gestalt, Graham-Kendall) and activity level yielded correlations near zero. On the other hand, the marble board progression score correlated .67 and the error score .53 with ballistographic activity level. These preliminary findings would support the notion that widely different phenomena are being measured in these different kinds of perceptual tasks.

It seems reasonable to state that perceptual variables have a bearing, directly or indirectly, on activity level. Defining perception separately from sensation on the one hand and from conceptual-verbal variables on the other is a difficult problem. (Perhaps it is as much a problem of overlapping constructs as it is a problem of methodology.) The question of whether inhibitory mechanisms, which seem to be measured by Rorschach *M*, are related to perceptual disturbances which Strauss and Lehtinen (1947) and Strauss and Kephart (1955) say are found in the brain injured child remains unanswered. Whether the range of perceptual determinants found by Wolfensberger et al. (1962) can be upheld in a further study, and whether they are related to a constriction-dilation or a general intelligence dimension, are also as yet unanswered questions.

Physiological and organismic correlates

Factors will now be discussed at a physiological level of description. This will include the influences of heredity, neural functions such as EEG and sleep, neural structural correlates, drugs, and such organismic correlates as age and sex.

Heredity. To the authors' knowledge, activity level of human parents in relation to the activity of their children has not been studied. What information we have concerning the relation of heredity to activity comes from studies of animals, particularly rats. By way of summary, it seems certain that in several species, at least, there is a genetic transmission of activity behavior, although there is still disagreement regarding the genetic aspects involved.

The effects of domestication on genetic transmission of activity are shown in Richter's (1953; Richter & Uhlenhuth, 1954) work on gonadectomy. He reported reduced running activity by domesticated Norway rats following gonadectomy, whereas there was little or no effect on the activity of wild Norway rats. Richter has attempted to explain the marked difference in activity between wild and domesticated rats. In the controlled environment of domestication, the gonads through natural selection have assumed control of functions that were, in the wild state, adrenal functions. A possible parallel may be drawn between the activity of human infants and

[12] Unpublished research.

adults. The developmental changes leading from uninhibited infant behavior to the inhibition of human adult activity may follow similar physiological changes due to domestication.

Neural functions. Brain anomalies, such as tumors and scar tissue, especially in the area of the motor cortex, very often are accompanied by abnormal bursts of activity (seizures). Murphy and Gellhorn (1945) have shown that simultaneous stimulation of the hypothalamus and motor cortex results in an intensification of motor discharge in the peripheral musculature. They conclude that stimulation of the hypothalamus has an excitatory effect on the cortex. Thus, it is abundantly clear that irrespective of environmental variables, there is also a need to account for activity in electrophysiological terms.

The blocking (desynchronization) of the alpha wave seen in the electroencephalogram (EEG) appears to be a correlate of psychological arousal. Such arousal does not have a one-to-one relationship to activity level, since it may lead to a "frozen," attentive reaction in some cases and to executive, voluntary reaction and motor activity in other cases. Nevertheless, since the absence of arousal inevitably means a reduced level of motor activity, the topic of arousal has relevance here.

Moruzzi and Magoun (1949) found that direct stimulation to the reticular formation in the brain stem brought a blocking of the alpha wave which was identical to the psychological arousal phenomenon. Since then, Magoun, Lindsley, and their associates have been able to show behavioral arousal signs by electrode stimulation to the reticular system in dozing animals. Also, patients with tumors in the ascending reticular formation have been found to have defects in arousal.

Jasper and Penfield (1949) seem to have ruled out beta waves as a direct correlate of motor activity. They observed that beta-wave blocking in the precentral gyrus followed the examiner's command to get ready to move one's finger. However, no change in the beta wave was observed when actual movement occurred. Jenkins and Downie (1960) have demonstrated a clearly significant relation between EEG slowing and lowered scores on several visuomotor tests, but no such relationship exists with respect to verbal tests.

What then is the relation of alpha rhythm to motor activity? This question must have occurred to Prast (1950) when he was developing techniques to record EEG protocols while subjects were in motion. About the same time, Kibbler, Boreham, and Richter (1949); Bates (1950); and Kibbler and Richter (1950) were reporting evidence that voluntary movements, such as eyeblinks and finger movements, tended to occur more during certain portions of the alpha phase. These observations may be viewed in the light of theories which consider the alpha wave to be a correlate of a perceptual scanning mechanism which allows objects to be perceived and reacted to during one part of the phase and, with a flickering shutter effect, disallows percepts during other parts of the phase. On the other hand, the alpha phase may have an on-off triggering effect for motor responses independent of perceptual intake. Following these earlier investigations, Lansing (1957) and Lansing, Schwartz, and Lindsley (1959) performed ingenious experiments to relate motor reaction time to the phase of the alpha wave. Lansing (1957) corrected for the peripheral conduction speed from the receptor organ to the occipital cortex and from the motor cortex to the finger operating the reaction time key and was able to demonstrate (1) that reaction time was optimal during a particular phase of the alpha, and (2) that the phase found optimal in the occipital recording corresponded to the phase found optimal in the motor cortex recording of alpha. Later, Lansing, Schwartz, and Lindsley (1959) found faster reaction time under conditions when the alpha was blocked. These findings present the strongest recent evidence that the phase of the alpha wave is a correlate of an overt motor response.

Aside from the alpha phase, other variables of alpha have been subjected to examination regarding possible behavioral correlates. Many of these studies have been notoriously poor because of inadequate research methodology and inadequate measures for vaguely defined personality variables. No firm evidence has yet been found for the often held hypothesis that slow alpha frequency is characteristic of the calm, inactive, or passive-dependent individual. A companion hypothesis that nervous individuals have higher alpha frequency, low voltage, and greater susceptibility to photic driving (e.g., see Gastaut, Gastaut, Roger, Corriol, & Naquet, 1951) has not been adequately confirmed. During a flurry of attention to relations between the Rorschach test and the EEG (of equal clinical reputation in many respects), Brudo (1954) found a significant relation between alpha index (per cent time alpha) and human movement responses on the Rorschach. At the same time, however, he found a significant negative correlation between alpha index and animal movement responses. In an extensive study, Rabinovitch, Kennard, and Fister (1955) failed to find this relationship. Furthermore, even though certain other comparisons between the Rorschach and the EEG were statistically significant, Rabinovitch et al. concluded that they are probably spurious because the number of statistically significant relationships was within the range of what one would expect by chance.

If activation occurs with the blocking of alpha, is the latency of a response shorter in subjects who have a shorter blocking latency? Stamm (1952) was the first to investigate this in a well-controlled study. He found a significant positive correlation between alpha-blocking latency (ABL) and finger reaction time (RT) to the same stimuli. The average of intraindividual correlations (correlating RT and ABL from trial to trial within the same individual) was low but significant. The interindividual correlation of averages (correlating the mean ABL and mean RT score for each subject) was higher, suggesting reliable individual differences in speed of arousal and response initiation. Lansing (1957) substantiated the findings of Stamm.

Cromwell. Wolf, and Palk[13] secured evidence that occipital ABL. temporal ABL, and RT, as a simultaneously measured intercorrelated cluster of latency measures, are positively and significantly correlated with ballistographic activity level in awake retarded subjects. That is, the superactive subjects

[13] R. Cromwell, G. Wolf, and B. E. Palk. Unpublished research.

are slower in RT and ABL. When the same subjects were measured in ballistographic activity while asleep, the reverse was true. The interrelated cluster of ABL and RT measures was negatively correlated with ballistographic activity in sleeping retarded subjects. That is, the faster subjects in RT and ABL show more movement at night. The findings in regard to the waking state suggest that neurological impairment may underlie both slow latencies and superactivity. On the other hand, the sleeping activity level may possibly be a manifestation of arousability. Also, if arousability is related to the concept of generalized drive, this interpretation suggests that sleeping activity might be a more appropriate measure of generalized drive level than waking activity. This may account for the failure of Foshee (1958) to support the Hullian hypotheses of the effect of drive on learning. Hullian learning theory (see Chapter 3 by G. N. Cantor) postulates that high drive will facilitate learning on simple tasks and retard learning on complex tasks. Foshee (1958) attempted to use superactive and subactive retarded subjects to define high and low generalized drive states. Their differential performance on simple and complex tasks failed to support the Hullian hypothesis. In a second attempt to examine this hypothesis, Cromwell, Palk, and Foshee (1961) examined the relationship between activity level and eyelid conditioning (viewed as a simple learning task) in mentally retarded subjects. Again, the findings revealed an absence of relationship between activity level and learning as predicted from Hullian theory.

Further substantiation for the distinction between sleeping and waking activity comes from the finding by Cromwell, Wolf, and Palk that the two measures are not correlated with each other in mentally retarded subjects. Schulman, Lipkin, Clarinda, and Mitchell (1961), measuring activity with the actometer, further substantiate this lack of relationship. This independence of sleeping and waking activity is reminiscent of the fact that spastic individuals are not spastic while asleep.

Since sleep clearly produces a lowered activity state, the well-known EEG manifestations of sleep may be viewed indirectly as a correlate of activity. Motor activity during sleep is at least as much in need of further research as waking activity level. In a recent study of eye movements, dream activity, and EEG, Dement and Kleitman (1957) point out that body movement decreases sharply at the onset of rapid eye movements while the subject is sleeping. Another observation is that eye movements are associated with spindles and delta activity.

Beckett, Bickford, and Keith (1956) clinically compared EEG records of hyperkinetic and quiet, easily managed mentally defective children. They found the highly active children to have fewer normal records, more dysrhythmia, and many more paroxysmal responses to light.

Neural structures. The *hyperkinetic syndrome* in children is described by Laufer and Denhoff (1957) as related to neural structural impairment. Its characteristics are constant motion, short attention span, an inability to delay gratification, irritability, and poor schoolwork. The syndrome appears related to mental retardation since there are reports that the intelligence of hyperkinetic children is lower than normal (Levin, 1938; Ounsted, 1955).

Levin found evidence of cerebral lesions in 75 per cent of a hyperkinetic group.

Laufer and his colleagues suspect the syndrome results from dysfunction of the diencephalon in early life. They use a photo-Metrazol EEG technique (Gastaut, 1950) to test diencephalic function. The test involves stimulating a subject under Metrazol with intermittent stroboscopic light. A photo-Metrazol threshold is obtained from the amount of Metrazol required to evoke a specific spike wave in the EEG record and a jerk of both forearms. In accordance with theory, low thresholds indicate diencephalic disorder. Laufer reasons that if children with hyperkinesis also have low photo-Metrazol thresholds, then these superactive children have diencephalic dysfunction. Such a notion finds support from animal research in which the diencephalon, particularly the hypothalamus, is associated with superactivity. Perhaps cross validation with some of the other human activity devices in conjunction with photo-Metrazol threshold measures might also add further support. The question arises whether Foshee's ballistograph scores, in lieu of clinical hyperkinetic diagnoses, relate in any way to photo-Metrazol thresholds.

A considerable amount of research on brain-damaged animals has attempted to correlate activity level with insult to various cortical and subcortical structures. This type of evidence would appear to bear heavily on the conceptions of Strauss and his associates as well as on the points raised by Laufer and Denhoff. In brief, the frontal areas of the brain, the hypothalamus, and the reticular activating system all seem to be invariably implicated in abnormal activity level. However, the specific areas involved and the nature of their relationship to efferent motor activity are less clear.

Drugs. Over the years a number of drugs have been used in an attempt to reduce the level of superactivity in children. Lippman (1928) is among the first to suggest atropine for the superactive, hypertonic infant. Believing the condition to be a result of heredity, congenital autonomic imbalance, or cerebral injury, a behavioral or environmental theory was rejected. Nevertheless, he suggested that along with atropine the mother should relax and someone other than the parents should assume the greater share of the management of the infant. He also suggests diet shifts until the best one is found since these infants gain less weight than normal infants. Air swallowing should be prevented, a drowsy state produced, and atropine should be used, even up to the point of tolerance.

According to Laufer and Denhoff (1957, p. 470):

Phenobarbital and other barbituates are ineffective in the hyperkinetic syndrome. Instead the great majority of children with this syndrome react adversely to such medication. They often become more irritable, unmanageable, and active. This reaction is so marked as almost to provide a specific diagnostic test in itself.

Similar observations are reported by Ingram (1956) with superactive brain-injured children and by Ounsted (1955) with hyperkinetic epileptic children. Burket (1955), however, reports favorable results and no adverse reactions while using sustained-release phenobarbital capsules with superactive children.

Numerous experiments have been conducted using reserpine with superactive retardates. A number of uncontrolled studies yield favorable results (Fischer, 1956; Horenstein, 1957; Noce, Williams, & Rapaport, 1955; Sprogis, Lezdins, White, Ming, Lanning, Drake, & Wyckoff, 1957). Kirk and Bauer (1956), on the other hand, find no decrease in superactivity in 31 educable retardates ranging in age from 8 to 28. Timberlake, Belmont, and Ogonik (1957), using reserpine on 200 superactive retardates, reported improved behavior in 40 per cent of the subjects. The average ages of the marked and moderately improved groups were 12 and 9, respectively; the average ages of the slight and not improved groups were 16 and 23, respectively. Another finding that the drug was more effective with mild than with severe retardates was also reported by Wardell, Rubin, and Ross (1958).

With chlorpromazine, again, poorly controlled studies report positive results (Bair & Herold, 1955; MacColl, 1956; Rettig, 1955; Sprogis et al., 1957). Freed and Peifer (1956) find behavior improvements with the drug in 21 of 25 superactive emotionally disturbed children. However, it is possible that the positive results might be attributed to a therapeutic interrelationship with the therapist and others in the child's environment. Craft (1957a) and Wardell et al. (1958) obtained no improvement with severely retarded adult subjects. The suggestion was made that the young and mildly disturbed child may have the better prognosis with or without the chlorpromazine. Craft found meprobamate (1957c) and hydroxyzine (1957b) to be unsuccessful with severely retarded adults. In a controlled study Foshee, Brooks, Spicker, and Cromwell,[14] using a placebo group and single and double dosage groups for the drug Pamabron, found no effects on resting ballistographic activity, working ballistographic activity, working efficiency, or ward ratings of behavior.

A more recent question has been the effect of amphetamines on activity level. Laufer and Denhoff (1957, p. 470) gave positive reports from their observations: "In our experience amphetamine is a specific for the treatment of the hyperkinetic syndrome. It is ineffective in other conditions. . . . A favorable response to amphetamine is supportive evidence for a diagnosis of the hyperkinetic syndrome."

While amphetamine is reported to decrease superactivity, it also appears to stimulate activity in subactive children. In addition, amphetamine seems to be effective in raising low photo-Metrazol thresholds in superactive children up to normal, and when the drug is removed, the threshold drops back and the superactivity reappears (Laufer, Denhoff, & Rubin, 1954; Laufer, Denhoff, & Solomons, 1957). Since other factors were not studied, one cannot conclude that the amphetamine alone produces this phenomenon.

The two available forms of amphetamine are racemic amphetamine, called Benzedrine, and dextro-amphetamine, called Dexedrine. According to Bradley (1937, 1950), Benzedrine is about 75 per cent effective with hyperkinetic children while Dexedrine is about 60 per cent effective.

[14] Unpublished research.

Benzedrine is only slightly more effective than Dexedrine with syndromes which are psychogenic in origin; however, Benzedrine is described as extremely more effective than Dexedrine (77 per cent versus 4 per cent) with syndromes which are associated with convulsions. Qualitatively, Benzedrine produces more dramatic favorable effects than Dexedrine, but it also produces two or three times as many unfavorable side effects. Differences have been noted concerning which form is more effective in an individual (Laufer & Denhoff, 1957).

Effective results with amphetamine, although not as dramatic as those reported above, have been obtained by Ingram (1956) and Ounsted (1955) in England. However, both writers report more effective results with primidone.

McConnell, Bialer, and Cromwell[15] have recently completed the first controlled study known to the authors on the effect of Dexedrine on activity. Superactive and subactive retarded children were given placebos, 7½-mg and 15-mg dosages of Dexedrine, respectively. Measures were made of ward activity level ratings as well as (and unrelated to) ballistographic activity. No effect was found among the different treatment groups on the activity of either the subactive or superactive groups. Thus, no evidence was forthcoming in this study to support the uncontrolled clinical observations that amphetamines affect activity.

Age. Superactive behavior in retarded children has been thought to decrease at pubescence (Laufer & Denhoff, 1957). Evidence in support of this notion was found by Cromwell, Palk, and Foshee (1961) in that ballistographic activity decreased greatly among institutionalized retarded subjects between 25 and 35 years of age. This finding may be related to play activity of young animals and children which appears to remain at high levels even when physiological needs seem to be at a minimum (Beach, 1945). As with animal research, the age-activity relationship with these human subjects is not linear.

Sex. Brody (1942) has shown that female rats run in revolving drums twice as much as do males. While this difference may be explained, in part, by the increased activity of the females in estrus, the consistency of the difference lends evidence to the notion that other factors are involved. Apparently, this finding cannot be extended to humans. Wolfensberger, Miller, Foshee, and Cromwell (1962) have taken ballistographic measures of activity in junior and senior high school students. They report that boys are more active than girls. Although this is a common observation in young children, cultural factors may be relevant here. Schulman, Lipkin, Clarinda, and Mitchell (1961) have found essentially the same thing in children, using the actometer as the measuring device. Childers (1935), on the other hand, reports no correlation of activity level with sex or race.

Response variables

Activity cycles. Some of the best predictions about activity in an organism can be made on the basis of information concerning his prior behavior or response pattern. As well as knowing the stimulus and organismic

[15] Unpublished research.

factors affecting the individual, it is well to ask the question, "How has he behaved in the past?" As previously noted, the test-retest correlations of activity measures not only reflect the reliability of the measuring devices but they also attest to the consistency with which a given level of activity is maintained over a period of time. Thus, the consistency in activity level which is reflected by these reliability coefficients is one of the most notable findings yet made about activity.

On the other hand, the activity which an organism displays over a period of time may not have the simple "level-line" function which test-retest coefficients might lead one to assume. Rhythms and cycles of activity are reported for various organisms (Harker, 1958). Richter (1953, 1957) and Ellis and Pryer (1959) have described cyclic variations which seem to occur in humans.

Other factors.   Perhaps one of the most fruitful approaches to response variable predictions of activity has been made recently by McKinney (1961). He did a factor analysis of 80 behaviors in mentally retarded boys. Among his eight factors were (1) *purposefulness* (relating meaningfully to remote objects and people), (2) *lack of restraint* (diversified, distractible, and superactive behavior emphasizing tactual, gustatory, and proprioceptive stimulation), (3) *self or bodily stimulation* (long-term superactivity leading to proprioceptive and genital stimulation and, therefore, often treated with the use of tranquilizers), (4) *age* (long-term institutionalization, often epileptic), (5) *social interaction* (socially appropriate seeking of tactually affectionate contact with others), (6) *neuromuscular control* (rocking, teeth-grating, and headbanging behavior associated with postnatal trauma), (7) *verbal behavior* (meaningful or meaningless use of speech apparatus), (8) *emotional adjustment* (disturbed hebephrenic-like behavior, admitted to an institution at a later age). These findings support the thesis of this chapter that distinct components of activity are important for individual consideration.

The factors have implications for the theories of Gellner, Zaporozhets, and Strauss with respect to the relationship of visual-autonomic deficit, motor-touch association, and distractibility to superactive behavior. The findings also point to more than one kind of relevant and irrelevant activity.

THEORETICAL FORMULATIONS

Any attempt to build a theoretical framework to handle activity level as a unitary, or homogeneous, phenomenon would probably be futile. The literature reviewed in this chapter indicates that different methods of activity measurement frequently do not correlate with each other and that the prediction of activity level comes from widely different classes of predictor variables. Thus, heterogeneity seems to be a hallmark of the concept.

So, instead of speaking of activity level, we should more appropriately be speaking of constructs which describe different components of activity level. However, such a theory dividing activity into useful subconstructs is yet to be devised. Therefore, the purpose of this section will be to describe some theoretical fragments and formulations which represent interesting leads and possible pathways toward an integrative conception of activity level components.

Motor neurone firing

A first, gross theoretical formulation is that activity level is a function of motor neurone firing. Whatever affects motor neurones will, in turn, affect activity level. One can hardly quarrel with such a formulation. However, one might be at somewhat of a loss to make extensive predictions about activity level from it. We might well suspect that lesions in the motor area causing abnormal discharges may increase activity level, perhaps in the form of seizures. But would diffuse lesions throughout the brain bring about the same effect as focal lesions at various places? Would irritations or excessive stimulation of afferent or sensory areas ultimately increase motor output as well? It would be reasonable to expect that prior learning of the organism which emphasizes responses with gross movements of skeletal muscles would produce a higher amount of motor output. But what is to account for activity which is not necessary to consummatory behavior resulting from prior learning? How is it mediated to the motor neurones? Also, how does motor activity occur at times when no previously learned responses are being acted out? These questions do not seem to be adequately answered.

A further step in the "neurone firing" approach to theory involves cortical damage. According to this explanation, if inhibitory functions of the cortex are knocked out by cortical lesions, a free expression of uninhibited superactive behavior is allowed.

Strauss-Lehtinen-Kephart theory

The theory of Strauss, Lehtinen, and Kephart (Straus & Kephart, 1955; Strauss & Lehtinen, 1947) might be described as a quasi-neurophysiological theory. Their concept of brain injury is based on behavioral rather than organic structural criteria. The energy reservoir concept has been criticized as a neurological fallacy. Moreover, expected effects of stimulation on the brain-injured child do not seem to be upheld by controlled research. Nevertheless, the theory is worth considering seriously. For one thing, it posits a series of intervening "brain events" between the external stimulus and the acted-out motor response, which have psychological significance regardless of their neurological purity. For another thing, the theory has had perhaps more heuristic value in generating hypotheses regarding methods of management than any other theory in the area of mental retardation. The reactions to the theory seem to illustrate two general foibles of scientists and others who react to scientific theories: They become so emotionally involved with a theory that they cannot modify or reject aspects of it in the face of contrary empirical evidence; or, they reject it completely, the valuable parts along with the weak parts, once it comes under criticism.

The essence of the Strauss theory can perhaps be described most briefly as follows: The brain, in order to complete the cycle between receiving a stimulus and acting out an overt response, must proceed through a

654 *Handbook of Mental Deficiency*

series of events. Chronologically, this involves (1) the sensory reception of the stimulus, (2) the organizing of the stimulus impact into a meaningful pattern, ordinarily called perception, (3) a consideration of the percept in the light of the needs (goals) of the person, (4) a decision-making, or response-choosing, process to select a "behavior" from the person's repertory, and (5) a final acting out of this overt behavior with the skeletal muscles and other effectors. A person with brain injury cannot carry out this sequence of events with the same fluency as a normal person. The store of energy normally alloted to these various events, therefore, does not get fully or evenly utilized. Proceeding sequentially again, neural damage may prevent a complete sensory reception of the stimulus. Thus, blindness, partial sight, deafness, etc., may result in such cases of peripheral afferent damage. Second, the individual may be impaired in organizing the stimulus into a meaningful pattern. Thus, defects may occur in perceiving various stimuli. The individual may be distracted by peripheral elements which the normal person would discard as irrelevant to the central meaningful pattern (gestalt). Also, defects may occur in coordinating the perceptual impact to motor output in copying forms. Third, a person may be impaired in considering a recognized percept in the light of his present needs. Thus, he would not be able to react to stimuli with sustained or long-term goal-directed activity. Such a person would be described as having short attention span, abrupt shifting of behavior, and inclusion of irrelevant behavior within a particular sequence of goal-directed behavior. Fourth, the individual may be impaired in the executive capacity for choosing an appropriate response or in having a hierarchy of responses closely linked with the different alternative stimulus conditions. If so, he might have a prolonged reaction time. He may perseverate with a response rather than shift to appropriate behavior. He may be described as rigid because of his tendency to repeat a previous response in a situation where it has been proved inappropriate or where the attempting of alternative responses would be appropriate. Fifth, he may be impaired in the final acting out of the overt response. Apart from the possible paralytic effects of efferent damage, Strauss and his colleagues emphasize the notion that energy which is normally utilized for these earlier processes does not get fully utilized. Therefore, when the final overt response does occur, the built-up reservoir of energy makes the response explosive, catastrophic, and forceful. The resulting behavior would be described as *hyperactive*. Whether or not this formulation has validity in all its aspects, it does attempt to tie together the various symptoms of brain damage with psychologically meaningful stimulus-response mediating events.

Arousal theory

Another major neurological conception having implications for activity level is arousal. The major impact of the conception of arousal has been to discard once and for all the naïve notions of earlier stimulus-response theory that the incoming stimulus stands in a one-to-one relation to brain activity and response, and that during periods of minimal or no stimulation the brain is inactive. To replace these notions, the brain is viewed as a highly active electrophysiological unit, whether the subject is aroused and responding to stimuli or not. During the normal waking, resting state the brain is typically involved in a hypersynchronous electric wave pattern, having something to do with its degree of readiness for incoming stimuli. Once a stimulus is presented, either overtly or experimentally by deep electrodes to the reticular system, the high-amplitude electrical wave action disappears or is diminished, and the individual attends and reacts to the stimulus. He is thus described as being aroused. The brain has ceased its high-amplitude, fast rhythm. One possible implication is that the brain is no longer acting as a unit. It is divided into elements which are out of phase with each other and which are perceiving, reacting to, and "disposing of" the stimulus which has been introduced.

The implication for activity level is that an inverse relation might exist between the amount of alpha activity of the brain and the overt motor-activity level. That is, subjects with low per cent–time alpha would be more often aroused and reactive to stimuli; subjects with high per cent–time alpha would be in an overt resting state and relatively less responsive to stimuli over a given time period. As mentioned before, the instance of arousal may not directly determine that the activity level will be high. Arousal may lend to "freezing," as well as to overt action of the skeletal musculature.

An important question, however, is whether or not there is such a thing as an abnormally high state of arousal. The fact that reliable differences exist among people regarding their speed of alpha recovery and per cent–time alpha is well known. However, when the alpha wave is blocked in a particular instance, can we say that one person blocks with greater intensity or in abnormal magnitude while another does not? If so, abnormal arousability may have an important direct bearing on activity level. Otherwise, arousal should probably be viewed as relevant to the "base-line activity" of the organism but not relevant to predicting excessively high activity level conditions.

Drive theory

Activity level has been construed still a different way in Hull-Spence learning theory. Here activity is viewed as a function of generalized drive. This theoretical approach has been discussed earlier in the chapter together with the experimental hypotheses which have been deduced from it. In Chapter 3, Cantor presents a more elaborate exposition of this theory. The theory leads to the prediction that generalized drive D multiplies with habit sHr to determine behavior. Theoretically, animals with high activity level, and presumably high drive, should learn simple tasks more rapidly than animals with low activity level. On the other hand, high-drive animals may be retarded in learning complex tasks since high D may be more likely to multiply the incorrect habits. Evidence for this in animal research is sufficient to advance the notion that activity level may be viewed as a general motivational phenomenon.

The exact nature of the relationship between activity and the general drive state is as yet unclear. Evidence from animal research indicates that, without stimulation, an increase in deprivation does not necessarily increase activity. This suggests that the increase in activity may be a secondary function owing to increased and perhaps learned responsiveness to differential stimuli. If so, generalized drive would not be viewed as directly related to activity level.

Gellner's theory

Still another conception about activity is by Gellner (1959; Hunt, 1959). This conception has remained unapplauded and, along with the theory of Strauss, has been criticized because of lack of evidence of the relationship between defective behavior and the neurological structures which are implicated. Again, it is important to look at the testable research hypotheses which are suggested from the formulation. Gellner conceives of the superior and inferior colliculi as involved in conditions of mental retardation and that four classifications can be made of the behavior impairments involved. These classifications—(1) visual-motor defect, (2) auditory-motor defect, (3) visual-autonomic defect, and (4) auditory-autonomic defect—are posited as having relationships to the local midbrain structures which may be individually or collectively damaged. The first two classes, involving impairments in sensorimotor coordination, are fairly easily understood. The latter two categories involve an inability to "appreciate emotionally" or to respond meaningfully to visual or auditory stimuli. It is in the visual-autonomic defect that the symptom of superactivity assumes a major role. The role of activity suggested by this formulation is novel enough to deserve attention regardless of the neurological credibility which the theory may have. It suggests that a child who is defective in his ability to react meaningfully and appreciatively to visual stimuli will compensate by getting as much kinesthetic, tactual, and proprioceptive stimulus input as possible. In order to do this, the child out of necessity must maintain a high rate of activity. He cannot sit still for the purely visual appreciations which other children enjoy. He cannot respond as meaningfully to visually presented instructions. Such a hypothesis deserves further investigation.

Zaporozhets' theory

Zaporozhets (1957, 1960), a contemporary Russian psychologist, has devoted his attention to the role of the senses in the development of voluntary movements. Describing three stages in the development of the normal child, he points out that, at a very early age, motor activity has a role in external-orienting and investigatory behavior. This provides a primal basis of motor-touch associations with the outside world. This foundation of tactual association then serves as a basis for the later development of visual associations, so that the child need not come directly into contact with objects in order to respond to them. Gradually, as the visual and the earlier association systems are built up, a transition is made so that word associations, as well as sensory associations, are also developed.

With this framework of normal development, one can ask what would happen if neurological or other impairment in the child prevented him from advancing to the later visual and verbal stages. The result would seem to be that the child would continue to be dependent at later ages on the motor-touch association system in order to react to external stimuli. At an early age such a system would be viewed as normal, but at a later stage in the child's life, it would be viewed as abnormally superactive. The older child with fluent visual and verbal associations need not invoke his motor-touch system as much. Again, as suggested by Gellner, the role of tactual stimulation is invoked as an explanation of superactivity.

Bindra's formulation

Bindra (1961) has recently attempted a formulation which is concerned with the kinds of acts which comprise general activity rather than the amount of general activity of the organism. These spontaneous acts are so pervasive and frequent that their occurrences and nonoccurrences must be considered when trying to formulate laws about the less frequent consummatory acts with which the psychologist is mostly concerned. As well as studying the relationship between stimulus conditions and the relevant responses in a situation, Bindra thinks that various factors, such as drugs, brain damage, and past learning, should be studied which affect the irrelevant responses which are competing with those that are relevant. Typically, the relevant response is already in the repertory of the organism, and learning consists in the elimination of the irrelevant responses. Bindra's term "novelty reactions," which he uses to describe the exploratory and nonexploratory behaviors which would be irrelevant in a simple maze-learning situation, reminds one of the fidgety, irrelevant kinds of behavior observed while a human subject is being measured in a ballistograph.

The formulation suggested by Bindra emphasizes that relevant versus irrelevant activity should be a major construct in analyzing the total activity matrix. Perhaps this is supported by the sometimes low correlations between different operational measures of general activity. Perhaps the correlation between activity wheel and straight alley activity is low because irrelevant and relevant activity show a different prominence in each measure. The lack of correlation between ballistographic and open-floor activity might merit a similar explanation. The relevant-irrelevant activity distinction also brings to mind the Straussian notion of impairment in ability to consider the perceived stimulus in relation to the goals of the organism. If one assumes such a condition could occur, it would seem that the probability of irrelevant behavior would be increased by neurological impairment.

SUMMARY

The study of activity level, although diversely explored, has never been a central organized focal point of attention in science. Perhaps the major reasons why it has been studied are associated with (1) the practical problems of managing superactive children, (2) its obvious role as a behavior correlate in the attempts made to understand brain function, (3) its role in the psychology of motivation and learning, (4) the recent attention to the importance of irrelevant activity, and (5) its obvious convenience in studying drug effects. The methodologies developed to measure activity

have found recent attention because of impressively high reliabilty coefficients which exist for many of them. However, the frequently found low
correlations between these reliable measures deny us the simple privilege
of assuming that the same thing is being measured in each case.

Meanwhile, a wide range of variables has been studied in relation to
activity measures. Stimulus conditions, perceptual conditions, organic and
central nervous system variables, and response variables are described in terms
of their effect on activity. Mutual exclusion does not exist among these classes
of correlates; they represent only arbitrary distinctions among a wide range
of variables. Since the brain impairment of a retarded child may affect
the mediation of functions elsewhere in the body, research on this broad
range of correlates must all be taken into consideration. The empirical and
theoretical separation of these correlates into clusters which relate to different kinds of activity is yet to be done.

The theoretical approaches to explaining activity level are, as expected,
somewhat fragmentary. However, one measure of an adequate theory is
the fertility it has in suggesting new research. In that sense, a number
of views about activity level seem to represent valuable sources for hypothesis
making. Of special interest is the stress which some theories have put on
motor-touch behavior as a substitute for other less motor-active behaviors
which cannot be developed owing to neurological impairment. Also, some
formulations emphasize the distinction of behavior relevance-irrelevance.

Whether activity level need be considered as a unitary topic of review
in the future is a question well worth considering. It seems inevitable that
a more sophisticated approach at some future time would have to deal
more seriously with constructs which would describe activity components.
In so doing, the factors which control the level of activity output would
have to be treated in terms of the different "levels" and "areas" where
they operate. Also, if the past is any basis for predicting the future, research
will continue to focus primarily where crucial pragmatic problems are at
hand.

REFERENCES

ALEXANDER, M. A., & ISAAC, W. The effects of sensory stimulation on activity level
of normal and prefrontal lobectomized rats. Paper read at Southeast. Psychol.
Ass., Gatlinburg, March, 1961.

BAIR, H. V., & HEROLD, W. Efficacy of chlorpromazine in hyperactive mentally retarded children. *Arch. Neurol. Psychiat.*, 1955, 74, 363–364.

BARRON, F. Threshold for the perception of human movement in inkblots. *J. consult. Psychol.*, 1955, 19, 33–38.

BATES, J. A. V. Electrical activity of the motor cortex accompanying voluntary
movement. *EEG clin. Neurophysiol.*, 1950, 2, 103. (Abstract)

BEACH, F. A. Effects of brain lesions upon running activity in the male rat. *J.
comp. Psychol.*, 1941, 31, 145–179.

BEACH, F. A. Current concepts of play in animals. *Amer. Natural.*, 1945, 79, 523–
541.

BECKETT, P. G., BICKFORD, B. G., & KEITH, H. M. The electroencephalogram and
various aspects of mental deficiency. *J. Dis. Child.*, 1956, 92, 374–381.

BEHNEY, W. H. Nocturnal explorations of the forest deermouse. *J. Mammal.*, 1936, 17, 225–230.

BERKSON, G. Stereotyped movements in mental defectives. Paper read at Southeast. Sect., Amer. Ass. ment. Def., Nashville, November, 1961.

BIERI, J., & BLACKER, E. External and internal stimulus factors in Rorschach performance. *J. consult. Psychol.*, 1956, 20, 1–7.

BINDRA, D. Components of general activity and the analysis of behavior. *Psychol. Rev.*, 1961, 68, 205–215.

BINDRA, D., & BLOND, J. A time-sample method for measuring general activity and its components. *Canad. J. Psychol.*, 1958, 12, 74–76.

BRADLEY, C. The behavior of children receiving Benzedrine. *Amer. J. Psychiat.*, 1937, 94, 557–585.

BRADLEY, C. Benzedrine and Dexedrine in treatment of children's behavior disorders. *Pediatrics*, 1950, 5, 24–36.

BRODY, E. G. Genetic basis of spontaneous activity in the albino rat. *Comp. Psychol. Monogr.*, 1942, 17, 1–24.

BRUDO, C. S. The alpha index in the electro-encephalogram and movement responses on the Rorschach and PMS tests. *Dissertation Abstr.*, 1954, 14, 393.

BURKET, L. C. New method of sedation in treatment of hyperkinetic children. *Amer. J. med. Sci.*, 1955, 229, 22–25.

CAMPBELL, B. A. Design and reliability of a new activity-recording device. *J. comp. physiol. Psychol.*, 1954, 47, 90–92.

CAMPBELL, C. J., & MCLEAN, R. A. An electronic integrating circuit for recording the spontaneous activity of animals. *Rev. scient. Instrum.*, 1948, 19, 302.

CASTANERA, T. J., KIMELDORF, D. J., & JONES, D. C. Apparatus for measurement of activity in small animals. *J. Lab. clin. Med.*, 1955, 45, 825–832.

CHILDERS, A. T. Hyper-activity in children having behavior disorders. *Amer. J. Orthopsychiat.*, 1935, 5, 227–243.

CRAFT, M. Tranquillizers in mental deficiency: chlorpromazine. *J. ment. Def. Res.*, 1957, 1, 91–95. (a)

CRAFT, M. Tranquillizers in mental deficiency: Hydroxyzine. *J. ment. Sci.*, 1957, 103, 855–857. (b)

CRAFT, M. Tranquillizers in mental deficiency: meprobamate. *J. ment. Def. Res.*, 1957, 2, 17–20. (c)

CROMWELL, R. L., & FOSHEE, J. G. Studies in activity level. IV. Effects of visual stimulation during task performance in mental defectives. *Amer. J. ment. Defic.*, 1960, 65, 248–251.

CROMWELL, R. L., PALK, B. E., FOSHEE, J. G. Studies in activity level. V. The relationships among eyelid conditioning, intelligence, activity level, and age. *Amer. J. ment. Defic.*, 1961, 65, 744–748.

DAWSON, W. W. An electronic tambour: the piezoelectric crystal. *Amer. J. Psychol.*, 1959, 72, 279–282.

DEMENT, W., & KLEITMAN, N. Cyclic variations in EEG during sleep and their relation to eye movements, body motility, and dreaming. *EEG clin. Neurophysiol.* 1957, 9, 673–690.

ELLIS, N. R., & PRYER, R. S. Quantification of gross bodily activity in children with severe neuropathology. *Amer. J. ment. Defic.*, 1959, 63, 1034–1037.

ESCALONA, S. K., & LEITCH, M. Early phases of personality development: a non-normative study of infant behavior. *Monogr. Soc. Res. Child Developm.*, 1952, 17, No. 1.

FINGER, F. W. 72 hours of food deprivation in wheels vs. photo-cage. Unpublished manuscript, Univer. of Virginia, 1958.

FISCHER, E. Reserpine (Serpasil) in mental deficiency practice. *J. ment. Sci.*, 1956, 102, 542–545.

FOSHEE, J. G. Studies in activity level. I. Simple and complex task performance in defectives. *Amer. J. ment. Defic.*, 1958, 62, 882–886.

FREDERICSON, E. The theory of psychomotion as applied to study of temperament. *J. comp. Psychol.*, 1946, 39, 77–89.

FREED, H., & PEIFER, C. A. Treatment of hyperkinetic emotionally disturbed children with prolonged administration of chlorpromazine. *Amer. J. Psychiat.*, 1956, 113, 22–26.

FURCHTGOTT, E., & ECHOLS, M. Activity and emotionality in pre- and neonatally x-irradiated rats. *J. comp. physiol. Psychol.*, 1958, 51, 541–545.

GALLAGHER, J. J. *The tutoring of brain-injured mentally retarded children.* Springfield, Ill.: Charles C Thomas, 1960.

GARDNER, W. I., CROMWELL, R. L., & FOSHEE, J. G. Studies in activity level. II. Effects of distal visual stimulation in organics, familials, hyperactives, and hypoactives. *Amer. J. ment. Defic.*, 1959, 63, 1028–1033.

GASTAUT, H. Combined photic and Metrazol activation of the brain. *EEG clin. Neurophysiol.*, 1950, 2, 249–261.

GASTAUT, H., GASTAUT, Y., ROGER, A., CORRIOL, J., & NAQUET, R. Étude electrographique du cycle d'excitabilité cortical. *EEG clin. Neurophysiol.*, 1951, 3, 401–428.

GELLNER, L. *A neurophysiological concept of mental retardation and its educational implications.* Chicago: J. Levinson Research Foundation, 1959.

GOLDEN, BEVERLY. A comparison of the distractibility of intellectually normal and mentally retarded subjects. *Dissertation Abstr.*, 1956, 16, 1718–1719.

GRIFFIN, D. R., & WELSH, J. H. Activity rhythms in bats under constant external conditions. *J. Mammal.*, 1937, 18, 337–342.

HARKER, J. E. Diurnal rhythms in the animal kingdom. *Biol. Rev.*, 1958, 33, 1–52.

HARNED, B. K., CUNNINGHAM, R. W., & GILL, E. R. An activity analyzer for small animals. *Science*, 1952, 116, 369–370.

HAYES, K. J. The effects of abnormal brain development on rat behavior. *Amer. Psychologist*, 1957, 12, 461. (Abstract)

HERON, W., DOANE, B. K., & SCOTT, T. H. Visual disturbances after prolonged perceptual isolation. *Canad. J. Psychol.*, 1956, 10, 13–18.

HORENSTEIN, S. Reserpine and chlorpromazine in hyperactive mental defectives. *Amer. J. ment. Defic.*, 1957, 61, 525–529.

HOSKINS, R. G. Studies on vigor. XVI. Endocrine factors in vigor. *Endocrinology*, 1927, 11, 97–105.

HUNT, B. M. Performance of mentally deficient brain-injured children and mentally deficient familial children on construction from patterns. *Amer. J. ment. Defic.*, 1959, 63, 679–687.

HUNT, J. MCV., & SCHLOSBERG, H. General activity in the male white rat. *J. comp. Psychol.*, 1939, 28, 23–38.

HURWITZ, I. A developmental study of the relationship between motor activity and perceptual processes as measured by the Rorschach test. *Dissertation Abstr.*, 1954, 14, 1805–1806.

INGRAM, T. T. S. A characteristic form of overactive behavior in brain-damaged children. *J. ment. Sci.*, 1956, 102, 550–558.

IRWIN, O. C. Infant responses to vertical movements. *Child Develpm.*, 1932, 3, 167–169.

IRWIN, O. C. Effect of strong light on the body activity of newborns. *J. comp. Psychol.*, 1941, 32, 233–236.

ISAAC, W., & RUCH, T. C. Evaluation of four activity techniques for monkeys. *Science*, 1956, 123, 1170.

JASPER, H. H., & PENFIELD, W. Electrocorticograms in man: effect of voluntary movement upon electrical activity of precentral gyrus. *Arch. Psychiat.*, 1949, 183, 163–174.

JENKINS, C. D., & DOWNIE, A. W. The relation of electro-encephalographic slowing to impairment of intellective function. Paper read at Amer. Psychol. Ass., Chicago, September, 1960.

KESSEN, W., HENDRY, L. S., & LEUTZENDORFF, A. Measurement of movement in the human newborn. *Child Develpm.*, 1961, 32, 95–105.

KIBBLER, G. O., BOREHAM, J. L., & RICHTER, D. Relation of the alpha rhythm of the brain to psychomotor phenomena. *Nature, Lond.*, 1949, 164, 371.

KIBBLER, G. O., & RICHTER, D. Alpha rhythm and motor activity. *EEG clin. Neurophysiol.*, 1950, 2, 227. (Abstract)

KIRK, D. L., & BAUER, A. M. Effects of Reserpine (Serpasil) on emotionally maladjusted high grade mental retardates. *Amer. J. ment. Defic.*, 1956, 60, 779–784.

KUHNKE, E. An objective proof of reflex immobilization in humans. *Z. Psychother. med. Psychol.*, 1952, 5, 208–213.

LANSING, R. W. Relation of brain and tremor rhythms to visual reaction time. *EEG. clin. Neurophysiol.*, 1957, 9, 497–504.

LANSING, R. W., SCHWARTZ, E., & LINDSLEY, D. B. Reaction time and EEG activation under alerted and nonalerted conditions. *J. exp. Psychol.*, 1959, 58, 1–7.

LAUFER, M. W., & DENHOFF, E. Hyperkinetic behavior syndrome in children. *J. Pediatr.*, 1957, 50, 463–474.

LAUFER, M. W., DENHOFF, E., & RUBIN, E. Z. Photo-Metrazol activation in children. *EEG. clin. Neurophysiol.*, 1954, 6, 1–8.

LAUFER, M. W., DENHOFF, E., & SOLOMONS, G. Hyperkinetic impulse disorder in children's behavior problems. *Psychosom. Med.*, 1957, 19, 38–49.

LEVIN, P. M. Restlessness in children. *Arch. Neurol. Psychiat.*, 1938, 39, 764–770.

LIPPMAN, H. S. Restlessness in infancy. *J. Amer. Med. Ass.*, 1928, 91, 1848–1852.

LIPSITT, L. P., & DeLUCIA, C. A. An apparatus for the measurement of specific response and general activity of the human neonate. *Amer. J. Psychol.*, 1960, 73, 630–632.

MACCOLL, K. Chlorpromazine hydrochloride (Largectil) in the treatment of the disturbed mental defective. *Amer. J. ment. Defic.*, 1956, 61, 378–389.

MCKINNEY, J. P. A multidimensional study of the behavior of severely retarded boys. Unpublished doctoral dissertation, Ohio State Univer., 1961.

MARQUIS, D. P. Can conditioned responses be established in the newborn infant? *J. genet. Psychol.*, 1931, 39, 479–492.

MELTZOFF, J., SINGER, J. L., & KORCHIN, S. J. Motor inhibition and Rorschach movement responses: a test of the sensory-tonic theory. *J. Pers.*, 1953, 21, 400–410.

MITCHELL, W. G. Differentiation of activity of three mouse strains with magnetic pickup apparatus. *Science*, 1959, 130, 455.

MONTGOMERY, K. C. The effect of activity deprivation upon exploratory behavior. *J. comp. physiol. Psychol.*, 1953, 46, 438–441. (a)

MONTGOMERY, K. C. The effect of the hunger and thirst drives upon exploratory behavior. *J. comp. physiol. Psychol.*, 1953, 46, 315–319. (b)

MORGAN, C. T. *Introduction to psychology.* (2nd ed.) New York: McGraw-Hill, 1961.

MORGAN, C. T., & STELLAR, E. *Physiological psychology.* New York: McGraw-Hill, 1950.

MORUZZI, G., & MAGOUN, H. W.   Brain stem reticular formation and activation of the EEG. *EEG clin. Neurophysiol.*, 1949, 1, 455–473.

MURPHY, J. P., & GELLHORN, E.   The influence of hypothalamic stimulation on cortically induced movements and on action potentials of the cortex. *J. Neurophysiol.*, 1945, 8, 341–364.

NOCE, R. H., WILLIAMS, D. B., & RAPAPORT, W.   Reserpine (Serpasil) in management of mentally ill. *J. Amer. med. Ass.*, 1955, 158, 11–15.

OUNSTED, C.   Hyperkinetic syndrome in epileptic children. *Lancet,* 1955, 2, 303–311.

PRAST, J. W.   Electroencephalography during motion. *EEG clin. Neurophysiol.,* 1950, 2, 230–231. (Abstract)

PRATT, K. C.   The neonate. In L. Carmichael (Ed.), *Manual of child psychology.* New York: Wiley, 1946.

PRATT, K. C., NELSON, A. K., & SUN, K. H.   *The behavior of the newborn infant.* Columbus: Ohio State Univer. Press, 1930.

RABINOVITCH, M. S., KENNARD, M. A., & FISTER, W. P.   Personality correlates of electroencephalographic patterns: Rorschach findings. *Canad. J. Psychol.*, 1955, 9, 29–41.

REED, J. D.   Spontaneous activity of animals. *Psychol. Bull.,* 1017, 11, 393–412.

REITIG, J. H.   Chlorpromazine for the control of psychomotor excitement in the mentally deficient. *J. nerv. ment. Dis.*, 1955, 122, 190–194.

RICHARDS, T. W.   The relationship between bodily and gastric activity of newborn infants. II. Simultaneous variations in the bodily and gastric activity of newborn infants under long-continued light stimulation. *Human Biol.*, 1936, 8, 381–386.

RICHTER, C. P.   Behavior cycles in man and animals. *Science,* 1953, 117, 470. (Abstract)

RICHTER, C. P.   Behavior and metabolic cycles in animals and men. In P. H. Hoch and J. Zubin (Eds.), *Experimental psychopathology.* New York: Grune & Stratton, 1957. Pp. 34–54.

RICHTER, C. P., & UHLENHUTH, E. H.   Comparison of effects of gonadectomy on spontaneous activity of wild and domesticated Norway rats. *Endocrinology,* 1954, 54, 311–322.

SAINSBURY, P.   A method of measuring spontaneous movements by time-sampling motion pictures. *J. ment. Sci.,* 1954, 100, 742–748.

SCHULMAN, J. L., LIPKIN, N. P., CLARINDA, M., & MITCHELL, J.   Studies on activity level in children. Paper read at Amer. Psychiatr. Ass., Chicago, May, 1961.

SCHULMAN, J. L., & REISMAN, J. M.   An objective measure of hyperactivity. *Amer. J. ment. Defic.*, 1959, 64, 455–456.

SHIRLEY, N.   Spontaneous activity. *Psychol. Bull.*, 1929, 26, 341–365.

SIEGEL, P. S.   A simple electronic device for the measurement of gross bodily activity of small animals. *J. Psychol.*, 1946, 21, 277–286.

SINGER, J. L., & HERMANN, J.   Motor and fantasy correlates of Rorschach human movement responses. *J. consult. Psychol.*, 1954, 18, 325–331.

SINGER, J. L., MELTZOFF, J., & GOLDMAN, G. D.   Rorschach movement responses following motor inhibition and hyperactivity. *J. consult. Psychol.*, 1952, 16, 359–364.

SINGER, J. L., & SPOHN, H. E.   Some behavioral correlates of Rorschach's experience-type. *J. consult. Psychol.*, 1954, 18, 1–9.

SPRADLIN, J. E., CROMWELL, R. L., & FOSHEE, J. G.   Studies in activity level. III. Effects of auditory stimulation in organics, familials, hyperactives, and hypoactives. *Amer. J. ment. Defic.*, 1959, 64, 754–757.

SPROGIS, G. R., LEZDINS, V., WHITE, S. D., MING, D., LANNING, M., DRAKE, M. E., & WYCKOFF, G· Comparative study on Thorazine and Serpasil in the mental defective. *Amer. J. ment. Defic.*, 1957, 61, 737–742.

STAMM, J. S. On the relationship between reaction time to light and latency of blocking of the alpha rhythm. *EEG clin. Neurophysiol.*, 1952, 4, 61–68.

STENGEL, E., OLDHAM, A. J., & EHRENBERG, A. S. C. Reactions of low grade mental defectives to pain. *J. ment. Sci.*, 1958, 104, 434–438.

STERN, J. A. The effect of frontal cortical lesions on activity wheel and open-field behavior. *J. genet. Psychol.*, 1957, 90, 203–212.

STEVENS, S. S. Rectilinear rectification applied to voltage integration. *Electronics,* 1942, 15 (1), 40–41.

STRAUSS, A. A., & KEPHART, N. C. *Psychopathology and education of the brain-injured child.* Vol. II. *Progress in theory and clinic.* New York: Grune & Stratton, 1955.

STRAUSS, A. A., & LEHTINEN, L. E. *Psychopathology and education of the brain-injured child.* New York: Grune & Stratton, 1947.

STRONG, P. N., JR. Activity in the white rat as a function of apparatus and hunger. *J. comp. physiol. Psychol.*, 1957, 50, 596–600.

TAINTER, M. L. The effects of certain analeptic drugs on spontaneous running activity of the white rat. *J. comp. Psychol.*, 1943, 36, 143–155.

THOMPSON, W. R., MELZACK, R., & SCOTT, T. H. "Whirling behavior" in dogs as related to early experience. *Science,* 1956, 123, 939.

TIMBERLAKE, W. H., BELMONT, E. H., & OGONIK, J. The effect of Reserpine on 200 mentally retarded children. *Amer. J. ment. Defic.*, 1957, 62, 61–66.

WARDELL, D. W., RUBIN, H. K., & ROSS, R. T. The use of Reserpine and chlorpromazine in disturbed mentally deficient patients. *Amer. J. ment. Defic.*, 1958, 63, 330–344.

WATSON, P. D., DIMASCIO, A., KANTER, S. S., SUTER, E., & GREENBLATT, M. A note on the influence of climatic factors of psychophysiological investigations. *Psychosom. Med.*, 1957, 19, 419–423.

WOLFENSBERGER, W. P., MILLER, M. B., FOSHEE, J. G., & CROMWELL, R. L. Rorschach correlates of activity level in high school children. *J. consult. Psychol.,* 1962, 26, 269–272.

ZAPOROZHETS, A. V. The development of voluntary movements. In B. Simon (Ed.), *Psychology in the Soviet Union.* Stanford: Stanford, 1957. Pp. 108–114.

ZAPOROZHETS, A. V. *Development of voluntary movements.* Moscow: The Publishing House, Academy of Pedagogical Sciences, 1960.

21

ACADEMIC SKILLS

Lorene Childs Quay

This chapter will discuss research related to academic skill development in the mentally retarded. Since the retarded at the lower end of the intelligence scale (IQ below 50) have not been demonstrated to be capable of developing academic skills to any appreciable extent, the concern here will be with those retardates classified for educational purposes as educable. They are defined as retardates "capable of some degree of achievement in traditional academic subjects such as reading and arithmetic . . ." (Heber, 1959, p. 98). The IQ range for this group is from 50 to 75 or 80. Although basic learning research is related to academic skill development, it will not be reviewed here because it is the major emphasis of other chapters. Educational procedures, including educational placement, curriculum development, and teaching method, are related to the development of academic skills; and this chapter will review theories, philosophies, and research on such educational procedures. At present these procedures are based mainly on subjective experience and untested assumptions, rather than on research. However, when the methodological problems involved in the conduct of research of this nature are considered, the paucity of adequate research is understandable. Before research contributions are reviewed, some of these methodological problems—the criterion problem, the sampling problem, and the problem of experimental controls—will be discussed.

The last part of the chapter will be a review of research on academic skills, per se, and on the relationship of other variables to the development of such skills.

METHODOLOGICAL PROBLEMS

The criterion problem

A prerequisite for evaluating educational procedures for the retarded is the development of criteria of effectiveness. It is difficult to find agreement on a single criterion, perhaps because educators have conceptualized such a wide variety of educational objectives and because objectives are often stated in extremely general terms. However, most writers (Kirk & Johnson, 1951) suggest that the educational objectives include occupational adequacy, social competence, and personal adequacy, all of which would seem to involve some academic achievement. Thus, the development of multiple criteria of effectiveness seems to be necessary. These criteria, with whatever differential weights they might have, need to be made explicit.

The second problem relating to criteria is the criterion measure. If the criterion is academic achievement, the available measures, standardized achievement tests, would seem to be adequate. However, their content validity might be inadequate for the retarded. That is, the items might not adequately sample the types of academic material which the retarded are expected to master, since most curricula planned for the retarded are based on the concrete and designed to have direct practical value. Standardized achievement tests sample the more abstract content of the standard curriculum. However, at the level of achievement expected of the retarded, whether content validity is a problem is perhaps questionable; it needs to be evaluated.

A problem in the measurement of achievement which occurs in comparisons of retarded and normal or bright subjects (Ss) is statistical regression. It is not uncommon to find studies showing greater gains in achievement for the retarded than for the normal, although these gains might simply be a function of regression toward the mean.

If the criterion of effectiveness is personal adequacy, measurement problems are even more acute. Most present personality measures, when used with normal children and adolescents for whom they were constructed, present numerous measurement problems. These instruments are likely to be completely inapplicable to the mentally retarded, who were not represented in their construction. Most investigators attempt to avoid this problem by developing measures of their own, often without validating them before using them in their research.

Many criteria of occupational adequacy have been used, examples being wages, length of time on the job, and employer ratings. Obtaining objective measures of many of these criteria may involve complex decisions. For example, such variables as wages and number of days worked are affected by absences due to illness or other such factors. The researcher has the problem of ascertaining whether the failure is actually due to factors beyond the S's control or whether he is malingering. In their attempts to handle this problem, most investigators exclude the absentee employee from their samples. However, in a comparison of two educational procedures, if one of the samples has had more Ss excluded for absenteeism, that sample is a selective one, biased in favor of the healthy. The interpretation of more malingering in the group having the exclusions might be more appropriate than the interpretation of greater occupational competence. Investigators should at least compare groups for such exclusions. In a discussion of this general problem in research, Campbell and Stanley (1961) recommend that exclusions not be made. They point out that while including these failures in the sample would attenuate the effects of one of the types of treatment, it would avoid sampling bias.

The sampling problem

Sampling affects both the internal validity of an experiment and the extent to which the results can be generalized. Most research in this area is replete with sampling difficulties in both the selection of individuals for various kinds of treatment and in the selection of the larger sample from which the individuals to be studied are chosen. Examples of these sampling problems are particularly apparent in research comparing educational placement procedures. Comparisons of special-class and regular-class placement in which the experimenter was able to preselect the subjects have not been made. Instead of using groups composed of randomly selected Ss, investigators, out of necessity, have used groups that were previously constituted. Two groups so selected are not comparable because of the bias of the educational practitioner in nominating the candidates for various types of placement. Special-class nominees are likely to have more exaggerated problems than retardates retained in the regular classroom, such as lower achievement, more physical defects which interfere with learning, and lower mean intelligence. Thus, the comparison is actually between retardates who are at the lower end of the scale and retardates who are at the upper end of the scale on many dimensions. It would be surprising if differences did not favor the regular-class group.

Some researchers (Blatt, 1958; Cassidy & Stanton, 1959) have attempted to equalize the groups by selecting the regular-class Ss from communities not having special classes. The notion is that retardates with exaggerated problems will be represented in the regular class. However, it is still unlikely that the groups are comparable because of the probability that the regular-class group will include a wide range of retardates, some of whom present no problems, while the special-class group from a different community will include retardates having a narrow range of severe problems. The difference should be reflected by variances within each group. Indeed, Blatt (1958) found larger standard deviations for his regular-class group on all physical and achievement measures; and in the Cassidy and Stanton study (1959) the standard deviation was larger for the regular-class group on all five subtests of the Stanford Achievement Test, although whether these differences were significant was not analyzed. Further, Cassidy and Stanton's difficulty in finding school children with IQs in the 50 to 59 range in communities not having special classes suggests that the two groups are not comparable intellectually. Presumably, special classes, were they available, would accommodate many retarded in this range, but regular classes do not.

The problem in the selection of the larger community from which the research sample is drawn is frequently overlooked. Often, investigators send letters to superintendents and principals requesting permission to use their school systems for research. They then use samples from schools whose administrators grant such permission. Since permission is likely to be granted by the most progressive administrators, or by those who wish to improve their program, the sample is biased. The use of this sampling procedure is especially unsatisfactoi, in the selection of regular-class *S*s from schools not having special classes. The resulting comparison may be between special-class retardates and regular-class retardates from schools having progressive administrators and teachers.

The use of this selection procedure to compare special classes and regular classes from the same community also restricts generalizations. The school staff which is motivated to cooperate in a research project is probably one which is enlightened concerning individual differences and motivated to deal with them effectively. In this situation regular-class teachers are likely to use specialized techniques and materials with the retarded in their classes. The regular teacher than "becomes a special education teacher in every important sense of the word" (Graham, 1959, p. 16), and comparisons are likely to yield no differences between the two treatments. On the other hand, a comparison in a school where the regular teachers do not perform at such a high level might yield the opposite results, indicating that the special teacher is far more effective; but the researcher is less likely to be invited to study this kind of situation. Findings concerning the effects of a specific program in the school are contaminated by the attitudes and practices in that particular school.

Although it is necessary for one who is doing research in an academic setting to use *S*s from such selective schools, the findings cannot be generalized to the universe of retardates irrespective of the school system in which they are found. Instead, findings concerning the effectiveness of differential treatment must be generalized only to the kinds of schools which volunteer to cooperate in research. This sampling difficulty might seem to be of minor significance in view of the more apparent sampling problems. However, this consideration suggests that in evaluating the effectiveness of any educational procedure, teacher, school, and community variables must be considered; and the interaction of such variables with the procedure should be evaluated.

The adverse effects of subject attrition have been mentioned in the discussion of the criterion problem, though more appropriately this is a sampling problem which seriously hampers the extent to which results can be generalized. This problem is almost always encountered in follow-up studies because of the difficulty in locating all the *S*s selected for the sample. Theoretically, *S*s who cannot be located may be either very poorly adjusted (in terms of instability) or very well adjusted (in simply being able to be absorbed into society); but, either way, their exclusion biases the results. Frequently an investigator handles this problem by substituting an available *S* for the one which cannot be located, but too rarely does he indicate how many *S*s had to be substituted in the various groups. A related problem is that of excluding *S*s from the statistical analysis for various reasons. An example of this practice is found in a postschool comparison of the weekly income of regular-class and special-class retardates (Carriker, 1957). The investigator concluded that there was no significant difference between the groups, but he excluded four *S*s from the special-class group because the information was unavailable on three of them and the other had been institutionalized. In the regular-class group only one S was excluded for lack of information. The institutionalized S from the special-class group apparently could not maintain himself in society. Quite probably, had this information been included in the analysis, the regular-class group would have significantly surpassed the special-class group in income (even with the exclusion, the absolute difference was in favor of the regular-class group).

The problem of experimental controls

A problem which is too broad to discuss in detail here, but which should be mentioned, is that of experimental control. Usually, when research is done in the schools, it is done at the convenience of school personnel. While a desire to protect the school from upheaval is understandable in view of the job the school is expected to do, such protection will prevent experimental manipulations which would permit unambiguous results. If definitive results are to be obtained, the research worker must be allowed to do such things as prescribe differential treatment for different groups, select the Ss within each group so as to minimize the effects of confounding variables, and control such variables as time and place of administering the treatment and evaluating its effects. While allowing the experimenter such freedom would temporarily inconvenience the educational practitioner, it might offer him solutions to some of the practical problems which have plagued him for years.

EDUCATIONAL PROCEDURES

In spite of the multitude of problems, some research has been attempted, often with the realization on the part of the researcher that it has been impossible to surmount some of the problems considered above. Many researchers have had to incorporate existing conditions into their research instead of designing studies with rigorous controls. This section will review research designed to yield information concerning the effectiveness of placement, curriculum, and method. To be reviewed a study must meet the following criteria: a control group must have been used, inferential statistics must have been employed in comparing groups, and significance levels must have been reported.

Placement

The three major types of placement for the educable mentally retarded are regular class, special class, and residential school, the largest group being in the regular class and the smallest group in residential schools. Other placement procedures, which involve only a minority of retardates, are special day schools, programs for the homebound, and regular-class programs with periodic help from an itinerant teacher (Dunn & Capobianco, 1959). However, only special- and regular-class placement procedures have been evaluated by studies meeting the criteria for inclusion in this review.

Only in recent years has any systematic research been attempted. Nevertheless, special education has greatly expanded during the last few years. Much energy has gone into planning programs, curricula, and teaching methods. A vast literature is filled with reports of efforts to make special-class placement effective. However, these efforts need to be empirically evaluated.

Although the research on the effectiveness of special-class placement is meager, some attempts have been made. The research reviewed in this section has been unable to overcome some of the problems discussed above, but it is important research in that it is a first attempt to bring some controls to an evaluation of placement procedures.

For comparing special- and regular-class placement various criteria of effectiveness have been used, including achievement test scores, intelligence test scores, physical or motor measures, speech responses, and adjustment as measured by both questionnaires and specific behavior in various situations (e.g., number of court referrals, marriage, income, financial self-sufficiency).

In the early 1930s Bennett (1932), Wassman (1933), and Pertsch (1936) compared the achievement of regular-class and special-class retardates in single school systems. Each found regular-class *S*s to be slightly superior in achievement to special-class *S*s. Bennett and Wassman felt that the differences between the groups were due to selective factors in placement. Pertsch concluded that instruction was inferior in special classes. Cowen (1938), in an attempt to determine whether the lower achievement of special-class *S*s was a function of selection, studied the amount of gain in achievement for the two groups. He found that the special-class group made greater gains. Whether statistical regression accounted for the results cannot be determined.

Blatt (1958) compared special-class and regular-class retardates on a number of variables. By selecting his regular-class *S*s from communities not having special classes, Blatt felt that he had handled the problem of sampling bias as adequately as he could. Children in special classes had significantly more physical defects than those in regular classes. Special-class *S*s were shown to be more socially mature and emotionally stable on scales having no established validity or reliability, but there were no differences between the groups on the California Test of Personality or on delinquency and behavior records. While there was no significant difference between the two groups in academic achievement as measured by the Total Achievement Scores of the California Achievement Tests, a comparison of achievement from year to year revealed that special-class *S*s made significantly greater annual improvement in reading than did regular-class *S*s. The finding concerning physical defects points to one possible selection bias, since these defects obviously were not caused by the special class. The finding concerning academic achievement also appears to be a function of sampling. Since the special-class group made greater gains than the regular-class group yet did not differ from it at the end of 2 years' differential treatment, the *S*s in that group had to be lower in achievement at the time they were placed.

The remainder of the studies comparing special-class and regular-class placement have been done with the support of the U.S. Office of Education. Carriker (1957) compared Nebraska special-class and regular-class retardates on postschool adjustment. He obtained the following results: (1) there were significantly more court referrals from the special-class group while they were in school, but no difference between the groups in postschool law violations; (2) no significant difference was found in weekly wages earned, although the mean wage for the control group was slightly higher (four exclusions were made from the special-class group, one because of institutionalization; one exclusion was made from the regular-class group); (3) the special-class group received a significantly higher mean rating from their employers; (4) a greater percentage of *S*s from the regular-class group were financially self-sufficient, but whether the difference was statistically significant was not reported; (5) the greatest majority of both groups were in semiskilled and unskilled occupations, although a few more *S*s from the regular-class group were in the higher-level occupational classifications.

Some data were presented on in-school adjustment: (1) the regular-class group was significantly older than the special-class group at the time of leaving school, having remained in school longer; (2) no significant difference was found between the two groups in absences during their school enrollment; (3) no differences were found in the number of absences for the special-class group when the prior period of enrollment in the regular class was compared with the period of enrollment in the special class.

Carriker's study was a follow-up study, the *S*s having been selected several years after they left school. This type of study involves a sampling problem in addition to those problems previously discussed. That is, the group of regular-class retardates had not been identified while they were in school. Thus, screening had to be done from cumulative record material which was several years old. After such screening, however, the investigator administered individual intelligence tests to the regular-class *S*s and matched the groups on intelligence. Since it was impossible to locate all of the *S*s selected from the records, exclusion figures were quite high for the regular-class group. The number excluded in the special-class group was not reported.

Concerning employment, Carriker concluded:

> It appears, from the available data in this study, that subjects from the experimental group (special class) have fared as well or better than the subjects from the control group (regular class) in terms of employment status. This, the writer feels, it important because in relation to the subjects from the control group, the subjects from the experimental group, as a whole are approximately one year younger, have been in school approximately one and one-half years less, and probably were less adjusted most of their years in school (1957, pp. 118–119).

However, a contrary conclusion is just as plausible. In view of cost involved, society might expect special-class retardates to fare *better* than regular-class retardates. Actually, they surpassed regular-class *S*s on only one measure, employer ratings on which the reliability was not reported. The fact that special-class retardates left school earlier than regular-class retardates might indicate that the special class did not have the holding power that the regular class had. This would raise a question concerning whether the special class is of benefit in providing a place of security and happiness for the retardate.

Cassidy and Stanton (1959) compared a group of special-class retardates from 16 different systems with a group of regular-class retardates from 20 school systems which had no special classes. The samples were stratified on age and IQ. No differences between the groups were obtained on the following tests: (1) Ammons Picture Vocabulary Test, (2) Goldstein-Sheerer Stick Test, (3) Kent E-G-Y, Scales A and D. Significant differences in favor of the special-class group were obtained on: (1) thirty select items from the California Test of Personality (these items were selected on the basis of a prior validity study using retarded *S*s), (2) Goodenough Draw-a-Man, raw score and total score, (3) Raven's Coloured Progressive Matrices, (4) WISC Block Designs Sub-Test, and (5) WISC Coding Sub-Test. It is difficult to interpret these differences, and their practical significance is not clear. The crucial difference, significant at the 1 per cent level of confidence, occurred on the Stanford Achievement Test and favored the regular-class group.

Thurstone and her associates (1959) compared the scores of regular-class and special-class retardates on the Stanford Achievement Test at an initial testing and at a second testing approximately 1 year later. They also compared the two groups on 1-year gains. On both the initial testing and the second testing, regular-class *S*s were significantly higher than special-class *S*s on all measures except arithmetic computation. This finding was also obtained when separate comparisons based on race, sex, age (6 to 10, 11 to 13, 14 to 16) and IQ (50 to 59, 60 to 69, 70 to 79) were made. The average time in the special class at the first testing was approximately one year, the range being from 4 months to over 46 months. An analysis of the gains in achievement over a 1-year period revealed no significant differences between the special- and regular-class groups.

This research apparently gives evidence of selectivity in placement and of biased findings resulting from selectivity. Even after the two groups made equal gains during a year's interval, the final comparison had to show lower achievement in special-class *S*s than in regular-class *S*s because of the difference in achievement at the initial testing. Assuming that statistical regression does not account for the achievement gains, special-class placement might actually be instrumental in equalizing the gains, since the special-class *S*s apparently had not kept pace with the regular-class *S*s prior to their placement in the special class. Perhaps the first few years in the special class are a warming-up period, a kind of readiness period, which emotionally or experience-wise prepares the retardate for later achievement. A follow-up study would provide evidence concerning whether the special-class *S*s continue to make gains which equal or surpass the gains of the regular-class *S*s. A study of achievement gains as related to number of years in special class would also be informative on this point.

In a comparison of the two groups on personal and social traits, special-class pupils fared better than did those in the regular class. Social acceptance was measured with a sociometric technique. Retardates in special classes were chosen by their classmates more frequently than were retardates in regular classes. Personal traits were measured by teacher ratings, the special-class teachers giving higher ratings than the regular-class teachers to the retarded in their respective classrooms. Neither of these measures permit an adequate comparison, and the conclusion that special-class retardates are superior on social and personal traits is not warranted. First, although the special-class retardates were told that they could choose children on the sociometric device from the general population, it is reasonable to expect them to name the children who are present at the time they take the test. Second, on the basis of their experiences, special-class teachers are likely to have lower internal norms for personal traits in children than are regular-class teachers.

Wilson (1960) compared special-class and regular-class retardates on various language and speech measures. Holding MA and social age constant, she found no significant difference between the two groups of younger retardates on the primary form of the Stanford Achievement word meaning test. She found a significant difference in favor of the older regular-class group on the elementary form of the test. Although the differences between the groups on the Dolch Basic Sight Vocabulary and the number of words used were not significant, the direction of all the differences was in favor of the regular-class groups. Generalizations from these results are not warranted, since Wilson's sample apparently was drawn from a Southern Negro population, and the sample was obtained by selecting schools whose administrators granted permission for the research in response to a written request.

The most that can be said for studies on placement is that the results are inconclusive. Not a single study has demonstrated that special-class placement is more effective than regular-class placement when the criterion of effectiveness is achievement. In fact, three of the four studies which used achievement as a criterion found regular-class retardates to be superior. However, two studies (Cowen, 1938; Blatt, 1958) showed greater yearly achievement gains in the special-class group and one study (Thurstone, 1960) showed equal gains for the two groups. These findings might suggest that the special class is more effective than final comparisons indicate. The results on adjustment are equivocal. Although the results of teacher ratings and personality questionnaires seemed to indicate that special-class retardates were superior, behavioral measures of adjustment did not differentiate between the groups. However, it should be pointed out that because of sampling problems and other methodological difficulties, special-class placement has not received an adequate evaluation.

Many observers feel that, regardless of the outcome, special-class placement is important from a humanitarian point of view. They point out that the special class places the retarded child with others who are similar to him, thus preventing frustration and feelings of inferiority derived from undue competition. These observers base their opinions on the study by Johnson (1959), which indicated that retarded children in the regular class were likely to be social isolates. Their subjective criterion of placement effectiveness is social acceptance, but is this a realistic criterion in view of the postschool adjustments required of the retardates? Whether the perceptions of the educator who views special-class placement as humanitarian coincide with the perceptions of the retarded who, in spite of the social difficulties involved, might still prefer the regular class is also questionable. It is possible that the retarded are better able to perceive that they are isolated from their normal peers when the isolation is physical than when it is social; therefore, they might have stronger negative feelings about being physically isolated. A study of the preferences of the retarded would contribute to the humanitarian's understanding of this problem.

Educators have interpreted the results of the research on special-class placement in various ways. Some have suggested that the retarded profit from the stimulation of being in a classroom with normal children. Others have suggested that special classes have a detrimental effect on motivation. One explanation might be conformity. Retarded children in the regular class might attempt to conform to the norm of that group, whereas children in the special class conform to the norm there. The difference in performance, then, would be accounted for by the difference in the norms. The most reasonable explanation is inadequate sampling, but it would be profitable to an understanding of the retarded to test the other hypotheses which have been suggested.

In an evaluation of the effectiveness of special-class placement, avoiding the methodological problems previously discussed would not be impossible. One way to surmount the sampling problem would be to initiate research in communities not having special classes. All children who are eligible for special-class placement could be identified and randomly assigned to various treatment groups. Criterion performance could be measured at specific intervals or at the end of the experiment, depending on the hypotheses to be tested. A way of handling the sampling problem in communities having special education is to identify retardates during their first year of school and randomly assign them to the treatment groups. The effects of community and teacher differences should be assessed or controlled.

There is a need for identifying variables which might interact with type of placement to yield a higher level of performance. Thus, teacher and pupil characteristics should be studied to determine whether certain kinds of teachers are more effective in special classes and whether special classes are more effective for some types of retardates than for others. Cronbach's statement best summarizes this position: "Applied psychologists should deal with treatments and persons simultaneously. Treatments are characterized by many dimensions; so are persons. . . . For any practical problem, there is some best group of treatments to use and some best allocation of persons to treatments. We can expect some attributes of persons to have strong interactions with treatment variables" (1957, p. 680). Actually, many person variables, such as age, sex, race, and intelligence level, have been studied in relation to academic achievement, and this research will be reviewed later. The interaction of these and other variables with educational treatment needs to be systematically studied.

Curriculum and method

Since curriculum and method are closely related, both will be presented in this section. A discussion of specific curriculum practices is beyond the scope of this chapter. A detailed review of these practices has been provided by Kirk and Johnson (1951). Wolk (1958) describes several trends in curriculum for the retarded: (1) studying the standard curriculum more slowly, (2) following the normal course of study with such modifications as are necessary because of personal limitations, and (3) emphasizing social development rather than academic development.

Kirk and Johnson (1951), summarizing present-day curriculum practices, point out that the curriculum must consider two major areas; the development of skills in the tool subjects, and experience in the areas of living. Differences among curriculum makers can be accounted for by differences of emphasis on these areas. Some (Inskeep, 1926) emphasize the development of skills in the tool subjects, patterning the curriculum of the special class after the standard curriculum. Others (Ingram, 1953) emphasize activities or units of experience, relating academic skills to these activities as they are needed.

Although the relative effectiveness of these approaches has not been empirically tested, at least in terms of the criterion of occupational self-sufficiency, both considerations seem to be important. Personal and social adequacy, as well as some academic skill, are necessary to job success. The familiar reviews of Engel (1952) and DiMicheal (1950) have indicated that factors such as ability to work with others, punctuality, courtesy, trustworthiness, ability to follow instructions, and appearance are more important in job performance than ability to do the work. Further, Shafter (1957), comparing occupationally successful and unsuccessful retardates who had been institutionalized, found that there was no differentiation between them in their ability to read, write, and tell time. Since the IQ range was not reported, it might be assumed that these Ss were so low intellectually that academic skills were not important in the kinds of jobs they could do. At any rate, the results of these studies would point to the importance of special training in good personal and social habits and attitudes. However, in an analysis of jobs held by the educable, Young (1958) found some academic skills to be required by practically all jobs. Too, some respect must be accorded standard curriculum practice since it has been tested by experience. Over the years many successful approaches have been retained and many unsuccessful ones discarded. These practices have been studied and evaluated and, with modifications and revisions, have stood the test of time. Whether they are appropriate for the retarded is perhaps questionable, but discarding the old for the new without rigid tests of their relative effectiveness is an unwise procedure.

A knowledge of the learning characteristics of the retarded would have important implications for both curriculum and method. Much educational practice is presently based on conflicting opinions concerning whether the retarded are quantitatively or qualitatively different from normals. Some educators (Hollingworth, 1920) feel that the retarded are only quantitatively different from normals and do not require special curricula and teaching methods; others (Baker, 1953) think the retarded are qualitatively different and do require specialized techniques.

One specific issue is whether basing educational practice on the mental age concept is a valid procedure. Although there is high agreement among authorities that MA is the best measure of achievement expectancy, Bijou (1952) states that from a learning-teaching point of view, the retarded child is different from the normal child of comparable mental age in that the retarded child appears unable to progress academically at the level expected on the basis of his mental age. If children of the same MA, regardless of IQ, are similar, teaching the standard curriculum more slowly would seem to be appropriate. If they are not similar, a different approach would be indicated.

Research in basic learning theory, reviewed in other chapters, should be of practical value in the education of the retarded. Sloan and Berg have pointed out that "a cardinal feature of mental retardation has been the defect in learning ability. Meticulous study of this area is imperative for the development of techniques of training and teaching of the retarded group" (1957, p. 565). Unfortunately, learning studies have yielded conflicting results. McPherson (1958) has said that the reason for the conflicting results probably lies in the fact that the various studies use different motivating techniques, study different aspects of learning, use different methods of sampling, and use *S*s of different intellectual levels and etiology.

More extensive and better-integrated investigations and replications should permit a complete description of the learning characteristics of the retarded and thus should influence educational practice. However, if the reports of these learning investigations are to be useful in describing learning characteristics for practical purposes, they must include more data on the characteristics of their *S*s. Many investigators simply do not describe their populations. Often such data as CA and MA are omitted, with only IQs being reported. In other studies CA and IQ are omitted, and data on whether or not the *S*s are institutionalized are frequently omitted. While these variables might not be important to the particular theoretical problem being studied, they are essential to the practical application of the results.

In spite of the limitations, some tentative generalizations applicable to educational practice can be made. Tentative though they may be, these generalizations should serve the purpose of stimulating the formation of hypotheses to be tested in the classroom. Since laboratory results cannot be assumed to be directly applicable to the complex classroom situation, these generalizations must be tested in the practical situation.

Many investigations have yielded a significant relationship between intellectual development and learning ability (Ellis, Pryer, Distefano, & Pryer, 1960; Ellis & Sloan, 1959; McCulloch, Reswick, & Roy, 1955). These studies have supported Hull's notion that individual differences in intelligence affect the rate and asymptote of learning but not the basic form of learning. These studies give some support to educators who would base educational practice on the notion of quantitative, rather than qualitative, differences between the retarded and the normal. However, conflicting evidence is presented when different populations are studied. For example, trainable *S*s appear to be qualitatively different from normal and educable *S*s of the same MA (Girardeau, 1959; Martin & Blum, 1960). These findings suggest the possibility that some types of retarded are different from other types in their intellectual performance. They tend to confirm the commonplace observation by educators that trainables and educables require different educational techniques.

The possibility that learning characteristics of the retarded are similar to those of the normal of the same MA on some tasks but different on others is also suggested. Sloan and Berg (1957) found a significant relationship betwen MA and the learning of meaningful verbal associations but no significant relationship between MA and maze learning. This finding might indicate a need for differential educational treatment in the different areas of education. Indeed, this finding might have some implications for the validity of the educational practice of placing the retarded and normal together and having equal expectations for both in some areas of the curriculum but not in others.

Methods advocated by most special educators are based on the assumption that the ability to form concepts and use symbols to permit delayed reactions is negligible in the retarded. Ingram (1953) states that, because retardates are unable to apply in one situation what they have learned in another and cannot anticipate consequences, they must learn through concrete experiences. Specific methods include teaching with concrete materials, avoiding the abstract, assisting transfer of training, and repeating the same concepts in a variety of situations.

Some knowledge of concept formation and symbolization in the retarded comes from the laboratory. Studying concept formation, Martin and Blum (1960) required *S*s to classify objects in terms of color, form, size, and orientation. They found no differences between normal and educable *S*s of the same MA, but they found differences between mongoloids and the other two groups. Studies by Griffith (1960), Griffith and Spitz (1958), and Griffith, Spitz, and Lipman (1959) suggest that in classifying words, normals are superior to retarded *S*s of the same MA. However, they found that verbal mediators assisted the retarded in forming concepts. That is, success in discovering a similarity between words was related to the number of the words defined in common with a suitable abstraction. Thus, if the *S* used the word big, or a synonym for it, in defining two of the words from the group elephant, mountain, and whale, he was likely to attain the abstraction of size when presented with the group of words. These findings suggest that the teaching of common words for various stimuli and operations should aid the retarded in forming a concept.

Verbal mediators have also been shown to aid in discrimination learning (Cantor & Hottel, 1957) and in delayed reaction (Barnett, Ellis, & Pryer, 1959), supporting the view that the teaching of names for various stimuli and operations is important in assisting symbolic processes and concept formation.

The complaint that motivation for learning is lacking in the retardate is often heard (Bijou, 1952), and many practical incentives are suggested. From the laboratory comes much evidence to support what most teachers of the retarded have already observed: that social approval is an effective incentive. That verbal urging and praise have a positive effect on performance was shown by Ellis and Distefano (1959). Verbal reinforcement also influences verbal response patterns (Barnett, Pryer, & Ellis, 1959). O'Connor and Tizard (1956) found that competition with oneself by using targets to beat is more effective motivation for trainables than constant verbal encouragement. Ellis and Pryer (1958) found that primary reinforcement is no more effective than secondary reinforcement with retarded Ss. All these findings could be incorporated into research on methods of motivating mentally retarded students in the classroom.

One method which has recently received much attention from general educators but scant attention from special educators is teaching machines. Stolurow (1960) raises the question, based on his work with college students, of whether the criterion performance of poorer students might become indistinguishable from that of more able students with this efficient method of learning. He points out that this position is supported by the theoretical position of Woodrow (1946), who thinks that level of intelligence as measured by ability tests is related to the initial level of performance but not to gain scores. Three studies using teaching machines or similar devices with normal and retarded children have yielded conflicting evidence on this point. Ordahl and Ordahl (1915), using a modified typewriter, compared the performance of retarded groups of MA 6, 8, and 10 on a serial learning task. They found a positive relationship between MA and rate of learning, thus providing evidence against Stolurow's position. Conversely, Smith (1959) reported that a program in English grammar designed for ninth graders produced 91 per cent correct responses in seventh-grade slow learners (IQ 75 to 90). Although Smith presented no data on bright students, he felt that the same program could be used for the bright and the dull. He suggested that dull students might require more steps to learn than the bright, but he felt that requiring the bright to take every step might better enable them to retrace their conceptual paths. Smith stated that retention is a problem with the dull, especially when the learner is chronically anxious and when the material to be learned is not meaningful (e.g., spelling). Porter (1959) programmed spelling for second and sixth graders. He found essentially no relationship between IQ and achievement in the experimental groups but a significant positive relationship in the control groups. Thus, his results indicate that low-IQ groups learn spelling just as effectively as high-IQ students by the teaching machine method, but not by the traditional method. However, since he did not report the IQ range, it is not known whether these findings apply to the retarded. Stolurow (1960) states a firm belief that teaching machines will contribute greatly to both special and general education.

Before this method can be said to be effective with the retarded, however, more research is needed, not only to evaluate overall effectiveness, but also to work out many programming problems. Galanter (1959) has considered several problems involved in the nature of optimum teaching machines. Among these problems are the order of presentation of material, the size of the steps, the type of response, and the generalization or testing problem. Since these are important problems not yet solved in general programming, their solution must be equally important to the programming of material for the retarded. Actually, a comprehensive research project under way at the Edward R. Johnstone Training and Research Center is designed to study some of these programming problems in the teaching of reading to the retarded.[1] Until the results of such studies are forthcoming, definite statements concerning the effectiveness of teaching machines for the retarded cannot be made.

While basic research has important implications for general educational practices for the retarded, empirical research on the learning of academic skills (achievement) is also important. This research will be reviewed in the next section.

ACHIEVEMENT

This section will review research on the learning of academic skills by the retarded, including studies of the level of achievement attained by the retarded as compared with the normal. It will also attempt to delineate factors related to achievement in specific skill areas.

It is common practice for educators to use mental age as an index of achievement expectancy. For normal children in regular grades correlations between expected reading achievement based on MA and actual reading achievement have ranged from .50 to .65 (Morphett & Washburne, 1931; Monroe, 1932). Boyle (1959), on the other hand, reported a correlation of .33 for the retarded, the restricted range yielding a lower correlation. Whether MA is a valid predictor of achievement for the mentally retarded is questionable. Surveys comparing expected achievement with actual achievement in the retarded and comparisons of the achievement of retarded and normal Ss of the same MA have yielded some evidence on this point.

Surveys comparing expected and actual achievement have focused on reading and arithmetic, the study of other skill subjects being incidental. Merrill (1921) found special-class retarded Ss with a median MA of 8.8 years to be below their mental age expectancy in achievement. Skill areas listed from most to least retardation were reading, arithmetic, writing, and spelling. Witty and McCafferty (1930) found that Ss in an opportunity school (median MA = 9–6; IQ range = 55 to 71) were below expectancy in all areas except arithmetic fundamentals. Kelly (1934), using special-class retardates, found median reading scores to indicate reading retardation of 1 year. Studying an older special-class group, Mullen (1952) found the mean reading level to be 1.4 years below mental age.

Jacobs (1957) attempted to ascertain whether MA, CA, or IQ was the best predictor of achievement for slow learners in special classes. In his sample the mean IQ was 62.8, and all Ss had a CA below 13 years. The Kuhlmann-Anderson Group Intelligence Test was employed as the measure

[1] Griffith, B. C. Personal communication, 1961.

of MA and IQ. Using total achievement on the California Achievement Battery, he found a correlation with CA of .139, with MA of .695, and with IQ of .668. Although mean total achievement scores were approximately equal to mean expected scores, the Ss were significantly higher in arithmetic than in reading and language and significantly higher in arithmetic fundamentals than in arithmetic reasoning.

Boyle (1959), studying special-class retardates aged 12 to 15, found that their mean reading achievement was lower than the level predicted by the MA even after 1 year of emphasis in reading during which they made significant gains.

Studying both special-class and regular-class retardates, Thurstone (1960) found both groups to be below expectancy on the battery median scores of the Stanford Achievement Test. However, the discrepancy was practically negligible on arithmetic computation. Spelling scores showed most variability. Special-class retardates were significantly below regular-class retardates on all Stanford Achievement Test measures except arithmetic computation.

Bensberg (1953) found the differences between expected and obtained grade achievement not to be significant in institutionalized retardates (IQ range = 38 to 87; mean CA = 18.8; mean MA = 7–11), but the average arithmetic achievement was 1 month below MA, whereas the average reading achievement was 2 months below MA. Using exogenous and endogenous institutionalized retardates, Capobianco (1954) found a discrepancy between performance and MA for the total group on the Compass Survey Test, a test of computational abilities, with the discrepancy being greater for the endogenous Ss. He found a discrepancy for the endogenous but not the exogenous Ss on the Arithmetic Reasoning Test of the Stanford Achievement Test.

The primary concern of studies comparing the achievement of retarded, normal, and bright children having the same MA has also been reading and arithmetic. Few studies have been concerned with achievement in other skill subjects.

In the most comprehensive of arithmetic studies Cruickshank (1948a, 1948b, 1948c) compared institutionalized retardates (mean IQ = 73.3; mean MA = 10.06) with normals (mean IQ = 110.4; mean MA = 9.96). He found normals to be superior to institutionalized retardates in their ability to differentiate extraneous materials from needed arithmetic facts, in arithmetic problem identification and computation, and in all four fundamentals of arithmetic. His results are in agreement with those obtained by Capobianco (1954), who also studied institutionalized retardates.

Using special-class retarded Ss, Merrill (1924) found the performance of the retarded to be below that of normals having the same MA on the Haggerty Group Reading Test, the Kansas Silent Reading Test, the Thorndike Alpha 2 Reading Test, the Woody Arithmetic Fundamentals Test, the Ayres Spelling List, and the Ayres Writing Scales. However, on the Stanford Achievement Tests the retarded and the superior read up to their mental age levels when compared with the age norms in the standardization.

In the most comprehensive of reading studies, Dunn (1954) compared special-class retarded boys (mean CA = 13–3, MA = 9–2) with normal boys (CA = 8 to 10) of the same MA. He found significant differences in favor of normals on: (1) silent reading as measured by the Gates Reading Tests and the Monroe Word Discrimination Test; (2) oral reading as measured by the Gray Oral Reading Tests and the Iowa World Recognition Test; (3) performance on a tachistoscopic test of phrase and word recognition, for both flashed and untimed presentations; and (4) the use of context clues. By analyzing types of reading errors he also found some qualitative differences in the reading process. The types of errors made more frequently by the retarded were faulty vowels, omission of sounds, and refusing or requiring aid on words. The types of errors made more frequently by the normals were repetitions and addition of words. Other errors, including reversals, did not differentiate between the groups. Unfortunately, Dunn also found the normal *S*s to be significantly superior to the retarded on auditory acuity, visual efficiency, home conditions (including cultural level of the home), and social and emotional adjustment, all of which have been related to reading difficulty in normal children. Thus, the obtained results are confounded by these conditions. Dunn must be commended for evaluating and reporting these possibly confounding variables. It is likely that these variables have not been controlled in many studies of this type, particularly those using special-class *S*s, and have been neither evaluated nor reported. Dunn also found the normal group to be significantly superior to the retarded group on oral spelling achievement and arithmetic reasoning, but he found no differences on arithmetic fundamentals.

Klausmeier, Feldhusen, and Check (1959), comparing special-class retardates with average and bright children of the same MA, found that in reading, arithmetic, and language, the retarded were lower than the average, and the average were lower than the bright. Also, on achievement in relation to capacity the same relationships were obtained.

In a comparison of regular-class retarded and bright children of the same MA Bliesmer (1952), using Durrell's Analysis of Reading Difficulty Examination, found no significant differences in reading rate, word recognition, and word meaning. However, significant differences favored the bright on all tests related to comprehension.

Wilson (1926) compared regular-class dull normal (IQ below 96) and bright *S*s of the same MA. He found no differences between the groups on reading and spelling, but the dull group was superior on arithmetic as measured by the Stanford Achievement Test. Torgerson and Shuman (1925) also found regular-class dull (IQ below 96) and bright *S*s achieving on the Thorndike-McCall Reading Tests above their mental age expectancy. In a survey of regular-grade *S*s, McGehee (1939) found that those scoring in the lowest 10 per cent on mental ability showed greater relative general achievement than normal and gifted *S*s on the Unit Scales of Attainment and scored higher on achievement than the MA expectancy.

A reconciliation of such varied results might seem impossible. However, considering the wide variety of measuring instruments and the differences in CA, MA, and IQ levels used, the studies yield surprisingly similar results when they are analyzed in terms of type of educational placement from which the *S*s were drawn. Four of the studies reviewed used institutionalized *S*s; nine used special-class *S*s; one used both special- and regular-class *S*s; and four used regular-class *S*s.

All studies except one using institutionalized *S*s found significant discrepancies from normal on reading and arithmetic reasoning. The studies were equally divided in their findings concerning arithmetic computation, two finding performance below normal, and two finding no significant discrepancy from normal.

All except two studies using special-class *S*s yielded definite discrepancies between actual achievement and that expected on the basis of MA, the performance of the retarded being below normal in all skill subjects studied except arithmetic computation. One study which yielded no discrepancy between actual and expected achievement (Jacobs, 1957) used the Kuhlmann-Anderson Group Intelligence Test as a measure of MA and the California Achievement Battery as a measure of achievement, a combination of instruments not used in other studies. The fact that the results of this study were reported in terms of total achievement and that significant differences were found between reading and arithmetic raises the question of whether a discrepancy might have been found on reading, had reading scores been analyzed separately.

In these studies of special-class *S*s, there is no disagreement with the ordering of skills. On the basis of the size of the discrepancy between actual achievement and expected achievement calculated from MA, the order of skills is as follows: reading, arithmetic reasoning, writing, spelling, and arithmetic computation. Even in the studies in which discrepancies were not significant, reading showed a greater absolute discrepancy than arithmetic.

Studies using regular-class *S*s generally found no significant discrepancies below normal. However, in three of these studies *S*s were dull normals and retarded combined. In the one study using bona fide retarded *S*s, there were no significant discrepancies from normal on any area of reading except comprehension. The one study using both regular- and special-class retarded *S*s found special-class *S*s below regular-class *S*s in all skills except arithmetic computation.

A tentative conclusion based on a synthesis of these results is that a relationship exists between type of placement and achievement discrepancies. Institutionalized retardates tend to show retardation in all academic areas; special-class retardates show no retardation on arithmetic computation but are retarded in all other skill areas. Regular-class retardates show no academic retardation except, as shown by one study, in some areas of reading comprehension. This conclusion must be very tentative, since the results of studies were not in complete agreement and since regular-class *S*s usually included dull normals. However, from this synthesis it might be hypothesized that mental retardation per se does not cause discrepancies between actual achievement and achievement expected on the basis of MA. Instead, as with normal children, other variables must be related to such discrepancies. If this assumption is valid, it would lend further support to the laboratory findings of no difference in performance of retarded and normals of the same MA. Thus, a relationship between intellectual development and learning in academic situations is assumed.

It is likely, in view of previously reviewed studies which demonstrated relationships between other variables and special-class placement, that educational placement is a result, not a cause, of achievement discrepancies. For instance, it might be hypothesized that retardates who have lowest relative achievement show greatest difficulty on other dimensions and are institutionalized; those who are intermediate in achievement are intermediate in other problems and are placed in special classes; and those who achieve most show few related difficulties and are retained in regular classes. An empirical comparison of institutionalized, special-class, and regular-class retardates of the same MA would yield evidence on the validity of the comparison made from a synthesis of research results.

However, if an empirical comparison should support the hypothesis of differences among the groups, it would yield no evidence on the cause of such differential achievement. Research on the cause of differential achievement would be of value in providing a better understanding of failure and in facilitating the prevention or treatment of failure. Since normal children of the same intellectual level vary in achievement and since many factors have been related to such variation, it is reasonable to expect relationships between achievement and other variables in the retarded. Studies of such relationships will be reviewed next. Variables which have been related to achievement, either systematically or incidentally, are teaching method, age, sex, IQ, etiology, length of institutionalization, race, and emotional disturbance.

Teaching method and skill development

Special-class placement can be broadly considered to be a teaching method. The results of studies previously reviewed give no evidence that this method facilitates skill development.

Boyle (1959) studied the effectiveness of different methods of teaching reading to Ss within special classes. Using retarded adolescents, she studied the effects of emphasis on reading and the effects of three different methods of teaching reading—traditional, semiexperience, and experience—on reading programs. She found that emphasis on reading, regardless of the teaching method used, significantly increased reading achievement. No significant differences in achievement resulted from the use of the three teaching methods.

The major finding of this study, that emphasis on reading facilitates reading achievement, supports curriculum planners who emphasize academic rather than social development—if the criterion of curriculum effectiveness is reading achievement. Boyle, in fact, concludes that the most important implication of her study is that special educators should raise their sights when planning programs for the retarded.

Daly and Lee (1960) studied the effects of two methods of grouping on reading speed. Their Ss were institutionalized and had MAs from 6–3 to 10–10. The investigators administered special reading instruction and stimulation to a group which was homogeneous in speed of reading and to a group which was heterogeneous on that dimension. After a 5-month period, they found no difference between the two groups in reading speed.

Klausmeier et al. (1959) reported a study which has implications for the teaching of arithmetic. They used ingenious methodology to grade arithmetic tasks to current levels of achievement. Then they studied acquisition and retention of arithmetic concepts when the material was graded to the achievement level of special-class retarded, average, and bright *S*s of the same MA. On counting, addition, subtraction, and arithmetic problem solving, the retarded acquired material graded to their level of difficulty more slowly than did the average and bright. However, there was no difference among the groups on retention of the material once it was learned. Since one measure of retention was the ability to use previous learning to solve novel problems, this study yielded some evidence that the retarded are able to generalize in a subject matter area. The authors state that an important implication is that teachers should ascertain the present achievement level of each child early in the year, select learnings at next higher levels, and offer individualized or small group instruction to facilitate retention. Although they felt that the arithmetic curriculum does not promote the most efficient learning because it is directed toward the average child, they did not compare this standard practice with their experimental procedure. Of all the studies on learning of academic skills this one is most similar to a laboratory study. The authors conclude that it is possible to conduct well-designed and well-executed studies which use socially useful material to measure acquisition and retention and which grade learning tasks to each child's level of achievement. Actually, similar studies on reading and other skill subjects would yield information on the effectiveness of the procedure of grading tasks to the child's level of achievement in other areas. Such studies, however, would require cooperation at the level of the design between the research worker and the educational practitioner, the practitioner providing types of materials used in the classroom with suggestions of their level of difficulty.

The limited number of studies on specific teaching methods suggests that emphasis on an area facilitates achievement; grading subject matter to the achievement level already attained facilitates retention but not acquisition; and grouping, whether homogeneous or heterogeneous, has no effect on level of achievement.

Age

Thurstone (1960), using a combination of special- and regular-class *S*s, compared the actual achievement in relation to the expected achievement of three age groups: 6 to 10 years, 11 to 13 years, and 14 to 16 years. She obtained significant differences: the younger the child, the higher his achievement in relation to capacity. Groelle (1961) studied reading age, as measured by the Gates Reading Tests, in relation to capacity at three levels: elementary, junior high, and high school. He found the reading age of elementary school *S*s to slightly surpass the MA; that of junior high school *S*s showed some discrepancy below MA; and that of high school *S*s showed marked discrepancy below MA. A replication 3 years later yielded the same results.

Jones, Gross, and Van Why (1960), using institutionalized *S*s, compared three age groups, 16, 17, and 18 years. They found no differences **among** age groups for boys, girls, or both sexes combined on reading scores of the California Test of Achievement. However, the age groups were older adolescents so close in age that the finding of no difference is not surprising.

Both Thurstone (1960) and Groelle (1961) raise the question of whether the schools are as effective in teaching academic skills to older retardates as they are in teaching them to younger retardates. These findings might also suggest that schools are emphasizing areas other than academic ones to the detriment of older groups. This consideration is particularly relevant in view of Boyle's (1959) findings that emphasis on reading was effective with retarded adolescents and in view of the incidental observation of Klausmeier et al. (1959) that children were able to acquire and retain arithmetic learnings considerably beyond those in their present curriculum. These findings suggest that the curriculum at every level needs further evaluation.

Sex

One variable which has been related to achievement in normal children is the sex of the child. Several investigators have shown sex to relate to achievement in the retarded also. The results of studies of both special-class and institutionalized retarded samples have been in agreement that girls achieve in reading significantly higher than boys. The results on arithmetic are inconclusive. Studying a combined group of special- and regular-class retardates, Thurstone (1960) found that the Stanford Achievement Test Battery median was significantly higher for girls than boys. All subtest scores were higher for girls except arithmetic computation, which was higher for boys. Jacobs (1957) also found special-class girls to be significantly higher than special-class boys on reading and language, but not on arithmetic, as measured by the California Achievement Tests. Klausmeier et al. (1959) found that girls have higher total achievement in relation to capacity than boys. Bensberg (1953), using an institutionalized sample, found that females matched with males on MA and CA with a mean CA of 18.8 significantly exceeded males in both reading and arithmetic. Jones et al. (1960), also using an institutionalized sample, ages 16, 17, and 18, found that females significantly exceeded males at each age level on California Achievement Test reading scores.

However, in terms of an interaction of sex and emphasis on reading, Boyle (1959) found no difference between boys and girls in amount of progress in an experimental program which emphasized reading. Both sexes made significant gains. This type of interaction needs further study to ascertain whether boys progress as well as girls with the use of certain teaching methods.

The relationship between sex and reading achievement is the same for retardates as it is for normal children.

Intelligence level

The relationship of IQ to the development of skills in the retarded is important for grouping. Recently, the suggestion that educable retardates of lower intelligence levels (IQ of 50 to 60 or 65) should not be considered educable and should be placed in trainable groups has been made. Studies on IQ and academic skill development should provide some evidence on the validity of that suggestion. The results of these studies might also suggest hypotheses on other grouping procedures for the educable retarded.

Thurstone (1960) compared groups of three different intelligence levels, IQ 50 to 59, 60 to 69, and 70 to 79. She concluded that the less intelligent the group, the better the achievement in relation to ability. Achievement was measured by median scores of the Stanford Achievement Battery. She found that at the beginning of her study regular-class performance was higher than special-class performance for all groups. However, after a year's interval, special-class Ss in the IQ range of 50 to 59 made significantly greater achievement gains than regular-class Ss in that IQ group, but no differences occurred between special and regular-class gains at the other two intelligence levels. This finding suggests that special-class placement compared with regular-class placement might be more effective for retardates at lower intellectual levels than for those at the upper levels.

Using the same IQ intervals that Thurstone used to compare retardates of different intellectual levels, Cassidy and Stanton (1959) found the achievement of regular-class Ss to be higher than that of special-class Ss in the lowest and highest IQ groups, but they found no difference between special and regular-class Ss in the middle (IQ 60 to 69) group. However, since they had great difficulty locating regular-class Ss in the 50 to 59 category, this sample is likely to be a highly selective one.

To study the effects of intellectual factors on progress in an experimental reading program, Boyle (1959) divided her special-class Ss into six IQ levels, each level consisting of an IQ range of five points. She found no relationship between progress and IQ, with the exception that very little progress was made by Ss in the 50 to 54 IQ range. However, since the number of Ss in this range was only six, results cannot be considered reliable.

The most reasonable conclusion to draw from the meager research comparing retardates of various intellectual levels is that intellectual level is not related to discrepancies of actual achievement from expected achievement. This conclusion would lend further support to the finding of a relationship between intelligence and learning ability within mentally retarded groups. However, achievement expectancies and limits for retardates at lower intellectual levels are below those for retardates at the upper intellectual levels, rate and asymptote of learning being related to intelligence. Thus, the decision of whether retardates presently considered to be at the lower limits of educability should be placed in educable classes must be a value judgment. However, if it is demonstrated that these retardates impede the progress of those at the upper intellectual levels, the decision would no longer be based solely on values. The effects of various methods of grouping on the academic progress of educable retardates of all intellectual levels need to be evaluated.

Etiology

Brain-injured and familial retardates have been considered to differ psychologically, and great effort has been expended in devising special instructional techniques for the brain-injured (Strauss & Lehtinen, 1947). However, studies reviewed by Barnett et al. (1960) present no evidence that the learning characteristics of the two groups are different. A knowledge of the relative achievement of these two groups would have implications for educational practice.

Bensberg (1953) found no differences between institutionalized familial and brain-injured retardates of the same MA on either reading or arithmetic. Capobianco (1954) compared institutionalized groups on arithmetic performance. No significant difference occurred between the groups on arithmetic reasoning, computation, or general arithmetic achievement as measured by the Compass Survey Test and the general tests of arithmetic ability devised by Hannum. However, the familial group scored below its mental age level on all three tests, whereas the brain-injured group performed closer to the mental age level, even working up to expectancy in arithmetic reasoning. In a qualitative analysis for which the Buswell-John Diagnostic Chart was used, no significant differences between the groups occurred on rigidity, reversals, or on the concept of zero. These findings raise the question of whether etiology is a person variable relevant to educational practice.

Miscellaneous variables

Other factors which have been related to achievement are length of institutionalization, race, and emotional disturbance. Since studies of these variables are limited in number and since no replications have been made, conclusions cannot be drawn from them.

Bensberg (1953) found no relationship between length of institutionalization and reading and arithmetic achievement.

Thurstone (1960) found the achievement of white retardates in North Carolina to be further from expectancy than the achievement of Negro retardates. Though the differences were small, they were statistically significant for all tests of the Stanford Achievement Test except that of arithmetic computation. Both Negro and white regular-class retardates were superior to special-class pupils. In terms of progress in an experimental reading program, Boyle (1959) found no difference between Negro and white retardates.

Studies of normal children (Axline, 1947) have suggested a relationship between reading difficulty and emotional disturbance. In a study of the mentally retarded, Vaughn (1941) compared the classroom behavior of poor and good readers. The poor readers showed more disinterest, overactivity, temper outbursts, and speech difficulties than the good readers in academic classrooms; but their behavior was no different from that of the good readers in handwork rooms, where they could succeed. Whether the behavior was the cause or the result of the reading disability is not known. This finding suggests that special classes, by enabling the retarded to have successful experiences, might ameliorate behavior problems. This fact might account for the results of some studies which indicate that special-class retardates are superior in adjustment to regular-class retardates.

SUMMARY

In this chapter three methodological difficulties in the conducting of research on educational procedures for the mentally retarded were considered: the criterion problem, the sampling problem, and the problem of experimental controls. Philosophy, theories, and research on educational placement, curriculum development, and teaching methods were also discussed. In the last part of the chapter a review of research on the academic achievement of the retarded, compared with the achievement expected on the basis of MA and compared with achievement of normals, was presented. Research relating teaching method, age, sex, IQ, etiology, length of institutionalization, race, and emotional disturbance to academic achievement in the retarded was also reviewed.

Throughout the chapter, syntheses of research results were made, and tentative conclusions concerning academic skill development in the retarded were drawn from these syntheses. Practical suggestions concerning the conducting of research in the education of the mentally retarded were also given.

REFERENCES

AXLINE, VIRGINIA M. Nondirective therapy for poor readers. *J. consult. Psychol.*, 1947, 11, 61–69.

BAKER, H. J. *Introduction to exceptional children.* New York: Macmillan, 1953.

BARNETT, C. D., ELLIS, N. R., & PRYER, MARGARET. Stimulus pre-training and the delayed reaction in defectives. *Amer. J. ment. Defic.*, 1959, 64, 104–111.

BARNETT, C. D., ELLIS, N. R., & PRYER, MARGARET. Learning in familial and brain-injured defectives. *Amer. J. ment. Defic.*, 1960, 64, 894–901.

BARNETT, C. D., PRYER, MARGARET, & ELLIS, N. R. Experimental manipulation of verbal behavior in defectives. *Psychol. Rep.*, 1959, 5, 593–596.

BENNETT, ANNETTE. *A comparative study of subnormal children in elementary grades.* New York: Teachers Coll., 1932.

BENSBERG, G. J. The relation of academic achievement of mental defectives to mental age, sex, institutionalization, and etiology. *Amer. J. ment. Defic.*, 1953, 327–330.

BIJOU, S. W. The special problem of motivation in the academic learning of the retarded child. *Except. Child.*, 19, 1952, 103–104, 120.

BLATT, B. The physical, personality, and academic status of children who are mentally retarded attending special classes as compared with children who are mentally retarded attending regular classes. *Amer. J. ment. Defic.*, 1958, 62, 810–818.

BLIESMER, E. P. A comparison of bright and dull children of comparable mental ages with respect to various reading abilities. Unpublished doctoral dissertation, State Univer. of Iowa, 1952.

BOYLE, RUTH C. *How can reading be taught to educable adolescents who have not learned to read?* (Project No. 162). Washington: U.S. Office of Education, 1959.

CAMPBELL, D. T., & STANLEY, J. C. Experimental and quasi-experimental designs for research on teaching. In N. L. Gage (Ed.), *Handbook of research on teaching.* Chicago: Rand McNally, 1963, 171–246.

CANTOR, G. N., & HOTTEL, J. V. Psychomotor learning in defectives as a function of verbal pretraining. *Psychol. Rec.*, 1957, 7, 79–85.

CAPOBIANCO, R. J. Quantitative and qualitative analyses of endogenous and exogenous boys on arithmetic achievement. *Monogr. soc. Res. Child Develpm.*, 1954, 19, 100–142.

CARRIKER, W. A. *A comparison of post-school adjustments of regular and special class retarded individuals served in Lincoln and Omaha, Nebraska Public Schools.* (Project No. 146). Washington: U.S. Office of Education, 1957.

CASSIDY, VIOLA M., & STANTON, JEANETTE E. *An investigation of factors involved in the educational placement of mentally retarded children.* (Project No. 043). Washington: U.S. Office of Education, 1959.

COWEN, P. A. Special classes vs. grade groups for subnormal pupils. *Sch. & Soc.*, 1938, 48, 27–28.

CRONBACH, L. J. The two disciplines of scientific psychology. *Amer. Psychologist*, 1957, 12, 671–684.

CRUICKSHANK, W. M. Arithmetic ability of mentally retarded children. I. Ability to differentiate extraneous materials from needed arithmetic facts. *J. educ. Res.*, 1948, 42, 161–170. (a)

CRUICKSHANK, W. M. Arithmetic ability of mentally retarded children. II. Understanding arithmetical processes. *J. educ. Res.*, 1948, 42, 279–288. (b)

CRUICKSHANK, W. M. Arithmetic work habits of mentally retarded boys. *Amer. J. ment. Defic.*, 1948, 52, 318–330. (c)

DALY, W. C., & LEE, R. H. Reading disabilities in a group of M-R children: incidence and treatment. *Train. Sch. Bull.*, 1960, 57, 85–93.

DiMICHAEL, S. G. (ED.). *Vocational rehabilitation of the mentally retarded.* Washington: U.S. Office of Vocational Rehabilitation, 1950.

DUNN, L. M. A comparison of the reading processes of mentally retarded and normal boys of the same mental age. *Monogr. soc. Child Develpm.*, 1954, 19, 1–99.

DUNN, L. M., & CAPOBIANCO, R. J. Mental retardation. *Rev. educ. Res.*, 1959, 29, 451–470.

ELLIS, N. R., & DISTEFANO, M. K., JR. Effects of verbal urging and praise upon rotary pursuit performance in mental defectives. *Amer. J. ment. Defic.*, 1959, 64, 486–490.

ELLIS, N. R., & PRYER, MARGARET W. Primary versus secondary reinforcement in simple discrimination learning of mental defectives. *Psy. Rep.*, 1958, 4, 67–70.

ELLIS, N. R., PRYER, MARGARET, W., DISTEFANO, M. K., JR., & PRYER, R. S. Learning in mentally defective, normal, and superior subjects. *Amer. J. ment. Defic.*, 1960, 64, 725–734.

ELLIS, N. R., & SLOAN, W. Oddity learning as a function of mental age. *J. comp. physiol. Psychol.*, 1959, 52, 228–230.

ENGEL, ANNA M. Employment of the mentally retarded. *Amer. J. ment. Defic.*, 1952, 57, 243–267.

GALANTER, E. The ideal teacher. In E. Galanter (Ed.), *Automatic teaching: the state of the art.* New York: Wiley, 1959, 1–11.

GIRARDEAU, F. L. The formation of discrimination learning sets in mongoloid and normal children. *J. comp. physiol. Psychol.*, 1959, 52, 556–570.

GRAHAM, R. Blueprints for CED action. *Except. Child.*, 1959, 26, 15–21.

GRIFFITH, B. C. The use of verbal mediators in concept formation by retarded subjects at different intellectual levels. *Child Develpm.*, 1960, 31, 633–641.

GRIFFITH, B. C., & SPITZ, H. H. Some relationships between abstraction and word meanings in retarded adolescents. *Amer. J. ment. Defic.*, 1958, 63, 247–251.

GRIFFITH, B. C., SPITZ, H. H., & LIPMAN, R. S. Verbal mediation and concept formation in retarded and normal subjects. *J. exp. Psychol.*, 1959, 58, 247–251.

GROELLE, M. C. Some results and implications of reading survey tests given to educable mentally retarded children. *Except. Child.*, 1961, 27, 443–448.

HEBER, R. A manual on terminology and classification in mental retardation. *Amer. J. ment. Defic., Monogr. Suppl.*, 1959, 64, No. 20.

HOLLINGWORTH, LETA S. *The psychology of subnormal children.* New York: Macmillan, 1920.

INGRAM, CHRISTINE P. *Education of the slow-learning child.* New York: Ronald, 1953.

INSKEEP, ANNIE D. *Teaching dull and retarded children.* New York: Macmillan, 1926.

JACOBS, J. N. A study of performance of slow learners in the Cincinnati public schools on mental and achievement tests. *Amer. J. ment. Defic.*, 1957, 63, 238–243.

JOHNSON, G. O. A study of the social position of mentally handicapped children in the regular grades. *Amer. J. ment. Defic.*, 1950, 55, 60–89.

JOHNSON, G. O., & KIRK, S. A. Are mentally-handicapped children segregated in the regular grades? *J. except. Child.*, 1950, 17, 65–68, 87–88.

JONES, R. L., GROSS, F. P., & VAN WHY, E. L. A longitudinal study of reading achievement in a group of adolescent institutionalized mentally retarded children. *Train. Sch. Bull.*, 1960, 57, 41–47.

KELLY, ELIZABETH M. The improvement of reading in special classes for mentally retarded children. *Proc. Amer. Ass. ment. Def.*, 1934, 39, 67–73.

KIRK, S. A., & JOHNSON, G. O. *Educating the retarded child.* Boston: Houghton Mifflin, 1951.

KLAUSMEIER, H. J., FELDHUSEN, J., & CHECK, J. *An analysis of learning efficiency in arithmetic of mentally retarded children in comparison with children of average and high intelligence.* (Project No. 153). Washington: U.S. Office of Education, 1959.

MARTIN, W. E., & BLUM, A. *Psychological characteristics underlying the educability of the mentally retarded child. I. Concept formation and transposition in young mentally retarded and normal children.* (Project No. 266). Washington: U.S. Office of Education, 1960.

MCCULLOCH, T. L., RESWICK, J., & ROY, I. Studies of word learning in mental defectives. I. Effects of mental level and age. *Amer. J. ment. Defic.*, 1955, 60, 133–139.

MCGEHEE, W. A study of retarded children in the elementary school. *Peabody Coll. Contr. Educ.*, 1939, No. 246.

MCPHERSON, M. W. Learning and mental deficiency. *Amer. J. ment. Defic.*, 1958, 62, 870–877.

MERRILL, MAUD A. The relation of intelligence to ability in the three r's in the case of retarded children. *Ped. Sem.*, 1921, 28, 249–274.

MERRILL, MAUD A. On the relation of intelligence to achievement in the case of mentally retarded children. *Comp. Psychol. Monogr.*, 1924, 2, 1–100.

MONROE, MARION. *Children who cannot read.* Chicago: Univer. of Chicago Press, 1932.

MORPHETT, MABLE V., & WASHBURNE, C. When should children begin to read? *Elem. Sch. J.*, 1931, 31, 496–503.

MULLEN, FRANCES A. *The reading ability of the older ungraded pupil.* Chicago: Bureau Mentally Handicapped Children, Chicago Public Schools, 1952.

O'CONNOR, N., & TIZARD, J. *The social problem of mental deficiency.* New York: Pergamon Press, 1956.

ORDAHL, LOUISE E., & ORDAHL, G. Qualitative differences between levels of intelligence in feeble-minded children. *J. Psycho-Asthenios, Monogr. Suppl.,* 1915, 1, 3–50.

PERTSCH, C. F. A comparative study of the progress of subnormal pupils in the grades and in special classes. Unpublished doctoral dissertation, Columbia Univer., 1936.

PORTER, D. Some effects of year long teaching machine instruction. In E. Galanter (Ed.), *Automatic teaching: the state of the art.* New York: Wiley, 1959, 85–90.

SHAFTER, A. J. Criteria for selecting institutionalized mental defectives for vocational placement. *Amer. J. ment. Defic.,* 1957, 61, 599–616.

SLOAN, W., & BERG, I. A. A comparison of two types of learning in mental defectives. *Amer. J. ment. Defic.,* 1957, 61, 556–566.

SMITH, D. E. P. Speculations: characteristics of successful programs and programmers. In E. Galanter (Ed.), *Automatic teaching: the state of the art.* New York: Wiley, 1959, 91–102.

STOLUROW, L. M. Teaching machines and special education. *Educ. Psychol. Measmt.,* 1960, 20, 429–448.

STRAUSS, A. A., & LEHTINEN, LAURA. *Psychopathology and education of the brain-injured child.* New York: Grune & Stratton, 1947.

THURSTONE, THELMA G. *An evaluation of educating mentally handicapped children in special classes and in regular classes.* (Project No. 168). Washington: U.S. Office of Education, 1960.

TORGERSON, T. L., & SHUMAN, IRENE. The variability of the accomplishments of pupils of the same mental level. *J. educ. Res.,* 1925, 11, 132–136.

VAUGHN, C. L. Classroom behavior problems encountered in attempting to teach illiterate defective boys how to read. *J. educ. Psychol.,* 1941, 32, 339–350.

WASSMAN, KATHERINE. A comparative study of mentally deficient children in regular and in special classes. Unpublished master's thesis, George Washington Univer., 1933.

WILSON, F. T. Some achievement of pupils of the same mental ages but different intelligence quotients. *J. educ. Res.,* 1926, 14, 43–53.

WILSON, MAMIE L. T. *A comparative study of the speech responses and social ages of two selected groups of educable mental retardates.*

WITTY, P. A., & MCCAFFERTY, ESTELLE. Attainment by feebleminded children. *Educ.,* 1930, 50, 588–597.

WOLK, SHIRLEY M. A survey of the literature on curriculum practices for the mentally retarded. *Amer. J. ment. Defic.,* 1958, 62, 826–839.

WOODROW, H. The ability to learn. *Psychol. Rev.,* 1946, 53, 147–158.

YOUNG, M. A. Academic requirements of jobs held by the educable mentally retarded in the state of Connecticut. *Amer. J. ment. Defic.,* 1958, 62, 792–802.

CONTRIBUTORS

Alfred Baumeister attended the University of Alaska, where he took his bachelor of arts degree. After 3 years of high school teaching, he went on to George Peabody College for Teachers, obtaining his master's degree in 1959 and his Ph.D. in 1961. His primary interests and research activities have centered around measurement problems in mental deficiency. He has also conducted research concerned with the physiological correlates of mental retardation, particularly the relationship between brain damage and retention. After graduate school Dr. Baumeister served as a research associate at George Peabody College. He is now at Central Michigan University.

Gershon Berkson did undergraduate work as Oberlin College and received the M.S. degree from the University of Wisconsin. He then became a Fellow in the mental deficiency program at George Peabody College for Teachers. His interest in comparisons of the mentally deficient with normals began with studies of learning and then turned to attentional mechanisms. After a research internship at UCLA, where he gained experience with psychophysiological methods, he did a dissertation at the Edward R. Johnstone Training and Research Center and received the doctorate from George Peabody College in 1959. In the following year, Dr. Berkson continued his comparative studies as a USPHS postdoctoral Fellow at the Social Psychiatry Research Unit, London, England. On his return to the United States, he became a research associate at the Yerkes Laboratories of Primate Biology, where he studied psychophysiological responses of newborn chimpanzees and abnormal stereotyped movements of chimpanzees and mental defectives. Currently, he is a research associate at the Illinois Pediatric

Institute, where he is investigating defects in responsiveness in early development.

Gordon N. Cantor received his B.A. and M.A. degrees from Syracuse University, and his Ph.D., in 1954, from the Iowa Child Welfare Research Station, State University of Iowa. His doctoral training was in the area of experimental child psychology. From 1954 to 1960 he was assistant and associate professor of psychology at George Peabody College for Teachers, his affiliation being with Peabody's doctoral training program in mental deficiency. During his tenure at Peabody College, Dr. Cantor's research was concerned with learning and motivational processes in mental defectives. He returned to the Iowa Child Welfare Research Station (now the Institute of Child Behavior and Development) in 1960 as associate professor of child psychology and is currently involved in research on motivation in normal children. In collaboration with his wife, Dr. Joan H. Cantor, he has recently initiated a series of studies dealing with observing and manipulative responses in infants and young children as a function of stimulus novelty and complexity. His research articles have appeared in a number of sources, including the *Journal of Experimental Psychology,* the *Journal of Educational Psychology,* and the *American Journal of Mental Deficiency.*

Rue L. Cromwell received his A.B. degree in psychology at Indiana University and his M.A. and Ph.D. degrees in clinical psychology at The Ohio State University. He had internship training at the Veterans Administration Hospital, Chillicothe, Ohio, and the V.A. Mental Hygiene Clinic, Columbus, Ohio. After serving 1 year as assistant instructor in the Psychological Clinic at Ohio State University, he accepted, in 1955, a faculty position in the NIMH mental deficiency graduate training program in psychology at George Peabody College for Teachers. Since that time he has conducted and supervised research, most of which has been in the area of mental retardation. During various summers he has worked as a psychologist at the Ohio Juvenile Diagnostic Center, South Florida State Hospital, and the Laboratory of Psychology, National Institute of Mental Health.

Norman R. Ellis received a bachelor's degree from Howard College in 1951, an M.A. from the University of Alabama in 1953, and a Ph.D. in experimental psychology from Louisiana State University in 1957. He has taught at the University of Alabama, L.S.U., and Louisiana College. From 1956 to 1960 he served as Director of psychological services at the State Colony and Training School, Pineville, Louisiana. Since 1960 he has been an associate professor of psychology at George Peabody College for Teachers. His interests are in the study of fundamental determinants of behavior and, in particular, in the analysis of behavioral inadequacy in the human organism.

Sol L. Garfield took his graduate work at Northwestern University, obtaining his Ph.D. degree in 1942. One of his main interests at that time was clinical work with children. Shortly after obtaining his degree, he entered the United States Army, where, among other duties, he served as a psychologist at an induction station and as chief psychologist at an army hospital. Upon discharge from military service in 1946, he accepted a position as chief psychologist at the Veterans Administration Hospital, Mendota, Wisconsin.

From 1947 to 1949 he was associate professor of psychology and director of the clinical psychology training program at the University of Connecticut. He then returned to the Veterans Administration, where he was successively chief psychologist, Mental Hygiene Clinic, Milwaukee, Wisconsin, chief of the psychology training unit for Illinois and Wisconsin, and then coordinator of psychological services at the hospital at Downey, Illinois. From 1957 to 1963 Dr. Garfield was professor of medical psychology and chief of the psychology division at the Psychiatric Institute, University of Nebraska. Presently, Dr. Garfield is on the staff of the Missouri Psychiatric Institute, St. Louis, Missouri, and Washington University.

He has published extensively in the areas of diagnostic testing and psychotherapy and more recently has been concerned with diagnostic problems in the area of mental retardation. He is the author of *Introductory Clinical Psychology* (Macmillan, 1957).

He is a diplomate in clinical psychology of the American Board of Examiners in Professional Psychology, a fellow of APA, and currently secretary-treasurer of the clinical division of APA.

Irving I. Gottesman took his B.S. in psychology at the Illinois Institute of Technology in 1953. After a stint in the Navy, he went on to the University of Minnesota, where he specialized in child clinical psychology and took a minor from the Institute of Child Development. He received the doctorate in 1960 after completing a dissertation on the psychogenetics of human personality, a study of twins. Gottesman interned at both the A. H. Wilder Child Guidance Clinic and the Minneapolis Veterans Administration Hospital. After graduation he obtained a position as lecturer on child psychology in the department of social relations at Harvard University. He is continuing his research, at the Center for Research in Personality, into the genetic aspects of personality under grants from the National Institutes of Health and Harvard's Laboratory of Social Relations. He is one of the few psychologists in this country interested in building a stronger bridge between human genetics and psychology; he participated in the Second International Conference for Human Genetics and is a member of the American Society for Human Genetics.

Samuel Guskin took his bachelor's degree at Brooklyn College and then went on to the University of North Carolina, where he specialized in personality and social psychology, obtaining the master's degree in 1955 and the doctorate in 1958. His dissertation involved a critique of concept and method in the field of social stereotypes and demonstrated a revised empirical approach to the topic. After graduate school, Dr. Guskin became a research assistant and later a Russell Sage postdoctoral resident with the Disaster Research Group of the National Academy of Science—National Research Council in Washington, D.C. During his tenure with the group he was engaged in research and analysis on problems of shelter living in natural and man-made disasters. He served as a research officer with Research Services Limited in London, planning and carrying out studies of consumer attitudes and behavior. In July, 1960, he returned to the United States to his present position as associate professor of psychology at George Peabody College for Teachers. He is now studying social aspects of mental deficiency.

William Hawkins was graduated from the United States Naval Academy, where he majored in marine engineering. After 5 years in the Marine Corps, he went to Southern Illinois University, obtaining the master's degree in 1959. While there he was a graduate assistant involved in perceptual research and in teaching undergraduate introductory psychology. He also attended the University of Virginia and was enrolled in their experimental psychology program; he was doing human research on short-term memory. Later he came to George Peabody College for Teachers on a mental deficiency fellowship. Mr. Hawkins is now working toward the Ph.D. degree in mental retardation with an emphasis on physiological psychology. His main research activities at Peabody have been in the areas of learning and retention of retardates.

Betty House (Mrs. David Zeaman) received her B.A. in 1948 from Oklahoma University, her M.A. in 1949 from Brown, and her Ph.D. in psychology from the University of Connecticut in 1952, where she is currently a research assistant professor of psychology. *David Zeaman* has an A.B. from Queens College, 1943, in chemistry. He spent 2 years in the Air Corps and then went on to Columbia, where he received the Ph.D. in 1948. He was an instructor of psychology at Brown from 1947 to 1949 before coming to the University of Connecticut, where he is professor of psychology.

Both House and Zeaman have been doing research on retardate learning processes for 7 years in their laboratory at the Mansfield State Training School.

Frank Kodman, Jr., received the B.S., B.A., and M.A. degrees from the University of Pittsburgh. He received his Ph.D. in 1954 from the University of Illinois, where he was a research assistant in the Speech Research Laboratory from 1951 to 1953 and a research assistant in the Control Systems Laboratory from 1953 to 1954. Currently he is associate professor of psychology at the University of Kentucky and the author or senior co-author of 46 publications in psychological, medical, educational, and acoustical journals covering a wide range of subject matter. Dr. Kodman is listed in *American Men of Science,* in the *National Registry of Technical and Scientific Personnel,* and in *Who's Who in the South and Southwest.* He is a member of Sigma Xi, APA, ASHA, and the Acoustical Society of America.

Ronald Lipman received his bachelor's degree from New York University and went on to major in social psychology at the University of Connecticut, where he received his master's degree in 1952 and his doctorate in 1957. During his last year at the University of Connecticut he worked as a research fellow on a Ford Foundation Grant aimed at evaluating the effectiveness of the educational program in the College of Arts and Sciences. He was awarded the Donald L. Kanter fellowship in 1956 for his promise as a social psychologist. In his dissertation he explored the future time perspective characteristics of anxiety. His first major position upon graduation was as a research associate at the E. R. Johnstone Training and Research Center, where he worked until November, 1961. During the 4 years that he was there, he published 13 articles, mostly in the areas of perception and learning. He has also acted as a research consultant to the Mentally Retarded Children's Clinic of Flower and Fifth Avenue Hospitals since September, 1959.

He is presently employed as a research psychologist with the Special Studies Unit, Psychopharmacology Service Center, National Institute of Mental Health. This unit is engaged in evaluating the combined effects of drugs and attitudinal variables on the social behavior of normal and clinic populations.

A. R. Luria, Ph.D., M.D., is professor of psychology at Moscow University. He was born in 1902 and graduated from the University of Kazan in 1921 and then from the Moscow Medical Institute in 1937. His principal work has been in experimental psychology, in psychological studies of mental development of normal and abnormal children, and in brain mechanisms of behavior. For many years he was head of psychological laboratories in the Institute of Psychology, the Institute of Defectology, and the Institute of Neurosurgery (Moscow). He is a Fellow of the Academy of Pedagogical Sciences of the Russian Federation. In 1932 he published *The Nature of Human Conflicts* (New York, Liveright); in 1947, *Traumatic Aphasia;* and in 1948, *Rehabilitation of Brain Functions after War Trauma* (the last two books dealing with results of his work as a head of the Neurosurgical Rehabilitation Hospital in World War II). In 1956 and 1958 his two volumes on *Problems of the Higher Nervous Activity in Normal and Abnormal Children* (Moscow, Academy of Pedagogical Science Press) appeared, summarizing his work with mentally retarded children. Objective analysis of his book *Speech and Development of the Mental Process in the Child* was published in 1959 in London (Staples Press).

During 1957 he was a visiting professor in London University, and his lectures in University College appeared as a book, *The Regulatory Role of Speech in Normal and Abnormal Behavior* (London, Pergamon Press, 1961). In 1959 he visited the United States, taking part in J. Macy Symposium on the Central Nervous System and Behavior and delivering three lectures in the Post Graduate Center for Psychotherapy, New York. Prof. A. R. Luria is editor of "Proceedings of the Academy of Pedagogical Sciences" and coeditor of "Questions of Psychology" (Russian).

Brendan Maher received the baccalaureate from the University of Manchester, England, in 1950; he entered graduate study in clinical psychology at The Ohio State University in the same year with Fulbright and Mundt-Smith Scholarships. He received the M.A. in 1951 and completed a clinical internship at the Neuropsychiatric Institute of the University of Illinois in Chicago. Receiving the Ph.D. in 1954, he returned to England as psychologist at H. M. Prison, Wakefield. This was followed by appointment as instructor at Ohio State (1955 to 1956), assistant professor at Northwestern University (1956 to 1958), associate professor and director of clinical training at Louisiana State University (1958 to 1960). He is currently lecturer in psychology in the department of social relations at Harvard University.

At the present time his interests lie in the area of experimental clinical psychology, with a special concern for the study of conflict.

Leslie F. Malpass attended the University of Cincinnati and Syracuse University as an undergraduate. He received the B.A., M.A., and Ph.D. degrees from Syracuse University in psychology. He was the psychologist at the Syracuse Child Guidance Center for 4 years before being appointed to the faculty of Southern Illinois University, where he served on the psychology staff for 8 years. While there Dr. Malpass conducted research projects dealing with perceptual-response potentials and learning activities of retarded, normal, and bright children. In 1960 he became professor and chairman of the behavioral sciences program at the University of South Florida. Currently, he is doing research with automated teaching procedures for retarded children.

Lorene Childs Quay received the A.B. degree in psychology from Southwestern Louisiana Institute in 1951 and the M.A. degree in psychology from Florida State University in 1952. From 1953 to 1955 she taught in the Laboratory School of the Georgia State College for Women. While studying for the doctorate in school psychology at the University of Illinois, she taught child development and was an intern in school psychology in the Champaign, Illinois, city schools. After receiving the Ph.D. in 1958, she became an assistant professor of psychology at George Peabody College for Teachers, where she remained until 1961. Dr. Quay is currently a school psychologist for the Niles Township (Illinois) public schools. She has published in the areas of concept formation, attitude measurement, and the assessment of attendant-employee training programs.

Sheldon Rosenberg obtained his bachelor's degree from Brooklyn College in 1954 and the M.A. and Ph.D. in 1956 and 1958 at the University of Minnesota. His first position after completing graduate study was at Indiana University, where he was involved in research on incidental learning. More recently Dr. Rosenberg was a member of the research department of the Training School at Vineland, where he conducted a series of experimental studies of learning in brain-injured mental defectives and participated in a study of ability structure in mentally defective and normal children. In September, 1961, he joined the faculty of George Peabody College for Teachers as assistant professor of psychology. His area of specialization is human learning, child development, and mental retardation.

Herman H. Spitz received his bachelor's degree at Lafayette College, and his Ph.D. in clinical psychology at New York University. After internships at the Paterson Mental Health Center and the New Jersey Diagnostic Center, he became a staff member at Trenton State Hospital, initially as an assistant psychologist and then, from 1955 to 1957, as head of the psychology department. At Trenton State Hospital he initiated and carried out an intensive group therapy program for sex offenders. But interest in brain processes, especially as they are reflected in geometric illusions and in stationary and movement aftereffects, led him to the research department of the Edward R. Johnstone Training and Research Center, where a population of mental retardates offered a rich field for the study of disturbed brain processes. In this regard, he has become interested recently not only in the origin of different types of optical illusions but in comparing the intensity of illusory processes in such diverse groups as college students, mental retardates, and pigeons. He is presently director of research at the Johnstone Training and Research Center.

George Spivack received his B.A. in English from Hunter College in 1949 and then went to Columbia University, where, in 1950, he received his master's degree in experimental psychology. He then attended the University of Pennsylvania, where he completed his doctorate in 1954. During this period he trained at the Veterans Administration Mental Health Clinic in Philadelphia and spent 1 year at the Perry Point Veterans Administration Hospital in Maryland. After graduate work, Dr. Spivack was a clinical psychologist and a psychological coordinator at the Devereux Schools in Devon, Pennsylvania. In 1957 he was made chief of the research and training department and since 1958 has been the director of psychological research at the Devereux Foundation Institute for Research and Training. From 1959 to the present, Dr. Spivack has been affiliated with the Philadelphia Psychiatric Hospital as research psychologist and therapist in a project on family treatment. He received his American Psychological Association Diplomate in clinical psychology in 1959.

Joseph Spradlin took his bachelor's degree at the University of Kansas in 1957, his master of science degree at Fort Hays Kansas State College in 1954, and his doctor of philosophy degree at George Peabody College for Teachers in 1959. His dissertation involved the study of effects of schedules of reinforcement on the extinction of a motor response in severely retarded children. Prior to going to George Peabody, Dr. Spradlin was a clinical psychologist at Winfield State Training School in Kansas. After leaving there he became a research associate on the Parsons Research Project, a cooperative language research project between the Bureau of Child Research at the University of Kansas and the Parsons State Hospital and Training Center. His current research interests include language evaluation, two-person interaction, and the application of descriptive learning theory to language.

Harold W. Stevenson is professor of child development and psychology as well as the director of the Institute of Child Development at the University of Minnesota. He received his bachelor's degree from the University of Colorado in 1947 and his master's degree and doctorate in 1948 and 1951 from Stanford University. Dr. Stevenson was assistant professor of psychology at Pomona College from 1950 to 1953, assistant and then associate professor of psychology at the University of Texas from 1953 to 1954, and since 1959 he has been at Minnesota. His primary interests are in experimental child psychology, and his major concerns have been in the study of children's learning and motivation.

Mary Woodward was educated at the University of London, where she read psychology, taking her first degree in 1950. This was followed by 2 years of postgraduate study at the same university, involving a research on the social activities and attitudes of mothers of young children. She was then appointed Research Fellow at the Institute for the Study and Treatment of Delinquency in London, where her main work included an investigation of the relation of intelligence to juvenile delinquency and a follow-up study of homosexuals referred to the psychiatric clinic. For the following 5½ years Miss Woodward worked as a clinical psychologist at the Fountain Hospital, London, which houses mentally defective children and has hostels for subnormal adolescents and adults. While dealing with problems of assessment for training and rehabilitation, she became aware of the need for new techniques in this field; and this led to the study of the applicability of Piaget's work to the problems. Other research interests during this time included the origin of behavior disorders in mentally defective children and certain features of their perceptual development. Miss Woodward is now lecturer in psychology at University College, Swansea, in the University of Wales.

NAME INDEX

Mautner, H., 468, 477
Mayer-Gross, W., 470, 478
Means, J. R., 548, 554
Mecham, M. J., 517, 519, 522, 523, 527, 528, 535, 540, 544, 553
Mednick, S. A., 34, 38
Meehl, P., 243, 247, 252
Meier, G. W., 570, 572
Meier, P., 500, 509
Melhado, J. W., 413, 414, 422
Mellman, W. J., 255, 284, 294
Meltzoff, J., 643, 661, 662
Melzack, R., 644, 663
Merachnik, D. A., 487, 509
Mercer, Margaret, 587, 600
Meredith, H. V., 612, 613, 630
Merrill, Maud A., 277, 290, 296, 329, 555, 678, 679, 689
Mescheriakov, A. I., 380, 383
Metheny, E., 612, 630
Metzger, R., 427, 438
Milgram, N., 577, 599
Mill, C. R., 495
Miller, M. B., 31, 38, 41, 60–61, 70–74, 76, 80, 89, 444, 451, 461, 498, 505, 509, 643, 644, 651, 663
Miller, N. E., 80, 81, 92, 132, 553
Miller, P. Y., 537, 540, 552
Miller, R. V., 327, 351
Milner, B., 249, 252, 558, 572
Ming, D., 650, 662
Missen, H. W., 317, 324
Mitchell, J., 636, 648, 651, 662
Mitchell, W. C., Jr., 399, 422
Mitchell, W. G., 637, 661
Mixson, A., 466, 478
Moekler, B., 326, 327, 343, 350
Moller, S., 606, 630
Monroe, Marion, 678, 689
Montessori, M., 218, 222
Montgomery, K. C., 635, 661
Moorhead, P. S., 255, 284, 294
Morgan, C. T., 639, 642, 661
Morphett, Mable V., 678, 689
Morrison, D. H., 244, 251
Morse, Sally, 489, 509
Morton, N. E., 253, 296
Moruzzi, G., 646, 662
Moss, J. W., 41, 47, 56–61, 88, 90, 466, 478
Moss, M., 466, 478
Mosteller, F., 166, 169, 173, 174, 213, 216, 221
Mowrer, C. H., 393, 417, 418
Mowrer, O. H., 92, 99, 110, 132, 135, 422, 536
Muench, G. A., 238, 252
Mullen, Frances A., 678, 689

Muller, G. E., 135, 136
Muller, H. J., 258, 291–294
Mundy, Lydia, 475, 478
Munn, N., 472, 478, 630, 633
Murphy, G., 481, 510
Murphy, J. P., 642, 662
Murphy, Mary M., 473, 478
Murray, J. G., 498
Muscio, B., 621, 630
Myklebust, H. R., 475, 478

Naquet, R., 647, 660
Nass, M. L., 312, 323
Naunton, R. F., 466, 477
Neel, J. V., 257, 259, 260, 291, 295
Neham, Sara, 574, 595, 600
Neilson, N. P., 630
Neisser, U., 503, 509
Nelson, A. K., 637, 662
Neuer, H., 584, 600
Newbigging, P. L., 31–32, 39
Newman, H. H., 280, 295
Nieman, L. V., 359
Nissen, H. W., 282
Noble, C. E., 141, 144, 146, 394, 396, 420, 422
Noce, R. H., 650, 662
Nolan, C. Y., 570, 572
North, A. J., 209, 211, 222

O'Connor, N., 126, 132, 142, 153, 398, 422, 426, 432, 438, 448, 460, 468, 478, 563–568, 570–572, 586–588, 592–595, 600, 610, 619, 625, 630, 677, 690
Odell, M., 76, 90
Oden, M. H., 277, 296
O'Donnell, J. P., 434, 438
Ogilvie, E., 312–315, 323
Ogonik, J., 650, 663
O'Gorman, G., 589, 600
Ohwaki, S., 494, 506, 509
Oldham, A. J., 470, 479, 644, 663
Ordahl, G., 419, 422, 677, 690
Ordahl, Louise E., 419, 422, 677, 690
Orlando, R., 143, 199, 204, 222, 429, 437, 438
Ornstein, G. N., 18, 37
Orton, K. D., 561, 619, 627
Orton, S. T., 475, 478
Osborn, W. J., 33, 38, 419, 422, 452, 461
Osgood, C. E., 27, 39, 141, 398, 418, 422, 519, 553
Osipova, V. N., 59, 369
Oster, J., 468, 479
Ounsted, C., 648, 649, 651, 662
Oyama, T., 21, 39

SUBJECT INDEX

Mongolism, biochemical genetics in, 284
twin studies, 283
Monte Carlo methods, 173
Motivation (*see* Drive)
Motor cortex, 647
Motor disability, 605–607
Motor reactions, 371
Multiple alternative discrimination
(MAD), 58
Multiple neurofibromatosis, 259
Muscle activity, 562, 563
Music therapy, 473
(*See also* Therapy)
Myxedema, 562, 568

Need achievement, 74, 76
Need value, 46
Negative time error, 135
Nerve impulses, 568
Neural functions, 646–648
Neural integrity, 138
Nomothetic laws, 73
Nonreinforcement, 113, 130
Novelty, and attention, 199, 200
and learning, 199, 200, 219
Noxious stimulation, 79, 111, 642
Number, of reinforcements, 100, 101, 117
of response evocations, 105

Observing-response theory, 166, 167
compared with attention theory, 71
relation to continuity-noncontinuity
theory, 214
Occipital cortex, 647
Oddity learning, 193, 202, 203, 446–447
(*See also* Learning)
Ohio State Psychological Examination
(OSPE), 76
Olfactory sensitivity, 470
(*See also* Discrimination)
Operant behavior, 639
fixed-interval, 143, 144
Operators applied to probabilities, 171
expected, 171
for partial reinforcement model, 205
for partially relevant stimuli, 69
Organic deficit, 88
Organic pathology (*see* Brain damage)
Organicity, 94, 97
Organismic correlates, 645–651
Orienting reflex, 560
Oscillation, 105, 106, 639
Oseretsky Motor Development Scale, 610,
617–619, 623, 624, 626, 628

Pain, 77, 470, 644, 663
Paired-associate learning, 145, 151, 152
Pamabron, 650

Parameters, 117–119
Paranoia, 69
Parental attitudes, 77
Parsons Language Sample (PLS), 520–
522, 525–527, 538, 539, 542, 543,
546, 547, 550
Partial reinforcement (*see* Reinforcements)
Partial relevance of cues, 208, 209
Patellar reflex, 562
Peabody Picture Vocabulary Test, 76, 89,
518, 522
Pedigree method, 254, 273–279
Pedometer, 636
Perception, 13–16, 23–26, 30–32, 480–
511
apparent movement, 32
and brain damage, 482–502
and CNS, 464
cutaneous, 491–492
definition, 481
of depth, 490
differences in, sex, 496, 497
double simultaneous tactile, 491–492
effects of brain injury, 482, 501
figure-ground, 15–16, 482–485
Necker cube, 24–26
reproduction method in, 505, 506
response indicators, 504, 505
reversible figures, 30–32
(*See also* Discrimination; Illusions;
Sensory processes)
Perceptual learning, 213, 474, 476
(*See also* Learning)
Perseveration, 654
Persistence, 61, 77, 90
Personality development, 88
Personality variables, 42, 63
Phenobarbital, 649, 650
Phenotypic variance, 265
Phenylalinine diet, 570
Phenylketonuria, 253, 260
Phosphenes, 567, 569
Photic driving, 565, 647
(*See also* Electroencephalogram)
Photoelectric technique, 635, 639
(*See also* Activity, measures of)
Photo-Metrazol EEG, 649, 650, 661
Physiological psychology, 35–36
Pleasure-approach and pain-avoidance
system, 7, 64, 65, 79
Polygenic inheritance, 235, 261–266,
289–291
Postulates, 26–35
application to retarded behavior, 30–35
deprivation, 26–27, 29–30
social-learning theory, 78–84

Scientific method (*see* Methodology)
Second signaling system, 371, 380
 (*See also* Signal system)
Secondary drive, 98, 99
Secondary senses, 469
Sensorineural organization, 464
Sensoriperceptual continuum, 463
Sensory defects and learning, 472
Sensory deprivation, 644
 (*See also* Deprivation)
Sensory processes, 472
 (*See also* Discrimination)
Sensory training, 474
Serial learning, 71–73, 85, 87, 145
 (*See also* Learning)
Serial position effects, 141
Severely mentally retarded, 88, 589–591
Sex, 651
 and achievement, 684
 differences in, 280, 281
 and differences in perception, 496, 497
Signal system, 355
Single organism approach, 7
Skin conductance (*see* Electrodermal measures)
Skin resistance (*see* Electrodermal measures)
Skin temperature, 642
Sleep, 644, 648
Social deprivation, 88
Social distrust scale, 76
Speaker, 512, 513, 550
Speech, 512, 514–515, 517–518, 521, 523, 549, 550
 development, 359
Speech audiometry, 465–468
Speech defects of institution patients, 524, 526, 535, 536, 538, 539, 542, 548, 550
Speech therapy, 534–538, 540, 542, 550
Spence theory of discrimination learning, 108
Stabilimeter, 637, 641
Stability of nervous processes, 370–372, 381
Stanford-Binet Intelligence Scale, 621, 623
 (*See also* Intelligence)
Startle reflex, 568, 569
Stat-children, backward curves for, 184, 185
 definition, 173
 partial reinforcement, 206, 207
 partially relevant cues, 208, 209
 variability, 182–184
Static sense, 470
 (*See also* Discrimination)
Stereotype, 644, 659

Stimulation, environmental, 472–474
 noxious, 79, 111, 642
 sensory, 474
Stimulus, 164, 166–169
 dimensions, 164, 166–169
 and intelligence, 187
 oddity, 202–204
 temporal duration, 204
 variability, 204
Stimulus generalization, 101, 102, 121, 213, 214
Stimulus intensity dynamism, 106
Stimulus trace, 106
 definition, 138
 theories of, 130ff.
Strauss-Lehtinen-Kephart theory, 653
Strauss marble board, 645
Stress, 128
Stylus-maze learning, 144, 145
Success and failure, 47–62, 67–70, 75 79, 80, 84, 87, 88
 awareness (conceptualization), 62–69
 success-striving individual, 58–62, 85, 87, 90
Success-approach and failure-avoidance (later) motivational system, 58, 65, 70, 76, 79, 82–84, 87
Success striving and failure avoiding, 59–62
Summation, temporal and spatial, in diffuse brain abnormality, 568
Superior colliculi, 656
Symbolic function, 307
Synaptic summation in diffuse brain abnormality, 568

Tactile inattention, 474
Tactile performance, 469–470
Tactual sense, 642, 656
Taylor Manifest Anxiety Scale, 59, 60, 62, 78, 88, 89
 (*See also* Anxiety)
Teaching methods, 682–683
Templin Sound Discrimination Test, 535
Temporal contiguity, importance for learning and memory, 139
Tendon reflexes, 562
Testing as service function, 2
Theories, continuity-noncontinuity, 214
 hypothetico-deductive, 94, 96, 107
 of retroactive inhibition, 135
 of social learning, 74, 75, 89, 90
 of stimulus trace, 130ff.
Theory construction, 90
Therapy, educational, 475
 music, 473
 speech, 534–538, 540, 542, 550
Thirst, 661